Mission Handbook:
U.S. and Canadian Protestant Ministries Overseas
21st Edition

Edited by Linda J. Weber

www.missionhandbook.com

Evangelism and Missions Information Service
P.O. Box 794, Wheaton, IL 60187

Mission Handbook:
U.S. and Canadian Protestant Ministries Overseas, 21st Edition

Edited by Linda J. Weber
Executive editor, Kenneth D. Gill
Cover design and layout, Dona Diehl

Published by EMIS, a division of the Billy Graham Center at Wheaton College, 500 College Ave., Wheaton, IL 60187

Printed in the United States of America.

For information about other resources or publications of EMIS or the Billy Graham Center:
Phone: 630.752.7158
Email: emis@wheaton.edu
Online: www.emisdirect.com

ISBN 978-1-879089-51-8

To update your agency's information, or to check on current updates for mission agencies, go to: www.missionhandbook.com.

"Only a book that is meeting a very significant need would ever reach twenty-one editions! The 21st edition of the *Mission Handbook* is such a publication. It is the one-stop shop to find out who is who in the Protestant world of missions from the U.S. and Canada. Meticulous in detail, this volume provides the contact and vision information for upwards of one thousand agencies, thousands of missionaries, and hundreds of thousands of volunteers and short-term missionaries."

—**Doug McConnell**, *dean of the School of Intercultural Studies at Fuller Seminary*

"The 21st edition of the *Mission Handbook* demonstrates that North America is still alive with a deep commitment to the continuing redemptive mission of Jesus Christ! This volume is far more than the listing of over one thousand mission agencies—it highlights the continued fervor and willingness of obedient followers of Jesus to represent, globally, our Lord and his transforming gospel."

—**Byron D. Klaus**, *president of Assemblies of God Theological Seminary*

"I do not know of any other source of information related to the mission effort of North American Christianity that comes close to the treasure of data found in the *Mission Handbook*. Any serious student or practitioner of missions, executive of a mission organization, strategist of church mission and ministry, or scholar in the area of missiology can only enhance his or her ministry by making the *Handbook* an indispensable helper for his or her particular area of the mission task."

—**Elias Dantas**, *president of the Center for Studies in Global Christianity, Inc.; international facilitator for the Global Kingdom Partnerships Network; professor of pastoral studies and missions at Alliance Theological Seminary in Nyack, N.Y.*

"I have kept a copy of the *Mission Handbook* on my desk for over a decade. Whether you need to know which organizations are working in a particular country, what the mission statement of a group is, or websites and contact information, it is all available in this single volume. I have found it to be one of the most helpful resources for myself and my students."

—**Timothy C. Tennent**, *president and professor of world missions at Asbury Theological Seminary*

"When God touches your heart for mission, where do you begin? If you want the big picture, where can you find it? I hand my students the *Mission Handbook* and say, "Look up your profession. Look up the region that is on your heart. Look up your interests. The opportunities are right here."

—**Miriam Adeney**, *associate professor of world Christian studies at Seattle Pacific University; teaching fellow at Regent College; author of* Kingdom without Borders: The Untold Story of Global Christianity

"This unique, comprehensive, reliable resource is indispensable to anyone interested in what God is doing around the world through mission agencies in the United States and Canada. I don't know what I would do without it!"

—**Ron Blue**, *international mobilizer of Latin missions, CAM International; coordinator of the Spanish Doctor of Ministries at Dallas Theological Seminary*

"A well-written news story explains who, what, where, when, and why. In one convenient volume the *Mission Handbook* conveys the stories of hundreds of ministries: who they are, what they do (and where), and when they began. Here also is the purpose for each ministry—the why and the interpretative trends essay that describes the current and potential story of North American overseas ministries."

—**Grant McClung**, *missiological advisor to the World Missions Commission and the Pentecostal World Fellowship*

"Long ago, the *Handbook* became an indispensible and frequently consulted part of my reference library. Each successive edition seems to excel the previous one in terms of content, organization, and analysis. More than a well organized, helpfully classified directory of U.S. and Canadian Protestant mission agencies, the volume includes extraordinarily useful interpretive essays by A. Scott Moreau, analyzing the data and offering insightful perspectives on the current state and prospects of Protestant missions."

—**Jonathan J. Bonk**, *executive director of Overseas Ministries Study Center; editor of* International Bulletin of Missionary Research

"The *Mission Handbook* is an excellent, ready reference book which I've used countless times over the years. I'm not sure where I'd go for a great deal of this information. Even the Web doesn't fill this void, in part, because one piece of info leads to another in categories you've never thought about and organizations you've never heard of. If you are interested in having contact information, basic stats, and helpful analysis of the current North American mission scene, this is a book for you!"

—**Greg H. Parsons**, *general director of the U.S. Center for World Mission*

"With over two hundred new ministry listings, this edition of the *Mission Handbook* is the most expansive edition to date! If you want to know what in the world these North American-based agencies are doing, then you must get this resource. While chocked full of a wealth of data, this volume is not designed to sit on your shelf and collect dust. Get it, rejoice in what the Lord is doing through our brothers and sisters, and use it to assist you in kingdom advancement!"

—**J. D. Payne**, *missionary with the North American Mission Board; associate professor of church planting and evangelism at The Southern Baptist Theological Seminary*

"A treasure-trove of data coupled with perceptive analytic insights make this 21st edition of the *Mission Handbook* an unparalleled resource for a constellation of users. Detailed agency information makes it a must-have reference for practitioners. Careful interpretation of trends is valued by professors of mission and students alike. This trustworthy and rich reference tool has a well-earned place on the bookshelves of all who care about global outreach."

—**Evvy Hay Campbell**, *chair of Intercultural Studies at the Wheaton College Graduate School*

"The *Mission Handbook* is an indispensable reference work that I use for quick access to essential facts about Protestant missions based in the U.S. and Canada. When it arrives on my desk, I am always impressed by the variety and diversity of agencies seeking to carry out Christ's Great Commission in all of its facets."

—**Todd M. Johnson**, *executive director of Center for the Study of Global Christianity at Gordon-Conwell Theological Seminary*

"When church leaders call me to ask what mission organizations are working in certain countries, I steer them toward the *Mission Handbook*. Here, they can quickly see which organizations are working in their area of interest, which ones are congruent with their theology and tradition, how long they have been on the field, and how many staff are there. Additionally, the assessment of trends is invaluable for strategic planning. I wish all church mission leaders had a copy of the *Handbook*."

—**David Mays**, *director of learning initiatives for The Mission Exchange*

"EMIS continues to provide the North American mission community with this invaluable one-stop comprehensive reference source. I keep it in arm's reach of my desk since I refer to it frequently, so I am glad that even in this age of electronics, the *Mission Handbook* is still in this easy-to-use format."

—**Marv Newell**, *executive director of CrossGlobal Link*

"Great Commission activity in North America is increasingly decentralized and very difficult to summarize. But nothing comes close to the snapshot provided by the *Mission Handbook*. I highly recommend this reference tool as one to reach for repeatedly."

—**Steve Moore**, *president and CEO of The Mission Exchange*

"The 21st edition of the *Mission Handbook* is an extremely valuable tool for me as a mission professor and my students in the West who are seeking to engage the Global Church with the gospel. It provides amazing detail on mission agencies and their ministries. Similarly, the *Handbook* is valuable for the Global Church as they learn to engage with Western missions for gospel proclamation."

—**Samuel Naaman**, *president of the South Asian Friendship Center in Chicago; professor in the Department of Missions at Moody Bible Institute*

"Our urban francophone theological network, URBANUS, has its roots in the *Handbook*. In 1995, a group of French-speaking urban practitioners wanted to know what was being done to raise up the next generation of men and women to pursue mission in the great cities of La Francophonie. Fifteen years later, this network works in the fifty largest French-speaking cities of the world providing the best missiological formation possible. God uses tools like this to birth the most amazing initiatives."

—**Glenn Smith**, *executive director of Direction Chrétienne in Montréal*

"The 21st edition of the *Mission Handbook* is a critical resource for pastors and mission leaders in North America. Often, as we engage in our own work and ministries, it is easy to lose sight of what is changing in the surrounding culture. It is possible to grow discouraged if our recruiting efforts are yielding fewer results. However, because of the research provided in the *Handbook*, it is easier for leaders to discern the cause. If the same problem is being faced by the broader mission community, it provides leaders the opportunity to pause and examine if God is working in new ways. If the struggle is unique to your specific ministry, the *Handbook* enables you to locate other ministries you can contact and from which you can learn."

—**Mary T. Lederleitner**, *cross-cultural consultant for Wycliffe International and author of* Cross-Cultural Partnerships: Navigating the Complexities of Money and Mission

Contents

**For additional information on other resources and agencies not listed
in the *Handbook*, visit www.missionhandbook.com.**

Abbreviations and Acronyms

Admin.	Administrative, administrator	Natl.	National
Am.	America, American	NE	Northeast
Apt.	Apartment	NIV	New International Version
Assoc.	Associate, Association	NR	Not Reported
Ave.	Avenue	NW	Northwest
Bd.	Board	Org.	Organization
Blvd.	Boulevard	Pres.	President
Cen.	Central	PO	Post Office
CEO	Chief Executive Officer	Rd.	Road
Ch(s).	Church (es)	Rev.	Reverend
Co.	Company	Rm.	Room
Comm.	Commission	Rep.	Republic
Conf.	Conference	S.	South
Cong.	Congregational	SE	Southeast
Conv.	Convention	Soc.	Society
COO	Chief Operating Officer	St.	Saint, Street
Coord.	Coordinator, Coordination	Sta.	Station
Ctr.	Center	Supt.	Superintendent
Dept.	Department	Ste.	Suite
Dev.	Development	SVC(s).	Services
Dir.	Director	SW	Southwest
Div.	Division	TEE	Theological Education by Extension
Dr.	Doctor, Drive	Theol.	Theology, Theological
E.	East	U., Univ.	University
Ed.	Education	VP	Vice President
Exec.	Executive	W.	West
Frgn.	Foreign	Wld.	World
Gen.	General		
Govt.	Government	**Canada**	
Hdq.	Headquarters	AB	Alberta
Hts.	Heights	BC	British Columbia
Hwy.	Highway	MB	Manitoba
Inc.	Incorporated	NB	New Brunswick
Inst.	Institute	NF	Newfoundland
Intl.	International	NS	Nova Scotia
Is (ls).	Islands	NT	Northwest Territories
Lit.	Literature	ON	Ontario
Mgr.	Manager	PE	Prince Edward Island
Min(s).	Ministry (ies)	PQ	Québec
Msn.	Mission	SK	Saskatchewan
Mtg.	Meeting	YT	Yukon Territory
N.	North		
NA	Not Applicable		
NASB	New American Standard Bible		

United States

AK	Alaska	NJ	New Jersey
AL	Alabama	NM	New Mexico
AR	Arkansas	NV	Nevada
AZ	Arizona	NY	New York
CA	California	OH	Ohio
CO	Colorado	OK	Oklahoma
CT	Connecticut	OR	Oregon
DE	Delaware	PA	Pennsylvania
DC	District of Columbia	PR	Puerto Rico
FL	Florida	RI	Rhode Island
GA	Georgia	SC	South Carolina
HI	Hawaii	SD	South Dakota
IA	Iowa	TN	Tennessee
ID	Idaho	TX	Texas
IL	Illinois	UT	Utah
IN	Indiana	VA	Virginia
KS	Kansas	VT	Vermont
KY	Kentucky	WA	Washington
LA	Louisiana	WI	Wisconsin
MA	Massachusetts	WV	West Virginia
MD	Maryland	WY	Wyoming
ME	Maine		
MI	Michigan		
MN	Minnesota		
MO	Missouri		
MS	Mississippi		
MT	Montana		
NC	North Carolina		
ND	North Dakota		
NE	Nebraska		
NH	New Hampshire		

Mission Associations

AERDO	Association of Evangelical Relief and Development Organizations
AIMS	Accelerating International Mission Strategies
ANAM	Association of North American Missions
CCRDA	Canadian Christian Relief and Development Organizations
CWS	Church World Service
	CrossGlobal Link (IFMA)
FOM	Fellowship of Missions
	The Mission Exchange (EFMA)
OCMC	Orthodox Christian Mission Center
USCMA	US Catholic Mission Association

Advertising Directory
of Schools and Services

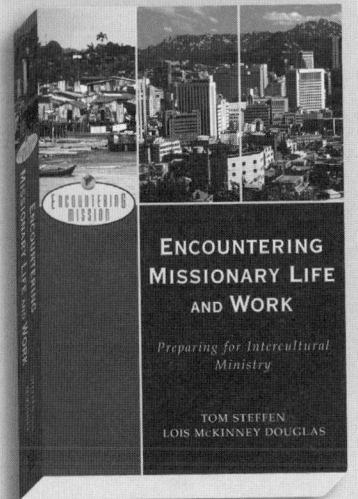
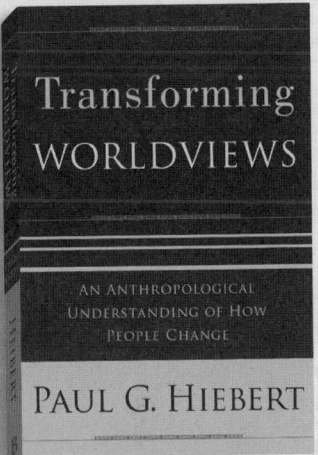
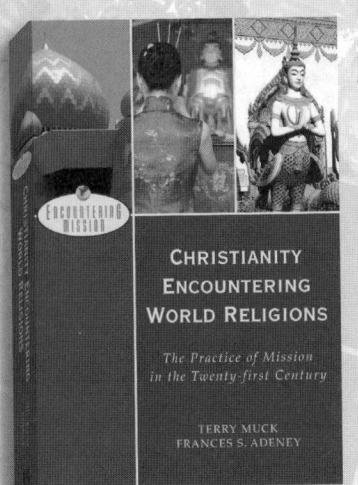

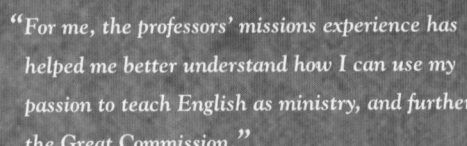

"For me, the professors' missions experience has helped me better understand how I can use my passion to teach English as ministry, and further the Great Commission."

MARK HERBST
('07, M.A. TESOL)

BIOLA UNIVERSITY IS PLEASED TO CELEBRATE

THE 25TH ANNIVERSARY
OF THE COOK SCHOOL OF INTERCULTURAL STUDIES

BIOLA UNIVERSITY · COOK SCHOOL OF INTERCULTURAL STUDIES · 25 YEARS

For the past 25 years, the School of Intercultural Studies has been all about the Great Commission. When Jesus said, "go and make disciples of all nations," we believe he meant it. Now celebrating its silver anniversary, the newly renamed Clyde and Anna Belle Cook School is committed to continuing and strengthening its tradition of disciple-making — of equipping cross-cultural servants for missions and global impact through doctoral or master's programs in missiology, intercultural studies, linguistics, education and anthropology.

Students like Mark Herbst come to the Cook School of Intercultural Studies with the ambition to impact the world for Christ. They leave with the tools to make it happen.

COOK
SCHOOL OF INTERCULTURAL STUDIES
BIOLA UNIVERSITY

LA MIRADA, CA | 1 800 OK BIOLA | WWW.BIOLA.EDU/COOK/MH

www.CrunchyLunch.com

Flying food. Grounded faith.

Your youth ministry leader said she hoped to learn more about herself on this mission trip. Little did she know the lesson would include a chapter on organic foods.

Ministry life is filled with unexpected moments. Wondering if you have the right insurance coverage shouldn't be one of them. For the expertise and specialized international mission travel insurance protection you need—count on Brotherhood Mutual.

Prepare for your next mission trip.
Free resources at www.crunchylunch.com

Brotherhood Mutual
Insurance Company

We understand why.

Insuring America's churches and related ministries.® | **www.brotherhoodmutual.com** | **800.333.3735**
Property & Liability Insurance | Commercial Vehicle | Workers' Compensation | Foreign Travel Insurance

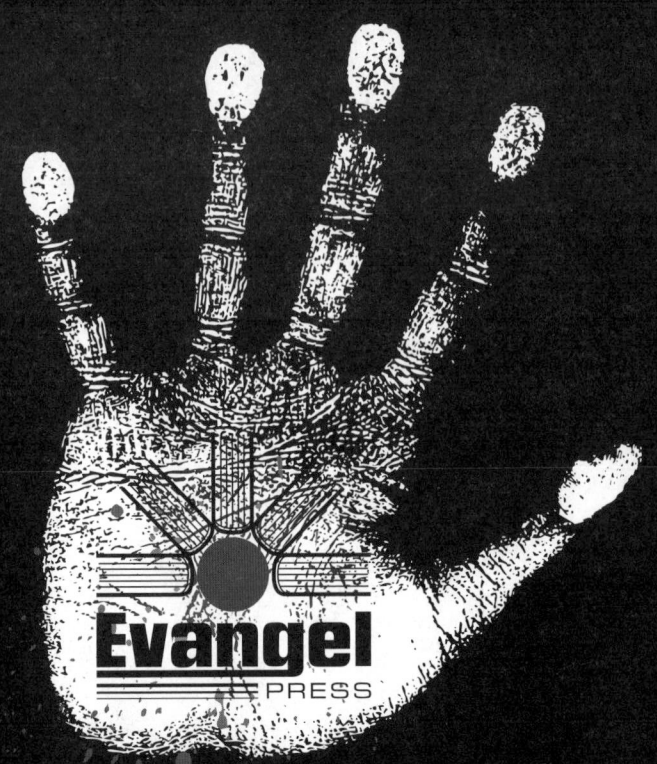

PREPARE FOR
CROSS-CULTURAL MISSIONS

**Pre-field training in
how to learn another language**

**Teaching English to
Speakers of Other Languages (TESOL)**

Intercultural Communication

Credit or non-credit courses
Three weeks each June

Institute for Cross-Cultural Training
Billy Graham Center, Wheaton College
Wheaton, IL 60187-5593
Phone: 630/752-7950   Fax 630/752-7125
E-mail: icct@wheaton.edu
Website: www.wheaton.edu/bgc/icct/

Wheaton College
For Christ and His Kingdom

NEW MODELS FOR MISSION

CROSS-CULTURAL PARTNERSHIPS

"Money is the defining and dividing issue in cross-cultural partnerships, and Mary Lederleitner has given us the essential cultural insights and very practical tools and applications to navigate these treacherous waters."

—**Sherwood Lingenfelter,** provost and senior vice president, Fuller Theological Seminary

231 pages, 978-0-8308-3747-2, $17.00

Mary T. Lederleitner is a cross-cultural consultant with Wycliffe International.

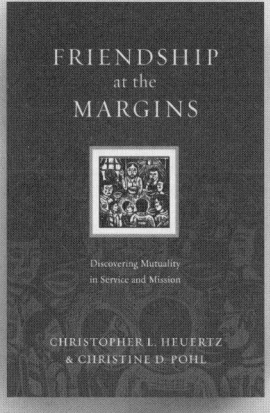

FRIENDSHIP AT THE MARGINS

"[Chris Heuertz and Christine Pohl] offer much to ponder about how, in a world of too many adversaries, the practice of friendship among the weak and unnoticed may be our hope for the future."

—**Walter Brueggemann,** Columbia Theological Seminary

120 pages, 978-0-8308-3454-9, $15.00

Christopher L. Heuertz is the international director of Word Made Flesh, an organization that serves Jesus among the most vulnerable of the world's poor.

Christine D. Pohl (Ph.D., Emory University) is professor of social ethics at Asbury Theological Seminary in Wilmore, Kentucky.

Resources for
Reconciliation

IVP Books
Think Deep. Live Smart.

800.843.9487 · *ivpress.com*

Some things are just comfortable...
and easier on the wallet than you think.

LUBBOCK CHRISTIAN UNIVERSITY

the Life Changing University

1.800.933.7601
www.lcu.edu

THE MASTER'S COLLEGE /

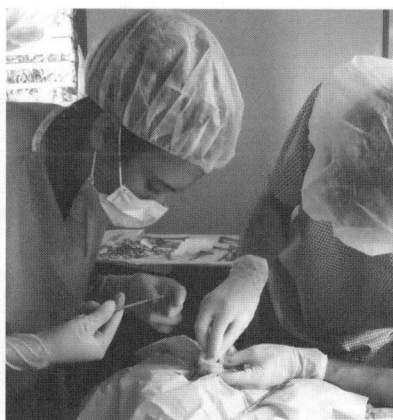

why *Intercultural Studies?*

*Study at NYACK
While Living Near
the Intercultural
Capital of the World*

*Nyack College and Alliance
Theological Seminary will prepare
you for a lifetime of participation
in intercultural and urban contexts,
here and around the world. Our
programs provide excellent academic
preparation with close proximity to
the intercultural capital of the
world–New York City!*

Programs available

- *B.A. Cross-Cultural Studies*
- *B.S. Pastoral Ministry:
  concentrations in Cross-Cultural
  Studies, Evangelism and Church
  Planting, Urban Ministries,
  and TESOL*
- *B.A. Sociology: concentrations
  in Community Development,
  Ethnic Studies*
- *B.S. TESOL*
- *M.A. Intercultural Studies*
- *M.Div. with specialized
  Missions track*
- *Master of Professional studies:
  emphasis on Urban Ministries*

NYACK
College · Seminary · Graduate Schools
Christian Higher Education Since 1882

*Your experience at NYACK will challenge you, excite
you, and prepare you for your calling. Contact us
today at www.nyack.edu or 800-336-9225.*

As he reads the paper, we're training
students to bring him far better news.

Preach the Word. Reach the World.

Training at Southwestern isn't just about understanding the Great
Commission, it's about obeying it. So every year, we train and mobilize
teams of students to take the gospel into the most difficult places of the
world even the impenetrable Buddhist strongholds of East Asia. Is
God calling you to join us? For more information and to apply online,
visit **WWW.SWBTS.EDU** or call **1.800.SWBTS.01.**

SOUTHWESTERN
BAPTIST THEOLOGICAL SEMINARY

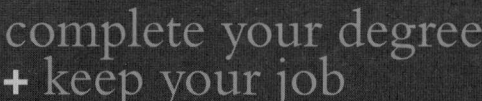

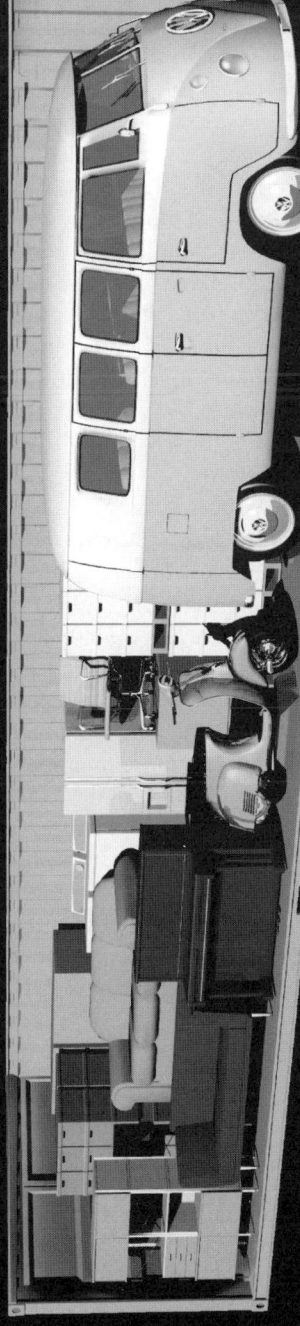

Introduction

For more than fifty years the *Mission Handbook,* under different names, different publishers, and in different formats, has been providing thousands of readers with comprehensive information on U.S. and Canadian-based Protestant mission agencies[1] engaged in overseas missions. With this 21st edition of the *Handbook* you will find complete information on more than 1,000 U.S. and Canadian-based ministries that are changing the world for Jesus Christ.

This invaluable resource includes information such as agency name and contact information, purpose statement, areas of ministry, countries of ministry, number of personnel, and more. It must be noted that although many of the agencies are involved in ministries in the U.S. and Canada, due to space concerns, this information is not included. The *Handbook* is concerned with what these agencies are doing overseas. As God continues to grow his Church, so too do mission organizations around the world continue to engage in both evangelistic and social ministry.

The *Handbook* includes only North American-based organizations. Mission activity for agencies based in other parts of the world can be found in other publications. See Appendix A for a list of these resources.

This Edition of the *Mission Handbook*

The research for the 21st edition of the *Mission Handbook* took over a year. Research was gathered via mail, email, fax, or phone. Each agency received the same questionnaire (see Appendices C and D). As times and mission agencies have changed, so too has certain aspects of the questionnaire. Key questions, however, have stayed the same. For example, questions relating to financial data have used the same definitions since the late 1970s. The countries of service and field personnel questions have remained the same since the early 1990s when the "more than four years" definition for long-term personnel was instituted. These definitions were determined in consultation with editors of other mission directories and leaders in national mission associations.

Dr. A. Scott Moreau, a former missionary to Africa who is currently serving as editor of *Evangelical Missions Quarterly* and as professor in the Intercultural Studies Department in the Wheaton College Graduate School (Wheaton, Illinois), did an overview of the survey database. The result was a comprehensive analysis of trends in U.S. and Canadian-based ministries serving overseas (see chapter 1).

History of the *Mission Handbook*

The *Mission Handbook* first appeared in 1953 with the title *Foreign Missionary Agencies in the United States: A Check List.* It was compiled and mimeographed by the Missionary Research Library (MRL) in New York. The MRL was founded in 1914 at the initiative of John R. Mott, who chaired the World Missionary Conference in Edinburgh in 1910 and headed its continuation committee.

In 1968 the publication became a cooperative effort of MRL and the Missions Advanced Research and Communication (MARC) Center, a division of World Vision International near Los Angeles. The title was changed to *North American Protestant Ministries Overseas Directory.* In 1973 the title included *"Mission Handbook"* as the publication began to include related articles and expanded analyses of the survey data. In 1976 MARC became the sole publisher. The *Mission Handbooks* of the 1990s contained chapters by MARC director Bryant L. Myers which provided a global perspective of evangelism and missions using maps, charts, graphs, and pictures. Also in the 1990s, chapters from the Catholic (www.uscatholicmission.org) and Orthodox (www.ocmc.org) mission communities were added and "Protestant" in the title was changed to "Christian." Presently, readers are referred to the websites of these two groups for their mission data.

A Word of Caution

Statistics relating to overseas missionary endeavors suffer from the same (and often more) problems as statistics in general. Although the questions have been worded to be as specific as possible, different interpretations will inevitably occur. Even within the same agency, some reporting practices may be inconsistent due to personnel changes or changes in the agency's policies or structure. Mission agencies may decide at different times and for various reasons not to report their activities in certain countries. The reader should exercise caution when comparing statistics either between agencies or within the same agency from different years. They must also be cautious in combining statistics from different agencies. Wrong conclusions about a particular agency or group of agencies or missions within a particular country may result without being aware of, or securing, additional information not in the scope of this survey.

Thanks and Acknowledgments

Our deep heartfelt thanks goes out to the individuals in each agency who completed the questionnaire. In larger agencies this may have been a collaborative effort involving executives, accountants, researchers, personnel department staff, and others. This edition of the *Handbook* is possible because of the dedicated efforts of many individuals and organizations. We also owe a tremendous debt of gratitude to Dr. Moreau for using his detailed research skills to create the analysis chapter and to John Hayward for offering his technical database assistance. We also could not have completed this edition without the following members of the EMIS team: executive editor Ken Gill, editor Linda J. Weber, designer Dona Diehl, advertising manager Vera McDonald, editorial coordinator Laurie Fortunak Nichols, data entry specialist Deborah Ferguson, and dedicated proofreaders Carolyn Larsen, Mallory Larsen, and Gloria McDowell.

Update Information

We would appreciate being updated on any changes to the mission agencies included in this volume. To update any of the information in this directory or to suggest a new listing, please contact us in one of the following ways:

Website: www.missionhandbook.com • Email: missionhandbook@wheaton.edu
Phone: 630.752.7159 • Fax: 630.752.7155
Address: EMIS, P.O. Box 794, Wheaton, IL 60187

Endnote

1. The term "agency" is used in the broad sense referring to all denominational and non-denominational boards and societies, and other specialized organizations involved in overseas mission.

Chapter 1

Putting the Survey in Perspective

A. Scott Moreau

What have we discovered in our survey for the 966 North American Protestant mission agencies listed in this edition of the *Handbook?* More than we have space to explain! Of the 966 agencies and organizations surveyed, 800 are in the United States and 166 in Canada. There are 144 more North American agencies in this *Handbook* than in the previous edition: we added 167 agencies (119 U.S. and 48 Canadian), reinstated 13 U.S. agencies, and dropped 36 agencies (32 U.S.; 4 Canadian). In this chapter we offer statistical overviews of the state of Protestant agencies in North America as well as helpful comparisons of the results of this survey with results from previous surveys.

For the past decade as we have presented this analysis, we have asked our readers to keep in mind that the tables and graphs throughout are only as valid as the numbers reported by the organizations themselves. Several factors contribute softness to these numbers. First, the numbers themselves fluctuate during the year (e.g., people leave their field of service unexpectedly, budgets change, administrative staff come and go, field assignments are changed and so on). Second, the agencies we survey use different methods for counting their own personnel. While some carefully tabulate and report painstakingly exact numbers for the month the survey is completed, others provide either highs or averages for the year. Still others provide estimates based on their best guesses, especially for categories such as short-term workers. Third, and finally, agencies do not always interpret the survey questions consistently with other agencies or even with their own answers in previous surveys. To help the reader keep this in mind, throughout this analysis we will typically use the term "reported" to refer to the numbers.

Table 1 summarizes the reported totals of the missionary force (for which we will use the terms missionary, worker and personnel interchangeably) employed by North American Protestant mission agencies from 2005 to 2008. The full-time[1] on-location North American missionary force deployed by those agencies for 2008 was 147,445 people serving in 217 different countries and territories around the world. The 147,445 includes 50,002 North Americans, 6,185 non-North Americans[2] serving in countries other than their own, and 91,258 non-North Americans serving in their own countries. This is a robust increase in the total reported missionary force mobilized by North American Protestant agencies of 9.7% over the adjusted numbers from the 2005 survey.[3]

In the seven year span from 2001 and 2008, the total full-time missionary force by North American agencies increased by 30.5%, while the North Americans grew by 5.6%, and non-North Americans grew by 48.5%. Once again, this is a vivid demonstration of the fact of the global presence of Christianity and the vibrancy of the

Table 1: North American Full-time Mobilization from 2005 to 2008

	United States			Canada			North American Totals		
	2005	2008	Change	2005	2008	Change	2005	2008	Change
U.S. or Canadian FT	43,263	47,261	9.0%	2,570	2,741	6.7%	45,833	50,002	8.9%
Non-U.S. or non-Canadian citizens in another country	5,428	5,537	2.0%	728	648	-11.0%	6,156	6,185	0.5%
Non-U.S. or non-Canadian citizens in home country	80,834	86,471	7.0%	1,510	4,787	217.0%	82,344	91,258	10.8%
Total FT on-location force	129,525	139,269	7.4%	4,808	8,176	70.0%	134,333	147,445	9.7%

faith of people from countries around the world who want to serve Christ in Christian service under the supervision of North American agencies.

The 2008 survey results indicate that for each U.S. or Canadian citizen reported as serving an agency from his or her own country, there are 2.06 non-U.S. or non-Canadian citizens also reported as serving a North American Protestant agency. The ratio in 2005 was one to 1.93. The continuing growth of this ratio over the past decade is another reminder of the global demographics of today's church.

It should be clear that this is a representative rather than a complete picture of Christians serving cross-culturally and mobilized by North American Protestant agencies. For example, numerous Christian organizations send Christian professionals to serve around the world which do not want themselves to be labeled as "mission" agencies. They are not included here. Additionally, churches (especially megachurches) send uncounted individuals as partial or fully supported cross-cultural workers. Finally, uncounted additional Christians faithfully go to serve Christ as business people or entrepreneurs without reporting to any Protestant organizational entity. Because the *Handbook* survey is limited to Protestant agencies, we cannot report numbers for these additional cross-cultural workers.

U.S. Agencies Overview

We compiled data on one-hundred more U.S. agencies for this edition than the previous *Handbook* (800 versus 700). We listed 700 agencies in the previous edition. We dropped 32 agencies and added 132 ones. Of these 132, we added 119 for the first time and restored 13 to the survey that we did not include in the previous edition.

Table 2 helps us better track some of the information in this edition. The "Agencies Tracked from 2001 to 2008" column lists the totals from 607 agencies that are included in this edition as well as in the past two editions of the *Handbook*. We will use information from these agencies to explore trends and shifts over the seven-year span they cover. The "Agencies Tracked from 2005 to 2008" column gives the numbers for the 668 agencies that are included in this edition as well as the previous edition. The "Agencies Newly Listed in 2008" column gives the totals for the 119 agencies added to this edition for the first time. We will use information on these agencies to see how they affect the totals for this edition. Finally, the "All Agencies 2008" column on the far right lists the totals for all 800 U.S. Protestant agencies listed in this *Handbook*. These numbers are our baseline for comparing with totals from previous editions.

Table 2: Summary of U.S. Protestant Missions Statistics Reported for 2008

	Agencies Tracked from 2001 to 2008		Agencies Tracked from 2005 to 2008		Agencies Newly Listed in 2008		All Agencies 2008
	Number	% of All	Number	% of All	Number	% of All	All agencies 2008
General							
Number of Agencies	607	75.9%	668	83.5%	119	14.9%	800
Income for Overseas	$5,459,363,107	95.8%	$5,492,917,012	96.4%	$187,032,941	3.3%	$5,700,848,815
Average Income for Overseas	$8,994,008	126.2%	$8,222,930	115.4%	$1,571,705	22.1%	$7,126,061
Full-time U.S. Personnel Serving Overseas							
Long-term (4+ years)	33,925	98.4%	34,227	99.3%	176	0.5%	34,480
Mid-term (1 to 4 years)	7,442	78.9%	9,267	98.3%	152	1.6%	9,427
Tentmakers	3,102	92.5%	3,183	94.9%	131	3.9%	3,354
Other U.S. Personnel Serving Overseas							
Short-term (< 2 weeks)	31,093	75.1%	31,684	76.6%	9,509	23.0%	41,378
Short-term (≥ 2 weeks)	59,772	77.3%	73,397	95.0%	3,758	4.9%	77,281
Nonresidential					99	2.4%	4,166
Fully Supported	3,915	94.0%	4,048	97.2%			1,489
Partially Supported	1,354	90.9%	1,415	95.0%	51	3.4%	
Non-U.S. Personnel Directly Supported							
In Home Country	73,397	84.9%	83,994	97.1%	1,387	1.6%	86,471
Outside Home Country	5,205	94.0%	5,352	96.7%	165	3.0%	5,537
U.S. Home Office and Support Staff							
Full-time Paid	20,989	94.1%	21,442	96.2%	731	3.3%	22,296
Part-time	3,352	87.0%	3,483	90.4%	306	7.9%	3,852
Short-term Support staff							
Full-time	868	81.0%	939	87.7%	129	12.0%	1,071
Part-time (≥ 50%)	427	84.4%	462	91.3%	39	7.7%	506
Part-time (10 to 49%)	638	61.4%	820	78.9%	207	19.9%	1,039
Selected Totals of People Mobilized by U.S. Agencies							
Grand Total	245,479	84.0%	273,713	93.6%	16,840	5.8%	292,347
U.S. Full-time On-location	44,469	94.1%	46,677	98.8%	459	1.0%	47,261
All Full-time On-location	123,071	88.4%	136,023	97.7%	2,011	1.4%	139,269
All Overseas	219,205	83.2%	246,567	93.5%	15,428	5.9%	263,583
All Support	26,274	91.3%	27,146	94.4%	1,412	4.9%	28,764

As indicated in the "All Agencies 2008" column, the reported on-location, full-time United States missionary force from 800 U.S. agencies was comprised of 139,269 people serving in 217 countries and territories.[4] As seen in Tables 1 and 2, 47,261 were U.S. citizens working in another country; 5,537 were non-U.S. citizens serving in countries other than their own, and 86,471 were non-U.S. citizens serving in their own countries (occasionally referred to in this chapter as nationals).

Table 2 gives us indicators about continuities and discontinuities from the various surveys for previous editions of the *Handbook*. We indicate the share of the totals contributed from the agencies carried over from 2001 to 2008 in the column to the right of the totals for those agencies. Altogether, these 607 agencies contributed 95.8% of the total reported overseas income, 88.4% of the full-time on-location personnel (including U.S. and non-U.S. citizens), 94.1% of the full-time on-location U.S. personnel (1 to 4+ years plus tentmakers), 98.4% of the long-term U.S. personnel and 91.3% of the administrative and short-term support staff for the 800 U.S. agencies.

Likewise, we indicate the share of the totals contributed from the agencies carried over from 2005 to 2008 in the column to the right of the totals for those agencies. Altogether, these 668 agencies contributed 96.4% of the total reported overseas income, 97.7% of the full-time on-location personnel (including U.S. and non-U.S. citizens), 98.8% of the full-time on-location U.S. personnel (1 to 4+ years plus tentmakers), 99.3% of the long-term U.S. personnel and 94.4% of the administrative and short-term support staff for the 800 U.S. agencies. Clearly in these two areas, the 2001 to 2008 and 2005 to 2008 carryovers well represent the totals for all 800 agencies surveyed.

Finally, the "Agencies Newly Listed in 2008" column offers us an opportunity to see emphases among the newly listed agencies. We indicate the share of the totals contributed from the agencies in the column to the right of their totals. Since 117 of these 119 agencies were founded after 1944 (and 101 after 1974), they offer us a snapshot of the types of emphases newer agencies pursue, as well as areas in which they place less emphasis. While adding almost 14.9% to the total list of agencies, for example, they added 23.0% to our newest category of short-term missions (those less than two weeks in duration). They also add 19.9% to the number of part-time (less than 50%) short-term support staff and 12% to the full-time short-term support staff. On the other hand, they only added 0.5% of the long-term workers. The latter confirms the former—these newly added agencies focus far more of their energy on what we might call micro-term missions (less than 2 weeks long) than on long-term work. Finally, we may also note that the average income for overseas work of these agencies is only 22.1% of the average budget for all 800 agencies. Together these indicate that the newly added agencies—while numerous—are by and large relatively small and relatively focused on short-term missions work in comparison with the other agencies.

In Table 3, we offer the comparative totals from the surveys since 1996,[5] together with indicators that help us discern the patterns in the data. The Annualized Growth Rate (AGR)[6] columns enable us to see difference between the AGR for 1996 to 2005 and 2005 to 2008. The final column simply shows the difference between the two growth rates, which indicates the severity of the change. In looking at the table, it will help to keep the following in mind. First, a negative number in AGR 1 (2005-2008) indicates a reduction in actual numbers between the two surveys. However, a negative number in the AGR 1—AGR 2 column indicates a slower growth between the two periods, but not necessarily negative growth in the 2005 to 2008 period. For example, the AGR 1—AGR 2 for non-residential fully supported workers was -11.2%. The actual number of non-residential fully supported workers *grew* from 2005 to 2008—at an AGR of 10.9%. However, this annualized growth rate was much slow-

Table 3: Summary of Reported U.S. Protestant Mission Agency Totals 1996-2008

	1996	1998	2001	2005	2008	Change (2005-08)	1. AGR 2005-08	2. AGR 1996-05	AGR 1-AGR 2
U.S. Personnel Serving Full-time Overseas									
Long-term (4+ years)	33,074	32,957	34,747	33,714	34,480	2.3%	0.8%	0.2%	0.5%
Mid-term (1 to 4 yrs.)	6,562	6,930	8,001	7,615	9,427	23.8%	7.4%	1.7%	5.7%
Tentmakers	1,336	1,853	1,780	1,934	3,354	73.4%	20.1%	4.2%	15.9%
Totals	**40,972**	**41,740**	**44,528**	**43,263**	**47,261**	**9.2%**	**3.0%**	**0.6%**	**2.4%**
Other U.S. Personnel Serving Overseas									
Short-term (< 2 weeks)	N/A	N/A	N/A	N/A	41,378	N/A	N/A	N/A	N/A
Short-term (> 2 wks.)	63,995	97,272	149,810	144,318	77,281	-46.5%	-18.8%	9.5%	-28.3%
Subtotals	**63,995**	**97,272**	**149,810**	**144,318**	**118,659**	**-17.8%**	**-6.3%**	**9.5%**	**-15.8%**
Non-residential full support	507	1,093	1,610	3,055	4,166	36.4%	10.9%	22.1%	-11.2%
Non-residential partial support	215	310	501	697	1,489	113.6%	28.8%	14.0%	14.8%
Subtotals	**722**	**1,403**	**2,111**	**3,752**	**5,655**	**50.7%**	**14.7%**	**20.1%**	**-5.4%**
Non-U.S. Personnel Directly Supported									
In home country	28,535	56,214	59,852	80,834	86,471	7.0%	2.3%	12.3%	-10.0%
Outside home country	1,791	3,179	3,744	5,428	5,537	2.0%	0.7%	13.1%	-12.4%
Subtotals	**30,326**	**59,393**	**63,596**	**86,262**	**92,008**	**6.7%**	**2.2%**	**12.3%**	**-10.1%**
U.S. Ministry and Home Office Staff									
Full-time paid staff	19,399	21,758	20,724	19,199	22,296	16.1%	5.1%	-0.1%	5.2%
Part-time staff/associates	2,850	2,946	2,896	4,547	3,852	-15.3%	-5.4%	5.3%	-10.7%
Subtotals	**22,249**	**24,704**	**23,620**	**23,746**	**26,148**	**10.1%**	**3.3%**	**0.7%**	**2.5%**
Short-term Support Staff									
Part-time (10 to 49%)	455	823	779	979	1,039	-25.6%	-9.4%	17.4%	-26.8%
Part-time (> 50%)	150	281	502	463	506	9.3%	3.0%	13.3%	-10.3%
Full-time	339	457	585	1,440	1,071	6.1%	2.0%	8.9%	-6.9%
Subtotals	**944**	**1,561**	**1,866**	**2,882**	**2,616**	**-9.2%**	**-3.2%**	**13.2%**	**-16.4%**
Total People Mobilized by U.S. Agencies									
Grand Total	**159,208**	**226,073**	**285,531**	**304,223**	**292,347**	**-3.9%**	**-1.3%**	**7.5%**	**-8.8%**
U.S. Full-time On-location	40,972	41,740	44,528	43,263	47,261	9.2%	3.0%	0.6%	2.4%
All Full-time On-location	71,298	101,133	108,124	129,525	139,269	7.5%	2.4%	6.9%	-4.4%
All Overseas, Any Duration	136,015	199,808	260,045	277,595	263,583	-5.0%	-1.7%	8.2%	-10.0%
All Support Staff (Home/ST)	23,193	26,265	25,486	26,628	28,764	8.0%	2.6%	1.5%	1.1%

Financial Support Raised in the U.S.—Income for Overseas Ministries (Adjusted for Inflation)

1996	1998	2001	2005	2008	Change (2005-2008)	AGR (2005-2008)
$3,179,656,881	$3,873,909,057	$4,560,026,911	$5,778,375,541	$5,700,848,815	-1.3%	-0.45%

er than the 22.1% AGR from 1996 to 2005, so even though the number of non-residential fully supported workers continued to grow from 2005 to 2008, it did so at a much slower pace than from 1996 to 2005. Together these columns help us identify areas of health as well as areas of concern in our analysis—and let us see relative strengths of health or concern.

Looking at the final column, then, gives a quick indicator of how agencies fared in 2005 to 2008 versus 1996 to 2005. The reported numbers of mid-term workers (1 to 4 years), tentmakers, non-residential partially supported workers, and full-time paid staff grew more quickly from 2005 to 2008 than from 1996 to 2005. However, the number of short-term workers, non-residential fully supported workers, nationals (whether serving in their own county or another country), part-time paid staff, and short-term support staff of all levels either shrank or grew less quickly from 2005 to 2008 than they did from 1996 to 2005. In sum, our relative "report card" for U.S. Protestant mission agency growth from 2005 to 2008 is mixed, and the news is more bad than good, as most clearly seen in the four totals categories above the financial categories in Table 3.

Throughout the discussion that follows, we will use the following terms to designate the types of changes:
- *TREND*—change consistent over a decade or more
- *trend*—change consistent from 2001 to 2008
- *SHIFT*—change shown by 2005-2008 data that is opposite a pattern previously seen for at least a decade
- *shift*—change shown by 2005-2008 data that differs from the pattern over the 2001-2005 period

In our analysis of the data, we discovered 15 *TRENDS* (all up), 140 *trends* (109 up, 31 down), 21 *SHIFTS* (12 up and 9 down), and 107 *shifts* (43 up and 64 down). Some of these we can combine with others for analysis, such as the two categories of nonresidential workers. Many others are simply not significant or large enough for our analysis. For example, agencies whose primary activity falls in the education and training category reported an increase in non-residential partially supported personnel from 9 in 2005 to 24 in 2008. While this is in fact a 250% increase, even so the number reported in 2008 comprises less than 2% of the 1,489 total non-residential partially supported workers, and space precludes discussion or analysis of such changes. With that in mind, we organize the material in three major categories: U.S. agency aggregate totals and changes, activity totals and changes, and deployment location totals and changes.

U.S. Agency Aggregate Totals and Changes

In every survey over the past several decades, we have asked each of the 800 U.S. organizations and agencies to provide us with general information about the leadership, denominational orientation, historic tradition, and the purpose of their organization. We also ask for statistical information. Some of this information is about the personnel they deploy (from short-term to long-term), the type of overseas engagement (full-time or nonresidential). For full-time personnel we ask them to identify the numbers in six categories: the country, the number of full-time U.S. workers, and the number of non-U.S. workers. We ask them to tell us how many personnel staff the agency (home staff and short-term staff) and whether they are full-time or part-time. The rest of the information we request relates to non-personnel issues, such as the date they were founded, general financial information (total income for the year, income for overseas work, and gifts in kind income) and the types of activities they engage in as an organization, including which one activity they consider to be one most associated with their organization. Finally, we ask them to identify among several methods those they use to recruit short-term workers.

TREND Up: Non-U.S. Citizens

The most significant upward *TREND* is that U.S. agencies continue to utilize ever more non-U.S. citizens to engage in their work. As seen in Figure 1, while the number continues to increase, the rate of growth has slowed down over the last period. From 1996 to 2005, the AGR was 12.32%, but it dropped to 2.17% from 2005 to 2008. As Figure 2 illustrates, however, due to an increase in U.S. workers we can report a small SHIFT down in the share of non-U.S. workers in the total pool working under U.S. agencies and organizations.

When U.S. Protestant agencies employ non-U.S. citizens, we primarily deploy them in their own countries (94%). However, the number of non-U.S. citizens serving U.S. agencies in their home countries grew at an AGR of 2.2% from 2005 to 2008, sharply lower than the 12.3% AGR from 1996 to 2005 (Table 3, also Figures 3

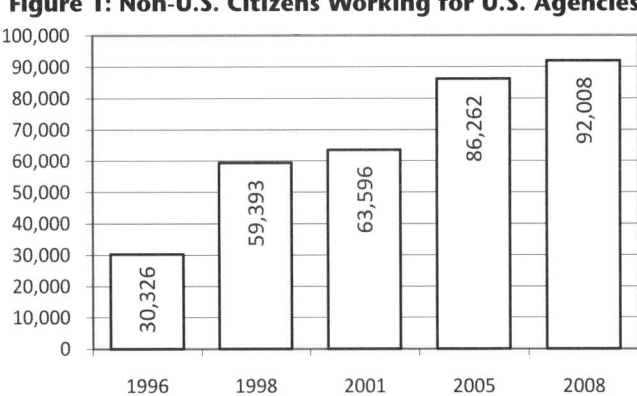

Figure 1: Non-U.S. Citizens Working for U.S. Agencies

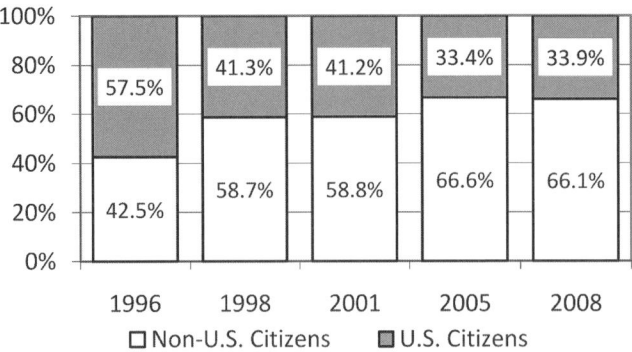

Figure 2: Share of U.S. and Non-U.S. Citizens Working for U.S. Agencies

and 4). We noted in the previous edition that while there should be no question of the potential effectiveness of the work of non-U.S. citizens, and across the majority world there are definite financial efficiencies gained through employing them rather than U.S. citizens, the extent to which these workers are actually serving as *cross-cultural workers* rather than same-culture workers is unknown. Further, we do not ask in our survey whether the reported non-U.S. workers are serving cross-culturally. It is easy to imagine an Indian working in India in a cross-cultural setting; likewise in our globalized world it is also easy to imagine a Nigerian working among same-culture Nigerians in England.

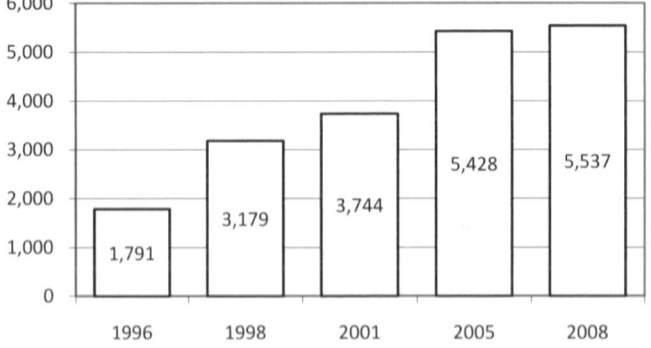

Figure 3: Non-U.S. Citizens Working outside Their Home Country for U.S. Agencies

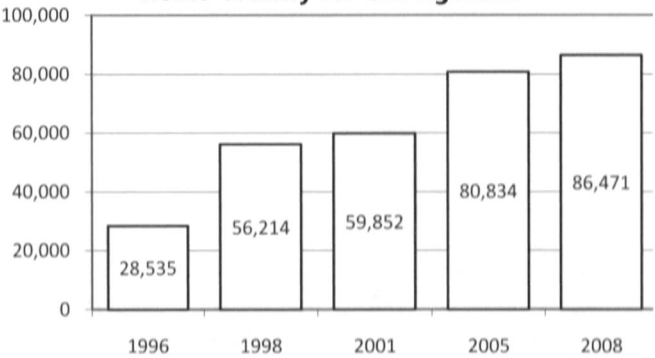

Figure 4: Non-U.S. Citizens Working in Their Home Country for U.S. Agencies

In Table 4 we list the U.S. agencies and organizations that reported 500 or more non-U.S. citizens working for them. In our listing for 2005, this included 26 agencies; for 2008 it includes 25. With the continuing globalization of mission agencies and organizations (which most recognize as healthy), we cannot ignore questions that have arisen in global conversation about multinational operations of all types. Is it ultimately good or bad to continue the trend of having ever more non-U.S. citizens work for U.S. agencies? What are the motivations driving this *TREND*? What will be the ultimate results? Answers to these and many other similar questions are

Table 4: Agencies with 500 or More Non-U.S. Citizen Workers

Rank	Agency	No.
1	Campus Crusade for Christ, Intl.	11,404
2	Christian Aid Mission	11,036
3	Gospel for Asia, Inc.	9,523
4	AMG International	8,293
5	Youth With A Mission (YWAM)	6,162
6	Partners International	4,278
7	India Gospel Outreach, Inc.	2,540
8	Compassion International, Inc.	1,531
9	World Relief	1,179
10	Gospelink, Inc.	1,113
11	Word of Life Fellowship, Inc.—International Ministries	1,015
12	Final Frontiers Foundation, Inc.	1,010
13	Dayspring International	1,000
14	India Gospel League, NA	908
15	World Concern	850
16	Christian Broadcasting Network Inc., The	847
17	Reaching Indians Ministries International	810
18	I. N. Network USA	804
19	Greater Grace World Outreach	793
20	Lott Carey Baptist Foreign Mission Convention	730
21	World Link Ministries	720
22	Baptist Missionary Association of America	704
23	HBI Global Partners	605
24	Far East Broadcasting Company, Inc.	515
25	Bible League, The	500

beyond the reach of our work here, and need to be taken up by missionaries, mission leaders, and missiologists if we are to walk the tensions created in ways that please God. Certainly one of the foundational realities of globalization is that "market-share" is driven by several factors, and choice at the local level for prospective cross-cultural workers to decide which organization to join is a fact that will not change in the foreseeable future.

TREND Up: Growth in Full-time On-location Workers

An important *TREND* is that the total of all full-time, on-location workers for U.S. agencies continued to rise (Figure 5). For every 4 U.S. citizens there are 7.79 non-U.S. citizens working under the employ of U.S. agencies. This is a slight decrease from the previous survey in which there were 7.97 nationals for every four Americans. A parallel *trend* was the growth in the number of all U.S. citizens working full-time for U.S. agencies (including home staff; Figure 6).

Figure 5: Full-time On Location Workers

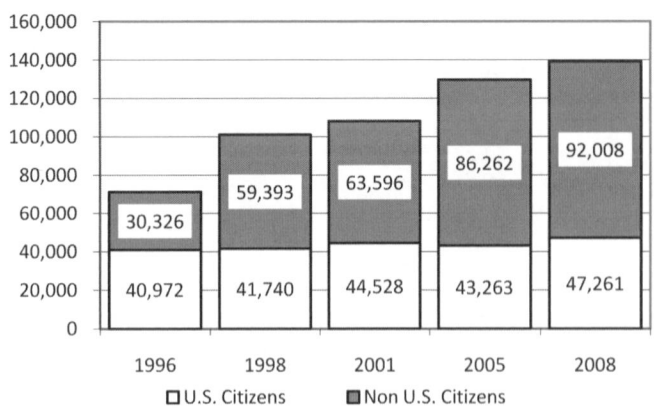

U.S. Citizens   Non U.S. Citizens

Figure 6: U.S. Citizens Working for U.S. Agencies

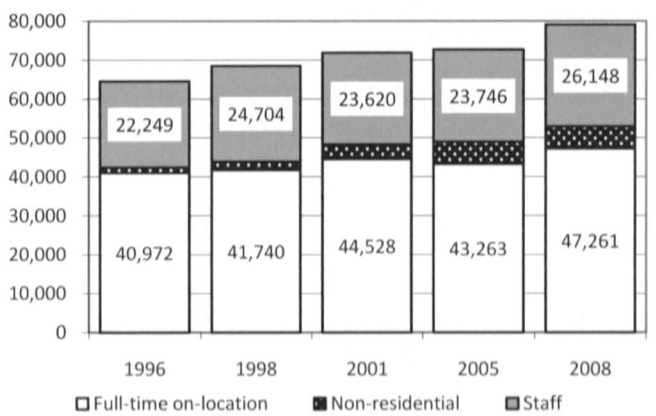

Full-time on-location   Non-residential   Staff

TREND Up: Nonresidential Workers

In addition to the full-time on-location workers, nonresidential workers continued the growth TREND seen since 1996, though the AGR was roughly three-quarters of the 1998 to 2005 rate (from 14.7% as opposed to 20.1%; Table 3).

SHIFT Up: Mid-term Workers

In our previous analysis, we reported a 5.2% decrease of U.S. citizens serving overseas for 1 to 4 years. The reported numbers turned around dramatically in this edition, with a 10.7% increase in 1 to 2 year full-time workers and a 32.7% increase in 2 to 4 year workers (Table 5) for a net increase of 23.8% (Table 3). The newly added agencies accounted for only 1.6% of the total for mid-term workers, so the increase was largely due to the same agencies listed in 2005 adding to their reported ranks.

Trend up: Tentmakers

The increase in reported tentmakers also continued as a trend. For this edition,

Table 5: Full-time U.S. Workers

	2001	2005	2008	Change (2005-08)	1: AGR 2005-08	2: AGR 2001-05	AGR 1 minus AGR 2
1 to 2 Years	2,755	3,077	3,406	10.7%	3.4%	2.8%	-0.2%
2 to 4 Years	5,246	4,538	6,021	32.7%	9.9%	-3.6%	10.9%
4+ Years	34,747	33,714	34,480	2.3%	0.8%	-0.8%	1.3%
Tentmakers	1,780	1,934	3,354	73.4%	20.1%	2.1%	12.7%
Totals	44,528	43,263	47,261	9.2%	3.0%	-0.7%	3.0%

the count grew a dramatic 73.4% (Table 5; an AGR of 20.1%). As we noted in the previous edition concerning tentmakers, the number reported from U.S. agencies is only a fraction of the actual total. A good number of tentmakers simply find employment with a company that allows overseas work. Churches are beginning to send others without necessarily connecting them with mission agencies. Individuals start businesses in international settings and live lives of Christian witness without any connections to U.S. groups or organizations. I have friends in all three categories and am sure there are additional types of tentmakers as well.

Together with this increase in long-term workers is the *trend* of an increasing reported number of 1 to 2 year full-time workers, the *shift* to an increase of 2 to 4 year as well as 4+ year workers and *trend* of a significant increase in the reported number of tentmakers. Showing the comparative growth rates in each category in the 2001 to 2005 and 2005 to 2008 periods best demonstrates the strength of the turnaround in three of the four categories (Figure 7). With the totals up in every category, the aggregate of U.S. on-location full-time workers in 2008 more than erased the dip seen in 2005.

Figure 7: AGR for Full-time U.S. Citizen by Category

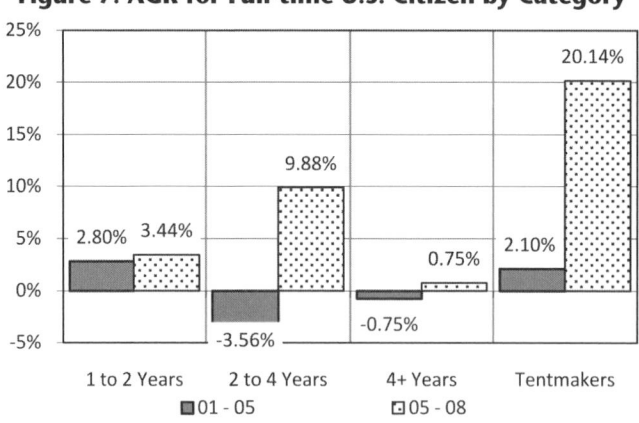

Trend up: Home Staff

Home staff for U.S. agencies is a mixed picture. The number of reported full-time home staff shifted from decline (1998 to 2005) to significant growth (Table 3 and Figure 8; adjusted from the previous edition of the *Handbook*). However, the number

Figure 8: All Home Staff for U.S. Agencies

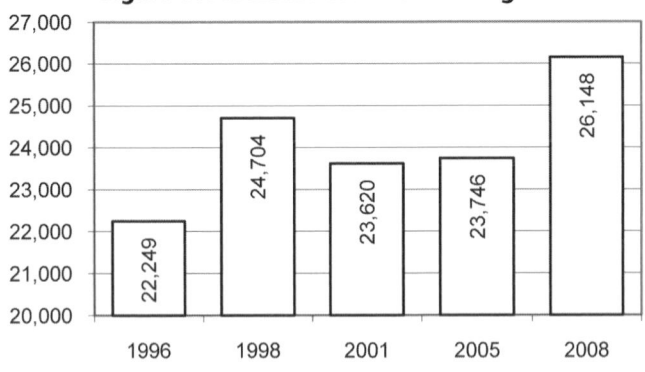

of part-time home staff declined, and the AGRs for both show a mixed picture. Ultimately, the increase in the number of full-time staff was large enough to give a net trend of an increase in the number of home support and administrative staff from 2001 to 2008. As with the 2005 survey, the numbers are significantly larger than might be expected for administrative staff only, but again that is primarily attributable to the different ways agencies legitimately count their home staff numbers—which are not limited to administrative staff. The average for all 599 agencies reporting at least one person in this category is 37.2 per agency. Discounting only the first two agencies results in an average of 27.2 per agency. Factoring out the top ten agencies, the other 589 average 17.6 per agency, 2 more staff per agency than in our last survey. This may be an indicator of an aging long-term force returning home to help out administratively as well as redeployments in the United States to have staff work cross-culturally among immigrants and ethnic pockets here.

TREND Down: Short-term Workers

The final *TREND* we note for agency totals is the continuing decrease in the number of short-term missionaries sent by U.S. agencies. In the 2008 survey, and as seen in Table 2, we asked agencies to report short-term trips of less than two weeks with the intention of catching a more accurate picture of the total number of people who do short-term trips through them. Even combining these with the reported number of trips two weeks or longer, the net decrease in reported short-term mission workers for 2008 is significant (17.78%; Table 3; Figure 9) and the growth rates for short-term workers appear to indicate that U.S. agencies are significantly cutting back on short-term mobilization (Figure 10).

Thus, in sum, while U.S. full-time workers increased, U.S. short-term workers decreased (Figure 11). The reasons are certainly complicated, and include numerous factors. At least from our survey no straight line correlation between the two trends is possible. One might say that given the lag between a short-term trip and a full term commitment, we might expect to see full-time numbers to rise at some point after the short-term rise, and that certainly is seen in the reported numbers. However, until we can demonstrate a correlation that takes place over time and that the two are related it is best not to connect them too directly. With the sheer number of evangelical Christians reaching a saturation stage, correlating short-term with full-time longer term would seem to be statistically impossible from here on out.

Figure 9: All Short-term Workers

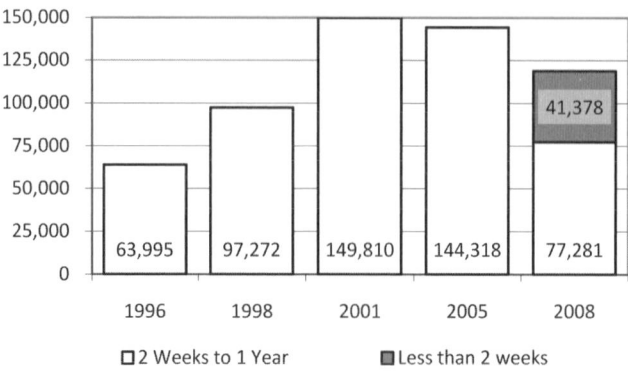

Figure 10: AGR of Short-term (> 2 Weeks) Workers

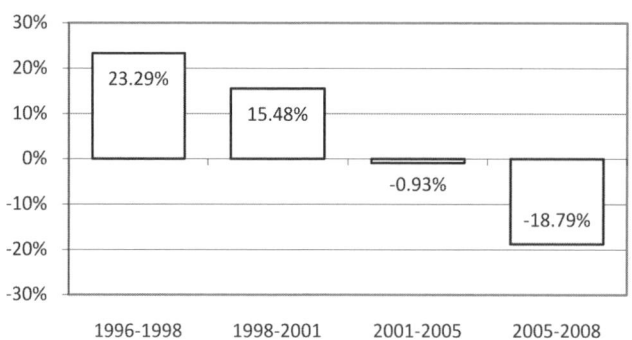

Figure 11: All Full-time, Long-term and Short-term Missionaries

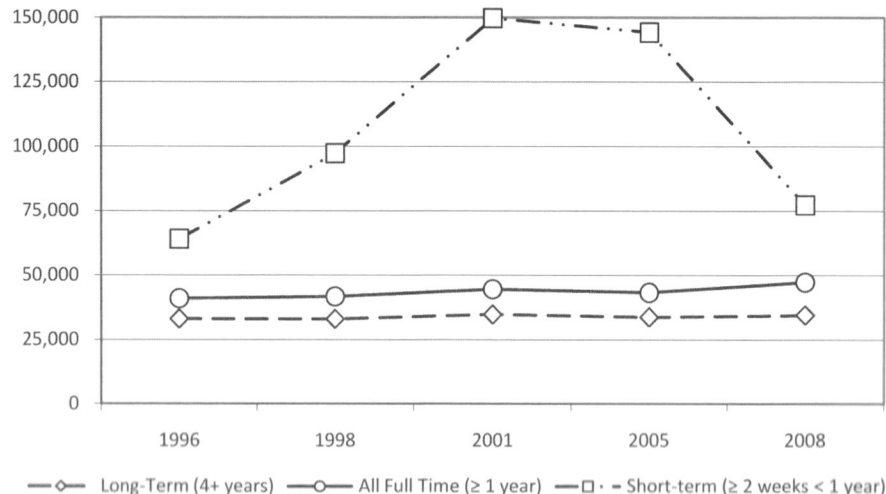

SHIFT down: Short-term Support Staff

Additionally, for the first time in more than a decade the number of people supporting short-term work among U.S. agencies shifted to a decline—and a significant one. Figure 12 shows the total number of personnel (whether in the U.S. or overseas) who devote at least 10% of their work to supporting short-term missions, and Figure 13 shows the breakdown by category. The 7.1% increase in part-time staff mitigated the 25.6% drop in full-time support staff. However, because of the focus on short-term mission by the 119 new agencies, the decline among previously listed agencies was far more significant than it appears. Excluding the new agencies, the number of reported part-time short-term support staff *dropped* 4.5% and the full-time dropped 40%. Perhaps the tightened budgets (see below) have deeply impacted this. Perhaps the longer established U.S. organizations are shifting focus. Whatever the reason, fewer people are going on short-term trips through U.S. agencies, and U.S. agencies are devoting fewer support staff to the venture, and—at least for now, newer agencies that focus on short-term efforts are stepping into the gap offering opportunities as well as support.

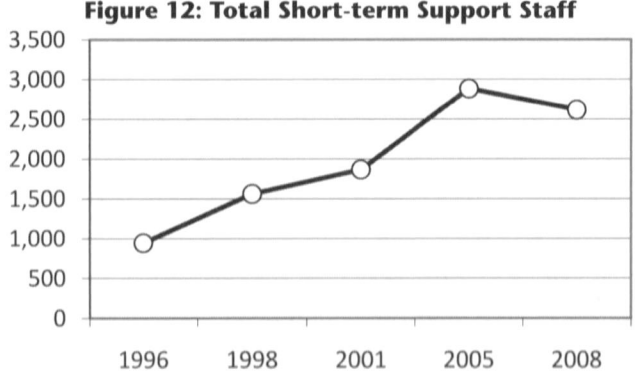

Figure 12: Total Short-term Support Staff

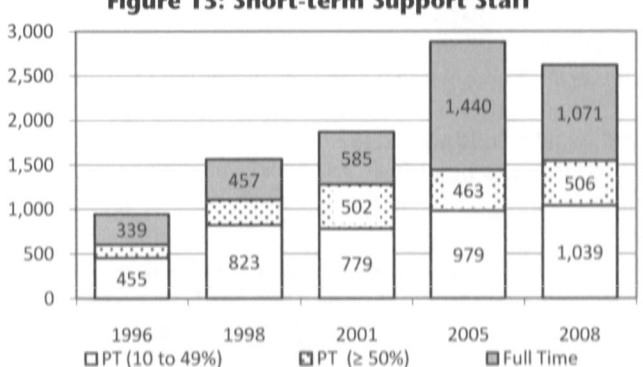

Figure 13: Short-term Support Staff

Figure 14 shows how the agencies contact people for short-term missions. The number of organizations that contacted potential workers through churches rose slightly; all other contact methods from the previous survey dropped. In this survey we added "Web" as a method for short-term contacts. 136 organizations indicated they used the Web in this fashion, making it third ranked among the five categories. With all organizations considered, the drop in contact methods was 3.3%. However, excluding the 119 newly listed organizations from the results yielded a 20.2% reduction in the total number of contact methods indicated by the agencies.

Figure 14: Contact Methods for Short-term Recruitment for All U.S. Agencies

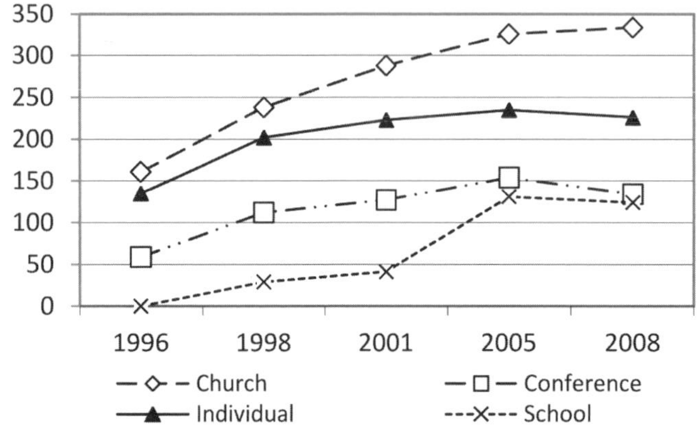

SHIFT Down: Income for Overseas Ministries

Certainly the *shift* seen among U.S. agencies with the greatest overall impact is the drop in reported income for overseas ministries (Table 6). Though this is the first time we have seen a drop in inflation-adjusted income between surveys, it is not surprising in light of the recent global financial collapse. As an overall picture, it is fair to say that on average U.S. agencies and organizations are operating at an inflation-adjusted budget roughly that of 2005. For this survey, the reported inflation-adjusted total income and the gifts in kind total income for all organizations also dropped. The fact that these are 2008 numbers is a sobering reminder, as that was the beginning of the financial meltdown. Agencies began tightening their belts in 2008, but there is no evidence that this is simply a short-phased issue. As of this writing, the final results of the impact of the global crunch is not yet known. It is hard to imagine that income for 2009 was better than for 2008, and agencies still face tremendous challenges funding ministry into the future.

**Table 6: Income for Overseas Ministries
1996 to 2008 (Adjusted for Inflation)**

1996	1998	2001	2005	2008
$3,179,656,881	$3,873,909,057	$4,560,026,911	$5,778,375,541	$5,700,848,815
1992 to 1996	1996 to 1998	1998 to 2001	2001 to 2005	2005 to 2008
0.27%	10.38%	5.59%	6.10%	-0.45%

Figure 15 clearly illustrates the differences. In it we indicate the aggregate total reported by all agencies for 2008. Figure 16 shows the annualized growth rates for each period. As noted, this is the first time the aggregate AGR dipped below zero between surveys—and it includes one-hundred more agencies than the 2005 survey.

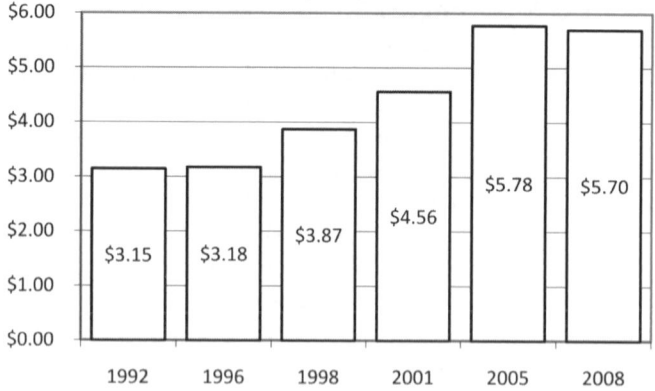

Figure 15: Inflation Adjusted Income for Overseas for U.S. Agencies (Billions of Dollars)

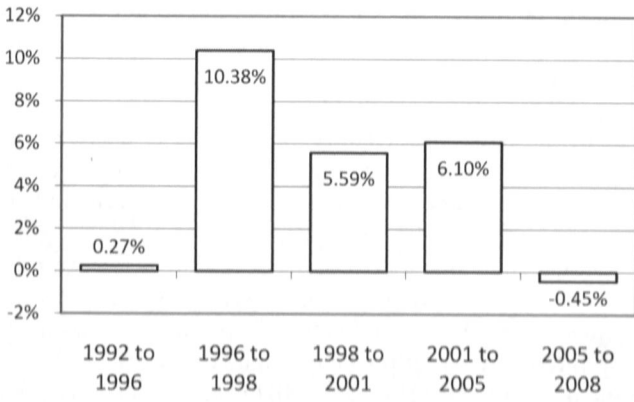

Figure 16: Inflation Adjusted AGR Income for Overseas for U.S. Agencies

At first glance, the drop appears to be broadly-based among the agencies. However, there are three types of evidence that suggest the total income for overseas ministries grew from 2005 to 2008. First, five agencies which reported an aggregate of more than $180 million in 2005 reported an aggregate of $0 as their income for overseas ministries in 2008. All five continue to operate today. Even if they operated at 2005 levels, the difference is greater than the total loss from 2005 to 2008. Second, 415 agencies reported income in each of the past three surveys (2001, 2005 and 2008). Of these, 146 reported an inflation-adjusted increase from 2005 to 2008, and their aggregate inflation-adjusted 2008 total is 1.6% *higher* than the 2005 totals. Third, 483 agencies reported incomes for the past two surveys (2005 and 2008). Of these, 172 reported an inflation-adjusted *increase* from 2005 to 2008. In fact, when we compare the totals of these 483 agencies, there is surprising inflation-adjusted to-tal *increase* of over 19.1% (an AGR of 6.0%)! Thus, it is accurate to say that it was the agencies which did not report incomes in either of the two years that had the great-est impact on the total difference, and that at *least* 172 of the 668 agencies (25.7%) common to both surveys reported an inflation-adjusted increase in income for over-seas ministries from 2005 to 2008.

Activities of U.S. Agencies

As has been our practice over the past several surveys, in our 2008 survey we asked agencies to identify up to six activities that are the primary activities of their organi-zation. We provide a list of options from which to choose, and include an "Other" option that lets them identify additional activities not in the current list. After each survey, we examine the "other" options and add to the following survey's list some of the "other" activities. In the 2008 survey, we added five new options to the previ-ous list (Business as Mission, Children at Risk, HIV/Aids, Sports Program Ministry, and Trafficking/Slavery Issues), resulting in 66 total activity choices.

We also ask agencies to indicate which **one** of the activities they most commonly associate with their organization. For our discussion, we refer to that activity as the "primary activity." We refer to the remaining activities identified by each organiza-tion (up to five) as "activities" or "all activities."

As we have noted over the past several surveys, for the following analysis we as-sume that the self-identified primary activity receives a larger share of an agency's re-sources and energy than any other activity. Thus, if an agency selects "National work-er support" as their primary activity, we assume that this will receive more personnel and financial resources than any of the other five activities reported by that agency, and that assumption guides the analysis which follows.

Further, as in the past, we categorize each of the 66 activities into five larger groups: evangelism & discipleship, education & training, relief & development, mis-sion agency support, and other. We list the groupings with the individual activities in Table 7.

Figure 17 shows the comparative share of resources for several categories for 2008. To keep the chart less cluttered, we only indicate the actual share when it is greater than 10%. Agencies who indicate their primary activity in the evangelism and discipleship category report the largest share of income for overseas ministries (with relief and development a close second), full-time workers (U.S. and non-U.S.), short-term workers and tentmakers.

Since 1998 we have tracked the ebb and flow of the number of agencies report-ing a primary activity within each major category. Table 8 gives the numerical results; Figure 18 shows the relative change in shares of each category. From 1998 to 2008, the percent of all agencies indicating a primary activity in evangelism and disciple-ship category dropped by 6.43%. On the other hand, the percent of all agencies indi-cating a primary activity in the relief and development category increased by 4.65%; those indicating an activity in the mission agency support category grew by 1.96%. This does not necessarily mean that these agencies are changing activities. In fact, the largest drops and gains took place in this survey came from the 100 agencies added to the mix in 2008. In effect, it was these 100 new agencies that changed the relative share rather than the previously listed agencies changing their focus.

Table 7: Primary Activities in Categories[7]

Evangelism & Discipleship		Mission Agency Support
Apologetics	Linguistics	Association of Missions
Bible distribution	Literacy	Aviation services
Bible memorization	Literature distribution	Furloughed missionary support
Broadcasting, radio	Literature production	Information services
and/or TV	National church nurture/	Management consulting/training
Camping programs	support	Member Care
Children's programs	Sports Program Ministry	Partnership development
Church construction	Support of national workers	Psychological counseling
Church establishing/	Tentmaking & Related	Purchasing services
planting	Translation, Bible	Recruiting/Mobilizing
Discipleship	Translation, other	Services for other agencies
Evangelism, mass	Urban Ministry	Short-term programs coordination
Evangelism, personal	Video/Film production/	Technical assistance
and small group	distribution	Training/Orientation, missionary
Evangelism, student	Youth programs	
Leadership development		
Relief & Development		**Education & Training**
Adoption	Justice & Related	Audio recording/distribution
Agricultural programs	Medical supplies	Correspondence courses
Childcare/orphanage	Medicine, incl. dental	Education, church/sch. general
Children at risk	and public health	Christian
Development, community	Relief and/or rehabilitation	Education, extension (other)
and/or other	Supplying equipment	Education, missionary
Disability assistance	Trafficking/slavery Issues	(certificate/degree)
programs		Education, theological
HIV/Aids		Education, theological by
		extension (TEE)
		Training, other
Other		
Business as Mission	Research	
Funds transmission	TESOL	

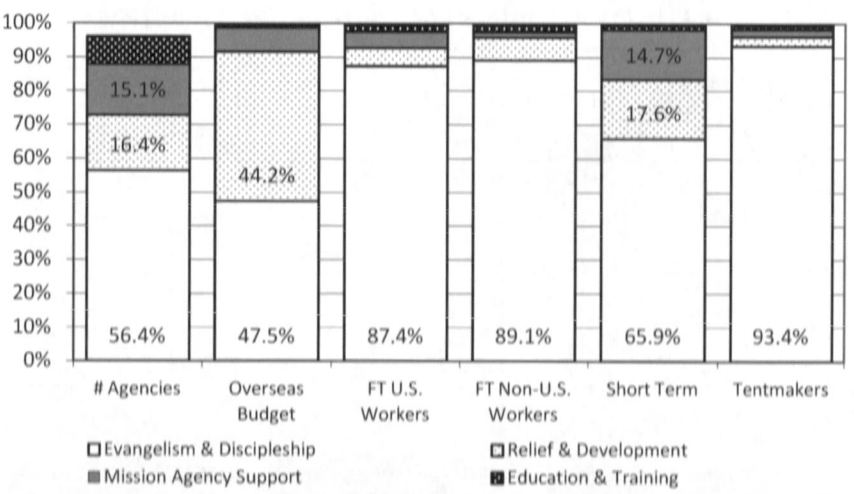

Figure 17: Comparison of Resources focused on Primary Activities Categories

- □ Evangelism & Discipleship
- ■ Mission Agency Support
- □ Relief & Development
- ▨ Education & Training

	# Agencies	Overseas Budget	FT U.S. Workers	FT Non-U.S. Workers	Short Term	Tentmakers
Evangelism & Discipleship	56.4%	47.5%	87.4%	89.1%	65.9%	93.4%
Relief & Development	16.4%	44.2%			17.6%	
Mission Agency Support	15.1%				14.7%	

Table 8: Share of Agencies per Primary Activity Category

Category	1998	2001	2005	2008
Education & Training	8.1%	8.2%	9.3%	8.3%
Evangelism & Discipleship	62.8%	61.8%	59.3%	56.4%
Mission Agency Support	13.2%	14.7%	16.6%	15.1%
Relief & Development	11.7%	11.7%	11.9%	16.4%
Other	4.2%	3.6%	2.9%	3.9%

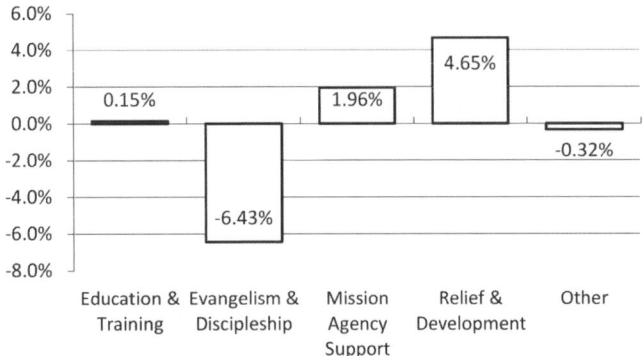

Figure 18: Total Change in Share of Agencies Reporting Primary Activities 1998 to 2009

To correct for the ways the 100 new agencies in the 2008 survey change the overall picture, we must limit our perspective to the 607 agencies that reported in all three surveys (2001, 2005 and 2008). We do this in Figure 19 (limited the categories with changes greater than 5% from 2001 to 2008).

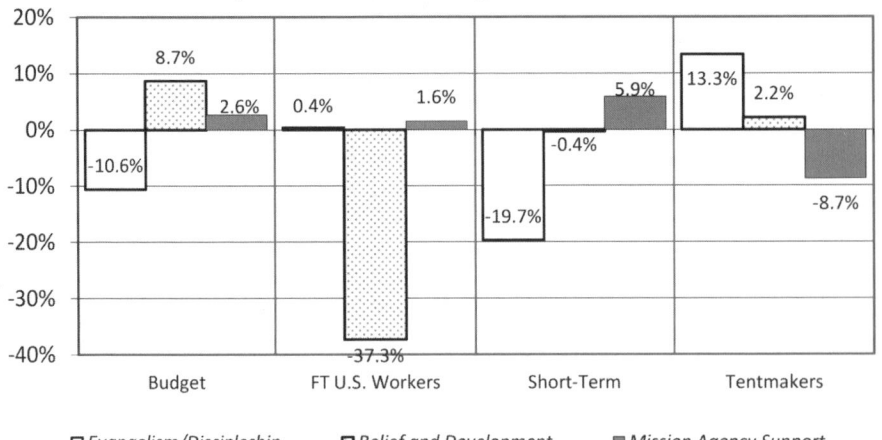

Figure 19: Change in Share for Selected Categories in Primary Activities of 607 Agencies 2001 and 2008

□ Evangelism/Discipleship   □ Relief and Development   ■ Mission Agency Support

For the 607 agencies reporting in all three surveys, those indicating primary activities in the evangelism and discipleship category gained in the share of tentmakers but lost in the share of budget for overseas ministries and short-term workers. Agencies indicating primary activities in relief and development gained in the share of budget for overseas ministries, but lost in the share of full-time U.S. workers. Finally, agencies indicating primary activities in the agency support category reported gained in the share of short-term workers, but lost in the share of the tentmakers. In the rest of this section we will focus on reported changes seen among the agencies with primary activities in each of the four major activity categories in turn.

Education and Training

Agencies whose primary activity fits into the education and training category reported solid growth from 2001 to 2008 in the total number of full-time workers deployed (Figure 20). Not shown in Figure 20 is the fact that agencies in this category reported a significant increase in the number of 1 to 2 year full-time workers for 2001 to 2008. The increase from 2005 to 2008 alone was over 600% (from 52 to 367). At the same time, however, they reported a downward trend in the number of U.S. full-time 2 to 4 year and 4+ year workers. It is unclear from the data whether this is from normal attrition of an aging mission force more committed to long-term work or the result of better recruitment of the 1 to 2 year workers.

Figure 20: Education and Training: Full-time Workers 2001 to 2008

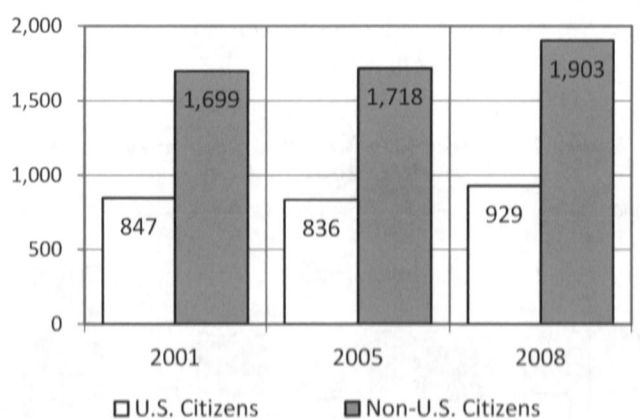

There were three areas in particular in which agencies in this category went the opposite direction of the aggregate for all U.S. agencies (Figure 21): 1) they reported upward changes in short-term workers, 2) downward changes in U.S. full-time 2 to 4 year and 3) downward changes in the U.S. full-time 4+ year workers.

The reported income for overseas work for these agencies dropped almost 29.4% from 2005 to 2008 (the inflation-adjusted AGR dropped from 5.3% for 2001 to 2005 down to -10.8% for 2005 to 2008). This may indicate major funding hurdles ahead for agencies whose primary activity focuses on education and training.

Figure 21: Areas of Significant AGR for Agencies with Primary Activities in Education and Training

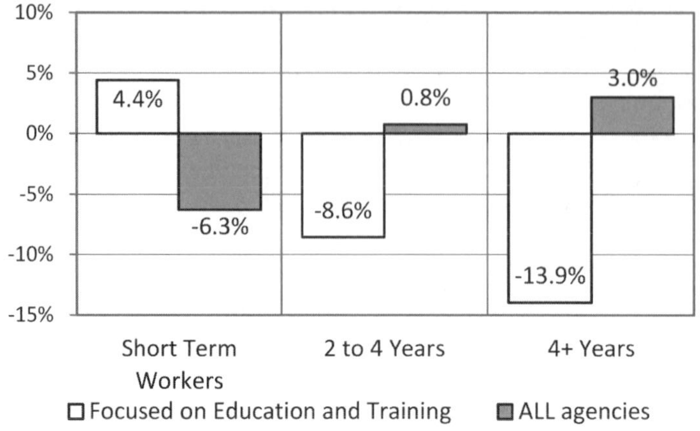

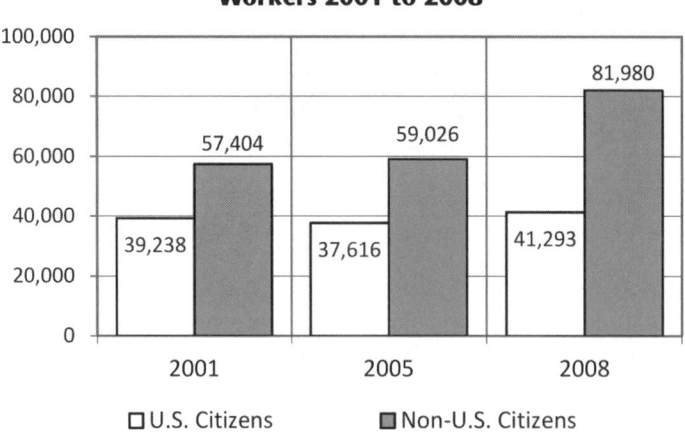

Evangelism and Discipleship

Overall agencies whose primary activity was in the evangelism and discipleship category reported gains in twelve of our indicators and drops in seven of them. In sum, the reported number of full-time workers increased for both U.S. citizen and non-U.S. citizen totals (Figure 22). The U.S. 2 to 4 year workers increased by 41.3%, accounting for almost all of the U.S. full-time worker growth. The non-U.S. citizens working in their own countries grew by 42.6%, while non-U.S. citizens working outside of their own countries shrank by 3.8%.

Figure 22: Evangelism and Discipleship: Full-time Workers 2001 to 2008

There were three areas in particular in which agencies in this category reported significant annual growth rates from 2005 to 2008 (Figure 23): 1) increase in 2 to 4 year full-time U.S. workers, 2) decrease in short-term workers, and 3) increase in non-U.S. workers serving in their own countries.

Figure 23: Areas of Significant AGR 2005 to 2008 for Agencies with Primary Activities in Evangelism and Discipleship

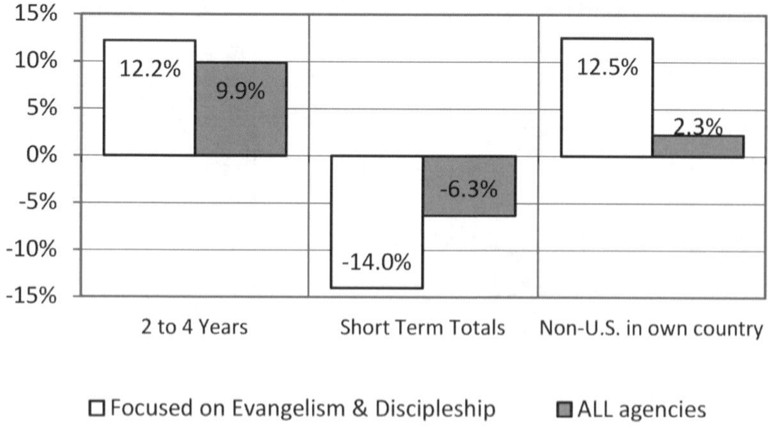

	2 to 4 Years	Short Term Totals	Non-U.S. in own country
Focused on Evangelism & Discipleship	12.2%	-14.0%	12.5%
ALL agencies	9.9%	-6.3%	2.3%

☐ Focused on Evangelism & Discipleship   ■ ALL agencies

Mission Agency Support

Agencies whose primary activity fits into the mission agency support category reported increases in full-time U.S. citizens but significant decreases in non-U.S. citizens (Figure 24). The relatively large decrease in the number of non-U.S. citizens working in their own country was the result of the largest agency in this category changing their primary activity to one that is in the evangelism and discipleship category rather than an actual loss of such workers. This is clearly an instance in which the fuzziness of the categories and primary activity designations can result in a large negative impact in particular categories from survey to survey, even though the aggregate totals may even increase.

Figure 24: Mission Agency Support: Full-time Workers 2001 to 2008

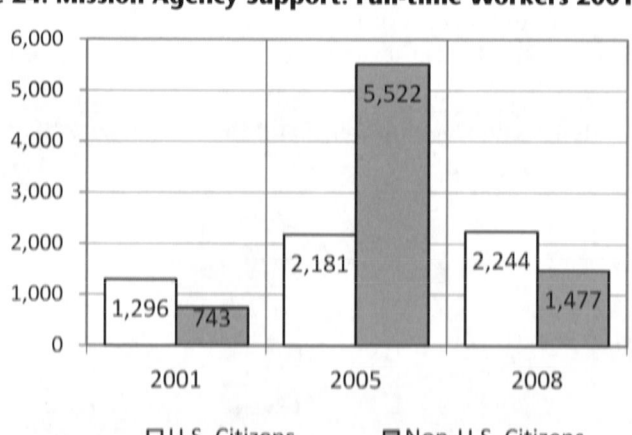

	2001	2005	2008
U.S. Citizens	1,296	2,181	2,244
Non-U.S. Citizens	743	5,522	1,477

☐ U.S. Citizens   ■ Non-U.S. Citizens

There were three areas in particular in which agencies in this category reported significant annual growth rates from 2005 to 2008 contrasting with the AGRs for all agencies (Figure 25): 1) increase in short-term workers, 2) increase in income for overseas ministries, and 3) decrease in full-time U.S. workers serving 1 to 2 years.

Figure 25: Areas of Significant AGR 2005 to 2008 for Agencies with Primary Activities in Mission Agency Support

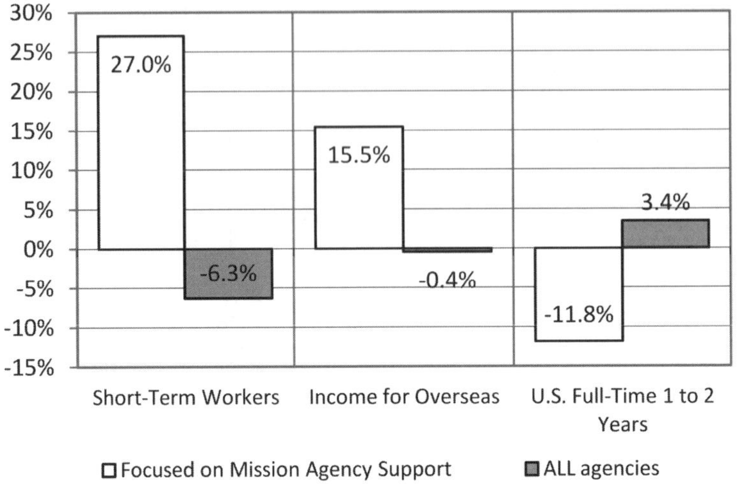

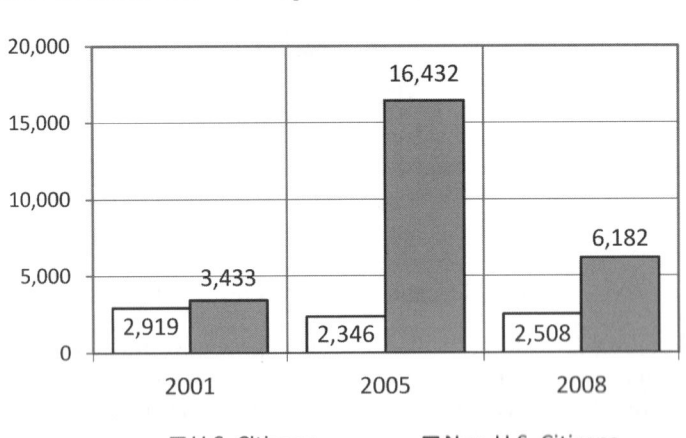

While the loss of 1 to 2 years is large in terms of percentage, the actual loss was only 56 workers, and the gains in the 2 to 4 year (51) and 4+ year (68) U.S. workers resulted in a net gain of all U.S. full-time workers for these agencies (Figure 27). The loss of 1 to 2 year workers may have been only the moving to the longer term categories. If so, this may reflect an increase in longevity for full-time U.S. workers with a corresponding decrease in getting new full-time workers to their assignments.

Relief and Development

Agencies whose primary activity fits into the relief and development reported increases in full-time U.S. citizens but significant decreases in non-U.S. citizens (Figure 26). However, as with the changes in the previous category, this was primarily due to the two largest agencies sponsoring non-U.S. citizens. The largest agency changed

Figure 26: Relief and Development: Full-time Workers 2001 to 2008

their primary activity from one listed in relief and development to one in evangelism and discipleship. The second largest dropped from over 2,000 non-U.S. workers in 2005 to 0 in 2008. Factoring those two out, the drop in non-U.S. citizens working in their own countries was from 5,681 to 5,632, a far more modest decline. Bear in mind that Figure 26 includes the total of non-U.S. workers, both those in their own countries and those outside of their own countries.

Three areas in which agencies in this category reported significant annual growth rates from 2005 to 2008 relative to the AGRs for all agencies (Figure 27) are: 1) increase in short-term workers, 2) decrease in non-U.S. citizens serving in their home countries, and 3) increase in full-time U.S. workers serving 4+ years.

Figure 27: Areas of Significant AGR 2005 to 2008 for Agencies th Primary Activities in Mission Agency Support

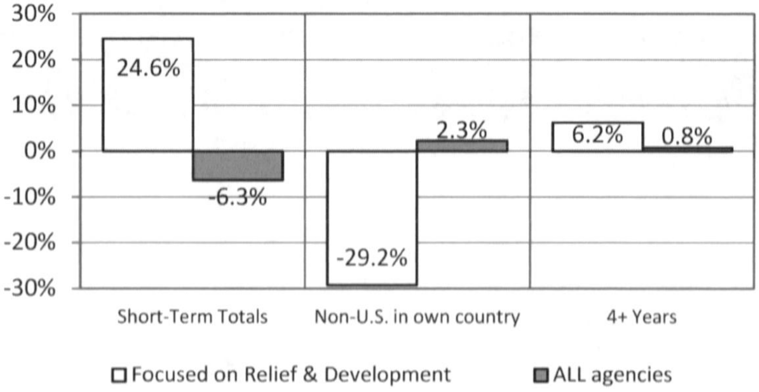

Deployment of U.S. Agencies and Missionaries

In previous editions of the *Handbook* we examined shifts in continental areas (e.g., increases in deployments to Asia, decreases in deployments to Oceania). In this edition, we will touch on three ways to configure the deployments reported by the agencies, looking for clues to help us understand the extent to which agencies focus resources on countries with greater populations of unreached or least-reached peoples. First, we will offer deployment shifts in relation to Asia and the Middle East. Second, we will look at deployment shifts in 10/40 Window countries.[8] Finally, we will examine shifts in deployment among Worlds A, B, and C (as used in *World Christian Trends*[9]). Bear in mind in this discussion that we do not ask agencies to identify where they send their short-term workers, nor to distinguish tentmakers from other full-time workers. Further, because agencies send their workers to more than one country or continent, we cannot accurately discern how they divide their financial or logistical support among the continents on which they have a presence. Thus the limitations of the survey confine our discussion on deployments to the reported shifts in full-time U.S. and non-U.S. workers.

Continental Deployments

In the previous edition, we noted a large shift to workers in Asia (incorporating

the Middle East). That shift reversed from 2005 to 2008. The fact that agencies in aggregate reported gains in both U.S. and non-U.S. citizens being deployed means that
it is theoretically possible that we could see more workers deployed on every continent. However, this did not happen. There were gains in the reported number of
full-time U.S. citizens for every continent except South America, and gains for full-
time non-U.S. citizens for every continent except Asia. The drop indicates the loss
of U.S. agencies deploying them and not necessarily an actual loss of them to mission as a whole. Some, for example, may have left U.S. agencies to join agencies from
their own country or other non-U.S. based agencies. These losses offset the gain in
full-time U.S. citizens, so that the net result was that there were gains for all full-time
workers (both U.S. and non-U.S. citizens) for every continent except Asia over the
2005 to 2008 span (Table 9 and Figure 28).

Table 9: U.S. Protestant Agency Deployments by Continent 2008

	U.S. Full-time	Change 2005 to 2008	Non-U.S. Full-time	Change 2005 to 2008	All Full-Time	Change 2005 to 2008
Africa	6,437	329	16,347	5,078	22,784	5,407
Asia	8,620	152	53,136	-4,586	61,756	-4,434
Central America/ Caribbean	3,896	335	5,909	1,144	9,805	1,479
Commonwealth of Independent States	1,152	6	3,126	700	4,278	706
Europe	6,674	497	4,487	1,194	11,161	1,691
Middle East	834	112	1,013	245	1,847	357
Oceania	1,767	68	882	214	2,649	282
South America	4,795	-538	5,546	2,291	10,341	1,753

Figure 28: Deployment of All Full-time Missionaries 2005 and 2008

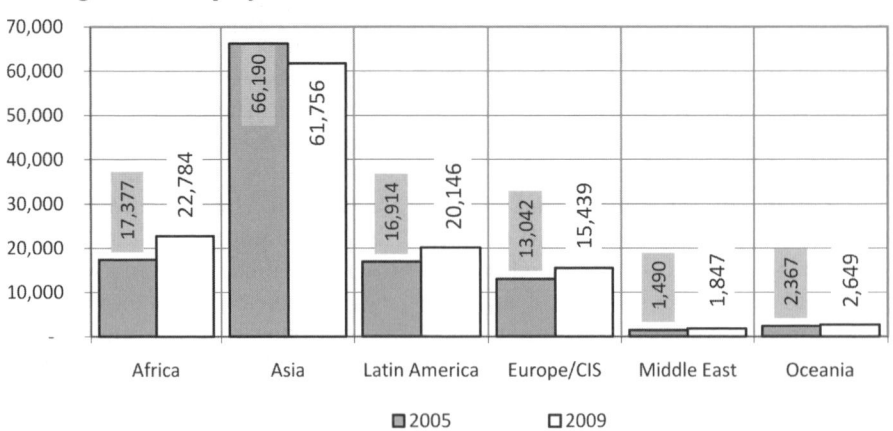

Figure 28 puts the *shift* in perspective. In it we combine some continental regions
(e.g., Central America and the Caribbean are combined with South America) and
omitted the unspecified category to simplify reading. While the drop in deployment

in Asia was significant (6.7%), even so the largest investment in full-time personnel of U.S. Protestant agencies remains in Asian countries. Figure 29 offers the percentage change for the same grouped regions, giving an additional way to understand the changes—especially the extent of the growth of all full-time personnel reported for countries in the Middle East.

Figures 29 through 34 help us focus the picture for the reported changes in regional deployments. In Figure 29 we show the total full-time deployments in Asia, and Figure 30 shows the percentage *share* of deployments reported in Asia. Figure 29 clearly indicates that the number of U.S. workers grew over the period (from 8,468 to 8,620). However, the *share* of U.S. workers in Asia dropped from 20.5% in 2005 to 19.6% in 2008. This means that increases of full-time workers reported for other regions of the world outpaced the increases reported for Asian deployments, with the result of a net loss of *share* of U.S. full-time workers in Asia even though the actual number increased.

Figure 29: Percent Change in Full-time Missionaries per Region 2005 to 2008

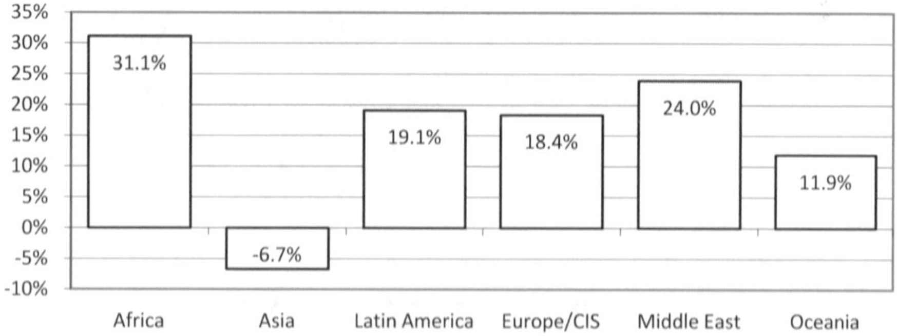

Region	Percent Change
Africa	31.1%
Asia	-6.7%
Latin America	19.1%
Europe/CIS	18.4%
Middle East	24.0%
Oceania	11.9%

Figure 30 : Full-time Workers Deployed in Asia

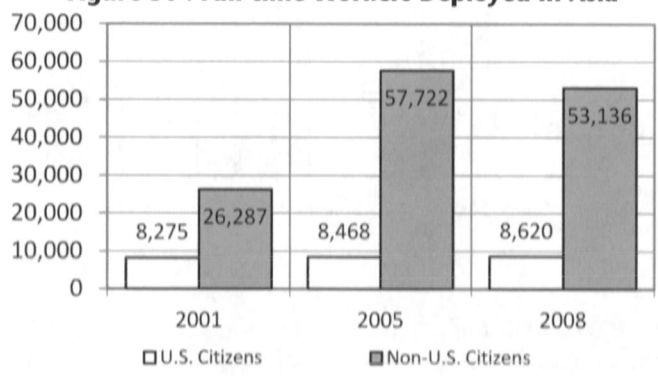

	U.S. Citizens	Non-U.S. Citizens
2001	8,275	26,287
2005	8,468	57,722
2008	8,620	53,136

On the other hand, the reported number of non-U.S. citizens can swing wildly from one survey to another for the same organization. In this case it was the reporting of the largest agency in this category, which reported a drop of almost 7,000 non-U.S. citizens between 2005 and 2008 (after reporting a gain of some 16,000 work-

Figure 31: Share of All Full-time Workers in Asia

Figure 32 : Adjusted Full-time Workers Deployed in Asia

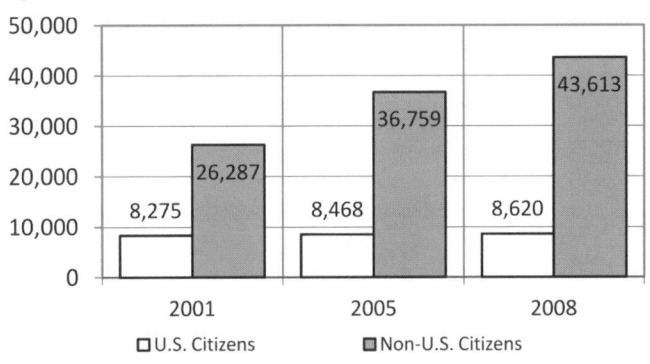

Figure 33: Adjusted Share of All Full-time Workers in Asia

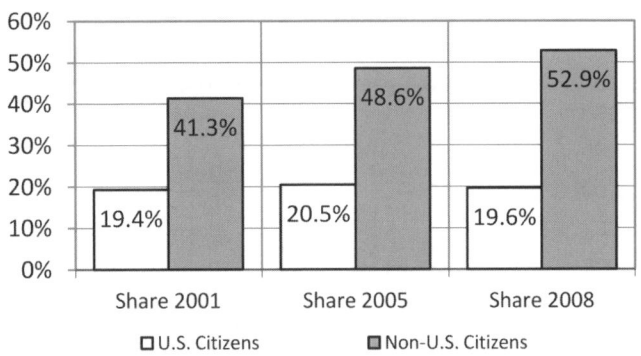

ers in 2001 to 2005). Adjusting the chart by excluding this agency from the totals yields a net increase in the reported numbers of non-U.S. citizens deployed in Asia from 2005 to 2008 (Figure 34) and a gain in share for the same period (Figure 35)!

The reported deployment shifts to the Middle East of all full-time workers were encouraging. The total number of all types of full-time workers continued an increasing *trend*, and the shares also increased. The growth in share indicates that growth in deployment in Middle East countries was higher than in other regions.

Figure 34 : Total Number of Full-time Workers Deployed in the Middle East

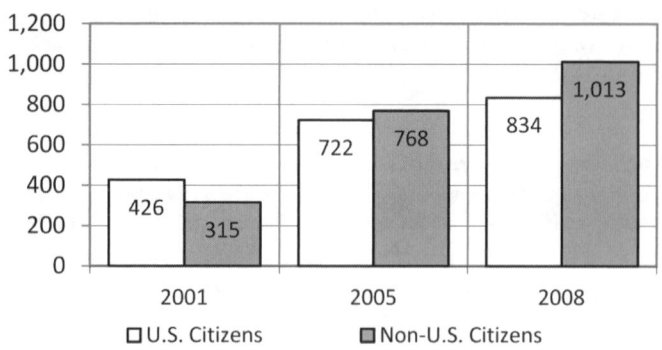

☐ U.S. Citizens   ▣ Non-U.S. Citizens

Figure 35: Share of All Reported Full-time Workers in Middle East

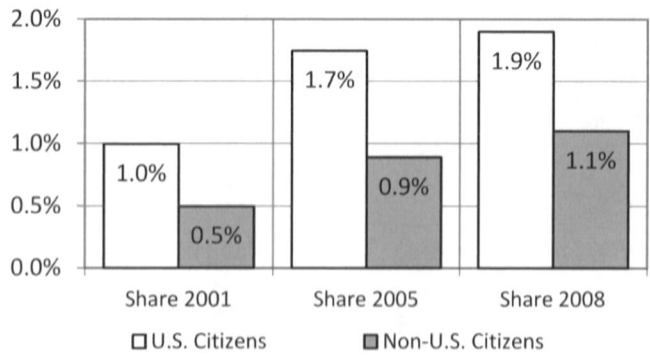

☐ U.S. Citizens   ▣ Non-U.S. Citizens

However, the actual size of the share (under 2% for both full-time categories) is a reminder of the relative lack of deployments across the Middle East. Agencies are gaining ground, but not at a pace which demonstrates *significant* deployment changes.[10]

10/40 Window Deployments

In addition to continental regions, we configured the database to enable us to determine whether deployments were in 10/40 Window countries or not—though we need to note several caveats on the following table and charts. First, the list for these countries is an evolving list (e.g. some lists include Indonesia, others do not). We chose to use the Joshua Project list (http://www.joshuaproject.net/10-40-window.php) in part because of their long-standing with groups such as the A.D. 2000 Movement and the U.S. Center for World Mission and in part because they recognize the diverse lists and have chosen criteria that are missionally focused while adhering to the core concept of the 10/40 Window. A second caveat is that countries in the 10/40 Window list have varying levels of reached and unreached populations. Third, deployments from a particular agency in various 10/40 Window countries are not automatically among unreached peoples in those countries. Finally, as noted in our discussion on deployments in Asia, we have adjusted the numbers in Table 10 factoring out the largest non-U.S. citizen deploying agency because the variations in reporting skew the entire picture. With those caveats in mind, in Table 10 and Figure 36 we offer the adjusted aggregate numbers of reported full-time workers, and show the percentages of all full-time workers in Figure 37 and the divisions of U.S. full-time workers in Figure 38.

Table 10: Adjusted Deployments In and Out of 10/40 Window 2001 to 2008

	2001		2005		2008	
	10/40	Other	10/40	Other	10/40	Other
# of Agencies	320	420	370	457	413	515
U.S. Citizens	8,929	33,819	9,121	32,208	9,474	34,433
Non-U.S. Citizens	25,679	37,917	58,196	28,066	53,936	38,072
Total	34,608	71,736	67,317	60,274	63,410	72,505

Figure 36: Adjusted Full-time Workers in 10/40 Window Countries

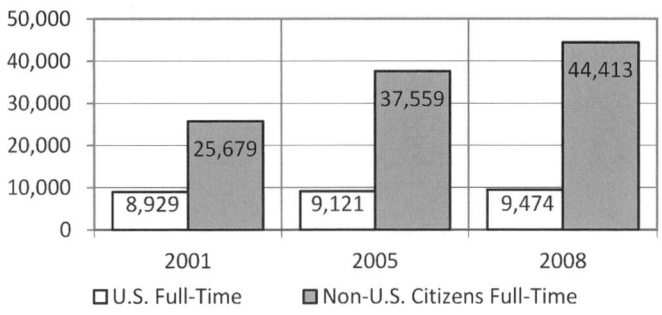

Figure 37: Adjusted Share of All Full-time Workers in 10/40 Window Countries

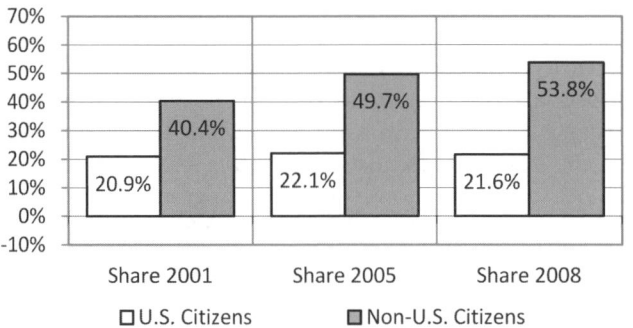

Figure 38: Adjusted 10/40 Window Deployment Ratio 2001 to 2009

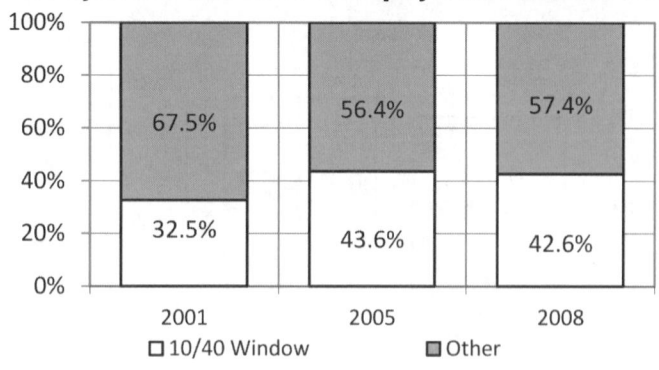

When adjusted, the clear signal is that U.S. agencies continue to shift more workers to 10/40 Window countries. While the share dropped somewhat in 2008, it still demonstrates a focus on deploying workers among the least reached or the unreached.

World A, B, C Deployments

In the *World Christian Encyclopedia*[11] David Barrett and editors identify three categories for categorizing countries (2001: I:30). World A countries are those in which more than 50% of the population is unevangelized. World B countries are those in which more than 50% of the population is evangelized, but fewer than 60% of the people are identified as Christians. World C countries are those in which those identified as Christians number more than 60% of the population.

In Figure 39, we present the adjusted[12] shares of workers in each segment of the world in the A, B, and C categories. The shares in the "Other" category refer to full-time workers for whom the agencies do not designate a specific country or area of the world. As Figure 40 shows, World A countries (the least accessible to Western missionaries) have by far the smallest number deployed. However, it should be kept in mind that when organizations do not specify assignments, likely it is because they are in such countries. The large shift from 2001 to 2005 is primarily due to more agencies indicating where their workers are deployed in 2005 than they did in 2001.

Figure 39: Adjusted World A, B & C Shares of All Full-time Workers

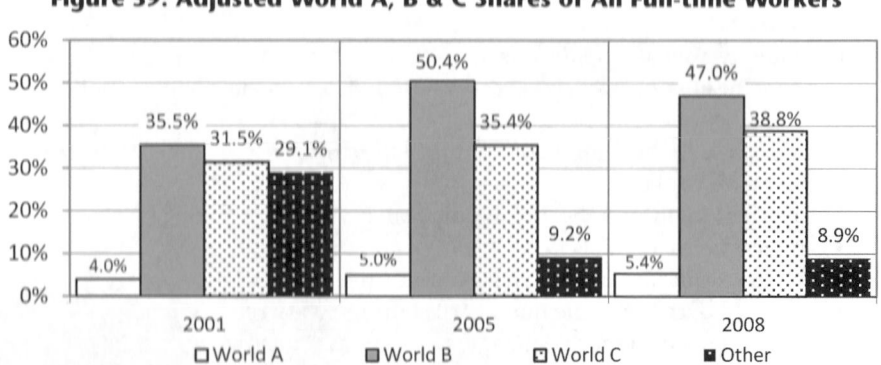

Figure 40: Adjusted Share of Full-time Workers in World A Countries

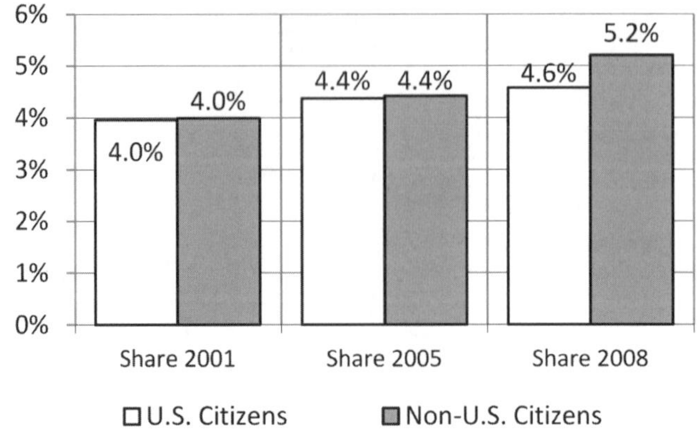

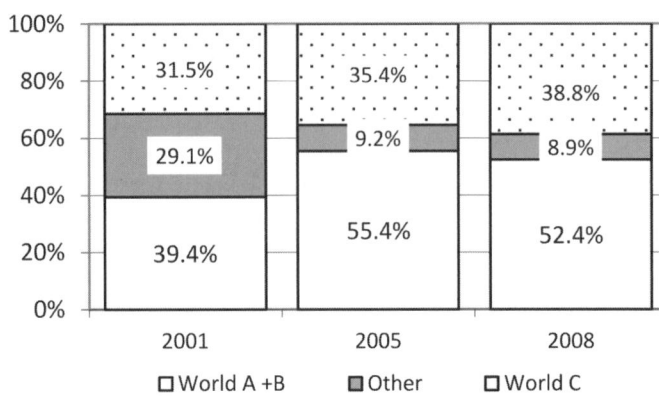

However, judging by the adjusted reported numbers for 2008 (Figure 41), we can say with confidence that well over half of the workers deployed by U.S. agencies are working in either World A or World B countries, so it is fair to say that U.S. agencies are indeed giving significant focus on the unreached.

Figure 41: World A +B, C and Other Shares of All Full-time Workers

Conclusion

In summary, we have identified several changes based on reported numbers from U.S. Protestant mission agencies over the past decade. General changes for the agencies include the following:

- An increase in the number of full-time U.S. citizens, and—most importantly— long-term workers
- An increase in the number of full-time non-U.S. citizens working for U.S. agencies
- An increase in tentmakers
- An increase in funding for overseas ministries
- A marked decrease in the number of short-term workers
- A decrease in the reported income for overseas ministries

A summary of the more significant changes in relation to the primary activities of agencies includes:

- For agencies whose primary activities are in the education and training category: increases in the number of U.S. 1 to 2 year full-time workers, full-time non-U.S. citizen workers, short-term workers and home support staff; a significant decrease in income for overseas ministries
- For agencies whose primary activities are in the evangelism and discipleship category: a significant increase in tentmakers; increases in the total of full-time U.S. and non-U.S. citizen workers and home support staff; a small decrease in income for overseas ministries; and significant decreases in short-term workers and total short-term support staff
- For agencies whose primary activities are in the mission agency support category: significant increases in short-term workers, income for overseas ministries and nonresidential workers; increases in full-time U.S. workers; decreases in the totals of home and short-term support staff
- For agencies whose primary activities are in the relief and development category: a significant increase in the number of short-term workers; increases in the number of full-time U.S. workers and full-time short-term support staff; a moderate decrease in income for overseas ministries; and significant decreases in the number of non-U.S. citizen workers and tentmakers

A summary of the deployment of full-time workers from U.S. agencies for 2008 include:

- More than half of all full-time workers deployed by U.S. agencies are working in Asian/Middle Eastern countries, but a smaller percentage than reported for the 2005 survey
- 10/40 Window: More than 40% of all full-time workers deployed by U.S. agencies are working in 10/40 Window countries
- World A, B, and C countries: Well over half of all full-time workers deployed by U.S. agencies are working in either World A or World B countries

Canadian Agencies Overview

We compiled data on 44 more Canadian agencies for this edition than the previous *Handbook* (166 versus 122). We listed 122 agencies in the previous edition. For this edition we dropped 4 from the 2005 list and added 48 new ones. Table 11 helps us better track some of the information in this edition on the Canadian agencies and organizations. The "Agencies Tracked from 2001 to 2008" column lists the totals from 105 agencies that are included in this edition as well as in the past two editions of the *Handbook*. We will use information from these agencies to explore trends and shifts over the seven-year span they cover. The "Agencies Tracked from 2005 to 2008" column gives the numbers for the 118 agencies that are included in this edition as well as the previous edition. The "Agencies Newly Listed in 2008" column gives the totals for the 48 agencies added to this edition for the first time. We will use information on these agencies to see how they affect the various totals for this edition. Finally, the "All Agencies 2008" column on the far right lists the totals for all 166 Canadian Protestant agencies listed in this *Handbook*. These numbers are our baseline for comparing totals from previous editions.

Table 11: Summary of Canadian Protestant Mission Statistics Reported for 2008

	Agencies Tracked from 2001 to 2008		Agencies Tracked from 2005 to 2008		Agencies Newly Listed in 2008		All Agencies 2008
	Number	% of All	Number	% of All	Number	% of All	All Agencies 2008
General							
Number of Agencies	105	63.3%	118	71.1%	48	28.9%	166
Income for Overseas	$675,276,442	94.2%	$686,294,853	95.8%	30,236,248	4.2%	$716,531,101
Average Income for Overseas	$6,431,204	149.0%	$5,816,058	134.7%	$629,922	14.6%	$4,316,452
Full-time Canadian Personnel Serving Overseas							
Long-term (4+ years)	2,089	92.9%	2,181	97.0%	68	3.0%	2,249
Mid-term (1 to 4 years)	397	80.7%	431	87.6%	61	12.4%	492
Tentmakers	40	26.8%	40	26.8%	109	73.2%	149
Other Canadian Personnel Serving Overseas							
Short-term (< 2 weeks)	1,436	40.5%	1,472	41.5%	2,073	58.5%	3,545
Short-term (≥ 2 weeks)	2,719	83.1%	2,836	86.7%	436	13.3%	3,272
Nonresidential							
Fully supported	369	90.7%	376	92.4%	31	7.6%	407
Partially supported	37	74.0%	45	90.0%	5	10.0%	50
Non-Canadian Personnel Directly Supported							
In home country	4,418	92.3%	4,454	93.0%	333	7.0%	4,787
Outside home country	530	81.8%	534	82.4%	114	17.6%	648
Canadian Home Office and Support Staff							
Full-time paid	2,395	94.5%	2,425	95.7%	110	4.3%	2,535
Part-time	726	91.7%	743	93.8%	49	6.2%	792
Short-term Support Staff							
Full-time	141	90.4%	141	90.4%	15	9.6%	156
Part-time (≥ 50%)	47	83.9%	49	87.5%	7	12.5%	56
Part-time (10 to 49%)	85	63.4%	91	67.9%	43	32.1%	134
Selected Totals of People Mobilized by Canadian Agencies							
Grand Total	**15,429**	**80.1%**	**15,818**	**82.1%**	**3,454**	**17.9%**	**19,272**
Canadian Full-time On-location	2,526	87.4%	2,652	91.8%	238	8.2%	2,890
All Full-time On-location	7,474	89.8%	7,640	91.8%	685	8.2%	8,325
All Overseas Workers	12,035	77.2%	12,369	79.3%	3,230	20.7%	15,599
All Support Staff	3,394	92.4%	3,449	93.9%	224	6.1%	3,673

As indicated in the "All Agencies 2008" column, the reported on-location, full-time Canadian missionary force from 166 Canadian agencies was comprised of 15,599 people serving in 145 countries and territories.[13] Of these, 2,890 were Canadian citizens working in another country; 648 were non-Canadian citizens serving in countries other than their own, and 4,787 were non-Canadian citizens serving in their own countries (occasionally referred to in this chapter as nationals).

To help put the following discussion in perspective,[14] throughout the analysis we refer to "reported" totals, since the totals we present are only as valid as the numbers received from each agency. Several factors contribute softness to these numbers. First, the actual numbers fluctuate during the year. Second, agencies use different methods for counting their personnel. For example, some carefully tabulate and report painstakingly exact numbers for the month the survey is completed. Others, however, provide either highs or averages for the year. Still others provide estimates, especially for categories such as short-term workers. Third, and finally, agencies do not always interpret the survey questions consistently with either other agencies or even with their own answers in previous surveys. To help the reader keep this in mind, throughout this analysis we will typically use the term "reported" to refer to the numbers.

Table 11 gives us indicators about continuities and discontinuities from the various surveys for previous editions of the *Handbook*. We indicate the share of the totals contributed from the agencies carried over from 2001 to 2008 in the column to the right of the totals for those agencies. Altogether, these 105 agencies contributed 94.2% of the total reported overseas income, 89.8% of the full-time on-location personnel (including Canadian and non-Canadian citizens), 87.4% of the full-time on-location Canadian personnel (1 to 4+ years plus tentmakers), 92.9% of the long-term Canadian personnel and 92.4% of the administrative and short-term support staff for the 166 Canadian agencies.

Likewise, we indicate the share of the totals contributed from the agencies carried over from 2005 to 2008 in the column to the right of the totals for those agencies. Altogether, these 118 agencies contributed 95.8% of the total reported overseas income, 91.8% of the full-time on-location personnel (including Canadian and non-Canadian citizens), 91.8% of the full-time on-location Canadian personnel (1 to 4+ years plus tentmakers), 97.0% of the long-term Canadian personnel and 93.9% of the administrative and short-term support staff for the 166 Canadian agencies. Thus, the agencies listed from 2001 to 2008 and those listed from 2005 to 2008 well represent the full-time personnel and income for overseas ministries of all 166 agencies surveyed.

Finally, the "Agencies Newly Listed in 2008" column offers us an opportunity to see emphases among the newly listed agencies. Since 44 of these 48 agencies were founded after 1944 (and 37 after 1974), they offer us a snapshot of the types of emphases newer agencies pursue, as well as areas in which they place less emphasis. While adding almost 29% to the total list of agencies, for example, they added 73.2% to the tentmaker totals, and 58.5% to the short-term trips of less than two weeks in duration. They also add 32.1% to the number of part-time (less than 50%) short-term support staff. On the other hand, they only added 3% of the long-term workers and their average reported income for overseas work is only 14.6% of the average budget of the rest of the Canadian agencies. In sum, relative to the other Canadian agencies, the newly added agencies are small and focused on deploying short-term workers and tentmakers. Even so, they are a solid and welcome sign of vibrancy and new growth springing up from mission-minded Canadian Christians.

In Table 12 we offer the comparative totals from the surveys since 1996, together with indicators that help us discern the patterns in the data. The Annualized Growth Rate (AGR)[15] columns enable us to see difference between the AGR for 1996 to 2005 and 2005 to 2008. The final column simply shows the difference between the two

Table 12: Summary of Reported Canadian Protestant Mission Agency Totals 1996-2008

	1996	1998	2001	2005	2008	Change (2005-08)	1. AGR 2005-08	2. AGR 1996-05	AGR 1-AGR 2
Canadian Personnel Serving Full-time Overseas									
Long-term (4+ years)	2,961	2,613	2,493	2,059	2,249	9.2%	3.0%	-4.0%	6.9%
Mid-term (1 to 4 years)	416	421	337	511	492	-3.7%	-1.3%	2.3%	-3.6%
Tentmakers	140	144	154	186	149	-19.9%	-7.1%	3.2%	-10.3%
Totals	**3,517**	**3,178**	**2,984**	**2,756**	**2,890**	**4.9%**	**1.6%**	**-2.7%**	**4.3%**
Other Canadian Personnel Serving Overseas									
Short-term (< 2 weeks)	N/A	N/A	N/A	N/A	3,545	N/A	N/A	N/A	N/A
Short-term (> 2 weeks)	2,470	3,186	3,395	3,534	3,272	-7.4%	-2.5%	4.1%	-6.6%
Subtotals	**2,470**	**3,186**	**3,395**	**3,534**	**6,817**	**92.9%**	**24.5%**	**4.1%**	**20.4%**
Non-residential full support	120	294	385	156	407	160.9%	37.7%	3.0%	34.7%
Non-residential partial support	17	38	27	38	50	31.6%	9.6%	9.3%	0.2%
Subtotals	**137**	**332**	**412**	**194**	**457**	**135.6%**	**33.1%**	**3.9%**	**29.1%**
Non-Canadian Personnel Directly Supported									
In home country	707	1,725	1,128	1,510	4,787	217.0%	46.9%	8.8%	38.1%
Outside home country	77	244	873	728	648	-11.0%	-3.8%	28.4%	-32.2%
Subtotals	**784**	**1,969**	**2,001**	**2,238**	**5,435**	**142.9%**	**34.4%**	**12.4%**	**22.1%**
Canadian Ministry and Home Office Staff									
Full-time paid staff	1,622	1,838	2,515	2,145	2,535	18.2%	5.7%	3.2%	2.6%
Part-time staff/associates	389	496	431	570	792	38.9%	11.6%	4.3%	7.3%
Subtotals	**2,011**	**2,334**	**2,946**	**2,715**	**3,327**	**22.5%**	**7.0%**	**3.4%**	**3.6%**
Short-term Support Staff									
Part-time (10 to 49%)	18	36	158	45	156	246.7%	51.3%	10.7%	40.6%
Part-time (> 50%)	8	39	32	38	56	47.4%	13.8%	18.9%	-5.1%
Full-time	84	81	130	86	134	55.8%	15.9%	0.3%	15.7%
Subtotals	**110**	**156**	**320**	**169**	**346**	**104.7%**	**27.0%**	**4.9%**	**22.1%**
Total People Mobilized by Canadian Agencies									
Grand Total	**9,029**	**11,155**	**12,058**	**11,606**	**19,272**	**66.1%**	**18.4%**	**2.8%**	**15.6%**
Canadian Full-time On-location	3,517	3,178	2,984	2,756	2,890	4.9%	1.6%	-2.7%	4.3%
All Full-time On-location	4,301	5,147	4,985	4,994	8,325	66.7%	18.6%	1.7%	16.9%
All Overseas, Any Duration	6,908	8,665	8,792	8,722	15,599	78.8%	21.4%	2.6%	18.8%
All Support Staff	2,121	2,490	3,266	2,884	3,673	27.4%	8.4%	3.5%	4.9%

Financial Support Raised in Canada: Income for Overseas Ministries (Adjusted for Inflation)						
1996	1998	2001	2005	2008	(Change (2005-08)	AGR (2005-08)
$299,659,824	$413,902,174	$495,266,175	$677,516,224	$716,513,1001	5.8%	1.88%

growth rates, which indicates the severity of the change. In looking at Table 12, it will help the reader to keep the following in mind. First, a negative number in AGR 1 (2005-2008) indicates a reduction in actual numbers between the two surveys. However, a negative number in the AGR 1 – AGR 2 column always indicates slower growth in 2005 to 2008 than in 1996 to 2005, but not necessarily negative growth from 2005 to 2008. For example, the AGR 1 – AGR 2 for part-time (more than 50%) short-term support staff was -5.1%. Canadian agencies reported more people in this category in 2008 than in 2005. However, the annualized growth rate of 13.8% during that time was lower than the 18.9% AGR from 1996 to 2005. Thus, even though the agencies reported more people in this category, the growth rate was smaller than during the previous span. Together, then, the last four columns help us identify areas of health as well as areas of concern in our analysis—and let us see relative strengths of the health or the concern.

Looking at the final column, then, gives a quick indicator of how agencies fared in 2005 to 2008 versus 1996 to 2005. The reported numbers of long-term workers (4+ years), total short-term and non-residential fully-supported workers, non-Canadians serving in their home country and support staff of all types except the more than half-time short-term support staff grew more quickly from 2005 to 2008 than from 1996 to 2005. However, the number of mid-term workers (1 to 4 years), nonresidential partially supported workers, non-Canadians serving in their own county and more than half-time short-term support staff either shrank or grew less quickly from 2005 to 2008 than they did from 1996 to 2005. In sum, our relative "report card" for Canadian Protestant mission agency growth from 2005 to 2008 is far more good than bad, as most clearly seen in the four totals categories near the bottom of Table 12.

For the rest of this analysis we follow (and supplement) the terminology conventions utilized in the previous edition of the *Handbook*. In this edition, we identify a change as a *TREND* (italicized upper case) if it has been consistent over the past decade or more. However, we identify as a *SHIFT* (italicized upper case) changes from 2005 to 2008 that are the opposite of what had happened over the previous decade. TRENDS and SHIFTS can be either up or down.

We supplement this with two new terms, drawing on information reported by the 105 agencies for which we have data in 2001, 2005 and 2008. We indicate a consistent change in the same agencies from 2001 to 2008 as a *trend* (italicized lower case). We also identify as a *shift* (italicized lower case) changes from 2005 to 2008 that differ from the change over the 2001 to 2005 period. Trends and shifts can be either up or down.

When we sifted through the Canadian agency data, we identified the reported totals for the types of workers and activities of the agencies (52 categories from 1996 to 2008), the sub-totals for each primary activity category (140 sets of sub-totals; all trends and shifts), and the sub-totals for deployment (146 sets of sub-totals; all trends and shifts). In the analysis, we identified 15 TRENDS (all up), 114 trends (98 up, 16 down), 25 SHIFTS (22 up and 3 down), and 134 shifts (98 up and 36 down). For discussion purposes we combine a number of these together (e.g., fully-supported and partially-supported nonresidential workers). Many of the sub-category sets were too trivial for analysis, such as the trend down in the number of Canadian agencies reporting deployments in North America from 2 (2001) to 1 (2005) to 0 (2008). With that in mind, we organize the presentation of the changes into three major categories: 1) aggregates for the types of workers and mobilization activities re-ported by Canadian agencies, 2) the types of workers and agency activities reported by major activity category, and 3) full-time workers reported by areas of deployment.

Canadian Agency Workers and Mobilization Activities

In each of our surveys over the past several decades we have asked the Canadian organizations and agencies to provide us with general information on the types of workers they deploy as well as specific information about how they mobilize their personnel. In this section we present an analysis of the changes reported by the Ca-nadian agencies for 2008.

TREND Up: Non-Canadian Citizens

From 1996 to 2008, in every survey Canadian agencies reported that they mo-bilized more non-Canadian citizens than in the previous survey. This up TREND accelerated from 2005 to 2008, growing at an AGR of 46.9%. As seen in Figure 42, the difference between 2005 and 2008 is enormous.

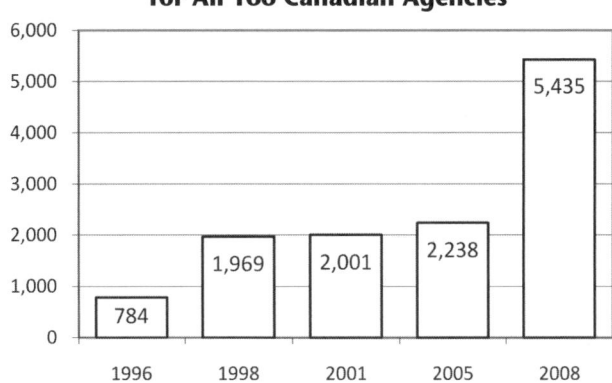

Figure 42: Total Non-Canadian Citizens Working for All 166 Canadian Agencies

The size of the jump in the AGR is due to a single agency, which reported 804 non-Canadians in 2005 but 3,668 in 2008. This one agency accounted for 53.2% of the totals in 2005—but 77.0% of the totals for 2008. They alone comprised 88.0% of the total increase. Thus, the number of full-time non-Canadians working in their own countries reported by this agency is so prominent in the Canadian totals that it could hide the reported changes for the other 165 Canadian agencies. However, the remaining 165 Canadian agencies reported an upward trend in total non-Canadian workers from 2001 to 2009 (from 1,197 to 1,747).

In Figure 43 we break down the total into those serving out of their home coun-try and those serving in their home country. In this we see changes going in oppo-site directions. While the number serving in their home countries grew from 2001 to 2008 (trend up), the number serving outside their home countries shrank over the same period (trend down). Thus, Canadian agencies are deploying more non-Cana-dians, but changing how they deploy them. More are serving in their own countries and fewer in countries other than their home countries.

Figure 43: Non-Canadian Citizens Working for All 166 Canadian Agencies

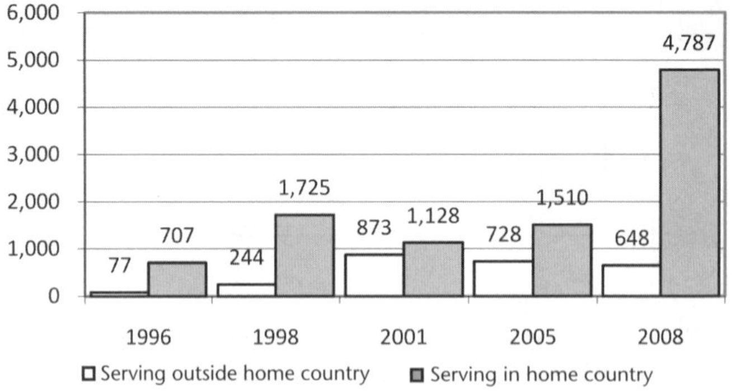

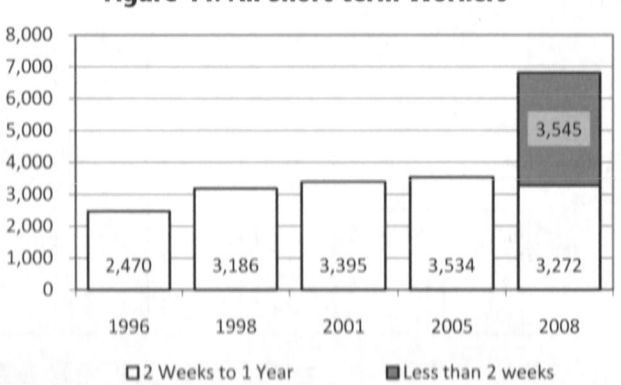

We noted in the first section of this chapter that there is no question of the potential effectiveness of the work of non-Canadian citizens across the majority world. Further, there are definite financial efficiencies gained through employing them rather than Canadian citizens. However, the survey does not enable us to determine the extent to which these workers are actually serving across cultural boundaries. It is easy to imagine an Indian working in India in a dramatically different cross-cultural setting. Likewise it is also easy to imagine a Nigerian working among ethnolinguistically similar Nigerians in England. Additionally, this ongoing TREND (Figure 42) could indicate an increase in non-Canadian support personnel in the administrative offices of their home countries rather than an increase of actual field workers.

TREND Up: Total Short-term Workers

The short-term workers deployed by Canadian agencies continued the growth seen in every survey since 1996. However, this is only when we use the combined total of those for 2 weeks to 1 year with those for less than 2 weeks (Figure 44). Figure 45 illustrates this by giving the AGR for only the short-term workers gone more than 2 weeks. The -2.53% AGR for 2005-2008 shows what we would be reporting if we did not combine the two segments in Figure 44. Even so, when compared to the U.S. negative rate of -6.32%, it appears that the Canadian agencies were not affected as deeply in short-term mobilization efforts as their U.S. counterparts.[16]

Figure 44: All Short-term Workers

Figure 45: AGR of Canadian Short-term (2 Weeks to 1 Year) Workers

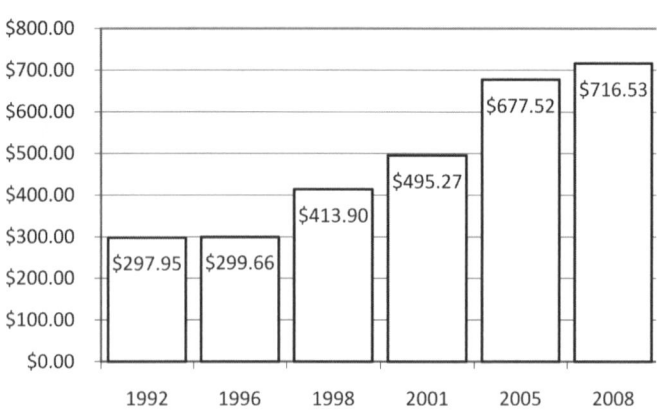

TREND Up: Incomes for Overseas Ministries

Figure 46 shows the inflation-adjusted income for overseas ministries for Canadian agencies from 1992 to 2008, and Figure 47 shows the AGR of that income. Together these show the slowing down of the pace of income gains from 1996. However, unlike the U.S. agencies, the Canadian agencies reported an inflation-adjusted gain of 5.8% in aggregate income for overseas ministries (Table 12), and AGR of 1.88%. Though anemic in comparison to prior gains, at least it is a gain rather than a loss (as reported by the U.S. agencies). This gain continues the TREND up in income for overseas ministries reported by Canadian agencies since 1992.

In light of the global financial crisis, we should rightly celebrate any gain. However, one sobering factor is that the reason the size of the gain is due to the introduction of the new agencies in this edition's survey. Even though they reported only 4.2% of the total income reported, that is 4.2% which would not have been otherwise reported. The aggregate income gain for the 118 agencies reporting in both the 2005 and 2008 surveys is only 1.3% (an AGR of 0.43%).

In sum, Canadian agencies reported more income for overseas ministries in 2008 than in 2005. However, they likely increased their overseas ministry budgets in both

Figure 46: Inflation-Adjusted Income for Overseas for Canadian Agencies (in $Millions)

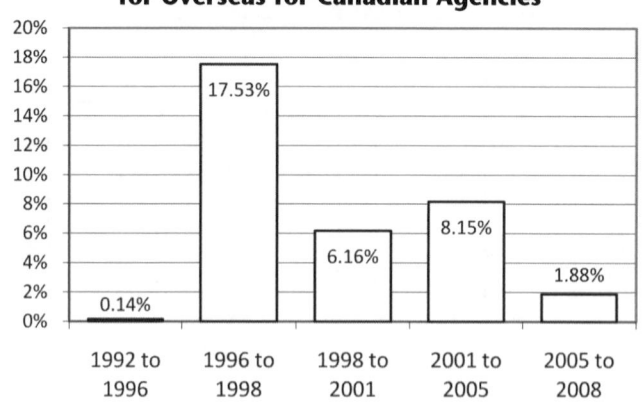

**Figure 47: Inflation Adjusted AGR Income
for Overseas for Canadian Agencies**

2006 and 2007. If so, the overall effect is a two or three year rollback. We also antic-
ipate that the 2009 income was even lower than in 2008, as the full strength of the
downturn was in effect by 2009. Finally, by any account the immediate financial future offers little assurance except that the agencies are now in a "new normal" rather than simply a temporary bump in an otherwise ever-rising growth in the future.

SHIFT Up: Long-term and All Full-time On-location Canadians and All Canadians

In this edition we are pleased to report a very welcome small SHIFT up in the
number of Canadians serving full-time overseas (including tentmakers; Table 13).

All together they grew by 4.9% from 2005 (Table 13; Figure 48). This is the first
increase in this category in since 1996 (Figure 61) and we detail the breakdown by
categories in Table 13 and Figure 49. This is very encouraging news for those watch-
ing the Canadian mission scene.

In Figure 50 we detail the AGRs for categories with important shifts. The 2 to 4
year full-time workers and tentmakers dropped since 2005, while 1 to 2 year full-
time and long-term (4+ year) workers grew—the latter adding a strong 9.2% to the
total reported in 2005 (Figure 51).

Table 13: Full-time Canadian Workers

	2001	2005	2008	Change (2005-08)	1: AGR 2005-08	2: AGR 2001-05	AGR 1 minus AGR 2
1 to 2 Years	106	158	223	41.1%	9.0%	10.5%	-1.5%
2 to 4 Years	231	353	269	-23.8%	-6.6%	11.2%	-17.8%
4+ Years	2,493	2,059	2,249	9.2%	2.2%	-4.7%	6.9%
Tentmakers	154	186	149	-19.9%	-5.4%	4.8%	-10.2%
Totals	2,984	2,756	2,890	4.9%	1.2%	-2.0%	3.2%

Figure 48: Full-time On-location Canadian Workers

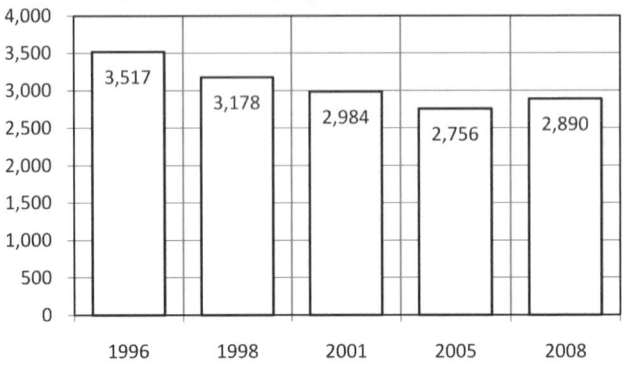

Figure 49: Full-time On-location Canadian Workers by Category

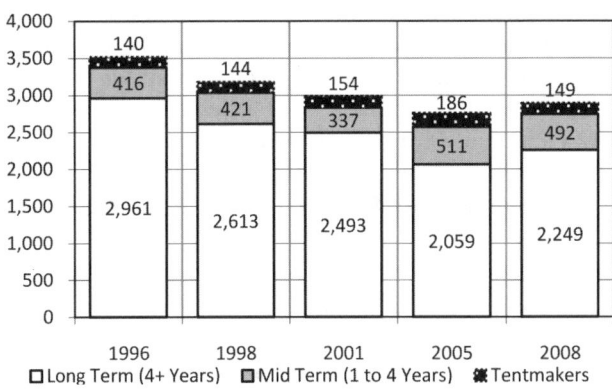

Figure 50: AGR Changes for Full-time Canadians by Category

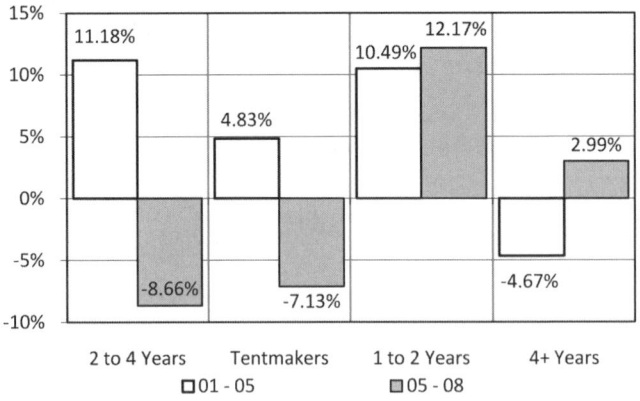

Figure 51: Changes in Full-time On-location Canadian Workers by Category

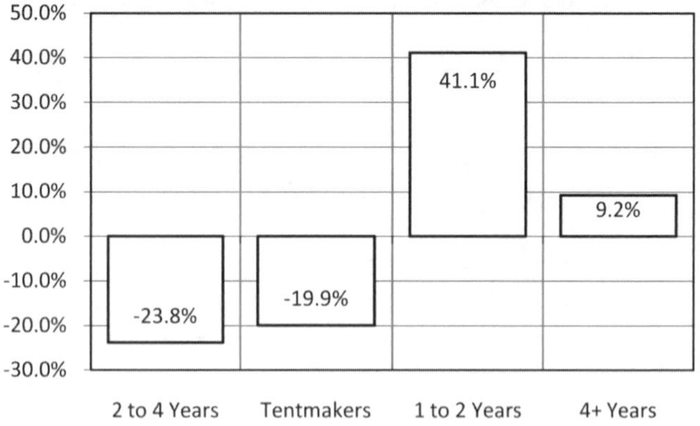

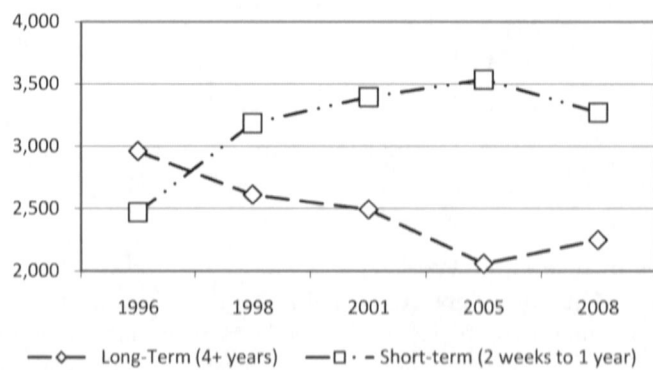

In the previous *Handbook* we noted that Canadians were sending fewer long-term workers and more short-term workers. Just the opposite happened in 2008, when Canadian agencies reported fewer short-term workers (of 2 weeks to 1 year) and more long-term workers (Figure 52).

Figure 52: Long-term and Short-term Canadian Workers

TREND Up: Ratio of Non-Canadians to Canadians

Even with the gain in full-time Canadians deployed by Canadian agencies, the larger increase in non-Canadians resulted in a net continuing TREND of an increasing ratio of non-Canadians to Canadians working for Canadian agencies (Figure 53). In the previous *Handbook*, for every five Canadians working with Canadian agencies there are four non-Canadians. This has now increased to 9.4 non-Canadians, a dramatic surge (Figure 53). However, the ratio for the remaining 165 agencies is 5.2 non-Canadians to 4 Canadians (Figure 54). Even so, Canadian agencies and organizations as a whole have crossed the threshold and now report that they deploy more non-Canadian citizens than Canadians in full-time on-location mission work.

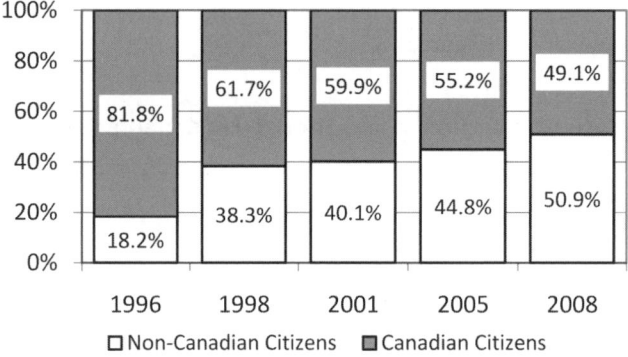

Figure 53: Share of Canadian and Non-Canadian Citizens Working forAll Canadian Agencies

	1996	1998	2001	2005	2008
Canadian Citizens	81.8%	61.7%	59.9%	55.2%	34.7%
Non-Canadian Citizens	18.2%	38.3%	40.1%	44.8%	65.3%

□ Non-Canadian Citizens   ■ Canadian Citizens

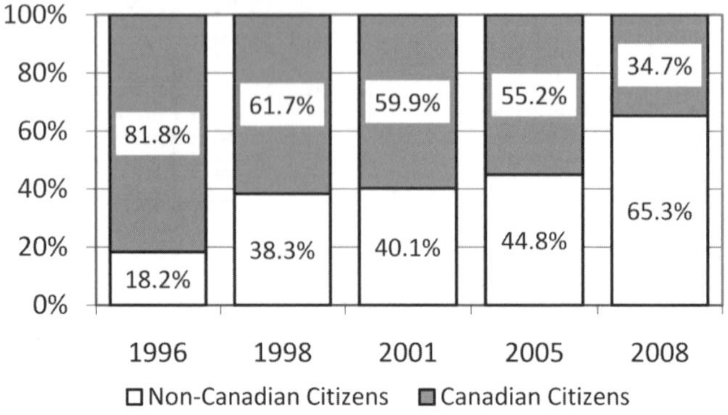

Figure 54: Share of Canadian and Non-Canadian Citizens Working for 165 Canadian Agencies

	1996	1998	2001	2005	2008
Canadian Citizens	81.8%	61.7%	59.9%	55.2%	49.1%
Non-Canadian Citizens	18.2%	38.3%	40.1%	44.8%	50.9%

□ Non-Canadian Citizens   ■ Canadian Citizens

Shift Up: Non-residential Workers

The reported number of non-residential workers is somewhat confusing. On one hand, after a significant drop in 2005, the 2008 total rebounded above the 2001 level (Figure 55). On the other hand, however, five agencies account for almost the entire changes reported across all three surveys. Three of these five reported an aggregate of 6 non-residential workers in 2001—but 253 in 2008. The other two showed the opposite pattern, reporting an aggregate of 271 non-residential workers in 2001—but only 10 in 2008. However, the combined total for these five agencies was only 7 non-residential workers in 2005! Thus, it was the massive shifts in reporting from these five agencies that gave rise to the dramatic aggregate swings for all Canadian agencies across the 2001, 2005 and 2008 surveys.

The implications of this are not completely clear. The changes may simply result from designations discrepancies among the five agencies over the seven-year span of the surveys. It could have been due to short-lived experiments with non-residential workers as a missional strategy tried by these five over different periods. Whatever the reason, the net adjusted picture is one of Canadian agencies deploying greater numbers of nonresidential workers.

Figure 55: All Non-residential Workers from Canadian Agencies

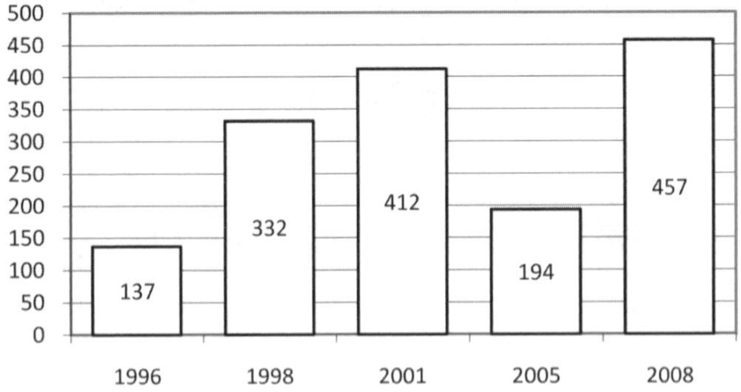

Bar chart:
- 1996: 137
- 1998: 332
- 2001: 412
- 2005: 194
- 2008: 457

Shift Up: Canadian Home Staff

Canadian agencies reported a shift up in the total number of home staff (Figure 56). Full-time home staff shifted up after a downturn in 2005. One agency reported over 150 for 2001, 0 in 2005 and over 250 in 2008, which impacted the strength of the changes in 2005 and 2008. However, there were numerous other large changes from other agencies with no identifiable cluster of patterns that can explain the net change in full-time home staff. However, from 2001 to 2008, the reported numbers of part-time home staff maintained an upward trend.

Figure 56: Home Staff for Canadian Agencies

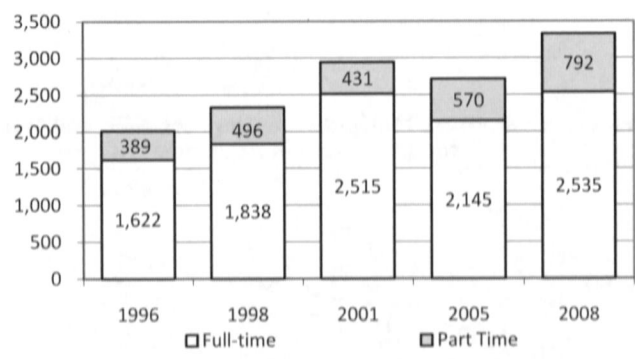

Stacked bar chart (Full-time / Part Time):
- 1996: 1,622 / 389
- 1998: 1,838 / 496
- 2001: 2,515 / 431
- 2005: 2,145 / 570
- 2008: 2,535 / 792

□ Full-time   □ Part Time

Shift Up: Short-term Support Staff

With the larger number of short-term workers reported, it is not surprising that Canadian agencies also reported larger numbers of short-term support staff (Figure 57). However, the infusion of new agencies into the totals made significant differences in the net numbers. Without the new listings, the 2008 numbers were still above the 2005 numbers, but below the 2001 numbers (Figure 58).

TREND Up: Short-term Contact Methods

With the increase in short-term staff, it is not surprising that Canadian agencies are also reporting increases in the number of every contact method they employ to recruit short-term workers. In Figure 59 we show the methods tracked since

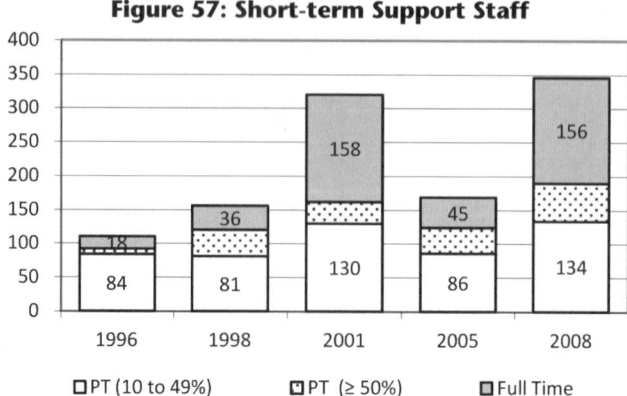

Figure 57: Short-term Support Staff

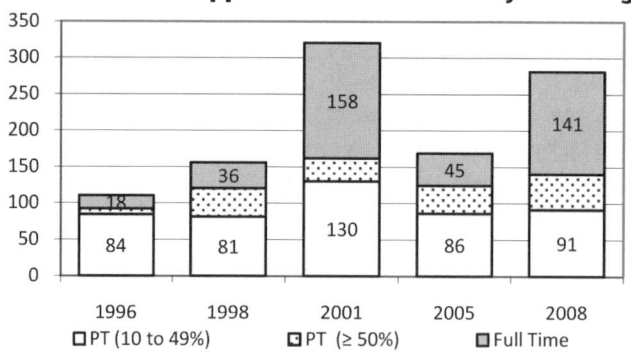

Figure 58: Short-term Support Staff without Newly Listed Agencies

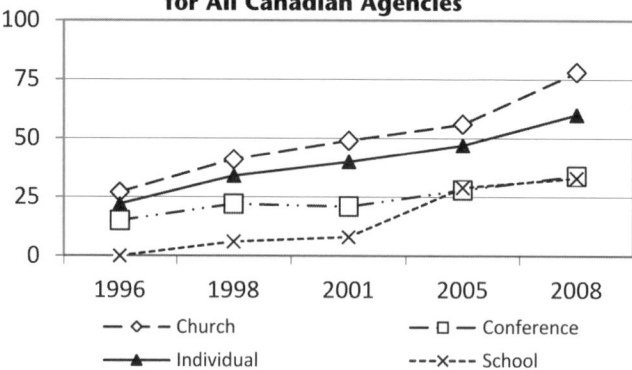

Figure 59: Contact Methods for Short-term Recruitment for All Canadian Agencies

1996. Keep in mind that in 2008, 52 agencies indicated they use the Web as a contact method (not indicated in Figure 59). However, as with short-term support staff, once we consider only the agencies reporting in 2005 and 2008, we see a slight decrease in the number of agencies using each of the contact methods (Figure 60), again demonstrating that the newly added agencies emphasize short-term (and micro-term) missions.

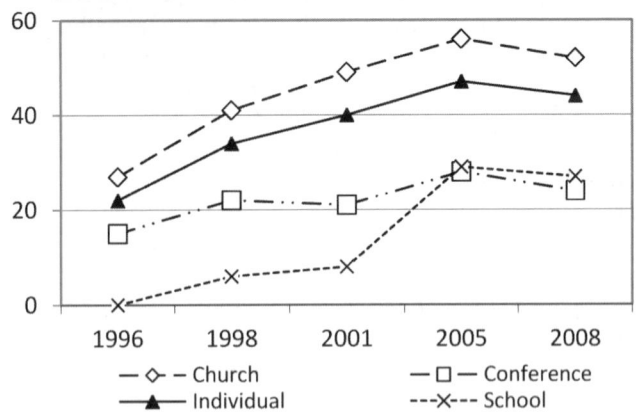

Figure 60: Contact Methods Used in Short-term Recruitment Excluding New Canadian Agencies

SHIFT Down: Tentmakers

As we previously noted, Canadian agencies reported a SHIFT down in tentmakers (Figure 61). However, the newly added agencies reported 73.2% of the aggregate numbers (109 out of 149). Factoring them out, the shift down for agencies listed in both 2005 and 2008 is 78.5% (from 186 to 40).

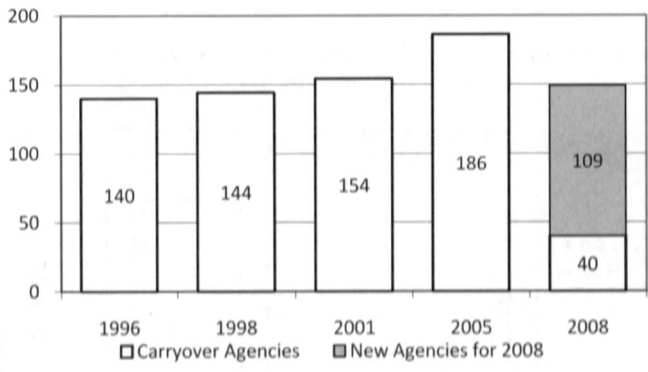

Figure 61: Canadian Agency Tentmakers

Several factors help us understand the nature of this precipitous drop for the previously listed agencies. First, in our 2005 survey nineteen Canadian agencies reported sending tentmakers. Only eleven did so in this edition. Second, the two largest organizations, which together in 2005 reported 78 tentmakers, reported a combined total of only 3 tentmakers in 2008. These two agencies alone accounted for almost 70% of the loss. Unfortunately, however, the remaining eleven agencies also reported a net loss. In fact, only one of the nineteen agencies reporting tentmakers in 2005 reported an increase in the 2008 survey. Because we do not ask for explanations from the agencies for such changes, further research is required before we can determine the reason or reasons for the large drop.

Activities of Canadian Agencies

As noted previously,[17] in our survey over the past several editions of the *Handbook* we have asked agencies to identify up to six activities that are the primary activities of their organization. We provide a list of options from which to choose, and include an "Other" option that lets them specify additional activities not in the current list. We also ask agencies to indicate which **one** of the activities they most commonly associate with their organization. For our discussion, we refer to that activity as the "primary activity." We refer to the remaining activities identified by each organization (up to five) as "activities" or "all activities." As shown in Table 8 (above), we categorize each of the 66 activities into five categories: evangelism & discipleship, education & training, relief & development, mission agency support, and other.

It is important to keep in mind in the following discussion that—for the purposes of our analysis—we assume that the self-identified primary activity receives a larger share of an agency's resources and energy than any other activity. Thus, if an agency selects "National worker support" as their primary activity, we assume that this will receive more personnel and financial resources than any of the other five activities reported by that agency.

Figure 62 shows the comparative share of resources for several categories for 2008. To keep the chart less cluttered, we only indicate the actual share when it is greater than 10%. Agencies whose primary activity is in the evangelism and discipleship category report the largest share of Canadian full-time workers (81.3%) and non-Canadian citizen full-time workers (78.2%). Agencies whose primary activity is in the relief and development category report the largest income for overseas ministries (74.0%) and short-term workers (47.8%).

Figure 62: Comparison of Resources focused on Primary Activities Categories for All Canadian Agencies

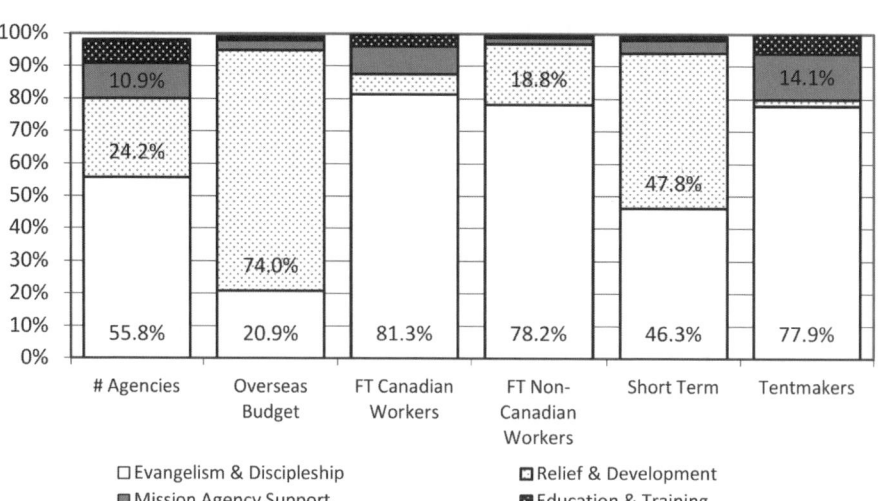

In comparison with 2005, Canadian agencies reported a large shift in the share of non-Canadian workers away from agencies whose primary activity is in the relief/development category and towards agencies primary activity is in the evangelism/discipleship category. Just the opposite is true for the reported number of short-term workers. Further, the relative shares of tentmakers increased for agencies whose primary activity is in the mission agency support category and decreased for agencies whose primary activity is in the evangelism/discipleship category.

The shares represented in Figure 62 for non-Canadian workers shift significantly when we exclude the agency reporting the largest share of them (as noted in previously). For the remaining 165 Canadian agencies, those with primary activities in the relief and development category report 58.4% (up from 18.8%) of the non-Canadian workers, while those with primary activities in the evangelism/discipleship category report 32.1% (down from 78.2%).

Since 1998 we have tracked the ebb and flow of the number of agencies reporting their primary activity within each major category. Table 14 gives the numerical results; Figure 63 shows the relative change in shares of each category.

Table 14: Share in Number of Agencies per Primary Activity Category

Category	1998	2001	2005	2008
Evangelism & Discipleship	68.8%	68.3%	72.1%	55.8%
Mission Agency Support	7.4%	6.7%	6.6%	10.9%
Education & Training	5.0%	5.8%	6.6%	7.3%
Relief & Development	15.7%	16.7%	13.9%	24.2%
Other	3.3%	2.5%	0.8%	1.8%

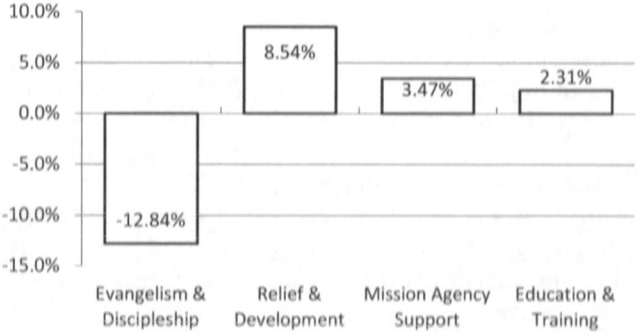

Figure 63: Net Change in Share of Agencies by Primary Category 1998 to 2008

From 1998 to 2008, the percent of all agencies indicating a primary activity in evangelism and discipleship category dropped while the percent of all agencies indicating a primary activity in the other three major categories all increased. This does not show a change in focus because the percentages in Table 14 for 2008 include the 48 newly listed agencies. In this case, while 68% of the previously listed agencies indicated primary activities in the evangelism and discipleship category, only 25.5% of the 48 agencies added in the 2008 survey did so. Thus, the shifts away from evangelism and discipleships in Figure 63 largely result from adding these agencies to the survey.

What about the agencies that were listed in all three surveys (2001, 2005 and 2008)? There were 105 such agencies, and Figure 64 shows areas that changed for them. To simplify, Figure 64 only shows categories with changes greater than 5%. Clearly the proportionate shares for the Canadian agencies whose primary activities are in evangelism and discipleship are shifting towards agencies whose primary activities are in the other categories.

Figure 64: Change in Share for Selected Categories in Primary Activities of 105 Agencies 2001 to 2008

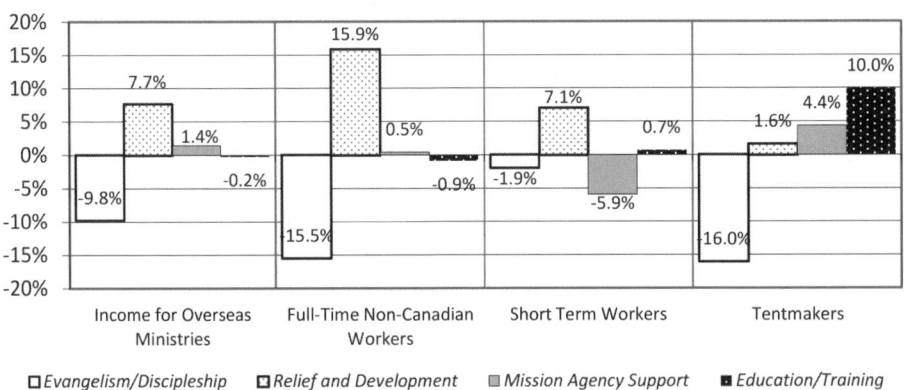

In the rest of this section we focus on reported changes seen among the agencies indicating primary activities in each of the four major activity categories in turn.

Education and Training

Agencies whose primary activity fits into the education and training category reported solid growth from 2001 to 2008 in the total number of full-time Canadian workers deployed (Figure 65), due to a 767% increase in full-time 2 to 4 year workers and 144% increase for 4+ year workers from 2005 to 2008. They also reported a shift up for non-Canadian citizens from 2001 to 2008.

There were three areas in particular in which agencies in this category reported increases while the aggregate for all Canadian agencies were decreases (Figure 66): 1) in 2 to 4 year full-time Canadian deployments, 2) short-term workers of more than 2 weeks, and 3) tentmakers.

The reported income for overseas work for these agencies grew 62.1% from 2005 to 2008 (the inflation-adjusted AGR rose from -0.2% for 2001 to 2005 to 17.5% for 2005 to 2008). However, when the newly listed agencies are excluded the growth was a more modest 14.1% (AGR of 3.4%).

Figure 65: Education and Training: Full-time Workers 2001 to 2008

Figure 66: Areas of Significant AGR for Agencies with Primary Activities in Education and Training

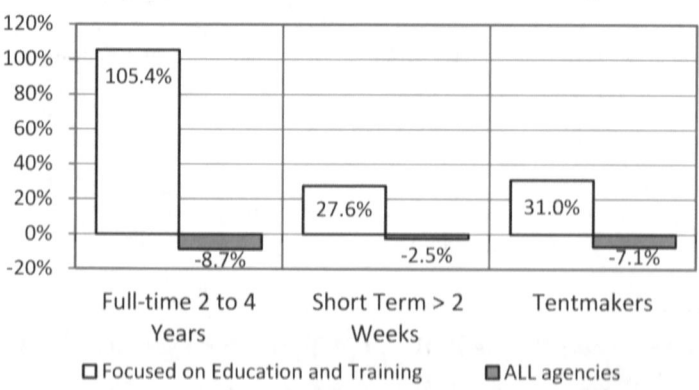

Evangelism and Discipleship

Agencies whose primary activity was in the evangelism and discipleship category reported gains the number of non-Canadian full-time workers but a drop in the number of full-time Canadian workers

Figure 67: Evangelism and Discipleship: Full-time Workers 2001 to 2008

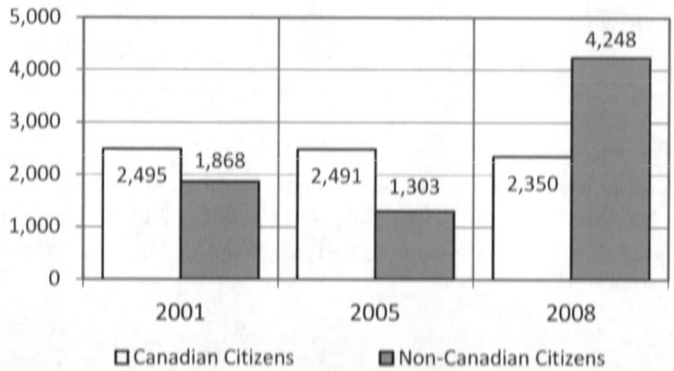

Three areas in which agencies in this category reported significant annual growth rates from 2005 to 2008 (Figure 68): 1) increase in 1 to 2 year full-time U.S. workers, 2) decrease in 2 to 4 year full-time workers, and 3) increase in non-Canadians working in their own countries.

Figure 68: Areas of Significant AGR for Agencies with Primary Activities in Evangelism and Discipleship

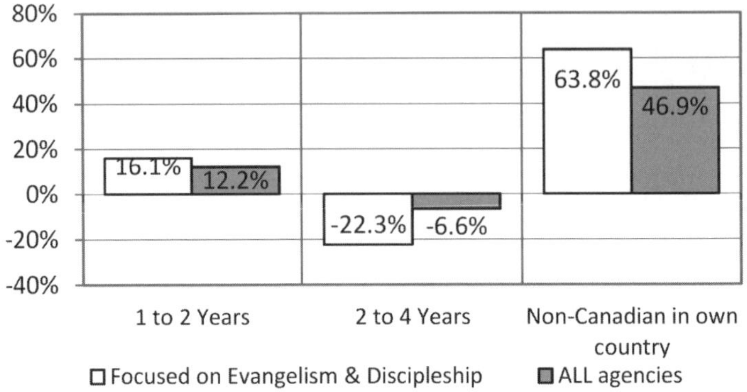

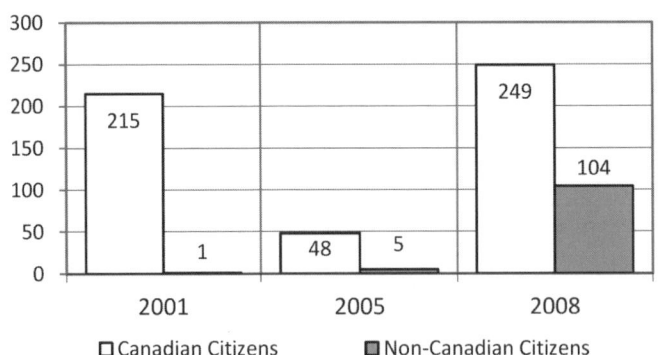

Mission Agency Support

Agencies whose primary activity fits into the mission agency support category reported increases in all categories of full-time workers (Figure 69), though the full-time Canadian gains were needed to offset the previous losses.

Figure 69: Evangelism and Discipleship: Full-time Workers 2001 to 2008

Three areas in which agencies in this category reported significant annual growth rates from 2005 to 2008 were (Figure 70): 1) increase in 2 to 4 year full-time workers, 2) increase 4+ year workers and 3) increase in non-Canadians working in their own countries.

Figure 70: Areas of Significant AGR for Agencies with Primary Activities in Mission Agency Suppport

Relief and Development

The number of all reported Canadian full-time workers for those agencies whose primary activity fits into the relief and development category remained steady in 2008, while the total non-Canadian citizens grew (Figure 71). Agencies in this category reported positive against-the-grain changes in the number of 2 to 4 year full-time Canadians, tentmakers, non-Canadians working out of their home countries, and short-term workers.

Figure 71: Relief and Development: Full-time Workers 2001 to 2008

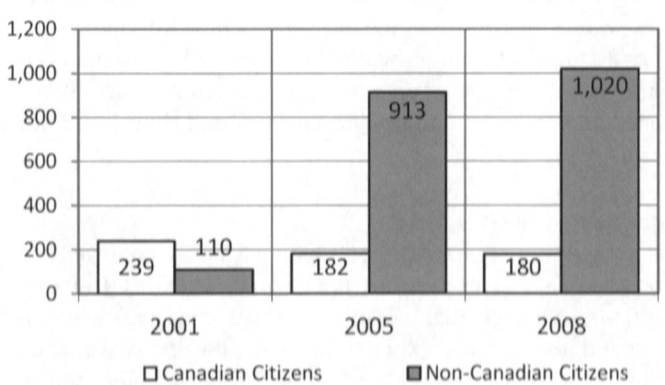

Four areas in which agencies in this category reported significant annual growth rates from 2005 to 2008 were (Figure 72): 1) increase in 2 to 4 year full-time workers, 2) increase in tentmakers, 3) increase in non-Canadians working out of their own countries, and 4) increase in short-term workers of 2 weeks to 1 year.

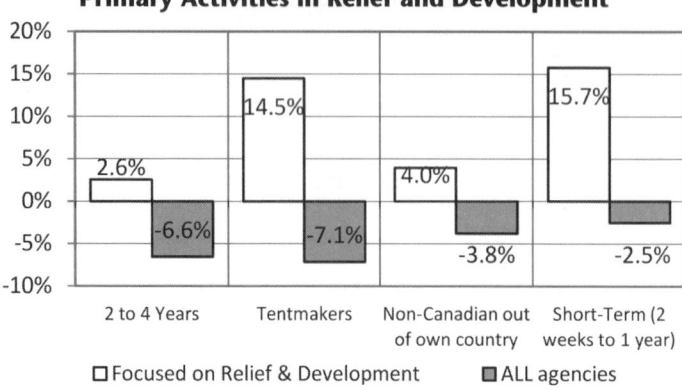

Figure 72: Areas of Significant AGR for Agencies with Primary Activities in Relief and Development

Deployment of Canadian Agencies and Missionaries

In the previous edition of the *Handbook* we examined shifts in continental areas (e.g., increases in deployments to Asia, decreases in deployments to Oceania).[18] In this edition, we present three ways to configure the deployment data, each offering a different glimpse on the extent to which Canadian agencies deploy their full-time workers. First, we offer deployment shifts in relation to the regions of Asia and the Middle East. Second, we look at deployment shifts in 10/40 Window countries.[19] Finally, we examine shifts in deployment among Worlds A, B, and C.[20]

Bear in mind in this discussion that we do not ask agencies to identify where they send their short-term workers, nor to distinguish tentmakers from other full-time workers. Nor do we ask them to disclose how they allocate their income for overseas ministries among the countries in which they deploy full-time workers. As a result, we cannot accurately discern how the agencies divide their financial or logistical support among the continents on which they have a presence. This means that we will confine our discussion in this section on reported shifts in full-time Canadian and non-Canadian workers.

Continental Deployments

In the previous edition, we noted that Canadian agencies deployed more Canadians and non-Canadian citizens in Africa and Central America/Caribbean and fewer Canadians in Europe. The fact that Canadian agencies in aggregate reported gains in both Canadian and non-Canadian citizens being deployed means that it is theoretically possible that we could see more workers deployed on every continent in 2008 than we did in 2005.

However, as Table 15 shows, this did not happen. To generate Table 15 we combined some continental regions (e.g., Central America and the Caribbean with South America; Europe with Commonwealth of Independent States) and omit the numbers for workers in unspecified countries. This simplifies the comparisons.

Canadian agencies reported the largest numerical deployment increase of Canadians to Asia (148) and Africa (140) and non-Canadians to Africa (2,729), Latin America (303) and Asia (201). On a percentage basis, the largest increase in all full-time workers was in Africa (250.3%), followed by gains in full-time workers deployed in the Middle East (90.3%), Oceania (84.1%) and Latin America (37.3%).

Table 15: Deployments for All Canadian Protestant Agencies by Continent 2008

	Canadians Full-time	05 to 08 Change		Non-Canadians Full-time	05 to 08 Change		All Full-time	05 to 08 Change	
Africa	704	140	24.8%	3,311	2,729	468.9%	4,015	2,869	250.3%
Asia	742	148	24.9%	1,171	201	20.7%	1,913	349	22.3%
Europe (and CIS)	453	-2	-0.4%	151	-59	-28.1%	604	-61	-9.2%
Latin America	535	42	8.5%	734	303	70.3%	1,269	345	37.3%
Middle East	114	52	83.9%	63	32	103.2%	177	84	90.3%
Oceania	111	62	126.5%	5	-9	-64.3%	116	53	84.1%

Figures 73 and 74 offer visual perspectives on these deployment changes. While Figure 76 shows the actual deployments, Figure 79 portrays the proportionate share changes. For example, while the percentage gain in actual full-time workers for Africa was 250.3%, the relative gain in share for Canadian full-time deployments was 25.3% (from 23.8% in 2005 to 49.4% in 2008).

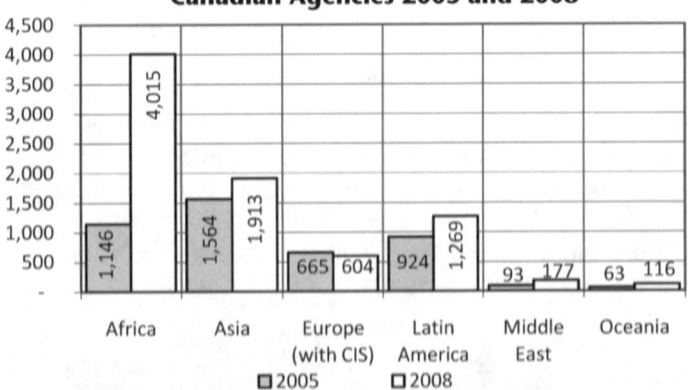

Figure 73: Deployment of Full-time Missionaries by All Canadian Agencies 2005 and 2008

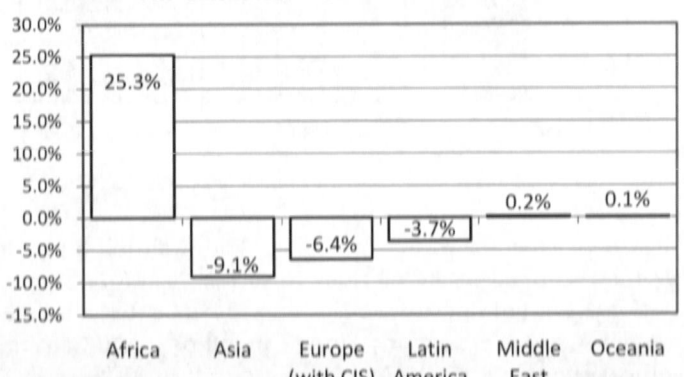

Figure 74: Share Change of Full-time Workers from All Canadian Agencies 2005 to 2008

Once again, however, many of the changes were due to a single agency. When we adjust for this, the remaining 165 Canadian agencies deployed more full-time workers to every region except Europe, and the share of Canadian workers rose everywhere except Europe and Latin America.

Figure 75 help us focus the picture for the reported changes in regional deployments by showing the upward trend in total full-time deployments in Asia from 2001 to 2008.

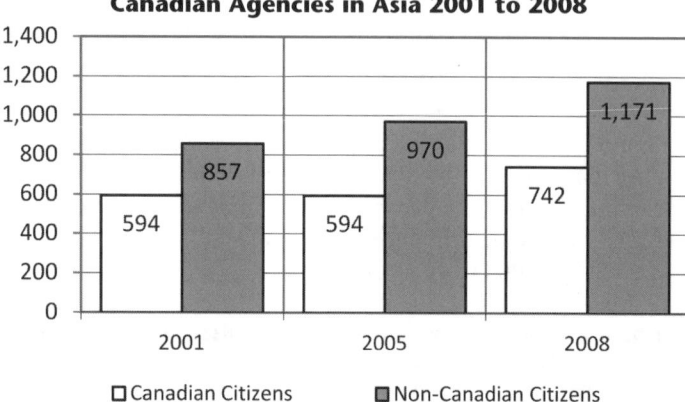

Figure 75: Full-time Workers Deployed by All Canadian Agencies in Asia 2001 to 2008

□ Canadian Citizens   ■ Non-Canadian Citizens

In Figure 76 we show the proportion of all full-time deployments reported in Asia, after adjusting for the largest agency. The share of non-Canadians shifted down in Asia for these agencies from 31.6% in 2005 to 27.6% in 2008, while the share of full-time Canadians increased from 26.1% to 27.3%.

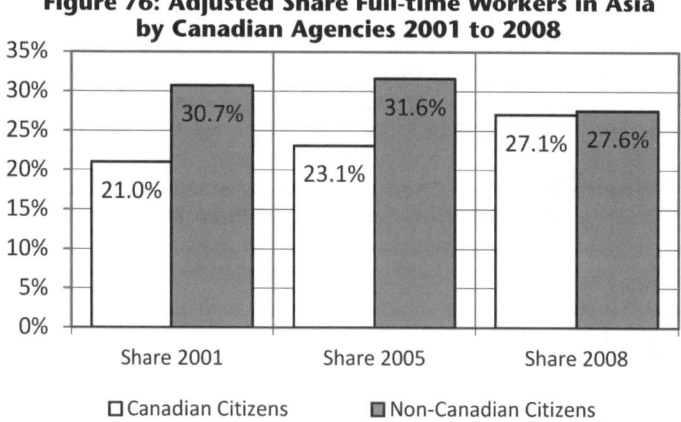

Figure 76: Adjusted Share Full-time Workers in Asia by Canadian Agencies 2001 to 2008

□ Canadian Citizens   ■ Non-Canadian Citizens

The reported deployment shifts to the Middle East of all full-time workers reversed the declines reported in the previous *Handbook*. Figure 77 shows that the number of both types of full-time workers increased in 2008. For full-time Canadians the increase was a trend up, and the increase in full-time non-Canadians was a shift up after the decline in 2005.

Figure 77: Full-time Workers Deployed by Canadian Agencies in the Middle East 2001 to 2008

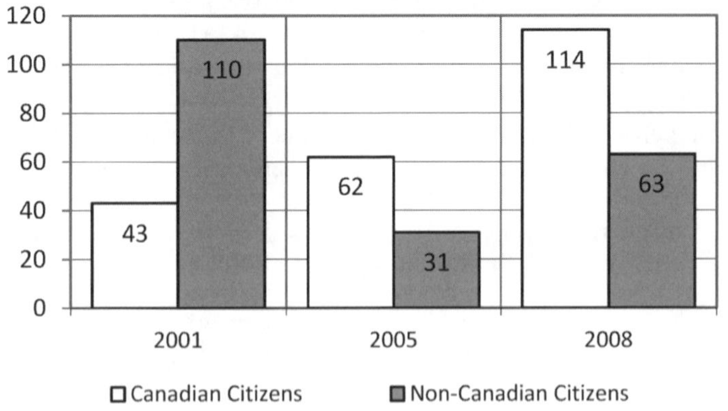

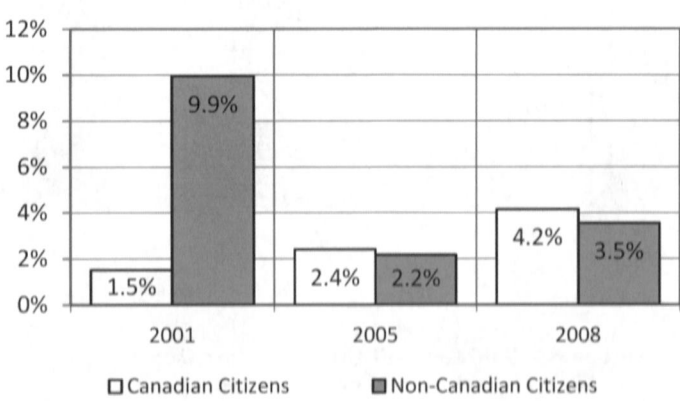

Adjusting for the agency noted previously results in a growth in the share of all Canadians to almost double the 2005 level (Figure 78), and the share of non-Canadians grew by over 50%. Thus, Canadians reported a greater adjusted share of their workers in Middle East countries in 2008 than they did in 2005.

Figure 78: Adjusted Share of Full-time Workers Deployed by Canadian Agencies in the Middle East

10/40 Window Deployments

In addition to continental regions, we configured the database to enable us to determine whether deployments were in 10/40 Window countries or not—though we need to note several caveats on the following table and charts.[21] First, the list for these countries is an evolving list (e.g. some lists include Indonesia, others do not). We chose to use the Joshua Project list (http://www.joshuaproject.net/10-40-window.php) in part because of their long-standing with groups such as the A.D. 2000 Movement and the U.S. Center for World Mission and in part because they recognize the diverse lists and have chosen criteria that are missionally-focused while adhering to the core ideas underlying the concept of the 10/40 Window. A second caveat is that countries in the 10/40 Window list have varying levels of reached and

unreached populations. As a result, deployments from a particular agency in countries listed in the 10/40 Window are not automatically among unreached peoples in
those countries. Third, and finally, we present the totals for the 165 Canadian agencies in Table 15 primarily so that we may more accurately see the broadest Canadian picture.[22] With those caveats in mind, in Table 16 and Figure 79 we offer the aggregate numbers of reported full-time workers for 165 of the 166 Canadian agencies.
We show the percentages of all full-time workers in Figure 80 and the divisions of
Canadian full-time workers in Figure 81 for the same 165 agencies.

Table 16: Deployments In and Out of 10/40 Window for 165 Canadian Agencies 2001 to 2008

	2001		2005		2008	
	10/40	Other	10/40	Other	10/40	Other
No. of Agencies	54	73	52	80	76	109
Canadians	607	2,223	469	2,101	512	2,229
Non-Canadians	377	1,624	959	1,279	1,107	4,328
Total	984	3,847	1,428	3,380	1,619	6,557

Figure 79: Full-time Workers Deployed in the 10/40 Window by 165 Canadian Agencies

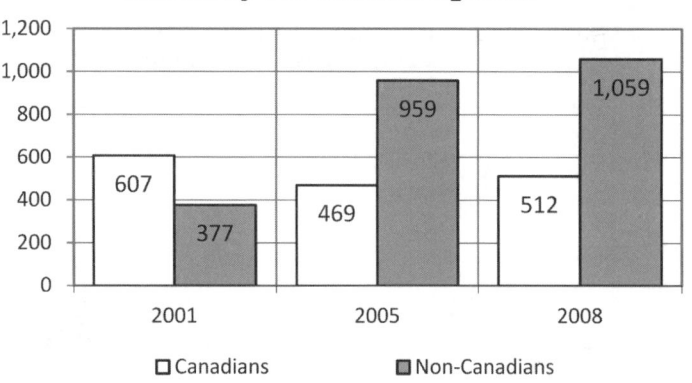

Figure 80: Share of Full-time Workers Deployed in 10/40 Window by 165 Canadian Agencies

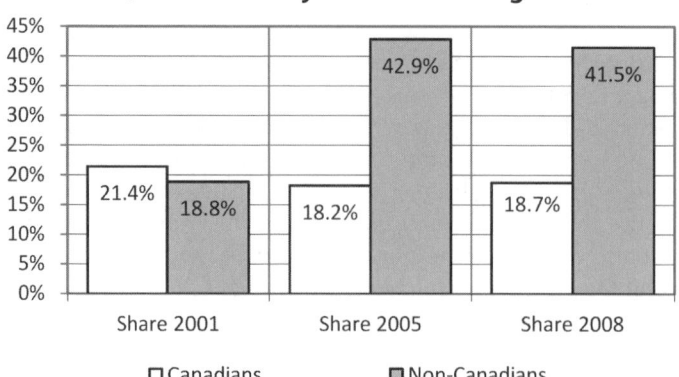

**Figure 81: 10/40 Window Deployment Ratio for 165
Canadian Agencies 2001 to 2008**

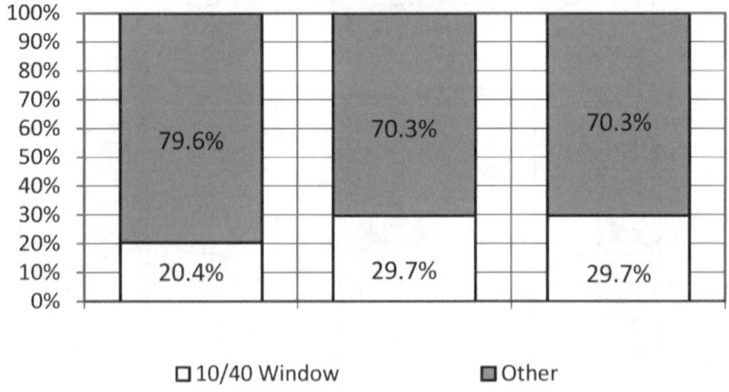

☐ 10/40 Window   ■ Other

When adjusted, the clear signal is that Canadian agencies continue to shift more workers to 10/40 Window countries. While the share remained the same in 2005 as in 2008, it still demonstrates a focus on deploying workers among the least reached or the unreached. It is also significant to note that when we limit the analysis to the 105 agencies surveyed in 2001, 2005 and 2008, they reported steady gains in the numbers of all full-time workers in 10/40 Window countries (up 19.5%).

World A, B, C Deployments

In the *World Christian Encyclopedia*[23] David Barrett and editors identify three categories for categorizing countries (2001, I:30). World A countries are those in which more than 50% of the population is unevangelized. World B countries are those in which more than 50% of the population is evangelized, but fewer than 60% of the people are identified as Christians. World C countries are those in which those identified as Christians number more than 60% of the population.

Figure 82 shows the shares of workers in each segment of the world in the A, B, and C categories for 165 Canadian agencies. The shares in the "Other" category refer to full-time workers for whom the agencies do not designate a specific country or area of the world. Bear in mind that when organizations choose to not specify deployments it is typically for security reasons and likely that those deployments are in World A or B countries.

Figure 83 clearly indicates that the Canadian agencies shifted deployments into World A countries over the seven year span. While we do not show a graph of the 105 Canadian agencies surveyed in 2001, 2005 and 2008, they reported steady gains in the numbers of all full-time workers in World A countries (up 62.5%) and World B countries (up 99.7%). While it is true that Figure 83 indicates that Canadian agencies deploy the smallest fraction of their full-time workers to World A countries, this is not the full story. As shown in Figures 85 and 87, in 2008 Canadian agencies reported that they deployed 55.8% of their full-time workers in World A or World B countries. Thus, based on information provided to us by the agencies themselves, it is accurate to say that Canadian agencies as a whole are deploying full-time workers in countries around the world with direct access to the unreached.

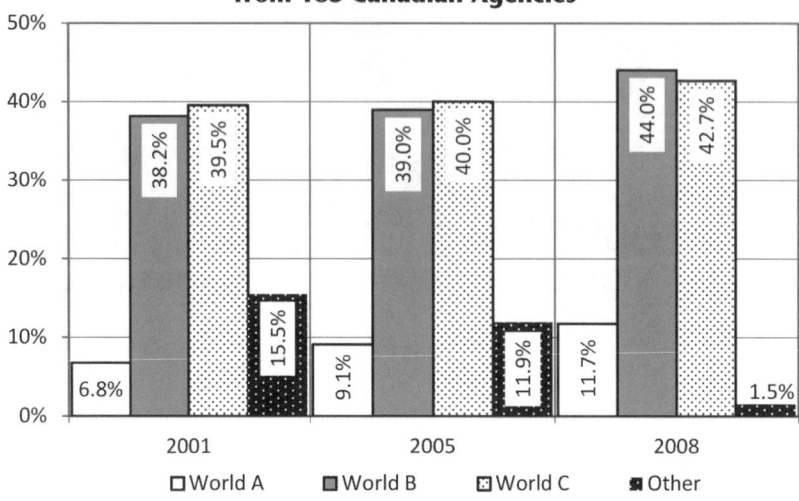

Figure 82: World A, B & C Shares of All Full-time Workers from 165 Canadian Agencies

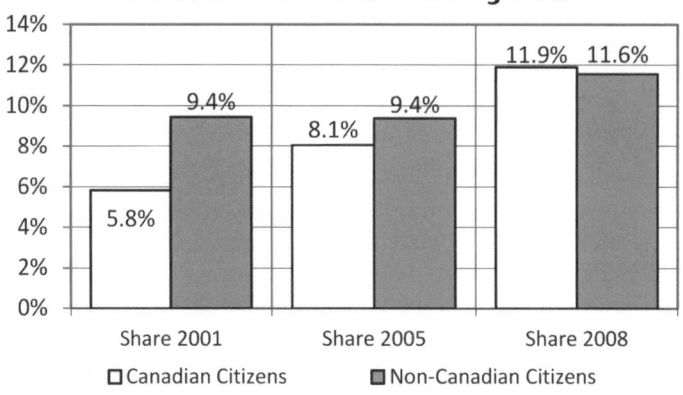

Figure 83: Share of Full-time Workers in World A Countries from 165 Canadian Agencies

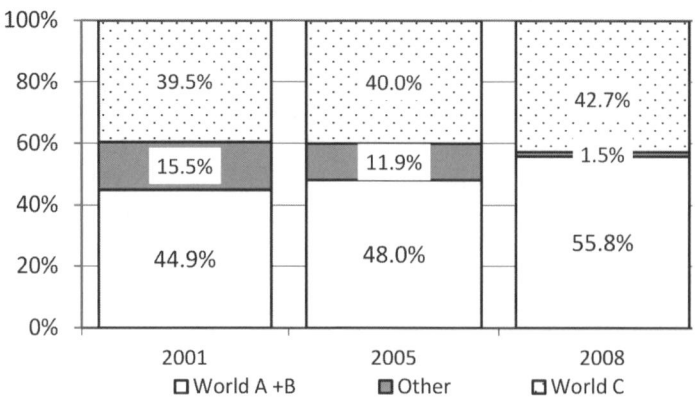

Figure 84: World A +B, C and Other Shares of Full-time Workers from 165 Canadian Agencies

Conclusion

In summary, we have identified several changes Canadian Protestant mission agencies have reported over the past decade. Changes for Canadian agencies, workers and mobilization include the following:

- An increase in the number of full-time Canadians—including a shift up in the number of long-term workers
- An ongoing trend in the increase in the number of full-time non-Canadian citizens
- An ongoing trend in the increase in income for overseas ministries with a corresponding trend in the increasing ratio of non-Canadians to Canadians
- A shift to a decrease in the number of short-term workers going for more than two weeks but an increase in the number of short-term support staff
- A shift to a decrease in the number of tentmakers
- The newly listed Canadian agencies—as compared with the agencies carried from 2005 to 2008—reported much smaller incomes for overseas ministries and greater numbers of tentmakers, short-term workers (less than 2 weeks), and part-time (less than 50%) short-term support staff

Concerning primary activities, the 105 agencies on which we have information over the past seven years have incrementally changed away from reporting primary activities in evangelism and discipleship and toward reporting primary activities in mission agency support or education and training. On the other hand, larger proportions of the agencies newly listed for this edition report primary activities in the relief and development, mission agency support and education and training categories. Other changes that Canadian agencies reported in relation to their primary activities include the following:

- Agencies whose primary activities are in the **education and training** category reported a greater proportion of full-time 2 to 4 year Canadian workers, short-term workers, and tentmakers for agencies
  - —*Newly listed* agencies in this category reported a greater proportion of the full-time Canadian and non-Canadian workers than the agencies carried from 2005 to 2008
- Agencies whose primary activities are in the **evangelism and discipleship** category reported a greater proportion of non-Canadian workers for but a smaller proportion in income for overseas ministries, the number of agencies and the number of full-time Canadian citizens, and
  - —*Newly listed* agencies in this category reported a greater proportion of the number of tentmakers than the agencies carried from 2005 to 2008
- Agencies whose primary activity is in the **relief and development** category reported a greater proportion of short-term workers for overseas ministries
  - —*Newly listed* agencies in this category reported a greater proportion of income for overseas ministries, full-time Canadian and non-Canadian workers and short-term workers than the agencies carried from 2005 to 2008
- Agencies whose primary activity is in the **mission agency support** category reported a greater proportion of tentmakers
  - —*Newly listed* agencies in this category reported a greater proportion of the number of agencies and full-time Canadian workers than the agencies carried from 2005 to 2008

Concerning deployments, the newly listed agencies for 2008 only contributed 8.2% (Table 14) of the total full-time workers listed by all agencies, and their deployments did not significantly change the deployment distributions for all agencies. Factoring out the agency reporting the largest number of non-Canadian workers, the remaining 165 Canadian agencies deployed more full-time workers to every region except Europe. However, they reported a greater proportion of their full-time workers to Africa, the Middle East, Asia and Oceania and a smaller proportion of their full-time workers to Europe and Latin America. They deployed the same share of all full-time workers to 10/40 Window countries in 2008 as they did in 2005, with slightly more full-time Canadians and slightly fewer full-time non-Canadians. They reported more full-time workers in World A countries, fewer in World B countries and more in World C countries. However, altogether they deployed over half of their full-time workers in World A or World B countries.

Altogether it is clear that we have a much stronger picture of missional engagement reported by Canadian agencies in 2008 than in 2005—including increasing of resources together with increasing attention focused on countries in which the least-reached reside. In sum, there is much to rejoice in for the picture of Canadian Protestant agencies portrayed in this chapter, and for that we give thanks to God.

Endnotes

1. By full-time we mean those who are in service for one year or longer; in this analysis we are including tentmakers as well, which is a shift from previous editions.

2. That these are all "non-North Americans" is not completely accurate. In the survey we ask agencies to report non-U.S. or non-Canadian citizens, but we do not ask them to separate out Canadian citizens working for U.S. agencies from non-Canadian citizens working for U.S. agencies. Thus, the non-U.S. (and non-Canadian) citizens number inevitably includes Canadians working for U.S. agencies as well as U.S. citizens working for Canadian agencies.

3. The 2005 numbers are slightly different than those given in the previous edition, due to changes received from the agencies after the previous edition went to press. Throughout this discussion, we will be using numbers adjusted from previous surveys which will accurately represent the actual numbers, though differ from those previously reported.

4. The numbers reported on country totals will always be the minimum confirmable number. There are two factors involved. First, this does not include countries of nonresidential personnel, short-term workers, tentmakers, or where agencies have ongoing programs they support financially but without personnel. Second, several agencies report a general region but not specific countries for their missionary personnel. As agencies continue to evaluate security concerns, it seems likely that country statistics will become increasingly hard to report reliably.

5. Bear in mind, as footnoted above, I adjusted the 1996 to 2005 totals from previous editions to eliminate discrepancies and correct the numbers in previous editions that changed after publication of the previous edition of the *Handbook*.

6. The AGR is calculated by this formula: ((Final Total)/Beginning Total)) ^ (1/(# years between totals)) – 1. Thus, for 2005 to 2008 numbers, the formula is ((2008 Total/2005 Total))^(1/3)-1.

7. As we noted in the previous edition, there were some cases in which the choice to list a particular activity in one category rather than another one was a matter of judgment on which not all will agree. Thus, there will be some fuzziness in the major categories used in the following analysis and care must be taken not to read too much into relatively minor changes in them.

8. As identified in the revised list posted at http://joshuaproject.net/10-40-window.php.

9. David B. Barrett, Todd M. Johnson, gen eds., 2001. *World Christian Trends: AD 30-AD 2200: Interpreting the Annual Christian Megacensus.* Pasadena: William Carey Library, pp. 426-

27 (Table 21-1 Column 163).

10. Keep in mind that many agencies have more workers in the Middle East than indicated here, as often they do not report those numbers for security reasons. In the 2008 survey, 8.25% of the deployments were "unspecified"—and those would almost all be to countries in which specifying deployments is a security risk. Not all of these workers are deployed in the Middle East, but it is safe to say that a sizeable proportion of them are.

11. David B. Barrett, George T. Kurian and Todd M. Johnson. 2001. *World Christian Encyclopedia: A Comparative Survey of Churches and Religions in the Modern World*, 2nd edition. Oxford: Oxford University Press.

12. Taking into account the agency discussed in Asia and 10/40 Window deployments above.

13. See note 4.

14. For those who have read the U.S. section prior to reading the Canadian section, we ask that you excuse our redundancy in repeating several explanations already found in the U.S. section. We assume that some readers will only be interested in the Canadian section, and we wanted those readers to be able to understand our methods and approach and terms without being forced to read the U.S. section.

15. See note 5 for the formula used to calculate the AGR.

16. Of course, having numbers for the intervening years would clarify the extent to which that was true, one of the limitations of administering the survey every three to four years.

17. See note 14.

18. Per our discussion above, Figure 76 includes 165 of the 166 Canadian agencies, excluding the agency reporting the largest number of non-Canadian citizen workers and giving a picture of the rest of the agencies.

19. To reduce visual clutter, we include labels in Figure 79 and 80 only when the share is greater than 10%.

20. See note 14.

21. See note 14.

22. See note 8.

23. See note 11.

Chapter 2
U.S. Protestant Agencies

This chapter contains the basic information for U.S. Protestant agencies engaged in Christian ministries outside the U.S. and Canada. It includes agencies that directly support the work of such ministries or the work of overseas national churches/workers. The agencies supplied the information. The survey used to gather the information is reproduced in the appendix.

The *Handbook* covers an agency's overseas ministry and support activities; it does not cover its mission work in the U.S. Agencies with both overseas and U.S. mission ministries, however, were asked to include U.S.-based ministry personnel in the total that appears in the "home ministry and office staff" line of the "Other Personnel" section. Each agency will have at least seven of the basic categories of information listed below, with others included as applicable.

Agency Name

Agencies are listed alphabetically. If the article "the" is in an agency's name, it will appear at the end of the name so the agency is in the most commonly referenced alphabetical order. Rare exceptions occur where the Christian public commonly uses the article "the" as the first word in the agency's name. Agencies that have changed their name since the previous *Handbook* have their prior name listed also, with a cross-reference to the current or new name. A subdivision of a larger organization may be listed separately if it is organized to also serve the larger mission community rather than just its parent organization.

Telephone and Fax Numbers

Area codes are in parentheses. Since area codes change rapidly, some may have changed since the time of publication.

Email Address

The Internet format and standards for capitalization are used. In some cases, agencies have a general email address. Others have supplied an individual's address within the organization. In cases where only a web address is given, it generally means a web page provides access to an email address that can be directed to the relevant department or person.

Web Address

The Internet format and standards for capitalization are used. Most agencies have a web address; however, a few have chosen not to list it for security reasons.

Postal Mailing Address

A post office box number usually appears whenever the agency has one. Exceptions occur when the agency prefers the street address.

Chief Executive Officer

In a few cases where there are multiple primary contacts, or due to agency preference, two officers may be listed.

Short Descriptive Paragraph

A brief description appears based upon the denominational orientation and primary activities information supplied by the agency. Additional specific information, such as name changes, mergers, or other unique aspects may also be included.

Purpose Statement

Purpose statements are included when available. Some of the statements are concise and shown in their entirety, straight from the agency or its promotional material. For most, however, common or similar phrases such as "exists for the purpose of" are replaced by ellipses to present a more concise statement.

Year Founded in USA

This date is the year the agency or overseas mission component of a larger organization was founded or incorporated in the U.S. In some cases, the denomination or organization may have existed earlier in another country. For some organizations, the founding date of the missionary-sending component may be later than the founding of the larger organization. For organizations that have experienced mergers, the founding date is generally that of the oldest component involved in the merger.

Income for Overseas Ministries

This is the part of an agency's overall income used or budgeted for ministry activities outside the U.S. and Canada or in activities that directly facilitate overseas ministries. "NA" indicates that income in this sense is not applicable, and usually applies to specialized service agencies or agencies whose income is reported under a sister or parent organization. "NR" indicates that the agency did not report income for overseas ministries, but may make this information available upon request.

Gifts-in-Kind

If applicable, this is the portion of the income received in the form of donated gifts-in-kind commodities and/or services used for overseas ministries. Please note that some agencies do not include gifts-in-kind as part of their financial audit process, so the value of such gifts may not be included in their income for overseas ministries.

Fully Supported U.S. Personnel Overseas

Since not all agencies have overseas personnel in the following categories, the above heading will not always appear. If applicable, the following lines will appear with the appropriate numbers:

"Expecting to serve more than four years" for persons from the U.S. who are fully supported by the agency

"Expecting to serve one up to four years" for persons from the U.S. who are fully supported by the agency

"Nonresidential mission personnel" for fully supported U.S. mission personnel not residing in the country or countries of their ministry, but assigned to work and travel overseas at least twelve weeks per year on operational aspects of the overseas ministry

Other Personnel

If applicable for the agency, the following lines will appear:

"Non-USA serving in own/other country" for persons with either citizenship in their country of service or another non-U.S. country, who are fully or partially supported from the U.S. Such individuals are not included in the specific numbers for individual countries listed under the "Countries" heading at the bottom of many entries.

"Bivocational/Tentmaker from USA" for persons sponsored or supervised by the agency, but who support themselves partially or fully through non-church/non-mission vocations and live overseas for the purpose of Christian witness and/or encouraging believers.

"Short-term less than one year from USA" for persons who went on overseas projects or mission trips that lasted less than one year through the agency, either fully or partially supported, or raising their own support.

"Home Ministry and office staff in USA" for persons assigned to ministry and/or office duties in the U.S. either as full-time or part-time paid staff/associates.

Countries

These are countries where the agency sends U.S. personnel or regularly supports national or other non-U.S. personnel. Following the name of the country is the number of U.S. personnel with terms of service of four years or more. In some cases, a continent or other general region is shown instead of a country. This may be due to several reasons, such as mission personnel whose ministry covers several countries.

Where an agency's work is maintained by nationals of countries other than the U.S. or Canada, or by personnel serving less than four years, the country of activity may be listed without a number. Refer to the chapter entitled "Countries of Activity for U.S. Protestant Agencies" for more detailed country personnel totals. "Unspecified Country" may also be listed for security reasons.

Abundant Life Association, Inc.

PO Box 883
Mount Prospect, IL 60056 USA
Phone: (630) 539-5481
Fax: (630) 539-5482
E-mail: eldon@abundantlifeassociation.com
Web Site: www.abundantlifeassociation.com

Mr. Eldon L. Tracy, President

A nondenominational sending agency
of Charismatic and Pentecostal tradition
engaged in rescuing children, adults and
communities, discipleship, association
of missions, children's programs, church
planting, development, Christian
education, missionary education, leadership
development, literacy work and missionary
training. Data from 2005.

Purpose: "...to take the whole Gospel to
the whole world so that men and women,
boys and girls might become disciples of
Christ Jesus."

Year Founded in US: 1997

Income for Overseas Min: $60,000.00

Gifts in Kind: $2,000.00

Fully Supported US Personnel Overseas:
  Expecting to serve 1 to 4 years: 2
  Non-residential mission personnel: 2
Other personnel:
  Non-US serving in own/other country: 213
  Home ministry & office staff in US: 2

Countries: Angola; Brazil; Guinea-Bissau;
Luxembourg; Mozambique; Portugal; Sao
Tome and Principe

ABWE, Inc.
(Association of Baptists
for World Evangelism)

PO Box 8585
Harrisburg, PA 17105-8585 USA
Phone: (717) 774-7000
Fax: (717) 774-1919
E-mail: abwe@abwe.org
Web Site: www.abwe.org
Associations: FOM

Mr. Michael G. Loftis, President

A denominational sending agency of
Baptist tradition engaged in evangelism,
camping programs, church planting,
discipleship, theological education and
medical work. Countries of service and field
personnel data from 2006.

Purpose: "...to be a spiritually empowered
family of servants committed to glorifying
Him by following His command to preach
the Gospel throughout the world."

Year Founded in US: 1927

Income for Overseas Min: $36,000,000.00

Fully Supported US Personnel Overseas:
  Expecting to serve more than 4 years: 599
  Expecting to serve 1 to 4 years: 186
Other personnel:
  Short-term less than 1 year: 275
  Home ministry & office staff in US: 100

Countries: Africa—General 79; Asia–General 141; Brazil 60; Caribbean—General 20;
Europe—General 160; South America—
General 70; Unspecified Country 69

ACM International

1270 Sandy Dr.
Florissant, MO 63031 USA
Phone: (314) 685-1226
Fax: (314) 685-1225
E-mail: usoffice@acminternational.com
Web Site: www.acminternational.com

Mr. Timothy Doggett, Exec. Director

A nondenominational sending agency of
Christian (Restoration Movement) tradition
engaged in church planting, business as
mission, childcare/orphanage programs,
children at risk, discipleship and TEE.
Financial and countries of service data from
2005.

Purpose: "...to establish and edify churches of
Christ in strategic populations of the world."

Year Founded in US: 1947

Income for Overseas Min: $995,000.00

Fully Supported US Personnel Overseas:
  Expecting to serve more than 4 years: 17
  Expecting to serve 1 to 4 years: 2
Other personnel:
  Short-term less than 1 year: 6
  Home ministry & office staff in US: 22

Countries: Asia—General; Kenya 5; Nigeria
2; Philippines 2; South Africa 2; Tanzania 4;
United Kingdom 2

Action Intl. Ministries, Inc.

PO Box 398
Mountlake Terrace, WA 98043-0398 USA
Phone: (425) 775-4800
Fax: (425) 775-0634

E-mail: info@actionusa.org
Web Site: www.actioninternational.org

Mr. Rex Lee Carlaw, USA Director

An interdenominational sending agency of Evangelical tradition engaged in children at risk, camping programs, theological education, literature distribution, discipleship and HIV/Aids.

Purpose: "...commits itself to the Great Commission of the Lord Jesus Christ... to cooperate with churches and other Christian organizations to present Jesus Christ as Savior and Lord...to assist Christians in their submission to Christ and their growth in His Body...to minister in the name of Christ to the whole person, especially the poor."

Year Founded in US: 1974

Income for Overseas Min: $4,553,750.00

Fully Supported US Personnel Overseas:
    Expecting to serve more than 4 years: 79
    Expecting to serve 1 to 4 years: 2

Other personnel:
    Non-US serving in own/other country: 26
    Home ministry & office staff in US: 19

Countries: Brazil 11; Cambodia 4; Colombia 2; Croatia; Ecuador 2; Honduras 4; India 3; Malawi 2; Mexico 4; Philippines 23; Rwanda 4; Spain 3; Uganda 6; Zambia 11

ACTS Intl. Ministries, Inc.

PO Box 64227
Colorado Springs, CO 80962 USA
Phone: (888) 719-2287
E-mail: info@actsinternational.net
Web Site: www.actsinternational.net

Mr. Alvin Low, President

A transdenominational support agency of Evangelical tradition engaged in church planting, theological education, leadership development, support of national churches, support of national workers and training.

Purpose: "...to equip indigenous missionaries for effective ministry and church planting among the unreached of Asia."

Year Founded in US: 1991

Personnel:
    Non-US serving in own/other country: 6
    Home ministry & office staff in US: 5

Countries: India; Myanmar/Burma; Nepal

Advancing Indigenous Missions

PO Box 1943
Boerne, TX 78006 USA
Phone: (830) 367-3513
E-mail: aim@hctc.net

Mr. James W. Colley, Exec. Director

A nondenominational support agency of Evangelical tradition engaged in support of indigenous ministries, support of national churches, funds transmission and support of national workers.

Purpose: "...to be a channel of the Holy Spirit...to educate, motivate, and mobilize Christian churches, organizations, and individuals for prayer, financial, and logistical support of quality indigenous missions."

Year Founded in US: 1990

Income for Overseas Min: $219,813.00

Personnel:
    Home ministry & office staff in US: 3

Advancing Native Missions

PO Box 5303
Charlottesville, VA 22905 USA
Phone: (540) 456-7111
Fax: (540) 456-7111
E-mail: anm@adnamis.org
Web Site: www.adnamis.org

Mr. Benjamin (Bo) Barredo, President/CEO

A nondenominational support agency of Baptist tradition engaged in support of national churches, church planting, funds transmission, support of national workers, mobilization for mission and short-term programs.

Purpose: "...to help take the Gospel of Jesus Christ to the world's remaining unreached peoples, standing behind 3,500 indigenous missionaries reaching their own people in more than 60 countries."

Year Founded in US: 1992

Income for Overseas Min: $4,509,182.00

Gifts in Kind: $931,670.00

Fully Supported US Personnel Overseas:
    Expecting to serve 1 to 4 years: 1

Other personnel:
    Home ministry & office staff in US: 35

Countries: Singapore

Advancing Renewal Ministries, Inc.

11616 Sir Francis Drake Dr.
Charlotte, NC 28277 USA

Phone: (704) 846-9355
Fax: (704) 846-9356
E-mail: arminc@carolina.rr.com
Web Site: www.advancingrenewalministries.org

Dr. Arthur M. Vincent, President

A nondenominational sending agency of Lutheran and Charismatic tradition engaged in leadership development, Bible distribution, church planting, theological education, evangelism and support of national workers. Data from 2005.

Year Founded in US: 1983
Income for Overseas Min: $146,925.00
Fully Supported US Personnel Overseas:
   Expecting to serve more than 4 years: 34
Other personnel:
   Non-US serving in own/other country: 34
   Home ministry & office staff in US: 1
Countries: Africa—General 2; China 5; India 15; Japan 2; Kazakhstan 4; Laos 2; Nepal 2; Unspecified Country 2

Advent Christian General Conf., Dept. of World Missions

PO Box 690848
Charlotte, NC 28227-7015 USA

Phone: (704) 545-6161
Fax: (704) 573-0712
E-mail: worldoutreach@acgc.us
Web Site: www.adventchristian.org
Associations: The Mission Exchange

Rev. Ronald P. Thomas III, Exec. Director

A denominational sending agency of Adventist tradition engaged in church planting, theological education, evangelism, furloughed missionary support, leadership development and support of national workers.

Purpose: "...to encourage, equip, and empower Advent Christians worldwide to be obedient to His Great Commandment and Great Commission."

Year Founded in US: 1865
Income for Overseas Min: $635,542.00
Fully Supported US Personnel Overseas:

Expecting to serve more than 4 years: 5
Expecting to serve 1 to 4 years: 1
Non-residential mission personnel: 3
Other personnel:
   Short-term less than 1 year: 250
   Home ministry & office staff in US: 2
Countries: India; Philippines 5

Adventist World Aviation

PO Box 251
Berrien Springs, MI 49103-0251 US

Phone: (269) 473-0135
Fax: (269) 471-4049
E-mail: donstarlin@cs.com
Web Site: www.flyawa.org

Mr. Donald B. Starlin, President

A denominational service agency of Adventist tradition engaged in aviation services.

Purpose: "...to provide aviation and communications support to those serving the physical, mental and spiritual needs of the forgotten peoples of the earth."

Year Founded in US: 1995
Income for Overseas Min: $379,175.00
Fully Supported US Personnel Overseas:
   Expecting to serve more than 4 years: 2
   Expecting to serve 1 to 4 years: 2
   Non-residential mission personnel: 1
Other personnel:
   Short-term less than 1 year: 40
   Non-US serving in own/other country: 1
   Home ministry & office staff in US: 2
Countries: Guyana 1; Philippines 1

Adventive Cross Cultural Initiatives—US

141 E. Main St.
Rock Hill, SC 29730 USA

Phone: (704) 607-5029
E-mail: johnhaley@adventive.ca
Web Site: www.adventive.ca

Mr. John Haley, Exec. Director

A support agency of Evangelical tradition engaged in evangelism, support of national churches, mobilization for mission, relief and/or rehabilitation, short-term programs and missionary training.

Purpose: "...to bring the hope of Jesus to a lost and suffering world through the power of God and by the direction of His Holy Spirit."

Year Founded in US: 2004
Income for Overseas Min: $109,193.00
Fully Supported US Personnel Overseas:
Expecting to serve more than 4 years: 1
Expecting to serve 1 to 4 years: 8
Other personnel:
Short-term less than 1 year: 3
Non-US serving in own/other country: 8
Countries: Africa—General; Asia—General 1; Brazil; Ecuador; Guatemala; Italy; New Zealand; Sri Lanka; Zambia

Adventures in Missions

6000 Wellspring Trail
Gainesville, GA 30506 USA
Phone: (770) 983-1060
Fax: (770) 983-1061
E-mail: info@adventures.org
Web Site: www.adventures.org
Mr. Seth Barnes, CEO

An interdenominational sending agency engaged in missionary training, childcare/orphanage programs, evangelism, mobilization for mission, short-term programs and youth programs. Data from 2005.
Year Founded in US: 1989
Income for Overseas Min: $4,000,000.00
Gifts in Kind: $200,000.00
Fully Supported US Personnel Overseas:
Expecting to serve more than 4 years: 25
Expecting to serve 1 to 4 years: 5
Non-residential mission personnel: 30
Other personnel:
Short-term less than 1 year: 500
Home ministry & office staff in US: 80
Countries: Dominican Republic 2; Kenya 3; Mexico 10; New Zealand 2; Swaziland 6; United Kingdom 2

AEGA Ministries Intl., Inc.

2149 Hwy. 139
Monroe, LA 71203 USA
Phone: (318) 345-1777
Fax: (318) 345-0350
E-mail: info@aega.org
Web Site: www.aega.org
Mr. Henry A. Harbuck, President/Gen. Overseer

A nondenominational & fellowship specialized agency of Charismatic, Evangelical and Full Gospel tradition engaged in credentialing of ministers & churches, church planting, TEE, leadership development, providing medical supplies and short-term programs.
Year Founded in US: 1976
Personnel:
Non-US serving in own/other country: 9
Countries: Benin; Cote d'Ivoire; Ghana; India; Kenya; Mexico; Nigeria; Pakistan; Philippines

Africa Inland Mission Intl., Inc.

PO Box 178
Pearl River, NY 10965 USA
Phone: (800) 254-0010
Fax: (845) 735-1814
E-mail: go@aimint.net
Web Site: www.aimint.org
Associations: CrossGlobal Link
Dr. W. Ted Barnett, U.S. Director

A nondenominational sending agency of Evangelical tradition engaged in church planting, business as mission, discipleship, theological education and evangelism.
Purpose: "...to declare the Glory of God to the peoples of Africa...to introduce those who have never heard of the One who died to save them—Jesus Christ...to help new believers grow strong and healthy in their faith...to see new believers enfolded into a maturing church...to invest in the lives of current and future church leaders, so they can effectively build into the lives of others and reach out in turn to the vast populations of Africa and beyond."
Year Founded in US: 1895
Income for Overseas Min: $17,163,000.00
Gifts in Kind: $1,674,000.00
Fully Supported US Personnel Overseas:
Expecting to serve more than 4 years: 450
Expecting to serve 1 to 4 years: 64
Non-residential mission personnel: 259
Other personnel:
Short-term less than 1 year: 135
Non-US serving in own/other country: 259
Home ministry & office staff in US: 37
Countries: Angola 2; Central African Republic 1; Chad 5; Congo, Democratic Republic of; Kenya 270; Lesotho 3; Madagascar 4; Mozambique 20; Namibia 13; Rwanda; Senegal 2; Sudan 8; Tanzania 39; Uganda 17; Unspecified Country 66

Africa Inter-Mennonite Mission International

PO Box 744
Goshen, IN 46527-0744 USA

Phone: (574) 535-0077
Fax: (574) 533-5275
E-mail: aimm@aimmintl.org
Web Site: www.aimmintl.org

Rod Hollinger-Janzen, Exec. Coordinator

An interdenominational sending agency of Evangelical and Mennonite tradition engaged in church planting, theological education, leadership development, support of national churches and partnership development. Countries of service data from 2005.

Purpose: "...to plant and nurture churches through authentic international mission partnerships."

Year Founded in US: 1912

Income for Overseas Min: $382,712.00

Fully Supported US Personnel Overseas:
  Expecting to serve more than 4 years: 7
  Expecting to serve 1 to 4 years: 9
  Non-residential mission personnel: 12

Other personnel:
  Short-term less than 1 year: 8
  Non-US serving in own/other country: 12
  Home ministry & office staff in US: 2

Countries: Botswana 3; Burkina Faso 4; Congo, Democratic Republic of; Lesotho; Senegal; South Africa

African Bible Colleges, Inc.

PO Box 103
Clinton, MS 39060 USA

Phone: (601) 922-1962
E-mail: ABCUSA@africanbiblecollege.com
Web Site: www.africanbiblecollege.com

Rev. William L. Mosal, U.S. Director

An interdenominational sending agency of Evangelical tradition engaged in leadership development, Bible distribution, broadcasting, correspondence courses, Christian education and evangelism. Data from 2001.

Purpose: "...to further evangelical Christian education through establishment and funding of Bible colleges in Africa and the acquisition of Christian teachers for African schools and colleges."

Year Founded in US: 1977

Income for Overseas Min: $1,007,862.00

Fully Supported US Personnel Overseas:
  Expecting to serve more than 4 years: 14
  Expecting to serve 1 to 4 years: 12

Other personnel:
  Non-US serving in own/other country: 25
  Home ministry & office staff in US: 2

Countries: Malawi 14; Uganda

African Children's Mission, Inc.

PO Box 26470
Birmingham, AL 35260 USA

Phone: (205) 824-5074
E-mail: acm-ea@att.net
Web Site: www.africanchildrensmission.org

Mr. Michael Wayne Daniel, Exec. Director

An interdenominational support agency of Baptist and Independent tradition engaged in childcare/orphanage programs, children at risk, children's programs, discipleship, theological education and medical work.

Purpose: "...to reach out to children in destitute circumstances, both physically and with the Gospel of Jesus Christ, to enable them to grow and develop in a secure environment, using Christian values and principles as the foundation of its ministry and programs, guiding them into a responsible, productive life, and discipling them through word and example."

Year Founded in US: 1996

Income for Overseas Min: $2,200.00

Gifts in Kind: $1,600.00

Fully Supported US Personnel Overseas:
  Expecting to serve more than 4 years: 2

Other personnel:
  Short-term less than 1 year: 26
  Home ministry & office staff in US: 1

Countries: Kenya; Uganda 2

African Enterprise

PO Box 727
Monrovia, CA 91017 USA

Phone: (626) 357-8811
Fax: (626) 359-2069
E-mail: info@aeusa.org
Web Site: www.africanenterprise.org
Associations: The Mission Exchange

Mr. Malcolm Graham, Exec. Director

An interdenominational support agency

of Evangelical tradition engaged in evangelism, development, leadership development, relief and/or rehabilitation and missionary training. Data from 2005.

Purpose: "...to evangelize the cities of Africa through Word & Deed in partnership with the Church."

Year Founded in US: 1962

Income for Overseas Min: $429,660.00

Personnel:
Short-term less than 1 year: 10
Non-US serving in own/other country: 73
Home ministry & office staff in US: 10

Countries: Congo, Republic of the; Ethiopia; Ghana; Kenya; Malawi; Rwanda; South Africa; Tanzania; Uganda; Zimbabwe

African Leadership Dev.

PO Box 176
Wheaton, IL 60187 USA

Phone: (630) 280-9401
Fax: (630) 588-0713
E-mail: rapiers@sbcglobal.net
Web Site: www.aldafrica.org

Dr. William R. Rapier, Exec. Director

A nondenominational service agency of Evangelical tradition engaged in leadership development, childcare/orphanage programs, discipleship, HIV/Aids and partnership development.

Purpose: "...to assist the church by mentoring, empowering and networking leaders in Africa."

Year Founded in US: 1997

Income for Overseas Min: $120,000.00

Fully Supported US Personnel Overseas:
Expecting to serve more than 4 years: 2

Other personnel:
Short-term less than 1 year: 5

Countries: Africa—General 2

African Leadership, Inc.

PO Box 2888
Brentwood, TN 37024-2888 USA

Phone: (615) 595-8238
Fax: (615) 595-7906
E-mail: info@africanleadership.org
Web Site: www.africanleadership.org

Mr. Larry Warren, President/Founder

A nondenominational support agency of

Baptist and Presbyterian tradition engaged in pastor training, childcare/orphanage programs, development, theological education, partnership development, relief and/or rehabilitation and HIV/Aids.

Purpose: "...a Christian education and development organization training pastors and church leaders in Africa and funding development projects in their communities."

Year Founded in US: 2000

Income for Overseas Min: $2,000,000.00

Fully Supported US Personnel Overseas:
Non-residential mission personnel: 2

Other personnel:
Short-term less than 1 year: 280
Non-US serving in own/other country: 25
Home ministry & office staff in US: 16

Countries: Angola; Botswana; Congo, Republic of the; Ethiopia; Ghana; Kenya; Liberia; Malawi; Mozambique; Nigeria; Rwanda; Sierra Leone; South Africa; Sudan; Tanzania; Uganda; Zambia; Zimbabwe

African Methodist Episcopal Church, Dept. Global Witness

PO Box 20852
Charleston, SC 29413-0852 USA

Phone: (843) 852-2645
Fax: (843) 852-2648
E-mail: gwmame@bellsouth.net
Web Site: www.ame-church.com
Associations: CWS

Rev. George F. Flowers, Exec. Director

A denominational support agency of Methodist tradition engaged in partnership development, Bible distribution, evangelism, providing medical supplies, missionary training and technical assistance. Data from 2005.

Purpose: "...ministry, witness and gospel proclamation so that people of God may be liberated spiritually and materially and reconciled to each other through the Holy Spirit."

Year Founded in US: 1787

Income for Overseas Min: $104,956.00

Gifts in Kind: $62,000.00

Personnel:
Home ministry & office staff in US: 2

African Mission Evangelism

C/O Carl Bridges
7900 Johnson Dr.
Knoxville, TN 37998 USA

Phone: (865) 579-1467
Fax: (865) 251-2285
E-mail: cbridges@jbc.edu
Web Site: www.ameghana.org

Dr. Carl B. Bridges, President

A nondenominational sending agency of Christian (Restoration Movement) tradition engaged in theological education and church planting.

Purpose: "...to teach people concerning salvation in Jesus Christ and to promote the general knowledge of the plan of the Church as outlined in the New Testament."

Year Founded in US: 1968

Income for Overseas Min: $287,000.00

Fully Supported US Personnel Overseas:
Expecting to serve more than 4 years: 6

Other personnel:
Non-US serving in own/other country: 10

Countries: Ghana 6

Agape Gospel Mission

PO Box 1458
Manassas, VA 20108-1458 USA

Phone: (703) 361-3331
E-mail: admin@agapegospelmission.org
Web Site: www.agapegospelmission.org

Mr. Richard Whitcomb, President

A nondenominational sending agency of Charismatic tradition engaged in childcare/orphanage programs, church planting, Christian education, evangelism and leadership development.

Purpose: "...to evangelize the lost, empower the Church, and embrace the poor."

Year Founded in US: 1982

Income for Overseas Min: $989,912.00

Fully Supported US Personnel Overseas:
Expecting to serve more than 4 years: 4
Expecting to serve 1 to 4 years: 6

Other personnel:
Home ministry & office staff in US: 3

Countries: Ghana 4

Agathos Foundation

PO Box 778
Everett, WA 98206-0778 USA

Phone: (360) 474-1320
Fax: (360) 474-1560
E-mail: info@agathosfoundation.org
Web Site: www.agathosfoundation.org
Associations: AERDO

Mr. Marc Fulmer, COO

A nondenominational sending agency of Evangelical and Reformed tradition engaged in childcare/orphanage programs, agricultural programs, business as mission, medical work, partnership development and relief and/or rehabilitation.

Purpose: "...to provide a Christ centered holistic approach to Sub-Saharan Africa's orphan crisis. With orphans and widows at our core, Agathos focuses programs on pastoral training, church partnerships, raising orphans, health care, and infrastructure development."

Year Founded in US: 2002

Income for Overseas Min: $11,500,000.00

Gifts in Kind: $11,000,000.00

Fully Supported US Personnel Overseas:
Expecting to serve more than 4 years: 1
Expecting to serve 1 to 4 years: 5

Other personnel:
Short-term less than 1 year: 30
Non-US serving in own/other country: 6
Home ministry & office staff in US: 3

Countries: Zambia 1

AIDS Family Fund, Inc.

3007 Bimini Bay
Boynton Beach, FL 33436 USA

Phone: (561) 676-9908
E-mail: director@aidsfam.org
Web Site: www.aidsfam.org

Mr. Terry Kennedy, Director

A support agency of Evangelical tradition engaged in development, childcare/orphanage programs, children at risk, church planting, HIV/Aids, leadership development and support of national churches.

Purpose: "...to minister to the needs of orphans, especially HIV-related, widows, national pastors and the poor...to develop micro-enterprise and self-help projects."

Year Founded in US: 2006

Income for Overseas Min: $175,000.00
Gifts in Kind: $2,500.00
Personnel:
  Non-US serving in own/other country: 30
Countries: India

AIMS (Accelerating Intl. Mission Strategies)

PO Box 64534
Virginia Beach, VA 23467-4534 USA

Phone: (757) 495-5850
Fax: (757) 495-5855
E-mail: aims@aims.org
Web Site: www.aims.org
Associations: The Mission Exchange
Mr. Howard Foltz, President

A nondenominational support agency of Evangelical tradition engaged in training of missionaries within the national church movements, recruiting/mobilizing, church planting, leadership development and missionary training.

Purpose: "...to empower the church to take the Gospel where it has never been proclaimed."

Year Founded in US: 1985
Income for Overseas Min: $370,709.00
Fully Supported US Personnel Overseas:
  Non-residential mission personnel: 5
Other personnel:
  Short-term less than 1 year: 25
  Home ministry & office staff in US: 17

Alberto Mottesi Evangelistic Association, Inc.

PO Box 6290
Santa Ana, CA 92706 USA

Phone: (714) 265-0400
Fax: (714) 265-0444
E-mail: info@albertomottesi.org
Web Site: www.albertomottesi.org
Dr. Alberto H. Mottesi, President

A nondenominational service agency of Evangelical tradition engaged in evangelism, audio recording/distribution, broadcasting, TEE, literature distribution, literature production and video/film production/distribution.

Purpose: "...to equip Hispanic Christian leaders and provide ministry resources for worldwide Hispanic churches."

Year Founded in US: 1977
Income for Overseas Min: $191,531.00
Gifts in Kind: $148,825.00

All About Orphans (David Livingstone KURE Foundation)

PO Box 716
Morgantown, WV 26507-0716 USA

Phone: (304) 2965873
E-mail: info@allaboutorphans.org
Web Site: www.allaboutorphans.org
Mr. H. Dwain Griffin, Chairman/CEO

A nondenominational service agency of Independent tradition engaged in support of national workers, childcare/orphanage programs, Christian education and development.
Year Founded in US: 1969
Countries: India; Philippines; Russia; Ukraine

All God's Children Intl.

3308 NE Peerless Pl.
Portland, OR 97232 USA

Phone: (800) 214-6719
Fax: (503) 282-2582
E-mail: missions@allgodschildren.org
Web Site: www.allgodschildren.org
Mr. John Blanchard, President

A nondenominational service agency engaged in adoption, childcare/orphanage programs, children at risk and short-term programs. Countries of service data from 2005.

Purpose: "...to passionately serve the world's forgotten children through life-changing ministries."

Year Founded in US: 1991
Fully Supported US Personnel Overseas:
  Expecting to serve 1 to 4 years: 3
Other personnel:
  Short-term less than 1 year: 8
  Non-US serving in own/other country: 181
Countries: China; Guatemala; Kazakhstan; Nepal; Vietnam

Allegheny Wesleyan Methodist Connection —Missions Department

PO Box 357
Salem, OH 44460 USA

Phone: (330) 337-9376
Fax: (330) 337-9700
E-mail: awmc@juno.com
Rev. Michael D. Marshall, Missions Director

A denominational sending agency of Holiness tradition engaged in evangelism, church construction, discipleship and Christian education.
Purpose: "...to promote and perform the Great Commission as it is recorded in the Holy Scriptures."
Year Founded in US: 1968
Income for Overseas Min: $463,375.00
Fully Supported US Personnel Overseas:
  Expecting to serve more than 4 years: 12
  Expecting to serve 1 to 4 years: 3
Other personnel:
  Short-term less than 1 year: 9
  Home ministry & office staff in US: 1
Countries: Ghana 2; Haiti 5; Peru 5

Alongside Ministries Intl.
PO Box 13159
Oakland, CA 94661-0159 USA
Phone: (510) 531-6530
Fax: (510) 531-6530
E-mail: alongside@alongside.org
Web Site: www.alongside.org
Margie L. Gilchrist, Exec. Director

An interdenominational sending agency of Evangelical and Presbyterian tradition engaged in support of national churches, discipleship, evangelism, leadership development, mobilization for mission and short-term programs.
Purpose: "...a fellowship of Christians working together to strengthen the Church in Europe, Great Britain, and the US, providing prayer, people, and practical help."
Year Founded in US: 1978
Income for Overseas Min: $520,803.00
Fully Supported US Personnel Overseas:
  Expecting to serve more than 4 years: 13
  Expecting to serve 1 to 4 years: 7
  Non-residential mission personnel: 4
Other personnel:
  Short-term less than 1 year: 21
  Non-US serving in own/other country: 20
  Home ministry & office staff in US: 3
Countries: Albania 6; Estonia 2; France 2; Germany 1; United Kingdom 2

Alongside, Inc.
PO Box 587
Richland, MI 49083 USA
Phone: (269) 671-4809
Fax: (269) 671-4977
E-mail: info@alongsidecares.net
Web Site: www.alongsidecares.net
Jeanne L. Jensma, Exec. Director

A nondenominational specialized agency of Evangelical tradition engaged in psychological counseling, furloughed missionary support, member care and services for other agencies.
Purpose: "...to restore hope, purpose, passion, and relationships among Christian leaders who are making an impact around the world."
Year Founded in US: 2000
Personnel:
  Home ministry & office staff in US: 4

Amazon Focus, Inc.
PO Box 271109
Littleton, CO 80127 USA
Phone: (720) 346-3000
E-mail: info@amazonfocus.com
Web Site: www.amazonfocus.com
Mr. Paul C. Johnson, CEO/Director

A nondenominational sending agency of Evangelical tradition engaged in partnership development, leadership development and support of national churches. Financial data from 2005.
Purpose: "...to empower and equip the indigenous tribes of the Amazon region to assume responsibility for their long-term spiritual, physical, and survival needs."
Year Founded in US: 1995
Income for Overseas Min: $170,015.00
Fully Supported US Personnel Overseas:
  Expecting to serve more than 4 years: 2
  Non-residential mission personnel: 17
Other personnel:
  Non-US serving in own/other country: 10
  Home ministry & office staff in US: 3
Countries: Peru 2

Amazon Outreach
PO Box 794763
Dallas, TX 75379 USA
Phone: (972) 931-5565

E-mail: jedt@amazonoutreach.org
Web Site: www.amazonoutreach.org
Mr. Jed Thompson, Exec. Director

An interdenominational service agency of Baptist tradition engaged in short-term programs, evangelism, medical work, support of national churches and water well drilling.
Purpose: "...to support Brazilian churches and other organized ministries in spreading the Gospel message of Jesus Christ throughout the Amazon Basin."
Year Founded in US: 1999
Income for Overseas Min: $1,667,671.00
Personnel:
    Short-term less than 1 year: 300
    Home ministry & office staff in US: 4
Countries: Brazil

Ambassadors for Christ International Ltd.

PO Box 470
Tucker, GA 30085 USA
Phone: (770) 921-4705
Fax: (888) 869-1049
E-mail: info@afciworld.org
Web Site: www.afciworld.org
Rev. Paul Hanak, Intl. Director

A nondenominational support agency of Evangelical tradition engaged in training, support of national workers and evangelism. Statistics from 2005.
Purpose: "...teams of Nationals accelerating the spread of the Gospel through local churches worldwide."
Year Founded in US: 1972
Income for Overseas Min: $100,000.00
Personnel:
    Home ministry & office staff in US: 9

Ambassadors for Christ, Inc.

21 Ambassador Dr.
Paradise, PA 17562 USA
Phone: (717) 687-8564
Fax: (717) 687-8891
E-mail: afc@afcinc.org
Web Site: www.afcinc.org
Mr. David Chow, Exec. Director

A nondenominational support agency of Evangelical tradition engaged in translation and distribution of English language books

into Chinese, Bible distribution, literature production and partnership development. Statistics and countries of service from 2005.
Purpose: "...to evangelize and disciple Chinese students and professionals in the United States, and other parts of the world, to motivate and equip them to impact the culture for the Lord."
Year Founded in US: 1964
Income for Overseas Min: $135,000.00
Personnel:
    Short-term less than 1 year: 2
    Home ministry & office staff in US: 13
Countries: China

American Association of Lutheran Churches—Commission for World Missions

921 E. Dupont Rd., #920
Fort Wayne, IN 46825-1551 USA
Phone: (260)452-3213
Fax: (260)452-3215
E-mail: theaalc@taalc.org
Web Site: www.taalc.org
Rev. Darrel Deuel, Chairman

A denominational support agency of Lutheran tradition engaged in funds transmission, church planting, member care, relief and/or rehabilitation and Bible translation. Data from 2005.
Year Founded in US: 1987
Income for Overseas Min: $45,000.00
Personnel:
    Home ministry & office staff in US: 4

American Baptist Churches of the U.S.A., Intl. Ministries

PO Box 851
Valley Forge, PA 19482-0851 USA
Phone: (610) 768-2201
Fax: (610) 768-2115
E-mail: patricia.williams@abc-usa.org
Web Site: www.internationalministries.org
Associations: CWS
Mr. Reid S. Trulson, Exec. Director

A denominational sending agency of Baptist tradition engaged in leadership development, trafficking/slavery issues, development, theological education, evangelism and medical work.

Purpose: "...to glorify God in all the earth by crossing cultural boundaries to make disciples of Jesus Christ."

Year Founded in US: 1814

Income for Overseas Min: $11,975,544.00

Fully Supported US Personnel Overseas:
Expecting to serve more than 4 years: 84
Non-residential mission personnel: 4

Other personnel:
Short-term less than 1 year: 1700
Non-US serving in own/other country: 19
Home ministry & office staff in US: 33

Countries: Bahamas, The 2; Bolivia 2; Brazil 4; Bulgaria 2; Chile 2; China 1; Congo, Democratic Republic of 11; Costa Rica 3; Cuba 1; Czech Republic; Dominican Republic 1; El Salvador; France 1; Haiti 2; India 4; Italy 2; Japan 9; Laos 2; Lebanon; Mexico 9; Nepal 2; Nicaragua; Panama; South Africa 2; Thailand 15; United Kingdom; Unspecified Country 5; Zambia 2

American Bible Society

1865 Broadway
New York, NY 10023-7505 USA

Phone: (212) 408-1200
Fax: (212) 408-1512
E-mail: info@americanbible.org
Web Site: www.americanbible.org

Dr. Lamar Vest, President

A specialized agency of Inter-confessional tradition engaged in Scripture advocacy & engagement, Bible distribution, children at risk, HIV/Aids, partnership development, Bible translation and youth programs. ABS prioritizes high-impact national & international programs that promote life-long Scripture engagement among those marginalized from God's Word.

Purpose: "...to make the Bible available to every person in a language and format each can understand and afford, so all people may experience its life-changing message."

Year Founded in US: 1816

Income for Overseas Min: $14,998,694.00

American Council of the Ramabai Mukti Mission, Inc.

PO Box 4912
Clinton, NJ 08809-0912 USA

Phone: (908) 735-8770

Fax: (908) 638-3113
E-mail: mukti1@eclipse.net
Web Site: www.ramabaimuktimission.com
Associations: CrossGlobal Link

Rev. David L. Scott, Exec. Director

A nondenominational support agency of Evangelical tradition engaged in childcare/orphanage programs, church planting, development, disability assistance programs, Christian education, support of national workers and short-term programs. Data from 2005.

Year Founded in US: 1889

Income for Overseas Min: $380,819.00

Personnel:
Short-term less than 1 year: 3
Non-US serving in own/other country: 2
Home ministry & office staff in US: 3

Countries: India

American Evangelical Christian Churches

PO Box 47312
Indianapolis, IN 46247-0312 USA

Phone: (317) 788-9280
Fax: (317) 788-1410
E-mail: aeccoffice@earthlink.net
Web Site: www.aeccministries.com

Dr. Charles Wasielewski Sr., Chairman of the Bd.

A nondenominational support agency of Evangelical tradition engaged in support of national churches, correspondence courses, extension education and evangelism.

Purpose: "...to provide credentials to workers, assisting with financial and prayer needs."

Year Founded in US: 1944

American Leprosy Missions, Inc.

1 ALM Way
Greenville, SC 29601 USA

Phone: (800) 537-7679
Fax: (864) 271-7062
E-mail: amlep@leprosy.org
Web Site: www.leprosy.org

Mr. Christopher J. Doyle, President/CEO

A nondenominational specialized agency of Evangelical tradition engaged in public health and medical work, development, disability assistance programs, providing medical supplies, relief and/or rehabilitation and technical assistance. Data from 2005.

Purpose: "to serve as a channel of Christ's love to persons affected by leprosy and related conditions, helping them to be healed in body and spirit and restored to lives of dignity and hope."

Year Founded in US: 1906
Income for Overseas Min: $5,038,555.00

Fully Supported US Personnel Overseas:
  Expecting to serve more than 4 years: 1
  Non-residential mission personnel: 3

Other personnel:
  Non-US serving in own/other country: 7
  Home ministry & office staff in US: 20

Countries: Angola; Brazil 1; Congo, Democratic Republic of; India; Myanmar/Burma; Philippines

American Missionary Fellowship
PO Box 370
Villanova, PA 19085 USA
Phone: (610) 527-4439
Web Site: www.americanmissionary.org
Dr. Ridge Burns, CEO

A nondenominational support agency of Evangelical and Independent tradition engaged in discipleship, camping programs, church planting and youth programs.

Purpose: "...to evangelize, disciple, and congregate unreached peoples in America for Jesus Christ."

Year Founded in US: 1817
Personnel:
  Home ministry & office staff in US: 175

American Scripture Gift Mission Inc. (SGM USA)
7862 W. Irlo Bronson Hwy., PMB 240
Kissimee, FL 34747 USA
Phone: (321) 251-8494
E-mail: usa@sgmlifewords.com
Web Site: www.asgm.com
Mr. James R. Powell, Chairman

A nondenominational support agency of Evangelical tradition distributing all-Scripture booklets and tracts in more than 400 languages, primarily for evangelism. The USA branch of SGM International, London,

England. Data from 2001.
Year Founded in US: 1937
Income for Overseas Min: $1,000.00
Personnel:
  Home ministry & office staff in US: 1

American Waldensian Society
PO Box 398
Valdese, NC 28690 USA
Phone: (866) 825-3373
E-mail: info@waldensian.org
Web Site: www.waldensian.org
Mr. Francis J. Rivers, Exec. Director

An interdenominational support agency of Ecumenical tradition engaged in partnership development, missions information service, funds transmission and leadership development.

Purpose: "...to foster dialogue and partnership among Waldensian churches in Italy and South America and Christian churches within North America in order to promote a compelling vision of Waldensian Christian witness for North America."

Year Founded in US: 1906
Personnel:
  Short-term less than 1 year: 4
  Home ministry & office staff in US: 2

AMG International
PO Box 182200
Chattanooga, TN 37422 USA
Phone: (800) 251-7206
Fax: (423) 894-6863
E-mail: missions@amginternational.org
Web Site: www.amginternational.org
Mr. Paul E. Jenks, President/CEO

An interdenominational sending agency of Baptist and Evangelical tradition engaged in support of national workers, childcare/orphanage programs, church planting, evangelism, medical work and relief and/or rehabilitation.

Purpose: "...to advance with compassion the command of Christ...to evangelize and make disciples around the world through national leaders engaged in life-changing transformation in partnership with like-minded Christians."

Year Founded in US: 1942

Income for Overseas Min: $6,096,530.00

Fully Supported US Personnel Overseas:
Expecting to serve more than 4 years: 14
Expecting to serve 1 to 4 years: 7

Other personnel:
Short-term less than 1 year: 214
Non-US serving in own/other country: 8315
Home ministry & office staff in US: 29

Countries: Argentina; Australia; Bangladesh; Brazil; Bulgaria; Cuba; Cyprus; Ghana; Greece 6; Guatemala 2; Haiti; India; Indonesia; Italy 2; Lebanon; Mexico 3; Mozambique; Myanmar/Burma; Peru; Philippines; Romania; Spain 1; Thailand; Turkey; Uganda

AMOR Ministries
1664 Precision Park Ln.
San Diego, CA 92713 USA
Phone: (619) 662-1200
Fax: (619) 662-1295
E-mail: missionservices@amor.org
Web Site: www.amor.org
Associations: AERDO

Mr. Scott Congdon, Founder/CEO

A nondenominational sending agency of Evangelical tradition engaged in development, support of national churches, partnership development, relief and/or rehabilitation and short-term programs. Data from 2005.

Year Founded in US: 1980

Income for Overseas Min: $4,250,000.00

Fully Supported US Personnel Overseas:
Expecting to serve 1 to 4 years: 37

Other personnel:
Non-US serving in own/other country: 10
Home ministry & office staff in US: 24

Countries: Mexico

Anglican Frontier Missions
PO Box 18038
Richmond, VA 23226-8038 USA
Phone: (804) 355-8468
Fax: (804) 355-8260
E-mail: info@afm-us.org
Web Site: www.afm-us.org

Rev. Julian Linnell, Exec. Director

A denominational sending agency of Anglican and Evangelical tradition engaged in church planting, evangelism, partnership development, mobilization for mission and mission-related research. Statistic and personnel data from 2005.

Purpose: "...to plant indigenous churches among the least evangelized people groups of the world."

Year Founded in US: 1993

Income for Overseas Min: $497,121.00

Fully Supported US Personnel Overseas:
Expecting to serve more than 4 years: 9
Expecting to serve 1 to 4 years: 2
Non-residential mission personnel: 6

Other personnel:
Short-term less than 1 year: 2
Non-US serving in own/other country: 6
Home ministry & office staff in US: 3

Countries: Asia—General 5; Middle East; Uganda

Anis Shorrosh Evangelistic Association
Omega 2001
PO Box 293627
Sacramento, CA 95829 USA
Web Site: www.islam-exposed.org

Dr. Anis Shorrosh, Evangelist

An interdenominational support agency of Baptist tradition engaged in evangelism, apologetics, audio recording/distribution, broadcasting and literature production. Data from 2005.

Year Founded in US: 1971

Fully Supported US Personnel Overseas:
Expecting to serve more than 4 years: 155
Non-residential mission personnel: 2

Other personnel:
Short-term less than 1 year: 5
Home ministry & office staff in US: 4

Countries: Ghana; India 35; Israel 40; Jordan 40; Palestine 40; South Africa

Apostolic Christian Church Foundation, Inc.— Missionary Committee
12666 Locust Rd.
Tremont, IL 61568 USA
Phone: (309) 925-9040
E-mail: info@accm.org
Web Site: www.accm.org

Mr. Jim Hodges, Exec. Director

A denominational sending agency of Anabaptist tradition engaged in funds transmission, church construction, relief aid, support of national workers and evangelism.

Purpose: "...exists to help fulfill Christ's Commission by sending out members of the AC Church who are called by God to become foreign missionaries."

Year Founded in US: 1953

Countries: Argentina; Australia; Brazil; Ghana; Japan; Mexico; Papua New Guinea; Paraguay

Apostolic Team Ministries, Intl.

529 North Walnut Street
Celina, OH 45822 USA

Phone: (419) 586-1095
E-mail: info@atmintl.org
Web Site: www.atmintl.org

Rev. Bill Lewis, Admin. Director

A nondenominational support agency of Charismatic tradition engaged in church planting and missionary training.

Year Founded in US: 1980

Arab World Ministries

PO Box 96
Upper Darby, PA 19082 USA

Phone: (800) 447-3566
Fax: (610) 352-2652
E-mail: awmusa@awm.org
Web Site: www.awm.org

Associations: CrossGlobal Link

Mr. Robert W. Sayer, U.S. Director

An interdenominational sending agency of Evangelical tradition engaged in church planting, TEE, support of national workers, video/film production/distribution, tentmaking and internet ministry.

Purpose: "...to exalt Jesus Christ through word and deed, making disciples and establishing mature, multiplying churches among Muslims of the Arab world wherever they may be found."

Year Founded in US: 1952

Income for Overseas Min: $4,768,691.00

Fully Supported US Personnel Overseas:
  Expecting to serve more than 4 years: 108
  Expecting to serve 1 to 4 years: 10
  Non-residential mission personnel: 6

Other personnel:
  Short-term less than 1 year: 15
  Non-US serving in own/other country: 151
  Home ministry & office staff in US: 42

Countries: Africa—General 29; Europe—General 6; France 14; Middle East 51; United Kingdom 6; Unspecified Country 2

ARISE International Mission
(See ad on page 113)

PO Box 1014
College Park, MD 20741 USA

Phone: (301) 395-2385
E-mail: aim@arise-mission.org
Web Site: www.arise-mission.org

Rev. C. Daniel Kim, President

A support agency of Charismatic and Evangelical tradition engaged in leadership development, literature distribution, partnership development, mobilization for mission and technical assistance.

Purpose: "...to reach the least evangelized world through literature distribution and leadership development."

Year Founded in US: 1990

Personnel:
  Short-term less than 1 year: 5
  Non-US serving in own/other country: 9
  Home ministry & office staff in US: 7

Countries: Africa—General; Asia—General

Armenian Missionary Association of America, Inc. (AMAA)

31 W. Century Rd.
Paramus, NJ 07652 USA

Phone: (201) 265-2607
Fax: (201) 265-6015
E-mail: amaa@amaa.org
Web Site: www.amaa.org

Mr. Andrew Torigian, Exec. Director

A nondenominational service agency of Evangelical tradition engaged in relief and/or rehabilitation, childcare/orphanage programs, church construction, church planting, Christian education and theological education.

Purpose: "...to serve the physical and spiritual needs of people everywhere, both at home and overseas...to fulfill this worldwide mission, the AMAA maintains a range

of educational, evangelistic, church-related relief, and social service, including various childcare ministries."

Year Founded in US: 1918

Fully Supported US Personnel Overseas:
   Expecting to serve more than 4 years: 16
   Non-residential mission personnel: 1

Other personnel:
   Home ministry & office staff in US: 14

Countries: Armenia 16

Artists In Christian Testimony International

PO Box 1649
Brentwood, TN 37024-1649 USA

Phone: (615) 376-7861
Fax: (615) 376-7863
E-mail: info@actinternational.org
Web Site: www.actinternational.org
Associations: The Mission Exchange

Mr. Byron L. Spradlin, President/CEO

An interdenominational sending agency of Evangelical tradition engaged in arts ministry, missionary equipping and sending, church planting, discipleship, evangelism, funds transmission and mobilization for mission.

Purpose: "...to equip and mobilize artistic ministries, ministers and missionaries for Christ's Kingdom work worldwide."

Year Founded in US: 1973

Fully Supported US Personnel Overseas:
   Expecting to serve more than 4 years: 8
   Non-residential mission personnel: 5

Other personnel:
   Short-term less than 1 year: 5
   Non-US serving in own/other country: 24
   Home ministry & office staff in US: 4

Countries: Africa—General; Brazil 3; China; France 2; Germany; Ghana; Hungary 1; Israel; Japan; Kenya 2; Lebanon; Russia; Tanzania; United Kingdom

Asian Access

PO Box 200
San Dimas, CA 91773 USA

Phone: (626) 914-8990
Fax: (866) 862-0968
E-mail: info@asianaccess.org
Web Site: www.asianaccess.org

Associations: The Mission Exchange

Mr. Joseph W. Handley, President

An interdenominational sending agency of Ecumenical tradition engaged in leadership development, church planting and evangelism.

Purpose: "...to identify, develop, and release emerging kingdom leaders to unite the Church, multiply leaders and congregations, and extend the transforming power of the Gospel of Jesus Christ."

Year Founded in US: 1967

Income for Overseas Min: $3,109,566.00

Fully Supported US Personnel Overseas:
   Expecting to serve more than 4 years: 28
   Expecting to serve 1 to 4 years: 7

Other personnel:
   Short-term less than 1 year: 39
   Non-US serving in own/other country: 23
   Home ministry & office staff in US: 15

Countries: Asia—General 4; Japan 22; Singapore 2

Asian Outreach U.S.A.

7330 N. Palm Ave. Ste. 106
Fresno, CA 93711 USA

Phone: (559) 436-4685
Fax: (559) 256-0523
E-mail: info@aousa.org
Web Site: www.aousa.org

Mr. David Ness, Exec. Director

A nondenominational support agency of Evangelical and Charismatic tradition engaged in church planting, Bible distribution, correspondence courses, theological education, evangelism, leadership development, literature distribution, literature production, short-term programs and training. Data from 2001.

Purpose: "...winning Asians to Christ."

Year Founded in US: 1965

Income for Overseas Min: $790,000.00

Personnel:
   Short-term less than 1 year: 40
   Home ministry & office staff in US: 1

Countries: Australia; Cambodia; China; Hong Kong; Indonesia; Japan; Malaysia; Mongolia; Myanmar/Burma; Nepal; New Zealand; Philippines; Singapore; South Africa; Taiwan; Thailand; United Kingdom; Vietnam

Assemblies of God World Missions

1445 Boonville Ave.
Springfield, MO 65802-1894 USA

Phone: (417) 862-2781
Fax: (417) 862-5274
E-mail: jbueno@ag.org
Web Site: www.ag.org/worldmissions
Associations: The Mission Exchange

Rev. L. John Bueno, Exec. Director

A denominational sending agency of Pentecostal tradition engaged in church planting, audio recording/distribution, Bible distribution, broadcasting, childcare/orphanage programs, children at risk and childrens programs. Countries of service data from 2005.

Purpose: "...to proclaim the message of Jesus Christ to the spiritually lost in all the world through every available means...to establish churches in more than 150 nations, following the New Testament pattern."

Year Founded in US: 1914

Income for Overseas Min:
$189,033,560.00

Fully Supported US Personnel Overseas:
Expecting to serve more than 4 years: 1769
Expecting to serve 1 to 4 years: 515
Non-residential mission personnel: 258

Other personnel:
Short-term less than 1 year: 31
Home ministry & office staff in US: 197

Countries: Algeria 2; American Samoa 1; Angola 6; Antigua; Argentina 26; Armenia 5; Asia—General 122; Austria 13; Azerbaijan 6; Bahamas, The 2; Bangladesh 8; Belarus 4; Belgium 20; Belize 10; Benin 4; Bhutan; Bosnia and Herzegovina 2; Bolivia 12; Botswana 8; Brazil 13; Bulgaria 4; Burkina Faso 7; Burundi 4; Cambodia 18; Cameroon 8; Cape Verde; Caribbean—General 2; Cayman Islands; Central African Republic; Central Asia—General 42; Chad 2; Chile 16; Colombia 22; Congo, Democratic Republic of 6; Congo, Republic of the 2; Cook Islands; Costa Rica 21; Cote d'Ivoire; Croatia 6; Cuba; Cyprus; Czech Republic 2; Denmark; Dominica 2; Dominican Republic 14; East Timor; Ecuador 27; Egypt 7; El Salvador 14; Equatorial Guinea 7; Eritrea; Estonia 2; Ethiopia 5; Europe—General 77; Fiji 7; Finland 2; France 13; French Polynesia 2; Gabon; Gambia, The 2; Georgia 4; Germany 40; Ghana 8; Greece 4; Greenland; Guam 2; Guatemala 12; Guinea-Bissau; Guyana; Haiti 2; Honduras 11; Hungary 6; Iceland 2; India 53; Indonesia 26; Ireland 14; Israel 11; Italy 10; Jamaica 10; Japan 37; Jordan 9; Kazakhstan 2; Kenya 32; Kiribati 1; Korea, South 4; Kosovo 4; Kyrgyzstan 10; Laos 4; Latin America—General 81; Latvia 3; Lebanon 8; Lesotho 2; Liberia; Lithuania 8; Luxembourg 2; Macedonia 2; Madagascar 8; Malawi 7; Malaysia; Maldives; Mali 6; Malta; Marshall Islands; Mauritius 2; Mexico 76; Middle East 21; Moldova 5; Mongolia 10; Mozambique 2; Myanmar/Burma 2; Namibia 11; Nauru; Netherlands 15; Netherlands Antilles 2; New Caledonia; Nicaragua 24; Niger 4; Nigeria 4; Oceania—General 9; Palau 2; Panama 8; Papua New Guinea; Paraguay 14; Peru 12; Philippines 53; Poland 8; Portugal 9; Romania 10; Russia 41; Rwanda 8; Saint Lucia 2; Senegal 7; Serbia and Montenegro 4 Sierra Leone 4; Singapore 10; Slovakia 3; Slovenia 2; Solomon Islands 4; South Africa 44; Spain 46; Sri Lanka 6; Suriname 2; Swaziland 10; Switzerland; Syria; Taiwan 8; Tajikistan 7; Tanzania 10; Thailand 19; Togo 11; Tonga 6; Trinidad and Tobago 2; Turkmenistan; Uganda; Ukraine 23; United Kingdom 15; Unspecified Country 68; Uruguay 10; Uzbekistan 4; Vanuatu 4; Venezuela 14; Vietnam 4; Yemen 2; Zambia 8; Zimbabwe 6

ASSIST Ministries & ASSIST News Service

PO Box 609
Lake Forest, CA 92609-0609 USA

Phone: (949) 472-0974
E-mail: danjuma1@aol.com
Web Site: www.assistnews.net

Mr. Dan Wooding, President

A nondenominational support agency of Independent tradition engaged in missions information service. Also runs ASSIST News Service.

Purpose: "...encourages and supports believers who, for religious, political or economic reasons, are unable to worship and witness freely for their faith."

Year Founded in US: 1989

Association of Christian Schools International (ACSI)

PO Box 65130
Colorado Springs, CO 80962-5130 US
Phone: (719) 528-6906
Fax: (719) 531-0631
E-mail: info@acsi.org
Web Site: www.acsi.org
Brian S. Simmons, President

A service agency of Evangelical tradition engaged in Christian education K-12 and colleges, extension education, leadership development, management consulting/training and short-term programs. Data from 2005.

Purpose: "...to enable Christian Educators and schools worldwide by offering effective Christian School Education."

Year Founded in US: 1978
Income for Overseas Min: $908,909.00
Gifts in Kind: $347,000.00
Fully Supported US Personnel Overseas:
    Expecting to serve more than 4 years: 3
    Non-residential mission personnel: 3
Other personnel:
    Short-term less than 1 year: 1
    Home ministry & office staff in US: 175
Countries: Philippines 1; Ukraine 2

Association of Free Lutheran Congregations —World Missions

3110 E. Medicine Lake Blvd.
Minneapolis, MN 55441 USA
Phone: (952) 545-5631
E-mail: worldmis@aflc.org
Web Site: www.aflc.org
Rev. Del Palmer, Director

A sending agency of Lutheran tradition engaged in evangelism, discipleship, theological education and leadership development.
Purpose: "...to make disciples of all nations through evangelism and training."
Year Founded in US: 1963
Income for Overseas Min: $981,691.00
Fully Supported US Personnel Overseas:
    Expecting to serve more than 4 years: 8
    Non-residential mission personnel: 2
Other personnel:
    Short-term less than 1 year: 15

Non-US serving in own/other country: 8
Home ministry & office staff in US: 3
Countries: Brazil 4; Mexico 2; Uganda 2

Audio Scripture Ministries

760 Waverly Rd.
Holland, MI 49423 USA
Phone: (616) 396-5291
Fax: (616) 396-5294
E-mail: info@asmtoday.org
Web Site: www.asmtoday.org
Mr. Tom Dudenhofer, Exec. Director

A nondenominational specialized agency of Evangelical tradition engaged in audio recording/distribution, support of national workers, technical assistance and training.
Purpose: "...to facilitate the recording, duplication, and distribution of audio Scriptures primarily for non-readers around the world."
Year Founded in US: 1967
Income for Overseas Min: $490,052.00
Fully Supported US Personnel Overseas:
    Expecting to serve more than 4 years: 1
Other personnel:
    Short-term less than 1 year: 3
    Non-US serving in own/other country: 1
    Home ministry & office staff in US: 3
Countries: India 1

Aurora Mission, Inc.

PO Box 1549
Bradenton, FL 34206 USA
Phone: (941) 748-4100
Fax: (941) 748-2625
E-mail: mission@auroramission.org
Web Site: www.auroramission.org
Mr. Joseph Aleppo, President/Exec. Director

A nondenominational support agency of Baptist tradition engaged in theological education, church planting, leadership development, literature production and support of national churches.
Purpose: "...exists as an evangelical, conservative, nondenominational mission agency whose purpose is evangelism and discipleship with the goal of planting and strengthening churches and developing church leadership and church training centers."
Year Founded in US: 1978

Fully Supported US Personnel Overseas:
Expecting to serve more than 4 years: 2
Expecting to serve 1 to 4 years: 13
Other personnel:
Short-term less than 1 year: 1
Home ministry & office staff in US: 3
Countries: Italy 2

Avant Ministries

10000 N. Oak Trafficway
Kansas City, MO 64155 USA
Phone: (816) 734-8500
Fax: (816) 734-4601
E-mail: info@avmi.org
Web Site: www.avantministires.org
Associations: CrossGlobal Link
Dr. J. Paul Nyquist, President

A nondenominational sending agency of
Evangelical and Independent tradition engaged in church planting, broadcasting,
camping programs and discipleship.

Purpose: "...to make a difference in time
for eternity by rapidly planting and developing churches where none exist."

Year Founded in US: 1892

Income for Overseas Min: $8,966,595.00

Gifts in Kind: $806,685.00

Fully Supported US Personnel Overseas:
Expecting to serve more than 4 years: 162
Expecting to serve 1 to 4 years: 5
Non-residential mission personnel: 1

Other personnel:
Non-US serving in own/other country: 52
Home ministry & office staff in US: 50

Countries: Argentina 10; Austria 1; Bahamas, The 3; Belgium 1; Belize; Bolivia 14;
Brazil 18; Czech Republic 4; Ecuador 13;
France 14; Germany 3; Greece; Guatemala
2; Italy 20; Jordan 2; Mali 2; Mexico 5; Panama 3; Poland 9; Slovenia 6 Spain 30; United Kingdom 2; Unspecified Country

Awana International

1 E. Bode Rd.
Streamwood, IL 60107 USA
Phone: (630) 213-2000
Fax: (630) 213-2715
E-mail: missions@awana.org
Web Site: www.awanainternational.org
Rev. Jack D. Eggar, President/CEO

A nondenominational specialized agency of
Evangelical tradition engaged in childrens
programs, bible memorization, discipleship,
evangelism, leadership development and
partnership development.

Purpose: "...to empower Christian leaders
worldwide to train children to know, love,
and serve Christ."

Year Founded in US: 1950

Income for Overseas Min: $5,005,665.00

Fully Supported US Personnel Overseas:
Expecting to serve more than 4 years: 17
Non-residential mission personnel: 4

Other personnel:
Non-US serving in own/other country: 264
Home ministry & office staff in US: 314

Countries: Antigua; Argentina; Aruba;
Asia—General 2; Australia; Bahamas, The;
Bangladesh 1; Belarus; Belize; Benin; Bolivia; Botswana; Brazil 2; Bulgaria; Burkina Faso;
Cameroon; Cayman Islands; Chad; Chile;
Colombia; Costa Rica 2; Cote d'Ivoire; Croa-
tia; Cuba; Czech Republic; Dominica 2; Do-
minican Republic; Ecuador 2; Egypt; El Sal-
vador; Fiji; France; Germany; Ghana; Guam;
Guatemala; Haiti 2; Honduras 2; Hong
Kong; Hungary; India; Jamaica; Japan; Kazakhstan; Kenya; Korea, South; Latvia; Liberia; Malawi; Malaysia; Mali; Mexico; Middle
East; Moldova; Mozambique; Nepal; Netherlands Antilles; Nicaragua; Nigeria; New Zealand; Papua New Guinea; Paraguay; Peru;
Philippines; Puerto Rico; Romania; Russia;
Senegal; Singapore; Slovakia; South Africa;
Spain; Sri Lanka; Suriname; Swaziland; Taiwan 2; Tanzania; Togo; Trinidad and Tobago; Tunisia; Uganda; Ukraine; United Kingdom; Uruguay; Venezuela; Virgin Islands;
Zambia; Zimbabwe

Back to the Bible Intl.

PO Box 82808
Lincoln, NE 68501 USA
Phone: (402) 464-7200
Fax: (402) 464-7474
E-mail: info@backtothebible.org
Web Site: www.backtothebible.org
Associations: CrossGlobal Link
Dr. Woodrow Kroll, President

A nondenominational service agency of Evangelical tradition engaged in broadcasting,
correspondence courses, discipleship, litera-

ture distribution and literature production.

Purpose: "...to lead people into a dynamic relationship with God."

Year Founded in US: 1939

Income for Overseas Min: $820,582.00

Personnel:
Short-term less than 1 year: 3
Non-US serving in own/other country: 132
Home ministry & office staff in US: 70

Countries: Brazil; Ecuador; India; Indonesia; Jamaica; Japan; Nepal; Philippines; Sri Lanka; Trinidad and Tobago

Baptist Bible Fellowship International

PO Box 191
Springfield, MO 65801-0191 USA

Phone: (417) 862-5001
Fax: (417) 865-0794
E-mail: info@bbfimissions.com
Web Site: www.bbfimissions.com

Dr. Jon Konnerup, Mission Director

A denominational sending agency of Baptist tradition engaged in church planting.

Year Founded in US: 1950

Income for Overseas Min: $38,500,000.00

Fully Supported US Personnel Overseas:
Expecting to serve more than 4 years: 750
Expecting to serve 1 to 4 years: 33

Other personnel:
Home ministry & office staff in US: 22

Countries: Argentina 19; Australia 30; Austria 4; Azores 2; Bahamas, The 2; Belgium 6; Belize 6; Bolivia 6; Botswana 4; Brazil 33; Bulgaria 2; Burkina Faso 10; Cambodia 4; Chile 8; Colombia 4; Congo, Democratic Republic of 1; Costa Rica 12; Cote d'Ivoire 2; Croatia 2; Dominican Republic 6; Ecuador 13; El Salvador 2; Estonia 2; Ethiopia 15; France 8; Germany 17; Greece 2; Guam 2; Guatemala 5; Haiti 3; Honduras 5; Hong Kong 6; Hungary 2; Iceland 2; Indonesia 4; Ireland 3; Italy 4; Jamaica 4; Japan 23; Kenya 34; Korea, South 11; Lithuania 2; Mexico 74; Mongolia 2; Nepal 2; Netherlands 6; Netherlands Antilles 2; Nicaragua 13; Nigeria 2; New Zealand 12; Pakistan 4; Panama 6; Papua New Guinea 6; Paraguay 2; Peru 19; Philippines 42; Poland 2; Portugal 12; Puerto Rico 3; Romania 9; Russia 10; Saint Vincent and the Grenadines 2; Sierra Le-

one 2; Singapore 4; Slovakia 2; Slovenia 2; South Africa 10; South Pacific 4; Spain 14; Sweden 2; Taiwan 10; Tanzania 10; Thailand 4; Uganda 2; Ukraine 2; United Kingdom 48; Unspecified Country 52; Uruguay 2; Vanuatu 2; Zambia 16

Baptist Bible Translators Institute

PO Box 1450
Bowie, TX 76230 USA

Phone: (940) 872-5751
E-mail: info@baptisttranslators.com
Web Site: www.baptisttranslators.com

Mr. Rex L. Cobb, Director

A denominational service agency of Baptist and Fundamental tradition engaged in missionary training, missionary education, linguistics and TESOL. Data from 2005.

Purpose: "...missionaries training missionaries to plant New Testament Baptist churches in every bibleless nation and translate the Scriptures into every bibleless language."

Year Founded in US: 1973

Baptist International Evangelistic Ministries

121 Commerce Dr., Ste. 50
Danville, IN 46122 USA

Phone: (317) 718-1633
Fax: (317) 718-1693
E-mail: missions@baptistinternational.org
Web Site: www.baptistinternational.org

Dr. Sam Slobodian, President

A denominational sending agency of Baptist and Fundamental tradition engaged in church planting, Bible distribution, church construction, theological education, literature distribution and support of national workers. Statistical and financial data from 2001.

Purpose: "...to fulfill the missionary mandate in Russia and Eastern Europe through the support, training, and equipping of dedicated and prepared nationals."

Year Founded in US: 1981

Income for Overseas Min: $880,035.00

Gifts in Kind: $27,740.00

Fully Supported US Personnel Overseas:
Expecting to serve more than 4 years: 3
Non-residential mission personnel: 2

Other personnel:
Short-term less than 1 year: 102
Non-US serving in own/other country: 93
Home ministry & office staff in US: 4

Countries: Asia—General; Belarus; Georgia; Kazakhstan; Kyrgyzstan; Moldova; Romania; Russia 3; Tajikistan; Turkmenistan; Ukraine; Uzbekistan

Baptist International Missions, Inc. (BIMI)
PO Box 9215
Chattanooga, TN 37412 USA
Phone: (423) 344-5050
Fax: (423) 344-4774
E-mail: info@bimi.org
Web Site: www.bimi.org

Dr. James R. Ray, President/Gen. Director

A sending agency of Baptist and Independent tradition engaged in church planting, Bible distribution, discipleship, evangelism and leadership development. Countries of service data from 2005.

Purpose: "...to assist fundamental Baptist churches in fulfilling our Lord's command to evangelize the world with the Gospel of Jesus Christ."

Year Founded in US: 1960

Income for Overseas Min: $31,325,542.00

Gifts in Kind: $305,000.00

Fully Supported US Personnel Overseas:
Expecting to serve more than 4 years: 708

Other personnel:
Short-term less than 1 year: 12
Home ministry & office staff in US: 30

Countries: Africa—General 2; American Samoa 2; Anguilla 2; Antigua 6; Argentina 4; Australia 31; Austria 2; Bahamas, The 5; Barbados 2; Bolivia 10; Brazil 48; Cambodia 8; Cayman Islands 6; Chile 2; Costa Rica 10; Cote d'Ivoire 10; Cuba 2; Czech Republic 2; Dominican Republic 24; Ecuador 4; El Salvador 4; Estonia 2; Fiji 4; France 8; French Polynesia 2; Germany 30; Ghana 8; Guadeloupe 2; Guatemala 2; Haiti 6; Hong Kong 2; Honduras 14; Hungary 2; India 7; Indonesia 2; Ireland 14; Italy 4; Jamaica 4; Japan 45; Kenya 4; Latvia 4; Malawi 1; Mexico 55; Nepal 2; New Caledonia 2; New Zealand 6; Niger 2; Nigeria 6; N. Mariana Isls 4; Norway 2; Panama 2; Papua New Guinea 4; Paraguay 2; Peru 13; Philippines 35; Poland 2; Puerto Rico 13; Romania 12; Russia 16; Saint Kitts and Nevis 2; Senegal 4; Singapore 3; Slovakia 4; South Africa 19; Spain 7; Switzerland 2; Tanzania 6; Thailand 2; Togo 8; Trinidad and Tobago 9; Turks and Caicos Islands 1; Uganda 36; Ukraine 13; United Kingdom 39; Venezuela 18; Virgin Islands 2; Zambia 2

Baptist International Outreach, Inc.
PO Box 639
Maynardville, TN 37807 USA
Phone: (865) 992-0999
Fax: (865) 992-4999
E-mail: secretary@biomissions.org
Web Site: www.biomissions.org

Dr. Garvin Dykes, Exec. Director

A sending agency of Baptist tradition engaged in church planting, childrens programs, discipleship, evangelism, funds transmission and support of national workers.

Purpose: "...to help local churches fulfill the Great Commission."

Year Founded in US: 1985

Income for Overseas Min: $2,350,000.00

Fully Supported US Personnel Overseas:
Expecting to serve more than 4 years: 110
Expecting to serve 1 to 4 years: 2
Non-residential mission personnel: 4

Other personnel:
Short-term less than 1 year: 1
Non-US serving in own/other country: 65
Home ministry & office staff in US: 9

Countries: Argentina; Asia—General 7; Belize 2; Botswana 4; Brazil 7; Cambodia 2; Chile 2; Costa Rica 2; Ethiopia 28; Mexico 4; Middle East 2; Nigeria 5; Peru 4; Philippines 7; Russia 2; South Africa 6; Venezuela 2; Zambia 24

Baptist Medical & Dental Mission International, Inc.
11 Plaza Dr.
Hattiesburg, MS 39402 USA
Phone: (601) 544-3586
Fax: (601) 544-6508
E-mail: info@bmdmi.org
Web Site: www.bmdmi.org

Mr. Dwight Carr, President

A denominational specialized agency of Baptist tradition engaged in medical work, church planting, discipleship, evangelism and support of national churches.

Purpose: "...to evangelize the lost, disciple the saved, and minister to the needs of the poor."

Year Founded in US: 1974

Income for Overseas Min: $17,500,000.00

Gifts in Kind: $11,000,000.00

Fully Supported US Personnel Overseas:
  Expecting to serve more than 4 years: 9
  Expecting to serve 1 to 4 years: 21

Other personnel:
  Short-term less than 1 year: 2158
  Non-US serving in own/other country: 84
  Home ministry & office staff in US: 7

Countries: Honduras 7; Nicaragua 2

Baptist Mid-Missions

PO Box 308011
Cleveland, OH 44130 USA
Phone: (440) 826-3930
Fax: (440) 826-4457
E-mail: info@bmm.org
Web Site: www.bmm.org

Dr. Gary L. Anderson, President

A sending agency of Baptist and Fundamental tradition engaged in church planting, broadcasting, theological education, medical work, relief and/or rehabilitation and Bible translation. Data from 2005.

Purpose: "...to strategically advance the building of Christ's church, with His passion and for His glory, in vital partnership with Baptist churches worldwide."

Year Founded in US: 1920

Income for Overseas Min: $18,600,000.00

Fully Supported US Personnel Overseas:
  Expecting to serve more than 4 years: 466

Other personnel:
  Short-term less than 1 year: 381
  Non-US serving in own/other country: 20
  Home ministry & office staff in US: 48

Countries: Asia—General 7; Argentina 5; Australia 17; Bangladesh; Botswana 2; Brazil 139; Cambodia 4; Cameroon 4; Central African Republic 5; Chad 7; Chile 4; Cote d'Ivoire 7; Dominican Republic 1; Ecuador 3; Ethiopia 2; Finland 2; France 29; Germany 17; Ghana 12; Guyana 2; Haiti 4; Honduras 10; India 8; Ireland 2; Italy 6; Jamaica 1; Japan 8; Kenya 2; Liberia 2; Luxembourg 2; Malta 2; Mexico 11; Micronesia, Federated States of 5; Middle East 2; Mozambique 2; Netherlands 10; New Zealand 6; Papua New Guinea 2; Peru 33; Puerto Rico 2; Romania 13; Russia 4; Saint Vincent and the Grenadines 6; Slovakia 2; Spain 8; Taiwan 2; Thailand 9; United Kingdom 11; Venezuela 7; Zambia 15

Baptist Missionary Association of America

PO Box 30910
Little Rock, AR 72260 USA
Phone: (501) 455-4977
Fax: (501) 455-3636
E-mail: bmaam@bmaam.com
Web Site: www.bmaam.com

Mr. Grady Higgs, Exec. Director

A denominational sending agency of Baptist tradition engaged in church planting, Bible distribution, childcare/orphanage programs, discipleship, missionary education, theological education, evangelism, relief and/or rehabilitation and TESOL.

Purpose: "...serves to influence the world for Jesus Christ by planting churches throughout all nations...to accomplish our goal by sending American missionaries, training and equipping believers, and by assisting every local church to be a Great Commission Church."

Year Founded in US: 1950

Income for Overseas Min: $3,600,000.00

Gifts in Kind: $1,000,000.00

Fully Supported US Personnel Overseas:
  Expecting to serve more than 4 years: 21
  Non-residential mission personnel: 32

Other personnel:
  Short-term less than 1 year: 200
  Non-US serving in own/other country: 721
  Home ministry & office staff in US: 23

Countries: Argentina; Armenia; Azerbaijan; Belarus; Belize; Benin; Bolivia; Brazil; Burkina Faso; Cambodia; Cape Verde; Chile 1; China 1; Colombia 1; Costa Rica; Cote d'Ivoire; Czech Republic; Dominican Republic; Egypt; El Salvador; Estonia 1; France; Georgia; Ghana 2; Guatemala 1; Guinea; Honduras; Hong Kong; India; Indonesia; Iran; Iraq; Japan; Kazakhstan; Korea,

South; Kyrgyzstan; Laos; Lebanon; Liberia; Mali; Mauritania; Mexico 4; Moldova; Mongolia 1; Myanmar/Burma; Nicaragua; Nigeria; Panama; Peru 1; Philippines 4; Portugal; Puerto Rico 1; Romania; Russia; Sierra Leone; Sudan; Syria; Taiwan; Tajikistan; Thailand; Togo; Turkmenistan; Ukraine 2; United Kingdom 1; Uruguay; Uzbekistan; Vietnam

Baptist Missions to Forgotten Peoples

PO Box 37043
Jacksonville, FL 32236-7043 USA
Phone: (904) 783-4007
Fax: (904) 778-8999
E-mail: bmfp@bmfp.org
Web Site: www.bmfp.org

Dr. Gene Burge, Pres./Exec. Dir.

A nondenominational sending agency of Baptist tradition engaged in church planting and evangelism. Data from 2001.

Purpose: "...to serve the local church by providing a faith-missions ministry committed to strategic church planting...among the unevangelized people groups of the world."

Fully Supported US Personnel Overseas:
   Expecting to serve more than 4 years: 125
Countries: Unspecified Country 125

Barnabas International

PO Box 11211
Rockford, IL 61108 USA
Phone: (815) 395-1335
Fax: (815) 395-1385
E-mail: Barnabas@barnabas.org
Web Site: www.barnabas.org

Perry Bradford, Exec. Director

An interdenominational support agency of Evangelical tradition engaged in member care, leadership development, support of national churches and psychological counseling. Data from 2005.

Purpose: "...to edify, enrich, encourage, and strengthen missionaries, pastors, national church leaders and their families... through personal, small group and conference ministries."

Year Founded in US: 1986
Income for Overseas Min: $964,095.00
Personnel:
   Home ministry & office staff in US: 2

BCM International

PO Box 249
Akron, PA 17501-0249 USA
Phone: (717) 859-6404
Fax: (717) 859-6914
E-mail: info@bcmintl.org
Web Site: www.bcmintl.org
Associations: CrossGlobal Link, The Mission Exchange

Rev. Martin Windle, President

A nondenominational sending agency of Evangelical tradition engaged in childrens programs, church development, camping programs, church planting, correspondence courses, evangelism and training.

Purpose: "...dedicated to making disciples of all age groups for the Lord Jesus Christ through evangelism, teaching, and training so that churches are established and the Church strengthened."

Year Founded in US: 1942
Fully Supported US Personnel Overseas:
   Expecting to serve more than 4 years: 534
Other personnel:
   Home ministry & office staff in US: 29

Countries: Antigua 1; Austria 1; Belgium 2; Belize 1; Bolivia 21; Brazil 7; Cambodia 2; Cuba 1; Dominican Republic 2; Egypt 10; Finland 2; France 6; Germany 9; Greece 1; Guyana 4; Hungary 2; India 211; Indonesia 12; Ireland 6; Italy 4; Jamaica 3; Mexico 6; Mozambique 1; Myanmar/Burma 7; Nepal 1; Netherlands 11; Peru 44; Philippines 89; Poland 2; Russia 4; Saint Vincent and the Grenadines 2; Singapore 1; South Africa 4; Spain 5; Sri Lanka 2; Suriname 4; Swaziland 2; Trinidad and Tobago 1; Ukraine 25; United Kingdom 13; Zambia 2

BEE World (Biblical Education by Extension)

PO Box 62805
Colorado Springs, CO 80962 USA
Phone: (719) 488-5837
Fax: (719) 488-0204
E-mail: info@beeworld.org
Web Site: www.beeworld.org

Mr. Al Bridges, President

A nondenominational sending agency of Evangelical tradition engaged in TEE, discipleship, extension education, theological education, leadership development and partnership development.

Purpose: "...to help the Church fulfill the Great Commission by providing Biblical training that results in the multiplication of servant leaders with priority given to countries with limited access to training."

Year Founded in US: 1994

Fully Supported US Personnel Overseas:
   Expecting to serve more than 4 years: 7
   Non-residential mission personnel: 26

Other personnel:
   Short-term less than 1 year: 8
   Non-US serving in own/other country: 2
   Home ministry & office staff in US: 17

Countries: Asia—General 7

Bethany Intl. Ministries
6820 Auto Club Rd., Ste. D
Bloomington, MN 55438 USA

Phone: (952) 829-2492
Fax: (952) 829-2767
E-mail: ministries@bethanyinternational.org
Web Site: www.bethanyinternational.org
Associations: The Mission Exchange

Mr. Dan Brokke, President

A nondenominational sending agency of Charismatic tradition engaged in missionary training, business as mission, church planting, missionary education, evangelism, literature distribution and partnership development. Countries of service data from 2005.

Purpose: "...to delight God's heart and extend His Kingdom by training and sending servant leaders to disciple the world's least reached people wherever they may be found."

Year Founded in US: 1963

Income for Overseas Min: $3,252,745.00

Fully Supported US Personnel Overseas:
   Expecting to serve more than 4 years: 92
   Expecting to serve 1 to 4 years: 11

Other personnel:
   Non-US serving in own/other country: 97
   Home ministry & office staff in US: 13

Countries: Bolivia 6; Brazil 15; Cambodia 2; Croatia 1; Dominican Republic 2; France 8; Ghana 2; Honduras 2; Hungary 2; Japan 2; Kenya 2; Kosovo 1; Mexico 10; Netherlands 1; Paraguay; Philippines 6; Slovenia 2; Spain 2; Thailand 1; Unspecified Country 25

Beyond Borders
PO Box 2132
Norristown, PA 19404 USA

Phone: (610) 277-5045
E-mail: mail@beyondborders.net
Web Site: www.beyondborders.net

Mr. David Diggs, Gen. Coord.

A support agency of Ecumenical tradition engaged in literacy work, children at risk, Christian education, leadership development, trafficking/slavery issues and training.

Purpose: "...a group of people who join together to work for justice and peace by fostering transformative learning within and across cultural and economic borders."

Year Founded in US: 1993

Income for Overseas Min: $830,000.00

Fully Supported US Personnel Overseas:
   Expecting to serve 1 to 4 years: 1
   Non-residential mission personnel: 2

Other personnel:
   Non-US serving in own/other country: 10
   Home ministry & office staff in US: 4

Countries: Haiti

Bible League, The
PO Box 28000
Chicago, IL 60628 USA

Phone: (866) 825-4636
Fax: (708) 367-8600
E-mail: info@bibleleague.org
Web Site: www.bibleleague.org

Mr. Robert Cole, President

A nondenominational specialized agency of Evangelical tradition engaged in Bible distribution, church planting, evangelism, literacy work, support of national workers, Bible translation and training in more than 55 countries. Data from 2005.

Purpose: "...to provide Scriptures and training worldwide to bring people into fellowship with Christ and His Church."

Year Founded in US: 1938

Income for Overseas Min: $22,179,947.00

Personnel:
   Non-US serving in own/other country: 500
   Home ministry & office staff in US: 150

Countries: Unspecified Country

Bible Training Centre for Pastors

2030 Tucker Industrial Rd., Ste. 126
Tucker, GA 30084 USA
Phone: (770) 938-6160
Fax: (770) 938-5884
E-mail: info@btcp.com
Web Site: www.bibletraining.com

Dr. Dennis J. Mock, President

A transdenominational support agency of Evangelical tradition engaged in theological education.

Purpose: "...an equipping ministry providing a Biblical, transferable, affordable concept and curriculum used by over 180 partnering organizations worldwide."

Year Founded in US: 1990

Personnel:
  Home ministry & office staff in US: 8

Bibles & Literature in French
(See ad on page 124)

PO Box 629
Wheaton, IL 60187 USA
Phone: (630) 221-1980
Fax: (630) 221-1982
E-mail: info@blfusa.org
Web Site: www.blfusa.org
Associations: CrossGlobal Link

Mr. Harry R. Enns, Exec. Director

A nondenominational specialized agency of Evangelical tradition engaged in literature production, Bible distribution, literature distribution and short-term programs.

Purpose: "...to glorify God through providing Christian materials to meet the needs of evangelism and discipleship in the French-speaking world."

Year Founded in US: 1958

Income for Overseas Min: $469,645.00

Fully Supported US Personnel Overseas:
  Expecting to serve more than 4 years: 7
  Expecting to serve 1 to 4 years: 3

Other personnel:
  Short-term less than 1 year: 51
  Home ministry & office staff in US: 5

Countries: Belgium 4; France 3

Bibles For The World, Inc.

PO Box 49759
Colorado Springs, CO 80949-9759 USA
Phone: (888) 382-4253
Fax: (719) 630-1449
E-mail: info@bftw.org
Web Site: www.biblesfortheworld.org

Dr. Rochunga Pudaite, President

A nondenominational support agency of Evangelical tradition engaged in Bible distribution, Christian education, theological education, support of national churches, support of national workers and childcare/orphanage programs. Data from 2001.

Year Founded in US: 1972

Income for Overseas Min: $690,457.00

Gifts in Kind: $564,295.00

Personnel:
  Short-term less than 1 year: 30
  Non-US serving in own/other country: 400
  Home ministry & office staff in US: 15

Countries: India

Biblical Ministries Worldwide

1595 Herrington Rd.
Lawrenceville, GA 30043 USA
Phone: (770) 339-3500
Fax: (770) 513-1254
E-mail: bmwhq@biblicalministries.org
Web Site: www.biblicalministries.org
Associations: FOM

Mr. Paul Seger, Gen. Director

A nondenominational sending agency of Independent tradition engaged in church planting, discipleship, evangelism and leadership development.

Purpose: "...to serve the Lord and local churches by establishing reproducing churches through evangelism, discipleship, and leadership development."

Year Founded in US: 1988

Income for Overseas Min: $8,000,000.00

Gifts in Kind: $200,000.00

Fully Supported US Personnel Overseas:
  Expecting to serve more than 4 years: 155
  Non-residential mission personnel: 8

Other personnel:
  Non-US serving in own/other country: 22
  Home ministry & office staff in US: 10

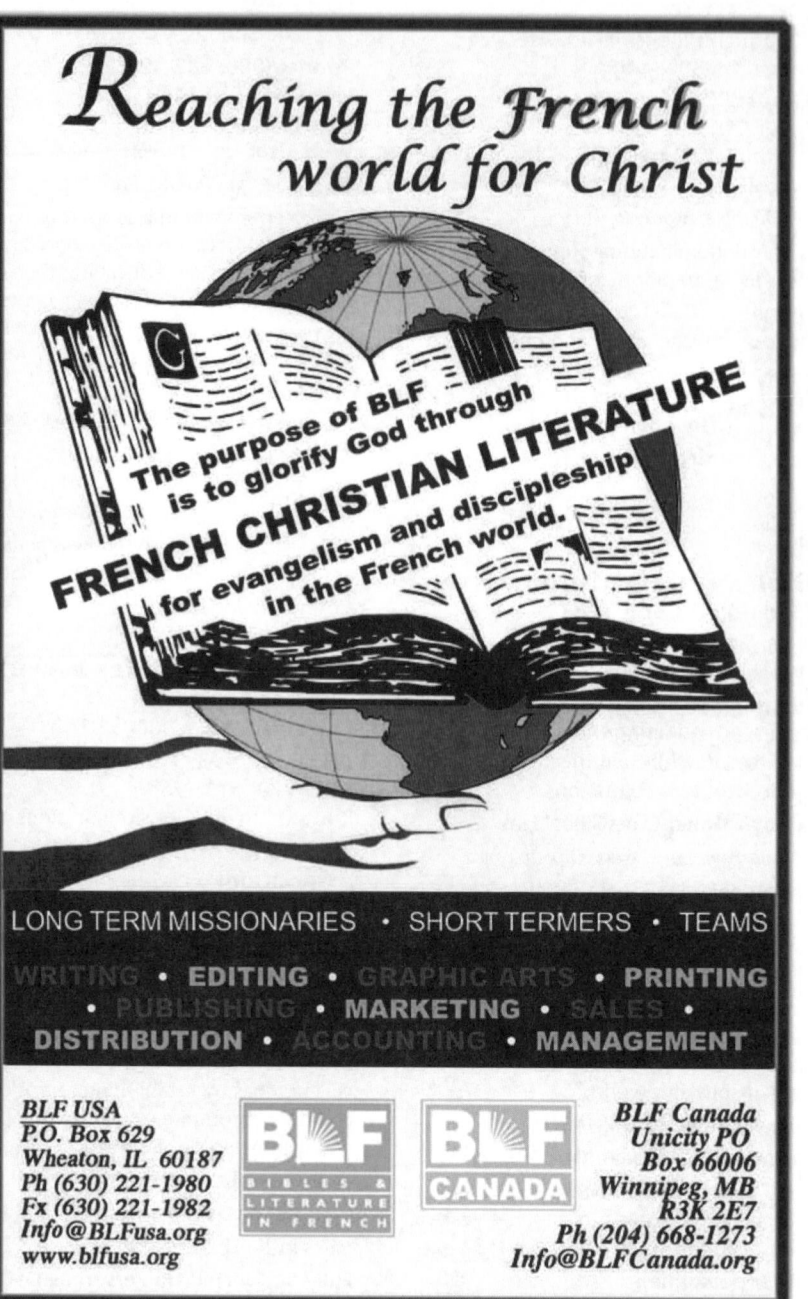

Countries: Antigua 2 Argentina 12; Australia 6; Austria 2; Croatia; Ecuador 10; Fiji 6; France 8; Germany 5; Hong Kong 5; Honduras 5; Ireland 8; Italy 4; Japan 2; Luxembourg 2; Mexico 12; Netherlands 2; New Zealand 2; Palau 4; Philippines 2; Puerto Rico 2; South Africa 11; Spain 4; Suriname 2; Sweden 4; United Kingdom 15; Uruguay 9; Vanuatu 9

BILD International

2400 Oakwood Rd.
Ames, IA 50014-8417 USA
Phone: (515) 292-7012
Fax: (515) 292-1933
E-mail: info@bild.org
Web Site: www.bild.org
Mr. Jeff Reed, President/CEO

A transdenominational support agency of Evangelical tradition engaged in leadership development, church planting, discipleship, Christian education, theological education and partnership development.

Purpose: "...to accelerate church-planting movements in each of the nine major civilizations by training key leaders of those movements in 'the way of Christ and His apostles,' equipping them with strategies and resources to train their leaders from grassroots to national."

Year Founded in US: 1974

Income for Overseas Min: $1,521,071.00

Gifts in Kind: $236,239.00

Fully Supported US Personnel Overseas:
  Non-residential mission personnel: 3

Other personnel:
  Short-term less than 1 year: 6
  Non-US serving in own/other country: 23
  Home ministry & office staff in US: 14

Countries: Albania; Australia; Cambodia; Chad; France; Guatemala; India; Indonesia; Japan; Mexico; Myanmar/Burma; Nigeria; Pakistan; Paraguay; Peru; Portugal

Billy Graham Center, The

500 College Ave.
Wheaton, IL 60187 USA
Phone: (630) 752-5918
Fax: (630) 752-5916
E-mail: bgcadm@wheaton.edu
Web Site: www.billygrahamcenter.org
Dr. Lon Allison, Exec. Director

A transdenominational service agency of Evangelical tradition engaged in training, evangelism, missions information service, leadership development and mission-related research. Activities data from 2005.

Purpose: "...to accelerate global evangelism...to envision every believer everywhere making Jesus Christ known until He returns."

Year Founded in US: 1975

Personnel:
  Home ministry & office staff in US: 33

Blessing the Children Intl.

2265 Fraser Road
Kawkawlin, MI 48631 USA
Phone: (989) 667-8850
Fax: (989) 684-2005
E-mail: melissa@blessingthechildren.org
Web Site: www.blessingthechildren.org
Mr. Keith V. Strawn, President/CEO

An interdenominational specialized agency of Evangelical tradition engaged in childcare/ orphanage programs, childrens programs, Christian education, evangelism, medical work and support of national churches.

Purpose: "...to enter into covenant relationships with ministries having the call to work with children...to minister to the physical and spiritual needs of children."

Year Founded in US: 2001

Income for Overseas Min: $298,407.00

Fully Supported US Personnel Overseas:
  Expecting to serve more than 4 years: 1
  Non-residential mission personnel: 16

Other personnel:
  Short-term less than 1 year: 65
  Non-US serving in own/other country: 16
  Home ministry & office staff in US: 3

Countries: Ethiopia 1

Blessings International

5881 S. Garnett
Tulsa, OK 74146 USA
Phone: (918) 250-8101
Fax: (918) 250-1281
E-mail: info@blessing.org
Web Site: www.blessing.org
Associations: AERDO
Dr. Harold C. Harder, Exec. Director

A nondenominational support agency of

Charismatic and Evangelical tradition engaged in medical supplies and medical work.

Purpose: "...to alleviate suffering and provide medicines world-wide by facilitating relationships that promote health."

Year Founded in US: 1981

Income for Overseas Min: $23,148,347.00

Gifts in Kind: $23,148,347.00

Personnel:
Home ministry & office staff in US: 9

Brazil Gospel Fellowship Mission

125 W. Ash St.
Springfield, IL 62704 USA

Phone: (217) 523-7176

Fax: (217) 523-7186

E-mail: bgfm@comcast.net

Web Site: www.bgfmission.com

Rev. Larry Lipka, Exec. Director

A sending agency of Baptist and Independent tradition engaged in church planting, camping programs, Christian education, TEE, evangelism and leadership development.

Purpose: "...to aid the evangelization of Brazil, South America."

Year Founded in US: 1945

Income for Overseas Min: $1,070,700.00

Fully Supported US Personnel Overseas:
Expecting to serve more than 4 years: 44
Expecting to serve 1 to 4 years: 1

Other personnel:
Short-term less than 1 year: 6
Home ministry & office staff in US: 4

Countries: Brazil 44

Bread for the World

50 F St., Ste. 500
Washington, DC 20001 USA

Phone: (202) 639-9400

Fax: (202) 639-9401

E-mail: bread@bread.org

Web Site: www.bread.org

Associations: AERDO

Rev. David Beckmann, President

A support agency of Ecumenical tradition engaged in advocacy, poverty education and justice.

Purpose: "...to urge our nation's decision

makers to end hunger at home and abroad."

Year Founded in US: 1972

Personnel:
Home ministry & office staff in US: 90

Brethren in Christ World Missions

PO Box 390
Grantham, PA 17027-0390 USA

Phone: (717) 697-2634

Fax: (717) 691-6053

E-mail: bicwm@bic-church.org

Web Site: www.bic-church.org/wm

Associations: The Mission Exchange

Rev. Christine A. Sharp, Exec. Director

A denominational sending agency of Brethren tradition engaged in church planting, apologetics, business as mission, discipleship, theological education and TEE.

Purpose: "...a church for every people...the Gospel to every person...Jesus worshipped in the nations...a mission from every church... to extend the Kingdom of God by laboring cross-culturally with other believers."

Year Founded in US: 1895

Income for Overseas Min: $1,325,192.00

Fully Supported US Personnel Overseas:
Expecting to serve more than 4 years: 35
Non-residential mission personnel: 2

Other personnel:
Short-term less than 1 year: 68
Non-US serving in own/other country: 3
Home ministry & office staff in US: 12

Countries: Colombia; Honduras 2; Malawi 6; Mexico 2; Spain 3; Unspecified Country 18; Zambia 2; Zimbabwe 2

Bridge Builders International

PO Box 4073
Salem, OR 97302 USA

Phone: (541) 602-6968

E-mail: naomi@bridgebuildersint.com

Web Site: www.bridgebuildersint.com

Rev. Charles D. Kelley, President/Founder

A nondenominational support agency of Baptist tradition engaged in partnership development, childrens programs, leadership development and training.

Purpose: "...to bring people together to develop and strengthen leaders, build vital partnerships, and connect resources with needs and opportunities."

Year Founded in US: 1994

Income for Overseas Min: $247,438.00

Fully Supported US Personnel Overseas:
  Expecting to serve more than 4 years: 6

Other personnel:
  Non-US serving in own/other country: 6
  Home ministry & office staff in US: 3

Countries: Latvia 6

Bright Hope International

2060 Stonington Ave.
Hoffman Estates, IL 60004 USA

Phone: (224) 520-6100
Fax: (847) 519-0024
E-mail: info@brighthope.org
Web Site: www.brighthope.org
Associations: AERDO

Mr. Craig Dyer, President

A service agency of Evangelical tradition engaged in international church empowerment, relief and/or rehabilitation, development, leadership development and partnership development. Countries of service data from 2005.

Purpose: "...to provide for the physical, economic, and spiritual needs of people living at the lowest economic level through personal, empowering, holistic, local church partnerships."

Year Founded in US: 1968

Income for Overseas Min: $4,648,574.00

Gifts in Kind: $1,295,418.00

Fully Supported US Personnel Overseas:
  Non-residential mission personnel: 1

Other personnel:
  Short-term less than 1 year: 4
  Non-US serving in own/other country: 348
  Home ministry & office staff in US: 20

Countries: Costa Rica; Cote d'Ivoire; Cuba; Ethiopia; Ghana; Haiti; India; Indonesia; Kenya; Malawi; Mozambique; Papua New Guinea; Philippines; Thailand; Uganda

Cadence International

PO Box 1268
Englewood, CO 80150 USA

Phone: (303) 762-1400
Fax: (303) 788-0661

E-mail: info@cadence.org
Web Site: www.cadence.org

Mr. David Schroeder, President

A nondenominational service agency of Evangelical tradition engaged in ministry to the military community, evangelism, childrens programs, youth programs and discipleship.

Purpose: "...to exalt Christ in the nations through the lives of transformed military people."

Year Founded in US: 1951

Income for Overseas Min: $3,683,602.00

Gifts in Kind: $8,715.00

Fully Supported US Personnel Overseas:
  Expecting to serve more than 4 years: 44
  Expecting to serve 1 to 4 years: 21
  Non-residential mission personnel: 3

Other personnel:
  Short-term less than 1 year: 16
  Home ministry & office staff in US: 12

Countries: Germany 25; Italy; Japan 9; Korea, South 4; Spain; Thailand 4; United Kingdom 2

Café 1040, Inc.

PO Box 110
Alpharetta, GA 30009 USA

Phone: (678) 938-5556
E-mail: information@cafe1040.com
Web Site: www.cafe1040.com

Rev. Charles Phillips, Founder/Exec. Director

A sending agency of Evangelical tradition engaged in moblilization for missions, leadership development, missionary training, justice, discipleship and business as mission.

Purpose: "...to provide practical training inside the 10/40 Window, where students can learn daily lessons in language, culture, history, technology and relational evangelism, and apply those skills."

Year Founded in US: 2001

Income for Overseas Min: $389,003.00

Fully Supported US Personnel Overseas:
  Expecting to serve 1 to 4 years: 7

Other personnel:
  Home ministry & office staff in US: 4

Countries: Asia—General; Middle East

Caleb Resources

10 West Dry Creek Cir.
Littleton, CO 80120 USA

Phone: (877) 662-1040
Fax: (303) 459-5401
E-mail: info@calebresources.org
Web Site: www.calebresources.org
Associations: CrossGlobal Link
Mr. Keith Swartley, Team Leader
A support agency of Evangelical tradition engaged in mobilization for mission, literature distribution, literature production, mission-related research, training and video/film production/distribution. Formerly a part of Initiative 360—Take it Global, known as Caleb Project.
Personnel:
    Home ministry & office staff in US: 13

Calvary Commission, Inc.
PO Box 100
Lindale, TX 75771 USA
Phone: (903) 882-5501
Fax: (903) 882-7282
E-mail: missions@calvarycommission.org
Web Site: www.calvarycommission.org
Rev. Joe L. Fauss, Intl. Director
A transdenominational sending agency of Charismatic and Evangelical tradition engaged in missionary training, childcare/orphanage programs, missionary education, evangelism, support of national workers and short-term programs. Data from 2001.
Year Founded in US: 1977
Income for Overseas Min: $150,000.00
Gifts in Kind: $125,000.00
Fully Supported US Personnel Overseas:
    Expecting to serve more than 4 years: 18
    Expecting to serve 1 to 4 years: 7
Other personnel:
    Short-term less than 1 year: 25
    Home ministry & office staff in US: 45
Countries: Belize 6; Mexico 10; Romania 2

Calvary Evangelistic Mission, Inc.
PO Box 367000
San Juan, PR 00936-7000 USA
Phone: (787) 724-2727
Fax: (787) 723-9633
E-mail: cem@therockradio.org
Web Site: www.therockradio.org
Janet Luttrell, President/CEO

An interdenominational specialized agency of Baptist tradition engaged in broadcasting and extension education. Data from 2005.
Purpose: "...to glorify God by assisting the church in fulfilling the Great Commission of Jesus Christ, primarily in the Caribbean."
Year Founded in US: 1953
Income for Overseas Min: $660,067.00
Gifts in Kind: $73,428.00
Fully Supported US Personnel Overseas:
    Expecting to serve more than 4 years: 7
    Expecting to serve 1 to 4 years: 8
    Non-residential mission personnel: 2
Other personnel:
    Home ministry & office staff in US: 11
Countries: Caribbean—General 7

Calvary International
3771 Spring Park Rd.
Jacksonville, FL 32207 USA
Phone: (904) 398-6559
Fax: (904) 398-6840
E-mail: info@gotonations.com
Web Site: www.gotonations.com
Associations: CrossGlobal Link
Dr. Jerry Williamson, President
An interdenominational sending agency of Charismatic and Evangelical tradition engaged in leadership development, childrens programs, church planting, development, evangelism and missionary training.
Purpose: "...a servant ministry helping the body of Christ reap a global harvest."
Year Founded in US: 1981
Income for Overseas Min: $3,506,976.00
Gifts in Kind: $2,549.00
Fully Supported US Personnel Overseas:
    Expecting to serve more than 4 years: 65
    Expecting to serve 1 to 4 years: 9
    Non-residential mission personnel: 6
Other personnel:
    Short-term less than 1 year: 110
    Non-US serving in own/other country: 62
    Home ministry & office staff in US: 59
Countries: Asia—General 3; Australia; Burkina Faso 3; Cambodia; Colombia; Costa Rica 7; Cuba; Ecuador; Equatorial Guinea; Estonia; Ethiopia; Ghana; Guatemala 11; Honduras 2; India; Indonesia; Jamaica; Jordan; Korea, North; Latvia 1; Malaysia; Mexico 7;

Nepal 1; Netherlands; Nigeria; Niger; Peru 1; Philippines 14; Russia 2; Singapore; South Africa 2; Tanzania 6; Thailand 3; Turkey; Ukraine 2; United Kingdom; Venezuela

CAM International

8625 La Prada Dr.
Dallas, TX 75228 USA
Phone: (214) 327-8206
Fax: (214) 239-9750
E-mail: smalphurs@caminternational.org
Web Site: www.caminternational.org
Associations: CrossGlobal Link
Mr. Daniel Wicher, President
A nondenominational sending agency of Evangelical tradition engaged in church establishing/planting, Christian education and theological education.

Purpose: "...to make disciples among the world's less-reached peoples by mobilizing multi-nation teams to win a hearing, teach the Word, and establish biblical churches."

Year Founded in US: 1888
Fully Supported US Personnel Overseas:
Expecting to serve more than 4 years: 162
Non-residential mission personnel: 4

Other personnel:
Short-term less than 1 year: 113
Non-US serving in own/other country: 3
Home ministry & office staff in US: 20

Countries: Albania 4; Guatemala 56; Honduras 23; Mexico 61; Spain 14; Uruguay 4

Campus Crusade for Christ, Intl.

100 Lake Hart Dr., Dept. 2100
Orlando, FL 32832 USA
Phone: (407) 826-2000
Fax: (407) 826-2067
Web Site: www.ccci.org
Associations: The Mission Exchange
Dr. Steven B. Douglass, President
An interdenominational sending agency of Evangelical tradition engaged in evangelism, support of national workers, training and discipleship. Countries of service data from 2005.

Purpose: "...to help build spiritual movements everywhere so that everyone knows someone who truly follows Jesus."

Year Founded in US: 1951
Income for Overseas Min:
$137,739,000.00
Fully Supported US Personnel Overseas:
Expecting to serve more than 4 years: 807
Expecting to serve 1 to 4 years: 480

Other personnel:
Short-term less than 1 year: 647
Non-US serving in own/other country: 12,228
Home ministry & office staff in US: 6,401

Countries: Africa—General 2; Albania 7; Angola; Argentina 6; Armenia; Asia—General 163; Australia 10; Austria; Bangladesh; Barbados; Belarus 9; Belgium; Benin; Bolivia 4; Bosnia and Herzegovina; Botswana; Brazil 9; Bulgaria 4; Burkina Faso 2; Burundi; Cambodia 2; Cameroon; Central African Republic; Central Asia—General 60; Chad; Chile 2; Colombia; Congo, Democratic Republic of; Congo, Republic of the; Costa Rica; Cote d'Ivoire; Croatia 16; Czech Republic 7; Dominican Republic; East Timor; Ecuador; Egypt 3; El Salvador 2; Estonia 2; Ethiopia; Europe—General 11; Fiji; France 57; Gabon; Germany 29; Ghana 1; Greece 3; Guatemala; Guinea; Guinea-Bissau; Guyana; Haiti; Hong Kong; Honduras; Hungary 69; India; Indonesia 2; Italy 13; Jamaica; Japan 18; Kenya 6; Korea, South; Latin America—General; Latvia 8; Lebanon; Lesotho; Liberia; Lithuania 5; Macau; Macedonia 4; Madagascar; Malawi; Malaysia; Mali; Mexico 9; Moldova; Mozambique; Myanmar/Burma; Namibia; Nepal; Netherlands 2; New Zealand 17; Nicaragua 2; Niger; Nigeria 4; Pakistan; Panama 2; Papua New Guinea; Paraguay; Peru; Philippines 21; Poland; Portugal; Romania 8; Russia 65; Rwanda; Senegal 1; Serbia and Montenegro; Sierra Leone; Singapore 41; Slovakia 9 Slovenia 3; Solomon Islands; South Africa 6; Spain 30; Sri Lanka; Suriname; Swaziland; Sweden; Switzerland; Taiwan; Tanzania; Thailand 8; Togo; Tonga; Trinidad and Tobago; Uganda 2; Ukraine 13; United Kingdom 17; Uruguay; Venezuela 3; Zambia; Zimbabwe 8

Caribbean Baptist Mission Society

PO Box 40247
Fort Worth, TX 76140-0247 USA
Phone: (817) 447-3722

E-mail: michaelmanire@cbms.org
Web Site: www.cbms.org
Mr. Albert Pack, President

A denominational sending agency of Baptist tradition engaged in business as mission, apologetics, church construction, church planting, evangelism and providing medical supplies.

Purpose: "...to collect and distribute support monies for national and international missionaries and mission organizations of like faith that practice and are actively proclaiming the Gospel."

Year Founded in US: 1993

Income for Overseas Min: $38,000.00

Fully Supported US Personnel Overseas:
Expecting to serve 1 to 4 years: 6

Countries: Haiti

Caring for Others
13355 Paddock Pkwy.
New Berlin, WI 53151 USA
Phone: (262) 641-9600
E-mail: john@caringforothers.org
Web Site: www.missionary-care.org
Mr. John Certalic, Exec. Director

A nondenominational support agency of Evangelical tradition engaged in member care, discipleship, leadership development, management consulting/training, psychological counseling and services for other agencies.

Purpose: "...to care for Christian workers so they can spread the Gospel as effectively as possible."

Year Founded in US: 2002

Income for Overseas Min: $52,631.00

Fully Supported US Personnel Overseas:
Expecting to serve more than 4 years: 2

Other personnel:
Short-term less than 1 year: 1
Home ministry & office staff in US: 1

Countries: Unspecified Country 2

Caring Partners Intl., Inc.
601 Shotwell Dr.
Franklin, OH 45005 USA
Phone: (937) 743-2744
Fax: (937) 743-2749
E-mail: r.reed@caringpartners.org
Web Site: www.caringpartners.org

Mr. Roy W. Cline, President/CEO

A transdenominational specialized agency of Evangelical tradition engaged in evangelism through medicine, short-term programs coordination, childrens programs, evangelism, providing medical supplies, and support of national churches.

Purpose: "...to open the minds and hearts of people around the world to the Gospel of Jesus Christ while serving their health needs with treatment, training, and materials."

Year Founded in US: 1975

Income for Overseas Min: $563,798.00

Gifts in Kind: $425,589.00

Personnel:
Short-term less than 1 year: 66
Non-US serving in own/other country: 8
Home ministry & office staff in US: 4

Countries: Cuba; Ecuador; Guatemala

Carpenter's Brothers Family Travel
PO Box 425
Sunderland, MA 01375 USA
Phone: (413) 665-3612
E-mail: bschulze@aol.com
Web Site: www.carpbrostravel.com/missionstravel.htm
Mr. Robert Schulze, Owner

A transdenominational specialized agency engaged in travel services.
Year Founded in US: 1996

Carver Intl. Missions, Inc.
PO Box 92543
Atlanta, GA 30314 USA
Phone: (404) 522-4000
E-mail: carverfm@aol.com
Rev. Glenn T. Mason, Exec. Director

A nondenominational missionary agency of Evangelical tradition specializing in training and deploying national disciples to biblically analyze, attack and resolve issues in their homes, communities, churches and workplaces. Data from 2005.

Year Founded in US: 1955

Income for Overseas Min: $300,000.00

Fully Supported US Personnel Overseas:
Expecting to serve more than 4 years: 5
Expecting to serve 1 to 4 years: 1

Other personnel:
Short-term less than 1 year: 2
Non-US serving in own/other country: 3
Home ministry & office staff in US: 1
Countries: Liberia 5

Casa Viva

PO Box 120
Wheaton, IL 60187-0120 USA
Phone: (630) 487-0079
E-mail: info@casaviva.org
Web Site: www.casaviva.org
Mr. Matthew Schulte, Director

A nondenominational support agency of Evangelical tradition engaged in childcare/orphanage programs, children at risk, justice, support of national churches and training.

Purpose: "...to provide family-based care for orphaned, abandoned, abused, and neglected children worldwide."
Year Founded in US: 2008
Income for Overseas Min: $275,000.00
Personnel:
Short-term less than 1 year: 129
Non-US serving in own/other country: 7
Home ministry & office staff in US: 1
Countries: Bolivia; Costa Rica

Catalyst Services

PO Box 152
Newtown, PA 18940 USA
Phone: (215) 579-4346
Fax: (215) 579-4346
E-mail: info@catalystservices.org
Web Site: www.catalystservices.org
Ellen Livingood, President

A service agency of Evangelical tradition engaged in services for other agencies, partnership development and mobilization for mission.

Purpose: "...to assist mission agencies and denominations to collaborate more effectively with local churches to accelerate their global impact."
Year Founded in US: 2006
Personnel:
Home ministry & office staff in US: 2

Cedar Lane Missionary Homes, Inc.

103 Cedar Lane
Laurel Springs, NJ 08021 USA
Phone: (856) 783-6525
Fax: (856) 783-6525
E-mail: cedarlane@furloughhomes.org
Web Site: www.furloughhomes.org
Rev. James Callahan, Director

A nondenominational support agency of Evangelical tradition engaged in furloughed missionary support and member care.

Purpose: "...providing restful homes and otherwise assisting missionaries on furlough."
Year Founded in US: 1957
Personnel:
Home ministry & office staff in US: 3

CEIFA Ministry International

PO Box 83
Bethalto, IL 62010 USA
Phone: (618) 581-6134
E-mail: runyanfg@juno.com
Web Site: www.ceifa-hgm.com
Mr. Jim Folsom, Chairman of Board/Director

A transdenominational service agency of Evangelical tradition engaged in TEE, Bible distribution, children at risk, childrens programs, church planting, missionary education, evangelism, literature distribution, literature production, providing medical supplies, support of national workers, short-term programs, missionary training and youth programs.

Purpose: "...to proclaim and demonstrate in word and deed the Gospel of Jesus Christ in conjunction with the local church."
Year Founded in US: 1990
Income for Overseas Min: $48,000.00
Fully Supported US Personnel Overseas:
Expecting to serve more than 4 years: 18
Non-residential mission personnel: 4
Other personnel:
Short-term less than 1 year: 35
Non-US serving in own/other country: 18
Countries: Albania; Asia—General 13; India 2; Nepal 2; Romania 1

Celebrant Singers

PO Box 1416
Visalia, CA 93291 USA

Phone: (559) 740-4000
Fax: (559) 740-4040
E-mail: celebrants@celebrants.org
Web Site: www.celebrants.org

Mr. Jon F. Stemkoski, Founder/President

An interdenominational service agency of Charismatic and Evangelical tradition engaged in music ministry evangelism, audio recording/distribution and broadcasting. Data from 2001.

Purpose: "...teaching young adults by proclaiming His greatness and sharing His love with a hurting world through music, testimony, the preaching of the Word and our lives."

Year Founded in US: 1977

Income for Overseas Min: $1,200,000.00

Fully Supported US Personnel Overseas:
Non-residential mission personnel: 44

Other personnel:
Short-term less than 1 year: 125
Home ministry & office staff in US: 22

Centers for Apologetics Research (CFAR), The

PO Box 1196
San Juan Capistrano, CA 92693 USA
Phone: (949) 496-2000
Fax: (949) 496-2244
E-mail: thecenters@aol.com
Web Site: www.thecenters.org

Mr. Paul Carden, Exec. Director

A transdenominational service agency of Evangelical tradition engaged in apologetics, evangelism, literature production, mission-related research, training and discipleship.

Purpose: "...to equip God's people across borders and cultures for discernment, the defense of the faith, and cult evangelism."

Year Founded in US: 1995

Personnel:
Short-term less than 1 year: 1
Non-US serving in own/other country: 8
Home ministry & office staff in US: 2

Countries: Brazil; Hungary; Russia; Ukraine

Central Yearly Meeting of Friends Missions

PO Box 542
Westfield, IN 46074 USA
Phone: (317) 896-5082

Web Site: www.centralyearlymeetingof-friends.org

Rev. Joseph A. Enyart, President

A denominational sending agency of Friends tradition engaged in church planting, Bible distribution and evangelism. Data from 2005.

Year Founded in US: 1925

Child Evangelism Fellowship, Inc.

PO Box 348
Warrenton, MO 63383 USA
Phone: (636) 456-4321
Fax: (636) 456-5000
E-mail: intlmin@cefonline.com
Web Site: www.cefonline.com

Mr. Reese R. Kauffman, President

A sending agency of Independent tradition engaged in evangelism, childrens programs, literature distribution, literature production, partnership development and training. Field personnel from 2002.

Purpose: "...to evangelize boys and girls... and establish them in the Word of God and the local church..."

Year Founded in US: 1937

Income for Overseas Min: $4,663,827.00

Fully Supported US Personnel Overseas:
Expecting to serve more than 4 years: 69
Expecting to serve 1 to 4 years: 3

Other personnel:
Short-term less than 1 year: 31
Non-US serving in own/other country: 196
Home ministry & office staff in US: 132

Countries: Albania 1; Angola; Argentina 1; Armenia 2; Australia 2; Austria 1; Belgium 2; Belize 2; Benin; Bolivia; Botswana 1; Brazil; Burkina Faso; Burundi; Cameroon; Congo, Democratic Republic of; Cote d'Ivoire; Chad; Chile; Colombia; Croatia 2; Cuba; Cyprus 7; Denmark 2; Ecuador; El Salvador; Estonia; Fiji 3; France 2; Gambia, The 2; Germany 4; Ghana; Greece 2; Guatemala; Guinea; Haiti 2; Hong Kong 1; Hungary 1; Israel 2; Japan; Jordan; Kenya 5; Liberia; Macau; Madagascar; Malawi; Mali; Mexico 1; Micronesia, Federated States of 2; Moldova 1; Mozambique; Namibia 3; Nepal; Netherlands Antilles 2; Niger; Nigeria; Pakistan; Peru; Philippines; Poland; Russia; Serbia and Montenegro 2; Singapore; Slovakia; Slovenia; South Africa 3; Suriname; Switzerland 6; Taiwan 2; Thailand; Togo; Uganda; Ukraine; Zambia; Zimbabwe

Childcare Worldwide

PO Box W
Bellingham, WA 98227 USA

Phone: (360) 647-2283
Fax: (360) 647-2392
E-mail: smiddleton@childcareworldwide.org
Web Site: www.childcareworldwide.org
Mr. G. Max Lange, President/Founder

A nondenominational service agency of Evangelical tradition engaged in child sponsorship, education, church/sch. general Christian, childcare/orphanage programs, children at risk, medical work and relief and/or rehabilitation.

Purpose: "...to build a bridge between concerned people in the West and children in the developing world...to help meet their spiritual and physical needs through a ministry that emphasizes education and is based on the Gospel of Jesus Christ."

Year Founded in US: 1981
Income for Overseas Min: $13,167,522.00
Gifts in Kind: $11,615,679.00
Personnel:
  Non-US serving in own/other country: 275
  Home ministry & office staff in US: 19
Countries: Haiti; India; Kenya; Liberia; Mexico; Peru; Philippines; Sri Lanka; Thailand; Uganda

Children of Promise Intl.

6844 Loop Rd.
Centerville, OH 45459-2159 USA

Phone: (888) 667-7426
Fax: (937) 438-4972
E-mail: info@promise.org
Web Site: www.promise.org
Mr. Robert J. Engimann, President

A sending agency of Evangelical tradition engaged in childcare/orphanage programs, evangelism, funds transmission and support of national workers.

Purpose: "...to care for orphans and love them into the Kingdom."

Year Founded in US: 1973

Income for Overseas Min: $994,559.00
Fully Supported US Personnel Overseas:
  Expecting to serve more than 4 years: 16
  Expecting to serve 1 to 4 years: 8
  Non-residential mission personnel: 7
Countries: Costa Rica 3; Guatemala 1; Haiti 6; Mexico 5; Venezuela 1

Children's Christian Concern Society

1000 SW 10th Ave.
Topeka, KS 66604 USA

Phone: (785) 357-7688
Fax: (785) 357-5071
E-mail: cccs@kslcms.org
Web Site: www.cccskids.org
Mr. David W. Saving, Exec. Director

A sending agency of Lutheran tradition engaged in Christian education, Bible distribution, childcare/orphanage programs, theological education, support of national churches and relief and/or rehabilitation.

Purpose: "...to share the love of Jesus with children throughout the world through Christian education."

Year Founded in US: 1968
Income for Overseas Min: $381,963.00
Fully Supported US Personnel Overseas:
  Non-residential mission personnel: 2
Other personnel:
  Short-term less than 1 year: 8
  Home ministry & office staff in US: 4
Countries: Africa—General; Bangladesh; Bolivia; Chad; El Salvador; Guatemala; Guinea; Haiti; Honduras; Israel; Liberia; Mexico; Nicaragua; Panama; Paraguay; Sierra Leone; Thailand; Uruguay; Venezuela

Children's Haven Intl.

400 E. Minnesota
Pharr, TX 78577 USA

Phone: (956) 787-7378
Fax: (956) 783-4637
E-mail: chii@childrenshaven.org
Web Site: www.childrenshaven.org
Elizabeth Chacon, General Director

A nondenominational service agency of Mennonite tradition engaged in childcare/orphanage programs, services for other agencies and short-term programs. Data from 2001.

Year Founded in US: 1972
Fully Supported US Personnel Overseas:
  Expecting to serve more than 4 years: 2
  Non-residential mission personnel: 12
Other personnel:
  Short-term less than 1 year: 4
Countries: Mexico 2

Children's HopeChest
9240 Explorer Dr., Ste. 202
Colorado Springs, CO 80920 USA
Phone: (719) 487-7800
Fax: (719) 487-7799
E-mail: bobmudd@hopechest.org
Web Site: www.hopechest.org
Mr. Tom Davis, CEO/President

A nondenominational support agency of
Evangelical tradition engaged in orphan
sponsorship programs, childcare/orphan-
age programs, children at risk, discipleship,
HIV/Aids and mobilization for mission.

Purpose: "...to respond to God's desire to
create a world where every orphan knows
Him, experiences the blessing of family,
and acquires the skills necessary for inde-
pendent life."
Year Founded in US: 1994
Income for Overseas Min: $3,398,782.00
Gifts in Kind: $234,520.00
Fully Supported US Personnel Overseas:
  Expecting to serve more than 4 years: 1
Other personnel:
  Short-term less than 1 year: 480
  Non-US serving in own/other country: 162
  Home ministry & office staff in US: 13
Countries: Ethiopia; Russia 1; Swaziland;
Uganda

Children's Intl. Lifeline
194 Sunset Dr.
Clay City, KY 40312 USA
Phone: (606) 663-3459
Fax: (606) 663-2175
E-mail: missionlifeline@bellsouth.net
Web Site: www.childrenslifeline.com
Mr. Donald L. Curtis, President/CEO

A nondenominational specialized agency
of Independent tradition engaged in childrens programs, church planting, Christian
education, evangelism, medical work and
short-term programs.

Purpose: "...to provide solid Bible teach-
ing, food, clothing, medical supplies, facil-
ities and educational assistance for the un-
derprivileged children and their families in
underdeveloped areas in Haiti."
Year Founded in US: 1989
Fully Supported US Personnel Overseas:
  Expecting to serve 1 to 4 years: 2
  Non-residential mission personnel: 2
Other personnel:
  Home ministry & office staff in US: 5
Countries: Haiti

Children's Ministry International, Inc. (CMI)
2368 Main St., Ste. #3
Tucker, GA 30084-8523 USA
Phone: (770) 493-8952
Fax: (770) 908-0849
E-mail: childrensministry1@earthlink.net
Web Site: www.childministry.com
Mr. Brad Winsted, Director

A specialized agency of Presbyterian and
Reformed tradition engaged in childrens
programs, Christian education, evangelism,
support of national churches, services for
other agencies and short-term programs.

Purpose: "...to develop and distribute chil-
dren's materials, translate materials with
the help of missionaries and nationals, and
teach missionary children at missionary re-
gional conferences."
Year Founded in US: 1982
Income for Overseas Min: $35,000.00
Personnel:
  Short-term less than 1 year: 20
  Home ministry & office staff in US: 2

Childspring International
1328 Peachtree St. NE
Atlanta, GA 30309-3902 USA
Phone: (404) 201-6450
Fax: (404) 228-7759
Web Site: www.childspringintl.org
Associations: The Mission Exchange
Mrs. Rose Emily Bermudez, Exec. Director

A denominational support agency of Christian (Restoration Movement) tradition
engaged in medical work and partnership

development.

Purpose: "...to become internationally recognized as the leading facilitator of medical care for children in need, resulting in 5,000 transformed lives throughout the global community by 2020."

Year Founded in US:

Fully Supported US Personnel Overseas:
Non-residential mission personnel: 4

Other personnel:
Home ministry & office staff in US: 10

China Connection
458 S. Pasadena Ave.
Pasadena, CA 91105 USA
Phone: (626) 793-3737
Fax: (626) 793-3362
E-mail: kathycall@sbcglobal.net
Web Site: www.chinaconnection.org
Ms. Kathy Call, Executive Director

A nondenominational support agency of Evangelical tradition engaged in missions information service, agricultural programs, Bible distribution, church construction, childcare/orphanage programs and medical work. Data from 2003.

Year Founded in US: 1989

Income for Overseas Min: $340,871.00

Gifts in Kind: $65,834.00

Personnel:
Home ministry & office staff in US: 1

China Ministries International
1605 E. Elizabeth St.
Pasadena, CA 91104 USA
Phone: (626) 398-2343
Fax: (626) 398-2361
E-mail: samuelchao@msn.com
Web Site: www.cmius.org
Mr. Samuel H. Chao, President

A nondenominational support agency of Evangelical tradition engaged in theological education, Bible distribution, evangelism, support of national workers, training and missionary training.

Purpose: "...for the evangelization of China, the strengthening of the Chinese Church...by engaging in ministries of research, training of workers and sending them to the harvest field..."

Year Founded in US: 1987

Income for Overseas Min: $522,376.00

Fully Supported US Personnel Overseas:
Expecting to serve more than 4 years: 8
Non-residential mission personnel: 2

Other personnel:
Short-term less than 1 year: 20
Non-US serving in own/other country: 8
Home ministry & office staff in US: 6

Countries: Asia—General 8

China Outreach Ministries, Inc.
555 Gettysburg Pike, Ste. A200
Mechanicsburg, PA 17055 USA
Phone: (717) 591-3500
Fax: (717) 591-0412
E-mail: chinaout@aol.com
Web Site: www.chinaoutreach.net
Rev. Glendon W. Osborn, President

An interdenominational support agency of Evangelical tradition engaged in evangelism.

Purpose: "...to focus on giving Christ to China's future leaders by showing them the love of Christ and by leading them to faith in Christ...to disciple, train, mentor, and equip them to minister creatively to other Chinese people."

Year Founded in US: 1949

Income for Overseas Min: $105,639.00

Fully Supported US Personnel Overseas:
Expecting to serve more than 4 years: 2
Non-residential mission personnel: 2

Other personnel:
Short-term less than 1 year: 8
Non-US serving in own/other country: 2
Home ministry & office staff in US: 10

Countries: Asia—General 2

China Service Ventures
1407 Cleveland Ave. N.
St. Paul, MN 55108 USA
Phone: (651) 659-1396
Fax: (651) 659-1397
E-mail: chinaserviceventures@hotmail.com
Web Site: www.chinaserviceventures.org
Mr. Paul Ofstedal, President

A denominational sending agency of Lutheran tradition engaged in childrens education, childrens programs, development, medical work and youth programs.

Purpose: "...to foster enriching relationships between Christian communities and individuals in North America with individuals and communities in China."
Year Founded in US: 2003
Income for Overseas Min: $380,000.00
Fully Supported US Personnel Overseas:
   Expecting to serve more than 4 years: 3
   Expecting to serve 1 to 4 years: 2
   Non-residential mission personnel: 2
Other personnel:
   Short-term less than 1 year: 30
   Non-US serving in own/other country: 2
   Home ministry & office staff in US: 1
Countries: China 3

ChinaSource
PO Box 4343
Fullerton, CA 92834-4343 USA
Phone: (714) 974-2400
Fax: (714) 974-2422
E-mail: info@chsource.org
Web Site: www.chsource.org
Dr. Brent Fulton, President
A specialized agency of Evangelical tradition engaged in partnership development and mission-related research. Founded as a cooperative effort of the EFMA, IFMA, WEF, Chinese Coordination Centre for World Evangelization, and the Billy Graham Center at Wheaton College.
Purpose: "...to identify critical issues, formulate strategies, convene resources, and evaluate results to advance the Kingdom of God in China."
Year Founded in US: 1995
Income for Overseas Min: $22,319.00
Fully Supported US Personnel Overseas:
   Expecting to serve more than 4 years: 1
Other personnel:
   Short-term less than 1 year: 2
   Home ministry & office staff in US: 4
Countries: China 1

Chosen Mission Project
3638 W. 26th St.
Erie, PA 16506 USA
Phone: (814) 833-3023
Fax: (814) 833-4091
E-mail: rick@chosenmissionproject.com

Web Site: www.chosenmissionproject.com
Mr. Rick King, Exec. Director
A nondenominational specialized agency of Evangelical tradition engaged in supplying equipment, providing medical supplies and technical assistance. Data from 2005.
Purpose: "...to promote health care programs in conjunction with missionaries and national Christian health care workers in a tangible effort to bring the love of Christ to those least able to help themselves."
Year Founded in US: 1969
Gifts in Kind: $787,622.00
Personnel:
   Home ministry & office staff in US: 4

Chosen People Ministries
241 E. 51st St.
New York, NY 10022 USA
Phone: (212) 223-2252
Fax: (212) 223-2581
E-mail: dsedaca@chosenpeople.com
Web Site: www.chosenpeople.com
Associations: CrossGlobal Link
Dr. Mitch Glaser, President/CEO
An interdenominational service agency of Evangelical and Messianic Jewish tradition engaged in evangelism, church planting, theological education, literature distribution, literature production and short-term programs.
Purpose: "...to evangelize and disciple Jewish people and to help the greater body of Messiah to do the same."
Year Founded in US: 1894
Income for Overseas Min: $624,287.00
Personnel:
   Short-term less than 1 year: 54
   Non-US serving in own/other country: 55
   Home ministry & office staff in US: 94
Countries: Argentina; Australia; France; Germany; Hong Kong; Israel; New Zealand; Russia; Ukraine; United Kingdom

Christ Community Church
2500 Dowie Dr.
Zion, IL 60099 USA
Phone: (847) 746-1411
E-mail: mmcdowell@ccczion.org
Web Site: www.ccczion.org

Dr. Mike McDowell, Missions Pastor

A nondenominational sending agency of Evangelical tradition engaged in partnership development, camping programs, church planting, discipleship, support of national workers, short-term programs and TESOL.

Purpose: "...to make known and promote the worship of God in obedience to the Great Commission and great commandments."

Year Founded in US: 1896

Income for Overseas Min: $325,000.00

Fully Supported US Personnel Overseas:
  Expecting to serve more than 4 years: 8
  Expecting to serve 1 to 4 years: 3

Other personnel:
  Short-term less than 1 year: 22
  Non-US serving in own/other country: 147
  Home ministry & office staff in US: 8

Countries: Guyana; Indonesia; Japan; Palestine; Philippines; South Africa 8

Christ for Children Intl.

PO Box 260
Wheaton, IL 60187-0260 USA

Phone: (205) 968-3004
E-mail: marydorset@aol.com
Web Site: www.christforchildren.com

Mary Dorsett, Exec. Director

An interdenominational sending agency of Anglican and Evangelical tradition engaged in Holistic care of impoverished families, children at risk, children's programs, discipleship and evangelism.

Year Founded in US: 1992

Income for Overseas Min: $217,000.00

Fully Supported US Personnel Overseas:
  Expecting to serve more than 4 years: 5
  Expecting to serve 1 to 4 years: 2

Other personnel:
  Non-US serving in own/other country: 3

Countries: Mexico 5

Christ for India, Inc.

PO Box 271086
Dallas, TX 75227 USA

Phone: (972) 771-7221
Fax: (972) 220-0069
E-mail: jtitus@christforindia.org
Web Site: www.christforindia.org

Mr. Jameson Titus, President

An interdenominational service agency of Charismatic and Pentecostal tradition engaged in theological education, childcare/orphanage programs, church construction, church planting, providing medical supplies and support of national workers.

Purpose: "...to fulfill Christ's Great Commission to India...to train nationals as pastors and evangelists...to establish native churches...to provide humanitarian aid...to educate India's future leaders."

Year Founded in US: 1981

Income for Overseas Min: $341,548.00

Fully Supported US Personnel Overseas:
  Expecting to serve more than 4 years: 1
  Non-residential mission personnel: 1

Other personnel:
  Short-term less than 1 year: 4
  Home ministry & office staff in US: 2

Countries: India 1

Christ for the City Intl.

PO Box 241827
Omaha, NE 68124-5827 USA

Phone: (402) 592-8332
Fax: (402) 592-8312
E-mail: info@cfci.org
Web Site: www.cfci.org

Associations: The Mission Exchange

Dr. Duane Anderson, President/CEO

An interdenominational sending agency of Evangelical tradition engaged in evangelism, childcare/orphanage programs, leadership development, children at risk, support of national churches and short-term programs. Countries of service data from 2005.

Purpose: "...to help people transform cities by transforming lives."

Year Founded in US: 1995

Income for Overseas Min: $1,165,000.00

Fully Supported US Personnel Overseas:
  Expecting to serve more than 4 years: 14
  Expecting to serve 1 to 4 years: 10
  Non-residential mission personnel: 2

Other personnel:
  Short-term less than 1 year: 25
  Non-US serving in own/other country: 63
  Home ministry & office staff in US: 1

Countries: Bolivia; Colombia 2; Costa Rica 7; Mali; Mexico; Nicaragua; Peru 1; Spain 2

Christ for the Nations, Inc.

3404 Conway St.
Dallas, TX 75224 USA
Phone: (214) 376-1711
Fax: (214) 302-6301
E-mail: info@cfni.org
Web Site: www.cfni.org

Dr. Dennis Lindsay, President/CEO

An interdenominational support agency
of Pentecostal tradition engaged in missionary education, church construction,
theological education, evangelism, literature distribution and literature production.
Data from 2005.

Purpose: "...to provide resources for the
completion of church buildings, caring
for orphans, supporting the nation of Israel, humanitarian relief efforts, establishing and strengthening international Bible
schools and the distribution of Christian
literature."

Year Founded in US: 1948

Income for Overseas Min: $1,500,000.00

Personnel:
 Short-term less than 1 year: 400
 Home ministry & office staff in US: 110

Christ to the Nations

PO Box 236713
Cocoa, FL 32923 USA
Phone: (321) 504-0778
Fax: (321) 504-0778
E-mail: harvesttoday@aol.com
Web Site: www.cttn.org

Dr. David L. Ralston, Founder/President

A sending agency of Baptist and Independent tradition engaged in support of
national workers, childcare/orphanage
programs, church planting, theological education, evangelism and missionary training.

Purpose: "...to help local churches and
God's people reach the unreached millions
with the Gospel of Jesus Christ and the
Word of God."

Year Founded in US: 1991

Income for Overseas Min: $180,000.00

Gifts in Kind: $5,000.00

Fully Supported US Personnel Overseas:
 Expecting to serve more than 4 years: 8
 Non-residential mission personnel: 2

Other personnel:
 Non-US serving in own/other country: 52
 Home ministry & office staff in US: 1

Countries: Bahamas, The 4; Caribbean—
General 2; India; Lithuania; Nigeria; Pakistan; Philippines; Uganda; Ukraine 2

Christar

(See ad on page 139)

PO Box 14866
Reading, PA 19612-4866 USA
Phone: (800) 755-7955
Fax: (610) 375-6862
E-mail: info@christar.org
Web Site: www.christar.org

Associations: CrossGlobal Link

Dr. Robert Kilgore, U.S. Director

An interdenominational sending agency
of Evangelical and Independent tradition
engaged in church planting, discipleship,
evangelism and language/culture studies.

Purpose: "...to glorify God by establish-
ing churches among the least-reached
Buddhists, Hindus, Muslims, and other
Asians worldwide."

Year Founded in US: 1930

Income for Overseas Min: $11,509,962.00

Fully Supported US Personnel Overseas:
 Expecting to serve more than 4 years: 235
 Expecting to serve 1 to 4 years: 2
 Non-residential mission personnel: 4

Other personnel:
 Short-term less than 1 year: 40
 Non-US serving in own/other country: 39
 Home ministry & office staff in US: 95

Countries: Africa—General 12; Albania 12;
Asia—General 11; China 38; France 13;
Germany 3; India 26; Japan 13; Jordan 13;
Kazakhstan 8; Middle East 15; Mongolia 1;
Netherlands 5; Pakistan 4; Philippines 17;
Sudan; Turkey 37; United Kingdom 7

Christian Aid Ministries (CAM)

PO Box 360
Berlin, OH 44610 USA
Phone: (330) 893-2428
Fax: (330) 893-2305
E-mail: cam@camoh.org

Mr. David N. Troyer, Gen. Director

A service agency of Mennonite tradition

Two thirds is not enough.

We refuse to leave the last third hanging.

One in three of the world's people—**2.7 billion**—have no access to the gospel in a way they can understand.

Does this bother you as much as it bothers us?

At Christar our passion is to glorify God by establishing churches among the very least-reached—Buddhists, Hindus, Muslims and other Asians worldwide. We work to cultivate Christ-honoring transformation in communities where he isn't being worshipped—yet.

Is this your passion, too?

Bringing light to the least-reached

www.christar.org
800-755-7955

engaged in relief and/or rehabilitation, Bible distribution, childcare/orphanage programs, literature distribution and medical work.

Purpose: "...to help and encourage God's people...to help bring the Gospel to a lost and dying world."

Year Founded in US: 1981

Income for Overseas Min: $183,415,214.00

Gifts in Kind: $161,893,562.00

Fully Supported US Personnel Overseas:
Expecting to serve more than 4 years: 16
Expecting to serve 1 to 4 years: 47

Other personnel:
Short-term less than 1 year: 15
Non-US serving in own/other country: 265
Home ministry & office staff in US: 63

Countries: Haiti 11; Israel; Liberia 3; Moldova; Nicaragua; Romania; Ukraine 2

Christian Aid Mission

1201 Fifth St. Extended
Charlottesville, VA 22902 USA

Phone: (434) 977-5650
Fax: (434) 295-6814
E-mail: info@christianaid.org
Web Site: www.christianaid.org

Mr. Robert V. Finley, Chairman

A nondenominational service agency of Evangelical and Fundamental tradition engaged in providing financial support for indigenous missionary ministries in poorer countries, church planting, evangelism, support of national workers, support of national churches, and missionary training.

Purpose: "...to provide financial assistance to indigenous evangelical missionary ministries in lands of great poverty, or where Christians are a persecuted minority."

Year Founded in US: 1953

Income for Overseas Min: $10,566,602.00

Personnel:
Short-term less than 1 year: 26
Non-US serving in own/other country: 11,036
Home ministry & office staff in US: 19

Countries: Albania; Algeria; Argentina; Australia; Bangladesh; Belarus; Benin; Burkina Faso; Bhutan; Bolivia; Brazil; Bulgaria; Burundi; Cambodia; Cameroon; Chad; Chile; China; Colombia; Congo, Democratic Republic of; Cote d'Ivoire; Cuba; Czech Republic; Ecuador; Egypt; Equatorial Guinea; Eritrea; Europe—General; Gabon; Gambia, The; Germany; Ghana; Guatemala; Guinea; Guinea-Bissau; Honduras; Hungary; India; Indonesia; Iraq; Jordan; Kazakhstan; Kenya; Kyrgyzstan; Laos; Lebanon; Liberia; Libya; Malawi; Mali; Mauritania; Mexico; Morocco; Mozambique; Myanmar/Burma; Nepal; Niger; Nigeria; Pakistan; Palestine; Papua New Guinea; Paraguay; Peru; Philippines; Poland; Russia; Senegal; Sierra Leone; South Africa; Sri Lanka; Sudan; Syria; Tanzania; Thailand; Togo; Uganda; Ukraine; Uruguay; Uzbekistan; Vietnam; Western Sahara; Zambia; Zimbabwe

Christian and Missionary Alliance, The

PO Box 35000
Colorado Springs, CO 80935-3500 USA

Phone: (719) 599-5999
Fax: (719) 599-8346
E-mail: im@cmalliance.org
Web Site: www.cmalliance.org

Dr. Gary M. Benedict, President

A denominational sending agency of Evangelical tradition engaged in church planting, discipleship, theological education, evangelism and leadership development.

Purpose: "...to know Jesus Christ as Savior, sanctifier, healer, second coming King and to complete His Great Commission."

Year Founded in US: 1887

Income for Overseas Min: $35,004,056.00

Fully Supported US Personnel Overseas:
Expecting to serve more than 4 years: 888

Other personnel:
Home ministry & office staff in US: 14

Countries: Africa—General 182; Asia—General 287; Central Asia—General 28; Europe—General 186; Latin America—General 144; Unspecified Country 61

Christian Associates Intl.

1534 N. Moorpark Rd. #356
Thousand Oaks, CA 91360 USA

Phone: (818) 865-1816
Fax: (818) 865-0317
E-mail: usoffice@christianassociates.org
Web Site: www.christianassociates.org

Dr. Linus J. Morris, President

A transdenominational sending agency of Evangelical tradition engaged in church planting and support of national churches, with 150 missionaries. Data from 2005.

Purpose: "...to reach the unchurched through the multiplication of high-impact leaders and high-impact churches."

Year Founded in US: 1968

Personnel:
Short-term less than 1 year: 100
Home ministry & office staff in US: 17

Countries: Belgium; Czech Republic; France; Germany; Ireland; Italy; Latvia; Netherlands; Poland; Portugal; Romania; Russia; Spain; Sweden; Switzerland; United Kingdom

Christian Aviation and Radio Mission

PO Box 514
Ankeny, IA 50021-0514 USA
Phone: (515) 480-9099
Fax: (515) 967-7128
E-mail: carmstan@aol.com
Web Site: www.carm-intl.org

Mr. Stanley Smelser, Admin./Mission Rep.

A nondenominational specialized agency of Christian (Restoration Movement) tradition engaged in audio recording/distribution, aviation services, broadcasting, leadership development, supplying equipment and technical assistance. Data from 2005.

Purpose: "...to strive to take on the responsibility of meeting the logistical and technical needs...in order to allow the ministers, evangelists and missionaries to give their attention to prayer and the ministry of the Word."

Year Founded in US: 1989

Income for Overseas Min: $27,476.00

Personnel:
Short-term less than 1 year: 1
Non-US serving in own/other country: 4

Countries: Philippines

Christian Blind Mission International (CBM-US)

450 E. Park Ave.
Greenville, SC 29602 USA
Phone: (864) 239-0065
Fax: (864) 239-0069
E-mail: info@cbm.org
Web Site: www.cbmus.org

Mr. Ron Nabors, CEO

A service agency engaged in disability assistance programs, development, leadership development and relief and/or rehabilitation. Countries of service data from 2005.

Purpose: "...to improve the quality of life of people with disabilities and those at risk of disability living in the world's most disadvantaged societies."

Year Founded in US: 1976

Income for Overseas Min: $28,038,213.00

Gifts in Kind: $26,405,186.00

Fully Supported US Personnel Overseas:
Expecting to serve more than 4 years: 1
Expecting to serve 1 to 4 years: 18

Other personnel:
Home ministry & office staff in US: 8

Countries: Cameroon; Congo, Republic of the; Dominican Republic; Ecuador; Jordan; Kenya; Madagascar; Nigeria; Pakistan; Papua New Guinea; Philippines; Tanzania 1; Thailand; Togo; Uganda

Christian Broadcasting Network Inc., The

977 Centerville Turnpike
Virginia Beach, VA 23463 USA
Phone: (757) 226-7000
Fax: (757) 226-2169
Web Site: www.cbn.com

Mr. Gordon Robertson, CEO

An interdenominational sending agency of Evangelical tradition engaged in broadcasting, radio and/or TV and video/film production/distribution. Countries of service data from 2005.

Purpose: "...to prepare the nations of the world for the coming of Jesus Christ and the establishment of His Kingdom on earth."

Year Founded in US: 1960

Income for Overseas Min: $128,854,919.00

Gifts in Kind: $100,795,335.00

Fully Supported US Personnel Overseas:
Expecting to serve more than 4 years: 6
Expecting to serve 1 to 4 years: 9
Non-residential mission personnel: 7

Other personnel:
Non-US serving in own/other country: 853
Home ministry & office staff in US: 1,288

Countries: Brazil; Cambodia; China 1; Costa Rica; Ghana; Hong Kong; India; Indonesia 1; Kazakhstan; Mexico; Nigeria; Philippines; Russia; Senegal 2; Singapore; South Africa; Thailand 1; Ukraine 1; United Kingdom

Christian Church (Disciples of Christ)—Global Ministries

PO Box 1986
Indianapolis, IN 46206 USA
Phone: (317) 709-8162
Fax: (317) 635-4323
E-mail: dom@disciples.org
Web Site: www.globalministries.org
Associations: CWS

Mr. David Vargas, Co-Executive

A denominational sending agency of Christian (Restoration Movement) and Congregational tradition engaged in support of national churches, development, Christian education, theological education, leadership development and partnership development. Working in partnership with United Church of Christ Global Ministries. Statistics include United Church of Christ Global Ministries.

Purpose: "...committed to a ministry of critical presence where we meet God's people and creation at the point of deepest need: spiritually, physically, emotionally, and/or economically."

Year Founded in US: 1849
Income for Overseas Min: $3,760,519.00
Fully Supported US Personnel Overseas:
  Expecting to serve 1 to 4 years: 49
Other personnel:
  Short-term less than 1 year: 12
  Home ministry & office staff in US: 43

Countries: Angola; Botswana; Chile; China; Colombia; East Timor; Egypt; Guadeloupe; Guatemala; Haiti; Hong Kong; Hungary; India; Indonesia; Japan; Kenya; Laos; Lesotho; Mexico; Palestine; Poland; South Africa; Thailand; Turkey; Venezuela; Zimbabwe

Christian Churches/ Churches of Christ

C/O Missions Resource Network
4001 Airport FWY, Ste. 550
Bedford, TX 76021 USA

A body of autonomous congregations and agencies of Christian (Restoration Movement) tradition (using instrumental music in worship) which sends and supports missionaries directly from local congregations. Data provided by Missions Resource Network (all information based upon best estimates for an independent brotherhood of churches). No central office. Data from 2005.

Income for Overseas Min: $52,000,000.00
Fully Supported US Personnel Overseas:
  Expecting to serve more than 4 years: 915
  Expecting to serve 1 to 4 years: 100
  Non-residential mission personnel: 50
Other personnel:
  Short-term less than 1 year: 2000
  Non-US serving in own/other country: 422

Countries: Africa—General 4; Asia—General 6; Argentina 4; Australia 20; Austria 6; Bahamas, The 2; Bangladesh; Barbados 6; Belgium 1; Bosnia and Herzegovina 2; Brazil 28; Cayman Islands 2; Chile 32; Cote d'Ivoire 6; Czech Republic 2; Dominica 5; Dominican Republic 12; Ecuador 4; Equatorial Guinea 2; Ethiopia 8; France 5; Germany 8; Ghana 13; Grenada 2; Guatemala 2; Guinea 15; Guyana; Haiti 4; Honduras 19; Hong Kong 10; India 17; Indonesia 15; Ireland 6; Israel 2; Italy 14; Jamaica 12; Japan 30; Kenya 35; Korea, South 4; Kosovo 2; Liberia 2; Mali 2; Mexico 50; Mozambique 6; Myanmar/Burma; New Zealand 8; Nigeria 2; Pakistan; Panama 2; Papua New Guinea 30; Philippines 40; Poland 2; Portugal 4; Puerto Rico 5; Russia 16; Singapore 4; South Africa 32; Spain 1; Taiwan 21; Tanzania 21; Thailand 41; Ukraine 30; United Kingdom 20; Unspecified Country 160; Venezuela 15; Zimbabwe 34

Christian Cultural Development Foundation

417 NE Third Ave
Fort Lauderdale, FL 33301 USA
Phone: (954) 828-1505
E-mail: robin@christiancultural.com
Web Site: www.christiancultural.com

Robin Haines Merrill, Founder/Director

An interdenominational service agency of Ecumenical and Evangelical tradition engaged in development, evangelism, prostitution ministry, justice, leadership development and support of national workers. Data from 2005.

Purpose: "...to provide creative alternatives to prostitutes and street children in the Philippines who want to change their lifestyles and follow Jesus Christ."

Year Founded in US: 1990

Income for Overseas Min: $14,408.00

Gifts in Kind: $2,000.00

Fully Supported US Personnel Overseas:
  Expecting to serve more than 4 years: 2
  Non-residential mission personnel: 1

Other personnel:
  Non-US serving in own/other country: 6
  Home ministry & office staff in US: 1

Countries: Philippines 2

Christian Dental Society

PO Box 296
Sumner, IA 50674 USA

Phone: (563) 578-8887
E-mail: info@christiandental.org
Web Site: www.christiandental.org

Dr. Robert F. Liebler, Exec. Director

An nondenominational specialized agency of Ecumenical tradition engaged in dental work, training local dentists in new techniques in 22 countries. Data from 2005.

Purpose: "...to carry out the Great Commission given by Christ in Matthew 28:19 & 20 through dentists and dentistry."

Year Founded in US: 1963

Personnel:
  Home ministry & office staff in US: 1

Christian Fellowship Union, Inc.

PO Box 909
McAllen, TX 78505 USA

Phone: (956) 686-5886
Fax: (956) 686-3049
E-mail: cfunion@sbcglobal.net
Mr. Steven P. Johnson, Gen. Director

An interdenominational support agency of Evangelical and Independent tradition engaged in leadership development, church planting, theological education, support of national churches, missionary training and discipleship.

Purpose: "...to proclaim Jesus Christ, make disciples, establish churches, and equip believers in Mexico and South Texas for worldwide ministry."

Year Founded in US: 1945

Income for Overseas Min: $22,562.00

Fully Supported US Personnel Overseas:
  Expecting to serve more than 4 years: 4
  Non-residential mission personnel: 2

Other personnel:
  Home ministry & office staff in US: 1

Countries: Mexico 2; Spain 2

Christian Flights Intl.

2150 Lexington Rd., Ste. J
Richmond, KY 40475 USA

Phone: (859) 623-6402
E-mail: scottmandl@aol.com
Web Site: www.christianflights.org

Mr. Scott Mandl, Exec. Director

A nondenominational sending agency of Ecumenical tradition engaged in Christian education, agricultural programs, development, medical work, short-term programs and supplying equipment.

Purpose: "...to further the Kingdom of God by providing resources and encouraging Haitians to facilitate wellness, community development, and excellence in education."

Year Founded in US: 1977

Income for Overseas Min: $298,000.00

Fully Supported US Personnel Overseas:
  Expecting to serve more than 4 years: 1
  Expecting to serve 1 to 4 years: 1

Other personnel:
  Short-term less than 1 year: 70
  Non-US serving in own/other country: 100
  Home ministry & office staff in US: 2

Countries: Haiti 1

Christian Involvement in Service (CIS)

PO Box 768
St. Joseph, MI 49085-0768 USA

Phone: (269) 429-0814
E-mail: jbettig@cisministries.org
Web Site: www.cisministries.org

Rev. John Bettig, President

An interdenominational support agency of Evangelical tradition engaged in support of national churches, church planting, Christian education, evangelism, support of national workers and relief and/or rehabilitation.

Purpose: "...to stimulate prayer and direct involvement in financing theological training of pastors in the CIS...to give financial support for missionaries and church planters...to give assistance in constructing new church buildings and to encourage, inform, inspire and instruct Christians regarding how they can be more involved in the Great Commission of Christ."

Year Founded in US: 2004

Income for Overseas Min: $67,400.00

Personnel:
  Short-term less than 1 year: 4
  Non-US serving in own/other country: 19

Countries: Russia; Ukraine

Christian Laymen's Missionary Evangelism Association

826 Ford St.
Prosser, WA 99350 USA
Phone: (509) 241-0530
E-mail: mhyh@clmea.com
Web Site: www.clmea.com
Mr. Larry Taylor, President

A support agency of Charismatic tradition engaged in evangelism, broadcasting, short-term programs and support of national workers. Data from 2005.

Purpose: "...to raise up laymen for world evangelism."

Year Founded in US: 1977

Income for Overseas Min: $2,982.00

Gifts in Kind: $300.00

Personnel:
  Short-term less than 1 year: 5
  Home ministry & office staff in US: 1

Christian Literacy Associates

541 Perry Highway
Pittsburgh, PA 15229-1851 USA
Phone: (412) 364-3777
E-mail: drliteracy@aol.com
Web Site: www.christianliteracy.com
Dr. William E. Kofmehl Jr., President

An interdenominational specialized agency of Ecumenical tradition engaged in literacy work.

Purpose: "...to develop basic reading program materials with Bible content...to train volunteers as reading tutors for children and

adults...to serve as consultants to churches, national churches, parachurch organizations, foreign missions and foreign governments."

Year Founded in US: 1975

Personnel:
  Home ministry & office staff in US: 4

Christian Literature Intl.

PO Box 777
Canby, OR 97266 USA
Phone: (503) 266-9734
Fax: (503) 266-1143
E-mail: newlife1@canby.com
Web Site: www.newlifebible.org
Joyce E. Moore, President

A nondenominational support agency of Evangelical tradition engaged in Bible distribution, literature distribution, literacy work and Bible translation.

Purpose: "...to publish and provide the Word of God in a form that can be read and understood by new readers and the well-educated alike...and at an affordable price."

Year Founded in US: 1967

Income for Overseas Min: $68,000.00

Personnel:
  Home ministry & office staff in US: 3

Christian Medical & Dental Associations

PO Box 7500
Bristol, TN 37621 USA
Phone: (423) 844-1000
Fax: (423) 764-1417
E-mail: gho@cmda.org
Web Site: www.cmda.org
Dr. David L. Stevens, CEO/CMDA

An interdenominational service agency of Evangelical tradition engaged in medical work, discipleship, Christian education, evangelism, leadership development and member care.

Purpose: "...to motivate, educate and equip Christian physicians and dentists to glorify God by living out the character of Christ in their homes, practices, communities, and around the world...."

Year Founded in US: 1931

Income for Overseas Min: $2,569,984.00

Gifts in Kind: $1,854,033.00

Fully Supported US Personnel Overseas:
Expecting to serve 1 to 4 years: 1
Other personnel:
Short-term less than 1 year: 1000
Home ministry & office staff in US: 66
Countries: Nicaragua

Christian Ministries International (CMI)

2615 Serenity Circle N
Port St. Lucie, FL 34981 USA
Phone: (772) 489-6721
Fax: (772) 489-6721
E-mail: lynnhood@cmimissions.com
Web Site: www.cmimissions.com
Dr. L. Lynn Hood, President

An interdenominational sending agency of Charismatic tradition engaged in leadership development, discipleship, theological education, management consulting/training, missionary training and training. Countries of service data from 2005.

Purpose: "...preparing national indigenous leaders of the local church to be empowered by New Testament principles of leadership to assist them in world evangelization and church planting in their generation."
Year Founded in US: 1985
Income for Overseas Min: $100,000.00
Gifts in Kind: $165,000.00
Fully Supported US Personnel Overseas:
Expecting to serve more than 4 years: 7
Non-residential mission personnel: 6
Other personnel:
Short-term less than 1 year: 127
Non-US serving in own/other country: 28
Home ministry & office staff in US: 6
Countries: Brazil 2; China 2; Colombia 2; Russia; Thailand 1; Ukraine

Christian Mission for the Deaf

PO Box 1651
Aledo, TX 76008 USA
Web Site: www.cmdeaf.org
Mrs. Berta Foster, Administrator

A denominational support agency of Brethren tradition engaged in Christian education, camping programs and funds transmission. Information from 2005.

Purpose: "...to organize, operate, maintain, promote and encourage Gospel and education work among the deaf of Africa."
Year Founded in US: 1956
Income for Overseas Min: $114,047.00
Fully Supported US Personnel Overseas:
Expecting to serve more than 4 years: 2
Other personnel:
Short-term less than 1 year: 1
Home ministry & office staff in US: 2
Countries: Congo, Democratic Republic of 2

Christian Missions in Many Lands, Inc.

PO Box 13
Spring Lake, NJ 07762-0013 USA
Phone: (732) 449-8880
Fax: (732) 974-0888
E-mail: cmml@cmmlusa.org
Web Site: www.cmmlusa.org
Mr. Thomas J. Turner, President

A nondenominational service agency of Christian/Plymouth Brethren tradition engaged in funds transmission and missions information service.

Purpose: "...to assist missionaries and to maintain an inviolable relationship to missionaries, assemblies and government authorities at home and abroad."
Year Founded in US: 1921
Income for Overseas Min: $12,700,000.00
Personnel:
Home ministry & office staff in US: 7

Christian Missions Unlimited

PO Box 58
Hope Hull, AL 36043 USA
Phone: (800) 355-1894
E-mail: info@christianmissions.org
Web Site: www.christianmissions.org
Mr. Charles Conner, Jr., Exec. Director

A specialized agency of Baptist tradition engaged in church construction, Bible distribution, evangelism, support of national workers, mobilization for mission and short-term programs. Data from 2001.

Purpose: "...church construction is the main focus."
Year Founded in US: 1973

Fully Supported US Personnel Overseas:
Non-residential mission personnel: 3

Other personnel:
Short-term less than 1 year: 300
Home ministry & office staff in US: 4

Countries: Brazil

Christian Outreach Intl.

PO Box 2823
Vero Beach, FL 32966 USA

Phone: (772) 778-0575
Fax: (888) 351-1318
E-mail: groupscoi@yahoo.com
Web Site: www.coiusa.com

Mary-Alice Isleib, Exec. Director

An interdenominational service agency of Charismatic and Evangelical tradition engaged in short-term programs, evangelism, relief and/or rehabilitation, sports program ministry and TESOL.

Purpose: "...a global mission network specializing in short-term projects that empower believers to action, volunteerism, leadership, full-time service, and disciplemaking through local and international outreach."

Year Founded in US: 1984

Fully Supported US Personnel Overseas:
Expecting to serve 1 to 4 years: 2

Other personnel:
Short-term less than 1 year: 1200
Non-US serving in own/other country: 8
Home ministry & office staff in US: 2

Countries: Asia—General; Dominican Republic; Honduras; Mexico; Ukraine

Christian Pilots Association

PO Box 90452
Los Angeles, CA 90009-0452 USA

Phone: (562) 208-2912
E-mail: info@christianpilots.org
Web Site: www.christianpilots.org

Mr. Andy Pike, Chairman

An interdenominational specialized agency of Evangelical tradition engaged in aviation services and providing medical supplies. Data from 2001.

Year Founded in US: 1972

Income for Overseas Min: $17,000.00

Gifts in Kind: $10,000.00

Christian Reformed World Missions

2850 Kalamazoo Ave., SE
Grand Rapids, MI 49560-0200 USA

Phone: (616) 224-0700
Fax: (616) 224-0707
E-mail: crwm@crcna.org
Web Site: www.crwm.org
Associations: The Mission Exchange

Dr. Gary J. Bekker, Director

A denominational sending agency of Evangelical tradition engaged in church planting, leadership development, Christian education, theological education, support of national churches and mobilization for mission. Countries of service data from 2005.

Purpose: "...to glorify God by leading the Christian Reformed Church (CRC) to respond obediently to our Lord's commission to witness to the Good News of God's Kingdom and make disciples of all nations."

Year Founded in US: 1888

Income for Overseas Min: $3,156,264.00

Fully Supported US Personnel Overseas:
Expecting to serve more than 4 years: 109
Expecting to serve 1 to 4 years: 25

Other personnel:
Home ministry & office staff in US: 20

Countries: Bangladesh; China 2; Costa Rica 3; Dominican Republic 8; El Salvador 1; France 2; Guinea 13; Haiti 4; Honduras 2; Hungary 5; Japan 12; Mali 6; Mexico 16; Nicaragua 2; Nigeria 22; Philippines 10; Russia 1

Christian Reformed World Relief Committee

2850 Kalamazoo Ave. SE
Grand Rapids, MI 49560 USA

Phone: (800) 552-7972
Fax: (616) 224-0806
E-mail: crwrc@crwrc.org
Web Site: www.crwrc.org
Associations: AERDO

Melissa Barnes, Chief Financial Officer

A denominational service agency of Reformed tradition engaged in relief and/or rehabilitation, agricultural programs, childrens programs, HIV/Aids, justice and literacy work.

Purpose: "...to engage God's people in redeeming resources and developing gifts in collaborative acts of love, mercy, justice, and compassion."

Year Founded in US: 1962

Income for Overseas Min: $100,000.00

Fully Supported US Personnel Overseas:
Expecting to serve more than 4 years: 12
Expecting to serve 1 to 4 years: 5
Non-residential mission personnel: 28

Other personnel:
Short-term less than 1 year: 84
Home ministry & office staff in US: 44

Countries: Bangladesh 1; Dominican Republic 1; Ecuador 2; Ghana; Haiti 1; Kenya 1; Laos; Malawi 2; Mali 1; Niger 1; Nigeria 1; Philippines 10; Russia 1

Christian Relief Fund, The

PO Box 19670
Amarillo, TX 79114 USA

Phone: (806) 352-5030
Fax: (806) 352-0251
E-mail: crfinfo@christianrelieffund.org
Web Site: www.christianrelieffund.org
Linda Purdy, Exec. Director

A sending agency of Christian (Restoration Movement) tradition engaged in child-care/orphanage programs, development, HIV/Aids and relief and/or rehabilitation.

Purpose: "...to follow Christ's example by feeding the hungry, healing disease and heartbreak, fighting ignorance and poverty through education, and preaching the Gospel through word and deed."

Year Founded in US: 1974

Income for Overseas Min: $2,783,995.00

Gifts in Kind: $1,787.00

Personnel:
Short-term less than 1 year: 2
Non-US serving in own/other country: 42
Home ministry & office staff in US: 10

Countries: Belarus; Dominican Republic; Ecuador; El Salvador; Ethiopia; Guatemala; Haiti; Honduras; India; Jamaica; Kenya; Liberia; Lithuania; Malawi; Mexico; Nicaragua; Niger; Nigeria; Romania; Uganda; Ukraine; Zambia; Zimbabwe

Christian Resources Intl.

PO Box 356
Fowlerville, MI 48836 USA
Phone: (517) 223-3193

Fax: (517) 223-7668
E-mail: admin@cribooks.org
Web Site: www.cribooks.org
Mr. Fred Palmerton, Exec. Director

A nondenominational specialized agency of Evangelical and Fundamental tradition engaged in literature distribution and Bible distribution, having reached 167 countries.

Purpose: "...to evangelize the world by distributing free Christian literature to spiritually-needy people."

Year Founded in US: 1956

Income for Overseas Min: $304,884.00

Personnel:
Short-term less than 1 year: 2
Home ministry & office staff in US: 9

Christian Union Churches of North America—Missions

PO Box 454
Liberty Corner, OH 43532 USA

Phone: (419) 237-2015
E-mail: joeroseredmond@juno.com
Web Site: www.christianunion.com
Rev. Marion Hunnerdosse, President

A sending agency of Evangelical tradition engaged in evangelism, broadcasting, camping programs, church construction, church planting and literature distribution. Data from 2005.

Year Founded in US: 1864

Fully Supported US Personnel Overseas:
Non-residential mission personnel: 5

Other personnel:
Short-term less than 1 year: 50
Home ministry & office staff in US: 2

ChristianCourses.Com

3000 Kraft Ave. SE
Grand Rapids, MI 49418 USA

Phone: (616) 942-6770
Fax: (616) 957-5741
Web Site: www.christiancourses.com
Mr. Evan Morgan, President

A nondenominational specialized agency of Evangelical tradition engaged in theological education, Christian education, TEE and leadership development.

Purpose: "...to provide affordable and accessible Christian worldview online learning opportunities to learners worldwide."

Year Founded in US: 1998

Personnel:
Home ministry & office staff in US: 5

Christians In Action Missions International

19880 Ave. 376
Woodlake, CA 93286 USA

Phone: (559) 564-3762
Fax: (559) 564-1231
E-mail: cinamissions@christiansinaction.org
Web Site: www.christiansinaction.org

Mr. Gordon Donoho, President/CEO

An interdenominational sending agency of Evangelical tradition engaged in evangelism, church planting, support of national churches, mobilization for mission, short-term programs and missionary training.

Purpose: "...to proclaim Christ to the nations by preparing and sending missionaries, planting indigenous churches, empowering national leaders, and personal evangelism."

Year Founded in US: 1957

Income for Overseas Min: $843,111.00

Fully Supported US Personnel Overseas:
Expecting to serve more than 4 years: 13

Other personnel:
Short-term less than 1 year: 15
Non-US serving in own/other country: 40
Home ministry & office staff in US: 5

Countries: Brazil 2; Colombia 2; Ecuador 2; Germany 1; Ghana; Guinea-Bissau; Guatemala 2; Honduras 1; India; Japan; Korea, South; Macau 1; Mexico; Peru; Philippines; Sierra Leone; United Kingdom 2

Christ's Mandate for Missions

375 Star Light Dr.
Ft. Mill, NC 29715 USA

Phone: (704) 225-3927
Fax: (888) 816-0725
E-mail: cmmarmy@gmail.com
Web Site: www.cmmissions.net

Dr. Jorge Parrott, President

An interdenominational service agency of Evangelical tradition engaged in support of national churches, childcare/orphanage programs, church planting, theological ed-

ucation, funds transmission, leadership development and support of national workers. Countries of service data from 2005.

Purpose: "...to equip leaders in many nations with the heart of the Father by connecting, strengthening, and expanding strategic relationships and stewarding donor relations with God's rising army of awakening people in all sectors of societies."

Year Founded in US: 1978

Income for Overseas Min: $525,000.00

Gifts in Kind: $10,000.00

Fully Supported US Personnel Overseas:
Expecting to serve more than 4 years: 17
Non-residential mission personnel: 275

Other personnel:
Short-term less than 1 year: 450
Non-US serving in own/other country: 287
Home ministry & office staff in US: 3

Countries: Bolivia; Dominican Republic; Ghana 5; Guatemala 5; Hong Kong 2; India; Mexico 5; Nigeria; Philippines; Spain; Thailand

Church Leadership Development International

8000 Research Forest Dr., Suite 115, #280
The Woodlands, TX 77382-1506 USA

Phone: (281) 363-2534
E-mail: admin@cldi.org
Web Site: www.cldi.org

Mr. Craig Ludrick, President

A nondenominational support agency of Evangelical tradition engaged in training pastors, church planting, leadership development and literature distribution. Data from 2005.

Purpose: "...to equip pastors in Eurasia and India with training, encouragement and resources to strengthen and multiply their churches."

Year Founded in US: 1996

Personnel:
Non-US serving in own/other country: 7
Home ministry & office staff in US: 1

Countries: Central Asia—General; Georgia; India; Ukraine

Church Ministries Intl.

2001 W. Plano Pkwy, Ste. 3100
Plano, TX 75075-8632 USA

Phone: (972) 941-4422

Fax: (972) 941-4422
E-mail: cmioffice@churchministries.org
Web Site: www.churchministries.org
James R. Murray, Exec. Director

An interdenominational support agency of Evangelical tradition engaged in church construction, church planting, partnership development, services for other agencies and training.

Purpose: "...to reach nations for Christ by serving as a catalyst for urban churches toward strategic planning, partnerships, leadership training, and ministries that address the goal of evangelizing and discipling entire countries."

Year Founded in US: 1989

Income for Overseas Min: $336,427.00

Personnel:
Home ministry & office staff in US: 6

Church Missions Link

PO Box 14175
Spokane Valley, WA 99214 USA

Phone: (509) 891-5595
Fax: (509) 924-8885
E-mail: churchmissionslink@gmail.com
Web Site: www.gracem.org
Rev. Ken Parker, Director

An interdenominational support agency of Evangelical and Independent tradition engaged in church missions development, leadership development, church planting, support of national workers, mission-related research, short-term programs and training.

Purpose: "...to expand the local church's vision for world missions through education."

Year Founded in US: 1998

Income for Overseas Min: $40,000.00

Gifts in Kind: $10,000.00

Fully Supported US Personnel Overseas:
Non-residential mission personnel: 1

Other personnel:
Short-term less than 1 year: 4
Home ministry & office staff in US: 1

Church of God (Anderson, Indiana), Global Missions

PO Box 2420
Anderson, IN 46018-2420 USA

Phone: (765) 648-2140

Fax: (765) 642-5652
E-mail: bedwards@chog.org
Web Site: www.chogmissions.org
Dr. Robert E. Edwards, Global Msns. Coordinator

A sending agency of Holiness and Wesleyan tradition engaged in leadership development, TEE, theological education, member care, support of national churches and missionary training.

Purpose: "...committed to world evangelism and discipleship, Global Missions will send missionaries, resource global ministry, and network through interdependent partnerships with the Church around the world."

Year Founded in US: 1909

Income for Overseas Min: $5,255,506.00

Fully Supported US Personnel Overseas:
Expecting to serve more than 4 years: 63
Expecting to serve 1 to 4 years: 10

Other personnel:
Short-term less than 1 year: 1700
Home ministry & office staff in US: 8

Countries: Asia—General 1; Belize 2; Bolivia 4; Bulgaria 2; Central Asia—General 1; Colombia; Cote d'Ivoire 5; Ecuador 4; Germany 3; Guam 2; Haiti 2; Hong Kong 2; Indonesia 2; Japan 6; Kenya 7; Malawi 1; New Zealand 4; Paraguay 2; Russia 2; Singapore 2; Tanzania 4; Thailand 2; Uganda 3

Church of God (Cleveland, Tenn.) World Missions

PO Box 8016
Cleveland, TN 37320-8016 USA

Phone: (423) 478-7190
Fax: (423) 478-7155
E-mail: kcooper@cogwm.org
Web Site: www.cogwm.org
Associations: The Mission Exchange
Dr. Douglas LeRoy, Gen. Director

A denominational sending agency of Pentecostal tradition engaged in church planting, childcare/orphanage programs, church construction, TEE, theological education and evangelism. Countries of service data from 2005.

Purpose: "...committed to obeying God by fulfilling Christ's Great Commission by proclaiming the Gospel through the power of the Holy Spirit to the unconverted everywhere and by discipling those Christ adds to His Kingdom."

Year Founded in US: 1910

Fully Supported US Personnel Overseas:
Expecting to serve more than 4 years: 159
Expecting to serve 1 to 4 years: 31
Non-residential mission personnel: 55

Other personnel:
Short-term less than 1 year: 98
Non-US serving in own/other country: 55
Home ministry & office staff in US: 66

Countries: Albania; Aruba 2; Australia; Austria 2; Bahrain; Belgium 5; Brazil 4; Bulgaria 1; Caribbean—General 2; Chile 3; China 6; Colombia 3; Croatia 2; Czech Republic 2; Ecuador 8; Europe—General 2; Fiji 2; France 3; Germany 10; Ghana 4; Greece 2; Guatemala 2; Haiti 2; Honduras 5; Indonesia 2; Ireland 4; Italy 2; Kenya 9; Liberia; Malaysia 4; Mexico; Nicaragua; Nigeria; Pakistan; Panama 2; Paraguay 2; Peru 2; Philippines 16; Romania 2; Russia 6; Singapore 2; South Africa 1; South America—General 2; Spain 4; Ukraine 3; United Kingdom; Unspecified Country 18; Venezuela 3; Vietnam; Zambia 3

Church of God (Holiness), World Mission Dept., Inc.

PO Box 4711
Overland Park, KS 66204 USA

Phone: (913) 432-0303
E-mail: worldmissions@cogh.net
Web Site: www.coghworldmissions.org

Mr. Silas McGehee, Exec. Secretary

A denominational sending agency of Holiness and Wesleyan tradition engaged in church planting, discipleship, Christian education, evangelism, support of national workers and Bible translation.

Purpose: "...to promote God's Kingdom through proclaiming the Gospel of Jesus Christ and providing opportunities to develop mission fields into self-propagating missionary forces."

Year Founded in US: 1917

Fully Supported US Personnel Overseas:
Expecting to serve more than 4 years: 2
Expecting to serve 1 to 4 years: 4

Other personnel:
Non-US serving in own/other country: 87
Home ministry & office staff in US: 2

Countries: Cayman Islands; Ghana; Haiti; India; Myanmar/Burma; Ukraine 2

Church of God (Seventh Day) General Conference— Missions Abroad

PO Box 33677
Denver, CO 80233 USA

Phone: (303) 452-7973
Fax: (303) 452-0657
E-mail: missions@cog7.org
Web Site: www.cog7.org

Mr. William C. Hicks, Missions Min. Director

A denominational support agency of Evangelical tradition engaged in funds transmission, Bible and literature distribution, and support of national churches in 16 countries. Data from 2001.

Year Founded in US: 1860

Income for Overseas Min: $109,950.00

Gifts in Kind: $30,000.00

Personnel:
Home ministry & office staff in US: 14

Church of God of Prophecy— Global Outreach

PO Box 2910
Cleveland, TN 37320-2910 USA

Phone: (423) 559-5100
Fax: (423) 472-5037
E-mail: Global@cogop.org
Web Site: www.cogop.org

Mr. Randy Howard, General Overseer

A denominational sending agency of Pentecostal tradition engaged in church planting, evangelism, leadership development, support of national churches and support of national workers. Data from 2001.

Year Founded in US: 1903

Income for Overseas Min: $2,000,000.00

Fully Supported US Personnel Overseas:
Expecting to serve more than 4 years: 15
Non-residential mission personnel: 8

Other personnel:
Short-term less than 1 year: 50
Non-US serving in own/other country: 352

Countries: Angola; Argentina; Australia 2; Azerbaijan; Barbados; Belarus; Belgium; Belize; Benin; Bermuda; Burkina Faso;

Bolivia; Botswana; Brazil; Bulgaria; Cameroon; Caribbean—General; Central African Republic; Chad; Chile; China 2; Colombia; Congo, Democratic Republic of; Congo, Republic of the; Costa Rica; Cote d'Ivoire; Cuba; Cyprus; Ecuador; Egypt; El Salvador; Ethiopia; Fiji; Finland; France; French Guiana; Gabon; Gambia, The; Germany 4; Greece; Guyana; Haiti; Hungary; India; Indonesia; Israel; Japan 2; Kazakhstan; Kenya; Korea, South; Liberia; Malawi; Malaysia; Malta; Mozambique; Namibia; Netherlands Antilles; New Zealand; Pakistan; Panama; Paraguay; Peru; Philippines; Portugal; Romania; Russia; Rwanda; Samoa 2; Senegal; Sierra Leone; South Africa; Spain; Sri Lanka; Sudan; Suriname; Swaziland; Tanzania; Thailand; Togo; Trinidad and Tobago; Uganda; Ukraine 3; Uruguay; Venezuela; Virgin Islands; Zambia; Zimbabwe

Church of God of the Apostolic Faith, Inc., The

PO Box 691745
Tulsa, OK 74169-1745 USA
Phone: (918) 437-7652
Fax: (918) 438-5633
E-mail: office@cogaf.org
Web Site: www.cogaf.org
Rev. Kelly Ward, Gen. Superintendent

A denominational sending agency of Pentecostal tradition engaged in theological education, Bible distribution, church construction, church planting, evangelism, literature distribution, providing medical supplies, training, video/film production/distribution and youth programs. Data from 2001.

Purpose: "...knowing Him...making Him known...that others may believe."

Year Founded in US: 1914

Fully Supported US Personnel Overseas:
  Expecting to serve more than 4 years: 5
  Non-residential mission personnel: 2

Other personnel:
  Short-term less than 1 year: 3
  Home ministry & office staff in US: 5

Countries: Honduras 1; Mexico 4

Church of the Brethren— Global Mission Partnerships

1451 Dundee Ave.
Elgin, IL 60120 USA
Phone: (847) 742-5100
Fax: (847) 742-6103
E-mail: mission@brethren.org
Web Site: www.brethren.org
Associations: CWS
Jay Wittmeyer, Exec. Director

A denominational sending agency of Brethren tradition engaged in peace and reconciliation, justice, support of national churches, Christian education, TEE and missionary training.

Purpose: "...to extend the church's witness around the world, leading out in God's mission, serving as a bridge between the local and the global, and creating opportunities for service and partnership."

Year Founded in US: 1719
Income for Overseas Min: $1,807,162.00
Fully Supported US Personnel Overseas:
  Expecting to serve more than 4 years: 3
  Expecting to serve 1 to 4 years: 36
  Non-residential mission personnel: 1
Other personnel:
  Home ministry & office staff in US: 7

Countries: Bosnia and Herzegovina; Brazil; Dominican Republic 2; El Salvador; France; Guatemala; Haiti; Honduras; Hungary; Ireland; Japan; Mexico; Netherlands; Nicaragua; Nigeria; Serbia and Montenegro; Slovakia; Sudan; Switzerland; Vietnam 1

Church of the Nazarene, World Mission Department

6401 The Paseo
Kansas City, MO 64131-1284 USA
Phone: (816) 333-7000
Fax: (816) 363-3100
Web Site: www.nazarene.worldmission.org
Associations: The Mission Exchange
Dr. Louie E. Bustle, Director

A sending agency engaged in church planting, TEE, evangelism, missionary education, providing medical supplies, medical work, relief and/or rehabilitation, missionary training, Christian education, theological education, evangelism, literature distribution, literature production, support of national workers, short-term programs and video/film production/distribution. Activities, financial, & countries of service data from 2005.

Purpose: "...to fulfill the Great Commission through a denominational structure and contextualized system of evangelism, discipleship, and development of a multiplying, indigenous, holiness church."

Year Founded in US: 1895

Income for Overseas Min: $56,606,056.00

Fully Supported US Personnel Overseas:
Expecting to serve more than 4 years: 363
Non-residential mission personnel: 973

Other personnel:
Short-term less than 1 year: 20209
Non-US serving in own/other country: 105
Home ministry & office staff in US: 49

Countries: Albania 3; American Samoa; Angola 2; Antigua; Argentina 17; Armenia; Aruba; Australia 5; Azores; Bahamas, The; Bangladesh; Barbados; Belize; Benin 6; Bolivia 2; Botswana 1; Brazil 6; Bulgaria 2; Burkina Faso; Burundi; Cambodia 2; Cameroon; Cape Verde; Chile 2; Colombia; Congo, Democratic Republic of; Congo, Republic of the; Costa Rica 11; Cote d'Ivoire 10; Croatia 1; Cuba; Cyprus 2; Denmark; Dominica 3; Dominican Republic 10; East Timor 2; Ecuador 6; Egypt; El Salvador; Equatorial Guinea; Eritrea; Ethiopia 6; Fiji 2; France 4; French Guiana; Gabon; Germany; Ghana 2; Greece; Grenada; Guadeloupe; Guam 2; Guatemala 20; Guinea-Bissau; Guyana; Haiti 6; Honduras; Hong Kong; Hungary; India; Indonesia 4; Ireland; Israel 3; Italy 2; Jamaica; Japan 2; Jordan 3; Kazakhstan; Kenya 20; Korea, South 6; Kosovo; Lebanon 2; Lesotho 2; Liberia; Macedonia 1; Madagascar 4; Malawi 5; Martinique; Mexico 3; Micronesia, Federated States of; Mozambique 9; Myanmar/Burma; Namibia 2; Nepal; Netherlands; Nicaragua; Nigeria; New Zealand; N. Mariana Isls; Pakistan; Palau; Panama; Papua New Guinea 28; Paraguay; Peru 8; Philippines 22; Poland; Portugal 3; Puerto Rico 1; Reunion 1; Romania 1; Russia 7; Rwanda; Saint Kitts and Nevis; Saint Lucia; Saint Vincent and the Grenadines; Samoa; Sao Tome and Principe 2; Senegal 2; Sierra Leone 2; Slovenia 1; Solomon Islands 2; South Africa 30; Spain; Sri Lanka; Sudan; Suriname; Swaziland 1; Switzerland 19; Syria; Taiwan; Tanzania; Thailand 6; Togo; Tonga; Trinidad and Tobago; Uganda 2; Ukraine; United Kingdom; Unspecified Country 10; Uruguay; Vanuatu 2; Venezuela 6; Virgin Islands; Zambia 4; Zimbabwe

Church Planting Intl., Inc.

PO Box 836
Gainesville, GA 30503 USA
Phone: (770) 535-7008
Fax: (770) 534-1025
E-mail: cpimission@juno.com
Rev. George P. Hutchinson, Exec. Director

A support agency of Presbyterian and Reformed tradition engaged in training national pastors, church planting, theological education, funds transmission, leadership development and support of national churches.

Purpose: "...to assist indigenous church planting ministries in developing nations."

Year Founded in US: 1983

Countries: Myanmar/Burma; Portugal; Uganda

Church Resource Ministries (CRM)

1240 N. Lakeview Ave., Ste.120
Anaheim, CA 92807 USA
Phone: (714) 779-0370
Fax: (714) 779-0189
E-mail: crm@crmleaders.org
Web Site: www.crmleaders.org
Dr. Samuel F. Metcalf, President

A transdenominational sending agency of Evangelical tradition engaged in leadership development, business as mission, church planting, development, member care and support of national churches.

Purpose: "...to envision movements of fresh, authentic churches, pioneered by godly leaders, fired by a passion for their world, compelled to multiply their lives and ministry, so that the name of God is renounced among the nations."

Year Founded in US: 1980

Income for Overseas Min: $5,000,000.00

Gifts in Kind: $10,000.00

Fully Supported US Personnel Overseas:

Expecting to serve more than 4 years: 77
Expecting to serve 1 to 4 years: 13
Non-residential mission personnel: 5

Other personnel:
Short-term less than 1 year: 30
Home ministry & office staff in US: 23

Countries: Asia—General 6; Australia 4; Cambodia 6; Costa Rica; Croatia 4; Guatemala 4; Hungary 6; India 1; Italy 2; Japan 4; Poland 2; Romania 3; Russia 6; Singapore 4; South Africa 4; Spain 3; United Kingdom 16; Venezuela 2

Church World Service

28606 Phillips St.
Elkhart, IN 46515 USA
Phone: (800) 297-1516
Fax: (574) 262-0966
E-mail: info@churchworldservice.org
Web Site: www.churchworldservice.org
Rev. John L. McCullough, CEO/Exec. Director

A denominational service agency of Ecumenical tradition engaged in development, agricultural programs, HIV/Aids, justice, literacy work and relief and/or rehabilitation.

Purpose: "...working with partners to build interfaith and intercultural coalitions to eradicate hunger and poverty and promote peace and justice around the world."

Year Founded in US: 1946

Churches of Christ

C/O Missions Resource Network
4001 Airport FWY, Ste. 550
Bedford, TX 76021 USA

A body of autonomous congregations and agencies of the Christian "Restoration Movement" (not using instrumental music in worship) which sends and supports missionaries directly from local congregations. Data furnished by Missions Resource Network. No central office.

Fully Supported US Personnel Overseas:
Expecting to serve more than 4 years: 746
Non-residential mission personnel: 51

Other personnel:
Home ministry & office staff in US: 35

Countries: Albania 17; American Samoa 5; Antigua; Argentina 4; Armenia; Australia 12; Austria 12; Bahamas, The 2; Bangladesh 1; Barbados 1; Belarus 5; Belgium 8; Belize 2;

Benin; Bolivia 8; Bosnia and Herzegovina 2; Botswana 2; Brazil 97; Bulgaria 5; Burkina Faso 8; Cambodia 14; Cameroon 3; Central African Republic; Chad 2; Chile 9; Colombia 2; Cook Islands; Costa Rica 2; Cote d'Ivoire 3; Croatia 4; Cuba; Cyprus; Czech Republic 7; Denmark; Dominica; Dominican Republic 6; Ecuador 6; Egypt; El Salvador 3; Estonia 7; Ethiopia; Fiji 3; Finland 3; France 8; French Polynesia; Gabon; Gambia, The; Georgia; Germany 10; Ghana 4; Greece; Grenada; Guam; Guatemala 6; Guinea 2; Guyana 14; Haiti 4; Honduras 6; Hungary 5; Iceland; India 10; Indonesia 6; Iran; Ireland 2; Israel; Italy 8; Jamaica 2; Japan 16; Jordan; Kenya 17; Kiribati; Korea, North; Korea, South 5; Laos 4; Latvia; Lebanon; Lesotho; Liberia; Libya; Lithuania 6; Madagascar 2; Malawi 2; Malaysia 3; Mali; Marshall Islands; Malta; Mauritius 2; Mexico 40; Micronesia, Federated States of 2; Moldova; Morocco; Mozambique 12; Myanmar/Burma; Namibia; Nepal; Netherlands; New Zealand 11; Nicaragua 2; Nigeria 5; Northern Mariana Islands 2; Norway; Pakistan; Panama 4; Papua New Guinea 9; Paraguay 8; Peru 13; Philippines 18; Poland 2; Portugal 2; Puerto Rico; Romania 8; Russia 3; Rwanda 16; Saint Lucia; Saint Vincent and the Grenadines; Samoa; Saudi Arabia; Senegal; Serbia and Montenegro 2; Seychelles; Sierra Leone; Singapore 3; Slovakia 2; Solomon Islands; South Africa 17; Spain; Sri Lanka; Sudan 2; Suriname; Swaziland 6; Sweden; Switzerland 6; Tanzania 29; Thailand 12; Togo 10; Tonga; Trinidad and Tobago 4; Tunisia 2; Turkey 4; Tuvalu; Uganda 24; Ukraine 10; United Kingdom 12; Unspecified Country 15; Uruguay; Vanuatu 3; Venezuela 3; Vietnam; Zambia 12; Zimbabwe 2

Churches of God, General Conference

700 E. Melrose Ave.
Findley, OH 45839 USA
Phone: (419) 424-1961
Fax: (419) 424-3433
E-mail: missions@cggc.org
Web Site: www.cggc.org
Associations: The Mission Exchange
Rev. Edward L. Rosenberry, Exec. Director

A denominational sending agency of Evangelical tradition engaged in support of national churches, church planting, Christian education, leadership development, medical work and support of national workers.

Purpose: "...to make Jesus Christ known to all people as Savior and Lord...to lead them into a personal relationship with God through Jesus Christ as Savior..."

Year Founded in US: 1825

Income for Overseas Min: $980,394.00

Fully Supported US Personnel Overseas:
  Expecting to serve more than 4 years: 8

Other personnel:
  Short-term less than 1 year: 5
  Home ministry & office staff in US: 6

Countries: Brazil 4; Haiti 4

Churches Together

PO Box 6003
Cabot, AR 72023 USA

Phone: (479) 774-1807
E-mail: info@churchestogether.com
Web Site: www.churchestogether.com
Associations: AERDO

Dr. Robert L. Brown, Exec. Director

A support agency of Evangelical tradition engaged in HIV/Aids, development, discipleship, support of national churches and partnership development.

Purpose: "...to join and equip North American and African churches in transforming ministry in communities impacted by HIV/AIDS and other social ills through vision-casting, network building, and equipping for partnership."

Year Founded in US: 2003

Gifts in Kind: $50,000.00

Personnel:
  Non-US serving in own/other country: 1
  Home ministry & office staff in US: 2

Countries: Africa—General

Cities for Christ Worldwide (CCW)

2474 Boise Ave.
Loveland, CO 80538 USA

Phone: (970) 663-0477
E-mail: Monsmatd@comcast.net

Dr. Timothy Monsma, Director

An interdenominational sending agency of Presbyterian and Reformed tradition engaged in childcare/orphanage programs,

children at risk, Christian education, missions information service, services for other agencies and work in cities. Partnering with Word and Deed Ministries. Countries of service from 2005.

Year Founded in US: 1985

Fully Supported US Personnel Overseas:
  Expecting to serve more than 4 years: 4

Countries: Africa—General 2; Asia—General 2

CityTeam Ministries—New Generations International

2304 Zanker Rd.
San Jose, CA 95131 USA

Phone: (408) 232-5600
Fax: (408) 436-0702
E-mail: info@newgenerationsintl.org
Web Site: www.newgenerationsintl.org

Patrick J. Robertson, President

A nondenominational support agency engaged in church planting, discipleship, partnership development, relief and/or rehabilitation and training. Data from 2005.

Purpose: "...serving people in need, proclaiming the gospel, and establishing disciples among disadvantaged people of cities."

Year Founded in US: 1957

Fully Supported US Personnel Overseas:
  Expecting to serve more than 4 years: 1
  Non-residential mission personnel: 3

Other personnel:
  Non-US serving in own/other country: 11

Countries: Cote d'Ivoire; Ethiopia 1; Indonesia; Sierra Leone; South Africa

CLC Ministries International

PO Box 1449
Ft. Washington, PA 19034 USA

Phone: (215) 542-1242
Fax: (215) 542-7580
E-mail: clcmail@clcusa.org
Web Site: www.clcusa.org
Associations: The Mission Exchange

Mr. David Almack, US Director

A nondenominational support agency of Evangelical tradition engaged in literature distribution, Bible distribution, business as mission and literature production.

Purpose: "...to make evangelical Christian literature available to all nations so that people may come to faith and maturity in the Lord Jesus Christ."

Year Founded in US: 1948
Income for Overseas Min: $324,898.00
Gifts in Kind: $2,288.00
Fully Supported US Personnel Overseas:
Expecting to serve more than 4 years: 5
Other personnel:
Short-term less than 1 year: 1
Home ministry & office staff in US: 37
Countries: Central Asia—General 1; Hong Kong 2; Italy 2

CMF International
5525 E. 82nd St.
Indianapolis, IN 46256 USA
Phone: (317) 578-2700
Fax: (317) 578-2827
E-mail: missions@cmfi.org
Web Site: www.cmfi.org
Dr. Doug Priest, Exec. Director

A nondenominational sending agency of Christian (Restoration Movement) tradition engaged in church planting, development, evangelism, leadership development and tentmaking.
Purpose: "...is compelled by Christ's love to transform lives and communities around the world."
Year Founded in US: 1949
Income for Overseas Min: $10,000,000.00
Gifts in Kind: $52,164.00
Fully Supported US Personnel Overseas:
Expecting to serve more than 4 years: 146
Expecting to serve 1 to 4 years: 22
Non-residential mission personnel: 2
Other personnel:
Short-term less than 1 year: 34
Non-US serving in own/other country: 7
Home ministry & office staff in US: 36
Countries: Asia—General 9; Brazil; Burkina Faso 4; Chile 8; Cote d'Ivoire 6; Ethiopia 14; Germany 6; Indonesia 8; Kenya 27; Mexico 16; Spain 4; Tanzania 9; Thailand 8; Ukraine 11; United Kingdom 16

CMTS Ministries, Inc.
321 Focht Rd.
Bernville, PA 19506 USA
Phone: (610) 488-6975

Fax: (610) 488-1331
E-mail: cmtsmin@aol.com
Web Site: www.cmtsministries.com
Mr. Andrew J. Merrick, Sr., Exec. Director

A nondenominational service agency of Evangelical tradition engaged in technical assistance, discipleship, furloughed missionary support, purchasing services, services for other agencies and supplying equipment.
Purpose: "...to provide technical assistance, materials, and equipment for use by Christian organizations and Bible-believing missionaries at home and abroad."
Year Founded in US: 1982
Income for Overseas Min: $106,626.00
Fully Supported US Personnel Overseas:
Non-residential mission personnel: 1
Other personnel:
Short-term less than 1 year: 65
Non-US serving in own/other country: 2
Countries: Mexico

Colorado Haiti Project, Inc.
4141 Arapahoe Ave.
Boulder, CO 80303 USA
Phone: (303) 938-5021
E-mail: info@coloradohaitiproject.org
Web Site: www.coloradohaitiproject.org
Mr. Paul Casey, Exec. Director

A support agency of Episcopal tradition engaged in medical work, development, Christian education, leadership development, partnership development and clean water..
Purpose: "...to share Christ's love through partnership with our brothers and sisters in Haiti to improve the human condidtion."
Year Founded in US: 1989
Income for Overseas Min: $472,000.00
Gifts in Kind: $12,000.00
Personnel:
Short-term less than 1 year: 25
Non-US serving in own/other country: 23
Home ministry & office staff in US: 3
Countries: Haiti

ComCare International
3027 Split Rock Circle
Bulverde, TX 78163 USA
Phone: (210) 317-9998
E-mail: cci@comcareinternational.org

Web Site: www.comcareinternational.org
Scotta Williams, Exec. Director
An interdenominational specialized agency of Evangelical tradition engaged in medical work, technical assistance, and training, including solar powered hearing aids for unreached people. Statistical data from 2001.
Year Founded in US: 1989
Income for Overseas Min: $24,000.00
Fully Supported US Personnel Overseas:
    Expecting to serve more than 4 years: 2
Other personnel:
    Short-term less than 1 year: 1
    Non-US serving in own/other country: 2
Countries: Mexico 2

COMHINA—Cooperacion Misionera De Hispanos De North America

PO Box 593754
Orlando, FL 32859-3754 USA
Phone: (407) 992-7726
Fax: (407) 382-1008
E-mail: comhinanacional@comhina.org
Web Site: www.comhina.org
Associations: The Mission Exchange
Rev. Victor Cuartas, Exec. Director
An interdenominational support agency of Christian (Restoration Movement) tradition engaged in mobilization for mission, children at risk, missionary education, leadership development and partnership development.
Purpose: "...to glorify God by fulfilling the mandate that our Lord Jesus Christ gave us in the Great Commission, collaborating with the Hispanic local churches in the United States and Canada in its missionary action..."
Year Founded in US:
Income for Overseas Min: $1,672,125.00
Fully Supported US Personnel Overseas:
    Non-residential mission personnel: 4
Other personnel:
    Short-term less than 1 year: 2
    Home ministry & office staff in US: 4

Commission to Every Nation
(See ad on page 157)
PO Box 291307
Kerrville, TX 78029-1307 USA
Phone: (830) 896-8326

Fax: (830) 896-5262
E-mail: usa@cten.org
Web Site: www.cten.org
Rev. Richard Mann, President
An interdenominational sending agency of Evangelical and Independent tradition engaged in member care, children at risk, church planting, development, funds transmission, leadership development, linguistics and Bible translation.
Purpose: "...to partner with churches to help Christians become personally involved in fulfilling the Great Commission to every nation."
Year Founded in US: 1994
Income for Overseas Min: $3,780,760.00
Gifts in Kind: $13,150.00
Fully Supported US Personnel Overseas:
    Expecting to serve more than 4 years: 173
    Expecting to serve 1 to 4 years: 65
    Non-residential mission personnel: 4
Other personnel:
    Non-US serving in own/other country: 240
    Home ministry & office staff in US: 10
Countries: Albania 2; Asia—General 2; Belize 2; Bolivia; Brazil 4; Burkina Faso 2; Cambodia; Cameroon 9; Chile 2; Costa Rica 8; Cyprus; Ecuador 8; El Salvador 2; Germany; Guatemala 52; Honduras; India; Ireland; Kenya; Liberia; Mexico 41; Mozambique 4; Nicaragua 2; Peru 4; Philippines 8; Poland 2; Romania 2; Rwanda; South Africa 1; Spain 2; Suriname 2; Sweden; Tanzania; Thailand 4; Trinidad and Tobago 4; Uganda; Ukraine 2; Zambia 2

Compassion Intl., Inc.
12290 Voyager Pkwy.
Colorado Springs, CO 80921 US
Phone: (719) 487-7000
Fax: (719) 487-6648
E-mail: ciinfo@us.ci.org
Web Site: www.compassion.com
Dr. Wesley K. Stafford, President/CEO
A support agency engaged in childrens programs, development, Christian education, evangelism, leadership development and medical work.
Purpose: "...an advocate for children, to release them from their spiritual, economic, social, and physical poverty and enable them to become responsible and fulfilled Christian adults."

Most mission agencies invite you to join them to accomplish their God-given mission.

But,

What if God has called you to do something unique that does not fit the mold?

CTEN serves by providing pastoral care, service and oversight to help missionaries fulfill their unique call.

Commission
TO EVERY NATION
International

Serving along side faith-based missionaries and their churches in the U.S. and Canada.

www.*CTEN*.org

In the U.S. 800.872.5404 or usa@cten.org

In Canada 866.321.8048 or canada@cten.org

Helping Ordinary People Partner With God To Accomplish The Extraordinary

Year Founded in US: 1952

Income for Overseas Min: $217,278,070.00

Gifts in Kind: $143,367.00

Fully Supported US Personnel Overseas:
Expecting to serve more than 4 years: 6
Expecting to serve 1 to 4 years: 5

Other personnel:
Non-US serving in own/other country: 1531
Home ministry & office staff in US: 762

Countries: Asia—General 2; Bangladesh 1;
Bolivia; Brazil; Burkina Faso; Colombia;
Dominican Republic; Ecuador; El Salvador;
Ethiopia; Ghana 1; Guatemala; Haiti; Honduras; India; Indonesia; Kenya; Mexico;
Nicaragua; Peru; Philippines; Rwanda 2;
Tanzania; Thailand; Togo; Uganda

Congregational Christian Churches, National Assoc. of
PO Box 288
Oak Creek, WI 53154 USA
Phone: (414)764-1620
Fax: (414)764-0319
E-mail: naccc@naccc.org
Web Site: www.naccc.org

Rev. John Carson, Assoc. Exec. Sec. for Missions

A nondenominational sending agency of
Congregational tradition engaged in relief
and/or rehabilitation, association of missions,
agricultural programs, church construction,
development and funds transmission. Entry
on database rebuilt using data from 2002.

Purpose: "...to encourage and assist local
churches in their development of vibrant
and effective witnesses to Christ in Congregational ways."

Year Founded in US: 1953

Income for Overseas Min: $450,000.00

Personnel:
Short-term less than 1 year: 125
Non-US serving in own/other country: 22

Countries: Unspecified Country

Congregational Holiness Church—World Missions
3888 Fayetteville Hwy.
Griffin, GA 30223 USA
Phone: (770) 228-4833
Fax: (770) 228-1177
E-mail: headquarters@chchurch.com

Web Site: www.chchurch.com

Rev. Charles Hanson, World Missions Director

A denominational support agency of Holiness
and Pentecostal tradition engaged in support
of national workers, church construction,
Christian education and providing medical
supplies in 17 countries. Data from 2001.

Year Founded in US: 1921

Personnel:
Home ministry & office staff in US: 4

Congregational Methodist Missions
PO Box 9
Florence, MS 39073 USA
Phone: (601) 845-8787
Fax: (601) 845-8788
Web Site: www.cmmission.com

Dr. Jerry M. Jones, Director

A denominational sending agency of Methodist and Wesleyan tradition engaged in
partnership development, church planting,
development, evangelism, leadership development and short-term programs.

Purpose: "...to promote evangelism of non-
Christans, equipping of believers, empowering of leaders, and the planting of churches
both within the United States and abroad."

Year Founded in US: 1852

Income for Overseas Min: $250,000.00

Fully Supported US Personnel Overseas:
Expecting to serve more than 4 years: 2
Expecting to serve 1 to 4 years: 2

Other personnel:
Short-term less than 1 year: 36
Non-US serving in own/other country: 4
Home ministry & office staff in US: 14

Countries: Belize; Mexico 2

Connecting Businessmen to Christ, Inc. (CBMC)
PO Box 8009
Chattanooga, TN 37414 USA
Phone: (423) 698-4444
Fax: (423) 629-4434
E-mail: info@cbmc.com
Web Site: www.cbmc.com

Mr. Patrick O'Neal, Exec. Director

A nondenominational support agency engaged in discipleship, evangelism, leadership development and training.

Purpose: "...to present Jesus Christ as Savior and Lord to business and professional men, and to develop Christian business and professional men to carry out the Great Commission."

Year Founded in US: 1930

Personnel:
Home ministry & office staff in US: 15

Conservative Congregational Christian Conference— Missions Committee

8941 Highway 5
Lake Elmo, MN 55042 USA

Phone: (651) 739-1474
Fax: (651) 739-0750
E-mail: missions@ccccusa.com
Web Site: www.ccccusa.org

Rev. Laurence M. Wood, President

A denominational support agency of Congregational and Evangelical tradition engaged in support of national churches and short-term programs. Data from 2005.

Year Founded in US: 1948

Income for Overseas Min: $6,375,000.00

Fully Supported US Personnel Overseas:
Expecting to serve more than 4 years: 4

Other personnel:
Short-term less than 1 year: 90
Home ministry & office staff in US: 3

Countries: Micronesia, Federated States of 4

Continent of Great Cities

3939 Belt Line Rd., Ste. 705
Addison, TX 75001 USA

Phone: (214) 466-6200
Fax: (214) 466-6205
E-mail: info@greatcities.org
Web Site: www.greatcities.org

Dr. Gary J. Sorrells, Exec. Director

A denominational sending agency of Christian (Restoration Movement) tradition engaged in church planting, member care, support of national churches, support of national workers, mobilization for mission and missionary training.

Year Founded in US: 1976

Income for Overseas Min: $1,600,000.00

Converge Worldwide

Mail Code 1000
100 Lake Hart Rd.
Orlando, FL 32832 USA

Phone: (800) 323-4215
Web Site: www.convergeww.org

Associations: The Mission Exchange

Rev. Stephen Doggett, Exec. Director Intl. Mins.

A denominational sending agency of Baptist tradition engaged in church planting, development, discipleship, theological education and medical work.

Purpose: "...to develop an expanding network of leaders and leadership teams serving together to mobilize and multiply vital, reproducing churches."

Year Founded in US: 1945

Income for Overseas Min: $6,880,000.00

Fully Supported US Personnel Overseas:
Expecting to serve more than 4 years: 129
Non-residential mission personnel: 2

Other personnel:
Short-term less than 1 year: 6
Home ministry & office staff in US: 9

Countries: Argentina 8; Asia—General 2; Belize 4; Brazil 12; Cambodia 3; Cameroon 14; Caribbean—General 3; Costa Rica 2; Cote d'Ivoire 2; Estonia 2; Ethiopia 1; France 5; Germany 4; Japan 10; Mexico 10; Nigeria 4; Philippines 17; Senegal 8; Singapore 2; Spain 4; Thailand 8; Ukraine 2; Uruguay 2

Cook Communications Ministries International

4050 Lee Vance View
Colorado Springs, CO 80920 USA

Phone: (719) 536-0100
Fax: (719) 536-3266
Web Site: www.ccmi.org

Mr. Chris Doornbos, President

An interdenominational ministry of evangelical tradition engaged in making Christian literature available from translations of their English language product and through training Christian publishers to provide Christian literature in their own language and country. Data from 2005.

Purpose: "...to encourage the acceptance of Jesus Christ as personal Savior and to aid, promote and contribute to the teaching and putting into practice of His two great commands..."

Year Founded in US: 1944

Income for Overseas Min: $1,900,000.00

Countries: Brazil; China; Europe—General; India; Latin America—General; Myanmar/Burma; Vietnam

Cooperative Baptist Fellowship—Global Missions

2930 Flowers Rd. S., Ste. 133
Atlanta, GA 30341 USA

Phone: (770) 220-1600
Fax: (770) 220-1685
E-mail: contact@thefellowship.info
Web Site: www.thefellowship.info

Mr. Rob Nash, Coord. Global Missions

A sending agency of Baptist tradition engaged in development, agricultural programs, justice, leadership development, support of national churches and tentmaking.

Purpose: "...to serve Christians and churches as they discover and fulfill their God-given mission."

Year Founded in US: 1990

Fully Supported US Personnel Overseas:
  Expecting to serve more than 4 years: 54
  Expecting to serve 1 to 4 years: 21
  Non-residential mission personnel: 66

Other personnel:
  Short-term less than 1 year: 275
  Home ministry & office staff in US: 63

Countries: Africa—General 6; Asia—General 12; Belgium 1; Belize; China 4; Greece 2; Haiti 2; Hungary 2; India 4; Kenya 2; Macedonia 2; Mexico; Middle East 7; Netherlands 2; Peru; Slovakia 2; South Africa 4; Spain; Uganda; Ukraine 2

Cornerstone International

PO Box 192
Wilmore, KY 40390 USA

Phone: (859) 858-4578
Fax: (859) 858-0981
E-mail: duane@cornerstoneinternational.org
Web Site: www.cornerstoneinternational.org

Mr. E. Duane Jones, Director

A nondenominational sending agency of Wesleyan and Charismatic tradition engaged in church planting, mobilization for mission, childrens programs, TEE, evangelism and

short-term programs. Data from 2001.

Purpose: "...to evangelize and disciple...[in] partnership with local churches in the launching of short-term and career missionaries."

Year Founded in US: 1972

Income for Overseas Min: $565,226.00

Personnel:
  Home ministry & office staff in US: 4

Crescent Project

PO Box 50986
Indianapolis, IN 46250 USA

Phone: (888) 446-5457
E-mail: info@crescentproject.org
Web Site: www.crescentproject.org

Mr. Fouad Masri, President

An interdenominational specialized agency of Evangelical tradition engaged in missionary training, missionary education, evangelism, literature distribution, literature production and training.

Purpose: "...to help Christians in North America reach out in love to our Muslim neighbors...to see the hope of Jesus Christ shared with each of the seven million Muslims in North America."

Year Founded in US: 1994

Income for Overseas Min: $63,000.00

Personnel:
  Short-term less than 1 year: 60
  Home ministry & office staff in US: 24

Crisis Consulting Intl.

9452 Telephone Rd., #223
Ventura, CA 93004 USA

Phone: (805) 642-2549
Fax: (805) 642-1748
E-mail: info@cricon.org
Web Site: www.cricon.org

Mr. Robert Klamser, Exec. Director

A nondenominational service agency of Evangelical tradition engaged in security training, hostage negotiations, management consulting/training, missions information service, services for other agencies and training.

Purpose: "...to assist the global Christian community in fulfilling the Great Commission by providing security and crisis management services."

Year Founded in US: 1985

Personnel:
Home ministry & office staff in US: 1

CrossGlobal Link

(See ad page 162)
PO Box 398
Wheaton, IL 60187-0398 USA

Phone: (630) 682-9270
Fax: (630) 682-9278
E-mail: info@crossgloballink.org
Web Site: www.crossgloballink.org
Associations: CrossGlobal Link

Dr. Marvin J. Newell, Exec. Director

An association of mission agencies, churches and mission training centers organized for the purpose of advancing the effectiveness of its members in global mission through fellowship, networking, training and providing educational and informational services.

Purpose: "...to network for the purpose of advancing the effectiveness of the North American mission enterprise to the world, and connecting globally with majority world missions, serving as an accrediting association for mission agencies."

Year Founded in US: 1917

Personnel:
Home ministry & office staff in US: 3

CrossLink International

427 N. Maple Ave.
Falls Church, VA 22046 USA

Phone: (703) 534-5465
Fax: (703) 536-8349
E-mail: info@crosslinkinternational.net
Web Site: www.crosslinkinternational.net
Associations: AERDO

Mr. Dan Henneberg, Exec. Director

An interdenominational specialized agency of Evangelical tradition engaged in providing medical supplies and medical work.

Purpose: "...to change the world one life at a time through Christ-like missions, by equipping mission volunteers, medical mission teams, and missionaries as they witness the love of Jesus Christ."

Year Founded in US: 1994
Income for Overseas Min: $3,870,000.00
Gifts in Kind: $3,870,000.00
Personnel:
Home ministry & office staff in US: 12

Crossover Communications International

PO Box 211755
Columbia, SC 29221-1755 USA

Phone: (803) 691-0688
Fax: (803) 691-9355
E-mail: info@crossoverusa.org
Web Site: www.crossoverusa.org
Associations: CrossGlobal Link

Dr. William H. Jones, President

An interdenominational service agency of Evangelical tradition engaged in church planting, business as mission, extension education, support of national churches and short-term programs.

Purpose: "...to glorify God by assisting and accelerating church planting movements among the least reached peoples of the world through culturally appropriate implementation of the ministry multiplication cycle."

Year Founded in US: 1987
Income for Overseas Min: $583,478.00
Gifts in Kind: $34,761.00
Fully Supported US Personnel Overseas:
Expecting to serve more than 4 years: 9

Other personnel:
Short-term less than 1 year: 126
Non-US serving in own/other country: 54
Home ministry & office staff in US: 10

Countries: Brazil 3; Central Asia—General 2; Moldova; Turkey 4

CrossWorld

PO Box 306
Bala Cynwyd, PA 19004 USA

Phone: (610) 667-7660
Fax: (610) 667-9068
Web Site: www.crossworld.org
Associations: CrossGlobal Link

Mr. Dale Losch, President

A nondenominational sending agency of Baptist and Evangelical tradition engaged in church planting, discipleship, Christian education, theological education, evangelism and leadership development.

Purpose: "...serves the Church by mobilizing teams to make disciples and train leaders which will result in movements of reproducing churches among the unreached."

Year Founded in US: 1943

CONNECT
INTERACT
NETWORK

Mission Agencies

Global Mission Movement

Churches and Schools

Income for Overseas Min: $13,341,350.00

Fully Supported US Personnel Overseas:
Expecting to serve more than 4 years: 242
Expecting to serve 1 to 4 years: 4
Non-residential mission personnel: 2

Other personnel:
Short-term less than 1 year: 115
Non-US serving in own/other country: 26
Home ministry & office staff in US: 48

Countries: Asia—General 16; Austria 2; Bosnia and Herzegovina 4; Brazil 35; Cambodia; Central Asia—General 8; Congo, Democratic Republic of 4; Dominican Republic 8; Ecuador 11; France 25; Germany 20; Guatemala 2; Guyana 6; Haiti 13; Indonesia 13; Ireland 11; Italy 16; Kenya 2; Kosovo 6; Mexico 10; Monaco 2; New Zealand; Philippines 5; Romania 2; Slovakia 2; South Africa 1; Spain 4; Sweden 2; Switzerland 4; Ukraine 6; United Kingdom 2

CSI Ministries
1714 W. Royale Dr.
Muncie, IN 47304 USA
Phone: (800) 286-5773
Fax: (765) 286-5773
E-mail: csi@csiministries.org
Web Site: www.csiministries.org
Mr. Ronn Oren, Exec. Director

An interdenominational service agency of Evangelical tradition engaged in short-term programs, childcare/orphanage programs, church construction, Christian education and medical work.

Purpose: "...to share the redeeming Gospel of Jesus Christ throughout the world."

Year Founded in US: 1963

Income for Overseas Min: $1,603,275.00

Fully Supported US Personnel Overseas:
Expecting to serve more than 4 years: 15

Other personnel:
Short-term less than 1 year: 950
Non-US serving in own/other country: 49
Home ministry & office staff in US: 5

Countries: Haiti 8; Jamaica 7

CTI Music Ministries (Carpenter's Tools Intl.)
PO Box 100
Willmar, MN 56201-0100 USA
Phone: (329) 235-0155

Fax: (320) 235-0185
E-mail: info@ctimusic.org
Web Site: www.ctimusic.org
Chris Reed, Exec. Director

An interdenominational support agency of Evangelical tradition engaged in evangelism, short-term programs, music performance and youth programs. An associate ministry of Youth for Christ International. Data from 2005.

Purpose: "...to recruit, train and send music teams to work with established Christian ministries worldwide to reach young people with the Gospel."

Year Founded in US: 1975

Income for Overseas Min: $230,000.00

Personnel:
Short-term less than 1 year: 45
Home ministry & office staff in US: 7

Cumberland Presbyterian Church Board of Missions
8207 Traditional Place
Cordova, TN 38016 USA
Phone: (901) 276-9988
Fax: (901) 276-4578
E-mail: watkr@mac.com
Web Site: www.cumberland.org/bom
Associations: CWS
Rev. Michael Sharpe, Exec. Director

A denominational sending agency of Presbyterian tradition engaged in church planting, missions information service, leadership development, partnership development, relief and/or rehabilitation and short-term programs. Data from 2005.

Year Founded in US: 1845

Income for Overseas Min: $437,720.00

Personnel:
Short-term less than 1 year: 30
Home ministry & office staff in US: 11

Cup of Cold Water Ministries
PO Box 318
Newark, IL 60541 USA
Phone: (815) 228-1442
E-mail: dan@ccwm.org
Web Site: www.ccwm.org
Mr. Dan Hennenfent, Exec. Director

A nondenominational service agency of Evangelical tradition engaged in Christian education, children at risk and short-term programs.

Purpose: "...to glorify our Lord Jesus Christ by faithful proclamation of His Word and by loving service to our fellow man, especially the poor and disadvantaged, both at home and abroad."

Year Founded in US: 1978
Income for Overseas Min: $299,958.00
Personnel:
   Short-term less than 1 year: 2
   Non-US serving in own/other country: 13
   Home ministry & office staff in US: 2
Countries: Bolivia; Honduras; Mongolia; Thailand

CWE
4301 W. South Ave.
Tampa, FL 33614 USA
Phone: (813) 877-8420
Fax: (813) 874-5408
E-mail: office@cwe-missions.org
Web Site: www.cwe-missions.org
Mr. Paul Puleo, President

A nondenominational service agency of Evangelical tradition engaged in church construction and medical work.

Purpose: "...to assist the local church in fulfilling the Great Commission by providing and facilitating spiritually effective construction and medical mission opportunities throughout the world."

Year Founded in US: 1991
Personnel:
   Short-term less than 1 year: 500

D & D Missionary Homes, Inc.
4020 58th Ave. North
St. Petersburg, FL 33714-1133 USA
Phone: (727) 522-0522
Fax: (727) 522-0524
Web Site: www.ddmissionaryhomes.org
Mr. Jerry Trask, Exec. Director

A nondenominational service agency of Evangelical tradition engaged in furloughed missionary support and homes for missionaries on furlough or transition..

Purpose: "...to provide temporary housing to Bible-believing missionaries doing deputation, on furlough or during the first year of retirement."

Year Founded in US: 1949
Personnel:
   Home ministry & office staff in US: 13

Dawn Ministries, Inc.
PO Box 690787
Orlando, FL 32869-0787 USA
Phone: (321) 395-4949
Fax: (321) 395-4951
E-mail: inquiries@dawnministries.org
Web Site: www.dawnministries.org
Berna Salcedo, President

A nondenominational service agency of Charismatic and Evangelical tradition engaged in church planting, discipleship, justice, leadership development, literature distribution, mission-related research and training. Data from 2005.

Purpose: "...to see saturation church planting become the generally accepted and fervently practiced strategy for completing the task of making disciples of all peoples in our generation."

Year Founded in US: 1985
Income for Overseas Min: $3,900,000.00
Personnel:
   Non-US serving in own/other country: 8
   Home ministry & office staff in US: 10
Countries: Africa—General; Asia—General; Central Asia—General; Eastern Europe—General; Latin America—General; Unspecified Country; Western Europe—General

Dayspring International
PO Box 3309
Virginia Beach, VA 23454 USA
Phone: (757) 428-1092
Fax: (757) 428-0257
E-mail: info@dayspringinternational.org
Web Site: www.dayspringinternational.org
Rev. John E. Gilman, President

A nondenominational support agency of Evangelical tradition engaged in evangelism, church planting, funds transmission, support of national workers and supplying equipment. Data from 2005.

Purpose: "...to be an enabling servant to the national church through culturally relevant multi-media tools and humanitarian programs to assist in evangelization and discipling of unreached and under-reached

people groups."
Year Founded in US: 1979
Income for Overseas Min: $11,947,641.00
Gifts in Kind: $9,544,533.00
Personnel:
Non-US serving in own/other country: 1000
Countries: India

Daystar U.S.
5701 Normandale Rd. #325
Edina, MN 55424 USA
Phone: (952) 928-2550
Fax: (952) 928-2551
E-mail: info@daystarus.org
Web Site: www.daystarus.org
Mr. Todd Rasmuson, Exec. Director

An interdenominational sending agency of Evangelical tradition engaged in theological education, Christian education, extension education and leadership development.
Purpose: "...to educate Jesus-centered servant leaders to transform Africa."
Year Founded in US: 1982
Income for Overseas Min: $661,000.00
Fully Supported US Personnel Overseas:
Expecting to serve more than 4 years: 4
Other personnel:
Home ministry & office staff in US: 5
Countries: Kenya 4

Deaf Missions Inc.
PO Box 8514
Clearwater, FL 33758 USA
Phone: (727) 530-3020
E-mail: deafmissions@netzero.net
M. Eldeny Hale, Director

A transdenominational specialized agency of Evangelical tradition engaged in ministry to those with hearing disabilities through mission projects including missionary orientation and training. Data from 2005.
Year Founded in US: 1967
Personnel:
Home ministry & office staff in US: 1

DeNike Ministries
PO Box 1231
McAlester, OK 74502 USA
Phone: (918) 423-2431

E-mail: info@denikeministries.org
Web Site: www.denikeministries.org
Mr. Frank DeNike, President

A nondenominational support agency of Charismatic and Independent tradition engaged in short-term programs, training the nationals in Mexico and Kenya, church construction, church planting, theological education, partnership development and supplying equipment. Data from 2005.
Purpose: "...to encourage others to come alongside of them to provide the necessary resources, both spiritual and physical, for the training and strengthening of God's people in Mexico, so they can more effectively fulfill their burden to reach the lost for Jesus as stated in Matt. 28:18-20."
Year Founded in US: 1995
Fully Supported US Personnel Overseas:
Expecting to serve more than 4 years: 1
Other personnel:
Short-term less than 1 year: 120
Home ministry & office staff in US: 1
Countries: Mexico 1

Development Associates International (DAI)
PO Box 49278
Colorado Springs, CO 80949 USA
Phone: (719) 598-7970
Fax: (719) 884-0668
E-mail: info@daintl.org
Web Site: www.daintl.org
Associations: The Mission Exchange
Jane D. Overstreet, President/CEO

A nondenominational support agency of Evangelical tradition engaged in leadership development, discipleship, theological education, partnership development and training.
Purpose: "...to enhance the integrity and effectiveness of Christian leaders worldwide so that the Church can fulfill its role in extending the Kingdom of God."
Year Founded in US: 1996
Income for Overseas Min: $4,166,022.00
Gifts in Kind: $56,297.00
Fully Supported US Personnel Overseas:
Expecting to serve more than 4 years: 1
Expecting to serve 1 to 4 years: 2

Non-residential mission personnel: 3
Other personnel:
Non-US serving in own/other country: 20
Home ministry & office staff in US: 15
Countries: Australia; Belgium; Cote d'Ivoire; Egypt; Ghana; India; Liberia; Middle East; Nepal 1; Nigeria; Russia; South Africa; Togo; Uganda; United Kingdom

Disciples International

PO Box 466
Wallingford, PA 19086 USA
Phone: (610) 872-8742
Fax: (610) 872-8762
E-mail: david.komarnicki@verizon.net
Web Site: www.disciplesinternational.org
Mr. David Komarnicki, President/CEO

A specialized agency of Evangelical tradition engaged in leadership development, Bible memorization, correspondence courses, discipleship, evangelism and literature distribution.
Purpose: "...to obtain translations of and distribute copies of the Apostles' Creed and certain Bible verses into the 100 most widely spoken languages."
Year Founded in US: 2002
Income for Overseas Min: $2,000.00

Discipleship Missions Intl.

5317 Annapolis Ct.
Ventura, CA 93003 USA
Phone: (805) 218-8331
E-mail: jdredit@yahoo.com
Web Site: www.discipleshipmissions.com
Joy Downing Riley, U.S. Coordinator

A nondenominational support agency of Pentecostal tradition engaged in church planting, agricultural programs, childcare/orphanage programs, development, extension education, evangelism and providing medical supplies.
Purpose: "...to preach and propagate the Gospel of our risen Master and King Jesus in villages and urban areas in Uganda, East Africa, and around the world for the forgiveness of sin and transformation of lives in the name of Jesus Christ...to plant biblically based churches where none are found...to train both men and women who are called to evangelism, church ministry, and pastoral ministry for the purpose of advancing

the Kingdom of God as we care for widows, orphans, the needy, and the poor."
Year Founded in US: 2008
Income for Overseas Min: $81,000.00
Personnel:
Short-term less than 1 year: 10
Non-US serving in own/other country: 3
Countries: Uganda

Door of Hope International

PO Box 303
Glendale, CA 91209 USA
Phone: (877) 440-3644
E-mail: info@dohi.org
Web Site: www.dohi.org
Paul H. Popov, Intl. President

An interdenominational support agency engaged in Bible distribution, childcare/orphanage programs, missions information service, relief and/or rehabilitation, Bible translation and youth programs. Data from 2005.
Purpose: "...to provide help and bring spiritual, practical and humanitarian assistance to Eastern Europe through the development and support of leadership in the indigenous church and the education of believers in the West."
Year Founded in US: 1972
Income for Overseas Min: $158,985.00
Gifts in Kind: $48,937.00
Personnel:
Home ministry & office staff in US: 4

DualReach

PO Box 427
Dana Point, CA 92629 USA
Phone: (949) 248-1236
E-mail: info@dualreach.org
Web Site: www.dualreach.org
Dr. Bruce Camp, Founder/CEO

A transdenominational service agency of Evangelical tradition engaged in missions mobilization of churches and assistance to the church-mobilization ministry of mission agencies via consulting, training and production of resources to increase their global impact.
Purpose: "...to provide resources, training and consulting to churches and mission agencies to help them mobilize local congregations' potential to reach the world

globally and locally."
Year Founded in US: 2001
Personnel:
Home ministry & office staff in US: 1

e3 Partners Ministry
2001 W. Plano Pkwy., Ste. 2600
Plano, TX 75075 USA
Phone: (214) 440-1101
Fax: (214) 440-1190
E-mail: information@e3partners.org
Web Site: www.e3partners.org
Mr. Curtis Hail, President
An interdenominational support agency of Evangelical tradition engaged in church planting, evangelism, leadership development, support of national churches, mobilization for mission and short-term programs.
Purpose: "...to equip God's people to evangelize His world and establish His Church."
Year Founded in US: 1987
Income for Overseas Min: $18,000,000.00
Personnel:
Short-term less than 1 year: 2,840
Home ministry & office staff in US: 36

East West Interknit
PO Box 270333
St. Paul, MN 55127 USA
Phone: (651) 765-2550
Fax: (651) 765-2523
E-mail: info@ew-interknit.org
Web Site: www.ew-interknit.org
Annette L. Jones, Exec. Director
A nondenominational support agency of Evangelical tradition engaged in support of national workers, funds transmission, literature distribution and supplying equipment.
Purpose: "...to provide training, tools, and resources that enhance the outreach efforts of developing world Christians serving to meet the spiritual and physical needs of people in their sphere of influence."
Year Founded in US: 1992
Income for Overseas Min: $64,500.00
Personnel:
Short-term less than 1 year: 15
Home ministry & office staff in US: 2

Eastern European Outreach, Inc.
PO Box 685
Murrieta, CA 92564 USA
Phone: (951) 696-5244
Fax: (951) 696-5247
E-mail: info@eeo.org
Web Site: www.eeo.org
Associations: AERDO
Mr. Jeff L. Thompson, President
A nondenominational service agency of Evangelical tradition engaged in children at risk, camping programs, literature distribution, support of national workers, short-term programs and child sponsorship.
Purpose: "...to make disciples (followers of Christ) of all peoples (Matt. 28:18-19)... to emphasize the millions of 'children at-risk' and the needy of Eastern Europe."
Year Founded in US: 1980
Income for Overseas Min: $1,400,000.00
Gifts in Kind: $10,000.00
Fully Supported US Personnel Overseas:
Expecting to serve more than 4 years: 2
Expecting to serve 1 to 4 years: 1
Non-residential mission personnel: 1
Other personnel:
Short-term less than 1 year: 74
Non-US serving in own/other country: 38
Home ministry & office staff in US: 6
Countries: Kosovo 2; Russia; Ukraine

Eastern Mennonite Missions
53 W. Brandt Blvd.
Salunga, PA 17538 USA
Phone: (717) 898-2251
Fax: (717) 898-8092
E-mail: info@emm.org
Web Site: www.emm.org
Associations: The Mission Exchange
Dr. Richard Showalter, President
A denominational sending agency of Mennonite tradition engaged in church planting, business as mission, HIV/Aids, support of national churches and short-term programs.
Purpose: "...in serving together, we share God's love, empower Christ-like leaders, and nurture Spirit-inspired partnerships to create transforming communities of worship so that the whole world will know Je-

sus Christ as Lord."
Year Founded in US: 1894
Income for Overseas Min: $5,006,919.00
Fully Supported US Personnel Overseas:
Expecting to serve more than 4 years: 68
Expecting to serve 1 to 4 years: 24
Non-residential mission personnel: 1
Other personnel:
Short-term less than 1 year: 79
Non-US serving in own/other country: 3
Home ministry & office staff in US: 57
Countries: Africa—General 4; Albania 3;
Asia—General 4; Australia; Belize; Bulgaria 2;
Cambodia; Central Asia—General 7; Chile 2;
China 10; Dominican Republic; El Salvador;
Ethiopia 2; Gambia, The 2; Germany 4; Gua-
temala 2; Guinea-Bissau; Honduras; Hong
Kong; India 2; Indonesia 1; Kenya 4; Kosovo
2; Lithuania 2; Macau; Middle East 3; Peru 6;
Philippines; Tanzania 1; Thailand 3; United
Kingdom 2; Venezuela

East-West Ministries Intl.
PO Box 701560
Dallas, TX 75370-1560 USA
Phone: (214) 265-8300
Fax: (214) 265-8503
E-mail: bdurman@eastwest.org
Web Site: www.eastwest.org
Associations: CrossGlobal Link
Mr. John Maisel, President/Founder
A nondenominational sending agency of
Evangelical tradition engaged in church
planting, business as mission, TEE, evange-
lism and leadership development.
Purpose: "...to evangelize and equip na-
tionals to establish grace oriented churches."
Year Founded in US: 1993
Income for Overseas Min: $12,240,000.00
Gifts in Kind: $317,356.00
Fully Supported US Personnel Overseas:
Expecting to serve more than 4 years: 17
Expecting to serve 1 to 4 years: 17
Non-residential mission personnel: 50
Other personnel:
Short-term less than 1 year: 21
Non-US serving in own/other country: 9
Home ministry & office staff in US: 27
Countries: Albania 1; China 2; Haiti; India;
Indonesia; Israel; Kazakhstan 8; Kenya 2;
Russia 2; Spain 2

ECHO Cuba
PO Box 546135
Miami, FL 33154 USA
Phone: (305) 884-0441
Fax: (305) 260-4214
E-mail: info@echocuba.org
Web Site: www.echocuba.org
Associations: AERDO
Dr. Teo A. Bobun, Jr., President/Exec. Director
An interdenominational service agency of
Evangelical tradition engaged in support of
national churches, development, theological
education, literature distribution, support of
national workers and short-term programs.
Purpose: "...is a mission community of
Christ-centered people committed to
reaching the people of Cuba with the Gos-
pel of Jesus Christ, promoting Christian ed-
ucation...help its Cuban citizens to enhance
their lives through captital projects, social
and human services, humanitarian needs,
agricultural entrepreneurship, and church
organizational capacity."
Year Founded in US: 1994
Income for Overseas Min: $1,002,931.00
Gifts in Kind: $158,368.00
Fully Supported US Personnel Overseas:
Non-residential mission personnel: 3
Other personnel:
Short-term less than 1 year: 7
Non-US serving in own/other country: 12
Home ministry & office staff in US: 13
Countries: Cuba

Educational Resources & Referrals—China (ERRC)
1405 Arch St.
Berkeley, CA 94708 USA
Phone: (510) 486-8170
Fax: (510) 486-8160
E-mail: errc@errchina.com
Web Site: www.errchina.com
Mrs. Martha T. Chan, President
A transdenominational specialized agency
of Evangelical and Reformed tradition en-
gaged in cross-cultural education, training/
orientation, discipleship, theological educa-
tion, evangelism, leadership development
and short-term programs.
Purpose: "...to offer educational servic-

es and academic resources to China...to send teachers, professionals, and academics to serve in educational institutions...to conduct local and international culturally relevant long-term programs, short-term seminars, conferences, and events of an educational nature consistent with the key values endorsed by the board."

Year Founded in US: 1986

Income for Overseas Min: $252,188.00

Gifts in Kind: $18,501.00

Fully Supported US Personnel Overseas:
   Expecting to serve more than 4 years: 8
   Expecting to serve 1 to 4 years: 37
   Non-residential mission personnel: 3

Other personnel:
   Short-term less than 1 year: 8
   Non-US serving in own/other country: 2
   Home ministry & office staff in US: 8

Countries: China 8

Educational Services Intl. (ESI)

444 E. Huntington Dr. Ste. 200
Arcadia, CA 91006 USA

Phone: (626) 294-9400
Fax: (626) 821-2022
E-mail: Serve@TeachOverseas.org
Web Site: www.teachoverseas.org

Mr. Ron Nicholas, President

An interdenominational specialized agency of Evangelical tradition engaged in TESOL and tentmaking. Data from 2005.

Purpose: "...to share Christ's love in creative-access nations through teaching."

Year Founded in US: 1989

Income for Overseas Min: $1,400,000.00

Fully Supported US Personnel Overseas:
   Expecting to serve 1 to 4 years: 165

Other personnel:
   Short-term less than 1 year: 105
   Home ministry & office staff in US: 20

Countries: China; CIS—General; Europe—General; Morocco; Vietnam

Edwin L. Hodges Ministries

PO Box 1921
Decatur, AL 35602 USA

Phone: (256) 355-3004
Fax: (256) 250-3502
E-mail: ehodges169@aol.com

Web Site: www.elhm.org
Associations: The Mission Exchange

Mr. Edwin L. Hodges, President/Founder

A nondenominational support agency of Evangelical tradition engaged in literature distribution, audio recording/distribution, Bible distribution, discipleship, leadership development and literature production.

Purpose: "...to collect and donate Christian literature from the United States and ship it to Christians overseas."

Year Founded in US: 1994

Income for Overseas Min: $233,494.00

Gifts in Kind: $9,250,000.00

Elim Fellowship— International Ministries

1703 Dalton Rd.
Lima, NY 14485-0857 USA

Phone: (585) 582-2790
Fax: (585) 624-1229
E-mail: international@elimfellowship.org
Web Site: www.elimfellowship.org

Rev./Dr. Ronald Burgio, President

A nondenominational sending agency of Charismatic and Pentecostal tradition engaged in church planting, theological education, evangelism, funds transmission, support of national churches and missionary training.

Purpose: "...to serve those who are called to reach the nations for Christ."

Year Founded in US: 1933

Income for Overseas Min: $2,939,129.00

Fully Supported US Personnel Overseas:
   Expecting to serve more than 4 years: 82
   Expecting to serve 1 to 4 years: 32
   Non-residential mission personnel: 13

Other personnel:
   Non-US serving in own/other country: 4
   Home ministry & office staff in US: 4

Countries: Andorra 2; Argentina 1; Asia—General 11; Australia 1; Bosnia and Herzegovina 1; Brazil 6; Congo, Democratic Republic of 1; Guam 2; Haiti 2; Kenya 13; Mexico 13; Middle East 3; New Zealand; Niger 4; Nigeria 2; Paraguay 1; Peru 1; Philippines 2; Poland 2; Sudan 2; Sweden 2; Tanzania 6; United Kingdom 2; Vietnam 2

Emmanuel Intl. Mission

3878 Concord Rd.
York, SC 29745 USA
Phone: (803) 831-1356
E-mail: agraham@e-i.org
Web Site: www.e-i.org
Mr. Alan C. Graham, Chairman/President

A nondenominational service agency of Ecumenical and Evangelical tradition engaged in support of national churches, Christian education, theological education, evangelism, relief and/or rehabilitation and WATSAN.

Purpose: "...to transform lives for now, for eternity."

Year Founded in US: 1976

Income for Overseas Min: $122,882.00

Fully Supported US Personnel Overseas:
Expecting to serve more than 4 years: 2
Expecting to serve 1 to 4 years: 1

Other personnel:
Short-term less than 1 year: 2
Non-US serving in own/other country: 29

Countries: Brazil; Haiti; Malawi 1; Philippines 1; South Africa; Tanzania; Uganda

Emmaus Road International

7150 Tanner Ct.
San Diego, CA 92111 USA
Phone: (858) 292-7020
Fax: (858) 292-7020
E-mail: neal_pirolo@eri.org
Web Site: www.eri.org
Mr. Neal Pirolo, Director

A transdenominational service agency engaged in member care, support of national churches, partnership development, mobilization for mission and missionary training.

Purpose: "...to assist the church to mobilize their cross-cultural outreach, train their cross-cultural team and network that church and team with ministries asking for help."

Year Founded in US: 1983

Income for Overseas Min: $50,000.00

Personnel:
Short-term less than 1 year: 12
Home ministry & office staff in US: 1

Empowering Lives Intl.

PO Box 67
Upland, CA 91785 USA
Phone: (909) 931-1311
Fax: (909) 931-9925
E-mail: info@empoweringlives.org
Web Site: www.empoweringlives.org
Mr. Donald P. Rogers, Founder/Director

A nondenominational service agency of Evangelical tradition engaged in development, agricultural programs, childcare/orphanage programs, Christian education, evangelism, medical work, support of national churches and short-term programs. Data from 2005.

Purpose: "...to provide training, resources and encouragement to break the cycle of poverty and help people recognize their importance in the eyes of God."

Year Founded in US: 1994

Income for Overseas Min: $600,464.00

Fully Supported US Personnel Overseas:
Expecting to serve more than 4 years: 2
Expecting to serve 1 to 4 years: 3
Non-residential mission personnel: 3

Other personnel:
Short-term less than 1 year: 65
Non-US serving in own/other country: 122
Home ministry & office staff in US: 4

Countries: Congo, Democratic Republic of; Kenya 2; Sudan; Tanzania

endPoverty.org

7910 Woodmont Ave, Ste. 800
Bethesda, MD 20814 US
Phone: (240) 396-1146
Fax: (240) 235-3550
E-mail: for-more-info@endpoverty.org
Web Site: www.endpoverty.org
Mr. Kenneth W. Wesche, Exec. Director

A nondenominational service agency of Evangelical tradition engaged in microenterprise development, community development, HIV/Aids, partnership development, technical assistance and training.

Purpose: "...to demonstrate God's love by enabling the poor to free themselves from poverty."

Year Founded in US: 1985

Income for Overseas Min: $858,649.00

Gifts in Kind: $92,247.00

Personnel:
Short-term less than 1 year: 10
Non-US serving in own/other country: 1
Home ministry & office staff in US: 6

Countries: Africa—General

Engineering Ministries International (EMI)

130 E. Kiowa St., Ste. 200
Colorado Springs, CO 80903 USA

Phone: (719) 633-2078
Fax: (719) 633-2970
E-mail: info@emiusa.org
Web Site: www.emiusa.org
Associations: AERDO

Mr. James Hall, CEO

An interdenominational specialized agency of Ecumenical tradition engaged in designing projects for other agencies, camping programs, development, Christian education, medical work, relief and/or rehabilitation and technical assistance.

Purpose: "...to design a world of hope for the physically and spiritually poor."

Year Founded in US: 1982

Income for Overseas Min: $5,459,000.00

Gifts in Kind: $3,252,000.00

Fully Supported US Personnel Overseas:
Expecting to serve more than 4 years: 10
Expecting to serve 1 to 4 years: 6
Non-residential mission personnel: 6

Other personnel:
Short-term less than 1 year: 230
Non-US serving in own/other country: 1
Home ministry & office staff in US: 2

Countries: Costa Rica 4; India 4; Uganda 2; United Kingdom

Entrust

PO Box 25520
Colorado Springs, CO 80936-5520 USA

Phone: (719) 622-1980
Fax: (719) 622-1992
E-mail: info@entrust4.org
Web Site: www.entrust4.org

Dr. David G. Goodman, President

A sending agency of Evangelical tradition engaged in leadership development, Christian education, missionary education, theological education and missionary training.

Purpose: "...to assist the Church in responding to the global cry for servant-leaders through accessible, transformational Biblical training."

Year Founded in US: 1979

Income for Overseas Min: $2,886,417.00

Fully Supported US Personnel Overseas:
Expecting to serve more than 4 years: 28
Expecting to serve 1 to 4 years: 3
Non-residential mission personnel: 3

Other personnel:
Short-term less than 1 year: 3
Non-US serving in own/other country: 14
Home ministry & office staff in US: 27

Countries: Czech Republic 2; Greece 2; Hungary 6; Kenya; Middle East 5; Moldova 1; Mozambique; Nigeria; Romania 7; Russia 3; Slovakia 2; South Africa

Envoy International

2051 Warrington
Rochester Hills, MI 48307 USA

Phone: (248) 650-8974
E-mail: dandersen@envoyseminars.org
Web Site: www.envoyseminars.org

Rev. David L. Andersen, President

A nondenominational service agency of Baptist and Evangelical tradition engaged in church mobilization, missions information service, leadership development, partnership development, services for other agencies, short-term programs and training, working in Central America, South America and Eastern Europe.

Purpose: "...to help the local church develop and implement a personalized involvement in world evangelization and discipleship."

Year Founded in US: 1995

Income for Overseas Min: $175,000.00

Fully Supported US Personnel Overseas:
Non-residential mission personnel: 3

Episcopal Church USA— Domestic & Foreign Missionary Society

815 Second Ave.
New York, NY 10017 USA

Phone: (212) 922-5461
Fax: (212) 682-5594

E-mail: dcopley@episcopalchurch.org
Web Site: www.episcopalchurch.org
Associations: CWS
Katharine Jefferts Schori, CEO
A denominational sending agency of Anglican and Episcopal tradition engaged in support of national churches, Christian education, evangelism, furloughed missionary support, partnership development and youth programs.
Purpose: "...to ensure, in the most comprehensive and coordinated manner possible, the full participation of Episcopalians in the worldwide mission of the Church..."
Year Founded in US: 1785
Income for Overseas Min: $13,000,000.00
Fully Supported US Personnel Overseas:
    Expecting to serve more than 4 years: 42
    Expecting to serve 1 to 4 years: 26
    Non-residential mission personnel: 68
Other personnel:
    Short-term less than 1 year: 14
Countries: Belize 42; Colombia; Israel; Namibia; Sierra Leone; Spain; Taiwan

Equip International
PO Box 1126
Marion, NC 28752-1126 USA
Phone: (828) 738-3891
Fax: (828) 738-3946
E-mail: webmaster@equipministries.org
Web Site: www.equipinternational.com
Associations: AERDO, The Mission Exchange
Rev. Barrie G. Flitcroft, Gen. Director
An interdenominational sending agency of Evangelical tradition engaged in missionary training, agricultural programs, development, evangelism, HIV/Aids and justice.
Purpose: "...engaged in specialized prefield training in Appropriate Technology, Missionary Medicine, Community Health, and Water Technologies for missionaries and missionary candidates, development, community health and medicine, and national vocational training."
Year Founded in US: 1983
Income for Overseas Min: $1,665,870.00
Fully Supported US Personnel Overseas:
    Expecting to serve more than 4 years: 16

Expecting to serve 1 to 4 years: 2
Other personnel:
    Non-US serving in own/other country: 10
    Home ministry & office staff in US: 14
Countries: Belize 2; Bolivia 1; Brazil 2; Ethiopia 3; Japan 1; Kenya; Liberia; Malawi 1; Mexico 2; Nicaragua 1; Nigeria; Spain 1; Uganda 2

EQUIP Intl. Ministries
12000 Findley Rd., Ste. 100
Johns Creek, GA 30097 USA
Phone: (678) 225-3300
Fax: (678) 225-3349
Web Site: www.iequip.org
Associations: The Mission Exchange
Dr. John D. Hull, President/CEO
An interdenominational support agency engaged in leadership development and discipleship.
Purpose: "...to see effective Christian leaders fulfill the Great Commission in every nation."
Year Founded in US: 1996

Equipping the Saints
1254 Keezletown Rd.
Weyers Cave, VA 24486 USA
Phone: (540) 234-6222
Fax: (540) 234-6262
E-mail: ets.usa@hotmail.com
Web Site: www.etsusa.org
Rev. Keith A. Jones, Exec. Director
An interdenominational service agency of Evangelical tradition engaged in supplying equipment, missions information service, literature distribution, providing medical supplies, purchasing services and services for other agencies.
Purpose: "...to serve evangelical Christian ministries worldwide by providing all types of information, materials, and equipment so that the body of Christ may be built up."
Year Founded in US: 1991
Income for Overseas Min: $729,804.00
Gifts in Kind: $675,784.00
Personnel:
    Home ministry & office staff in US: 5

Eternal Hope in Haiti

PO Box 307
Hoschton, GA 30548 USA
Phone: (706) 367-7302
Fax: (706) 367-7304
E-mail: thaynes123@aol.com
Web Site: www.eternalhopeinhaiti.org

Twilla L. Haynes, President

An interdenominational sending agency of Baptist, Evangelical, and Friends tradition engaged in childcare/orphanage programs, Bible distribution, discipleship, extension education, medical work and partnership development.

Purpose: "...to provide healthcare to the most impoverished Haitians and to help each child at Hope Haven to grow up healthy and safe in an atmosphere guided by the love of Jesus Christ."

Year Founded in US: 1996

Income for Overseas Min: $116,000.00

Gifts in Kind: $200,000.00

Fully Supported US Personnel Overseas:
Expecting to serve more than 4 years: 4

Other personnel:
Short-term less than 1 year: 106

Countries: Haiti 4

EurAsian Baptist Mission

PO Box 7689
Pensacola, FL 32534 US
Phone: (866) 999-7729
E-mail: chapmaneric57@gmail.com
Web Site: www.eurasianbaptistmission.com

Dr. Eric Chapman, President

A support agency of Baptist and Fundamental tradition engaged in church planting, camping programs, discipleship, Christian education, theological education and evangelism.

Year Founded in US: 1997

Income for Overseas Min: $276,025.00

Personnel:
Short-term less than 1 year: 33
Non-US serving in own/other country: 14

Countries: Malawi; Moldova

European Christian Mission International—USA
(See ad on page 174)

PO Box 181
West Unity, OH 43570-0181 USA
Phone: (419) 924-2056
Fax: (419) 924-2056
E-mail: ecmi.usa@ecmi.org
Web Site: www.ecmi.org

Mr. George Brown, Exec. Director

An interdenominational sending agency of Evangelical tradition engaged in church planting, discipleship, theological education, evangelism, support of national workers and mobilization for mission.

Purpose: "...to establish and develop local reproducing churches that evangelize and disciple the peoples of Europe."

Year Founded in US: 1923

Income for Overseas Min: $464,000.00

Fully Supported US Personnel Overseas:
Expecting to serve more than 4 years: 13
Expecting to serve 1 to 4 years: 1
Non-residential mission personnel: 2

Other personnel:
Short-term less than 1 year: 50
Non-US serving in own/other country: 46
Home ministry & office staff in US: 4

Countries: Albania; Austria 2; Belgium; Bosnia and Herzegovina 2; France 1; Germany; Kosovo 1; Netherlands; Portugal; Romania; Serbia and Montenegro; Spain 7; United Kingdom

European Evangelistic Society

PO Box 90150
East Point, GA 30364 USA
Phone: (404) 460-2443
Fax: (404) 460-2446
E-mail: wye@eesatlanta.org
Web Site: www.eesatlanta.org

Mr. Samuel W. Huxford, Exec. Director

A nondenominational specialized agency of Christian (Restoration Movement) tradition engaged in theological education, church planting, evangelism and mission-related research. Statistical data from 2001.

Purpose: "...to study, disseminate, and demonstrate the gospel, primarily, but not

EUROPEAN CHRISTIAN MISSION INTERNATIONAL USA

PO BOX 181
WEST UNITY OH 43570
419.924.2056

Sharing Christ's love in Europe

Europe is the only continent in which the church is in decline. ECMI exists to establish and develop churches that evangelize and disciple the peoples of Europe. Will you partner with us?

PRAYER PARTNERS
join those praying since 1904 for the unevangelized

MINISTRY PARTNERS
join 197 missionaries from every continent in 20 countries

CHURCH PLANTING PARTNERS
join a sister church in one of 42 outreach projects

FINANCIAL PARTNERS
join 1500 in the US who support 68 missionaries and 13 outreach projects

For more information please contact us at:
www.ecmi-usa.org
Email: ecmi.usa@ecmi.org

exclusively in Europe ...through scholarly research in Christian origins, the publication of research, and the establishment and development of congregations reflecting the understanding of the early church..."

Year Founded in US: 1932

Income for Overseas Min: $205,817.00

Personnel:
Home ministry & office staff in US: 2

Evangel Bible Translators

PO Box 669
Rockwall, TX 75087-0669 USA

Phone: (972) 771-8886
Fax: (972) 722-1721
E-mail: info@evangelbible.org
Web Site: www.evangelbible.org

Rev. H. Syvelle Phillips, Founder/President

A nondenominational sending agency of Pentecostal tradition engaged in Bible translation, Bible distribution, church planting, literacy work and translation work. Data from 2005.

Year Founded in US: 1976

Income for Overseas Min: $701,405.00

Fully Supported US Personnel Overseas:
Expecting to serve more than 4 years: 17
Residential mission personnel: 36

Other personnel:
Short-term less than 1 year: 8
Non-US serving in own/other country: 37
Home ministry & office staff in US: 10

Countries: Azerbaijan 1; Benin; France 2; Ghana 2; Guatemala 2; India 6; Israel 1; Kenya; Liberia 1; Myanmar/Burma; Nepal; Papua New Guinea 2

Evangelical Baptist Missions

PO Box 781438
Indianapolis, IN 46278 USA

Phone: (866) 531-7380
Fax: (317) 872-4489
E-mail: ebm@ebm.org
Web Site: www.ebm.org

Dr. W. Paul Jackson, President

A denominational sending agency of Baptist tradition engaged in church planting, children at risk, theological education, HIV/ Aids, leadership development and video/ film production/distribution.

Purpose: "...to help churches around the

world lead the way in global ministry."

Year Founded in US: 1928

Income for Overseas Min: $4,000,000.00

Gifts in Kind: $5,000.00

Fully Supported US Personnel Overseas:
Expecting to serve more than 4 years: 101
Expecting to serve 1 to 4 years: 1
Non-residential mission personnel: 14

Other personnel:
Short-term less than 1 year: 15
Non-US serving in own/other country: 15
Home ministry & office staff in US: 13

Countries: Argentina 6; Belgium 2; Benin 2; Brazil 3; France 11; Germany 9; Haiti; Italy 4; Japan 4; Mali 9; Mexico 4; Niger 8; Nigeria; Romania 3; Russia 1; South Africa 16; South Pacific 2; Sweden 1; United Arab Emirates; Unspecified Country 14; Zambia 2

Evangelical Bible Mission

5200 SE 145th Street
Summerfield, FL 34491 USA

Phone: (352) 245-2560
Fax: (352) 245-9783
E-mail: info@ebminternational.com
Web Site: www.ebminternational.com

Rev. Gerald Bustin, President

An interdenominational sending agency of Holiness tradition engaged in church planting, Bible distribution, evangelism, literature distribution and supplying equipment. Data from 2001.

Year Founded in US: 1939

Personnel:
Home ministry & office staff in US: 5

Evangelical Congregational Church—Global Ministries Commission

100 W. Park Ave.
Myerstown, PA 17067 USA

Phone: (717) 866-7584
Fax: (717) 866-7383
E-mail: ecglobal@eccenter.com
Web Site: www.ecglobal.org

Rev. Randall Sizemore, Director

A service agency of Wesleyan tradition engaged in missionary kids education, support of national churches, aviation services, church planting and Bible translation. Additional missionaries are sent under other mission agencies.

Year Founded in US: 1928

Income for Overseas Min: $760,000.00

Fully Supported US Personnel Overseas:
Expecting to serve more than 4 years: 23

Other personnel:
Home ministry & office staff in US: 3

Countries: Belize 1; Brazil 2; Caribbean—General 2; Kenya 5; Papua New Guinea 5; Spain 4; Thailand 3; Ukraine 1

Evangelical Covenant Church—Covenant World Mission

5101 N. Francisco Ave.
Chicago, IL 60625 USA

Phone: (773) 784-3000
Fax: (773) 784-4366
E-mail: world.mission@covchurch.org
Web Site: www.covchurch.org

Mr. Gary Walter, President

A denominational sending agency of Evangelical tradition engaged in national church nurture/support, church planting, development, leadership development and partnership development.

Purpose: "...to facilitate intercultural ministries around the world and partner with churches and international believers to glorify God by bringing the whole Gospel to the whole world."

Year Founded in US: 1885

Income for Overseas Min: $8,530,000.00

Fully Supported US Personnel Overseas:
Expecting to serve more than 4 years: 76
Expecting to serve 1 to 4 years: 29
Non-residential mission personnel: 6

Other personnel:
Short-term less than 1 year: 1500
Home ministry & office staff in US: 14

Countries: Argentina; Asia—General 5; Belgium 1; Brazil 2; Burkina Faso 2; Cameroon 8; Central African Republic 3; Chile; Colombia 3; Congo, Democratic Republic of 1; Czech Republic 2; Dominican Republic; Ecuador 2; Equatorial Guinea 2; France 5; Germany; Guam; India; Japan 10; Kenya; Mexico 12; Mongolia 2; Nigeria; Philippines; Russia 2; South Africa; Spain 4; Sudan; Sweden; Taiwan 2; Thailand 8

Evangelical Friends Church Southwest

18639 Yorba Linda Blvd.
Yorba Linda, CA 92886-1436 USA

Phone: (888) 704-9393
Fax: (714) 779-7740
E-mail: office@friendschurchsw.org
Web Site: www.friendschurchsw.org

Mr. Stan Leach, Superintendent

A denominational sending agency of Friends tradition engaged in church planting, association of missions, TEE, leadership development and member care.

Purpose: "...to seek to live our lives as Jesus would live if He were in our shoes, and together fuel a worldwide church multiplication movement that our grandchildren's grandchildren will be compelled to expand."

Year Founded in US: 1895

Fully Supported US Personnel Overseas:
Expecting to serve 1 to 4 years: 2
Non-residential mission personnel: 12

Other personnel:
Short-term less than 1 year: 33
Non-US serving in own/other country: 7
Home ministry & office staff in US: 4

Countries: Cambodia

Evangelical Friends Mission

PO Box 525
Arvada, CO 80001 USA

Phone: (303) 421-8100
Fax: (303) 431-6455
E-mail: efm@friendsmission.com
Web Site: www.friendsmission.com

Associations: The Mission Exchange

Dr. Charles Mylander, Exec. Director

A denominational sending agency of Evangelical tradition engaged in church planting, discipleship, TEE, evangelism, leadership development and support of national churches.

Purpose: "...to lead our people worldwide to live so close to Jesus Christ that we will worship, serve, and obey God as faithful witnesses...to live and die for the cause of fulfilling the Great Commission in the spirit of the Great Commission."

Year Founded in US: 1978

Income for Overseas Min: $1,523,819.00

Personnel:

Short-term less than 1 year: 7
Home ministry & office staff in US: 6

Countries: Bangladesh; Bhutan; India; Ireland; Mexico; Nepal; Philippines; Rwanda; Unspecified Country

Evangelical Lutheran Church in America, Div. for Global Mission

8765 W. Higgins Rd.
Chicago, IL 60631 USA
Phone: (773) 380-2650
Fax: (773) 380-2410
E-mail: GMInfo@elca.org
Web Site: www.elca.org
Associations: CWS
Rev. Rafael Malpica-Padilla, Exec. Director

A denominational sending agency of Lutheran tradition engaged in partnership development, development, evangelism, leadership development and relief and/or rehabilitation. Data from 2005.

Purpose: "...marked with the cross of Christ forever, we are claimed, gathered and sent for the sake of the world."

Year Founded in US: 1987

Income for Overseas Min: $34,434,240.00

Fully Supported US Personnel Overseas:
Expecting to serve more than 4 years: 101
Expecting to serve 1 to 4 years: 62

Other personnel:
Short-term less than 1 year: 83
Non-US serving in own/other country: 15
Home ministry & office staff in US: 44

Countries: Argentina 1; Brazil 2; Cameroon 6; Central African Republic 1; China 4; Costa Rica 1; Denmark 2; Egypt 2; El Salvador; Ethiopia 2; Germany 6; Guam 2; Guyana 2; Hong Kong 6; Honduras; India 1; Indonesia 1; Jamaica 2; Japan 13; Kenya 4; Korea, South; Lebanon; Liberia 1; Madagascar 5; Mexico 2; Namibia 1; Nigeria 1; Palestine; Papua New Guinea 2; Russia 1; Senegal 7; Singapore 1; Slovakia 2; South Africa 1; Tanzania 19; Thailand

Evangelical Methodist Church, Inc.—Board of Missions

PO Box 17070
Indianapolis, IN 46217 USA
Phone: (317) 780-8017

Fax: (317) 780-8078
Web Site: www.emchurch.org
Dr. Edward W. Williamson, General Supt.

A denominational sending agency of Wesleyan tradition engaged in evangelism, childrens programs, church planting, discipleship and theological education. Data from 2005.

Year Founded in US: 1946

Income for Overseas Min: $344,145.00

Fully Supported US Personnel Overseas:
Expecting to serve more than 4 years: 5
Non-residential mission personnel: 1

Other personnel:
Non-US serving in own/other country: 1
Home ministry & office staff in US: 3

Countries: Mexico 5; Spain

Evangelical Mission Ministries, Inc.

PO Box 636
Pharr, TX 78577 USA
Phone: (956) 787-3543
Fax: (956) 787-3566
E-mail: emm-mex@sbcglobal.net
Web Site: www.emm-mexico.org
Mr. Keith B. Anderson, Exec. Director

A nondenominational sending agency of Evangelical and Independent tradition engaged in support of national churches, church construction, correspondence courses, theological education, evangelism and literature distribution.

Purpose: "...to make Christ known to the Spanish speaking world."

Year Founded in US: 1954

Income for Overseas Min: $437,100.00

Fully Supported US Personnel Overseas:
Expecting to serve 1 to 4 years: 9

Other personnel:
Short-term less than 1 year: 1
Home ministry & office staff in US: 11

Countries: Mexico

Evangelical Presbyterian Church—World Outreach

17197 N. Laurel Park Dr., Ste. 567
Livonia, MI 48152 USA
Phone: (734) 742-2020
Fax: (734) 742-2033
E-mail: wo@epc.org

Web Site: www.epcwo.org

Associations: The Mission Exchange

Mr. John McCurry, Director

A denominational sending agency of Evangelical tradition engaged in church planting, discipleship, theological education, evangelism, support of national churches and leadership development.

Purpose: "...to glorify God through full-cycle church planting which firmly establishes the Church of Jesus Christ among least reached people, with a primary focus on the Muslim world."

Year Founded in US: 1981

Income for Overseas Min: $2,314,697.00

Fully Supported US Personnel Overseas:
Expecting to serve more than 4 years: 4
Expecting to serve 1 to 4 years: 2

Other personnel:
Home ministry & office staff in US: 4

Countries: Ethiopia 4; Nigeria

Evangelism and Missions Information Service (EMIS)

PO Box 794
Wheaton, IL 60187 USA

Phone: (630) 752-7158
Fax: (630) 752-7155
E-mail: emis@wheaton.edu
Web Site: www.emisdirect.com

Dr. Kenneth D. Gill, Director

The publishing department of the Billy Graham Center, providing evangelism and missions information through publications such as *Evangelical Missions Quarterly, Lausanne World Pulse, Mission Handbook*, and books about evangelism and missions.

Year Founded in US: 1964

Personnel:
Home ministry & office staff in US: 9

Evangelism Explosion Intl.

PO Box 23820
Ft. Lauderdale, FL 33307-3820 USA

Phone: (954) 491-6100
Fax: (954) 771-2256
E-mail: info@eeinternational.org
Web Site: www.eeinternational.org

Associations: The Mission Exchange

Rev. John B. Sorensen, President

An interdenominational support agency of Evangelical tradition engaged in evangelism, discipleship, training and youth programs. Countries of service data from 2005.

Purpose: "...to equip pastors and lay people to be bold witnesses for Jesus Christ and to be able to train others to take the Gospel to the very ends of the earth."

Year Founded in US: 1970

Income for Overseas Min: $2,289,356.00

Fully Supported US Personnel Overseas:
Expecting to serve more than 4 years: 2
Non-residential mission personnel: 11

Other personnel:
Non-US serving in own/other country: 64
Home ministry & office staff in US: 19

Countries: Argentina; Armenia; Belgium; Ghana; Guatemala; India 2; Indonesia; Kazakhstan; Kyrgyzstan; Mexico; Moldova; Papua New Guinea; Russia; Turkmenistan; Ukraine; Uzbekistan

Evangelism Resources, Inc.

425 Epworth Ave.
Wilmore, KY 40390 USA

Phone: (859) 858-0777
Fax: (859) 858-2907
E-mail: eroffice@qx.net
Web Site: www.erinfo.org

Rev. Stephen P. Liversedge, President

A sending agency of Evangelical tradition engaged in evangelism, church planting, Christian education, evangelism, leadership development and literature distribution.

Purpose: "...to deliver time-tested curriculum, blended with cutting-edge practices...to equip churches to make evangelism an everyday, every-member, every-activity way of life."

Year Founded in US: 1976

Income for Overseas Min: $739,016.00

Fully Supported US Personnel Overseas:
Expecting to serve 1 to 4 years: 2

Other personnel:
Short-term less than 1 year: 7
Non-US serving in own/other country: 2
Home ministry & office staff in US: 2

Countries: India; Nigeria

Evangelistic Faith Missions

PO Box 609
Bedford, IN 47421 USA
Phone: (812) 275-7531
Fax: (812) 275-7532
E-mail: efmjsm@juno.com
Web Site: www.efm-missions.org
Associations: The Mission Exchange

Rev. J. Stevan Manley, President

An interdenominational sending agency of Holiness tradition engaged in theological education, broadcasting, childcare/orphanage programs, church planting, medical work and support of national churches. Countries of service data from 2005.

Purpose: "...to win the lost to Jesus Christ...to conduct a strong program of evangelism..."

Year Founded in US: 1905

Income for Overseas Min: $1,133,440.00

Fully Supported US Personnel Overseas:
  Expecting to serve 1 to 4 years: 14
  Non-residential mission personnel: 4

Other personnel:
  Short-term less than 1 year: 6
  Non-US serving in own/other country: 4
  Home ministry & office staff in US: 10

Countries: Bolivia; Costa Rica; Dominican Republic; Egypt; El Salvador; Eritrea; Ethiopia; Guatemala; Honduras; Korea, South; Unspecified Country

Evangelize China Fellowship, Inc.

435 S. Garfield Ave.
Monterey Park, CA 91754 USA

Phone: (626) 288-8828
Fax: (626) 288-6727
E-mail: info@ecfusa.org
Web Site: www.ecfinternational.org

Dr. Paul C.C. Szteo, Gen. Director

A support agency of Baptist tradition engaged in evangelism, broadcasting, childcare/orphanage programs, church construction, Christian education and relief and/or rehabilitation.

Year Founded in US: 1947

Personnel:
  Short-term less than 1 year: 17

Non-US serving in own/other country: 2
Home ministry & office staff in US: 10
Countries: Hong Kong; Philippines

Every Child Ministries, Inc.

PO Box 810
Hebron, IN 46341 USA

Phone: (219) 996-4201
Fax: (219) 996-4203
E-mail: ecmafrica@ecmafrica.org
Web Site: www.ecmafrica.org

John & Lorella Rouster, Intl. Co-Directors

A transdenominational service agency of Evangelical tradition engaged in children at risk, childcare/orphanage programs, childrens programs, evangelism, relief and/or rehabilitation and trafficking/slavery issues.

Purpose: "...dedicated to offering hope to the new generation in Africa by training, equipping, and providing resources for African churches..."

Year Founded in US: 1985

Income for Overseas Min: $800,160.00

Fully Supported US Personnel Overseas:
  Expecting to serve more than 4 years: 4
  Expecting to serve 1 to 4 years: 7
  Non-residential mission personnel: 1

Other personnel:
  Short-term less than 1 year: 31
  Non-US serving in own/other country: 38
  Home ministry & office staff in US: 4

Countries: Angola; Benin; Congo, Democratic Republic of; Ghana 4; Togo; Uganda

Every Home for Christ Intl.

PO Box 64000
Colorado Springs, CO 80962 USA

Phone: (800) 423-5054
E-mail: info@ehc.org
Web Site: www.ehc.org
Associations: CrossGlobal Link

Dr. Dick Eastman, Intl. President

A service agency of Evangelical tradition engaged in evangelism, church planting, correspondence courses, literature distribution, Bible distribution and training. Financial data from 2005.

Purpose: "...to serve, mobilize, and train the Church to actively participate and pray for the systematic personal presentation of a printed or repeatable message of the Gospel of Jesus Christ to every home in the whole world, adding new believers as functioning members of the body of Christ."

Year Founded in US: 1946
Income for Overseas Min: $13,648,253.00
Personnel:
Non-US serving in own/other country: 36
Home ministry & office staff in US: 30
Countries: Albania; Angola; Armenia; Asia—General; Austria; Bangladesh; Belgium; Bosnia and Herzegovina; Bulgaria; Burundi; Cambodia; Croatia; Czech Republic; Ethiopia; France; Germany; Ghana; Honduras; Hungary; India; Indonesia; Italy; Japan; Kenya; Kosovo; Lesotho; Liberia; Madagascar; Malawi; Mexico; Mongolia; Mozambique; Myanmar/Burma; Namibia; Nepal; Nicaragua; Philippines; Russia; Rwanda; Sierra Leone; South Africa; Sri Lanka; Swaziland; Tanzania; Thailand; Uganda; Ukraine; Uruguay

Face to Face International

PO Box 6045
Scottsdale, AZ 85261 USA
Phone: (480) 835-5080
Fax: (480) 835-8905
Web Site: www.face.org
Dr. Don Orvis, President

An interdenominational specialized agency of Evangelical and Independent tradition engaged in short-term programs.

Purpose: "...to assist local churches and mission agencies to take well prepared short-term teams throughout the world to meet a variety of needs."

Year Founded in US: 1995
Income for Overseas Min: $500,000.00
Gifts in Kind: $150,000.00
Personnel:
Short-term less than 1 year: 50
Home ministry & office staff in US: 8

Faith Christian Fellowship Intl.

PO Box 35443
Tulsa, OK 74153 USA
Phone: (918) 492-5800
Fax: (918) 492-6140
Web Site: www.fcf.org
Pat Harrison, President

A nondenominational sending agency of Charismatic tradition engaged in church planting, association of missions, discipleship, Christian education, theological education, missions information service, leadership development, support of national churches, support of national workers and partnership development.

Purpose: "...to reach the world for Christ... to demonstrate the power of the Holy Spirit...to build covenant relationships."

Year Founded in US: 1977
Income for Overseas Min: $205,000.00
Fully Supported US Personnel Overseas:
Expecting to serve more than 4 years: 24
Non-residential mission personnel: 1
Other personnel:
Short-term less than 1 year: 54
Non-US serving in own/other country: 273
Countries: Africa—General 2; Belgium 1; Czech Republic 1; Germany 1; Guatemala 1; India 2; Ireland 1; Jamaica 2; Kenya 2; Korea, South 1; Malawi 2; Mexico 2; Russia 1; Singapore 1; South Africa 1; Sri Lanka 1; Turkey 1; Zimbabwe 1

Faith Comes By Hearing/ Hosanna

2421 Aztec Rd. NE
Albuquerque, NM 87107 USA
Phone: (505) 881-3321
Fax: (505) 881-1681
E-mail: info@fcbhmail.org
Web Site: www.faithcomesbyhearing.com
Mr. Gerald A. Jackson, President

A service agency which works with over 140 different denominations engaged in Bible audio recording and Bible distribution.

Purpose: "...to bring His Church together and make disciples from every nation, tribe, language, and people."

Year Founded in US: 1972
Income for Overseas Min: $15,412,094.00
Fully Supported US Personnel Overseas:
Expecting to serve more than 4 years: 15
Non-residential mission personnel: 7
Other personnel:
Home ministry & office staff in US: 112
Countries: Africa—General 4; Asia—General 5; Central Asia—General 1; Latin America—General 4; Middle East 1

Faith Life Ministries, Inc.

12000 Leeward Walk Circle
Alpharetta, GA 30005 USA
Phone: (770) 619-9939
Fax: (678) 205-2198
E-mail: barryvoss@comcast.net
Web Site: www.faithlifeministries.net
Mr. Barry Voss, President
A nondenominational service agency of Lutheran tradition engaged in leadership development, childrens programs, discipleship, management consulting/training and youth programs.
Purpose: "...to provide biblcal, practical, basic leadership and management training in a standardized format to help pastors and church leaders in 2nd and 3rd world nations make disciples."
Year Founded in US: 2001
Income for Overseas Min: $40,000.00
Personnel:
  Short-term less than 1 year: 15
  Home ministry & office staff in US: 1
Countries: India; Kazakhstan; Kenya; Latvia; Peru; Philippines; Uganda

Faith Missions International

PO Box 34038
Omaha, NE 68134 USA
Phone: (402) 391-0657
E-mail: info@fmisent.org
Web Site: www.fmisent.org
Mr. Daniel Jensen, President
A nondenominational support agency of Evangelical tradition engaged in childcare/orphanage programs, development and Christian newspaper.
Year Founded in US: 1998
Income for Overseas Min: $210,077.00
Personnel:
  Non-US serving in own/other country: 11
  Home ministry & office staff in US: 2
Countries: Haiti

FAME (Fellowship of Associates of Medical Evangelism)

4545 Southeastern Ave.
Indianapolis, IN 46203 USA
Phone: (317) 358-2480
Fax: (317) 358-2483

E-mail: medicalmissions@fameworld.org
Web Site: www.fameworld.org
Dr. Richard Wolford, Exec. Director
A nondenominational specialized agency of Christian (Restoration Movement) tradition engaged in medical work, evangelism, providing medical supplies, short-term programs, supplying equipment and community health evangelism.
Purpose: "...to spread the FAME of Jesus Christ to all nations through medical evangelism."
Year Founded in US: 1970
Income for Overseas Min: $11,464,097.00
Gifts in Kind: $10,746,645.00
Personnel:
  Short-term less than 1 year: 140
  Home ministry & office staff in US: 10

Far East Broadcasting Company, Inc.

PO Box 1
La Mirada, CA 90638 USA
Phone: (562) 947-4651
Fax: (562) 947-0391
E-mail: info@febc.org
Web Site: www.febc.org
Associations: The Mission Exchange
Rev. Gregg J. Harris, President
A sending agency engaged in broadcasting, audio recording/distribution, evangelism, funds transmission and support of national workers. Activities & countries of service data from 2005.
Purpose: "...to develop radio programming and deliver it to listeners in Asia in such a way that they move toward Jesus Christ and into His Kingdom, that they know Him as Saviour, Lord, and King, follow His teaching, and live in obedience to Him..."
Year Founded in US: 1945
Income for Overseas Min: $4,545,948.00
Fully Supported US Personnel Overseas:
  Expecting to serve more than 4 years: 14
Other personnel:
  Non-US serving in own/other country: 516
  Home ministry & office staff in US: 53
Countries: Cambodia; Finland 1; Indonesia; Korea, South 1; Mongolia; N. Mariana Isls. 4; Philippines 7; Russia; United Kingdom 1

FARMS International

PO Box 270
Knife River, MN 55609 USA
Phone: (218) 834-2676
Fax: (218) 834-2676
E-mail: nathan@farmsinternational.com
Web Site: www.farmsinternational.com
Associations: AERDO

Mr. Joseph E. Richter, Exec. Director

A nondenominational specialized agency of Evangelical tradition engaged in development, agricultural programs, discipleship, funds transmission, management consulting/training and technical assistance. Data from 2005.

Purpose: "...serving the church by equipping Christian families in poverty with the means for self-support...[to help]...families find a biblical path out of poverty."

Year Founded in US: 1967

Income for Overseas Min: $117,580.00

Personnel:
   Home ministry & office staff in US: 4

Fellowship Intl. Mission

555 S. 24th St.
Allentown, PA 18104 USA
Phone: (610) 435-9099
Fax: (610) 435-2641
E-mail: info@fim.org
Web Site: www.fim.org
Associations: CrossGlobal Link

Mr. Stephen Wilt, Gen. Director

A nondenominational sending agency of Independent tradition engaged in church planting, camping programs, childcare/orphanage programs, childrens programs, discipleship and youth programs.

Purpose: "...to assist local churches to fulfill their missionary vision and missionaries to fulfill their call."

Year Founded in US: 1950

Income for Overseas Min: $2,946,218.00

Fully Supported US Personnel Overseas:
   Expecting to serve more than 4 years: 74
   Expecting to serve 1 to 4 years: 1

Other personnel:
   Short-term less than 1 year: 2
   Non-US serving in own/other country: 30
   Home ministry & office staff in US: 4

Countries: Australia 1; Belgium; Benin 2; Bolivia 2; Brazil 11; China 1; Fiji; Germany 2; Ghana 3; Greece; Haiti 2; Italy 2; Japan 1; Kenya 2; Mexico 13; Morocco 10; Nepal 2; New Zealand 1; Niger 1; Nigeria 4; Senegal 2; Sweden 3; Thailand 2; Uganda; United Kingdom 2; Venezuela 5

Fellowship of Companies for Christ International (FCCI)

4201 N. Peachtree Rd.,Ste. 200
Atlanta, GA 30341 USA
Phone: (770) 685-6000
Fax: (770) 685-6001
E-mail: doug@fcci.org
Web Site: www.fcci.org

Mr. Douglas Hunter, President/CEO

A specialized agency of Evangelical tradition engaged in business as mission, discipleship, evangelism, leadership development, management consulting/training and training.

Purpose: "...to equip and encourage Christian business leaders to operate their businesses and conduct their personal lives in accordance with Biblical principles."

Year Founded in US: 1977

Income for Overseas Min: $182,115.00

Personnel:
   Non-US serving in own/other country: 4
   Home ministry & office staff in US: 4

Countries: Africa—General; Asia—General; Europe—General; Latin America—General

Fellowship of Evangelical Churches—Intl. Ministries

1420 Kerrway Ct.
Fort Wayne, IN 46805 USA
Phone: (260) 423-3649
Fax: (260) 420-1905
Web Site: www.fecministries.org

Rev. Earl I. Cecil, Director

A denominational sending agency of Evangelical and Anabaptist tradition engaged in leadership development, church planting, discipleship, extension education and evangelism.

Purpose: "...to facilitate local churches to spread the Gospel among unreached and unevangelized peoples with the goal of generating and reproducing a church planting movement."

Year Founded in US: 1865
Income for Overseas Min: $947,780.00
Fully Supported US Personnel Overseas:
  Expecting to serve more than 4 years: 21
  Non-residential mission personnel: 1
Other personnel:
  Short-term less than 1 year: 57
  Home ministry & office staff in US: 3
Countries: Albania 6; Asia—General 2; Hungary 2; Middle East 2; Spain 2; United Kingdom 3; Venezuela 3; Zimbabwe 1

Fellowship Travel Intl.
10220 Timber Ridge Dr.
Ashland, VA 23005 USA
Phone: (800) 235-9384
Fax: (804) 550-2525
E-mail: mail@fellowship.com
Web Site: www.fellowship.com
Mr. G. Wayne Lawhorn, President

A service agency of Evangelical tradition engaged in mission travel, short-term programs and sports program ministry.
Year Founded in US: 1982

Final Frontiers Foundation, Inc.
1200 Peachtree St.
Louisville, GA 30434 USA
Phone: (706) 955-4916
E-mail: postmaster@finalfrontiers.org
Web Site: www.finalfrontiers.org
Rev. Jon Nelms, President

A nondenominational support agency of Baptist tradition engaged in support of national workers, Bible distribution, childcare/orphanage programs, church planting, funds transmission and support of national churches, serving in 73 countries and more than 25,000 churches. Data from 2005.
Year Founded in US: 1986
Income for Overseas Min: $806,561.00
Personnel:
  Short-term less than 1 year: 4
  Non-US serving in own/other country: 1010
  Home ministry & office staff in US: 6
Countries: Africa—General; Asia—General; Caribbean—General; Central Asia—General; Eastern Europe—General; Europe—General; Latin America—General; Middle East; Oceania—General

Finishers Project
3303 S. Lindsay Rd., Ste. 108
Gilbert, AZ 85297 USA
Phone: (480) 854-4444
Fax: (480) 854-4741
E-mail: azoffice@finishers.org
Web Site: www.finishers.org
Mr. Donald Parrott, CEO/President

A nondenominational service agency of Baptist and Evangelical tradition engaged in recruiting/mobilizing, business as mission and services for other agencies.
Purpose: "...to connect mid-life adults with global impact opportunities for God."
Year Founded in US: 1998
Personnel:
  Home ministry & office staff in US: 8

FLET University/ Universidad FLET
14540 SW 136 St., Ste. 108
Miami, FL 33186 USA
Phone: (305) 378-8700
Fax: (305) 232-5832
E-mail: informacion@flet.edu
Web Site: www.flet.edu
Dr. Jeffery De Leon, President

An interdenominational service agency of Evangelical tradition engaged in theological education, correspondence courses, Christian education, TEE, extension education and leadership development, with students located in 29 countries. Data from 2005.
Purpose: "...to provide biblical and theological training to pastors, teachers and church leaders by means of distance education throughout the Spanish-speaking world."
Year Founded in US: 1968
Personnel:
  Home ministry & office staff in US: 5

Floresta USA, Inc.
4903 Morena Blvd., Ste.1215
San Diego, CA 92117-7352 USA
Phone: (858) 274-3718
Fax: (858) 274-3728
E-mail: info@floresta.org
Web Site: www.floresta.org
Associations: AERDO
Mr. Scott C. Sabin, Exec. Director

A nondenominational support agency of Evangelical tradition engaged in agricultural programs, development and discipleship. Data from 2005.

Purpose: "...reversing deforestation and poverty by transforming the lives of the rural poor."

Year Founded in US: 1984

Income for Overseas Min: $814,837.00

Personnel:
   Non-US serving in own/other country: 47
   Home ministry & office staff in US: 7

Countries: Dominican Republic; Haiti; Mexico; Tanzania

Flying Doctors of America (Medical Mercy Missions, Inc.)

PO Box 923563
Norcross, GA 30010 USA

Phone: (770) 558-330
E-mail: missiontrip@aol.com
Web Site: www.fdoamerica.org

Dr. Allan M. Gathercoal, President

An interdenominational service agency engaged in providing medical and dental work, providing medical supplies and rehabilitation through short-term medical missions in 14 countries. A division of Medical Mercy Missions, Inc. Data from 2005.

Purpose: "...helping people help people...[by]...creating a network of God's love that reaches into the farthest corners of the world and the human heart."

Year Founded in US: 1990

Income for Overseas Min: $70,984.00

Personnel:
   Short-term less than 1 year: 60

Countries: Guatemala; Honduras; Mexico; Peru

FOCAS (Foundation of Compassionate American Samaritans)

PO Box 428760
Cincinnati, OH 45242 USA

Phone: (513) 621-5300
Fax: (513) 621-5307
E-mail: FOCAS@focas-us.org
Web Site: www.focas-us.org
Associations: AERDO

Mr. Richard P. Taylor, Exec. Director

An interdenominational service agency of Charismatic tradition engaged in medical work, childrens programs, Christian education, evangelism and short-term programs. Data from 2005.

Purpose: "...to seek the transformation of lives by proclaiming the gospel of Jesus Christ and, through discipleship and practical expressions of God's love, to open hearts to the work of the Holy Spirit."

Year Founded in US: 1986

Income for Overseas Min: $400,000.00

Gifts in Kind: $80,000.00

Personnel:
   Non-US serving in own/other country: 8
   Home ministry & office staff in US: 3

Countries: Haiti

FOM (Fellowship of Missions)

35 Maranatha Blvd.
Sebring, FL 33870 USA

Phone: (863) 214-4859
Web Site: www.fellowshipofmissions.org

Dr. Daniel Anderson, Chairman

An inter-mission service agency of fundamental tradition engaged in research and information service, acting as an accrediting agency for its constituents and encouraging the formation of missionary and church fellowships.

Year Founded in US: 1969

Food for the Hungry, Inc.

1224 E. Washington St.
Phoenix, AZ 85034 USA

Phone: (480) 998-3100
Fax: (480) 998-9448
Web Site: www.fh.org
Associations: The Mission Exchange

Mr. Benjamin Homan, President/CEO

An interdenominational sending agency of Evangelical tradition engaged in development, agricultural programs, children at risk, childrens programs, HIV/Aids and justice. Countries of service data from 2005.

Purpose: "...to walk with churches, leaders, and families in overcoming all forms of human poverty..."

Year Founded in US: 1971

Income for Overseas Min: $82,768,788.00

Fully Supported US Personnel Overseas:
Expecting to serve more than 4 years: 19
Expecting to serve 1 to 4 years: 63
Non-residential mission personnel: 2

Other personnel:
Non-US serving in own/other country: 6
Home ministry & office staff in US: 4

Countries: Bangladesh; Bolivia 4; Brazil; Cambodia; China 2; Congo, Democratic Republic of; Costa Rica; Dominican Republic; Ethiopia; Guatemala 3; India; Kenya 1; Laos; Malaysia 2; Mongolia; Mozambique; Nicaragua; Nigeria; Peru; Philippines 1; Romania 4; Rwanda; Thailand 2; Tajikistan; Uzbekistan

For God's Children Intl.
PO Box 434
Council Bluffs, IA 51502-0434 USA
Phone: (712) 328-3776
Fax: (712) 328-3776
E-mail: fgci@fgci.org
Web Site: www.fgci.org
Mr. Joel Burkum, Exec. Director

A nondenominational specialized agency of Christian (Restoration Movement) tradition engaged in childrens programs, camping programs, childcare/orphanage programs, evangelism, relief and/or rehabilitation and youth programs.

Purpose: "...to provide hope, dignity and love in Jesus' name for God's children."

Year Founded in US: 1995

Income for Overseas Min: $150,000.00

Fully Supported US Personnel Overseas:
Expecting to serve 1 to 4 years: 1

Other personnel:
Short-term less than 1 year: 22
Non-US serving in own/other country: 7
Home ministry & office staff in US: 5

Countries: Moldova; Romania

For Haiti with Love, Inc.
PO Box 1017
Palm Harbor, FL 34682-1017 USA
Phone: (727) 938-3245
Fax: (727) 942-6945
E-mail: forhaiti@aol.com
Web Site: www.forhaitiwithlove.org
Eva DeHart, President

An interdenominational service agency engaged in medicine, including a burn clinic, dental and public health and emergency food and housing.

Purpose: "...to make life better for Haiti's poor by sharing God's love and increasing awareness of needs to those in the US and elsewhere."

Year Founded in US: 1969

Income for Overseas Min: $583,000.00

Gifts in Kind: $264,000.00

Fully Supported US Personnel Overseas:
Expecting to serve more than 4 years: 7

Other personnel:
Non-US serving in own/other country: 7

Countries: Haiti 7

For His Glory Evangelistic Ministries
PO Box 4107
Wheaton, IL 60189 USA
Phone: (630) 728-8012
E-mail: rob.welch@forhisglorymin.org
Web Site: www.forhisglorymin.org
Mr. Rob Welch, President

An interdenominational specialized agency of Evangelical tradition engaged in evangelism and leadership development.

Purpose: "...to proclaim the Good News of Jesus Christ...to equip and mobilize His Church to reach those without Christ."

Year Founded in US: 2006

Income for Overseas Min: $91,520.00

Personnel:
Short-term less than 1 year: 17
Home ministry & office staff in US: 2

Forgotten Voices Intl.
PO Box 1368
Mechanicsburg, PA 17055-1368 USA
Phone: (717) 506-0633
E-mail: info@forgottenvoices.org
Web Site: www.forgottenvoices.org
Mr. Ryan Keith, President

A support agency of Brethren and Evangelical tradition engaged in children at risk, development, HIV/Aids, leadership development, support of national churches and psychological counseling.

Purpose: "...to demonstrate the love of Jesus Christ by equipping local churches in southern Africa to meet the physical and spiritual needs of children orphaned by AIDS in their communities."

Year Founded in US: 2005

Income for Overseas Min: $198,733.00

Fully Supported US Personnel Overseas:
   Non-residential mission personnel: 1

Other personnel:
   Short-term less than 1 year: 3
   Non-US serving in own/other country: 3
   Home ministry & office staff in US: 2

Countries: Zambia; Zimbabwe

Forward Edge International

15121- A NE 72nd Ave.
Vancouver, WA 98686 USA

Phone: (360) 574-3343
Fax: (360) 574-2118
E-mail: fei@forwardedge.org
Web Site: www.forwardedge.org

Rev. Joseph Anfuso, Founder/Director

A transdenominational service agency of Evangelical tradition engaged in short-term programs, childcare/orphanage programs, development, medical work and relief and/ or rehabilitation. Data from 2005.

Purpose: "...mobilizing ordinary Christians to spread the gospel and serve the poor... on U.S. Indian reservations and overseas."

Year Founded in US: 1983

Income for Overseas Min: $165,000.00

Fully Supported US Personnel Overseas:
   Expecting to serve 1 to 4 years: 1

Other personnel:
   Short-term less than 1 year: 950
   Non-US serving in own/other country: 1
   Home ministry & office staff in US: 13

Countries: Nicaragua

Foundation For His Ministry

PO Box 74000
San Clemente, CA 92673-0134 USA

Phone: (949) 492-2200
Fax: (949) 492-0900
E-mail: charla@ffhm.org
Web Site: www.ffhm.org

Charla Pereau, Exec. Director

An interdenominational service agency of Charismatic and Ecumenical tradition engaged in childcare/orphanage programs, evangelism, broadcasting, church planting, disability assistance programs, discipleship and medical work.

Purpose: "...to glorify God by making disciples of Jesus Christ...by sharing and demonstrating God's love through the power of the Holy Spirit by meeting basic spiritual, emotional, physical and educational needs of those in Mexico and beyond."

Year Founded in US: 1967

Income for Overseas Min: $3,092,054.00

Gifts in Kind: $951,067.00

Fully Supported US Personnel Overseas:
   Expecting to serve more than 4 years: 20
   Expecting to serve 1 to 4 years: 10

Other personnel:
   Short-term less than 1 year: 2500
   Non-US serving in own/other country: 114
   Home ministry & office staff in US: 8

Countries: Mexico 20

Foursquare Missions Intl.

PO Box 26902
Los Angeles, CA 90026-0176 USA

Phone: (213) 989-4320
Fax: (213) 989-4559
Web Site: www.foursquare.org

Associations: The Mission Exchange

Dr. Jack Hayford, President

A denominational sending agency of Charismatic tradition engaged in church planting, discipleship, evangelism, leadership development and support of national churches. Countries of service data from 2005.

Purpose: "...to evangelize, release indigenous leadership, cultivate church planting, and reproduce missionary-sending churches in obedience to the mandate of Jesus Christ to 'make disciples of all nations'..."

Year Founded in US: 1923

Fully Supported US Personnel Overseas:
   Expecting to serve more than 4 years: 61
   Expecting to serve 1 to 4 years: 13
   Non-residential mission personnel: 5

Other personnel:
   Short-term less than 1 year: 25
   Home ministry & office staff in US: 18

Countries: Albania 2; Australia 2; Brazil 2;

Cambodia 2; Costa Rica 2; Croatia; Dominican Republic 2; Grenada 1; India 2; Israel 4; Italy 2; Japan 4; Malaysia; Mexico 4; Nepal 2; Nigeria 2; Panama 2; Papua New Guinea 2; Paraguay 2; Puerto Rico 2; Rwanda 2; Singapore 2; South Africa 4; Spain 2; Taiwan 2; Tajikistan 2; Thailand 2; Uganda 4; Unspecified Country

Free Gospel Church, Inc.— Missions Department
PO Box 477
Export, PA 15632 USA
Phone: (412) 373-0307
Fax: (412) 373-0307
E-mail: fgmd@juno.com
Mr. Chester H. Heath, Gen. Superintendent

A support agency of Holiness and Pentecostal tradition engaged in support/nurture of national churches, church construction, church planting, theological education, evangelism and support of national workers.
Year Founded in US: 1916
Income for Overseas Min: $188,523.00
Fully Supported US Personnel Overseas:
  Expecting to serve 1 to 4 years: 2
Other personnel:
  Short-term less than 1 year: 10
  Non-US serving in own/other country: 59
Countries: India; Philippines; Sierra Leone

Free Methodist World Missions
PO Box 535002
Indianapolis, IN 46253-5002 USA
Phone: (800) 342-5531
Fax: (317) 241-1248
E-mail: missions@fmcna.org
Web Site: www.fmwm.org
Associations: The Mission Exchange
Dr. Arthur Brown, Exec. Director

A denominational sending agency of Methodist and Wesleyan tradition engaged in leadership development, church planting, evangelism, support of national churches, partnership development and child sponsorship.
Purpose: "...to serve Free Methodists as together we make disciples of Jesus Christ among the peoples of the world."
Year Founded in US: 1885

Income for Overseas Min: $13,814,031.00
Fully Supported US Personnel Overseas:
  Expecting to serve more than 4 years: 84
  Expecting to serve 1 to 4 years: 25
  Non-residential mission personnel: 4
Other personnel:
  Short-term less than 1 year: 815
  Home ministry & office staff in US: 24
Countries: Asia—General 17; Belgium; Brazil 2; Bulgaria 2; Burundi 2; Cambodia 2; Chile 3; Costa Rica 2; Egypt 2; France 2; Greece 2; Haiti 4; Hungary 4; Liberia 2; Malawi 2; Mexico 8; Nigeria 1; Peru 4; Philippines 4; Romania 2; Rwanda 1; Slovakia 2; Spain 4; Taiwan 4; Thailand 2; Ukraine 3; United Kingdom 1; Venezuela

Free Will Baptist, Inc. Board of International Missions
PO Box 5002
Antioch, TN 37011-5002 USA
Phone: (615) 731-4950
Fax: (615) 731-5345
E-mail: kiley@fwbgo.com
Web Site: www.fwbgo.com
Associations: The Mission Exchange
Rev. James Forlines, Gen. Director

A denominational sending agency of Baptist tradition engaged in church planting, church construction, discipleship, evangelism, furloughed missionary support and short-term programs. Countries of service data from 2005.
Purpose: "...to serve our churches, pastors, and people by helping them fulfill their role in establishing churches beyond North America so unreached peoples can know the joy of a worshipping relationship with the living God."
Year Founded in US: 1935
Income for Overseas Min: $6,300,000.00
Fully Supported US Personnel Overseas:
  Expecting to serve more than 4 years: 84
  Expecting to serve 1 to 4 years: 10
Other personnel:
  Short-term less than 1 year: 124
  Home ministry & office staff in US: 16
Countries: Brazil 16; Cote d'Ivoire 15; France 18; India 1; Japan 10; Panama 8; Russia 2; Spain 9; Uruguay 5

FRIENDS in Action Intl.

PO Box 323
Elizabethtown, PA 17022-0323 USA

Phone: (717) 546-0208
Fax: (717) 546-0214
E-mail: FIA-USA@fiaintl.org
Web Site: www.fiaintl.org

Mr. Timothy Johnston, Exec. Director

A service agency of Evangelical tradition engaged in services for other agencies, development, support of national churches, support of national workers, partnership development and supplying equipment.

Purpose: "...to accelerate the work of proclaiming the Gospel to people groups around the world that have not had the opportunity to hear the Good News of Jesus Christ."

Year Founded in US: 1992
Income for Overseas Min: $767,697.00
Fully Supported US Personnel Overseas:
  Expecting to serve 1 to 4 years: 6
Other personnel:
  Short-term less than 1 year: 112
  Home ministry & office staff in US: 3
Countries: Burkina Faso; Bolivia; India; Mexico; Moldova; Nicaragua; Papua New Guinea; Vanuatu

Friends of Donetsk Christian University (DCU)

PO Box 805
San Dimas, CA 91773 USA

Phone: (909) 969-0175
E-mail: fdcupr@gmail.com
Web Site: www.dcu.org.ua

Mr. Gerry Hawkins, Director

A nondenominational specialized agency engaged in university education, Christian education, theological education, missionary education, TEE, evangelism and leadership development. Countries of service data from 2005.

Purpose: "...to work on behalf of the evangelical community of the former Soviet Union to engage in theological as well as other academic research and reflection, and to prepare people to fulfill the mission of the Church in both the spiritual and social spheres."

Year Founded in US: 2001
Income for Overseas Min: $300,000.00

Fully Supported US Personnel Overseas:
  Expecting to serve more than 4 years: 5
  Expecting to serve 1 to 4 years: 2
Other personnel:
  Non-US serving in own/other country: 50
  Home ministry & office staff in US: 2
Countries: Ukraine 5

Friends of Israel Gospel Ministry, Inc.

PO Box 908
Bellmawr, NJ 08099 USA

Phone: (800) 257-7843
Fax: (856) 853-9565
E-mail: foi@foi.org
Web Site: www.foi.org

Mr. William E. Sutter, Exec. Director

A nondenominational support agency of Evangelical tradition engaged in evangelism, audio recording/distribution, broadcasting, development, theological education, literature distribution and literature production. Data from 2005.

Purpose: "...to communicate Biblical truth about Israel and the Messiah, while fostering solidarity with the Jewish people."

Year Founded in US: 1938
Income for Overseas Min: $842,234.00
Fully Supported US Personnel Overseas:
  Non-residential mission personnel: 1
Other personnel:
  Non-US serving in own/other country: 32
  Home ministry & office staff in US: 37
Countries: Argentina; Australia; France; India; Israel; Poland; Russia; United Kingdom

Friends United Meeting

101 Quaker Hill Dr.
Richmond, IN 47374 USA

Phone: (765) 962-7573
Fax: (765) 966-1293
E-mail: info@fum.org
Web Site: www.fum.org

Sylvia Graves, Gen. Secretary

A denominational sending agency of Friends tradition engaged in foreign missions, support of national churches, childcare/orphanage programs, theological education, leadership development, literature production and medical work.

Purpose: "...to energize and equip

Friends, through the power of the Holy Spirit, to gather people into fellowships where Jesus Christ is known, loved, and obeyed as teacher and Lord."

Year Founded in US: 1902

Income for Overseas Min: $1,080,015.00

Gifts in Kind: $30,000.00

Fully Supported US Personnel Overseas:
Expecting to serve more than 4 years: 3
Expecting to serve 1 to 4 years: 3

Other personnel:
Short-term less than 1 year: 23
Non-US serving in own/other country: 1
Home ministry & office staff in US: 6

Countries: Belize 2; Cuba; Jamaica; Kenya 1; Palestine

Friendship International Ministries, Inc.

PO Box 50884
Colorado Springs, CO 80949-0884 USA

Phone: (719) 386-8808
Fax: (719) 594-4992
E-mail: FRINT@aol.com
Web Site: www.friendshipintl.org

Rev. Del Huff, Exec. Director

An interdenominational service agency of Evangelical tradition engaged in evangelism, camping programs, discipleship, short-term programs and youth programs. Data from 2005.

Year Founded in US: 1990

Income for Overseas Min: $200,000.00

Gifts in Kind: $50,000.00

Fully Supported US Personnel Overseas:
Expecting to serve more than 4 years: 7
Expecting to serve 1 to 4 years: 7
Non-residential mission personnel: 3

Other personnel:
Short-term less than 1 year: 25
Non-US serving in own/other country: 14
Home ministry & office staff in US: 4

Countries: Chile 1; Hungary 4; Romania 2

Frontiers

P.O. Box 60670
Phoenix, AZ 85082-0670 USA

Phone: (480) 834-1500
Fax: (480) 834-1974
Web Site: www.frontiers.org
Associations: The Mission Exchange

Rev. Robert A. Blincoe, CEO

A nondenominational sending agency of Evangelical tradition engaged in church planting, agricultural programs, business as mission, evangelism, mobilization for mission and tentmaking. Personnel data from 2005.

Purpose: "...planting reproducing churches among unreached Muslim peoples."

Year Founded in US: 1982

Fully Supported US Personnel Overseas:
Expecting to serve more than 4 years: 288
Non-residential mission personnel: 9

Other personnel:
Short-term less than 1 year: 121
Non-US serving in own/other country: 9
Home ministry & office staff in US: 86

Countries: Unspecified Country 288

Full Gospel Evangelistic Association

PO Box 702378
Tulsa, OK 74170-2378 USA

Phone: (918) 749-3432
Fax: (918) 749-1171
E-mail: admin@fgeaonline.org
Web Site: www.fgeaonline.org

Mr. Curt Bezingve, President

An association of missions of Pentecostal and Full Gospel tradition helping to support full-time missionaries and national churches engaged in church construction, church planting, member care and services for other agencies. Data from 2005.

Year Founded in US: 1951

Fully Supported US Personnel Overseas:
Expecting to serve more than 4 years: 12
Expecting to serve 1 to 4 years: 6
Non-residential mission personnel: 1

Other personnel:
Short-term less than 1 year: 25
Non-US serving in own/other country: 2
Home ministry & office staff in US: 2

Countries: El Salvador 2; Honduras 2; Kenya 1; Mexico 5; Nicaragua 2; Pakistan; Russia

Full Gospel Fellowship of Churches and Ministries Intl.—World Missions

1000 N. Belt Line Rd, Ste. 201
Irving, TX 75061-4000 USA

Phone: (214) 492-1254
Fax: (214) 492-1736
E-mail: fgfcmi@aol.com
Web Site: www.fgfcmi.org
Mr. Gene Evans, President

A sending agency of Charismatic and Pentecostal tradition engaged in association of missions, Christian education and the fellowship of ministers, churches, and organizations.
Year Founded in US: 1962

Full Gospel Grace Fellowship
PO Box 1054
Sapulpa, OK 74057-1054 USA
Phone: (918) 512-6057
E-mail: fggf@juno.com
Web Site: www.fggf.org
Rev. Harley Hunt, Chairman

A nondenominational sending agency of Pentecostal and Independent tradition engaged in funds transmission and literature distribution. Data from 2005.
Year Founded in US: 1945
Income for Overseas Min: $70,000.00
Personnel:
  Short-term less than 1 year: 2
  Non-US serving in own/other country: 8
Countries: Argentina; Belarus; Belize; Paraguay

Fundamental Baptist Mission of Trinidad & Tobago
3050 Magazine Drive
Winston-Salem, NC 27106 US
Phone: (336) 499-7189
E-mail: fbmtt@earthlink.net
Web Site: www.fbmtt.org
Rev. Ken Best, Exec. Director

A sending agency of Baptist and Fundamental tradition engaged in church planting, evangelism and support of national workers. Data from 2005.
Year Founded in US: 1921
Countries: Trinidad and Tobago

Fundamental Baptist Missions International
523 Sibley St.
Hammond, IN 46320 USA
Phone: (219) 932-0711

Fax: (219) 852-3838
E-mail: helpdesk@fbmi.org
Web Site: www.fbmi.org
Mr. Daniel Wruck, Admin. Assistant

An Independent sending agency of Baptist tradition engaged in church planting, Bible distribution, Christian education, evangelism, funds transmission and Bible translation.
Year Founded in US: 1994
Income for Overseas Min: $6,470,000.00
Personnel:
  Home ministry & office staff in US: 21

Galcom Intl. USA, Inc.
PO Box 270956
Tampa, FL 33618-0956 USA
Phone: (813) 933-8111
Fax: (813) 933-8886
E-mail: galcomusa@galcom.org
Web Site: www.galcom.org
Associations: CrossGlobal Link
Mr. Gary Nelson, President

A nondenominational support agency of Independent and Evangelical tradition engaged in radio distribution for Christian broadcasting, Bible distribution, church planting and evangelism in 124 countries. Data from 2005.
Purpose: "...to provide durable technical equipment for communicating the Gospel worldwide."
Year Founded in US: 1991
Personnel:
  Home ministry & office staff in US: 2

General Association of Regular Baptist Churches— International Ministries
1300 N. Meacham Rd.
Schaumburg, IL 60173 USA
Phone: (847) 843-1600
Fax: (847) 843-3757
Web Site: www.garbcinternational.org
Rev. Chris Hindal, Intl. Min. Director

An association of Baptist tradition providing information for its associated local churches relative to cooperating mission agencies. Data from 2005.
Year Founded in US: 1932

General Baptists Intl.

100 Stinson Dr.
Poplar Bluff, MO 63901 USA
Phone: (573) 785-7746
Fax: (573) 785-0564
E-mail: jack.eberhardt@generalbaptist.com
Web Site: www.generalbaptist.com
Associations: The Mission Exchange
Rev. Jack Eberhardt, Director

A denominational sending agency of Baptist tradition engaged in church planting, agricultural programs, childcare/orphanage programs, literacy work, short-term programs and training. Countries of service data from 2005.

Purpose: "...to win and disciple people around the world."

Year Founded in US: 1903

Fully Supported US Personnel Overseas:
  Expecting to serve more than 4 years: 20
  Expecting to serve 1 to 4 years: 7
  Non-residential mission personnel: 16

Other personnel:
  Short-term less than 1 year: 500
  Non-US serving in own/other country: 1
  Home ministry & office staff in US: 5

Countries: Honduras 8; India; Mexico 4; N. Mariana Isls 2; Philippines 6; Unspecified Country

Gideons International, The

PO Box 140800
Nashville, TN 37214-0800 USA
Phone: (615) 564-5000
Fax: (615) 564-6000
E-mail: jburden@gideons.org
Web Site: www.gideons.org
Mr. Jerry D. Burden, Exec. Director

An interdenominational service agency of Evangelical and Fundamental tradition engaged in Bible distribution and evangelism.

Purpose: "...to win others to Christ through personal witnessing and scripture distribution."

Year Founded in US: 1899

Income for Overseas Min: $95,600,000.00

Fully Supported US Personnel Overseas:
  Non-residential mission personnel: 8

Other personnel:
  Short-term less than 1 year: 150

Non-US serving in own/other country: 58
Home ministry & office staff in US: 107

Countries: Africa—General; Asia—General; Europe—General; Latin America—General

Global Action

7680 Goddard Street, Ste. 200
Colorado Springs, CO 80920 USA
Phone: (719) 528-8728
Fax: (719) 528-8718
E-mail: globalaction@global-act.org
Web Site: www.global-act.org
Dr. Lars B. Dunberg, President

A nondenominational sending agency engaged in evangelism, childrens programs, church planting, short-term programs, training and youth programs. Data from 2001.

Purpose: "To proclaim the Kingdom of God in word and deed around the world and to serve the Church by empowering, training, motivating and mobilizing people to become fully devoted followers of Christ."

Year Founded in US: 1998

Income for Overseas Min: $966,077.00

Gifts in Kind: $222,333.00

Fully Supported US Personnel Overseas:
  Expecting to serve more than 4 years: 3
  Non-residential mission personnel: 2

Other personnel:
  Short-term less than 1 year: 108
  Non-US serving in own/other country: 21
  Home ministry & office staff in US: 10

Countries: Asia—General; India; Latin America—General 2; Serbia and Montenegro; Ukraine 1

Global Adopt-A-People Network

1443 E. Washington Blvd., #308
Pasadena, CA 91104 USA
Phone: (626) 205-3413
Fax: (626) 836-9364
E-mail: philbogosian@gaapc.org
Mr. Phil Bogosian, Director

A transdenominational service agency of Evangelical tradition engaged in support of national churches.

Purpose: "...to equip and educate local denominational churches to pray for their own denominational missionaries who are specifically working to plant Christ's Church among unreached peoples; this is done through seminars, publications, and short-term missionaries."

Year Founded in US: 1995

Income for Overseas Min: $230,000.00

Fully Supported US Personnel Overseas:
   Expecting to serve more than 4 years: 9
   Non-residential mission personnel: 2

Countries: El Salvador; Mexico; Philippines 9

Global Advance

PO Box 742077
Dallas, TX 75374-2077 USA

Phone: (972) 771-9042
Fax: (972) 771-3315
E-mail: info@globaladvance.org
Web Site: www.globaladvance.org

Dr. David Shibley, Founder/President

An interdenominational service agency of Evangelical tradition engaged in leadership development, discipleship, theological education, evangelism, support of national churches and training. Staff does short-term trips to more than 72 nations. Data from 2005.

Purpose: "...to help fulfill the Great Commission...by empowering national leaders to evangelize and disciple their own and surrounding nations..."

Year Founded in US: 1990

Income for Overseas Min: $1,068,645.00

Fully Supported US Personnel Overseas:
   Expecting to serve more than 4 years: 8

Other personnel:
   Short-term less than 1 year: 3
   Home ministry & office staff in US: 9

Countries: Unspecified Country 8

Global Aid Network (GAiN USA)

PO Box 139020
Dallas, TX 75313-9020 USA

Phone: (972) 234-0800
Fax: (972) 669-4053
E-mail: info@gainusa.org
Web Site: www.gainusa.org

Associations: AERDO

Mr. Duane E. Zook, CEO

An interdenominational specialized agency of Evangelical tradition engaged in relief and/

or rehabilitation, humanitarian aid, children at risk, evangelism, providing medical supplies and short-term programs, with short-term mission trips to more than 10 countries.

Purpose: "...to demonstrate the love of God, in word and deed, to hurting and needy people around the world."

Year Founded in US: 1994

Income for Overseas Min: $33,854,534.00

Gifts in Kind: $30,813,578.00

Fully Supported US Personnel Overseas:
   Non-residential mission personnel: 1

Other personnel:
   Short-term less than 1 year: 235
   Non-US serving in own/other country: 6
   Home ministry & office staff in US: 58

Countries: Eastern Europe—General; France

Global Fellowship, Inc.

PO Box 1
Meadow Vista, CA 95722 USA

Phone: (530) 888-9208
E-mail: globalraymond@gmail.com
Web Site: www.globalfellowship.org

Mr. Don Oates, President

An interdenominational sending agency of Evangelical tradition engaged in church planting, evangelism, support of national workers, missionary training and women's ministries.

Purpose: "...to serve indigenous ministries including financial assistance, technological assistance, prayer relief and human resources as well as spiritual encouragement, exhortation and equipping."

Year Founded in US: 1989

Income for Overseas Min: $500,000.00

Gifts in Kind: $75,000.00

Fully Supported US Personnel Overseas:
   Expecting to serve more than 4 years: 8
   Non-residential mission personnel: 2

Other personnel:
   Short-term less than 1 year: 4
   Non-US serving in own/other country: 6
   Home ministry & office staff in US: 4

Countries: Asia—General 7; Singapore 1

Global Focus

PO Box 1058
Acworth, GA 30101 USA

Phone: (770) 529-8610

Fax: (770) 529-8611
E-mail: contact.info@globalfocus.info
Web Site: www.globalfocus.info
Associations: The Mission Exchange
Dr. Larry D. Reesor, President

A nondenominational service agency of Baptist and Evangelical tradition engaged in church mobilization, church mission development, missions information service and Acts 1:8 strategies. Data from 2005.

Purpose: "...to glorify God by helping pastors or church leaders to be more effective in mobilizing the church to reach the world for Christ."

Year Founded in US: 1995
Personnel:
  Home ministry & office staff in US: 8

Global Harvest Ministries
PO Box 63060
Colorado Springs, CO 80962-3060 USA
Phone: (719) 262-9922
Fax: (719) 262-9920
E-mail: info@globalharvest.org
Web Site: www.globalharvest.org
Dr. C. Peter Wagner, President

A transdenominational support agency of Evangelical and Charismatic tradition engaged in leadership development and training. Data from 2005.

Purpose: "...to strengthen global forces for evangelism; engage in apostolic ministries to train, encourage, network, and resource leaders; mobilize prayer for world evangelization; train leaders in prayer, spiritual warfare, practical ministry and deliverance."

Year Founded in US: 1991
Personnel:
  Short-term less than 1 year: 8
  Home ministry & office staff in US: 19

Global Health Ministries
7831 Hickory St. NE
Minneapolis, MN 55432 USA
Phone: (763) 586-9590
Fax: (763) 586-9591
E-mail: ghmoffice@cs.com
Web Site: www.ghm.org
Rev. Timon C. Iverson, Exec. Director

An interdenominational support agency of Lutheran tradition engaged in providing medical supplies, development, management consulting/training, medical work, partnership development and mobilization for mission. Ongoing programs in 21 countries.

Purpose: "...to enhance the health care programs of Lutheran churches in the developing world."

Year Founded in US: 1987
Income for Overseas Min: $2,255,177.00
Gifts in Kind: $940,569.00
Personnel:
  Short-term less than 1 year: 6
  Non-US serving in own/other country: 2
  Home ministry & office staff in US: 8
Countries: Central African Republic; Madagascar

Global Impact Services
PO Box 336
Jenison, MI 49429 USA
Phone: (616) 821-7117
Fax: (616) 457-6014
E-mail: mark@globalimpactservices.org
Web Site: www.globalimpactservices.org
Mr. Mark Sigmon, Director

A nondenominational service agency of Evangelical tradition engaged in management consulting/training, missions information service and mission-related research.

Purpose: "...to maximize the resources and mobilize the people of the Church and her agencies for greater global impact."

Year Founded in US: 2007
Personnel:
  Home ministry & office staff in US: 1

Global Mapping Intl.
PO Box 63719
Colorado Springs, CO 80962-3719 USA
Phone: (719) 531-3599
Fax: (719) 548-7459
E-mail: info@gmi.org
Web Site: www.gmi.org
Associations: The Mission Exchange
Mr. Michael O'Rear, President

An interdenominational support agency of Evangelical tradition engaged in mission-related research, missions information service, leadership development, management consulting/training, services for other agencies and training.

Purpose: "...to produce and present world-class research that fuels emerging mission movements and leaders."

Year Founded in US: 1983

Global Ministries, Church of the United Brethren in Christ

302 Lake St.
Huntington, IN 46750 USA
Phone: (260) 356-2312
Fax: (260) 356-4730
E-mail: jeffbleijerveld@mac.com
Web Site: www.ubmissions.org
Associations: The Mission Exchange
Rev. Jeff Bleijerveld, Dir. Global Ministries

A denominational sending agency of Brethren tradition engaged in church planting, discipleship, evangelism, leadership development, support of national churches and TESOL.

Purpose: "...to help United Brethren churches fulfill the global mandate of the Great Commission."

Year Founded in US: 1853

Income for Overseas Min: $50,000.00

Fully Supported US Personnel Overseas:
   Non-residential mission personnel: 50

Other personnel:
   Short-term less than 1 year: 325
   Home ministry & office staff in US: 3

Countries: China; Costa Rica; El Salvador; Germany; Guatemala; Honduras; India; Macau; Myanmar/Burma; Poland; Sierra Leone; Somalia; Thailand

Global Opportunities

8400 Cypress Lake Dr.
Ft. Myers, FL 33919 USA
Phone: (239) 243-0881
E-mail: goemail@globalopps.org
Web Site: www.globalopps.org
Mr. David E. English, Exec. Director

A nondenominational support agency of Evangelical tradition engaged in tentmaking, business as mission, member care and training. GO people go as self-supporting cross-cultural witnesses and disciple-makers

as workplace professionals in education, engineering, marketing, management, etc. in 85 countries.

Purpose: "...to call the Church to engage the power of tentmaking as lay missions...to mobilize and equip missions-committed lay Christians to serve abroad as effective tentmakers, primarily to least-reached peoples."

Year Founded in US: 1984

Personnel:
   Home ministry & office staff in US: 4

Global Outreach Intl.

PO Box 1
Tupelo, MS 38802 USA
Phone: (662) 842-4615
Fax: (662) 842-4620
E-mail: go@globaloutreach.org
Web Site: www.globaloutreach.org
Dr. Sammy Simpson, Founder

A nondenominational sending agency of Evangelical tradition engaged in missionary training, childcare/orphanage programs, church construction, evangelism, leadership development and medical work. Data from 2005.

Year Founded in US: 1970

Income for Overseas Min: $4,789,009.00

Fully Supported US Personnel Overseas:
   Expecting to serve more than 4 years: 165

Other personnel:
   Short-term less than 1 year: 1007
   Non-US serving in own/other country: 9
   Home ministry & office staff in US: 9

Countries: Argentina 5; Barbados 2; Belize 11; Brazil 3; Cambodia 2; Cameroon 2; Chile 1; China 13; Costa Rica 2; Ecuador 13; Guatemala 1; Guyana 5; Haiti 8; Honduras 11; India 4; Kenya 7; Mexico 9; Moldova 2; Mozambique 2; Myanmar/Burma 2; Nicaragua 2; Peru 2; Philippines 2; Poland 2; Romania 14; Rwanda 2; Slovakia 1; Sudan 1; Uganda 22; Ukraine 5; United Kingdom 5; Vietnam 2

Global Outreach Mission, Inc.

PO Box 2010
Buffalo, NY 14231-2010 USA
Phone: (716) 688-5048
Fax: (716) 688-5049
E-mail: gom@missiongo.org
Web Site: www.missiongo.org

Associations: CrossGlobal Link

Mr. Brian Albrecht, President

A nondenominational sending agency of Evangelical and Independent tradition engaged in church planting, broadcasting, evangelism, medical work, support of national workers, relief and/or rehabilitation and short-term programs.

Purpose: "...to share the Gospel of Jesus Christ around the world...to plant and encourage His church...to help the hurting physically and to serve in every area of Christian development."

Year Founded in US: 1943

Income for Overseas Min: $3,421,928.00

Fully Supported US Personnel Overseas:
Expecting to serve more than 4 years: 178
Expecting to serve 1 to 4 years: 10

Other personnel:
Short-term less than 1 year: 95
Home ministry & office staff in US: 14

Countries: Antigua 1; Australia 2; Austria 1; Belgium 2; Belize 2; Bolivia 2; Brazil 6; Chile 2; Congo, Republic of the 12; Costa Rica 9; Dominican Republic 2; France 38; Gabon 1; Germany 6; Ghana 1; Guatemala 11; Haiti 2; Honduras 5; India 8; Ireland 9; Jamaica 2; Jordan 3; Kosovo 1; Mexico 10; Myanmar/Burma 5; Netherlands 1; Netherlands Antilles 1; Paraguay 4; Peru 4; Romania 2; Russia 5; Sierra Leone 4; Spain; Switzerland 1; Thailand 2; United Kingdom 9; Ukraine 2

Global Partners/Wesleyan World Missions

PO Box 50434
Indianapolis, IN 46250-0434 USA

Phone: (317) 774-7950
Fax: (317) 774-7958
Web Site: www.praygivego.org
Associations: The Mission Exchange

Dr. H.C. Wilson, Gen. Director

A denominational sending agency of Wesleyan tradition engaged in church planting, theological education, TEE, evangelism, leadership development and support of national churches. Countries of service data from 2005.

Purpose: "...to exalt Jesus Christ by calling and mobilizing believers to global ministries of evangelism, church planting, leadership development, and ministries of compassion."

Year Founded in US: 1889

Fully Supported US Personnel Overseas:
Expecting to serve 1 to 4 years: 115
Non-residential mission personnel: 13

Other personnel:
Short-term less than 1 year: 21
Non-US serving in own/other country: 13
Home ministry & office staff in US: 20

Countries: Africa—General; Albania; Australia; Austria; Brazil; Cambodia; Caribbean—General; Chile; Colombia; Congo, Democratic Republic of; Costa Rica; Croatia; Czech Republic; Dominican Republic; Ecuador; Egypt; El Salvador; Germany; Ghana; Guatemala; Guyana; Haiti; Honduras; India; Indonesia; Japan; Kenya; Korea, South; Liberia; Mexico; Mongolia; Mozambique; Myanmar/Burma; Nepal; Nicaragua; New Zealand; Pakistan; Panama; Papua New Guinea; Peru; Philippines; Puerto Rico; Russia; Sierra Leone; South Africa; Sri Lanka; Suriname; Thailand; United Kingdom; Unspecified Country; Venezuela; Zambia

Global Recordings Network

41823 Enterprise Cir. N., Ste. 200
Temecula, CA 92590 USA

Phone: (951) 719-1650
Fax: (951) 719-1651
E-mail: info@globalrecordings.net
Web Site: www.globalrecordings.net
Associations: CrossGlobal Link

Mr. Colin Stott, Exec. Director

An interdenominational specialized agency of Evangelical tradition engaged in audio recording/distribution, evangelism, mission-related research, services for other agencies and supplying equipment.

Purpose: "...to help spread the Gospel by recording and distributing evangelistic messages in thousands of languages and dialects."

Year Founded in US: 1939

Income for Overseas Min: $672,719.00

Fully Supported US Personnel Overseas:
Expecting to serve more than 4 years: 74

Other personnel:
Short-term less than 1 year: 4
Non-US serving in own/other country: 211
Home ministry & office staff in US: 31

Countries: Australia; Bangladesh; Benin

2; Bolivia 2; Brazil 1; Burkina Faso 6; Cameroon 8; Chad 5; Colombia; Ecuador 2; France; Gabon 2; Germany; Guinea 2; India; Indonesia; Kenya 6; Korea, South; Liberia 6; Mexico 2; Mozambique; Myanmar/Burma; Nepal; Netherlands; Nigeria 12; Pakistan; Papua New Guinea; Peru; Philippines; Russia 2; Senegal; Sierra Leone 12; Singapore; Solomon Islands; South Africa; Switzerland; Tanzania; Thailand 4; Togo; United Kingdom; Vanuatu; Zimbabwe

Global Teams Intl., Inc.

212 21st St., Ste. 2
Bakersfield, CA 93301 USA
Phone: (661) 323-1214
Fax: (661) 323-1216
E-mail: inquiries@global-teams.net
Web Site: www.global-teams.net
The Rev. Kevin Higgins, Intl. Director

An interdenominational sending agency of Evangelical tradition engaged in church planting, business as mission, leadership development, member care, mobilization for mission and Bible translation.

Purpose: "...to equip and send teams of missionaries from many nations to multiply disciples of Jesus within cultures least familiar with the Gospel."
Year Founded in US: 1983
Income for Overseas Min: $1,128,000.00
Personnel:
  Short-term less than 1 year: 9
  Home ministry & office staff in US: 5

Global University

1211 S. Glenstone Ave.
Springfield, MO 65804 USA
Phone: (417) 862-9533
Fax: (417) 865-7167
E-mail: info@globaluniversity.edu
Web Site: www.globaluniversity.edu
Dr. George M. Flattery, President

A denominational service agency of Pentecostal tradition engaged in correspondence courses, missionary education, TEE, extension education, theological education and evangelism. Data from 2005.

Purpose: "...to integrate education and service through a worldwide network for student support."

Year Founded in US: 1999
Personnel:
  Home ministry & office staff in US: 83

Global Youth Ministry Network

91 Park Ave. W. Ste. G
Mansfield, OH 44902-1630 USA
Phone: (419) 756-4433
Fax: (419) 756-3041
E-mail: office@global-youth.com
Web Site: www.global-youth.com
Mr. Chris Davis, Exec. Director

A transdenominational specialized agency of Evangelical and Reformed tradition engaged in leadership development, evangelism, support of national workers, support of national churches, training and youth programs. Data from 2005.

Year Founded in US: 1997
Income for Overseas Min: $75,000.00
Gifts in Kind: $1,000.00
Fully Supported US Personnel Overseas:
  Expecting to serve more than 4 years: 1
Other personnel:
  Non-US serving in own/other country: 6
  Home ministry & office staff in US: 2
Countries: Africa—General; Asia—General; Latin America—General; Unspecified Country 1

Globe International

PO Box 3040
Pensacola, FL 32516-3040 USA
Phone: (850) 453-3453
Fax: (850) 456-6001
E-mail: info@gme.org
Web Site: www.gme.org
Associations: The Mission Exchange
Mr. J. Douglas Gehman, President

An interdenominational sending agency of Charismatic and Evangelical tradition engaged in church planting, discipleship, evangelism, funds transmission, leadership development and missionary training. Countries of service data from 2005.

Purpose: "...to carry the Gospel across cultural boundaries to unreached people, encouraging them to accept Christ as Lord and Savior...to draw disciples together into clusters of churches...to help the churches, under the Holy Spirit's leadership, to multiply, serve their communities and send out their own cross-cultural missionaries."

Year Founded in US: 1973

Income for Overseas Min: $3,000,000.00

Fully Supported US Personnel Overseas:
Expecting to serve more than 4 years: 97
Expecting to serve 1 to 4 years: 4

Countries: Africa—General 2; Albania 6; Argentina 2; China 2; Costa Rica; Ecuador 2; Germany 2; Guatemala 6; Haiti 2; Honduras 2; India 7; Indonesia 2; Israel 6; Italy 2; Kenya 2; Laos 2; Malaysia 2; Mexico 11; Mozambique 2; Nepal 2; Nicaragua 3; Philippines 2; Russia 2; South Africa 2; Sri Lanka 2; Taiwan 2; Thailand 6; Ukraine 2; United Kingdom 10; Vietnam 2

GO InterNational

PO Box 123
Wilmore, KY 40390 USA

Phone: (859) 858-3171
Fax: (859) 858-4324
E-mail: ceo@gointernational.org
Web Site: www.gointernational.org

Mr. Bert Jones, President/CEO

An interdenominational support agency of Wesleyan tradition engaged in development, childrens programs, church planting, evangelism, leadership development and short-term programs. Data from 2003.

Purpose: "...[to] collaborate with indigenous ministries [and] give Christians in the USA the opportunity to become directly involved in the life and ministry of the church in the Two-Thirds World..."

Year Founded in US: 1968

Go Ye Fellowship

PO Box 40039
Pasadena, CA 91114-7039 USA

Phone: (626) 398-2305
Fax: (626) 797-5576
E-mail: gyfint@cs.com
Web Site: www.goyefellowship.org

Rev. Gordon Rohn, President

An interdenominational sending agency of Evangelical tradition engaged in sending missionaries, church establishing/planting, discipleship, evangelism and tentmaking.

Purpose: "...to enable missionaries to pursue their God-given call and vision by serving as the link between missionaries and those who send them."

Year Founded in US: 1932

Income for Overseas Min: $1,367,000.00

Fully Supported US Personnel Overseas:
Expecting to serve more than 4 years: 30
Expecting to serve 1 to 4 years: 3

Other personnel:
Short-term less than 1 year: 5
Non-US serving in own/other country: 9
Home ministry & office staff in US: 5

Countries: Asia—General 3; Argentina 1; Austria 2; Brazil 3; Central Asia—General 2; Costa Rica; Egypt 1; Equatorial Guinea; France 2; Germany 2; Indonesia 1; Israel 2; Korea, South 1; Mexico 4; Philippines; Rwanda 2; Slovakia 2; Tanzania 1; Uganda; United Kingdom 1

God Reports

PO Box 7269
Capistrano Beach, CA 92624 USA

Phone: (949) 230-2843
E-mail: markellis4@cox.net
Web Site: www.godreports.com

Mr. Mark Ellis, President

A nondenominational specialized agency of Evangelical tradition engaged in missions information service, funds transmission and mobilization for mission.

Purpose: "...to spread the Good News of the Gospel of Jesus Christ and serve the Church worldwide."

Year Founded in US: 2008

Personnel:
Home ministry & office staff in US: 1

GOGF Ministries

160 E. Main St.
Lansdale, PA 19446 USA

Phone: (215) 361-8111
Fax: (215) 361-3970
E-mail: admin@gogf.org
Web Site: www.gogf.org

Dr. Tony Hart, President

A nondenominational support agency of Brethren and Christian/Plymouth Brethren tradition engaged in church planting, broadcasting, support of national churches and training.

Purpose: "...to plant churches, to prepare leaders, and to proclaim the Gospel until the whole world hears."
Year Founded in US: 1961
Income for Overseas Min: $50,000.00
Gifts in Kind: $2,000.00
Personnel:
Short-term less than 1 year: 20
Non-US serving in own/other country: 2
Home ministry & office staff in US: 2
Countries: India; Jamaica

Good Neighbor Insurance, Inc.
690 E. Warner Rd., Ste. 117
Gilbert, AZ 85296 USA
Phone: (480) 813-9100
Fax: (480) 813-9930
E-mail: info@gninsurance.com
Web Site: www.gninsurance.com
Mr. Jeff Gulleson, President
A specialized agency engaged in international & domestic health insurance.
Year Founded in US: 1997

Good News for India
PO Box 7576
LaVerne, CA 91750-7576 USA
Phone: (909) 593-7753
Fax: (909) 593-1155
E-mail: gnficea@gmail.com
Web Site: www.goodnewsforindia.org
Mr. George Chavanikamannil, President
An interdenominational support agency of Charismatic tradition engaged in theological education, childcare/orphanage programs, church planting, evangelism, leadership development and support of national workers.
Purpose: "...to train, send and support national Christians to preach the Gospel and plant churches among the unreached people groups/places in the Indian subcontinent."
Year Founded in US: 1986
Income for Overseas Min: $1,100,000.00
Personnel:
Short-term less than 1 year: 30
Non-US serving in own/other country: 350
Home ministry & office staff in US: 1
Countries: India

Good News Productions International
PO Box 222
Joplin, MO 64802-0222 USA
Phone: (417) 782-0060
Fax: (417) 782-3999
E-mail: gnpi@gnpi.org
Web Site: www.gnpi.org
Mr. Rich Sheeley, Exec. Director
A nondenominational specialized agency of Christian (Restoration Movement) tradition engaged in video/film production/distribution, broadcasting, evangelism, partnership development and mission-related research. Data from 2001.
Purpose: "...works in partnership with Christians around the world to develop culturally-relevant strategies and resources which are used to effectively proclaim the gospel of Christ to the peoples of the world."
Year Founded in US: 1976
Income for Overseas Min: $800,000.00
Fully Supported US Personnel Overseas:
Expecting to serve more than 4 years: 15
Expecting to serve 1 to 4 years: 2
Non-residential mission personnel: 2
Other personnel:
Short-term less than 1 year: 5
Non-US serving in own/other country: 34
Home ministry & office staff in US: 18
Countries: Africa—General 2; India 2; Mexico 2; Myanmar/Burma; Philippines 1; Singapore 2; Thailand 4; Ukraine 2

Good Shepherd Ministries Intl.
PO Box 11909
San Bernardino, CA 92423 USA
Phone: (909) 478-3330
Fax: (909) 478-3331
E-mail: info@isom.org
Web Site: www.isom.org
Dr. Berin Gilfillan, President/CEO
A nondenominational sending agency of Charismatic and Pentecostal tradition engaged in Christian education, correspondence courses, discipleship, training, video/film production/distribution and youth programs. Works with 13,575 school. In 88 countries.
Year Founded in US: 1991
Personnel:

Short-term less than 1 year: 15
Home ministry & office staff in US: 25

Good Shepherd Ministries, Inc.

PO Box 360963
Melbourne, FL 32936-0963 USA

Phone: (321) 752-0072
Fax: (321) 752-7209
E-mail: lamar@gsmi-haiti.org
Web Site: www.gsmi-haiti.org

Mr. Lamar Lyon, Administrator

An interdenominational support agency of Baptist and Evangelical tradition engaged in theological education, extension education, evangelism, literature distribution, providing medical supplies, medical work and supplying equipment. Data from 2005.

Year Founded in US: 1975

Income for Overseas Min: $203,343.00

Fully Supported US Personnel Overseas:
  Expecting to serve more than 4 years: 2
  Non-residential mission personnel: 1

Other personnel:
  Short-term less than 1 year: 6
  Non-US serving in own/other country: 48
  Home ministry & office staff in US: 1

Countries: Haiti 2

Gospel Fellowship Association

1809 Wade Hampton Blvd., #110
Greenville, SC 29609 USA

Phone: (864) 609-5500
Fax: (864) 609-5501
E-mail: GFA@gfamissions.org
Web Site: www.gfamissions.org

Dr. Mark Batory, Exec. Director

A nondenominational sending agency of Fundamental tradition engaged in church planting, camping programs, correspondence courses, theological education, evangelism and medical work.

Purpose: "...to get the Gospel to as many people as possible in the shortest time possible."

Year Founded in US: 1961

Fully Supported US Personnel Overseas:
  Expecting to serve more than 4 years: 163
  Expecting to serve 1 to 4 years: 35
  Non-residential mission personnel: 3

Other personnel:
  Home ministry & office staff in US: 9

Countries: Albania 2; Argentina 2; Australia 6; Austria 7; Brazil 4; Cambodia 4; Cameroon 16; Costa Rica 4; Dominica 2; Ecuador 4; Germany 18; Italy 2; Japan 1; Korea, South 4; Marshall Islands 4; Mexico 9; Netherlands 2; New Zealand 2; Panama 2; Papua New Guinea 13; Philippines 15; Puerto Rico 2; South Africa 2; Spain 4; United Kingdom 17; Unspecified Country 4; Zambia 11

Gospel for Asia, Inc.

1800 Golden Trail Ct.
Carrollton, TX 75010 USA

Phone: (972) 300-7777
Fax: (972) 300-7778
E-mail: info@gfa.org
Web Site: www.gfa.org

Rev. K. P. Yohannan, Intl. Director

An interdenominational service agency of Evangelical tradition engaged in church planting, broadcasting, childrens programs, leadership development, support of national workers and missionary training.

Purpose: "...to be devout followers of Christ and fulfill the Great Commission among the unreached in Asia through training, sending, and assisting qualified laborers who will win the lost and plant local churches in partnership with the Body of Christ."

Year Founded in US: 1979

Personnel:
  Non-US serving in own/other country: 9523
  Home ministry & office staff in US: 80

Countries: Asia—General

Gospel Literature International (GLINT)

PO Box 4060
Ontario, CA 91764 USA

Phone: (909) 481-5222
Fax: (909) 481-5216
E-mail: glintint@aol.com
Web Site: www.glint.org

Georgalyn B. Wilkinson, President

A nondenominational service agency engaged in translation work.

Purpose: "...to provide resources for literature projects worldwide for effective Bible teaching and learning materials in national languages, with the goal of making disciples, developing godly Christian leaders, and building the Church."

Year Founded in US: 1961

Gospel Mission of South America, Inc.

1401 SW 21st Ave.
Fort Lauderdale, FL 33312 USA
Phone: (954) 587-2975
Fax: (954) 587-2975
E-mail: gmsausa@gmsa.org
Web Site: www.gmsa.org
Mr. David L. Rozelle, U.S. Director

A nondenominational sending agency of Baptist and Fundamental tradition engaged in church planting, theological education and leadership development. Data from 2005.

Purpose: "...to evangelize the people of Latin America by means of itinerant and localized work, with the object of establishing and developing indigenous churches."

Year Founded in US: 1923

Income for Overseas Min: $930,930.00

Fully Supported US Personnel Overseas:
Expecting to serve more than 4 years: 24

Other personnel:
Short-term less than 1 year: 5
Home ministry & office staff in US: 4

Countries: Argentina 8; Chile 10; Uruguay 6

Gospel Operation Intl. for Chinese Christians (GO Intl. US)

PO Box 99
San Bruno, CA 94066-0099 USA
Phone: (650) 344-2299
Fax: (650) 344-9922
E-mail: gointl@pacbell.net
Web Site: www.gointl.org
Rev./Dr. Cyrus Lam, Intl. Director

An interdenominational sending agency of Evangelical tradition engaged in church planting, discipleship, evangelism, literature production, mobilization for mission and short-term programs.

Purpose: "...to reach the Chinese, touching all nations."

Year Founded in US: 1995

Income for Overseas Min: $1,657,716.00

Fully Supported US Personnel Overseas:
Expecting to serve more than 4 years: 5
Expecting to serve 1 to 4 years: 7

Other personnel:
Non-US serving in own/other country: 57
Home ministry & office staff in US: 13

Countries: Brazil; Cambodia; China 2; Cyprus; Kenya; Korea, South; Kyrgyzstan 2; Mexico; Mongolia; Myanmar/Burma; Peru; Thailand 1; Turkey; Ukraine; United Arab Emirates

Gospel Outbound

131 Morton Avenue
Millville, NJ 08332 USA
Phone: (609) 506-0570
Fax: (609) 506-0053
E-mail: info@gospeloutbound.org
Web Site: www.gospeloutbound.org
Mr. Brian Wheaton, President

A sending agency of Evangelical tradition engaged in business as mission, childcare/orphanage programs, missionary education, theological education, evangelism and partnership development.

Purpose: "...to serve 'the least of these,' the world's hungry, sick and disenfranchised...to mobilize the Church of Jesus Christ to fulfill her God-given mandate to 'go and make disciples of all nations.' "

Year Founded in US: 1997

Income for Overseas Min: $132,866.00

Fully Supported US Personnel Overseas:
Expecting to serve more than 4 years: 1

Other personnel:
Short-term less than 1 year: 20

Countries: Guatemala; India; Myanmar/Burma; Uganda 1

Gospel Outreach Ministries International

PO Box 380
Hillsboro, MO 63050-0380 USA
Phone: (636) 948-9836
Fax: (636) 948-9835
E-mail: gomint@aol.com
Dr. Sam Paul Gokanakonda, Pres./CEO

A nondenominational support agency of Evangelical tradition engaged in evangelism, church planting, support of national workers, mission-related research, literacy work, development, childcare/orphanage programs, leadership development, short-term programs and relief and/or rehabilitation. Primary focus is the most unreached people groups in India. Data from 2005.

Purpose: "...to fulfill the responsibility of the Great Commission to disciple the lost through a relationship with God and forming a community of local believers."

Year Founded in US: 1988

Income for Overseas Min: $144,000.00

Personnel:
   Short-term less than 1 year: 7
   Non-US serving in own/other country: 250
   Home ministry & office staff in US: 2

Countries: India

Gospel Revival Ministries

PO Box 705
DeSoto, TX 75115 USA
Phone: (972) 230-4660
Fax: (972) 274-1318
E-mail: staff@gogoodnews.com
Web Site: www.gogoodnews.com
Mr. John Musser, President

A nondenominational support agency of Pentecostal tradition engaged in support of national workers, Bible distribution, church construction, development, evangelism, funds transmission, literature distribution, mobilization for mission, mission-related research, short-term programs and supplying equipment. Data from 2005.

Purpose: "...to equip native workers to reach their nations for Christ, especially the unreached people groups—small rural villages that are usually inaccessible to western missionaries..."

Year Founded in US: 1980

Income for Overseas Min: $159,000.00

Gifts in Kind: $40,000.00

Personnel:
   Short-term less than 1 year: 5
   Non-US serving in own/other country: 59
   Home ministry & office staff in US: 8

Countries: Cameroon; Chad; Ghana; India; Malaysia; Niger; Nigeria; Pakistan; Philippines; Sri Lanka; Sudan

Gospelink, Inc.

PO Box 4299
Lynchburg, VA 24502 USA
Phone: (434) 485-7007
Fax: (434) 485-7008
E-mail: lnelms@gospelink.org
Web Site: www.nationalpreachers.com
Mr. Lewis Nelms, President

A nondenominational support agency of Evangelical tradition engaged in national church nurture/support, childcare/orphanage programs, church planting, theological education, evangelism and support of national workers.

Purpose: "...to advance the Gospel of Jesus Christ by assisting national preachers."

Year Founded in US: 1998

Income for Overseas Min: $1,818,900.00

Personnel:
   Short-term less than 1 year: 75
   Non-US serving in own/other country: 1113
   Home ministry & office staff in US: 18

Countries: Congo, Democratic Republic of; Ethiopia; India; Malawi; Mozambique; Russia; Tanzania; Ukraine; Vietnam; Zambia; Zimbabwe

Grace and Truth, Inc.

210 Chestnut St.
Danville, IL 61832 USA
Phone: (217) 442-1120
Fax: (217) 442-1163
E-mail: gtpress@gtpress.org
Web Site: www.gtpress.org
Mr. Sam O. Hadley, President

A nondenominational support agency of Brethren tradition engaged in literature production and correspondence courses.

Purpose: "...to disseminate and propagate the Gospel of our Lord Jesus Christ and all other scriptural truths by means of the publication and distribution of tracts, periodicals, booklets and magazines worldwide."

Year Founded in US: 1931

Income for Overseas Min: $288,000.00

Personnel:
   Home ministry & office staff in US: 7

Grace Brethren Intl. Missions

PO Box 588
Winona Lake, IN 46590 USA
Phone: (574) 268-1888
Fax: (574) 269-5210
E-mail: info@gbim.org
Web Site: www.gbim.org
Associations: The Mission Exchange
Rev. David Guiles, Exec. Director

A sending agency of Brethren and Evangelical tradition engaged in church planting, development, discipleship, evangelism, leadership development and support of national churches.

Purpose: "...to spread the knowledge and glory of God by mobilizing men and women to evangelize and disciple the nations through church multiplication movements."

Year Founded in US: 1900
Income for Overseas Min: $6,643,542.00
Fully Supported US Personnel Overseas:
  Expecting to serve more than 4 years: 68
  Expecting to serve 1 to 4 years: 21
  Non-residential mission personnel: 3
Other personnel:
  Short-term less than 1 year: 107
  Non-US serving in own/other country: 59
  Home ministry & office staff in US: 26
Countries: Argentina 7; Brazil 6; Cambodia 4; Cameroon 3; Central African Republic; Central Asia—General 6; Chad; Chile; Czech Republic 2; France 13; Germany 2; Ireland 4; Japan 2; Mexico 2; Philippines 2; Portugal 4; Russia; Spain 2; Thailand 4; United Kingdom 5

Grace Ministries Intl.

PO Box 9405
Grand Rapids, MI 49509 USA
Phone: (616) 241-5666
Fax: (616) 538-0599
E-mail: gmi@gracem.org
Web Site: www.gracem.org
Associations: The Mission Exchange
Mr. Samuel R. Vinton, Jr., Exec. Director

A nondenominational sending agency of Evangelical tradition engaged in church planting, childcare/orphanage programs, Christian education, theological education, leadership development and literature production.

Purpose: "...to send missionaries into various countries with the purpose of evangelism, establishing churches, leadership training, and meeting the needs of people through medical and community development ministries."

Year Founded in US: 1939
Income for Overseas Min: $2,177,230.00
Fully Supported US Personnel Overseas:
  Expecting to serve 1 to 4 years: 54
  Non-residential mission personnel: 2
Other personnel:
  Short-term less than 1 year: 56
  Non-US serving in own/other country: 2
  Home ministry & office staff in US: 5
Countries: Australia; Bolivia; Congo, Democratic Republic of; Costa Rica; India; Malawi; Puerto Rico; Tanzania; Uruguay; Zambia

Great Commission Center International

848 Stewart Dr., Ste. 200
Sunnyvale, CA 94085 USA
Phone: (408) 636-0030
Fax: (408) 636-0033
E-mail: info@gcciusa.org
Web Site: www.gcciusa.org
Sharon Chan, President

An interdenominational support agency of Evangelical tradition engaged in mobilization for mission, missions information service, literature production, mission-related research and training.

Purpose: "...to serve alongside the evangelical churches and para-church groups for the progressive realization of the Great Commission."

Year Founded in US: 1989
Income for Overseas Min: $178,217.00
Personnel:
  Home ministry & office staff in US: 5

Great Commission Ministries, Inc.

PO Box 7101
Winter Park, FL 32793-7101 USA
Phone: (407) 671-9700
Fax: (407) 671-9776
E-mail: info@gcmweb.org
Web Site: www.gcmweb.org
Associations: The Mission Exchange

Mr. Thomas Mauriello, Exec. Director

A nondenominational sending agency of Evangelical tradition engaged in leadership development, church planting, discipleship, evangelism and mobilization for mission. Countries of service data from 2005.

Purpose: "...to serve churches by multiplying missionaries for the Great Commission...to mobilize missionaries to locally governed, missional churches, and church networks...to direct employment, funding, and management for the staff with the local church..."

Year Founded in US: 1990

Income for Overseas Min: $2,339,874.00

Fully Supported US Personnel Overseas:
Expecting to serve more than 4 years: 32
Expecting to serve 1 to 4 years: 18

Other personnel:
Short-term less than 1 year: 1
Non-US serving in own/other country: 5
Home ministry & office staff in US: 230

Countries: Germany 4; Italy 7; Netherlands 9; Philippines; Poland 2; Taiwan; Ukraine 10

Greater Europe Mission

18950 Base Camp Rd.
Monument, CO 80132-8009 USA
Phone: (719) 488-8008
Fax: (719) 488-8018
E-mail: info@gemission.com
Web Site: www.gemission.org
Associations: CrossGlobal Link, The Mission Exchange

Mr. Henry Deneen, President

A nondenominational sending agency of Evangelical tradition engaged in church planting, discipleship, TEE, evangelism, short-term programs and TESOL.

Purpose: "...to disciple all peoples of Europe through rapidly reproducing churches."

Year Founded in US: 1949

Fully Supported US Personnel Overseas:
Expecting to serve more than 4 years: 274
Expecting to serve 1 to 4 years: 195
Non-residential mission personnel: 6

Other personnel:
Short-term less than 1 year: 293
Home ministry & office staff in US: 45

Countries: Albania 2; Austria 14; Azerbaijan; Belarus; Belgium 4; Bulgaria 3; Croatia 8; Czech Republic 8; Estonia; Finland 1; France 24; Georgia; Germany 73; Greece 12; Hungary 4; Iceland 2; Ireland 25; Italy 10; Kosovo 2; Latvia 4; Malta 2; Morocco; Netherlands 12; Poland 5; Portugal 8; Romania 16; Russia 1; Serbia and Montenegro 4; Slovakia 2; Slovenia; Spain 12; Sweden 8; Ukraine 6; United Kingdom 2

Greater Grace World Outreach

6025 Moravia Park Dr.
Baltimore, MD 21206 USA
Phone: (410) 483-3700
Fax: (410) 483-3708
E-mail: missions@ggwo.org
Web Site: www.ggwo.org

Mr. Thomas Schaller, Sr. Pastor

A nondenominational support agency of Baptist and Evangelical tradition engaged in church planting, broadcasting, childcare/orphanage programs, discipleship, Christian education, theological education, evangelism and missionary training.

Purpose: "...to propagate the finished work of the Gospel of Jesus Christ locally, nationally and internationally...to teach, in word and deed, those within our sphere of influence...to practice and promote a Christian lifestyle."

Year Founded in US: 1987

Income for Overseas Min: $1,400,000.00

Gifts in Kind: $200,000.00

Fully Supported US Personnel Overseas:
Expecting to serve more than 4 years: 49
Expecting to serve 1 to 4 years: 34
Non-residential mission personnel: 2

Other personnel:
Short-term less than 1 year: 349
Non-US serving in own/other country: 875
Home ministry & office staff in US: 4

Countries: Albania; Argentina; Asia—General; Austria; Azerbaijan; Benin; Burkina Faso; Brazil 1; Brunei; Burundi; Chile; Congo, Democratic Republic of; Cote d'Ivoire; Croatia 2; Czech Republic; Ecuador 3; Finland; France; Gabon; Germany 2; Ghana 2; Guyana; Hungary 10; India 2; Ireland 1; Italy; Jamaica; Kazakhstan 2; Kenya; Korea, South 3; Kyrgyzstan 2; Liberia; Lithuania; Mexico 4;

Middle East 3; Moldova; Mozambique; Nepal; Niger; Nigeria; Pakistan; Peru 2; Philippines 1; Poland; Portugal 1; Puerto Rico; Romania; Russia; Rwanda; Somalia; South Africa 2; Sudan; Swaziland; Sweden; Switzerland; Tajikistan; Tanzania; Thailand 3; Togo; Turkey; Turkmenistan; Uganda; Ukraine; United Kingdom 1; Uzbekistan; Zambia 2

Habitat for Humanity Intl.

121 Habitat St.
Americus, GA 31709 USA
Phone: (229) 924-6935
Fax: (229) 928-4157
E-mail: publicinfo@habitat.org
Web Site: www.habitat.org
Mr. Jonathan T.M. Reckford, CEO

An interdenominational specialized service agency of Ecumenical tradition engaged in building low-income housing in partnership with/for people in need. Since 1976, Habitat has built more than 200,000 houses in nearly 100 countries. Data from 2005.

Purpose: "...works in partnership with God and people everywhere to develop communities with God's people in need by building and renovating houses...in which people can live and grow into all that God intended."

Year Founded in US: 1976

Income for Overseas Min: $95,475,655.00

Gifts in Kind: $2,348,081.00

Fully Supported US Personnel Overseas:
  Expecting to serve more than 4 years: 22
  Expecting to serve 1 to 4 years: 184
  Non-residential mission personnel: 50

Other personnel:
  Short-term less than 1 year: 4600
  Non-US serving in own/other country: 206
  Home ministry & office staff in US: 568

Countries: Afghanistan; Australia; Bangladesh; Botswana; Brazil; China; Congo, Democratic Republic of; Costa Rica 6; Dominican Republic; Ecuador; Fiji; Ghana; Hong Kong; Hungary 4; India; Indonesia; Jordan; Kenya; Lesotho; Malawi; Mongolia; Mozambique; Nepal; Nicaragua; Philippines; Senegal; Singapore 3; South Africa 4; Sri Lanka; Tanzania; Thailand 5; Uganda; United Kingdom; Vietnam

Haiti Lutheran Mission Society

PO Box 22544
Lincoln, NE 68542-2544 USA
Phone: (402) 474-2063
Fax: (402) 474-2596
E-mail: rnnbuethe@yahoo.com
Web Site: www.haitilutheran.org
Dick Buethe, Executive Director

A denominational support agency of Lutheran tradition engaged in church planting, Christian education, theological education, medical work and relief and/or rehabilitation. Data from 2005.

Purpose: "...to minister to the spiritual and physical needs of the Haitian people so that they might be won by the Holy Spirit to be disciples of Jesus Christ."

Year Founded in US: 1979

Income for Overseas Min: $250,000.00

Gifts in Kind: $40,000.00

Personnel:
  Short-term less than 1 year: 300
  Non-US serving in own/other country: 75

Countries: Haiti

Haitian Christian Outreach

PO Box 1052
Mahomet, IL 61853 USA
Phone: (217) 778-6023
E-mail: mac@haitianchristian.org
Web Site: www.haitianchristian.org
Mr. Mac Burberry, Exec. Director

A nondenominational support agency of Christian (Restoration Movement) tradition engaged in church planting, discipleship, Christian education, theological education, medical work and support of national workers.

Purpose: "...to partner with Haitian Christians to transform their culture for Christ."

Year Founded in US: 1985

Income for Overseas Min: $300,000.00

Fully Supported US Personnel Overseas:
  Expecting to serve more than 4 years: 3
  Non-residential mission personnel: 1

Other personnel:
  Short-term less than 1 year: 94
  Non-US serving in own/other country: 86
  Home ministry & office staff in US: 1

Countries: Haiti 3

Handclasp International, Inc.

PO 3287
Lake Arrowhead, CA 92352-3287 USA
Phone: (909) 337-1894
Fax: (909) 336-1674
E-mail: cri@pobox.com

Mr. Daniel J. Henrich, President

An interdenominational service agency of Evangelical tradition engaged in video/film production/distribution, extension education, mission-related research and services for other agencies.

Year Founded in US: 1970

Harvest

PO Box 2670
Phoenix, AZ 85002 USA
Phone: (602) 258-1083
Fax: (602) 258-1318
E-mail: bmoffitt@harvestfoundation.org
Web Site: www.harvestfoundation.org
Associations: AERDO

Mr. Bob Moffitt, President

A nondenominational service agency of Christian tradition engaged in wholistic ministry, leadership development, Christian education, development, support of national churches and missionary training.

Purpose: "...to equip local churches worldwide to demonstrate God's intentions in every area of life."

Year Founded in US: 1983

Fully Supported US Personnel Overseas:
Non-residential mission personnel: 3

Other personnel:
Non-US serving in own/other country: 27
Home ministry & office staff in US: 1

Countries: Bolivia; Brazil; Congo, Democratic Republic of; Dominican Republic; Ethiopia; Ghana; Haiti; Honduras; India; Kenya; Myanmar/Burma; Nepal; Peru; Philippines; Rwanda; Venezuela

Harvest International, Inc.

PO Box 6690
Ocala, FL 34478-6690 USA
Phone: (352) 622-1818
Fax: (352) 622-2569
E-mail: danny@harvestinternational.org
Web Site: www.harvestinternational.org

Mr. Daniel Thomas, Exec. Director

A sending agency of Evangelical tradition engaged in short-term programs, childcare/orphanage programs, church construction, evangelism, providing medical supplies and services for other agencies.

Purpose: "...to meet the physical needs of people in order to earn the right to minister to their spiritual needs."

Year Founded in US: 1987

Income for Overseas Min: $1,366,382.00

Gifts in Kind: $154,505.00

Fully Supported US Personnel Overseas:
Expecting to serve 1 to 4 years: 11
Non-residential mission personnel: 2

Other personnel:
Short-term less than 1 year: 120
Non-US serving in own/other country: 12
Home ministry & office staff in US: 5

Countries: Haiti; India; Kenya; Romania; Uganda; Ukraine; Zimbabwe

Harvest Mission to the Unreached

PO Box 16656
Sugar Land, TX 77496-6656 USA
Phone: (281) 841-8607
E-mail: harvestmission@yahoo.com
Web Site: www.harvestmission.org

Rev. Matthew Oommen, President

A nondenominational support agency of Evangelical tradition engaged in church planting, childcare/orphanage programs, theological education, support of national workers, missionary training, youth programs and leper ministry.

Purpose: "...to reach Northern India through native missionaries for the glory of God."

Year Founded in US: 1998

Income for Overseas Min: $207,595.00

Personnel:
Short-term less than 1 year: 12
Non-US serving in own/other country: 120

Countries: India

Harvesting In Spanish (HIS)

VIP SAL 723
PO Box 25364
Miami, FL 33102-5364 USA
E-mail: don.benner@harvesting.org

Web Site: www.harvesting.org

Teri Benner de Dominguez, President

An interdenominational sending agency of Evangelical, Independent, and Pentecostal tradition engaged in childcare/orphanage programs, Bible distribution, Christian education, literature distribution, medical work and short-term programs.

Purpose: "...to prepare disadvantaged children to become ethical, productive Christian men and women through superior scholastic and spiritual education which promotes intellectual growth, social grace, an attitude of servanthood, and emotional stability.

Year Founded in US: 1980

Income for Overseas Min: $624,550.00

Fully Supported US Personnel Overseas:
    Expecting to serve more than 4 years: 3
    Non-residential mission personnel: 3

Other personnel:
    Short-term less than 1 year: 125
    Non-US serving in own/other country: 3
    Home ministry & office staff in US: 6

Countries: El Salvador 3

Have Christ Will Travel Ministries, Inc.

528 E. Church Ln.
Philadelphia, PA 19144 USA

Phone: (215) 438-6308

Fax: (215) 438-6308

Dr. Joseph C. Jeter, President/Director

An interdenominational support agency of Baptist and Evangelical tradition engaged in evangelism, broadcasting, camping programs, childrens programs, church planting and short-term programs.

Year Founded in US: 1965

Fully Supported US Personnel Overseas:
    Expecting to serve more than 4 years: 2
    Non-residential mission personnel: 2

Other personnel:
    Short-term less than 1 year: 48
    Non-US serving in own/other country: 104
    Home ministry & office staff in US: 3

Countries: Haiti; India; Kenya 2; Liberia

HBI Global Partners

PO Box 584
Forest, VA 24551 US

Phone: (336) 595-3891

E-mail: info@globalpartners.org

Web Site: www.globalpartners.org

Dr. Paul R. Gupta, President/Director

A sending agency of Baptist tradition engaged in leadership development, church planting, discipleship, support of national workers, relief and/or rehabilitation and short-term programs. Data from 2005.

Purpose: "...enabling the North American Church to develop partnerships with national movements to reach the unreached in India and beyond."

Year Founded in US: 1950

Income for Overseas Min: $1,069,020.00

Personnel:
    Short-term less than 1 year: 40
    Non-US serving in own/other country: 605
    Home ministry & office staff in US: 2

Countries: India; Nepal

HCJB Global

1065 Garden of the Gods Rd.
Colorado Springs, CO 80907 USA

Phone: (719) 590-9800

Fax: (719) 590-9801

E-mail: info@hcjb.org

Web Site: www.hcjb.org

Associations: CrossGlobal Link

Mr. Wayne Pederson, President

A nondenominational service agency of Independent tradition engaged in broadcasting, discipleship, leadership development, medical work, support of national churches and partnership development.

Purpose: "...to empower dynamic media and healthcare ministries that declare and demonstrate Jesus Christ."

Year Founded in US: 1931

Income for Overseas Min: $13,256,000.00

Gifts in Kind: $1,574,123.00

Fully Supported US Personnel Overseas:
    Expecting to serve more than 4 years: 120
    Expecting to serve 1 to 4 years: 2
    Non-residential mission personnel: 220

Other personnel:
    Short-term less than 1 year: 86
    Non-US serving in own/other country: 161
    Home ministry & office staff in US: 76

Countries: Argentina; Australia 4; Brazil

2; Cuba 2; Czech Republic 2; Ecuador 91; France; Ghana 2; Guatemala 2; Malawi 3; Papua New Guinea 2; Singapore 6; South Africa 1; Spain 1; Switzerland; United Kingdom 2

Health Emergent International Services

PO Box 1225
Issaquah, WA 98027 USA
Phone: (425) 837-0991
Fax: (425) 837-0992
E-mail: medicalteams@comcast.net
Web Site: www.heis.org
Mr. Marvin G. Taylor, Medical Director

A service agency of Evangelical and Pentecostal tradition engaged in medical work, development, management consulting/training, providing medical supplies, relief and/or rehabilitation and Christian education. Data from 2001.

Purpose: "...strives to show love and compassion to international communities, continually delivering health care services, medical education and supporting indigenous medical communities."

Year Founded in US: 1999
Income for Overseas Min: $2,700,000.00
Gifts in Kind: $1,200,000.00
Fully Supported US Personnel Overseas:
Expecting to serve more than 4 years: 4
Expecting to serve 1 to 4 years: 12
Non-residential mission personnel: 2
Other personnel:
Short-term less than 1 year: 53
Non-US serving in own/other country: 1
Countries: Afghanistan 2; Tajikistan 2

Health Teams International

10056 Applegate Ln.
Brighton, MI 48114 USA
Phone: (810) 229-9346
Fax: (810) 229-4336
E-mail: ddchar@earthlink.net
Web Site: www.healthteamsintl.org
Dr. Richard Charlick, President/CEO

An interdenominational specialized agency engaged in evangelism and short-term health care teams.

Purpose: "...to assist in the evangelization of the unreached people groups of the

world through the ministration of short-term Christian health care teams."
Year Founded in US: 1986
Income for Overseas Min: $40,000.00
Personnel:
Short-term less than 1 year: 50
Home ministry & office staff in US: 2

Heart for Honduras

22601 Lutheran Church Rd.
Tomball, TX 77377 USA
Phone: (281) 290-1206
Fax: (281) 290-1255
E-mail: kpieper@salem4u.com
Web Site: www.heartforhonduras.org
Dana Boehm, President

A denominational service agency of Lutheran tradition engaged in evangelism, medical work, partnership development and short-term programs.

Purpose: "...to obey Jesus Christ's great commandment."
Year Founded in US: 1998
Income for Overseas Min: $180,526.00
Personnel:
Short-term less than 1 year: 60
Home ministry & office staff in US: 3
Countries: Honduras

Heart of God Ministries

3720 S. Hiwassee Rd.
Choctaw, OK 73020 USA
Phone: (405) 737-9446
Fax: (405) 737-9448
E-mail: hgm@heartofgod.com
Web Site: www.heartofgod.com
Mr. John Willis Zumwalt, Director

A specialized agency engaged in church planting, missionary education, justice, mobilization for mission, trafficking/slavery issues and missionary training.

Purpose: "...to take the Good News to the ends of the earth."
Year Founded in US: 1995
Income for Overseas Min: $897,000.00
Fully Supported US Personnel Overseas:
Expecting to serve more than 4 years: 28
Other personnel:
Non-US serving in own/other country: 66
Home ministry & office staff in US: 13

Countries: Africa—General; India 8; Middle East 5; Senegal 12; Taiwan 3

Heart of the Bride Ministries

PO Box 786
Niceville, FL 32588 USA
Phone: (850) 678-9008
Fax: (850) 678-1192
E-mail: info@heartofthebride.org
Web Site: www.heartofthebride.org
Associations: The Mission Exchange
Rev. Tony L. Gibson, Jr., Founder

A nondenominational sending agency of Baptist tradition engaged in childcare/orphanage programs, children at risk, childrens programs, discipleship, evangelism and HIV/Aids.

Purpose: "...to send people and resources from places of abundance to places of need within the body of Christ...to care for and disciple orphans in developing countries through partnerships with indigenous believers."

Year Founded in US:
Income for Overseas Min: $871,170.00
Fully Supported US Personnel Overseas:
Expecting to serve 1 to 4 years: 7
Non-residential mission personnel: 2
Other personnel:
Short-term less than 1 year: 45
Home ministry & office staff in US: 5
Countries: Kenya; Uganda; Zambia;

Heart to Heart Intl. Ministries (H2H)

PO Box 1832
Ramona, CA 92065 USA
Phone: (760) 789-8798
Fax: (760) 789-8798
E-mail: info@h2hint.org
Web Site: www.h2hint.org
Mr. James Sorrels, President

An interdenominational support agency of Evangelical tradition engaged in childcare/orphanage programs, camping programs, children at risk, evangelism, medical work and short-term programs.

Purpose: "...to share God's love with the poor and orphaned in Romania by proclaiming the Gospel message...to offer physi-

cal help to those in need...to train people to become faithful followers of the Lord Jesus Christ."

Year Founded in US: 1994
Income for Overseas Min: $639,558.00
Fully Supported US Personnel Overseas:
Expecting to serve more than 4 years: 11
Non-residential mission personnel: 2
Other personnel:
Short-term less than 1 year: 231
Non-US serving in own/other country: 9
Home ministry & office staff in US: 2
Countries: Romania 11

Heifer Project International

1 World Ave.
Little Rock, AR 72202 USA
Phone: (501) 907-2600
Fax: (501) 907-2602
E-mail: info@heifer.org
Web Site: www.heifer.org
Jo Luck, President/CEO

A transdenominational support agency of Independent tradition engaged in development, agricultural programs, justice and training.

Purpose: "...to work with communities to end hunger and poverty and to care for the earth."

Year Founded in US: 1944
Income for Overseas Min: $81,973,237.00
Personnel:
Short-term less than 1 year: 50
Home ministry & office staff in US: 267
Countries: Asia—General; Europe—General; Latin America—General

Helimission, Inc.—USA

7245 College St.
Lima, NY 14485 USA
Phone: (585) 624-5509
Fax: (585) 582-6165
E-mail: helimission-usa@rochester.rr.com
Mr. Benjamin J. Dodzweit, USA Director

A nondenominational service agency of Charismatic and Pentecostal tradition engaged in evangelism, aviation services, church planting, services for other agencies, Bible translation and natural disaster relief.

Purpose: "...to use helicopters to bring

medical material and spiritual help to people in remote and inaccessible areas to assist in catastrophic emergencies in cooperation with international relief organizations."

Year Founded in US: 1983

Income for Overseas Min: $30,774.00

Personnel:
  Short-term less than 1 year: 1
  Non-US serving in own/other country: 16
  Home ministry & office staff in US: 3

Countries: Ethiopia; Indonesia; Madagascar

Hellenic Ministries/USA
PO Box 726
Wheaton, IL 60187 USA
Phone: (630) 520-0372
Fax: (630) 520-0417
E-mail: info@hmnet.org
Web Site: www.hellenicministries.com
Mr. Daniel A. Bostrom, Exec. Director

A sending agency engaged in evangelism, church planting, discipleship, evangelism, relief and/or rehabilitation and youth programs. Activities data from 2005.

Purpose: "Christ for Greece and the nations."

Year Founded in US: 1986

Fully Supported US Personnel Overseas:
  Expecting to serve more than 4 years: 6
  Expecting to serve 1 to 4 years: 8

Other personnel:
  Short-term less than 1 year: 97
  Non-US serving in own/other country: 25
  Home ministry & office staff in US: 1

Countries: Greece 6

Help for Christian Nationals, Inc.
PO Box 381006
Duncanville, TX 75138 USA
Phone: (972) 780-5909
Fax: (972) 780-5909
E-mail: hcninc@swbell.net
Dr. John S. Jauchen, President

An interdenominational sending agency of Evangelical tradition engaged in leadership development, theological education and evangelism. Data from 2005.

Purpose: "...serving Christian national workers through economic and educational assistance, equipping them to be more effective in reaching their own people for Jesus Christ."

Year Founded in US: 1982

Income for Overseas Min: $674,000.00

Fully Supported US Personnel Overseas:
  Expecting to serve more than 4 years: 7
  Non-residential mission personnel: 1

Other personnel:
  Non-US serving in own/other country: 7
  Home ministry & office staff in US: 2

Countries: Guatemala 2; India 1; Latin America—General 2; Philippines; Russia; Spain 2

Help for Haiti, Inc.
1129 South B St.
Lake Worth, FL 33460 USA
Phone: (561) 540-8784
Fax: (561) 585-4019
E-mail: helpforhaiti.inc@gmail.com
Web Site: www.helpforhaitiinc.org
Associations: AERDO
Sandra Koch, Exec. Director

A nondenominational service agency of Evangelical and Independent tradition engaged in relief and/or rehabilitation, development and services for other agencies.

Purpose: "...to care for the poor, sick, and hungry of Haiti, regardless of race, creed, or religious affiliation."

Year Founded in US: 1995

Income for Overseas Min: $27,000.00

Fully Supported US Personnel Overseas:
  Non-residential mission personnel: 3

Other personnel:
  Short-term less than 1 year: 2
  Non-US serving in own/other country: 3
  Home ministry & office staff in US: 1

Countries: Haiti

Helps Intl. Ministries
573 Fairview Rd.
Asheville, NC 28803 USA
Phone: (828) 277-3812
Fax: (828) 274-7770
E-mail: him@helpsintl.com
Web Site: www.helpsintl.com
Rev. David A. Summey, CEO

A nondenominational specialized agency of Evangelical and Fundamental tradition engaged in services for other agencies and technical assistance. Data from 2001.

Purpose: "...strengthening and equipping ministries serving God's kingdom by providing various 'helps'..."

Year Founded in US: 1976

Hermano Pablo Ministries

PO Box 100
Costa Mesa, CA 92628 USA

Phone: (949) 645-0676
Fax: (949) 645-0374
E-mail: hpm@box100.org
Web Site: www.box100.org

Mr. Charles R. Stewart, President

A nondenominational service agency of Evangelical tradition engaged in evangelistic broadcasting, audio recording/distribution, evangelism and video/film production/distribution, whose program "A Message to the Conscience" is broadcast 4,600 times each day in 32 countries throughout the Spanish-speaking world.

Purpose: "...to be God's voice to the conscience of every Hispanic in the world."

Year Founded in US: 1964

Income for Overseas Min: $320,260.00

Personnel:
Home ministry & office staff in US: 6

High Adventure Ministries/ Voice of Hope Broadcasting Network

PO Box 197569
Louisville, KY 40259 USA

Phone: (502) 254-9960
Fax: (502) 254-9962
E-mail: mail@highadventure.net
Web Site: www.highadventure.org

Jacqueline G. Yockey, President/CEO

An interdenominational service agency of Evangelical tradition engaged in broadcasting, evangelism and relief and/or rehabilitation. Data from 2005.

Year Founded in US: 1972

Personnel:
Non-US serving in own/other country: 3
Home ministry & office staff in US: 6

Countries: Israel

His Healing Helping Hands Intl. Ministries (4 H.I.M.)

2410 W. Memorial Rd.
Suite C, #133
Oklahoma City, OK 73134 USA

Phone: (405) 752-9861
Fax: (405) 753-9870
E-mail: okc4him@yahoo.com
Web Site: www.4-him.net

Mr. Steve Hollingsworth, President

An interdenominational service agency of Evangelical tradition engaged in development, church planting, evangelism, providing medical supplies, medical work and relief and/or rehabilitation.

Purpose: "...to facilitate and mobilize ministry teams and the essential resources required to bring relief to those who are in need."

Year Founded in US: 1999

Income for Overseas Min: $1,200,000.00

Gifts in Kind: $200,000.00

Fully Supported US Personnel Overseas:
Non-residential mission personnel: 1

Other personnel:
Short-term less than 1 year: 50
Non-US serving in own/other country: 11
Home ministry & office staff in US: 3

Countries: India; Sierra Leone; Togo

HIS Servants Ministries

PO Box 461
Ferguson, KY 42533 USA

Phone: (606) 451-0914
Web Site: www.hsministries.org

Mr. Curt Williams, President

A nondenominational service agency of Evangelical tradition engaged in medical work and providing medical supplies.

Purpose: "...to use medicine to create ministry opportunities."

Year Founded in US: 1999

Income for Overseas Min: $95,000.00

Personnel:
Short-term less than 1 year: 55

Countries: Belize; Guatemala; Kenya; Mexico; Thailand

Hisportic Christian Mission
4015 FM 2351 Road, Ste. 207
Friendswood, TX 77546 USA
Phone: (281) 482-3800
Fax: (281) 482-3802
E-mail: cbookout@hcm.org
Web Site: www.hcm.org
Mr. Carl Bookout, Exec. Director

A denominational support agency of Christian (Restoration Movement) tradition engaged in church planting. Data from 2005.

Purpose: "...enables mission-minded Christians to evangelize and plant churches among Portuguese speaking people."
Year Founded in US: 1984
Income for Overseas Min: $1,200.00
Personnel:
  Non-US serving in own/other country: 1
  Home ministry & office staff in US: 5
Countries: Guinea-Bissau

Holt International Children's Services, Inc.
PO Box 2880
Eugene, OR 97402 USA
Phone: (541) 687-2202
Fax: (541) 683-6175
E-mail: info@holtinternational.org
Web Site: www.holtinternational.org
Kim Brown, President/CEO

A nondenominational service agency of Evangelical tradition engaged in adoption, childcare/orphanage programs, children at risk, childrens programs and disability assistance programs.

Purpose: "...to carry out God's plan for every child to have a permanent, loving family."
Year Founded in US: 1956
Income for Overseas Min: $8,550,000.00
Fully Supported US Personnel Overseas:
  Non-residential mission personnel: 2
Other personnel:
  Non-US serving in own/other country: 102
  Home ministry & office staff in US: 135
Countries: Cambodia; China; Ethiopia; Guatemala; Nepal; Vietnam; Ukraine

Hope for the Hungry
PO Box 786
Belton, TX 76513 USA
Phone: (254) 939-0124
Fax: (254) 939-0882
E-mail: hope@hopeforthehungry.org
Web Site: www.hopeforthehungry.org
Mr. Daniel R. Kirkley, President

An interdenominational sending agency of Evangelical tradition engaged in childcare/orphanage programs, business as mission, children at risk, childrens programs, church planting, development, Christian education, missionary education, evangelism, funds transmission, leadership development, relief and/or rehabilitation, short-term programs and youth programs.

Purpose: "...to share the Bread of Life with a starving world."
Year Founded in US: 1982
Income for Overseas Min: $786,059.00
Fully Supported US Personnel Overseas:
  Expecting to serve more than 4 years: 16
  Expecting to serve 1 to 4 years: 3
  Non-residential mission personnel: 3
Other personnel:
  Short-term less than 1 year: 11
  Non-US serving in own/other country: 24
  Home ministry & office staff in US: 21
Countries: Asia—General 2; Colombia 1; Costa Rica 2; Ghana; Guatemala 1; Haiti 5; India; Israel; Japan 1; Kenya; South Africa; Sri Lanka; Taiwan 2; Uganda 2; Zimbabwe

Hope Haven Intl. Ministries
1800 19th St.
Rock Valley, IA 51247 USA
Phone: (712) 476-2737
Fax: (712) 476-2989
Web Site: www.hopehaven.org
Associations: AERDO
Mr. David R. Van Ningen, CEO

A denominational support agency of Reformed tradition engaged in disability assistance programs and camping programs.

Purpose: "...to assist persons with disabilities...to develop opportunities for improving the economic and social welfare and independence of people with disabilities within countries and cultures throughout the world."
Year Founded in US: 1964
Income for Overseas Min: $2,084,582.00
Gifts in Kind: $1,132,680.00

Fully Supported US Personnel Overseas:
Expecting to serve more than 4 years: 1
Non-residential mission personnel: 1

Other personnel:
Short-term less than 1 year: 50
Non-US serving in own/other country: 16
Home ministry & office staff in US: 5

Countries: Guatemala 1; Romania; Vietnam

HOPE International

227 Granite Run Dr., Ste. 250
Lancaster, PA 17601 USA
Phone: (717) 464-3220
Fax: (717) 735-2034
E-mail: info@hopeinternational.org
Web Site: www.hopeinternational.org

Mr. Peter Greer, President

A nondenominational support agency engaged in business as mission, development, evangelism and training.

Purpose: "...to invest in the dreams of the poor in the world's underserved communities so that they might be released from physical and spiritual poverty."

Year Founded in US: 1997

Income for Overseas Min: $5,409,838.00

Fully Supported US Personnel Overseas:
Expecting to serve more than 4 years: 4
Expecting to serve 1 to 4 years: 7
Non-residential mission personnel: 4

Other personnel:
Non-US serving in own/other country: 7
Home ministry & office staff in US: 29

Countries: Afghanistan 1; Burundi; China 1; Congo, Democratic Republic of 1; Congo, Republic of the; Haiti; India 1; Rwanda; Ukraine

I. N. Network USA

10432 Chicago Dr., Ste. 2
Zeeland, MI 49464 USA
Phone: (616) 748-9620
Fax: (616) 748-9641
E-mail: info@innetworkusa.org
Web Site: www.innetworkusa.org

Mr. LaDoyt "Rody" Rodeheaver, President/CEO

A nondenominational service agency of Evangelical and Reformed tradition engaged in support of national workers, church planting, development, Christian education,

evangelism and child sponsorship program. Field personnel data from 2002.

Year Founded in US: 1975

Income for Overseas Min: $1,369,236.00

Personnel:
Non-US serving in own/other country: 804
Home ministry & office staff in US: 7

Countries: Bangladesh; Colombia; Czech Republic; Egypt; Eritrea; Ethiopia; Ghana; India; Morocco; Nepal; Philippines; Romania; Slovakia; Sri Lanka; Tanzania; Uganda; Vietnam; Zambia

IFCA World Missions

1294 Rutledge Rd.
Transfer, PA 16154 USA
Phone: (724) 962-3501
Fax: (724) 962-1766
E-mail: ifcaworldimpact@neohio.twcbc.com
Web Site: www.ifcaministry.org

Rev. Dale Russo, Director of World Missions

A denominational support agency of Pentecostal tradition engaged in mobilization for mission, church planting, funds transmission, support of national churches, support of national workers and missionary training.

Purpose: "...to accelerate the Gospel to the unreached peoples of the world."

Year Founded in US: 1924

Income for Overseas Min: $393,332.00

Fully Supported US Personnel Overseas:
Expecting to serve more than 4 years: 8

Other personnel:
Non-US serving in own/other country: 20
Home ministry & office staff in US: 2

Countries: Argentina; Australia; Barbados; Bolivia; Botswana; Brazil; Chile; Colombia; Ecuador; Guyana 2; India 3; Italy 1; Madagascar; Malawi; Philippines; South Africa 2; Ukraine; Uruguay; Venezuela

IMA World Health

PO Box 429
Old Main Bldg.
New Windsor, MD 21776 USA
Phone: (410) 635-8720
Fax: (410) 635-8726
E-mail: imainfo@worldhealth.org
Web Site: www.imaworldhealth.org
Associations: CWS

Mr. Rick Santos, President

An interdenominational support agency of Christian ("Restoration Movement") and Ecumenical tradition distributing medical supplies to healthcare facilities in more than 50 countries affiliated with member and associate organizations. Data from 2005.

Purpose: "...to provide essential products and services for emergency, health and development programs of interest to members, which serve people in need with preference given to the poorest of the poor..."

Year Founded in US: 1960

Income for Overseas Min: $20,511,465.00

Gifts in Kind: $75,654,708.00

Personnel:
  Home ministry & office staff in US: 23

Impact International, Inc.
PO Box 160
Boca Raton, FL 33429 USA

Phone: (561) 338-7000
E-mail: bdm4@msn.com
Web Site: www.impactinternational.org

Rev. Bruce Woodman, Director

A nondenominational sending agency of Baptist tradition engaged in evangelism, broadcasting and church planting.

Purpose: "...to evangelize the lost and edify the Church in the Spanish-speaking world."

Year Founded in US: 1959

Income for Overseas Min: $500,000.00

Fully Supported US Personnel Overseas:
  Expecting to serve more than 4 years: 4

Other personnel:
  Non-US serving in own/other country: 18
  Home ministry & office staff in US: 4

Countries: Argentina; El Salvador; Guatemala; Honduras; Mexico; Peru; South America—General 4; Venezuela

In Motion Ministries
PO Box 337507
Greeley, CO 80633 USA

Phone: (970) 352-5640
E-mail: info@inmotionministries.org
Web Site: www.inmotionministries.org

Mr. Seth Dunn, Exec. Director

A transdenominational support agency of Charismatic and Independent tradition engaged in short-term programs, literature distribution, support of national churches, mobilization for mission, support of national workers and missionary training.

Purpose: "...to provide education, training, and worldwide opportunities to minister God's love."

Year Founded in US: 1986

Income for Overseas Min: $110,000.00

Fully Supported US Personnel Overseas:
  Non-residential mission personnel: 4

Other personnel:
  Short-term less than 1 year: 100
  Home ministry & office staff in US: 3

In Touch Mission Intl.
PO Box 7575
Tempe, AZ 85281 USA

Phone: (480) 968-4100
Fax: (480) 968-5462
E-mail: itmi@intouchmission.org
Web Site: www.intouchmission.org

Mr. Steve Evers, Director

A nondenominational sending agency of Evangelical tradition engaged in support of national workers, childcare/orphanage programs, support of national churches, partnership development, relief and/or rehabilitation and Bible translation.

Purpose: "...to find and partner with Christians who are already living and doing ministry in their home country for the purpose of connecting them with resources that will empower them to fulfill their calling by exposing their ministries to others in the Body of Christ."

Year Founded in US: 1981

Income for Overseas Min: $767,620.00

Gifts in Kind: $23,190.00

Fully Supported US Personnel Overseas:
  Expecting to serve more than 4 years: 10
  Expecting to serve 1 to 4 years: 1
  Non-residential mission personnel: 1

Other personnel:
  Short-term less than 1 year: 2
  Non-US serving in own/other country: 30
  Home ministry & office staff in US: 3

Countries: India; Poland 5; Romania; South Africa 2; Sudan; Uganda 1; Zambia 2

Independent Faith Mission, Inc.

PO Box 7791
Greensboro, NC 27417 USA
Phone: (336) 292-1255
Fax: (336) 292-9348
E-mail: kurtz.robert@ifmnews.com
Web Site: www.ifmnews.com

Rev. Robert F. Kurtz, Exec. Director

A sending agency of Baptist tradition engaged in church planting, evangelism, short-term programs, training and Bible translation.

Year Founded in US: 1950

Income for Overseas Min: $2,650,000.00

Fully Supported US Personnel Overseas:
  Expecting to serve more than 4 years: 47

Other personnel:
  Short-term less than 1 year: 14
  Non-US serving in own/other country: 14
  Home ministry & office staff in US: 7

Countries: Botswana 2; Congo, Democratic Republic of; Israel 2; Kenya 6; Korea, South 2; Marshall Islands 2; Mexico 2; Micronesia, Federated States of; Philippines 2; Saint Vincent and the Grenadines; South Africa 12; Suriname 7; Trinidad and Tobago; Zambia 7; Zimbabwe 3

Independent Gospel Missions: A Baptist Mission Agency

990 Calkins Rd.
Rochester, NY 14623 USA
Phone: (585) 334-9048
Fax: (585) 334-9048
E-mail: igm@igmonline.org
Web Site: www.igmonline.org

Rev. Gary E. Newhart, Exec. Director

An agency of Baptist and Independent tradition engaged in church planting, childcare/orphanage programs, leadership development, national worker support, short-term programs and training. IGM is a total faith missionary agency, operating solely on the support of individuals and churches. Data from 2005.

Purpose: "...serving the church, missionary, and national pastor to produce a concerted effort in the areas of accountability, responsibility, need, and the harvest of souls for the glory and kingdom of God."

Year Founded in US: 1968

Personnel:
  Home ministry & office staff in US: 1

India Evangelical Mission

PO Box 1633
Lakewood, CA 90716-0633 USA
Phone: (562) 484-0881
E-mail: iemusa@jps.net
Web Site: www.indiaevangelical.org

Dr. G. V. Mathai, President

A nondenominational service agency of Evangelical tradition engaged in evangelism, Bible distribution, childcare/orphanage programs and training. Data from 2005.

Purpose: "...winning the lost, building and equipping the saints and then sending them forth to fulfill the Great Commission of our Lord."

Year Founded in US: 1966

Personnel:
  Short-term less than 1 year: 10
  Home ministry & office staff in US: 1

India Gospel League, NA

1521 Georgetown Rd., Ste. 305
Hudson, OH 44236 US
Phone: (888) 352-4451
E-mail: david@iglworld.org
Web Site: www.iglworld.org
Associations: The Mission Exchange

Dr. David Rice, Exec. Director

An interdenominational support agency of Evangelical tradition engaged in church planting, evangelism, Christian education, childcare/orphanage programs, development and medical work.

Purpose: "...to bring the Gospel and the love of Jesus Christ to unreached people through effective discipleship to extend God's reign over the nations."

Year Founded in US: 1994

Income for Overseas Min: $3,370,519.00

Gifts in Kind: $54,000.00

Fully Supported US Personnel Overseas:
  Non-residential mission personnel: 3

Other personnel:
  Short-term less than 1 year: 114
  Non-US serving in own/other country: 908
  Home ministry & office staff in US: 7

Countries: India

India Gospel Outreach, Inc.

PO Box 550
Rancho Cucamonga, CA 91729-0550 USA
Phone: (909) 948-2404
Fax: (909) 948-2406
E-mail: igo@indiago.org
Web Site: www.indiago.org

Rev. T. Valson Abraham, Founder/President

A service agency of Charismatic and Evangelical tradition engaged in church planting, evangelism, leadership development, support of national workers, mobilization for mission and training evangelists.

Purpose: "...dedicated to evangelizing all 3,000 ethnic groups of India by planting dynamic churches in all 27,000+ zip codes."

Year Founded in US: 1984

Income for Overseas Min: $2,018,160.00

Fully Supported US Personnel Overseas:
Expecting to serve more than 4 years: 1
Non-residential mission personnel: 1

Other personnel:
Short-term less than 1 year: 26
Non-US serving in own/other country: 2540
Home ministry & office staff in US: 7

Countries: Bhutan; India 1; Nepal

India National Inland Mission

PO Box 13422
Roanoke, VA 24033-3422 USA
Phone: (540) 400-8684
E-mail: ajaybpillai@hotmail.com

Dr. Ajay Pillai, Director

A nondenominational support agency of Evangelical tradition engaged in church planting, Bible distribution, childcare/orphanage programs, discipleship, theological education and evangelism. Data from 2005.

Year Founded in US: 1963

Income for Overseas Min: $1,632,000.00

Personnel:
Non-US serving in own/other country: 350
Home ministry & office staff in US: 1

Countries: Asia—General; India

India Partners

PO Box 5470
Eugene, OR 97405-0470 USA
Phone: (541) 683-0696

Fax: (541) 683-2773
E-mail: info@indiapartners.org
Web Site: www.indiapartners.org
Associations: AERDO

Mr. Brent Hample, President/CEO

A nondenominational service agency engaged in childcare/orphanage programs, Christian education, medical work, partnership development, short-term programs and trafficking/slavery issues.

Purpose: "...to partner with the people of India in ministry by cultivating relationships, sharing resources, and encouraging self-sufficiency through the compassion and wisdom of Jesus Christ."

Year Founded in US: 1994

Income for Overseas Min: $254,676.00

Gifts in Kind: $176,072.00

Personnel:
Short-term less than 1 year: 10
Non-US serving in own/other country: 1
Home ministry & office staff in US: 5

Countries: India

Institute of Strategic Languages and Cultures

PO Box 212667
Columbia, SC 29221 USA
Phone: (803) 333-9119
Fax: (803) 333-9117
E-mail: islcoffice@strategiclanguages.org
Web Site: www.strategiclanguages.org

Mr. Marc T. Canner, Director

A nondenominational support agency of Evangelical tradition engaged in linguistics, services for other agencies and missionary training.

Purpose: "...to provide cross-cultural and linguistic training for missionaries and other workers serving Christ in Arabic, Chinese, and Russian speaking cultures."

Year Founded in US: 1992

Personnel:
Home ministry & office staff in US: 6

Institute of Theological Studies—Division of Outreach Inc.

3000 Kraft Ave.
Grand Rapids, MI 49512 USA
Phone: (616) 363-7864

Fax: (616) 363-7880
E-mail: itsinfo@rbc.org
Web Site: www.itscourses.org
Mr. Darrell Yoder, COO

A nondenominational theological education agency of Evangelical tradition engaged in independent study course development and training resources for students, pastors and laity worldwide. Data from 2005.

Purpose: "...to make the proven resources of ITS more available and more affordable to more people worldwide, through global partnerships, new delivery systems, translated and contextualized versions and creative financial options."

Year Founded in US: 1973

Income for Overseas Min: $6,344.00

Personnel:
Home ministry & office staff in US: 4

InterAct Ministries

31000 SE Kelso Rd.
Boring, OR 97009 USA
Phone: (503) 668-5571
E-mail: info@interactministries.org
Web Site: www.interactministries.org
Associations: CrossGlobal Link

Rev. Gary Brumbelow, Exec. Director

A nondenominational sending agency of Evangelical tradition engaged in church planting, discipleship, evangelism and leadership development.

Purpose: "...to glorify God by fulfilling the Great Commission among unreached people groups."

Year Founded in US: 1951

Income for Overseas Min: $337,353.00

Fully Supported US Personnel Overseas:
Expecting to serve more than 4 years: 9
Expecting to serve 1 to 4 years: 2

Other personnel:
Short-term less than 1 year: 19
Home ministry & office staff in US: 8

Countries: Russia 9

Interaction International

PO Box 863
Wheaton, IL 60189 USA
Phone: (630) 653-8780
Fax: (815) 846-1778

E-mail: office@interactionintl.org
Web Site: www.interactionintl.org
Janet Blomberg, Exec. Director

An interdenominational service agency of Evangelical tradition engaged in training and orientation of missionaries/third-culture kids, Christian education, furloughed missionary support, member care and services for other agencies. Data from 2005.

Purpose: "...to be a catalyst and resource working cooperatively in the development of programs, services and publications to provide and contribute to a flow of care that meets the needs of third-culture kids (TCKS) and internationally mobile personnel."

Year Founded in US: 1968

Personnel:
Home ministry & office staff in US: 7

INTERCOMM, Inc.

PO Box 618
Winona Lake, IN 46590 USA
Phone: (574) 267-5774
Fax: (574) 267-5876
E-mail: lane@intercommedia.org
Web Site: www.intercommedia.org
Mr. Lane Anderson, Exec. Director

An interdenominational support agency of Evangelical and Independent tradition engaged in media distribution, video foreign language dubbing, video/film production/distribution, audio recording/distribution and evangelism.

Purpose: "...to equip national Christian leaders with appropriate media to help them win their countries to Christ."

Year Founded in US: 1991

Income for Overseas Min: $300,000.00

Personnel:
Short-term less than 1 year: 2
Home ministry & office staff in US: 3

International Aid

17011 W. Hickory St.
Spring Lake, MI 49456 USA
Phone: (616) 846-7490
Fax: (616) 846-3842
E-mail: ia@internationalaid.org
Web Site: www.internationalaid.org
Associations: AERDO

Gordon Loux, President/CEO

A nondenominational specialized agency of Evangelical tradition engaged in services for other agencies, development, providing medical supplies, relief and/or rehabilitation, supplying equipment and training. Data from 2005.

Purpose: "...responding to Biblical mandates by providing and supporting solutions in healthcare."

Year Founded in US: 1980

Income for Overseas Min: $36,611,986.00

Gifts in Kind: $31,792,434.00

Personnel:
 Home ministry & office staff in US: 66

International Board of Jewish Missions, Inc.

1928 Hamill Rd.
Hixson, TN 37343 USA

Phone: (423) 876-8150
Fax: (423) 876-8156
E-mail: amolam@ibjm.org
Web Site: www.ibjm.org

Dr. Orman L. Norwood, President

A sending agency of Baptist and Evangelical tradition engaged in missionary training, broadcasting, evangelism, literature distribution and video/film production/distribution.

Year Founded in US: 1949

Fully Supported US Personnel Overseas:
 Expecting to serve more than 4 years: 8
 Expecting to serve 1 to 4 years: 15
 Non-residential mission personnel: 14

Other personnel:
 Short-term less than 1 year: 3
 Non-US serving in own/other country: 31
 Home ministry & office staff in US: 29

Countries: Argentina; Australia; Belgium 1; France 4; Israel; Mexico; Peru; South Africa; Ukraine; Uruguay 3; Venezuela

International Child Care, USA

3506 Lovers Ln., Ste. 8
Kalamazoo, MI 49001 USA

Phone: (800) 722-4453
Fax: (269) 382-2416
E-mail: iccusa@intlchildcare.org
Web Site: www.internationalchildcare.org

Mr. Keith Mumma, U.S. Natl. Director

An interdenominational service agency of Methodist tradition engaged in fundraising/funds transmission to national organizations, Christian education, HIV/Aids, missions information service and support of national workers.

Purpose: "...to respond to a loving God by promoting health and well-being for the children and families of Haiti and the Dominican Republic through caring service and the education of others."

Year Founded in US: 1965

Income for Overseas Min: $551,994.00

Personnel:
 Home ministry & office staff in US: 4

International Christian Leprosy Mission, Inc. (USA)

PO Box 596
Forest Grove, OR 97116 USA

Phone: (503) 357-7830
E-mail: HealingHands8414@aol.com

Rev. Daniel G. Pulliam, President

An interdenominational support agency of Evangelical tradition engaged in childcare/orphanage programs, church planting, disability assistance programs, evangelism and relief and/or rehabilitation.

Year Founded in US: 1948

Income for Overseas Min: $30,000.00

Personnel:
 Non-US serving in own/other country: 6

Countries: Asia—General; India; Philippines

International Christian Ministries

4201 Ardmore Ave., Ste. 6
Bakersfield, CA 93309 USA

Phone: (661) 832-9740
Fax: (661) 832-9741
E-mail: info@icmusa.org
Web Site: www.icmusa.org

Mr. Phillip Walker, President

An interdenominational sending agency of Evangelical tradition engaged in theological education, TEE, leadership development and partnership development. Countries of service data from 2005.

Purpose: "...to serve the Church by disci-

pling and equipping its leaders."
Year Founded in US: 1990
Income for Overseas Min: $1,500,000.00
Fully Supported US Personnel Overseas:
  Expecting to serve more than 4 years: 2
  Expecting to serve 1 to 4 years: 2
  Non-residential mission personnel: 4
Other personnel:
  Short-term less than 1 year: 20
  Non-US serving in own/other country: 33
  Home ministry & office staff in US: 5
Countries: Congo, Democratic Republic of;
Egypt; Ethiopia; Kenya 2; Nigeria; Sierra Le-
one; South Africa; Tanzania; Uganda

International Cooperating Ministries (ICM)
606 Aberdeen Rd.
Hampton, VA 23661 USA
Phone: (757) 224-7102
Fax: (757) 838-6486
E-mail: egoodwin@icm.org
Web Site: www.icm.org
Janice Rosser Allen, Exec. Chair

A transdenominational support agency of
Evangelical tradition engaged in national
church nurture/support, broadcasting, church
planting and sports program ministry.
Purpose: "...to nurture believers and assist
Church growth worldwide."
Year Founded in US: 1988
Income for Overseas Min: $6,924,906.00
Personnel:
  Home ministry & office staff in US: 25
Countries: Africa—General; Asia—General;
Caribbean—General; Eastern Europe—Gen-
eral; Latin America—General; South Ameri-
ca—General

International Crisis Aid
PO Box 510167
St, Louis, MO 63151-0167 USA
Phone: (888) 740-7779
Fax: (314) 487-1409
E-mail: info@crisisaid.org
Web Site: www.crisisaid.org
Associations: AERDO
Mr. Patrick Bradley, President

A nondenominational service agency of
Evangelical tradition engaged in relief and/

or rehabilitation, childcare/orphanage pro-
grams, childrens programs, development,
medical work and trafficking/slavery issues.
Year Founded in US: 2000
Income for Overseas Min: $1,117,855.00
Gifts in Kind: $105.00
Personnel:
  Short-term less than 1 year: 40
  Non-US serving in own/other country: 5
  Home ministry & office staff in US: 1
Countries: Ethiopia

International Family Missions
PO Box 309
Lafayette, CO 80026 USA
Phone: (303) 665-7635
Fax: (303) 287-7617
E-mail: ifm@ifmus.org
Web Site: www.ifmus.org
Rev. Joseph Hart, President, Minister/Dir.

A transdenominational support agency of
Evangelical tradition engaged in short-term
programs, Bible distribution, discipleship,
evangelism, partnership development, mo-
bilization for mission and missionary train-
ing. Data from 2005.
Year Founded in US: 1987
Income for Overseas Min: $175,000.00
Gifts in Kind: $40,000.00
Fully Supported US Personnel Overseas:
  Expecting to serve more than 4 years: 8
Other personnel:
  Short-term less than 1 year: 420
  Home ministry & office staff in US: 33
Countries: Mexico 8

International Foundation for EWHA Woman's University
475 Riverside Dr. Rm. 1359
New York, NY 10115 USA
Phone: (212) 864-5759
Fax: (212) 864-2552
E-mail: ewhafdn@aol.com
Web Site: www.ewhafoundation.org
Mrs. Ji-yei Park, Exec. Director

An interdenominational support agency
of Ecumenical tradition providing financial
and other support to EWHA University in
South Korea. Data from 2005.
Year Founded in US: 1969

International Gospel Outreach

PO Box 1008
Semmes, AL 36575 USA
Phone: (251) 645-2117
Fax: (251) 645-2118
Web Site: www.igoministries.org

Dr. James G. Graham, President

An interdenominational sending agency of Charismatic and Wesleyan tradition engaged in mobilization for mission, discipleship, theological education, leadership development, relief and/or rehabilitation and training.

Purpose: "...to serve the body of Christ through educating, equipping, and employing believers into the world harvest."

Year Founded in US: 1973

Income for Overseas Min: $1,100,000.00

Fully Supported US Personnel Overseas:
  Expecting to serve more than 4 years: 45
  Expecting to serve 1 to 4 years: 13
  Non-residential mission personnel: 72

Other personnel:
  Short-term less than 1 year: 3
  Non-US serving in own/other country: 54
  Home ministry & office staff in US: 11

Countries: Argentina 2; Botswana; Brazil; Cameroon 1; Chile; Cuba; Ethiopia; Finland 2; Gambia, The 3; Georgia 2; Guinea 1; Guinea-Bissau 1; Honduras 4; India; Ireland; Israel; Italy 4; Kenya 4; Korea, South; Liberia 1; Mexico 4; Philippines 2; Romania; Russia 4; Rwanda; Senegal 1; Sierra Leone 1; Sudan; Taiwan 2; Tanzania 2; Turkey 2; Uganda 2

International Institute for Christian Studies

PO Box 12147
Overland Park, KS 66282-2147 USA
Phone: (913) 962-4422
E-mail: iics@iics.com
Web Site: www.iics.com
Associations: The Mission Exchange

Dr. Daryl McCarthy, President

An interdenominational sending agency of Evangelical tradition engaged in extension education, theological education, evangelism, HIV/Aids and TESOL.

Purpose: "...to bring glory to God and impact the world by developing godly leaders for every sector of society—government, business, home, church, the arts, law, the sciences, education—as we provide key universities and academic institutions outside North America with educational services and Christian faculty who teach and live in such a way as to draw others to faith and transformation in Christ."

Year Founded in US: 1986

Income for Overseas Min: $1,850,386.00

Gifts in Kind: $780,053.00

Fully Supported US Personnel Overseas:
  Expecting to serve more than 4 years: 29
  Expecting to serve 1 to 4 years: 9

Other personnel:
  Short-term less than 1 year: 10
  Non-US serving in own/other country: 38
  Home ministry & office staff in US: 8

Countries: Brazil 3; Bulgaria 1; Czech Republic 8; Japan 1; Kazakhstan 1; Lithuania 1; Mexico 1; Nigeria 4; Romania 1; Uganda; Unspecified Country 8

International Justice Mission

PO Box 58147
Washington, DC 20037-8147 USA
Phone: (703) 465-5495
Fax: (703) 465-5499
E-mail: contact@ijm.org
Web Site: www.ijm.org
Associations: AERDO

Mr. Gary A. Haugen, President/CEO

A nondenominational service agency engaged in justice, Christian education, relief and/or rehabilitation and trafficking/slavery issues.

Purpose: "...to secure justice for victims of slavery, sexual exploitation, and other forms of violent oppression...to work with local governments to ensure victim rescue...to prosecute perpetrators...to strengthen the community and civic factors that promote functioning public justice systems."

Year Founded in US: 1997

Income for Overseas Min: $8,000,000.00

Fully Supported US Personnel Overseas:
  Expecting to serve 1 to 4 years: 15
  Non-residential mission personnel: 3

Other personnel:
  Short-term less than 1 year: 85

Non-US serving in own/other country: 234
Home ministry & office staff in US: 102

Countries: Bolivia; Cambodia; Guatemala; India; Kenya; Philippines; Rwanda; Thailand; Uganda; Zambia

International Messengers

PO Box R
Clearlake, IA 50428 USA
Phone: (641) 357-6700
Fax: (641) 357-6791
E-mail: office@internationalmessengers.org
Web Site: www.internationalmessengers.org
Darwin Anderson, President

A nondenominational sending agency of Evangelical tradition engaged in evangelism, camping programs, childcare/orphanage programs, childrens programs, church construction, short-term programs and missionary training. Statistics from 2003.

Purpose: "…partnering with local churches to renew, train and mobilize believers for active involvement in reaching the world for Christ."

Year Founded in US: 1984

Fully Supported US Personnel Overseas:
Expecting to serve more than 4 years: 24
Expecting to serve 1 to 4 years: 4

Other personnel:
Short-term less than 1 year: 300
Non-US serving in own/other country: 47
Home ministry & office staff in US: 33

Countries: Czech Republic; Germany; Hungary 2; Poland 12; Romania 7; Slovakia 3; Ukraine

International Partnership Associates

PO Box 1331
Edmonds, WA 98020 USA
Phone: (425) 775-3362
Fax: (425) 640-3671
E-mail: tricia@interdev.org
Web Site: www.ipassociates.org
Mr. Alex Araujo, IPA USA Bd. President

A nondenominational service agency of Evangelical tradition engaged in partnership development.

Purpose: "…to serve the Church in its mission to the least-reached peoples by equipping, encouraging, and catalyzing the part-

nering movement."

Year Founded in US: 2003

Income for Overseas Min: $45,000.00

Fully Supported US Personnel Overseas:
Non-residential mission personnel: 1

Other personnel:
Home ministry & office staff in US: 1

International Partnership Ministries, Inc.

PO Box 337
Hanover, PA 17331-0337 USA
Phone: (717) 637-7388
Fax: (717) 637-1618
E-mail: ipm@ipmworld.org
Web Site: www.ipmworld.org
Rev. Kevin M. Callahan, President

A sending agency of Baptist and Independent tradition engaged in church planting, childcare/orphanage programs, theological education, evangelism and partnership development.

Purpose: "…to glorify God through the reaching of men and women with the Gospel, the training of Christian leaders, and the planting of fundamental churches through partnerships with national missionaries and indigenous national ministries."

Year Founded in US: 1982

Income for Overseas Min: $1,511,447.00

Fully Supported US Personnel Overseas:
Expecting to serve more than 4 years: 3
Non-residential mission personnel: 1

Other personnel:
Non-US serving in own/other country: 390
Home ministry & office staff in US: 19

Countries: Bangladesh; Bhutan; Bolivia; Chad; Chile; China; Cote d'Ivoire; Cuba; Dominican Republic; Ghana; Guatemala; Haiti; India; Iraq; Lebanon; Liberia; Mexico; Myanmar/Burma; Nepal; Peru; Philippines; Puerto Rico; Spain; Taiwan 1; Togo; Uruguay; Zambia 2

International Pentecostal Church of Christ—Global Missions Dept.

PO Box 439
London, OH 43140-0439 USA
Phone: (740) 852-4722

Fax: (740) 852-0348
E-mail: hqipcc@aol.com
Web Site: www.ipcc.cc

Bishop Clyde M. Hughes, General Overseer

A denominational sending agency of Pentecostal tradition engaged in support of national churches, church planting, discipleship, evangelism, leadership development and youth programs.

Purpose: "...to assist the International Pentecostal Church of Christ in fulfilling its three-fold purpose of evangelism, discipleship, and worship across the world through seeking out neglected regions, to evangelize through sending missionaries and establishing indigenous churches."

Year Founded in US: 1917

Income for Overseas Min: $139,857.00

Fully Supported US Personnel Overseas:
Expecting to serve more than 4 years: 7
Expecting to serve 1 to 4 years: 3

Other personnel:
Short-term less than 1 year: 13
Non-US serving in own/other country: 7
Home ministry & office staff in US: 1

Countries: Brazil; India 1; Kenya 3; Mexico 1; Philippines 2; Uruguay; Venezuela

International Pentecostal Holiness Church World Missions Ministries

PO Box 12609
Oklahoma City, OK 73157 USA

Phone: (405) 787-7110
Fax: (405) 787-7729
E-mail: WMMInfo@iphc.org
Web Site: www.iphc.org

Associations: The Mission Exchange

Dr. Doug Beacham, Exec. Director

A denominational sending agency of Holiness tradition engaged in church planting, theological education, leadership development, support of national churches, mobilization for mission and short-term programs. Countries of service data from 2005.

Purpose: "...to fulfill the Great Commission of our Lord Jesus Christ."

Year Founded in US: 1904

Income for Overseas Min: $8,397,124.00

Fully Supported US Personnel Overseas:

Expecting to serve more than 4 years: 128
Expecting to serve 1 to 4 years: 7
Non-residential mission personnel: 6

Other personnel:
Short-term less than 1 year: 8
Non-US serving in own/other country: 35
Home ministry & office staff in US: 16

Countries: Albania; Argentina; Australia; Azerbaijan; Barbados; Belgium 6; Belize 2; Benin; Bolivia; Botswana; Brazil; Burundi; Cameroon; Chile; Colombia; Congo, Democratic Republic of; Costa Rica 4; Cote d'Ivoire 2; Croatia; Cuba; Dominican Republic 2; Ecuador 2; Egypt; Estonia 2; Ethiopia; France 1; Germany 2; Ghana 2; Guatemala 2; Guyana 2; Haiti; Honduras 2; Hong Kong; Hungary 4; India 2; Indonesia; Italy; Jamaica; Japan 4; Kenya 6; Korea, South; Lesotho; Liberia; Malawi 4; Malaysia; Malta; Mauritius; Mexico 6; Moldova; Mozambique; Myanmar/Burma; Netherlands 2; Nicaragua 1; Nigeria; Norway 2; Panama 2; Paraguay; Peru 2; Philippines 6; Portugal 2; Romania 2; Rwanda; Seychelles; Sierra Leone; Singapore 6; South Africa 19; Spain 4; Sri Lanka; Sudan; Swaziland; Tanzania 4; Thailand 4; Togo; Trinidad and Tobago; Turkey; Uganda 2; Ukraine; United Kingdom 8; Unspecified Country 5; Uruguay; Venezuela; Vietnam; Zambia; Zimbabwe

International Steward

3528 Lousma Dr. SE
Grand Rapids, MI 49548-2259 USA

Phone: (616) 734-0950
Fax: (616) 734-0954
E-mail: info@intsteward.org
Web Site: www.intsteward.org

Associations: The Mission Exchange

Dr. H. Charles Roost, Founding Partner

A nondenominational support agency of Evangelical tradition engaged in stewardship & fund development training, leadership development, management consulting/training and partnership development.

Purpose: "...Stewardship Training and Education for Worldwide Advancement in Resource Development."

Year Founded in US: 1999

Income for Overseas Min: $570,000.00

Personnel:
Short-term less than 1 year: 5
Home ministry & office staff in US: 8

International Street Kids Outreach Ministries (ISKOM)
PO Box 8551
Clearwater, FL 33758-8551 USA
Phone: (800) 265-1970
E-mail: contactus@internationalstreetkids.com
Web Site: www.internationalstreetkids.com
Rev. John M. Schmidt, President

A support agency of Evangelical tradition engaged in children at risk, discipleship, childcare/orphanage programs, justice and trafficking/slavery issues. Countries of service data from 2005.

Purpose: "...to reach, rescue, and make disciples of orphaned & abandoned children where the gospel of Christ has little or no access."
Year Founded in US: 1995
Income for Overseas Min: $337,531.00
Fully Supported US Personnel Overseas:
   Expecting to serve more than 4 years: 2
   Expecting to serve 1 to 4 years: 2
   Non-residential mission personnel: 4
Other personnel:
   Non-US serving in own/other country: 232
Countries: Asia—General; Brazil 2; Eastern Europe—General

International Students, Inc (ISI)
PO Box C
Colorado Springs, CO 80901-2901 USA
Phone: (719) 576-2700
Fax: (719) 576-5363
E-mail: president@isiwebnet.net
Web Site: www.isionline.org
Dr. Douglas Shaw, President/CEO

A transdenominational support agency of Ecumenical tradition engaged in evangelism, discipleship, mobilization for mission and training.

Purpose: "...exists to share Christ's love with international students and to equip them for effective service in cooperation with the local church and others."
Year Founded in US: 1953
Fully Supported US Personnel Overseas:
   Expecting to serve 1 to 4 years: 2
Other personnel:
   Non-US serving in own/other country: 2

Home ministry & office staff in US: 216
Countries: China; Hong Kong

International Teams, U.S.A.
411 W. River Rd.
Elgin, IL 60123-1570 USA
Phone: (847) 429-0900
Fax: (847) 429-0800
E-mail: info@iteams.org
Web Site: www.iteams.org
Associations: The Mission Exchange
Mr. Scott R. Olson, President, IT USA

An interdenominational sending agency of Evangelical tradition engaged in discipleship, children at risk, development, support of national churches, relief and/or rehabilitation and trafficking/slavery issues. Countries of service data from 2005.

Purpose: "...mobilizing international teams to build transforming communities."
Year Founded in US: 1960
Income for Overseas Min: $8,647,062.00
Gifts in Kind: $87,280.00
Fully Supported US Personnel Overseas:
   Expecting to serve more than 4 years: 211
   Expecting to serve 1 to 4 years: 38
Other personnel:
   Short-term less than 1 year: 710
   Non-US serving in own/other country: 487
   Home ministry & office staff in US: 34
Countries: Albania 4; Argentina; Australia 3; Austria 28; Belarus; Belgium; Bhutan; Bolivia 3; Bosnia and Herzegovina 3; Brazil; Bulgaria 3; Cambodia 6; Colombia 2; Costa Rica 15; Cuba; Czech Republic 3; Ecuador 18; Fiji; France 16; Greece 9; Honduras 2; Indonesia 3; Ireland 4; Israel 2; Italy; Japan; Kenya 2; Kosovo 2; Mexico 13; Nepal 2; Netherlands; New Zealand 2; Nicaragua; Norway; Philippines 2; Romania 6; Russia 4; Rwanda; Spain 6; Taiwan; Thailand; Turkey 3; Uganda; Ukraine 9; United Kingdom 13; Unspecified Country 23; Zambia

Interserve USA (International Service Fellowship)
PO Box 418
Upper Darby, PA 19082-0418 USA
Phone: (610) 352-0581
E-mail: pd@ludlow.net

Web Site: www.interserveusa.org
Associations: CrossGlobal Link
Rev. Doug Van Bronkhorst, Exec. Director
An interdenominational sending agency of Evangelical tradition engaged in tentmaking, business as mission, development, education/university/international faculty, medical work, member care and partnership development.
Purpose: "...to transform lives and communities through encounters with Jesus Christ."
Year Founded in US: 1852
Income for Overseas Min: $6,542,872.00
Fully Supported US Personnel Overseas:
  Expecting to serve more than 4 years: 102
  Non-residential mission personnel: 1
Other personnel:
  Short-term less than 1 year: 27
  Non-US serving in own/other country: 2
  Home ministry & office staff in US: 18
Countries: Afghanistan 22; Bahrain 3; Bangladesh 4; Cambodia 1; China 16; Cyprus 2; Egypt 2; India 8; Indonesia 1; Jordan 4; Oman 1; Pakistan 11; Turkey 15; United Arab Emirates 2; Tajikistan 3; Uzbekistan 2; Yemen 5

InterVarsity Christian Fellowship/USA— Missions Department

PO Box 7895
Madison, WI 53707-7895 USA
Phone: (608) 443-3702
Fax: (608) 274-7882
E-mail: jtebbe@intervarsity.org
Web Site: www.intervarsity.org
Associations: The Mission Exchange
Dr. James Tebbe, VP Missions/Urbana Director
A nondenominational sending agency of Evangelical tradition engaged in discipleship, evangelism, leadership development, short-term programs and missionary training.
Year Founded in US: 1941
Income for Overseas Min: $2,400,000.00
Fully Supported US Personnel Overseas:
  Expecting to serve more than 4 years: 26
  Expecting to serve 1 to 4 years: 17
  Non-residential mission personnel: 44
Other personnel:
  Short-term less than 1 year: 789
  Home ministry & office staff in US: 4
Countries: Asia—General 4; Belgium; Bos-

nia and Herzegovina; Bulgaria; Croatia; Europe—General 5; France 2; Germany; Kenya 1; Middle East 4; Moldova 2; Paraguay 2; Romania 3; Spain; Ukraine 3; United Kingdom

Iranian Christians Intl.

PO Box 25607
Colorado Springs, CO 80936 USA
Phone: (719) 596-0010
Fax: (719) 574-1141
E-mail: ici@iranchristians.org
Web Site: www.iranchristians.org
Mr. Ebrahim (Abe) Ghaffari, President
A transdenominational support agency of Evangelical tradition engaged in helping persecuted Christians, refugees & immigration, evangelism, justice, leadership development, literature distribution and literature production.
Year Founded in US: 1980
Income for Overseas Min: $2,000.00
Personnel:
  Home ministry & office staff in US: 2

Ireland Outreach Intl. Inc.

PO Box 1772
Waterloo, IA 50704-1772 USA
Phone: (972) 724-2463
E-mail: charleville@eircom.net
Web Site: www.irelandoutreach.org
Mr. James W. Gillett, President
A nondenominational sending agency of Christian/Plymouth Brethren tradition engaged in evangelism, Bible distribution, church planting, correspondence courses, theological education, literature distribution, literature production, literacy work, medical work, short-term programs. Gospel literature and correspondence courses are sent from Ireland to 40 countries around the world. Data from 2005.
Year Founded in US: 1981
Fully Supported US Personnel Overseas:
  Expecting to serve more than 4 years: 10
  Expecting to serve 1 to 4 years: 3
Other personnel:
  Short-term less than 1 year: 50
  Non-US serving in own/other country: 19
Countries: Ghana; Ireland 10; Kenya; Nigeria; Togo; Zambia

ISOH/IMPACT
25182 W. River Rd.
Perrysburg, OH 43551 USA
Phone: (419) 878-8548
Fax: (419) 878-3098
E-mail: ministries@isohimpact.org
Web Site: www.isohimpact.org
Dr. Linda Greene, President/CEO
A nondenominational service agency of Holiness tradition engaged in relief and/or rehabilitation, childrens programs, development, evangelism, providing medical supplies and partnership development.
Purpose: "...to reach out and serve others in the name of Christ through disaster relief and development projects at home, across the United States, and around the world."
Year Founded in US: 1982
Income for Overseas Min: $6,000,372.00
Gifts in Kind: $5,969,390.00
Fully Supported US Personnel Overseas:
Expecting to serve more than 4 years: 4
Other personnel:
Short-term less than 1 year: 16
Home ministry & office staff in US: 4
Countries: Bulgaria 1; Honduras 1; Tajikistan 2

Italy for Christ, Inc.
1301 Shiloh Rd., Ste. 1720
Kennesaw, GA 30144-7170 USA
Phone: (770) 274-2800
Fax: (770) 274-2833
E-mail: info@italyforchrist.com
Web Site: www.italyforchrist.it
Gaetano Sottile, President/Founder
A nondenominational sending agency of Evangelical tradition engaged in evangelism, church planting, leadership development and training.
Purpose: "...to reach all Italians with the Gospel of Christ in this generation, in cooperation with the local church."
Year Founded in US: 1983
Fully Supported US Personnel Overseas:
Expecting to serve more than 4 years: 5
Other personnel:
Home ministry & office staff in US: 1
Countries: Italy 5

JAARS, Inc.
PO Box 248
Waxhaw, NC 28173 USA
Phone: (704) 843-6000
Fax: (704) 843-6355
E-mail: info@jaars.org
Web Site: www.jaars.org
Mr. David Reeves, President
An interdenominational service agency of Evangelical tradition serving Wycliffe Bible Translators with various technical support services including aviation and radio. Personnel serve more than 70 countries. Overseas income and gifts in kind data from 2005.
Purpose: "...to provide quality technical support services and resources to speed Bible translation for all people."
Year Founded in US: 1948
Income for Overseas Min: $4,460,743.00
Gifts in Kind: $394,727.00

Japanese Evangelical Missionary Society (JEMS)
948 E. 2nd St.
Los Angeles, CA 90012 USA
Phone: (213) 613-0022
Fax: (213) 613-0211
E-mail: info@jems.org
Web Site: www.jems.org
Mr. Richard E. Chuman, Exec. Director
An interdenominational service agency of Evangelical tradition engaged in missions—short-term/summer/career, association of missions, camping programs and evangelism.
Year Founded in US: 1950
Income for Overseas Min: $262,085.00
Fully Supported US Personnel Overseas:
Expecting to serve more than 4 years: 2
Expecting to serve 1 to 4 years: 5
Other personnel:
Short-term less than 1 year: 6
Non-US serving in own/other country: 1
Home ministry & office staff in US: 6
Countries: Japan 2

Japanese Evangelization Center (Institute of Japanese Studies)
1605 Elizabeth St.
Pasadena, CA 91104 USA

Phone: (626) 797-1111

Dr. John Mizuki, Exec. Director

A nondenominational specialized agency of Evangelical tradition engaged in research and information on Japanese evangelization and church planting. Data from 2005.

Purpose: "...to provide information to churches, mission agencies, pastors, missionaries, missionary candidates, students and to serve as consultants to those interested in Japanese culture and evangelization."

Year Founded in US: 1981

JARON Ministries Intl.

4710 N. Maple Ave
Fresno, CA 93726-1204 USA

Phone: (559) 227-7997
Fax: (559) 227-9603
E-mail: info@jaron.org
Web Site: www.jaron.org

Rev. Eugene E. Beck, Exec. Director

An interdenominational support agency of Baptist tradition engaged in leadership development, theological education, literature production and short-term programs. Statistical data from 2001.

Purpose: "...to teach, disciple, counsel, and encourage Christian leaders...serve as a ministry of instruction and motivation...produce and provide biblically sound and currently relevant written, audio, and video training materials and organize and lead short-term ministry teams to other parts of the world."

Year Founded in US: 1992

Income for Overseas Min: $96,328.00

Fully Supported US Personnel Overseas:
  Non-residential mission personnel: 6

Other personnel:
  Short-term less than 1 year: 68
  Home ministry & office staff in US: 6

Jewish Awareness Mins., Inc.

PO Box 35
Holly Springs, NC 27540 USA

Phone: (919) 577-6331
Fax: (919) 557-6331
E-mail: office@jewishawareness.org
Web Site: www.jewishawareness.org
Associations: FOM

Mr. Mark Robinson, Exec. Director

A nondenominational sending agency of Baptist and Fundamental tradition engaged in evangelism, broadcasting, discipleship, literature distribution, literature production and missionary training.

Purpose: "...to proclaim the Messiah, preach the Word and pray for Israel."

Year Founded in US: 1946

Income for Overseas Min: $37,500.00

Fully Supported US Personnel Overseas:
  Expecting to serve more than 4 years: 2

Other personnel:
  Home ministry & office staff in US: 12

Countries: Israel 2

Jews for Jesus
(See ad on page 226)

60 Haight St.
San Francisco, CA 94102-5895 USA

Phone: (415) 864-2600
Fax: (415) 552-8325
E-mail: jfj@jewsforjesus.org
Web Site: www.jewsforjesus.org
Associations: The Mission Exchange

Mr. David Brickner, Exec. Director

A nondenominational sending agency engaged in evangelism, missionary education, literature distribution, short-term programs and youth programs.

Purpose: "...to make the Messiahship of Jesus an unavoidable issue to our Jewish people worldwide."

Year Founded in US: 1973

Income for Overseas Min: $1,859,800.00

Fully Supported US Personnel Overseas:
  Expecting to serve more than 4 years: 5
  Non-residential mission personnel: 4

Other personnel:
  Non-US serving in own/other country: 4
  Home ministry & office staff in US: 123

Countries: Brazil 1; France 1; Germany 1; Israel 2

Joni and Friends

PO Box 3333
Agoura Hills, CA 91376 USA

Phone: (818) 707-5664
Fax: (818) 707-2391
Web Site: www.joniandfriends.org

JEWS F✡R JESUS ™

We exist to make the Messiahship of Jesus an unavoidable issue to our Jewish people worldwide.

If you'd like to partner with us in any of the 22 cities we're working in, we'd love to hear from you!

U.S. BRANCH LOCATIONS

Boston, Chicago, Fort Lauderdale, Los Angeles, Phoenix, New York, San Francisco and Washington, D.C. (contact: jfj@jewsforjesus.org)

INTERNATIONAL LOCATIONS

Sydney, Australia
mail@jewsforjesus.org.au
www.jewsforjesus.org.au

Rio De Janeiro, Brazil
jpj@judeusporjesus.org.br
www.judeusporjesus.org.br

Montreal, Canada
montreal@jewsforjesus.ca
www.juifspourjesus.ca

Toronto, Canada
jfjcda@jewsforjesus.ca
www.jewsforjesus.ca

London, England
staff@jews-for-jesus.org.uk
www.jewsforjesus.org.uk

Paris, France
info@juifspourjesus.org
www.juifspourjesus.org

Essen, Germany
judenfuerjesus@googlemail.com
www.judenfuerjesus.de

Tel Aviv, Israel
info@jewsforjesus.co.il
www.yeshua4u.co.il

Russia
moscow@jewsforjesus.org
cis.jewsforjesus.org

Johannesburg, South Africa
info@jewsforjesus.co.za
www.jewsforjesus.co.za

Ukraine
dnepr@jewsforjesus.org
kharkov@jewsforjesus.org
kiev@jewsforjesus.org
odessa@jewsforjesus.org
cis.jewsforjesus.org

INTERNATIONAL HEADQUARTERS
60 Haight Street, San Francisco, CA 94102 U.S.A.
Phone: (415) 864-2600 Fax: (415) 552-8325
jfj@jewsforjesus.org • www.jewsforjesus.org

Mrs. Joni Eareckson Tada, Founder/CEO

An interdenominational service agency of Evangelical tradition engaged in disability assistance programs, broadcasting, Christian education, evangelism, short-term programs and missionary training. Data from 2005.

Purpose: "...to communicate the Gospel and equip Christ-honoring churches worldwide to evangelize and disciple people affected by disabilities."

Year Founded in US: 1979

Income for Overseas Min: $6,218,959.00

Gifts in Kind: $4,796,959.00

Personnel:
  Short-term less than 1 year: 194
  Home ministry & office staff in US: 99

Joshua Expeditions

6841 Virginia Parkway, Ste. 103-452
McKinney, TX 75071 USA

Phone: (972) 542-3024
Fax: (972) 542-3025
E-mail: trips@joshuaexpeditions.org
Web Site: www.joshuaexpeditions.org

Mr. Amir Mahadi, CEO

A nondenominational service agency of Baptist tradition engaged in short-term programs, Christian education, missionary education, extension education, evangelism and youth programs.

Purpose: "...to inspire students through hands-on education."

Year Founded in US: 1997

Income for Overseas Min: $4,297,000.00

Fully Supported US Personnel Overseas:
  Non-residential mission personnel: 36

Other personnel:
  Short-term less than 1 year: 3010
  Home ministry & office staff in US: 36

Josue Yrion World Evangelism and Missions, Inc.

PO Box 876018
Los Angeles, CA 90087-1118 USA

Phone: (562) 928-8892
Fax: (562) 947-2268
E-mail: josueyrion@josueyrion.org
Web Site: www.josueyrion.org

Rev. Josue Yrion, President/CEO

An interdenominational sending agency of Evangelical and Pentecostal tradition engaged in evangelism, audio recording/distribution, theological education, leadership development, missionary training and video/film production/distribution.

Purpose: "...to serve the Body of Christ, to edify, teach and prepare an effective evangelistic ministry that can change lives by the power of God's Word."

Year Founded in US: 1986

Income for Overseas Min: $36,864.00

Personnel:
  Non-US serving in own/other country: 27
  Home ministry & office staff in US: 6

Countries: Africa—General; Argentina; Australia; Brazil; India; Mexico; Myanmar/Burma; Peru; Spain; Turkey; United Kingdom

Kerus Global Education

245 Newman Ave., Ste. B
Harrisonburg, VA 22801 USA

Phone: (540) 438-8782
Fax: (540) 438-1342
E-mail: kerus@kerusglobal.org
Web Site: www.kerusglobal.org

Dr. Marcia L. Ball, Co-Founder/Exec. Director

A nondenominational support agency engaged in training, childcare/orphanage programs, children at risk, development, Christian education, HIV/Aids, services for other agencies and youth programs.

Year Founded in US: 2000

Fully Supported US Personnel Overseas:
  Non-residential mission personnel: 2

Other personnel:
  Short-term less than 1 year: 15
  Home ministry & office staff in US: 3

Key Communications

PO Box 13620
Portland, OR 97213-0620 USA

Phone: (503) 233-7680
Fax: (503) 236-0733
E-mail: lee@keycom.org

B. L. Turner, Director

A nondenominational specialized agency of Christian (Restoration Movement) tradition engaged in broadcasting, audio recording/distribution, church planting, leadership development and literature distribution.

Purpose: "...to provide people with enough information that they can make an intelligent decision whether to accept Christ or reject Him."

Year Founded in US: 1977

Income for Overseas Min: $30,980.00

Personnel:
  Short-term less than 1 year: 4
  Non-US serving in own/other country: 1
  Home ministry & office staff in US: 6

Countries: Pakistan

Kids Alive International
2507 Cumberland Dr.
Valparaiso, IN 46383 USA
Phone: (219) 464-9035
Fax: (219) 462-5611
E-mail: kidsalive@kidsalive.org
Web Site: www.kidsalive.org
Associations: CrossGlobal Link
Mr. Alfred R. Lackey, President

An interdenominational sending agency of Evangelical tradition engaged in childcare/orphanage programs, children at risk, childrens programs, development, Christian education and short-term programs.

Purpose: "...to reflect the love of Christ by rescuing suffering children at risk, nurturing them with quality holistic care, and introducing them to the transforming power of Jesus Christ so they are enabled to instill hope in others."

Year Founded in US: 1916

Income for Overseas Min: $4,828,332.00

Gifts in Kind: $96,198.00

Fully Supported US Personnel Overseas:
  Expecting to serve more than 4 years: 22
  Expecting to serve 1 to 4 years: 26
  Non-residential mission personnel: 2

Other personnel:
  Short-term less than 1 year: 972
  Non-US serving in own/other country: 442
  Home ministry & office staff in US: 14

Countries: Dominican Republic 10; Guatemala 3; Haiti 2; Kenya; Lebanon; Papua New Guinea; Peru 5; Sudan; Taiwan 2; Zambia

Kids Around the World, Inc.
2424 Charles St.
Rockford, IL 61108 USA

Phone: (815) 229-8731
Fax: (815) 229-8931
Web Site: www.kidsaroundtheworld.com
Mr. Jim Rosene, President

A nondenominational service agency of Independent tradition engaged in playground installation, food program, Christian education, HIV/Aids, short-term programs and training teachers/child workers.

Purpose: "...to reach children around the world with the Gospel of Jesus Christ through teaching and evangelizing, and to help those who work with children...to build playgrounds where children can play and where they can feel the happiness that is a gift of God's love..."

Year Founded in US: 1994

Income for Overseas Min: $1,498,000.00

Gifts in Kind: $577,005.00

Personnel:
  Short-term less than 1 year: 188
  Non-US serving in own/other country: 2
  Home ministry & office staff in US: 11

Countries: Ghana; Peru

Kids for Christ International
PO Box 963
Florissant, MO 63033 USA
Phone: (314) 972-7880
Fax: (314) 972-7880
Web Site: www.kidsforchristonline.com
Mr. Charles E. Seevers, President/CEO

A nondenominational support agency of Christian (Restoration Movement) and Independent tradition engaged in childrens programs, Bible distribution, Bible memorization, children at risk, church planting, discipleship, Christian education, missionary education, evangelism, mobilization for mission, TESOL and missionary training.

Purpose: "...to bring hope to children in a hopeless world."

Year Founded in US: 1994

Fully Supported US Personnel Overseas:
  Non-residential mission personnel: 1

Other personnel:
  Short-term less than 1 year: 1
  Non-US serving in own/other country: 5
  Home ministry & office staff in US: 1

Countries: China; Liberia; Myanmar/Burma; Philippines; Thailand

Kidzana Ministries

8229 44th Ave West, Ste. G
Mukilteo, WA 98275 USA
Phone: (425) 353-8027
Fax: (425) 954-4006
E-mail: info@kidzana.org
Web Site: www.kidzana.org
Sylvia Foth, President

An interdenominational support agency of Evangelical tradition engaged in children's ministry training, childrens programs, discipleship, literature production, support of national churches, support of national workers and training.

Purpose: "...to equip people to reach and disciple children around the world for Christ."
Year Founded in US: 1998
Income for Overseas Min: $500,000.00
Gifts in Kind: $150,000.00
Personnel:
  Short-term less than 1 year: 5

Latin America Mission

PO Box 52-7900
Miami, FL 33152-7900 USA
Phone: (305) 884-8400
Fax: (305) 885-8649
E-mail: info@lam.org
Web Site: www.lam.org
Mr. Steven R. Johnson, President

A sending agency of Evangelical tradition engaged in support of national churches, camping programs, children at risk, theological education, leadership development and short-term programs.

Purpose: "...to encourage, assist, and participate with the Latin church in the task of building the Church of Jesus Christ in the Latin world and beyond."
Year Founded in US: 1921
Income for Overseas Min: $5,508,739.00
Gifts in Kind: $45,634.00
Fully Supported US Personnel Overseas:
  Expecting to serve more than 4 years: 107
  Expecting to serve 1 to 4 years: 28
Other personnel:
  Short-term less than 1 year: 56
  Non-US serving in own/other country: 135
  Home ministry & office staff in US: 17
Countries: Argentina; Brazil 8; Chile 2; Colombia 8; Costa Rica 38; Ecuador 4; El Salvador 2; Honduras 5; Mexico 25; Paraguay 4; Peru 6; Spain 4; Venezuela 1

Latin American Indian Mins.

PO Box 2050
Orange, CA 92859 USA
Phone: (626) 398-2105
Web Site: www.laim.org
Mr. Dale W. Kietzman, President

A nondenominational service agency of Evangelical and Independent tradition engaged in support of national churches and support of national workers. Data from 2005.

Purpose: "...to encourage, strengthen and support the indigenous communities of Latin America in their efforts to evangelize and disciple their own people, as well as to help them improve living standards for their families..."
Year Founded in US: 1976
Income for Overseas Min: $68,000.00
Fully Supported US Personnel Overseas:
  Non-residential mission personnel: 1
Other personnel:
  Short-term less than 1 year: 4
  Home ministry & office staff in US: 1
Countries: Brazil; Mexico; Peru

Latin American Lutheran Mission

3519 Salinas Ave.
Laredo, TX 78041 USA
Phone: (956) 722-4047
Fax: (956) 727-0997
E-mail: lalmelcm@sbcglobal.net
Web Site: www.lalm-elcm.org
Mr. Richard G. Erickson, Director

A denominational support agency of Lutheran tradition engaged in support of national workers, leadership development, support of national churches, short-term programs and training.

Purpose: "...to develop the capacities of the Lutheran churches in Mexico and stir up vision for cross-cultural mission among USA Lutherans."
Year Founded in US: 1937
Income for Overseas Min: $130,000.00
Gifts in Kind: $10,000.00

Fully Supported US Personnel Overseas:
Expecting to serve more than 4 years: 3
Non-residential mission personnel: 3
Other personnel:
Short-term less than 1 year: 350
Non-US serving in own/other country: 1
Home ministry & office staff in US: 3
Countries: Mexico 3

Launch Out Ministries Intl.
PO Box 543102
Merritt Island, FL 32954 USA
Phone: (321) 637-0722
Fax: (321) 637-0722
E-mail: office@launchoutministries.com
Web Site: www.launchoutministries.com
Mr. Ryan Finnie, President

A nondenominational sending agency of
Evangelical tradition engaged in mobiliza-
tion for mission, childcare/orphanage pro-
grams, HIV/Aids, relief and/or rehabilita-
tion, short-term programs and trafficking/
slavery issues.
Purpose: "...to take the Gospel to the un-
reached...however...whenever...wherever."
Year Founded in US: 2003
Income for Overseas Min: $101,000.00
Fully Supported US Personnel Overseas:
Expecting to serve 1 to 4 years: 2
Other personnel:
Short-term less than 1 year: 100
Non-US serving in own/other country: 20
Home ministry & office staff in US: 2
Countries: Botswana; Brazil; Malawi; Mo-
zambique; South Africa; Swaziland; Tanza-
nia; Thailand; Zambia

Leadership Ministries Worldwide
3755 Pilot Point
Chattanooga, TN 37416 USA
Phone: (423) 855-2181
Fax: (423) 855-8616
E-mail: johnb@outlinebible.org
Web Site: www.lmworldwide.org
John W. Burkett, Exec. Director

A nondenominational service agency of
Evangelical tradition engaged in leadership
development, Bible distribution, Christian
education, literature production, training

and translation work.
Purpose: "...to equip ministers, teachers,
and laymen in their understanding, preach-
ing, and teaching of God's Word by publish-
ing and distributing worldwide The Preacher's
Outline & Sermon Bible and related Outline
Bible Resources to reach and disciple men,
women, boys, and girls for Jesus Christ."
Year Founded in US: 1992
Income for Overseas Min: $215,405.00
Gifts in Kind: $6,000.00
Personnel:
Short-term less than 1 year: 2
Home ministry & office staff in US: 9

Leadership Training Intl.
PO Box 9882
Chesapeake, VA 23321 USA
Phone: (757) 673-6581
Fax: (757) 673-6584
E-mail: info@ltiworld.org
Web Site: www.ltiworld.com
Mr. Kevin Hinman, Founder/President

An interdenominational service agency of
Charismatic and Evangelical tradition en-
gaged in leadership development. Data
from 2005.
Purpose: "...to provide training and re-
sources to multiply ministry leaders to fulfill
the Great Commission."
Year Founded in US: 1992
Income for Overseas Min: $23,000.00
Gifts in Kind: $10,000.00
Personnel:
Home ministry & office staff in US: 6

LeaderTreks
25W560 Geneva Rd., #30
Carol Stream, IL 60188 USA
Phone: (630) 668-0936
Fax: (630) 668-0980
E-mail: info@leadertreks.com
Web Site: www.leadertreks.com
Mr. Doug Franklin, President

An interdenominational service agency engaged in leadership development. Data
from 2005.
Purpose: "...developing leaders to fulfill
the Great Commission."
Year Founded in US: 1994

Fully Supported US Personnel Overseas:
Expecting to serve 1 to 4 years: 18

Other personnel:
Short-term less than 1 year: 1100
Home ministry & office staff in US: 17

Countries: Bolivia; Costa Rica; South Africa

Liberty Corner Mission
PO Box 204
Liberty Corner, NJ 07938-0204 US
Phone: (908) 647-1777
Fax: (908) 647-4117
E-mail: mariabaha@mac.com
Sister Maria Baha, Director

An interdenominational sending agency of Evangelical tradition engaged in evangelism, church planting and discipleship.

Year Founded in US: 1935

Income for Overseas Min: $147,000.00

Fully Supported US Personnel Overseas:
Expecting to serve more than 4 years: 3
Non-residential mission personnel: 9

Other personnel:
Short-term less than 1 year: 1
Non-US serving in own/other country: 9
Home ministry & office staff in US: 3

Countries: Japan 1; Taiwan 2

Liebenzell Mission of USA, Inc.
PO Box 66
Schooleys Mtn., NJ 07870 USA
Phone: (908) 852-3044
Fax: (908) 852-4531
E-mail: missions@liebenzellusa.org
Web Site: www.liebenzellusa.org
Associations: CrossGlobal Link

Mr. Tom Cooper

An interdenominational sending agency of Evangelical tradition engaged in church planting, Christian education, extension education, theological education, leadership development, Bible translation and discipleship.

Purpose: "...to help fulfill the Great Commission of our Lord by sharing the Gospel of Jesus Christ and by instructing believers in obedience to the Word of God and to Scriptural maturity wherever God may lead around the world."

Year Founded in US: 1941

Income for Overseas Min: $997,424.00

Fully Supported US Personnel Overseas:
Expecting to serve more than 4 years: 20
Expecting to serve 1 to 4 years: 1
Non-residential mission personnel: 1

Countries: China; Ecuador 5; Germany 3; Guam 9; Ireland; Japan; Micronesia, Federated States of; Nigeria 1; Palau 1; Papua New Guinea; Spain; Zambia 1

Life in Messiah International
PO Box 5470
Lansing, IL 60438 USA
Phone: (708) 418-0020
Fax: (708) 418-0132
E-mail: office@lifeinmessiah.org
Web Site: www.lifeinmessiah.org
Associations: CrossGlobal Link

Mr. Wesley N. Taber, Exec. Director

A nondenominational sending agency of Evangelical tradition engaged in evangelism, discipleship, literature distribution, mobilization for mission, short-term programs and training.

Purpose: "...building bridges of understanding between Jewish and Christian communities worldwide for over 100 years."

Year Founded in US: 1887

Income for Overseas Min: $180,000.00

Fully Supported US Personnel Overseas:
Expecting to serve more than 4 years: 11

Other personnel:
Short-term less than 1 year: 21
Non-US serving in own/other country: 14
Home ministry & office staff in US: 13

Countries: France 3; Israel 3; Japan 2; Mexico 2; Netherlands 1

Lifewater International, Inc.
PO Box 3131
San Luis Obispo, CA 93403-3131 USA
Phone: (805) 541-6634
Fax: (805) 541-6649
E-mail: info@lifewater.org
Web Site: www.lifewater.org

Mr. Daniel Stevens, Exec. Director

A nondenominational specialized agency of multi-denominational tradition engaged in development, extension education, medical work, partnership development, technical assistance and training.

Purpose: "...to equip partner organizations and work with them to empower communities in developing countries to gain safe water, adequate sanitation, effective hygiene, and the knowledge of Jesus' love."

Year Founded in US: 1979

Income for Overseas Min: $2,427,614.00

Gifts in Kind: $362,700.00

Fully Supported US Personnel Overseas:
Non-residential mission personnel: 4

Other personnel:
Short-term less than 1 year: 8
Home ministry & office staff in US: 17

LifeWind International

PO Box 576645
Modesto, CA 95357-6645 USA

Phone: (209) 543-7500
Fax: (209) 543-7550
E-mail: info@lifewind.org
Web Site: www.lifewind.org
Associations: AERDO

Dr. John Payne, President

An interdenominational support agency of Evangelical tradition engaged in development, discipleship, evangelism, management consulting/training, support of national workers and partnership development. Countries of service data from 2005.

Purpose: "...to permeate the world with the Gospel through a seamless integration of evangelism, discipleship, disease prevention, and community-owned development."

Year Founded in US: 1974

Income for Overseas Min: $1,999,884.00

Gifts in Kind: $5,100.00

Fully Supported US Personnel Overseas:
Expecting to serve more than 4 years: 13
Non-residential mission personnel: 6

Other personnel:
Non-US serving in own/other country: 354
Home ministry & office staff in US: 4

Countries: Albania 2; Argentina; Bangladesh; Belize; Bosnia and Herzegovina; Brazil; Cambodia; Congo, Democratic Republic of; Costa Rica; Cuba; Dominican Republic; East Timor; El Salvador; Ethiopia; Gabon; Guatemala; Haiti; Honduras; India; Indonesia; Kenya 6; Kiribati; Kosovo; Laos; Malaysia; Mexico 1; Mozambique; Myanmar/Burma; Nepal;

Nicaragua; Niger; Nigeria; Panama; Papua New Guinea; Paraguay; Peru; Philippines; Romania; Russia; Sierra Leone; Solomon Islands; South Africa; Sudan; Tanzania; Thailand; Uganda 2; Ukraine; Unspecified Country 2 Uruguay; Venezuela; Vietnam; Zambia

LIGHT International, Inc.

4344 E. Juanita Ave
Gilbert, AZ 852334 USA

Phone: (480) 570-9499
Web Site: www.lightinternationalinc.org

Suzanne Mendenhall, CEO

A nondenominational specialized agency of Evangelical tradition engaged in church mobilization and mission-related research and training in 65 countries. Statistical information from 2003.

Year Founded in US: 1991

Income for Overseas Min: $30,000.00

Gifts in Kind: $30,000.00

Personnel:
Home ministry & office staff in US: 2

Link Care Foundation
(See ad on page 233)

1734 W. Shaw Ave.
Fresno, CA 93711-3486 USA

Phone: (559) 439-5920
Fax: (559) 439-2214
E-mail: info@linkcare.org
Web Site: www.linkcare.org
Associations: The Mission Exchange

Dr. Phil Collier, Exec. Director/CEO

A nondenominational specialized agency of Evangelical tradition engaged in psychological counseling, discipleship and member care.

Year Founded in US: 1965

Literacy & Evangelism Intl.

1800 S. Jackson Ave.
Tulsa, OK 74107-1897 USA

Phone: (918) 585-3826
Fax: (918) 585-3224
E-mail: general@literacyevangelism.org
Web Site: www.literacyevangelism.org

Rev. Sid Rice, Exec. Director

An interdenominational sending agency of Evangelical tradition engaged in litera-

LINK CARE CENTER

Restoring Hearts, Celebrating Wholeness

Link Care Center educates, trains and counsels pastors, missionaries and our community to help them be more effective in life and ministry.

Link Care serves mission organizations and their staff

~~Restoration and Personal Growth
> Participants live on campus while participating in clinical and pastoral counseling designed for Christian Workers who have encountered difficulties while in ministry.

~Consultation
> Link Care staff is able to offer help for the personnel issues faced in cross-cultural Ministry.

~Re-entry
> A week of interaction, dealing with the issues of leaving, grieving, transitions, adaptations, closure and future action plans.

Link Care comes alongside hurting missionaries and their families by providing counseling. Our professional clinical team and pastoral counselors determine the best method of care and create a plan to promote healing and growth. The missionary will meet with our clinical staff and pastoral counselors as well as receive encouragement from fellow missionaries who are at Link Care for help.

Link Care Center   1734 West Shaw Avenue Fresno, California 93711
559-439-5920 info@linkcare.org www.linkcare.org fax 559-439-2214

cy work, literature production, services for other agencies, TESOL and missionary and other training. Data from 2005.

Purpose: "...to encourage, equip and enable the Church worldwide to empower the functionally illiterate with God's Word, through literacy ministries."

Year Founded in US: 1967

Income for Overseas Min: $200,000.00

Fully Supported US Personnel Overseas:
  Expecting to serve more than 4 years: 4

Other personnel:
  Short-term less than 1 year: 4
  Non-US serving in own/other country: 14
  Home ministry & office staff in US: 6

Countries: Asia—General; Benin; Bolivia; Brazil; Burundi; China; Dominican Republic; Ghana; India; Malawi; Pakistan; Peru 2; Philippines 2; Poland; Switzerland; Togo

Living Hope Ministries International, Inc.

PO Box 2765
Acworth, GA 30102 USA

Phone: (770) 917-1307
Fax: (770) 917-1307
E-mail: info@lhmi.org
Web Site: www.lhmi.org

Mr. Robert A. Carter, President

An interdenominational service agency of Baptist tradition engaged in childcare/orphanage programs, Bible distribution, children at risk, development and evangelism.

Purpose: "...to build Hope House Orphanages to care for the beautiful children of Kenya who have lost their parents to disease or the AIDS pandemic and who otherwise grow up with no hope for the future, physically or spiritually...to meet all their physical needs but most importantly, to teach them about our Lord and Savior Jesus Christ."

Year Founded in US: 2001

Personnel:
  Short-term less than 1 year: 7

Countries: Kenya

Living Water International

PO Box 35496
Houston, TX 77235-5496 USA

Phone: (281) 207-7800
Fax: (281) 207-7845

E-mail: info@water.cc
Web Site: www.water.cc

Mr. Gary L. Evans, Exec. Director

An interdenominational service agency of Baptist and Evangelical tradition engaged in water project construction, partnership development, Bible distribution, evangelism, relief and/or rehabilitation, short-term programs and training.

Purpose: "...to demonstrate the love of God by helping communities acquire desperately needed clean water, and to experience 'living water,' the Gospel of Jesus Christ, which alone satisfies the deepest thirst."

Year Founded in US: 1990

Income for Overseas Min: $10,588,000.00

Gifts in Kind: $61,196.00

Fully Supported US Personnel Overseas:
  Non-residential mission personnel: 4

Other personnel:
  Short-term less than 1 year: 10
  Home ministry & office staff in US: 39

Countries: Angola; Brazil; Central African Republic; El Salvador; Ethiopia; Ghana; Guatemala; Haiti; Honduras; India; Kenya; Liberia; Malawi; Mexico; Namibia; Nicaragua; Nigeria; Peru; Romania; Rwanda; Sierra Leone; Sudan; Tanzania; Uganda; Zambia

Living Water Teaching

PO Box 1190
Caddo Mills, TX 75135 USA

Phone: (903) 527-4160
Fax: (903) 527-2134
E-mail: lwt@lwtusa.org
Web Site: www.livingwaterteaching.org

Keith & Debbie Spanberger, Exec. Directors

A nondenominational sending agency of Evangelical and Pentecostal tradition engaged in theological education, childrens programs, evangelism, medical work, short-term programs, missionary training and youth programs.

Purpose: "...to make disciples through training and demonstration."

Year Founded in US: 1979

Fully Supported US Personnel Overseas:
  Expecting to serve more than 4 years: 15
  Expecting to serve 1 to 4 years: 2

Other personnel:

Short-term less than 1 year: 205
Non-US serving in own/other country: 10
Home ministry & office staff in US: 7

Countries: Belize; Brazil 2; El Salvador 3; Guatemala 5; Honduras 3; Nicaragua; Panama; Paraguay 2

Living Word Missions

PO Box 687
Wilmington, MA 01887 USA
Phone: (978) 258-3188
Fax: (978) 258-3188
E-mail: admin@lwmcentral.com
Web Site: www.livingwordmissions.org
Wendy Tatro, Director

A sending agency of Charismatic and Independent tradition engaged in discipleship, children at risk, church planting, Christian education, evangelism and translation work.

Purpose: "...to bring closure to the Great Commission by being missionaries to missionaries and making disciples in all nations."

Year Founded in US: 1993

Income for Overseas Min: $192,676.00

Fully Supported US Personnel Overseas:
Expecting to serve more than 4 years: 1
Non-residential mission personnel: 5

Other personnel:
Short-term less than 1 year: 5
Non-US serving in own/other country: 4
Home ministry & office staff in US: 3

Countries: Gambia, The; Guatemala 1; Sierra Leone

LOGOI Ministries

14540 SW 136th St., Ste. 200
Miami, FL 33186 USA
Phone: (305) 232-5880
Fax: (305) 232-3592
E-mail: logoi@logoi.org
Web Site: www.logoi.org
Mr. Ed Thompson, President

A nondenominational service agency of Reformed tradition engaged in national Spanish pastoral training & resources, discipleship, theological education, leadership development and support of national churches. Countries of service data from 2005.

Purpose: "...to prepare God's people for works of service, so that the body of Christ may be built up..." Eph. 4:12-13

Year Founded in US: 1968

Fully Supported US Personnel Overseas:
Non-residential mission personnel: 12

Other personnel:
Short-term less than 1 year: 6
Non-US serving in own/other country: 19
Home ministry & office staff in US: 9

Countries: Argentina; Bolivia; Chile; Colombia; Cuba; Ecuador; Mexico; Peru; Uruguay; Venezuela

Lott Carey Baptist Foreign Mission Convention

220 I Street NE, Ste. 220
Washington, DC 20002 USA
Phone: (202) 543-3200
Fax: (202) 543-6300
E-mail: lottcarey@lottcarey.org
Web Site: www.lottcarey.org
Dr. David Emmanuel Goatley, Exec. Sec.-Treas.

A transdenominational sending agency of Baptist tradition engaged in support of national churches, theological education, HIV/Aids, medical work, trafficking/slavery issues and youth programs.

Purpose: "...to help churches extend their Christian witness to the ends of the earth."

Year Founded in US: 1897

Income for Overseas Min: $2,250,000.00

Personnel:
Short-term less than 1 year: 125
Non-US serving in own/other country: 730
Home ministry & office staff in US: 10

Countries: Guyana; India; Jamaica; Kenya; Liberia; Nigeria; South Africa; Zimbabwe

Ludhiana Christian Medical College Board, USA, Inc.

PO Box 9583
Panama City Beach, FL 32417 USA
Phone: (850) 819-2753
E-mail: Ludhianamc@aol.com
Web Site: www.ludhianaus.org
Rev. Roberta K. Jones, Exec. Director

An interdenominational service agency of Methodist tradition engaged in medical work, extension education, leadership development, providing medical supplies, relief and/or rehabilitation and missionary training. Data from 2005.

Year Founded in US: 1910
Income for Overseas Min: $200,000.00
Gifts in Kind: $150,000.00
Personnel:
  Short-term less than 1 year: 25
  Home ministry & office staff in US: 1

Luis Palau Evangelistic Association
PO Box 50
Portland, OR 97207 USA
Phone: (503) 614-1500
Fax: (503) 614-1599
E-mail: info@palau.org
Web Site: www.palau.org
Mr. Luis Palau, President
A nondenominational service agency of Evangelical tradition engaged in evangelism, broadcasting, training and community service.
Purpose: "...to proclaim the Gospel, mobilize the Church, and equip the next generation."
Year Founded in US: 1978
Income for Overseas Min: $8,590,083.00
Gifts in Kind: $2,595,704.00
Fully Supported US Personnel Overseas:
  Expecting to serve more than 4 years: 18
  Non-residential mission personnel: 6
Other personnel:
  Non-US serving in own/other country: 18
  Home ministry & office staff in US: 66
Countries: Argentina 2; Latin America—General 13; United Kingdom 3

Luke Society, Inc., The
3409 Gateway Blvd., Ste. 1000
Sioux Falls, SD 57106 US
Phone: (605) 373-9686
Fax: (605) 373-9711
E-mail: office@lukesociety.org
Web Site: www.lukesociety.org
Dr. Wrede Vogel, Exec. Director
An interdenominational service agency of Evangelical tradition engaged in support of national workers, development, discipleship, evangelism and medical work. Data from 2005.
Year Founded in US: 1964
Income for Overseas Min: $1,941,529.00

Personnel:
  Home ministry & office staff in US: 7
Countries: Bolivia; Colombia; Ecuador; Guatemala; Honduras; Mexico; Nicaragua; Paraguay; Peru

Lutheran Bible Translators, Inc.
PO Box 2050
Aurora, IL 60507 USA
Phone: (630) 897-0660
Fax: (630) 897-3567
E-mail: info@lbt.org
Web Site: www.lbt.org
Associations: The Mission Exchange
Dr. Marshall R. Gillam, Exec. Director
A denominational sending agency of Lutheran tradition engaged in Bible translation, Bible distribution, literature distribution, literacy work and translation work. Countries of service data from 2005.
Purpose: "...to help bring people to faith in Jesus Christ by making the Word of God available to those who do not yet have it in the language of their hearts."
Year Founded in US: 1964
Income for Overseas Min: $3,498,296.00
Fully Supported US Personnel Overseas:
  Expecting to serve more than 4 years: 25
  Expecting to serve 1 to 4 years: 5
  Non-residential mission personnel: 4
Other personnel:
  Short-term less than 1 year: 1
  Non-US serving in own/other country: 94
  Home ministry & office staff in US: 18
Countries: Botswana 6; Cameroon; Ecuador; Ghana 5; Guatemala 10; Liberia; Namibia; Nigeria 2; Papua New Guinea 2; Sierra Leone; Togo

Lutheran Brethren World Missions
PO Box 655
Fergus Falls, MN 56538 USA
Phone: (218) 739-3336
Fax: (218) 739-5514
E-mail: lbwm@lbwm.org
Web Site: www.lbwm.org
Associations: The Mission Exchange
Mr. Matthew Rogness, Exec. Director
A denominational sending agency of Evan-

gelical and Lutheran tradition engaged in church planting, development, leadership development, literature production, partnership development and Bible translation.

Purpose: "...to glorify God by being a church that proclaims the Gospel with an intensity and scope proportionate to our responsibility within the larger body of Christ, so that the Great Commission is fulfilled in and on behalf of our generation."

Year Founded in US: 1900

Income for Overseas Min: $1,000,000.00

Fully Supported US Personnel Overseas:
Expecting to serve more than 4 years: 18

Other personnel:
Home ministry & office staff in US: 5

Countries: Cameroon; Chad 8; Japan 4; Taiwan 6

Lutheran Church-Missouri Synod, World Mission

1333 S. Kirkwood Rd.
St. Louis, MO 63122-7295 USA

Phone: (800) 433-3954
Fax: (314) 965-0959
Web Site: www.lcmsworldmission.org
Associations: The Mission Exchange

Dr. Thomas Zehnder, Exec. Director

A denominational sending agency of Lutheran tradition engaged in church planting, Christian education, theological education, TEE, leadership development and support of national churches. Countries of service data from 2005.

Purpose: "...praying to the Lord of the harvest, LCMS World Mission, in collaboration with its North American and worldwide partners, will share the Good News of Jesus with 100 million unreached people or uncommitted people by the 500th anniversary of the Reformation in 2017."

Year Founded in US: 1839

Income for Overseas Min: $13,408,952.00

Fully Supported US Personnel Overseas:
Expecting to serve more than 4 years: 59
Expecting to serve 1 to 4 years: 9

Other personnel:
Short-term less than 1 year: 247
Home ministry & office staff in US: 71

Countries: Argentina 1; Asia—General 2;

Central Asia—General 2; Guatemala 1; Jamaica 2; Japan 7; Kenya 2; Macau 3; Nigeria 2; Panama 6; Papua New Guinea 1; Poland 3; Puerto Rico 8; Russia 5; Taiwan 9; Togo 2; Venezuela 3

Lutheran Hour Ministries

660 Mason Ridge Center Dr.
St. Louis, MO 63141 USA

Phone: (314) 317-4100
Fax: (314) 317-4297
E-mail:lh_min@lhm.org.
Web Site: www.lhm.org

Mr. Greg Lewis, Exec. Director

A denominational specialized agency of Lutheran tradition engaged in evangelism through broadcasting in 41 countries through 290 national staff. Data from 2005.

Purpose: "...to bring Christ to the nations and the nations to the church through Christian radio and TV programming, the internet, print communications, dramas, music and congregational outreach training."

Year Founded in US: 1917

Income for Overseas Min: $650,000.00

Fully Supported US Personnel Overseas:
Expecting to serve more than 4 years: 1
Non-residential mission personnel: 4

Other personnel:
Short-term less than 1 year: 72
Non-US serving in own/other country: 290
Home ministry & office staff in US: 142

Countries: Unspecified Country 1

Lutheran World Relief

700 Light St.
Baltimore, MD 21230 USA

Phone: (410) 230-2800
Fax: (410) 230-2882
E-mail: lwr@lwr.org
Web Site: www.lwr.org

Mr. John A. Nunes, President/CEO

A denominational service agency of Lutheran tradition engaged in relief and/or rehabilitation, development, leadership development and agricultural programs. Activities from 2001.

Purpose: "...to alleviate suffering caused by natural disaster, conflict or poverty; through development efforts to enable marginalized people to realize more fully their God-given potential; and through education and advocacy efforts to promote a peaceful, just and sustainable global community."

Year Founded in US: 1945

Personnel:
Home ministry & office staff in US: 27

M/E International, Inc. (Missionary Electronics)
655 Shadow Lake Dr.
Brea, CA 92821 USA
Phone: (714) 624-3547
Fax: (909) 336-1674
E-mail: jford767@aol.com
Web Site: www.me-intl.org
Mr. James R. Ford, President

An interdenominational support agency of Baptist and Evangelical tradition engaged in discipleship, evangelism, supplying equipment, Bible translation and translation work.

Purpose: "...to enable nationals to reach their own ignored and forgotten villagers with the Gospel of the Lord Jesus Christ, augmented with teaching aids of various types as acceptable."

Year Founded in US: 1948

Income for Overseas Min: $60,726.00

Countries: China; Cote d'Ivoire; Ghana; India; Kenya; Liberia; Nigeria; Sierra Leone; Sudan; Togo

Macedonia World Baptist Missions, Inc.
PO Box 519
Braselton, GA 30517 USA
Phone: (706) 654-2818
Fax: (706) 654-2816
E-mail: dhamby@mwbm.org
Web Site: www.mwbm.org
Dr. Thurman Wade, Gen. Director

A denominational sending agency of Baptist and Independent tradition engaged in church planting, broadcasting, childcare/orphanage programs, Christian education, TEE, evangelism, short-term programs and missionary training.

Purpose: "...to assist local independent Baptist churches in servicing their missionary families as they are sent forth around the world to propagate the Gospel of Jesus Christ with the goal of establishing local

New Testament churches."

Year Founded in US: 1967

Income for Overseas Min: $7,100,000.00

Fully Supported US Personnel Overseas:
Expecting to serve more than 4 years: 160

Other personnel:
Short-term less than 1 year: 40
Non-US serving in own/other country: 9
Home ministry & office staff in US: 10

Countries: Africa—General 5; Argentina 4; Armenia 2; Asia—General 10; Australia 2; Bahamas, The 2; Bolivia 2; Brazil 14; Bulgaria 2; Burkina Faso 2; Caribbean—General 2; Chile 10; Colombia 2; Costa Rica 2; Cyprus 2; Germany 2; Guyana 4; Haiti 1; Honduras 2; Indonesia 4; Ireland 4; Jamaica 2; Japan 2; Kenya 2; Korea, South 2; Macedonia 2; Mali 2; Mexico 16; Peru 15; Portugal 2; Puerto Rico 9; Romania 2; Saint Lucia 4; South Africa 4; Spain 6; Taiwan 2; United Kingdom 2; Venezuela 6

Macedonian Missionary Service
PO Box 68
Polk City, FL 33868-0068 USA
Phone: (863) 984-4060
E-mail: leon@macedonianms.org
Web Site: www.macedonianms.org
Mr. Leon Jasper, President

A denominational support agency of Baptist tradition engaged in church construction, Bible distribution, broadcasting, church planting, correspondence courses, medical work and short-term programs.

Year Founded in US: 1973

Income for Overseas Min: $400,000.00

Gifts in Kind: $25,000.00

Personnel:
Short-term less than 1 year: 350
Home ministry & office staff in US: 6

Mahesh Chavda Ministries International
PO Box 411008
Charlotte, NC 28241-1008 USA
Phone: (800) 730-6264
E-mail: Info@maheshchavda.com
Web Site: www.maheshchavda.com
Rev. Mahesh Chavda, Founder/President

A nondenominational support agency of Charismatic tradition engaged in evangelism, leadership development, literature production and support of national churches. Data from 2003.

Year Founded in US: 1985

Personnel:
Home ministry & office staff in US: 9

Mailbox Club Intl. Inc., The

404 Eager Rd.
Valdosta, GA 31602 USA

Phone: (229) 244-6812
Fax: (229) 245-8977
E-mail: email@mailboxclub.org
Web Site: www.mailboxclub.org

Associations: ANAM

Mr. John Mark Eager, Director/CEO

A nondenominational support agency of Evangelical tradition engaged in correspondence courses, childrens programs, discipleship, evangelism and literature distribution.

Purpose: "...to win the children and young people of the world to Christ, help nurture them into spiritual maturity through Bible correspondence courses and into local churches...accomplished through direct ministry and by multiplying our efforts through key partnerships and the body of Christ around the world."

Year Founded in US: 1965

Income for Overseas Min: $3,096,000.00

Gifts in Kind: $4,300.00

Fully Supported US Personnel Overseas:
Non-residential mission personnel: 4

Other personnel:
Non-US serving in own/other country: 14
Home ministry & office staff in US: 11

Countries: Cameroon; India; Kenya; Nicaragua; Poland; Russia; South Africa; Uganda; Uruguay

MAP International

4700 Glynco Pkwy
Brunswick, GA 31525-6901 USA

Phone: (912) 265-6010
Fax: (912) 265-6170
E-mail: map@map.org
Web Site: www.map.org

Associations: AERDO

Mr. Michael Nyenhuis, President/CEO

A nondenominational specialized agency engaged in providing medical supplies, childrens programs, development, theological education, partnership development and relief and/or rehabilitation. Data from 2005.

Purpose: "...to promote the total health of people living in the world's poorest communities by partnering in the provision of essential medicines, prevention and eradication of disease and the promotion of community health development."

Year Founded in US: 1954

Income for Overseas Min: $319,511,995.00

Gifts in Kind: $338,971,358.00

Personnel:
Non-US serving in own/other country: 111
Home ministry & office staff in US: 58

Countries: Bolivia; Cote d'Ivoire; Ecuador; Honduras; Indonesia; Kenya; Tanzania; Uganda

MATS International, Inc.

4444 National Rd. E.
Richmond, IN 47374 USA

Phone: (765) 966-0101
Fax: (765) 962-9966
E-mail: mark@mats.org
Web Site: www.mats.org

Mr. Mike Nottingham, Chairman

A support agency engaged in purchasing services, furloughed missionary support, services for other agencies and supplying equipment.

Purpose: "...to provide reliable and affordable transportation to ministries and their staff."

Year Founded in US: 1977

Income for Overseas Min: $50,000.00

Personnel:
Home ministry & office staff in US: 27

MBMS International

4867 E. Townsend Ave.
Fresno, CA 93727 USA

Phone: (559) 456-4600
Fax: (559) 251-1432
E-mail: mbmsi@mbmsi.org
Web Site: www.mbmsinternational.org

Associations: The Mission Exchange

Mr. Randy Friesen, Gen. Director

A denominational sending agency of Mennonite tradition engaged in church planting, development, evangelism, recruiting/mobilizing, training and youth programs. MBMS is a bi-national organization and statistics cannot be separated into U.S. and Canadian. For statistical information see the Canadian listing.

Purpose: "Transforming lives in mission."

Year Founded in US: 1878

Media Associates Intl.
351 S. Main Place, Ste. 230
Carol Stream, IL 60188 USA

Phone: (630) 260-9063
Fax: (630) 260-9265
E-mail: mai@littworld.org
Web Site: www.littworld.org

Mr. John D. Maust, President/CEO

An interdenominational specialized agency of Evangelical tradition engaged in training of Christian publishers, editors and authors in countries where Christian publishing and witness are limited and difficult, literature distribution, literature production and training.

Purpose: "...to train, particularly in countries and cultures with limited Christian publishing or witness, MAI stimulates the creation of books, periodicals, and other written materials that nurture the church and attract general readers to Christ."

Year Founded in US: 1985

Income for Overseas Min: $268,247.00

Gifts in Kind: $53,567.00

Personnel:
Home ministry & office staff in US: 3

Medical Ministry Intl.
PO Box 1339
Allen, TX 75013 USA

Phone: (972) 727-5864
Fax: (972) 727-7810
E-mail: mmitx@mmint.org
Web Site: www.mmint.org

Mr. William T. Hunter, Jr., CEO

An interdenominational support agency engaged in medical work.

Year Founded in US: 1995

Income for Overseas Min: $3,700,426.00

Fully Supported US Personnel Overseas:
Expecting to serve more than 4 years: 2
Expecting to serve 1 to 4 years: 4

Other personnel:
Non-US serving in own/other country: 35
Home ministry & office staff in US: 10

Countries: Armenia; Bolivia; Colombia; Dominican Republic 2; Ecuador; Ethiopia; Fiji; Ghana; Haiti; Honduras; Jamaica; Jordan; Mexico; Nicaragua; Peru; Philippines

Medical Missions Philippines, Inc.
PO Box 3656
Modesto, CA 95352 USA

Phone: (209) 531-3031
Fax: (209) 848-2346

Mr. Richard G. Hagerty, President

A support agency of Evangelical tradition engaged in funds transmission to their Manila-based charitable corporation for community health ministry. Data from 2005.

Year Founded in US: 1987

Income for Overseas Min: $46,771.00

Countries: Philippines

Medical Teams International
PO Box 10
Portland, OR 97207 USA

Phone: (503) 624-1000
Fax: (503) 624-1001
E-mail: info@medicalteams.org
Web Site: www.medicalteams.org
Associations: AERDO

Mr. Bas Vanderzalm, President

An interdenominational specialized agency of Ecumenical and Evangelical tradition engaged in short-term medical teams, development, HIV/Aids, providing medical supplies, medical work and relief and/or rehabilitation.

Purpose: "...to demonstrate the love of Christ to those affected by disaster, conflict, and poverty around the world."

Year Founded in US: 1979

Income for Overseas Min: $136,847,845.00

Gifts in Kind: $126,215,972.00

Fully Supported US Personnel Overseas:

Expecting to serve 1 to 4 years: 6

Other personnel:
Short-term less than 1 year: 500
Non-US serving in own/other country: 8
Home ministry & office staff in US: 77

Countries: Guatemala; Indonesia; Liberia; Mexico; Mozambique; Sri Lanka; Uganda

Men for Missions Intl.

941 Fry Road
Greenwood, IN 46142 USA
Phone: (317) 881-6752
Fax: (317) 865-1076
E-mail: whardig@omsinternational.org
Web Site: www.mfmi.org
Associations: The Mission Exchange
Mr. Warren Hardig, Intl. Exec. Director

A nondenominational support agency of Wesleyan tradition engaged in short-term programs, action groups, church planting, and providing medical supplies.

Purpose: "...to do, go, and give of your God-given talents."

Year Founded in US: 1954

Personnel:
Short-term less than 1 year: 473

Mennonite Central Committee (MCC)

PO Box 500
Akron, PA 17501-0500 USA
Phone: (717) 859-1151
Fax: (717) 859-2171
E-mail: mailbox@mcc.org
Web Site: www.mcc.org
Rolando Santiago, Exec. Director

A denominational service agency of Mennonite and Brethren tradition engaged in development, agricultural programs, extension education, justice, medical work, relief and/or rehabilitation, technical assistance and training. Overseas personnel includes 287 locally appointed citizens within more than 70 countries where MCC works. Data from 2005.

Purpose: "...to demonstrate God's love by working among people suffering from poverty, conflict, oppression and natural disaster."

Year Founded in US: 1920

Income for Overseas Min: $40,614,000.00

Gifts in Kind: $6,345,000.00

Fully Supported US Personnel Overseas:
Expecting to serve more than 4 years: 606

Other personnel:
Home ministry & office staff in US: 217

Countries: Africa—General 153; Asia—General 212; Europe—General 26; Latin America—General 181; Middle East 34

Mennonite Economic Development Associates—US (MEDA)

32C E. Roseville Rd.
Lancaster, PA 17601-3861 USA
Phone: (717) 560-6546
Fax: (717) 560-6549

A service agency. Details for MEDA—US listed under their Canadian corporate office.

Mennonite Mission Network

PO Box 370
Elkhart, IN 46515-0370 US
Phone: (574) 294-7523
Fax: (574) 294-8669
E-mail: info@mennonitemission.net
Web Site: www.mennonitemission.net
Mr. Stanley W. Green, Exec. Director/CEO

A denominational sending agency of Mennonite tradition engaged in support of national churches, church planting, theological education, leadership development, partnership development and short-term programs.

Purpose: "...for every congregation and all parts of the Church to be fully engaged in God's mission, reaching from across the street, all through the market places to around the world."

Year Founded in US: 2002

Fully Supported US Personnel Overseas:
Expecting to serve more than 4 years: 40
Expecting to serve 1 to 4 years: 16
Non-residential mission personnel: 4

Other personnel:
Short-term less than 1 year: 78
Non-US serving in own/other country: 35
Home ministry & office staff in US: 95

Countries: Argentina 6; Australia 1; Benin 2; Bolivia; Botswana; Brazil; Burkina Faso; China 2; Colombia 2; Congo, Democratic Republic of; Ecuador; France 3; Germany 2; Ghana; India; Israel 1; Japan 3; Korea, South; Lebanon; Lithuania 3; Macau; Middle East; Mongolia 4; Nepal 1; Nigeria; Senegal 2; South Africa 4; Spain 3; Sweden; Thailand; United Kingdom; Ukraine 1

Mercy Ships

PO Box 2020
Lindale, TX 75771 USA
Phone: (903) 939-7000
Fax: (903) 939-7114
E-mail: jobs@mercyships.org
Web Site: www.mercyships.org
Associations: AERDO
Mr. Samuel Smith, CEO

An interdenominational service agency of Evangelical tradition engaged in medical work/surgical intervention, agricultural programs, development, leadership development, psychological counseling and training.

Purpose: "...Mercy Ships, a global charity, has operated a fleet of hospital ships in developing nations since 1978. Following the model of Jesus, Mercy Ships brings hope and healing to the poor, mobilizing people and resources worldwide."

Year Founded in US: 1978

Income for Overseas Min: $31,260,623.00

Fully Supported US Personnel Overseas:
Expecting to serve more than 4 years: 50
Expecting to serve 1 to 4 years: 400
Non-residential mission personnel: 300

Other personnel:
Short-term less than 1 year: 1200
Non-US serving in own/other country: 90
Home ministry & office staff in US: 40

Countries: Africa—General 50

Messianic Jewish Movement International, Inc. The (MJMI)

PO Box 1212
Chandler, AZ 85244-1212 USA
Phone: (480) 786-6564
Fax: (480) 897-8389
E-mail: office@mjmi.org
Web Site: www.mjmi.org
Mr. Nathan L. Jacobus, President

A Messianic Jewish support agency of Charismatic tradition engaged in evangelism, church planting, discipleship, leadership development and missionary training.

Year Founded in US: 1963

Income for Overseas Min: $120,000.00

Personnel:
Non-US serving in own/other country: 7
Home ministry & office staff in US: 2

Countries: Israel

Mexican Medical Ministries

7850 Lester Ave
Lemon Grove, CA 91945 USA
Phone: (619) 463-4777
Fax: (619) 463-4770
E-mail: information@mexicanmedical.com
Web Site: www.mexicanmedical.com
Pastor Steve Crews, President

A nondenominational service agency of Evangelical tradition engaged in medicine, including dental and public health, childrens programs, evangelism, providing medical supplies, short-term programs and health education.

Purpose: "...to bring healing and hope to the people of Mexico...to bring God's healing touch to the total person. The redemptive work of God touches the physical, emotional, intellectual, and spiritual condition of humankind. In accomplishing this mission, Mexican Medical Ministries seeks to empower people to work together to accomplish the Great Commission."

Year Founded in US: 1963

Income for Overseas Min: $1,615,000.00

Fully Supported US Personnel Overseas:
Expecting to serve more than 4 years: 13
Non-residential mission personnel: 2

Other personnel:
Short-term less than 1 year: 2006
Non-US serving in own/other country: 11
Home ministry & office staff in US: 7

Countries: Mexico 13

Mexico Medical Missions

4001 County Rd. 114
Glenwood Springs, CO 81601 USA
Phone: (970) 945-5432
E-mail: vicky@mexicomedical.org
Web Site: www.mexicomedical.org

Dr. Michael Berkeley, Director

An interdenominational support agency of Evangelical tradition engaged in medical work, aviation services, development and support of national churches.

Purpose: "...to provide an excellent level of integrated health care to the indigenous people of the Sierra Madre of Mexico, thereby proclaiming the transforming love of Jesus Christ."

Year Founded in US: 1989

Income for Overseas Min: $1,083,326.00

Gifts in Kind: $111,438.00

Personnel:
   Short-term less than 1 year: 45
   Non-US serving in own/other country: 45
   Home ministry & office staff in US: 1

Countries: Mexico

Middle East Christian Outreach (MECO)

PO Box 14896
Bradenton, FL 34280 USA

Phone: (941) 567-4053

E-mail: usa@aboutmeco.org

Web Site: www.aboutmeco.org

Associations: The Mission Exchange

Dr. J. Keith Bateman, Director

An interdenominational support agency of Evangelical tradition engaged in support of national churches, disability assistance programs, Christian education, TEE, partnership development and video/film production/distribution. Countries of service data from 2005.

Purpose: "...to assist the already-existing churches in the Middle East to do the work of mission in their region."

Year Founded in US: 1979

Income for Overseas Min: $146,000.00

Fully Supported US Personnel Overseas:
   Expecting to serve more than 4 years: 4
   Expecting to serve 1 to 4 years: 2
   Non-residential mission personnel: 50

Other personnel:
   Non-US serving in own/other country: 50
   Home ministry & office staff in US: 2

Countries: Australia; Cyprus; Middle East; Unspecified Country 4

Middle East Media—USA

PO Box 4949
Wheaton, IL 60189-4949 USA

Phone: (425) 488-9429

Fax: (425) 488-9429

E-mail: info@mem-usa.org

Web Site: www.mem.org

Associations: The Mission Exchange

Wayne Larson, Exec. Director

A nondenominational support agency engaged in video/film production/distribution, broadcasting, evangelism, support of national churches, missionary training, literature production and translation work. Data from 2005.

Year Founded in US: 1976

Income for Overseas Min: $286,870.00

Fully Supported US Personnel Overseas:
   Expecting to serve more than 4 years: 2

Other personnel:
   Non-US serving in own/other country: 89
   Home ministry & office staff in US: 4

Countries: Africa—General; Iran; Middle East; Turkey; Unspecified Country 2

Middle Eastern Outreach

PO Box 405
Duarte, CA 91009-0405 USA

Phone: (818) 482-5242

E-mail: meo.e@usa.net

Web Site: www.middleeasternoutreach.com

Dr./Rev. Elie Elbayadi, Founder/President

A support agency engaged in evangelism, missions information service, missionary training, literature distribution, support of national churches, and Muslim and jail ministry. Statistics are from 2003.

Year Founded in US: 1995

Income for Overseas Min: $22,000.00

Personnel:
   Home ministry & office staff in US: 3

Ministries in Action

PO Box 571357
Miami, FL 33257-1357 USA

Phone: (305) 234-7855

Fax: (305) 234-7825

E-mail: helpingchurches@mia.org

Web Site: www.mia.org

Rev. Steve McGee, President

An interdenominational sending agency of Evangelical tradition engaged in support of national churches, development, discipleship, TEE, evangelism, relief and/or rehabilitation and short-term programs. Data from 2005.

Purpose: "...to help the Church internationally to grow holistically and in accordance with the Great Commission."

Year Founded in US: 1961

Income for Overseas Min: $345,035.00

Fully Supported US Personnel Overseas:
Expecting to serve more than 4 years: 5
Non-residential mission personnel: 6

Other personnel:
Short-term less than 1 year: 302
Non-US serving in own/other country: 10
Home ministry & office staff in US: 11

Countries: Bolivia; Brazil; Dominican Republic; Grenada; Guadeloupe; Haiti 1; Jamaica 2; Mexico; Peru; Puerto Rico 2; Saint Lucia; Saint Martin; Saint Vincent and the Grenadines

Ministry to Educate and Equip, International (MTEE)

2520 Professional Rd., Ste. C
Richmond, VA 23229 USA
Phone: (804) 320-6456
Fax: (804) 320-6456
E-mail: mtee@verizon.net
Web Site: www.mtee.org
Associations: The Mission Exchange
Mr. Ernest R. Campe, President

A transdenominational sending agency of Pentecostal tradition engaged in TEE, childcare/orphanage programs, Christian education, theological education and leadership development.

Purpose: "...to equip God's people for works of service so the body of Christ may be built up." (Eph. 4:12)

Year Founded in US: 1986

Income for Overseas Min: $355,474.00

Fully Supported US Personnel Overseas:
Expecting to serve 1 to 4 years: 14
Non-residential mission personnel: 6

Other personnel:
Non-US serving in own/other country: 14
Home ministry & office staff in US: 2

Countries: Bulgaria; Hungary; Moldova; Ukraine

Mission Aviation Fellowship

PO Box 47
Nampa, ID 83653-0047 USA
Phone: (208) 498-0800
Fax: (208) 498-0801
E-mail: mafus@maf.org
Web Site: www.maf.org
Associations: The Mission Exchange, AER-DO, CrossGlobal Link
Mr. John Boyd, President

A specialized agency of Evangelical tradition engaged in aviation services, extension education, support of national churches and technical assistance.

Purpose: "...to share the love of Jesus Christ through aviation and technology so that isolated people may be physically and spiritually transformed."

Year Founded in US: 1945

Income for Overseas Min: $24,000,000.00

Gifts in Kind: $1,091,000.00

Fully Supported US Personnel Overseas:
Expecting to serve more than 4 years: 117
Expecting to serve 1 to 4 years: 44

Other personnel:
Short-term less than 1 year: 20
Non-US serving in own/other country: 28
Home ministry & office staff in US: 130

Countries: Africa—General 2; Asia—General 20; Brazil; Congo, Democratic Republic of; Costa Rica; Ecuador; Guatemala; Haiti; Indonesia 70; Lesotho 13; Mexico 2; Mozambique 4; Uganda 6

Mission Catalyst Intl., Inc.

PO Box 73047
Houston, TX 77273-3047 USA
Phone: (281) 507-8888
Fax: (936) 756-3451
E-mail: jre@mci3.org
Web Site: www.mci3.org
Associations: The Mission Exchange
Mr. James R. Eby, Founder/President

An interdenominational support agency of Charismatic and Pentecostal tradition engaged in leadership development, church planting, discipleship, support of national workers, mission-related research and missionary training.

Purpose: "...to help finish the Great Commission in this generation by training national workers in the 10/40 Window to plant effective, reproducing churches among the world's least-reached peoples."

Year Founded in US: 2002

Income for Overseas Min: $127,000.00

Fully Supported US Personnel Overseas:
Expecting to serve 1 to 4 years: 4

Other personnel:
Short-term less than 1 year: 10
Home ministry & office staff in US: 1

Countries: Asia—General

Mission Data International
PO Box 725
Siloam Springs, AR 72761 USA
Phone: (479) 524-9110
Fax: (610) 466-8857
E-mail: info@mdat.org
Web Site: www.mdat.org
Mr. Peter Armstrong, Exec. Director

A nondenominational specialized agency of Evangelical tradition engaged in recruiting/mobilizing, missions information service and services for other agencies.

Purpose: "...to bring people and missions together using internet technology."

Year Founded in US: 2000

Personnel:
Home ministry & office staff in US: 3

Mission Generation, Inc.
PO Box 327
Texas City, TX 77592 USA
Phone: (409) 515-1973
Fax: (591) 333-6623
E-mail: rmalloy@missiongeneration.org
Web Site: www.missiongeneration.org
Mr. Kyle Dickson, Exec. Director

A Christian development organization of Evangelical and Independent tradition engaged in children at risk, childrens programs, evangelism and leadership development.

Purpose: "...to give children the tools they need to make quality life decisions."

Year Founded in US: 1998

Income for Overseas Min: $39,029.00

Fully Supported US Personnel Overseas:
Expecting to serve more than 4 years: 2

Other personnel:

Short-term less than 1 year: 4
Non-US serving in own/other country: 60

Countries: Bolivia 2; Colombia; Costa Rica; Dominican Republic; Palestine; Paraguay; Peru

Mission India
PO Box 141312
Grand Rapids, MI 49514 USA
Phone: (616) 453-8855
Fax: (616) 791-9926
E-mail: info@missionindia.org
Web Site: www.missionindia.org
Rev. David Stravers, President

A nondenominational support agency of Evangelical tradition engaged in church planting, childrens programs, evangelism, literacy work and missionary training.

Purpose: "...to assist Indian churches and indigenous mission agencies in planting reproducing churches in a systematic, measureable way."

Year Founded in US: 1981

Income for Overseas Min: $10,452,453.00

Fully Supported US Personnel Overseas:
Non-residential mission personnel: 3

Other personnel:
Non-US serving in own/other country: 2
Home ministry & office staff in US: 25

Countries: India

Mission International
PO Box 7632
Woodland Park, CO 80863 USA
Phone: (719) 686-7761
Fax: (719) 686-7761
E-mail: missionintl@msn.com
Web Site: www.missionintl.org
Mr. William Agius, President

An interdenominational support agency of Evangelical tradition engaged in church planting, Bible distribution, discipleship, leadership development and literature distribution.

Purpose: "...to assist local churches and believers living in the Middle East and Northern Africa by equipping them in God's Word, in order for them to plant new churches in their nations."

Year Founded in US: 1993

Income for Overseas Min: $214,324.00

Fully Supported US Personnel Overseas:

Non-residential mission personnel: 2
Other personnel:
    Home ministry & office staff in US: 2

Mission Nannys
PO Box 61805
Santa Barbara, CA 93110 USA
Phone: (805) 683-7476
E-mail: bettysullins@juno.com
Web Site: www.missionnannys.org
Betty Sullins, Director

A nondenominational service agency of Baptist and Evangelical tradition engaged in childcare/orphanage programs, home schooling and providing domestic help for missionary families.

Purpose: "...to seek to glorify God among missionary families through domestic and teaching services of women volunteers to travel and meet particular needs."

Year Founded in US: 1991
Personnel:
    Short-term less than 1 year: 16

Mission of Mercy
PO Box 62600
Colorado Springs, CO 80962 USA
Phone: (800) 864-0200
Fax: (719) 481-4649
E-mail: mominfo@mofm.org
Web Site: www.missionofmercy.org
Associations: AERDO
Mr. Mark Pluimer, President

A nondenominational support agency of Evangelical tradition engaged in childrens programs, childcare/orphanage programs, development, discipleship, Christian education and youth programs in more than 23 countries. Data from 2005.

Purpose: "...to rescue forgotten children, with Jesus' love."

Year Founded in US: 1954
Income for Overseas Min: $13,736,718.00
Fully Supported US Personnel Overseas:
    Expecting to serve more than 4 years: 1
Other personnel:
    Non-US serving in own/other country: 1
    Home ministry & office staff in US: 18
Countries: India 1

Mission ONE, Inc.
PO Box 5960
Scottsdale, AZ 85261 USA
Phone: (480) 951-0900
Fax: (480) 951-1016
E-mail: info@mission1.org
Web Site: www.mission1.org
Rev. Robert Schindler, President/Founder

A support agency of Evangelical tradition engaged in partnership development, support of national workers, church planting, extension education, evangelism and support of national churches.

Purpose: "...to mobilize the Church for partnership with national missionaries, focusing on unreached people groups, and serving the poor and oppressed."

Year Founded in US: 1991
Income for Overseas Min: $386,882.00
Personnel:
    Short-term less than 1 year: 12
    Non-US serving in own/other country: 409
    Home ministry & office staff in US: 6
Countries: Asia—General; Benin; Ethiopia; Ghana; India; Kenya; Middle East; Nepal; Nigeria; Pakistan; Sudan; Tanzania; Thailand; Togo; Uganda

Mission Possible Foundation, Inc.
404 E. Gregory St., Ste. 8
Mount Prospect, IL 60056 USA
Phone: (847) 259-1270
Fax: (847) 259-1270
E-mail: mpusa@mp.org
Web Site: www.mp.org
Nasko Lazarov, USA Director

An interdenominational support agency of Evangelical and Pentecostal tradition engaged in church planting, childrens programs, leadership development, literature distribution and literature production. Data from 2005.

Purpose: "...to serve local national churches and enable them to evangelize unbelievers and disciple new believers..."

Year Founded in US: 1974
Income for Overseas Min: $139,526.00
Personnel:
    Non-US serving in own/other country: 52

Home ministry & office staff in US: 1

Countries: Albania; Bulgaria; Finland; Sweden; Russia; Ukraine

Mission Possible, Inc.

PO Box 1026
Findlay, OH 45839-1026 US
Phone: (419) 422-3364
Fax: (419) 422-3364
E-mail: office@ourmissionispossible.org
Web Site: www.ourmissionispossible.org
Mr. Kurt Bishop, President

An interdenominational support agency engaged in student Christian education, evangelism, discipleship, theological education, leadership development and medical work.

Purpose: "...to equip a new generation of Christ-centered leaders for the harvest."

Year Founded in US: 1979

Income for Overseas Min: $792,232.00

Personnel:
  Short-term less than 1 year: 106
  Non-US serving in own/other country: 204
  Home ministry & office staff in US: 6

Countries: Dominican Republic; Haiti

Mission Safety International

328 E. Elk Ave. #1
Elizabethton, TN 37643-3351 USA
Phone: (423) 542-8892
Fax: (423) 542-5464
E-mail: info@msisafety.org
Web Site: www.msisafety.org
Mr. Jonathan A. Egeler, President/CEO

A nondenominational specialized agency engaged in aviation safety services for other agencies in 10 countries. Data from 2005.

Purpose: "...to provide educational and consulting services to mission and mission aviation training organizations and related agencies in the areas of operational safety and organizational security."

Year Founded in US: 1983

Income for Overseas Min: $10,258.00

Gifts in Kind: $211,045.00

Personnel:
  Home ministry & office staff in US: 3

Mission Services Association, Inc.

2004 E. Magnolia Ave
Knoxville, TN 37917-8026 USA
Phone: (865) 577-9740
Web Site: www.missionservices.org
Mr. W. Reggie Hundley, Exec. Director

A nondenominational support agency of Christian (Restoration Movement) tradition engaged in communication, print publishing, web development and missions information service. Data from 2005.

Year Founded in US: 1960

Income for Overseas Min: $400,000.00

Personnel:
  Short-term less than 1 year: 2
  Home ministry & office staff in US: 8

Mission to Children, Inc.

PO Box 2217
Escondido, CA 92033-2217 USA
Phone: (877) 766-2400
Fax: (760) 839-1620
E-mail: info@missiontochildren.org
Web Site: www.missiontochildren.org
Dr. John Garmo, President

A nondenominational specialized agency of Evangelical tradition engaged in children at risk, childcare/orphanage programs, childrens programs, evangelism and character training & development.

Purpose: "...to care for and cultivate Christ-like character in children, especially those at risk."

Year Founded in US: 1971

Income for Overseas Min: $449,575.00

Personnel:
  Non-US serving in own/other country: 1
  Home ministry & office staff in US: 7

Countries: Bolivia; Costa Rica; El Salvador; India; Philippines

Mission to the World (PCA), Inc.

1600 North Brown Rd.
Lawrenceville, GA 30043 USA
Phone: (678) 823-0004
Fax: (678) 823-0027
E-mail: info@mtw.org
Web Site: www.mtw.org

Associations: The Mission Exchange

Mr. Paul D. Kooistra, Coordinator

A denominational sending agency of Presbyterian tradition engaged in support of national churches, church planting, theological education, leadership development, medical work and youth programs.

Purpose: "...to fulfill the Great Commission by advancing Reformed and covenantal church-planting movements through word and deed in strategic areas worldwide."

Year Founded in US: 1973

Income for Overseas Min: $38,588,608.00

Gifts in Kind: $9,095.00

Fully Supported US Personnel Overseas:
  Expecting to serve more than 4 years: 517
  Expecting to serve 1 to 4 years: 145
  Non-residential mission personnel: 9

Other personnel:
  Short-term less than 1 year: 6520
  Home ministry & office staff in US: 99

Countries: Australia 20; Austria 2; Bangladesh 1; Belgium 14; Belize 5; Bolivia 2; Brazil 5; Bulgaria 18; Cambodia 7; Chile 12; Colombia 4; Costa Rica 1; Czech Republic 6; Ecuador 8; Ethiopia 4; France 22; Germany 11; Guam 2; Haiti 2; Honduras; Hong Kong 2; India 10; Ireland 4; Italy 2; Japan 36; Kenya 2; Korea, South 2; Latvia 2; Mexico 49; Nicaragua 2; Panama 2; Papua New Guinea 2; Peru 34; Philippines 8; Portugal 3; Puerto Rico 4; Romania 7; Singapore 2; Slovakia 11; South Africa 24; Spain 8; Sweden 2; Taiwan 12; Thailand 8; Trinidad and Tobago 2; Uganda 10; Ukraine 21; United Kingdom 28; Unspecified Country 70; Zambia 2

Mission To Unreached Peoples

2401 Silver Holly Ln.
Richardson, TX 75082 USA
E-mail: mupinfo@mup.org
Web Site: www.mup.org

Associations: The Mission Exchange

Mr. Kent Parks, Intl. Director

A nondenominational sending agency of Evangelical tradition engaged in church planting, childcare/orphanage programs, children at risk, childrens programs, development and discipleship. Countries of service data from 2005.

Purpose: " ...to obey the Great Commission of Jesus Christ by investing our lives, gifts, resources, and vocational skills in God's work throughout Asia and Europe...to commit ourselves personally and corporately to the Word of God, to prayer, and to worship."

Year Founded in US: 1982

Income for Overseas Min: $4,878,929.00

Fully Supported US Personnel Overseas:
  Expecting to serve more than 4 years: 130
  Non-residential mission personnel: 14

Other personnel:
  Short-term less than 1 year: 32
  Non-US serving in own/other country: 10
  Home ministry & office staff in US: 29

Countries: Albania 2; Cambodia 16; China 30; Hungary 3; India 12; Indonesia 4; Japan 5; Kazakhstan; Korea, South; Macedonia 2; Malaysia; Mongolia 2; Nepal 3; Philippines 4; Poland 4; Russia 2; Taiwan 2; Thailand 27; Turkey 8; Ukraine 2; Vietnam 2

Mission Training and Resource Center

PO Box 41155
Pasadena, CA 91114 USA
Phone: (626) 797-7903
Fax: (626) 797-7906
E-mail: phil@paraclete.net

Mr. Phillip Elkins, President

A specialized agency engaged in development, leadership development, management consulting/training, services for other agencies, tentmaking and missionary training.

Purpose: "...to create innovative, experience-based training programs for cross cultural workers."

Year Founded in US: 1979

Income for Overseas Min: $160,000.00

Personnel:
  Non-US serving in own/other country: 4
  Home ministry & office staff in US: 2

Countries: Ethiopia; Zimbabwe

Mission Training Intl.

PO Box 1220
Palmer Lake, CO 80133-1220 USA
Phone: (719) 487-0111
Fax: (719) 487-9350

E-mail: info@mti.org
Web Site: www.mti.org
Associations: The Mission Exchange

Dr. Stephen M. Sweatman, President/CEO

A support agency of Evangelical tradition engaged in pre-field training & debriefing, missionary training, furloughed missionary support and services for other agencies.

Purpose: "...to serve mission boards, churches, and other sending organizations by developing and equipping their cross-cultural workers for the furtherance of Christ's Kingdom."

Year Founded in US: 1954

Mission Without Borders Intl.

PO Box 6008
Camarillo, CA 93011 USA
Phone: (805) 987-8880
Fax: (805) 484-8378
E-mail: mwb-us@mwbi.org
Web Site: www.mwb.org
Associations: AERDO

Mr. Loren N. Pine, Natl. Director

A nondenominational service agency of Evangelical tradition engaged in childcare/orphanage programs, Christian education, evangelism, literature distribution, support of national workers, relief and/or rehabilitation and family care/community centers.

Purpose: "...to reach people for Christ."
Year Founded in US: 1960
Income for Overseas Min: $1,274,013.00
Gifts in Kind: $1,162,883.00
Personnel:
  Non-US serving in own/other country: 209
  Home ministry & office staff in US: 3
Countries: Albania; Bosnia and Herzegovina; Bulgaria; Moldova; Romania; Ukraine

Mission: Moving Mountains, Inc.

PO Box 6000
Colorado Springs, CO 80934 USA
Phone: (719) 594-2727
Fax: (719) 260-0479
E-mail: d4d@navigators.org
Web Site: www.movingmountains.org

Dr. Gary T. Hipp, CEO

An interdenominational sending agency of Evangelical tradition engaged in development, agricultural programs, church planting,evangelism, leadership development and medical work. Data from 2005.

Purpose: "...to facilitate the physical and spiritual well-being of impoverished people in developing countries."
Year Founded in US: 1978
Income for Overseas Min: $602,980.00
Fully Supported US Personnel Overseas:
  Expecting to serve more than 4 years: 26
  Non-residential mission personnel: 5
Other personnel:
  Short-term less than 1 year: 17
  Non-US serving in own/other country: 27
  Home ministry & office staff in US: 13
Countries: Ghana; Kenya 16; Nigeria; Senegal 10; Uganda

Missionaire International

PO Box 335
Tompkinsville, KY 42167 USA
Phone: (270) 407-9816
Fax: (270) 487-0888
E-mail: serve@missionaire.org
Web Site: www.missionaire.org

Mr. Jon O. Foote, Director of Operations

An interdenominational service agency of Evangelical tradition engaged in aviation services, missionary education, leadership development, services for other agencies, training and youth programs.

Purpose: "...to prepare people and aircraft for Christian mission service throughout the world."
Year Founded in US: 1987
Personnel:
  Home ministry & office staff in US: 11

Missionary Athletes Intl.

1020 Crews Rd. N.
Matthews, NC 28105-7587 USA
Phone: (704) 841-8644
Fax: (704) 841-8652
E-mail: info@maisoccer.com
Web Site: www.maisoccer.com

Mr. Patrick Stewart, President

A nondenominational specialized agency of Evangelical tradition engaged in sports program ministry, discipleship, evangelism and youth programs.

Purpose: "...to communicate the message of Jesus Christ through the environment of soccer."

Year Founded in US: 1983

Income for Overseas Min: $579,995.00

Fully Supported US Personnel Overseas:
Expecting to serve more than 4 years: 1
Expecting to serve 1 to 4 years: 1

Other personnel:
Short-term less than 1 year: 153
Home ministry & office staff in US: 23

Countries: Asia—General; Ukraine 1

Missionary Expediters, Inc.

5620 Tchoupitoulas St.
New Orleans, LA 70115 USA

Phone: (504) 891-6300
Fax: (504) 891-6365
E-mail: matthewg@mxshipping.com
Web Site: www.missionaryexpediters.com

Associations: AERDO

Mr. Jack Fong, President

A specialized agency engaged in logistics and shipping GIK & personal effects.

Year Founded in US: 1955

Personnel:
Home ministry & office staff in US: 21

Missionary Flights Intl.

3170 Airmans Dr.
Ft. Pierce, FL 34951 USA

Phone: (772) 462-2395
Fax: (772) 462-2397
E-mail: mfi@missionaryflights.org
Web Site: www.missionaryflights.org

Mr. Richard Snook, President

A nondenominational support agency of Evangelical tradition engaged in missionary air transportation of personnel and cargo, Bible distribution and relief and/or rehabilitation. Data from 2005.

Year Founded in US: 1964

Income for Overseas Min: $2,600,000.00

Gifts in Kind: $2,600,000.00

Personnel:
Home ministry & office staff in US: 16

Missionary Furlough Homes Foundation

PO Box 943
Wheaton, IL 60187 USA

Phone: (630) 665-0020
Fax: (630) 665-8504
E-mail: furlough.homes@juno.com

Mr. Don Holwerda, President

A nondenominational specialized agency of Evangelical tradition engaged in furloughed missionary support.

Purpose: "...to provide comfortable and affordable housing for missionaries on furlough."

Year Founded in US: 1962

Missionary Gospel Fellowship

PO Box 1535
Turlock, CA 95381 USA

Phone: (209) 634-8575
Fax: (209) 634-8576
E-mail: mgfhq@mgfhq.org
Web Site: www.mgfhq.org

Associations: ANAM

Mr. A. J. Hyatt, Gen. Director

An interdenominational sending agency of Evangelical tradition engaged in discipleship, church construction, church planting, theological education, evangelism and medical work.

Purpose: "...to evangelize and disciple the unreached people groups with the Gospel."

Year Founded in US: 1939

Income for Overseas Min: $248,679.00

Fully Supported US Personnel Overseas:
Expecting to serve more than 4 years: 11
Expecting to serve 1 to 4 years: 6

Other personnel:
Non-US serving in own/other country: 17
Home ministry & office staff in US: 3

Countries: Mexico 11

Missionary Outreach Support Services (MOSS)

1000 Regent University Dr., CRB 163
Virginia Beach, VA 23464 USA

Phone: (757) 226-4341
E-mail: support@missionaryoutreach.net
Web Site: www.missionaryoutreach.net

Mr. Glen L. Moriarty, Director

A nondenominational specialized agency of

Evangelical tradition engaged in member care, furloughed missionary support, missions information service, leadership development, psychological counseling and relief and/or rehabilitation. Data from 2005.

Year Founded in US: 2005

Missionary Retreat Fellowship, Inc.

R.R. #4, Box 4590
Lake Ariel, PA 18436 USA
Phone: (570) 689-2984
Fax: (570) 689-2984
E-mail: MRF65@juno.com
Web Site: www.missionaryretreat.org
Mr. Donald E. Schuit, Exec. Director

A nondenominational support agency of Evangelical tradition engaged in furloughed missionary support and housing.

Purpose: "...to provide the furloughing missionary with fully furnished housing...at subsidized rates."

Year Founded in US: 1965

Missionary Revival Crusade

PO Box 764979
Dallas, TX 75376-4979 USA
Phone: (972) 283-8900
Fax: (972) 283-8900
E-mail: mrcsupport@sbcglobal.net
Web Site: www.thevinefellowship.com/MRC
Rev. Roger J. West, President

A support agency of Charismatic and Pentecostal tradition engaged in church planting, audio recording/distribution, broadcasting, correspondence courses, discipleship and leadership development. Also does ministry as "Master's Resourcing Commission."

Purpose: "...to fulfill a three-fold purpose: revival among God's people, preparation of workers for the harvest, and to reach the lost, at any cost, with the saving message of Jesus Christ."

Year Founded in US: 1955

Income for Overseas Min: $611,000.00

Personnel:
  Home ministry & office staff in US: 1

Countries: Argentina; Brazil; Colombia; France; Mexico; Nicaragua; Spain

Missionary TECH Team

25 FRJ Dr.
Longview, TX 75602-4703 USA
Phone: (903) 757-4530
Fax: (903) 758-2799
E-mail: bwiley@techteam.org
Web Site: www.techteam.org
Associations: CrossGlobal Link, ANAM
Mr. Birne D. Wiley, Founder/President

An interdenominational service agency of Independent tradition engaged in technical assistance, church construction, literature production, services for other agencies and short-term programs.

Purpose: "...to be the service mission that like-minded ministries may turn to for technical assistance and know-how."

Year Founded in US: 1969

Income for Overseas Min: $500,000.00

Gifts in Kind: $100,000.00

Fully Supported US Personnel Overseas:
  Non-residential mission personnel: 3

Other personnel:
  Short-term less than 1 year: 12

Missionary Ventures Intl.

PO Box 593550
Orlando, FL 32859-3550 USA
Phone: (407) 859-7322
Fax: (407) 856-7934
E-mail: info@mvi.org
Web Site: www.mvi.org
Mr. Glen P. Dubois, President

An interdenominational specialized agency of Evangelical tradition engaged in support of national churches, childrens programs, church planting, support of national workers and short-term programs. Data from 2005.

Purpose: "...to encourage and support indigenous missions through personal involvement, financial sponsorship and ministry development."

Year Founded in US: 1984

Income for Overseas Min: $6,031,772.00

Fully Supported US Personnel Overseas:
  Expecting to serve more than 4 years: 64
  Non-residential mission personnel: 19

Other personnel:
  Short-term less than 1 year: 1800

Non-US serving in own/other country: 30
Home ministry & office staff in US: 14

Countries: Belize 2; Bolivia 4; Colombia 2; Costa Rica 1; Dominican Republic 5; Ecuador 4; Egypt; Gabon; Guatemala 8; Haiti 1; Honduras 4; Indonesia 2; Ireland; Israel; Malaysia; Marshall Islands 2; Mexico 4; Nicaragua 6; Nigeria; Paraguay 2; Peru 8; Philippines 2; Russia; Singapore 1; South Africa; Thailand 2; Uganda; United Kingdom 2; Zambia 2

MissionaryHealth.net

1757 E. Baseline Rd., Ste. 126
Gilbert, AZ 85233 USA

Phone: (800) 647-4589
Fax: (480) 821-9297
E-mail: health@missionaryhealth.net
Web Site: www.missionaryhealth.net

Mr. Graham Bates, President

A nondenominational specialized agency of Evangelical tradition engaged in services for other agencies.

Year Founded in US: 1995

Personnel:
Home ministry & office staff in US: 8

Missions Door

2530 Washington St.
Denver, CO 80205-3142 USA

Phone: (303) 308-1818
Fax: (303) 295-9090
E-mail: info@missionsdoor.org
Web Site: www.missionsdoor.org

Rev. Richard A. Miller, President

An associational sending agency of Baptist and Evangelical tradition engaged in church planting, discipleship, TEE, leadership development and support of national churches.

Purpose: " ...to assist local churches of like faith and practice in their efforts to evangelize, disciple and plant churches among the unreached, including economic development and humanitarian ministries, in obedience to the Gospel of Jesus Christ."

Year Founded in US: 1948

Income for Overseas Min: $1,656,289.00

Fully Supported US Personnel Overseas:

Expecting to serve more than 4 years: 12
Non-residential mission personnel: 1

Other personnel:
Short-term less than 1 year: 150
Non-US serving in own/other country: 44
Home ministry & office staff in US: 14

Countries: Bahamas, The 1; Belize 2; Cambodia 2; China; Costa Rica; Dominican Republic; El Salvador; Guatemala 2; Haiti; Honduras 2; Kenya 1; Liberia; Mexico 2; Nicaragua; Panama

Missions Resource Network

4001 Airport Fwy., Ste. 550
Bedford, TX 76021 USA

Phone: (817) 267-2727
Fax: (817) 267-2626
E-mail: missions@mrnet.org
Web Site: www.mrnet.org

Mr. Bob Waldron, Exec. Director

A service agency of Christian (Restoration Movement) tradition engaged in church planting, discipleship, member care, partnership development, mobilization for mission and missionary training.

Purpose: "...to equip the body of Christ to steward the mission of God...to help churches vision strategically, equip for missions, plant churches worldwide, and nurture missionaries and their families."

Year Founded in US: 1998

Fully Supported US Personnel Overseas:
Expecting to serve more than 4 years: 39

Other personnel:
Home ministry & office staff in US: 11

Countries: Australia 6; Austria 8; Czech Republic 7; New Zealand 6; Rwanda 6; Ukraine 6

Missions To Japan, Inc.

PO Box 1203
Campbell, CA 95009-1203 USA

Phone: (408) 998-1768

Rev. Joe Weigand, President

An interdenominational support agency of Charismatic and Evangelical tradition engaged in discipleship, Bible distribution, bible memorization, broadcasting, evangelism and funds transmission. Data from 2005.

Purpose: "...to promote fellowship, cooperation, protection, recognition and the propagation of the Christian gospel at home and abroad..."

Year Founded in US: 1959

Income for Overseas Min: $17,801.00

Personnel:
Home ministry & office staff in US: 2

Missions to Military, Inc.
2221 Centerville Turnpike
Virginia Beach, VA 23464 USA

Phone: (757) 479-2288
Fax: (757) 479-3705
E-mail: hqs@missionstomilitary.org
Web Site: www.missionstomilitary.org
Associations: FOM
Dr. Keith H. Davey, President

A sending agency of Baptist tradition engaged in winning & training the military for Jesus Christ, discipleship, evangelism, literature distribution, mobilization for mission and missionary training.

Purpose: "...to win and train the military for Jesus Christ."

Year Founded in US: 1958

Fully Supported US Personnel Overseas:
Expecting to serve more than 4 years: 7
Expecting to serve 1 to 4 years: 2

Other personnel:
Non-US serving in own/other country: 2
Home ministry & office staff in US: 4

Countries: France 7; Ukraine

MMS Aviation (Missionary Maintenance Services)
PO Box 1118
Coshocton, OH 43812 USA

Phone: (740) 622-6848
Fax: (740) 622-8277
E-mail: admin@mmsaviation.org
Web Site: www.mmsaviation.org
Mr. Dwight Jarboe, President/CEO

A nondenominational support agency of Evangelical tradition engaged in aviation services, missionary training and training.

Purpose: "...to prepare people and planes for worldwide mission service."

Year Founded in US: 1975

Personnel:
Home ministry & office staff in US: 18

Moravian Church in North America, Board of World Mission
PO Box 1245
Bethlehem, PA 18016-1245 US

Phone: (610) 868-1732
Fax: (610) 868-1732
E-mail: will@mcnp.org
Web Site: www.moravianmission.org
Associations: CWS
Mr. William C. Sibert, Jr., Exec. Director

A denominational sending agency of Ecumenical and Moravian tradition engaged in short-term programs, Christian education, leadership development, missionary training and youth programs. Data from 2005.

Year Founded in US: 1742

Income for Overseas Min: $1,200,000.00

Fully Supported US Personnel Overseas:
Non-residential mission personnel: 6

Other personnel:
Short-term less than 1 year: 12
Non-US serving in own/other country: 4
Home ministry & office staff in US: 5

Countries: Honduras; Kenya; Tanzania

Morelli Ministries Intl., Inc.
PO Box 700026
Tulsa, OK 74170 USA

Phone: (225) 788-3022
Fax: (225) 293-2327
E-mail: michael@morelliministries.org
Web Site: www.morelliministries.org
Mr. Michael Morelli, President/Founder

A nondenominational support agency of Pentecostal tradition engaged in evangelism, church planting, discipleship, support of national churches, support of national workers and training.

Year Founded in US: 1995

Income for Overseas Min: $124,000.00

Personnel:
Short-term less than 1 year: 1
Non-US serving in own/other country: 65
Home ministry & office staff in US: 4

Countries: Africa—General

mPower
106 N. Watterson Tr.
Louisville, KY 40243 USA

Phone: (502) 365-5540
Fax: (502) 632-1419
E-mail: eowen@mpowerapproach.org
Web Site: www.mpowerapproach.org
Mr. Mark Franco, Exec. Director

A nondenominational service agency of Evangelical tradition engaged in medical work, business as mission, support of national workers, services for other agencies, supplying equipment and tentmaking.

Year Founded in US: 2006
Personnel:
Home ministry & office staff in US: 3

Muslim Hope
PO Box 144441
Austin, TX 78714 USA
Phone: (512) 218-8022
Fax: (512) 218-8022
E-mail: info@muslimhope.com
Web Site: www.muslimhope.com
Mr. Larry Wessels, Director

An interdenominational specialized agency of Baptist tradition engaged in apologetics, theological education, evangelism, services for other agencies and missionary training.

Year Founded in US: 1996

Mustard Seed International
PO Box 20188
Charleston, SC 29413-0188 USA
Phone: (843) 388-9314
Fax: (843) 388-9315
E-mail: info@mustardseed.org
Web Site: www.mustardseed.org
Mr. William N. Deans, President/CEO

An interdenominational sending agency of Evangelical tradition engaged in Christian education, agricultural programs, childcare/orphanage programs, church planting, TEE and medical work. Data from 2005.

Purpose: "...to present Christ to all we meet, to heal disease and all manner of suffering and to love sincerely and deeply those people whose lives we are privileged to touch."

Year Founded in US: 1948
Income for Overseas Min: $837,916.00
Fully Supported US Personnel Overseas:
Expecting to serve more than 4 years: 7
Other personnel:

Short-term less than 1 year: 100
Countries: India; Indonesia 7; Papua New Guinea; Sudan; Taiwan

Mutual Faith Ministries Intl.
PO Box 951060
Mission Hills, CA 91395-1060 USA
Phone: (818) 837-3400
Fax: (818) 837-4686
E-mail: ckrouzian@mutualfaith.org
Web Site: www.mutualfaith.org
Keith Hershey, President/Founder

A nondenominational support agency of Independent tradition engaged in short-term programs for evangelism teams in Central America, Africa, Asia, India and other nations. Data from 2005.

Year Founded in US: 1984
Fully Supported US Personnel Overseas:
Expecting to serve more than 4 years: 3
Other personnel:
Short-term less than 1 year: 100
Home ministry & office staff in US: 5
Countries: Costa Rica 1; Ghana; Guatemala 2; Lebanon; Nigeria; Philippines

Myanmar Christian Mission
PO Box 72
Lyman, NE 69352 USA
Phone: (308) 247-3293
E-mail: wayneford@myanmarchristianmission.com
Web Site: www.myanmarchristianmission.com
Mr. Wayne Ford, President/Exec. Director

A nondenominational support agency of Christian (Restoration Movement) tradition engaged in theological education (the Eastern Bible Institute of Myanmar), agricultural programs, church construction, church planting, providing medical supplies and relief and/or rehabilitation.

Purpose: "...to continue growing resources to support the men and women who are now and who will in the future be serving the Lord and preaching the Gospel of Jesus Christ."

Year Founded in US: 1996
Personnel:
Short-term less than 1 year: 8
Home ministry & office staff in US: 4
Countries: Myanmar/Burma

Narramore Christian Foundation

250 W. Colorado Blvd. Ste. 200
Arcadia, CA 91007 USA

Phone: (626) 821-8400
Fax: (626) 821-8409
E-mail: bruce@ncfliving.org
Web Site: www.ncfliving.org

Dr. Bruce Narramore, President

A nondenominational specialized agency of Evangelical tradition providing missionary kids reentry training and literature and also helps develop and support overseas missionary counseling and training programs. NCF's ministries include a Christian mental health website, literature on psychological problems and issues, reentry programs for missionary children and overseas seminars for missionaries. Data from 2005.

Purpose: "...to serve individuals and families through biblically-based psychological counseling, consulting, publications, education, research and training...targeting toward missionaries and pastors and their families, laypersons and counseling/psychology students."

Year Founded in US: 1958
Income for Overseas Min: $48,000.00
Personnel:
  Home ministry & office staff in US: 8

National Baptist Convention of America—Foreign Mission Board

PO Box 223665
Dallas, TX 75222 USA
Web Site: www.nbca-inc.com

Rev. John C. Raphael, Jr., Exec. Sec./Treasurer

A denominational support agency of Baptist tradition engaged in evangelism, Christian education, providing medical supplies and medical work.

Purpose: "...to operate as 'partner in ministry' with indigenous Christians and church bodies."

Year Founded in US: 1915
Income for Overseas Min: $325,200.00
Personnel:
  Non-US serving in own/other country: 118

Home ministry & office staff in US: 4
Countries: Ghana; Haiti; Jamaica; Panama; Virgin Islands

National Baptist Convention USA, Inc.—Foreign Mission Board

PO Box 15783
Philadelphia, PA 19103 USA

Phone: (215) 735-7868
Fax: (215) 735-1721
E-mail: fmbnbc@comcast.net
Web Site: www.nationalbaptist.com
Associations: CWS

Dr. J. Albert Bush, Sr., Exec. Secretary

A denominational sending agency of Baptist tradition engaged in evangelism, children at risk, church planting, Christian education, furloughed missionary support and HIV/Aids.

Purpose: "...to accomplish the Great Commission by training ministers and mission workers and providing health services and occupational training and services at each mission station with the goal of self-sufficiency."

Year Founded in US: 1880
Fully Supported US Personnel Overseas:
  Expecting to serve more than 4 years: 2
  Expecting to serve 1 to 4 years: 2

Other personnel:
  Non-US serving in own/other country: 130
  Home ministry & office staff in US: 6

Countries: Barbados; Guinea 2; Lesotho; Malawi; Nicaragua; Sierra Leone; South Africa; Swaziland

National Religious Broadcasters

9510 Technology Dr.
Manassas, VA 20110 USA

Phone: (703) 330-7000
Fax: (703) 330-7100
Web Site: www.nrb.org

Dr. Frank Wright, President/CEO

An interdenominational service agency of Evangelical tradition engaged in broadcasting and leadership development, including a Caribbean chapter and International Committee involving overseas associate members. Data from 2005.

Year Founded in US: 1944

Personnel:
Home ministry & office staff in US: 19

Navigators, U.S. Intl. Missions Group

PO Box 6000
Colorado Springs, CO 80934 USA

Phone: (719) 598-1212

Fax: (719) 260-0479

E-mail: info@navigators.org

Web Site: www.navigators.org

Associations: The Mission Exchange

Dr. Doug Nuenke, U.S. President

An interdenominational sending agency of Evangelical tradition engaged in discipleship, Bible memorization, camping programs, evangelism and literature production. Countries of service data from 2005.

Purpose: "...to advance the Gospel of Jesus and His Kingdom into the nations through spiritual generations of laborers living and discipling among the lost."

Year Founded in US: 1933

Income for Overseas Min: $20,000,000.00

Fully Supported US Personnel Overseas:
Expecting to serve more than 4 years: 301
Expecting to serve 1 to 4 years: 33
Non-residential mission personnel: 29

Other personnel:
Short-term less than 1 year: 372
Home ministry & office staff in US: 17

Countries: Argentina 6; Australia 6; Brazil 10; Bulgaria 6; Cameroon 4; Chile 4; Costa Rica 1; France 2; Germany; Ghana 1; Guatemala 1; Hungary 3; Iceland 2; Italy 4; Japan 24; Kenya 2; Mexico 8; New Zealand 4; Nigeria 2; Norway 2; Philippines 10; South Africa 4; Spain 8; Taiwan 4; United Kingdom 2; Unspecified Country 179; Zambia 2

Nehemiah Teams Intl.

PO Box 86
Buffalo Gap, SD 57722 USA

Phone: (605) 833-2244

E-mail: chamberlandm@hotmail.com

Web Site: www.nehemiahteamsinternational.com

Associations: FOM

Matthew Chamberland, Gen. Director

A nondenominational specialized agency of Fundamental and Independent tradition engaged in short-term programs, church construction, discipleship, leadership development and services for other agencies.

Purpose: "...to assist in the construction of mission-related building projects."

Year Founded in US: 2006

Income for Overseas Min: $32,000.00

Personnel:
Short-term less than 1 year: 22

Network of International Christian Schools

3790 Goodman Rd. E.
Southaven, MS 38672 USA

Phone: (662) 895-4300

Fax: (662) 895-4310

E-mail: info@nics.org

Web Site: www.nics.org

Associations: CrossGlobal Link

Dr. Joe Hale, President/Founder

A nondenominational service agency of Evangelical and Independent tradition engaged in Christian education, missionary education, evangelism, mobilization for mission and discipleship.

Purpose: "...to establish a worldwide network of international Christian schools staffed by qualified Christian educators, instilling in each student a Biblical worldview in an environment of academic excellence and respect for people of all cultures and religions."

Year Founded in US: 1990

Income for Overseas Min: $2,659,301.00

Gifts in Kind: $13,590.00

Fully Supported US Personnel Overseas:
Expecting to serve more than 4 years: 116
Expecting to serve 1 to 4 years: 449

Other personnel:
Short-term less than 1 year: 3
Non-US serving in own/other country: 170
Home ministry & office staff in US: 21

Countries: Argentina; Asia—General 6; Bolivia 1; Brazil 6; Central Asia—General 6; Germany 3; Ghana; Indonesia 7; Japan 9; Kenya 2; Korea, South 54; Peru 7; Singapore 15; Suriname; Venezuela

New Directions Intl., Inc.

PO Box 2347
Burlington, NC 27216 USA

Phone: (336) 227-1273
Fax: (336) 570-1392
E-mail: ndi@newdirections.org
Web Site: www.newdirections.org

Dr. J. L. Williams, Founder & Director

A nondenominational support agency of Evangelical tradition engaged in leadership development, childcare/orphanage programs, childrens programs, church construction, church planting, support of national churches and support of national workers. Data from 2005.

Purpose: "...encouraging, equipping and empowering indigenous national leaders to evangelize the unreached and edify the church in their respective countries."

Year Founded in US: 1968

Income for Overseas Min: $1,339,917.00

Gifts in Kind: $309,102.00

Fully Supported US Personnel Overseas:
Non-residential mission personnel: 4

Other personnel:
Short-term less than 1 year: 4
Non-US serving in own/other country: 81
Home ministry & office staff in US: 15

Countries: Bhutan; Haiti; India; Kenya; Nepal

New Hope International

PO Box 25490
Colorado Springs, CO 80936 USA

Phone: (719) 577-4450
Fax: (719) 577-4453
E-mail: info@newhopeinternational.org
Web Site: www.newhopeinternational.org

Mr. Hank Paulson, Founder/President

A nondenominational support agency of Evangelical and Presbyterian tradition engaged in youth programs, childcare/orphanage programs, correspondence courses, leadership development, support of national workers and translation work. Countries of service data from 2005.

Purpose: "...to establish a strong national NHI ministry in six former Communist countries; Czech Republic, Slovakia, Ukraine, Moldova, Hungary, and Romania."

Year Founded in US: 1971

Fully Supported US Personnel Overseas:
Expecting to serve more than 4 years: 3
Expecting to serve 1 to 4 years: 3

Other personnel:
Short-term less than 1 year: 150
Non-US serving in own/other country: 34
Home ministry & office staff in US: 8

Countries: Czech Republic; Eastern Europe —General 3; Hungary; Moldova; Romania; Slovakia; Ukraine

New Hope Uganda Ministries

PO Box 154
Belle Fourche, SD 57717-0154 USA

Phone: (605) 892-2058
Web Site: www.newhopeuganda.org

Mr. Gary Wood, N. A. Director

A nondenominational sending agency of Evangelical tradition engaged in childcare/orphanage programs, children at risk, childrens programs, Christian education, evangelism and relief and/or rehabilitation.

Year Founded in US: 1988

Income for Overseas Min: $1,450,000.00

Fully Supported US Personnel Overseas:
Expecting to serve more than 4 years: 20

Other personnel:
Home ministry & office staff in US: 1

Countries: Uganda 20

New Life Advance Intl.

PO 35857
Houston, TX 77235 USA

Phone: (832)242-7750
Fax: (832)242-7751
E-mail: Info@nlai.org
Web Site: www.nlai.org

Mr. David Depew, President

A nondenominational sending agency of Charismatic and Evangelical tradition engaged in Bible distribution, childcare/orphanage programs, church planting, development, evangelism, mobilization for mission and relief and/or rehabilitation. Data from 2001.

Purpose: "...in partnership with local churches, to make disciples among the nations, to plant churches, to work for the relief of human suffering and to print the Word of God and distribute it to the nations of the world."

Year Founded in US: 1954
Income for Overseas Min: $728,595.00
Gifts in Kind: $8,000.00
Fully Supported US Personnel Overseas:
  Expecting to serve more than 4 years: 14
  Expecting to serve 1 to 4 years: 1
  Non-residential mission personnel: 4
Other personnel:
  Short-term less than 1 year: 60
  Non-US serving in own/other country: 12
  Home ministry & office staff in US: 1
Countries: Bhutan; Brazil 1; China; Cuba; Guatemala 6; Haiti 2; India; Israel; Japan; Mexico 1; Nepal; Papua New Guinea; Philippines; Thailand 2; Turkey 2; Ukraine

New Mission Systems Intl.
PO Box 547
Fort Myers, FL 33902 USA
Phone: (239) 337-4336
Fax: (239) 461-0686
E-mail: info@nmsi.org
Web Site: www.nmsi.org
Associations: The Mission Exchange
Mr. Tim Dammon, President/CEO
An interdenominational sending agency engaged in discipleship, church planting, development, leadership development, relief and/or rehabilitation, youth programs and a variety of ministries.
Purpose: "...to foster the emergence of Christian communities globally."
Year Founded in US: 1991
Income for Overseas Min: $4,485,666.00
Fully Supported US Personnel Overseas:
  Expecting to serve more than 4 years: 34
  Expecting to serve 1 to 4 years: 62
  Non-residential mission personnel: 6
Other personnel:
  Short-term less than 1 year: 60
  Non-US serving in own/other country: 96
  Home ministry & office staff in US: 21
Countries: Africa—General 10; Asia—General 12; Europe—General 6; Latin America —General 6

New Tribes Mission
1000 E. First St.
Sanford, FL 32771 USA
Phone: (407) 323-3430

Fax: (407) 330-0376
E-mail: NTM@ntm.org
Web Site: www.ntm.org
Mr. Larry Brown, CEO USA
A nondenominational sending agency of Evangelical tradition engaged in church planting, linguistics, literacy work and Bible translation.
Purpose: "...to assist the ministry of the local church through mobilizing, equipping, and coordinating of missionaries to evangelize unreached people groups, translate the Scriptures, and see indigenous New Testament churches established."
Year Founded in US: 1942
Fully Supported US Personnel Overseas:
  Expecting to serve more than 4 years: 874
  Expecting to serve 1 to 4 years: 48
  Non-residential mission personnel: 22
Other personnel:
  Short-term less than 1 year: 236
  Non-US serving in own/other country: 421
  Home ministry & office staff in US: 597
Countries: Africa—General 6; Asia—General 42; Australia 2; Bolivia 59; Brazil 119; Cambodia 8; Colombia 20; Germany 2; Guinea 35; Mexico 103; Mozambique 16; Netherlands; Panama 9; Papua New Guinea 266; Paraguay 47; Philippines 66; Senegal 30; Singapore 2; Thailand 36; United Kingdom 6

New Way Missions
1501 Loretta Ct.
Brandon, FL 33511 USA
Phone: (813) 684-1289
Fax: (813) 684-1289
Web Site: www.newwaymissions.org
Linda H. Parker, Co-Founder/President
An interdenominational specialized agency of Charismatic and Pentecostal tradition engaged in short-term mission projects/ministry trips, Bible distribution, discipleship, evangelism, medical work and support of national churches. Data from 2005.
Year Founded in US: 2000
Income for Overseas Min: $13,470.00
Personnel:
  Short-term less than 1 year: 18
Countries: Dominican Republic; Mexico; Peru

New Wineskins Missionary Network

PO Box 278
Ambridge, PA 15003-0278 USA
Phone: (724) 266-2810
Fax: (724) 266-6773
E-mail: info@newwineskins.org
Web Site: www.newwineskins.org
Sharon Stockdale Steinmiller, Director

A denominational support agency of Anglican tradition engaged in mobilization
for mission, missions information service
and missionary training. Statistical information from 2005.

Purpose: "...a voluntary society, raising
mission vision in parishes and dioceses,
promoting and providing training for missionaries and mission committees, equipping Anglicans to reach unreached people groups around the world and raising
prayer support for Anglican missionaries."
Year Founded in US: 1974
Income for Overseas Min: $5,020.00
Personnel:
  Home ministry & office staff in US: 3

Ninos de Mexico

PO Box 309
Union, MO 63084 USA
Phone: (636) 583-2000
Fax: (636) 583-2724
E-mail: ndm@ninosdemexico.org
Web Site: www.ninosdemexico.org
Mr. Seth Thomas, Exec. Director

A nondenominational sending agency of
Christian (Restoration Movement) tradition engaged in childcare/orphanage programs, church planting, evangelism, support of national churches, short-term
programs and missionary training.

Purpose: "...to share the Gospel message
of salvation through Jesus Christ with as
many people as possible by raising at-risk
children in Mexico to love God and grow
to be mature, educated, Spirit-filled Christians with the ability and passion to evangelize their culture."
Year Founded in US: 1967
Income for Overseas Min: $704,000.00

Fully Supported US Personnel Overseas:
  Expecting to serve more than 4 years: 6
  Expecting to serve 1 to 4 years: 3
  Non-residential mission personnel: 1
Other personnel:
  Short-term less than 1 year: 182
  Non-US serving in own/other country: 25
  Home ministry & office staff in US: 4
Countries: Mexico 6

North American Baptist Conference—Worldwide Outreach

1 S. 210 Summit Ave.
Oakbrook Terrace, IL 60181-3994 USA
Phone: (630) 495-2000
Fax: (630) 495-3301
E-mail: nabmissions@nabconf.org
Web Site: www.nabconference.org
Associations: The Mission Exchange
Rev. Norm Poehlke, VP of Ministry Outreach

A denominational sending agency of Baptist tradition engaged in church planting,
childcare/orphanage programs, children at
risk, development, discipleship and theological education.

Purpose: "...to glorify God by making
disciples of Jesus Christ at home and inter-
nationally."
Year Founded in US: 1891
Income for Overseas Min: $2,626,575.00
Fully Supported US Personnel Overseas:
  Expecting to serve more than 4 years: 28
  Expecting to serve 1 to 4 years: 2
  Non-residential mission personnel: 1
Other personnel:
  Short-term less than 1 year: 227
  Non-US serving in own/other country: 15
  Home ministry & office staff in US: 4
Countries: Brazil; Cameroon 11; Japan 9;
Mexico 8; Nigeria

Northwest Haiti Christian Mission

PO Box 829
Versailles, KY 40383 USA
Phone: (502) 695-7870
Fax: (502) 695-8348
E-mail: hope@nwhcm.org
Web Site: www.nwhcm.org

Janeil Owen, Exec. Director

An interdenominational service agency of Christian (Restoration Movement) tradition engaged in development, childcare/orphanage programs, church planting, disability assistance programs, Christian education and medical work.

Purpose: "...to establish and partner with indigenous churches to help bring people in Northwest Haiti out of spiritual, physical, and social poverty to demonstrate God's love for all."

Year Founded in US: 1979

Personnel:
   Short-term less than 1 year: 980
   Home ministry & office staff in US: 5

OC International, Inc.

PO Box 36900
Colorado Springs, CO 80936-6900 USA
Phone: (719) 592-9292
Fax: (719) 592-0693
Web Site: www.onechallenge.org
Associations: The Mission Exchange

Dr. Greg Gripentrog, President

An interdenominational sending agency of Christian (Restoration Movement) tradition engaged in missionary training, church planting, theological education, leadership development, support of national churches, partnership development and mission-related research. Countries of service data from 2005.

Purpose: "...to mobilize Godly and effective church leaders to disciple all nations."

Year Founded in US: 1950

Income for Overseas Min: $10,831,601.00

Fully Supported US Personnel Overseas:
   Expecting to serve more than 4 years: 200
   Non-residential mission personnel: 449

Other personnel:
   Short-term less than 1 year: 28
   Non-US serving in own/other country: 17

Countries: Argentina; Brazil 13; Bulgaria 4; Colombia 2; Germany 13; Guatemala 13; India; Japan 2; Kenya 6; Mexico 4; Mozambique 2; Philippines 18; Romania 11; Singapore 6; South Africa 14; Spain 13; Taiwan 5; United Kingdom 4; Unspecified Country 70

OMF International

10 W. Dry Creek Cir.
Littleton, CO 80120 USA
Phone: (3037 30-4160
Fax: (303) 730-4165
E-mail: omfus@omf.org
Web Site: www.omf.org/us
Associations: CrossGlobal Link

Dr. Neil O.Thompson, US Natl. Director

An interdenominational sending agency of Evangelical tradition engaged in church planting, development, evangelism, leadership development and mobilization for mission.

Purpose: "...to glorify God by the urgent evangelization of East Asia's millions."

Year Founded in US: 1888

Income for Overseas Min: $10,645,608.00

Fully Supported US Personnel Overseas:
   Expecting to serve more than 4 years: 242
   Expecting to serve 1 to 4 years: 31
   Non-residential mission personnel: 6

Other personnel:
   Short-term less than 1 year: 215
   Non-US serving in own/other country: 273
   Home ministry & office staff in US: 60

Countries: Asia—General 126; Cambodia 20; Japan 25; Philippines 17; Singapore 3; Taiwan 29; Thailand 22

OMS International, Inc.

PO Box A
Greenwood, IN 46142-1841 USA
Phone: (317) 881-6751
Fax: (317) 888-5275
Web Site: www.omsinternational.org
Associations: The Mission Exchange

Mr. David Long, President

An interdenominational sending agency of Evangelical tradition engaged in evangelism, church planting, discipleship, theological education and TEE. Countries of service data from 2005.

Purpose: "...to establish responsible, reproducing, Christ-centered churches among the nations."

Year Founded in US: 1901

Fully Supported US Personnel Overseas:
   Expecting to serve more than 4 years: 125
   Expecting to serve 1 to 4 years: 2
   Non-residential mission personnel: 73

Other personnel:
Short-term less than 1 year: 481
Non-US serving in own/other country: 73
Home ministry & office staff in US: 123

Countries: Australia; Brazil 6; China 3; Colombia 6; Ecuador 7; Haiti 10; Hong Kong 5; Hungary 8; India 1; Indonesia 9; Ireland 1; Japan 12; Kazakhstan 1; Korea, South 2; Mexico 9; Mozambique 8; Philippines 6; Russia 5; South Africa; Spain 11; Taiwan 5; Ukraine 4 United Kingdom; Unspecified Country; Uruguay 6

On The Go Ministries/ Keith Cook Team

PO Box 963
Springfield, TN 37172 USA

Phone: (615) 299-0222
Fax: (615) 299-0232
E-mail: keithcook@onthego.org
Web Site: www.onthego.org
Rev. Keith Cook Sr., President

A transdenominational support agency of Baptist and Evangelical tradition engaged in evangelism, theological education, leadership development, short-term programs and training.

Purpose: "...to be On the Go sharing Christ across the street and around the world."

Year Founded in US: 1974
Income for Overseas Min: $350,000.00
Gifts in Kind: $200,000.00

Fully Supported US Personnel Overseas:
Expecting to serve more than 4 years: 4
Expecting to serve 1 to 4 years: 2
Non-residential mission personnel: 16

Other personnel:
Short-term less than 1 year: 1500
Non-US serving in own/other country: 2
Home ministry & office staff in US: 4

Countries: United Arab Emirates 4

OneHope

600 SW 3rd St.
Pompano Beach, FL 33060 USA

Phone: (954) 975-7777
Fax: (954)975-0620
E-mail: info@onehope.net
Web Site: www.onehope.net
Mr. Rob Hoskins, President

A nondenominational sending agency engaged in evangelism, Bible distribution, mission-related research and video/film production/distribution.

Purpose: "...to affect destiny by providing God's eternal Word to all children and youth of the world."

Year Founded in US: 1987
Income for Overseas Min: $20,038,303.00
Personnel:
Short-term less than 1 year: 574
Home ministry & office staff in US: 127

Countries: Angola; Argentina; Armenia; Benin; Brazil; Bulgaria; Burkina Faso; Cambodia; Cameroon; Chile; China; Colombia; Congo, Democratic Republic of; Cuba; Dominican Republic; Ecuador; Ghana; Haiti; Honduras; India; Indonesia; Japan; Kenya; Lesotho; Madagascar; Malaysia; Mexico; Mozambique; Nicaragua; Niger; Nigeria; Middle East; Peru; Philippines; Romania; Russia; Sierra Leone; South Africa; Spain; Swaziland; Taiwan; Tanzania; Thailand; Togo; Uganda; Ukraine; United Kingdom; Venezuela

Open Air Campaigners— Overseas Ministries

PO Box 4454
St. Augustine, FL 32085 USA

Phone: (904) 827-9715
Fax: (904) 827-9716
E-mail: djwils39@bellsouth.net
Web Site: www.oacom.org
Mr. David Wilson, Director

An interdenominational ministry of Evangelical tradition engaged in evangelism, correspondence courses, literature distribution and training. Each national branch is autonomous, with national evangelists.

Purpose: "...committed to preaching the gospel to the unreached through open air and other outreaches in partnership with the church."

Year Founded in US: 1989
Income for Overseas Min: $592,631.00

Fully Supported US Personnel Overseas:
Non-residential mission personnel: 1

Other personnel:
Non-US serving in own/other country: 58
Home ministry & office staff in US: 1

Countries: Argentina; Brazil; Ecuador; India; Jamaica; Mexico; Paraguay; Russia; Ukraine

Open Bible Churches, International Ministries

2020 Bell Ave.
Des Moines, IA 50315-1096 USA
Phone: (515) 288-6761
Fax: (515) 288-2510
E-mail: missions@openbible.org
Web Site: www.openbible.org/intl
Associations: The Mission Exchange

Rev. Vincent S. McCarty, Exec. Director Intl.

A denominational sending agency of Charismatic tradition engaged in church planting, childcare/orphanage programs, church construction, discipleship, theological education and TEE.

Purpose: "...to serve, equip, and resource churches, missionaries, and leaders committed to global evangelism, discipleship, and church planting."

Year Founded in US: 1935

Income for Overseas Min: $1,407,651.00

Fully Supported US Personnel Overseas:
  Expecting to serve more than 4 years: 21

Other personnel:
  Home ministry & office staff in US: 4

Countries: El Salvador 2; Guinea 2; Hungary 2; Mexico 8; Nicaragua 2; Ukraine 1; Unspecified Country 4

Open Door Baptist Missions

1115 Pelham Rd.
Greenville, SC 29615 USA
Phone: (864) 297-7890
Fax: (864) 297-5222
E-mail: info@odbm.org
Web Site: www.odbm.org

Dr. John Burnette, Director

A nondenominational sending agency of Baptist and Independent tradition engaged in church planting, Christian education, theological education and evangelism.

Purpose: "...to promote the work of Christ in regions that have been closed to the Gospel or that presently have little or no fundamental gospel witness."

Year Founded in US: 1990

Income for Overseas Min: $1,000,000.00

Fully Supported US Personnel Overseas:
  Expecting to serve more than 4 years: 43

Other personnel:

Short-term less than 1 year: 1
Non-US serving in own/other country: 5
Home ministry & office staff in US: 4

Countries: Asia—General 7; Cameroon 1; France 1; Ghana 2; Haiti 6; Japan 1; Lithuania 2; Middle East 5; Peru 2; Puerto Rico 2; South Africa 6; Spain 4; Taiwan 1; Uganda 2; United Kingdom 1

Open Doors, USA

PO Box 27001
Santa Ana, CA 92799 USA
Phone: (949) 752-6600
Fax: (949) 752-6442
Web Site: www.opendoorsusa.org

Mr. Carl A. Moeller, President/CEO

A support agency of Evangelical tradition engaged in Bible distribution, justice, leadership development, literature distribution and support of national churches.

Purpose: "...to strengthen and equip the Body of Christ living under or facing restriction and persecution because of their faith in Jesus Christ, and to encourage their involvement in world evangelism..."

Year Founded in US: 1973

Income for Overseas Min: $6,813,818.00

Gifts in Kind: $197.00

Personnel:
  Short-term less than 1 year: 50
  Home ministry & office staff in US: 41

Operation Blessing Intl. Relief and Development Corporation

977 Centerville Turnpike
Virginia Beach, VA 23463 USA
Phone: (757) 226-3401
Fax: (757) 226-6228
E-mail: operation.blessing@ob.org
Web Site: www.ob.org
Associations: AERDO

Mr. William Horan, President/COO

A nondenominational relief agency that has helped more than 184.9 million people in 96 countries, distributing more than $1.1 billion in goods. Engaged in hunger relief, medical aid, disaster relief, childrens programs and community development that will make a significant, long-term impact. Operating methodology focuses on capacity building and collaboration between indigenously-staffed field offices and local indigenous partners (including other NGOs, government agencies, community-based social service agencies, and grassroots relief groups). Data from 2005.

Purpose: "...to demonstrate God's love by alleviating human need and suffering in the United States and around the world."

Year Founded in US: 1978

Personnel:
Home ministry & office staff in US: 85

Operation Bootstrap Africa

122 W. Franklin Ave., Ste. 306
Minneapolis, MN 55404 USA

Phone: (612) 230-3344
Fax: (612) 871-1695
E-mail: info@operationbootstrapafrica.org
Web Site: www.operationbootstrapafrica.org

Mr. Jim Cornell, Exec. Director

A support agency of Lutheran and Methodist tradition engaged in community development and international development & relief services.

Purpose: "...to partner with Africans in educating their children."

Year Founded in US: 1965

Income for Overseas Min: $726,409.00

Gifts in Kind: $37,578.00

Personnel:
Home ministry & office staff in US: 2

Operation Mobilization

PO Box 444
Tyrone, GA 30290-0444 USA

Phone: (770) 631-0432
Fax: (770) 631-0439
Web Site: www.usa.om.org
Associations: The Mission Exchange

Dr. Steven R. Hicks, President OM USA

A nondenominational sending agency of Evangelical tradition engaged in evangelism, childrens programs, church planting, development and literature distribution. Countries of service data from 2005.

Purpose: "...the mission of OM USA is that Americans pray, give, go, and grow so that Operation Mobilization around the world is helped to accomplish its purpose... to motivate, develop, and equip people for worship in the body of Christ."

Year Founded in US: 1957

Income for Overseas Min: $17,227,000.00

Fully Supported US Personnel Overseas:
Expecting to serve more than 4 years: 173
Expecting to serve 1 to 4 years: 158
Non-residential mission personnel: 4

Other personnel:
Short-term less than 1 year: 6
Non-US serving in own/other country: 67
Home ministry & office staff in US: 109

Countries: Africa—General 13; Albania 2; Asia—General 2; Australia; Belgium 5; Caucasus; Central Asia—General 17; Chile; Czech Republic 1; Egypt 7; Europe—General 14; France 2; Hungary 3; India 7; Ireland 2; Israel; Italy 4; Latin America—General 6; Mexico 2; Middle East 23; Nepal 2; Netherlands; Romania; Russia; South Africa 6; Spain 3; Sweden 1; Turkey 8; Ukraine; United Kingdom 21; Unspecified Country 21; Uzbekistan 1

Operation Serve Intl.

PO Box 18070
Fairfield, OH 45018 USA

Phone: (513) 939-2000
E-mail: info@operationserve.org
Web Site: www.operationserve.org

Dr. Sameh Sadik, Exec. Director

An interdenominational and transdenominational sending agency of Evangelical and Independent tradition engaged in medical work, mercy mission/health care, development, leadership development, linguistics, literacy work, support of national workers, TESOL and translation.

Purpose: "...to motivate and mobilize concerned Christians to assist in the work of God among the poor and the destitute in under-served and unreached places."

Year Founded in US: 1983

Income for Overseas Min: $485,000.00

Gifts in Kind: $18,000.00

Fully Supported US Personnel Overseas:
Expecting to serve more than 4 years: 18
Expecting to serve 1 to 4 years: 16
Non-residential mission personnel: 5

Other personnel:

Short-term less than 1 year: 394
Non-US serving in own/other country: 5
Home ministry & office staff in US: 5
Countries: Egypt 12; Mexico 6

Opportunity International

2122 York Rd., Ste. 150
Oak Brook, IL 60523-1999 USA
Phone: (630) 242-4100
Fax: (630) 645-1458
E-mail: getinfo@opportunity.org
Web Site: www.opportunity.org
Mr. Kadita Tshibaka, President/CEO

An interdenominational service agency of
Ecumenical tradition engaged in microfi-
nancing, leadership development, funds
transmission and training, working in 26
countries. Data from 2005.

Purpose: "...to provide opportunities for
people in chronic poverty to transform
their lives."

Year Founded in US: 1971

Income for Overseas Min: $112,064,000.00

Personnel:
Home ministry & office staff in US: 65

ORPHANetwork

1500 N. Great Neck Rd.
Virginia Beach, VA 23454 USA
Phone: (757) 333-7200
E-mail: dick.anderson@orphanetwork.org
Web Site: www.orphanetwork.org
Mr. Dick Anderson, Exec. Director

A nondenominational specialized agency
of Evangelical tradition engaged in child-
care/orphanage programs, children at risk
and short-term programs.

Purpose: "...to rescue abandoned children...to prevent at-risk children from
being abandoned...to share Christ with
everyone."

Year Founded in US: 2000

Income for Overseas Min: $1,500,000.00

Personnel:
Short-term less than 1 year: 800
Non-US serving in own/other country: 1
Home ministry & office staff in US: 2

Countries: Nicaragua

Orthodox Presbyterian Church—Committee on Foreign Missions

PO Box P
Willow Grove, PA 19090-0920 USA
Phone: (215) 830-0900
Fax: (215) 830-0350
E-mail: OPForeignMissions@opc.org
Web Site: www.opc.org
Mr. Mark T. Bube, Gen. Secretary

A denominational sending agency committed to the establishment of indigenous
churches in the Presbyterian and Reformed
tradition, primarily through the ministry
of the Word. Actively engaged in church
planting, theological education, evangelism and literature distribution, medicine
and national church support. Medical ministries of mercy supplement the gospel
proclamation.

Purpose: "...to establish a healthy indigenous national church that is firmly and fully committed to the Reformed standards;
that is self-supporting, self-governing and
self-propagating; with whom the OPC
may have fraternal relations; that is itself
sending out foreign missionaries to other
nations; which no longer needs the services of OP foreign missionaries."

Year Founded in US: 1937

Income for Overseas Min: $1,700,000.00

Fully Supported US Personnel Overseas:
Expecting to serve more than 4 years: 26
Expecting to serve 1 to 4 years: 11
Non-residential mission personnel: 2

Other personnel:
Short-term less than 1 year: 45
Home ministry & office staff in US: 5

Countries: China 4; Eritrea 4; Ethiopia; Haiti 2; Japan 6; Kenya; Korea, South; Suriname 2; Uganda 8

Outreach To Asia Nationals

PO Box 2440
Winchester, VA 22604 USA
Phone: (540) 665-6418
Fax: (540) 665-0793
Web Site: www.outreachtoasianationals.org
Associations: CrossGlobal Link
Mr. Otis S. Goodwin, President/CEO

A denominational support agency of Baptist and Independent tradition engaged in support of national workers, Bible distribution, childcare/orphanage programs, church planting, theological education, evangelism and translation work. Data from 2005.

Purpose: "...to serve, train, equip and empower national church workers in Asia to plant evangelistic, disciple-making and reproducing churches among the different people groups."

Year Founded in US: 1986

Income for Overseas Min: $1,300,000.00

Fully Supported US Personnel Overseas:
  Expecting to serve more than 4 years: 7
  Expecting to serve 1 to 4 years: 11
  Non-residential mission personnel: 4

Other personnel:
  Short-term less than 1 year: 188
  Non-US serving in own/other country: 188
  Home ministry & office staff in US: 45

Countries: Asia—General 7; Central Asia—General

Overseas Council Intl.

3830 East Southport Rd. Ste. B
Indianapolis, IN 46237 USA

Phone: (317) 788-7250
Fax: (317) 788-7257
E-mail: info@overseas.org
Web Site: www.overseas.org
Associations: The Mission Exchange

Dr. David A. Baer, President/CEO

An interdenominational support agency of Evangelical tradition engaged in establishing partnerships between Western Christians and non-Western students and evangelical theological schools. Affiliated organizations in Australia, Canada, Europe, New Zealand, and UK. Data from 2005.

Purpose: "...to equip biblical leaders to be effective pastors, teachers, evangelists, missionaries and Christian leaders in their own countries."

Year Founded in US: 1974

Income for Overseas Min: $3,370,383.00

Personnel:
  Home ministry & office staff in US: 28

Overseas Insurance Consultants

425 Tribble Gap Rd.
Cumming, GA 30040 USA

Phone: (770) 663-0114
Fax: (770) 663-0628
E-mail: ovrccinsur@aol.com
Web Site: www.globalnsure.com

Mr. J. Stuart Elder, Jr., Owner/President

A specialized agency engaged in overseas medical protection.

Year Founded in US: 1986

Overseas Ministries Study Center

490 Prospect St.
New Haven, CT 06511 USA

Phone: (203) 624-6672
Fax: (203) 865-2857
Web Site: www.omsc.org

Dr. Jonathan J. Bonk, Exec. Director

A nondenominational study center of Ecumenical tradition providing education and related activities. Publishes the "International Bulletin of Missionary Research" (www.internationalbulletin.org) and the "Dictionary of African Christian Biography" (web only at www.dacb.org). Statistical data from 2005.

Purpose: "...to strengthen the Christian world mission by providing residential programs for the renewal of missionaries and international church leaders, continuing education in cross-cultural Christian ministries and advancement of mission scholarship through research and publication."

Year Founded in US: 1922

Personnel:
  Home ministry & office staff in US: 17

Overseas Radio & Television, Inc. (ORTV)

130 S. First St.
Arcadia, CA 91006 USA

Phone: (626) 462-0880
Fax: (626) 462-0008
E-mail: us@ortv.com
Web Site: www.ortv.com

An interdenominational support agency engaged in TESOL, audio recording/distribution, extension education, evangelism, short-term programs and video/film production/distribution. Data from 2005.

Year Founded in US: 1952

Fully Supported US Personnel Overseas:
Non-residential mission personnel: 25

Other personnel:
Non-US serving in own/other country: 225
Home ministry & office staff in US: 12

Countries: Taiwan

Palm Missionary Ministries, Inc.
1702 Parks Lake Rd.
Lake Wales, FL 33898-8430 USA
Phone: (863) 632-0230
Fax: (305) 665-0859
E-mail: info@palmministries.com
Web Site: www.palmministries.com

Mr. Art Patray, President

An interdenominational sending agency of Evangelical tradition engaged in support of national workers, Christian education, evangelism, literacy work, support of national churches and short-term programs.

Purpose: "...to enable and facilitate the development of national missionaries and workers to go into all nations."

Year Founded in US: 1986

Income for Overseas Min: $229,151.00

Fully Supported US Personnel Overseas:
Expecting to serve more than 4 years: 2

Other personnel:
Short-term less than 1 year: 50
Non-US serving in own/other country: 39
Home ministry & office staff in US: 5

Countries: Argentina; Bolivia 1; Colombia; Ecuador 1; Mexico; Spain

Pan American Missions
PO Box 710097
Santee, CA 92072-0097 USA
Phone: (619) 469-0970
Fax: (619) 469-0970
E-mail: dllasher@cox.net

Mr. Fred Jappe, President

An interdenominational support agency of Baptist and Wesleyan tradition engaged in Bible distribution, childcare/orphanage programs and church planting. Data from 2005.

Purpose: "...ministers in Mexico and other Spanish-speaking countries of Latin America for the establishing and building up of indigenous churches."

Year Founded in US: 1960

Income for Overseas Min: $33,000.00

Fully Supported US Personnel Overseas:
Expecting to serve more than 4 years: 2

Other personnel:
Home ministry & office staff in US: 2

Countries: Mexico 2

Paraclete Mission Group, Inc.
3303 S. Lindsay Rd., Ste. 108
Gilbert, AZ 85297 USA
Phone: (480) 854-4444
Fax: (480) 854-4741
E-mail: info@paraclete.net
Web Site: www.paraclete.net
Associations: The Mission Exchange

Mr. Glen Volkhardt, CEO

An interdenominational sending agency of Evangelical tradition engaged in services for other agencies, management consulting/training, member care, support of national churches, partnership development and training.

Purpose: "...to come alongside the missions community to enhance Kingdom effectiveness."

Year Founded in US: 1988

Income for Overseas Min: $120,732.00

Fully Supported US Personnel Overseas:
Expecting to serve more than 4 years: 4
Non-residential mission personnel: 2

Other personnel:
Short-term less than 1 year: 6
Home ministry & office staff in US: 4

Countries: Austria 2; Kosovo 2

Paradigm Shift
3472 Research Pky Ste. 104-401
Colorado Springs, CO 80920 USA
Phone: (719) 321-2477
E-mail: jedd@shiftingparadigm.org
Web Site: www.shiftingparadigms.org

Mr. Jedd Schroy, Exec. Director

A nondenominational sending agency of Evangelical tradition engaged in business as mission, development, discipleship, evangelism and leadership development.

Purpose: "...to train local churches and ministries in developing countries to provide business training, microcredit, mentoring and discipleship to the urban poor."

Year Founded in US: 2007

Fully Supported US Personnel Overseas:
Expecting to serve 1 to 4 years: 6

Other personnel:
Short-term less than 1 year: 6
Home ministry & office staff in US: 1

Countries: South Africa

Partners in Asian Missions

PO Box 531011
Birmingham, AL 35253 USA

Phone: (205) 854-8418
E-mail: js1@quickbox.com
Web Site: www.pam-ee.org

Rev. Jerry F. Sharpe, Intl. Director

A nondenominational support agency of Reformed tradition engaged in support of national workers, childcare/orphanage programs, church construction, church planting, evangelism and leadership development. Data from 2005.

Purpose: "...to mobilize and equip top leaders in every Asian country for developing and implementing an effective national church-planting project...to enlist groups that will take responsibility for evangelization of a particular geographic territory or ethnolinguistic group..."

Year Founded in US: 1972

Income for Overseas Min: $150,000.00

Fully Supported US Personnel Overseas:
Non-residential mission personnel: 1

Other personnel:
Non-US serving in own/other country: 159
Home ministry & office staff in US: 1

Countries: Asia—General

Partners in Christ Intl.

PO Box 237
Tempe, AZ 85280 USA

Phone: (480) 731-9170
Fax: (480) 731-9166
E-mail: partnersinchrist@qwest.net
Web Site: www.picinternational.org

Mr. Nicholas J. Beezhold, CEO

A nondenominational sending agency of Evangelical tradition engaged in training, development, TEE, leadership development and support of national churches.

Purpose: "...to empower and equip national churches to create their own vision and strategy for ministry, mission, and community transformation."

Year Founded in US: 1986

Income for Overseas Min: $375,000.00

Fully Supported US Personnel Overseas:
Expecting to serve more than 4 years: 3

Other personnel:
Short-term less than 1 year: 232
Non-US serving in own/other country: 13
Home ministry & office staff in US: 3

Countries: India; Mexico 1; Nicaragua 2; Slovenia

Partners International

1117 E. Westview Ct.
Spokane, WA 99218 USA

Phone: (509) 343-4000
Fax: (509) 343-4015
E-mail: info@partnersintl.org
Web Site: www.partnersintl.org

Associations: The Mission Exchange

Mr. Jon Lewis, President/CEO

A nondenominational sending agency of Evangelical tradition engaged in church planting, children at risk, development, leadership development, support of national workers and partnership development.

Purpose: "...to create and grow communities of Christian witness in partnership with God's people in the least Christian regions of the world."

Year Founded in US: 1943

Income for Overseas Min: $10,935,748.00

Gifts in Kind: $2,063,918.00

Fully Supported US Personnel Overseas:
Expecting to serve more than 4 years: 11
Non-residential mission personnel: 2

Other personnel:
Short-term less than 1 year: 124
Non-US serving in own/other country: 4278
Home ministry & office staff in US: 50

Countries: Africa—General; Albania 1; Cambodia 2; China; Ghana; Hong Kong; India; Indonesia 3; Iran; Iraq; Jordan 3;

Kenya; Malaysia; Mali; Malta; Mauritania; Myanmar/Burma; Nepal; Niger; Philippines; Senegal; Singapore 2; Sri Lanka; Sudan; Taiwan; Tajikistan; Thailand; Turkey; Vietnam

Partners Worldwide

6139 Tahoe Dr. SE
Grand Rapids, MI 49546 USA
Phone: (616) 818-4900
Fax: (616) 818-4899
E-mail: dougs@partnersworldwide.org
Web Site: www.partnersworldwide.org
Associations: AERDO

Mr. Doug Seebeck, Exec. Director

A specialized agency of Reformed tradition engaged in business as mission, development, management consulting/training and partnership development.

Purpose: "...to encourage, equip, and connect business and professional people in global partnerships that grow enterprises and create sustainable jobs, transforming the lives of all involved."
Year Founded in US: 1994
Income for Overseas Min: $2,460,861.00
Gifts in Kind: $241,438.00

Countries: Kenya; Uganda

Pass the Torch Ministries/ Church of Acts

PO Box 7392
Bismarck, ND 58507 USA
Phone: (701) 667-6325
E-mail: ptm@btinet.net
Web Site: www.churchofacts.net

Mr. Greg S. Runyon, President

An interdenominational and interdependent support agency of Christian (Restoration Movement) and Charismatic tradition engaged in leadership development, discipleship, support of national churches, support of national workers and training.

Purpose: "...to equip national Christian leaders to be supernatural laborers."
Income for Overseas Min: $18,000.00

Fully Supported US Personnel Overseas:
Non-residential mission personnel: 3

Other personnel:
Short-term less than 1 year: 3
Non-US serving in own/other country: 8

Home ministry & office staff in US: 3
Countries: Nepal; Philippines; Thailand

Pentecostal Assemblies of God of America, Inc.— Trans World Missions

15226 Parthenia St.
North Hills, CA 91343-5305 USA
Phone: (951) 742-2062
E-mail: transworldmissions@hotmail.com
Web Site: www.transworldmissions.com

Dr. Judith Leeper, PAGA, TWM World Director

A nondenominational support agency of Charismatic and Evangelical tradition engaged in church planting, camping programs, childcare/orphanage programs, discipleship, evangelism and leadership development. Data from 2005.

Purpose: "...ministering to the whole man spiritually, physically, emotionally and mentally..."
Year Founded in US: 1949
Income for Overseas Min: $138,728.00
Personnel:
Non-US serving in own/other country: 21
Home ministry & office staff in US: 3
Countries: Colombia; Costa Rica; El Salvador; Guatemala; Honduras; Nicaragua; Panama; Venezuela

Pentecostal Church of God— World Missions Department

PO Box 2248
Joplin, MO 64803 USA
Phone: (417) 624-7050
Fax: (417) 624-7102
E-mail: wm@pcg.org
Web Site: www.pcg.org

Loyd L. Naten, Director of World Missions

A denominational sending agency of Pentecostal tradition engaged in church planting, support of national churches, support of national workers, church construction, evangelism, literature distribution and Bible distribution. Activities from 2001.

Year Founded in US: 1919

Pentecostal Free Will Baptist Church, Inc. —World Witness Dept.

PO Box 1568
Dunn, NC 28335 USA
Phone: (910) 892-4161
Fax: (910) 892-6876
E-mail: pheath@intrstar.net
Web Site: www.pfwb.org
Dr. Preston Heath, Gen. Superintendent

A denominational sending agency of Holiness and Pentecostal tradition engaged in youth programs, missionary education, theological education, support of national churches, church planting and Christian education. Countries of service data from 2005.

Year Founded in US: 1600

Fully Supported US Personnel Overseas:
  Expecting to serve more than 4 years: 2
  Non-residential mission personnel: 2

Other personnel:
  Short-term less than 1 year: 40
  Non-US serving in own/other country: 10
  Home ministry & office staff in US: 11

Countries: Costa Rica; Dominican Republic; Guatemala; Honduras; Mexico; Nicaragua; Nigeria; Peru; Philippines 2; Puerto Rico; Venezuela

People International USA

PO Box 3005
Vancouver, WA 98668-3005 USA
Phone: (360) 567-3757
Fax: (360) 567-3757
E-mail: team@gopeople.org
Web Site: www.gopeople.org
Mr. Tom Houser, Exec. Director

An interdenominational sending agency engaged in church planting, childcare/orphanage programs, discipleship, evangelism, leadership development and Bible translation.

Purpose: "...to glorify God by bringing the love of Jesus Christ to the Muslim peoples of Central Asia."

Year Founded in US: 1987

Income for Overseas Min: $1,150,000.00

Fully Supported US Personnel Overseas:
  Expecting to serve more than 4 years: 37
  Expecting to serve 1 to 4 years: 2
  Non-residential mission personnel: 65

Other personnel:
  Short-term less than 1 year: 12
  Non-US serving in own/other country: 65
  Home ministry & office staff in US: 6

Countries: Afghanistan 7; Kazakhstan 6; Kyrgyzstan 3; Tajikistan 2; Turkey 7; Uzbekistan 12

Perimeter Church— Global Outreach

9500 Medlock Bridge Rd.
Duluth, GA 30097 USA
Phone: (678) 405-2270
Fax: (678) 405-2009
E-mail: go@perimeter.org
Web Site: www.goperimeter.org
Associations: The Mission Exchange
Mr. Tom Mullis, Dir. Global Outreach

A denominational support agency of Presbyterian tradition engaged in support of national churches, development, discipleship, theological education, leadership development and partnership development. Countries of service data from 2005.

Purpose: "...to partner with externally focused churches and church planters to make mature and equipped followers of Jesus Christ deployed for global city transformation."

Year Founded in US: 1996

Income for Overseas Min: $1,100,000.00

Fully Supported US Personnel Overseas:
  Non-residential mission personnel: 3

Other personnel:
  Short-term less than 1 year: 298
  Home ministry & office staff in US: 13

Countries: China; India; Russia; Tanzania; Thailand

Peter Deyneka Russian Ministries

PO Box 496
Wheaton, IL 60187 USA
Phone: (630) 462-1739
Fax: (630) 690-2976
E-mail: info@russian-ministries.org
Web Site: www.russian-ministries.org
Associations: The Mission Exchange
Mrs. Anita Deyneka, President

A nondenominational support agency of Evangelical tradition engaged in children at risk, camping programs, Christian education, HIV/Aids, literature distribution and relief and/or rehabilitation.

Purpose: "...to promote indigenous evangelism, church planting, church growth, and Christian leadership in the former Soviet Union by developing creative strategic ministries and facilitating partnerships between nationals and Western Christians."

Year Founded in US: 1991

Income for Overseas Min: $4,267,083.00

Gifts in Kind: $397,901.00

Fully Supported US Personnel Overseas:
Non-residential mission personnel: 1

Other personnel:
Home ministry & office staff in US: 9

Pilgrim

4401 2nd Ave NE, #204
Seattle, WA 98011 USA
Phone: (206) 706-0350
Fax: (206) 402-2478
E-mail: helen@pilgrimafrica.org
Web Site: www.pilgrimafrica.org
Associations: AERDO

Mr. Calvin David Echodu, Exec. Director

A nondenominational service agency of Evangelical tradition engaged in development, agricultural programs, Christian education, medical work, psychological counseling and relief and/or rehabilitation.

Purpose: "...to restore hope, dignity, and love to the needy, that God may be glorified."

Year Founded in US: 2004

Income for Overseas Min: $11,488,520.00

Gifts in Kind: $10,288,000.00

Fully Supported US Personnel Overseas:
Non-residential mission personnel: 14

Other personnel:
Home ministry & office staff in US: 5

Pillar of Fire Missions Intl.

1302 Sherman St.
Denver, CO 80203 USA
Phone: (303) 839-1500
Fax: (303) 832-8560
E-mail: pillaroffiredenver@msn.com

Rev. Bernard Dawson, Director

A sending agency of Holiness tradition engaged in Christian education, church construction, theological education and support of national workers. Data from 2005.

Year Founded in US: 1960

Income for Overseas Min: $113,204.00

Personnel:
Home ministry & office staff in US: 4

Pioneer Bible Translators

7500 W. Camp Wisdom Rd.
Dallas, TX 75137 USA
Phone: (972) 708-7460
Fax: (972) 708-7463
E-mail: secretary@pbtusa.org
Web Site: www.pioneerbible.org

Greg Pruett, President

A nondenominational sending agency of Christian (Restoration Movement) tradition engaged in Bible translation, development, evangelism, literacy work, support of national churches and mobilization for mission. Statistical data from 2003.

Purpose: "...discipling of the nations by: providing Scripture in the language of the people, developing mother-tongue literacy programs, establishing and strengthening congregations, and training leadership among nationals for partnership in reaching our goals."

Year Founded in US: 1976

Income for Overseas Min: $2,245,982.00

Gifts in Kind: $29,954.00

Fully Supported US Personnel Overseas:
Expecting to serve more than 4 years: 70
Non-residential mission personnel: 70

Other personnel:
Short-term less than 1 year: 10
Non-US serving in own/other country: 3
Home ministry & office staff in US: 27

Countries: Guinea 27; Papua New Guinea 33; Tanzania 6; Ukraine 4

Pioneer Clubs

PO Box 788
Wheaton, IL 60189-0788 USA
Phone: (630) 293-1600
Fax: (630) 293-3053
E-mail: info@pioneerclubs.org
Web Site: www.pioneerclubs.org

Judy Bryson, President/CEO

A nondenominational and interdenominational service agency of Evangelical tradition engaged in childrens programs and camping programs.

Purpose: "...to serve God by providing the most effective and educationally sound programs to help children follow Christ in every aspect of life."

Year Founded in US: 1939

Personnel:
Home ministry & office staff in US: 25

Pioneers USA
10123 William Carey Dr.
Orlando, FL 32832-6931 USA
Phone: (407) 382-6000
Fax: (407) 382-1008
E-mail: info@pioneers.org
Web Site: www.pioneers.org
Associations: CrossGlobal Link, The Mission Exchange
Mr. Stephen L. Richardson, President

An interdenominational sending agency of Evangelical tradition engaged in church establishing/planting, business as mission, discipleship, evangelism, support of national churches and tentmaking.

Purpose: "...to glorify God among unreached peoples by initiating church planting movements in partnership with local churches."

Year Founded in US: 1979

Income for Overseas Min: $26,905,000.00

Gifts in Kind: $1,700.00

Fully Supported US Personnel Overseas:
Expecting to serve more than 4 years: 612
Expecting to serve 1 to 4 years: 16

Other personnel:
Short-term less than 1 year: 119
Non-US serving in own/other country: 28
Home ministry & office staff in US: 165

Countries: Asia—General 324; Bolivia 11; Bosnia and Herzegovina 16; Brazil 4; Cambodia 4; Chad 7; CIS—General 5; Croatia 8; Colombia 2; Czech Republic 2; Eastern Europe—General 8; Ethiopia 1; Fiji 2; France 9; Greece 2; Guinea 2; Hungary 16; India 45; Japan 8; Kenya 7; Kosovo 2; Lithuania 2; Middle East 26; Moldova 2; Papua New Guinea 10; Peru 15; Poland 6; Senegal 9; Slovakia 2; Slovenia 2; Spain 1; Thailand 44; United Kingdom 6; Zambia 2

Prakash Association, USA
2130 Stoney Point Farms Rd.
Cumming, GA 30041 USA
Phone: (831) 234-9568
Fax: (770) 844-1651
E-mail: prakash4india@bellsouth.net
Web Site: www.prakash4india.org
Mr. Loren D. Eckhardt, Exec. Director

An interdenominational support agency of Baptist tradition engaged in vocational training, agricultural programs, development, leadership development and youth programs.

Purpose: "...to empower marginalized young Indian nationals by teaching marketable trades and life skills so they can build self-supporting, spiritually vibrant, transformed lives."

Year Founded in US: 1968

Income for Overseas Min: $200,000.00

Fully Supported US Personnel Overseas:
Non-residential mission personnel: 1

Other personnel:
Non-US serving in own/other country: 40
Home ministry & office staff in US: 3

Countries: India

Prayer Baptist Missions International, Inc.
PO Box 160849
Boiling Springs, SC 29349 USA
Phone: (864) 599-5132
Fax: (864) 599-5132
E-mail: pbmioffice@gmail.com
Web Site: www.prayerbaptistmissions.com
Bro. Gary W. Tingen, Gen. Director

A denominational sending agency of Baptist, Fundamental and Independent tradition engaged in church planting, Bible distribution, discipleship, evangelism, literature distribution and prison evangelism.

Purpose: "...to unite independent, fundamental Baptist churches with like-minded missionaries for the purpose of evangelizing the lost and establishing churches worldwide."

Year Founded in US: 1989

Income for Overseas Min: $500,000.00

Fully Supported US Personnel Overseas:
Expecting to serve more than 4 years: 22

Expecting to serve 1 to 4 years: 2
Non-residential mission personnel: 2
Other personnel:
Short-term less than 1 year: 8
Non-US serving in own/other country: 10
Home ministry & office staff in US: 3
Countries: Germany 2; Guyana 2; India; Ireland; Kenya; Mexico 10; Nicaragua 2; Romania 2; Russia 2; Saint Lucia 2

Precept Ministries Intl.

PO Box 182218
Chattanooga, TN 37422 USA
Phone: (423) 892-6814
Fax: (423) 894-2449
E-mail: info@precept.org
Web Site: www.precept.org
Mr. Tom Hall, Exec. Director

A nondenominational sending agency of Baptist and Evangelical tradition engaged in inductive Bible study materials, broadcasting, discipleship, leadership development, training and translation work.
Purpose: "...to establish people in God's Word."
Year Founded in US: 1970
Fully Supported US Personnel Overseas:
Expecting to serve more than 4 years: 2
Non-residential mission personnel: 7
Other personnel:
Short-term less than 1 year: 9
Non-US serving in own/other country: 153
Home ministry & office staff in US: 109
Countries: Afghanistan; Angola; Argentina; Armenia; Australia; Bahamas, The; Bolivia; Brazil; Bulgaria; Chile; China; Colombia; Costa Rica; Cuba; Czech Republic; Ecuador; Egypt; El Salvador; Estonia; Germany 1; Guatemala; Guinea-Bissau; Honduras; Hungary; India; Iran; Iraq; Ireland; Israel; Italy; Kenya; Korea, South; Macedonia; Mexico; Moldova; Mozambique; New Zealand; Nicaragua; Panama; Peru; Philippines; Poland; Portugal; Romania; Russia; Serbia and Montenegro; Singapore; Slovakia; South Africa; Syria; Taiwan 1; Tajikistan; Ukraine; United Kingdom; Uzbekistan; Venezuela

Precious Seed Ministries

1115 S. Maryland St.
Alton, TX 78573 USA
Phone: (956) 585-9966
Fax: (956) 583-7838
E-mail: wymanpylant@yahoo.com
Mr. Wyman Pylant, President

A nondenominational support agency of Charismatic tradition engaged in childcare/orphanage programs, church construction, church planting, theological education, leadership development and relief and/or rehabilitation. Data from 2005.
Year Founded in US: 1985
Income for Overseas Min: $57,000.00
Fully Supported US Personnel Overseas:
Expecting to serve more than 4 years: 1
Non-residential mission personnel: 3
Other personnel:
Non-US serving in own/other country: 10
Home ministry & office staff in US: 2
Countries: Mexico 1; Nicaragua

Presbyterian Church (USA), Worldwide Ministries

100 Witherspoon St.
Louisville, KY 40202 USA
Phone: (502) 569-5000
Fax: (502) 569-8039
Web Site: www.pcusa.org/worldmission
Associations: CWS
Hunter Farrell, Director

A denominational sending agency of Presbyterian and Reformed tradition engaged in mobilization for mission, development, leadership development, medical work, partnership development and relief and/or rehabilitation. Data from 2005.
Purpose: "...to share the transforming power of the Gospel of Jesus Christ and to carry out this mission by being committed to the whole church, the whole Gospel and the whole inhabited earth...assist the church in the quest for Christian unity and ecumenical commitment...nourish and strengthen the global perspective and mission effort of the General Assembly Council, the Divisions and the church-at-large."
Year Founded in US: 1837
Income for Overseas Min: $40,000,000.00
Fully Supported US Personnel Overseas:
Expecting to serve more than 4 years: 350
Expecting to serve 1 to 4 years: 385

Non-residential mission personnel: 375

Countries: Africa—General 80; Asia—General 65; Australia 2; Europe—General 37; Latin America—General 88; Unspecified Country 78

Presbyterian Evangelistic Fellowship

425 State St. Ste. 312
Bristol, VA 24201 USA

Phone: (276) 591-5336
Fax: (276) 591-5349
E-mail: admin@pefministry.org
Web Site: www.pefministry.org

Rev. Rick Light, Exec. Director

An interdenominational sending agency of Presbyterian and Reformed tradition engaged in evangelism, camping programs, evangelism, literature distribution, support of national workers and youth programs. Activities from 2001.

Purpose: "...to practice, train and equip God's people to do Biblical evangelism, anywhere, anytime, with anyone."

Year Founded in US: 1958

Presbyterian Mission International (PMI)

12330 Conway Rd.
St. Louis, MO 63141 USA

Phone: (314) 392-4120
Fax: (314) 434-4819
E-mail: pmi@covenantseminary.edu
Web Site: www.pmiweb.org

Mr. J. Nelson Jennings, President

An interdenominational sending agency of Presbyterian and Reformed tradition engaged in support of national workers, church planting, childcare/orphanage programs, development, theological education and evangelism.

Purpose: "...to enhance worldwide Reformed and Presbyterian gospel ministry through relationships with nationals who labor in evangelism, church planting, leadership training, holistic ministries, and connecting churches internationally."

Year Founded in US: 1988
Income for Overseas Min: $1,038,054.00
Personnel:

Non-US serving in own/other country: 31
Home ministry & office staff in US: 2

Countries: Brazil; France; Hungary; India; Italy; Japan; Kenya; Netherlands; New Zealand; Philippines; Thailand; Ukraine

Presbyterian Missionary Union

1650 Love Rd.
Grand Island, NY 14072 USA

Phone: (716) 775-0442
Fax: (716) 775-0442
E-mail: office@presbyterianmissions.org
Web Site: www.presbyterianmissions.org

Dr. Leonard W. Pine, Field Director

A denominational sending agency of Presbyterian and Reformed tradition engaged in church planting, evangelism, leadership development, support of national workers, short-term programs and translation work.

Purpose: "...to establish and strengthen indigenous Bible believing churches, related institutions, and works agreeable to the (Westminster) doctrinal standards and principles of (Presbyterian) church government."

Year Founded in US: 1985

Income for Overseas Min: $101,200.00

Fully Supported US Personnel Overseas:
Expecting to serve more than 4 years: 4
Non-residential mission personnel: 1

Other personnel:
Short-term less than 1 year: 12
Non-US serving in own/other country: 4
Home ministry & office staff in US: 2

Countries: Asia—General 1; Australia 2; Bolivia; Cambodia 1; Myanmar/Burma

Presbyterian Order for World Evangelization

542 E. Ingram
Mesa, AZ 95203 USA

Phone: (480) 834-1500
Fax: (480) 834-6643
E-mail: robertblincoe@cox.net

Rev. Robert Blincoe, Gen. Director

A denominational support agency of Presbyterian tradition engaged in evangelism, mobilization for mission, mission-related research and training. Data from 2005.

Purpose: "...attracting, coordinating, sponsoring, managing and establishing whatever project, activities, program or organizations that contribute strategically toward the fulfilment of the Great Commission."

Year Founded in US: 1974
Income for Overseas Min: $50,000.00
Fully Supported US Personnel Overseas:
  Non-residential mission personnel: 2
Other personnel:
  Home ministry & office staff in US: 3

Primitive Methodist Church in the USA—International Mission Board

33 W. Barrows St.
Cumberland, RI 02864 USA
Phone: (401) 722-7365
E-mail: fjeffrey1@cox.net
Web Site: www.ccmcri.com
Rev. Fred Jeffrey, Director

A denominational sending agency of Methodist tradition engaged in church planting, Bible translation, Christian education and evangelism.

Year Founded in US: 1921
Fully Supported US Personnel Overseas:
  Non-residential mission personnel: 1
Countries: Dominican Republic; Guatemala; Papua New Guinea; Spain

Proclaim! International, Inc.

PO Box 56888
Jacksonville, FL 32241 USA
Phone: (904) 739-0065
Fax: (904) 739-4737
E-mail: info@proclaiminternational.com
Web Site: www.proclaiminternational.com
Mr. John P. Bowers, Director for the Americas

A sending agency of Evangelical tradition engaged in evangelism, broadcasting, support of national churches and mobilization for mission.

Purpose: "...to proclaim the Gospel with creativity, humility and boldness, in obedience to the authority of Jesus Christ and labor alongside believers of integrity, by bringing our gifts to serve so that the Church may express itself in its fullness by doing all things with excellence and above all to 'love one another' providing ourselves

to be His disciples."
Year Founded in US: 2000
Income for Overseas Min: $1,233,000.00
Gifts in Kind: $13,200.00
Fully Supported US Personnel Overseas:
  Expecting to serve more than 4 years: 13
  Expecting to serve 1 to 4 years: 2
  Non-residential mission personnel: 8
Other personnel:
  Short-term less than 1 year: 17
  Non-US serving in own/other country: 5
  Home ministry & office staff in US: 1
Countries: Africa—General 1; Croatia; Eastern Europe—General; Germany 10; Peru; Spain 2

Progressive National Baptist Convention, Inc. (PNBC)— Missions

601 50th St., NE
Washington, DC 20019 USA
Phone: (202) 396-0558
Fax: (202) 398-4998
E-mail: info@pnbc.org
Web Site: www.pnbc.org
Dr. T. DeWitt Smith, Jr., President

A denominational support agency of Baptist tradition engaged in justice, Christian education, evangelism, literature production, training and youth programs.

Purpose: "...to develop, support, and empower Christian churches, communities, and PNBC partners to improve the quality of life of people domestically and internationally."
Year Founded in US: 1962
Personnel:
  Home ministry & office staff in US: 1
Countries: Haiti; Jamaica; Kenya; South Africa; Tanzania; United Kingdom

Project AmaZon

PO Box 3253
Peoria, IL 61612 USA
Phone: (309) 263-2299
Web Site: www.projectamazon.org
Mr. Paul Augustine, President

An interdenominational sending agency of Charismatic and Evangelical tradition engaged in evangelism, business as mission, church planting, discipleship, medical work and training.

Purpose: "...to glorify God, fulfilling the Great Commission by planting nationally led churches, emphasizing the making of disciple-making disciples; the training, equipping, and sending of nationals; ministering to the whole person—spirit, soul, and body; and focusing on the Amazon basin.

Year Founded in US:

Income for Overseas Min: $1,678,102.00

Fully Supported US Personnel Overseas:
    Expecting to serve more than 4 years: 40
    Expecting to serve 1 to 4 years: 1

Other personnel:
    Short-term less than 1 year: 82
    Non-US serving in own/other country: 5
    Home ministry & office staff in US: 3

Countries: Brazil 38; Japan 2

Project Christ International

124-08 Linden Blvd.
Jamaica, NY 11420 USA
Phone: (718) 845-6992
E-mail: pcintl@aol.com
Web Site: www.projectchristinternational.org
Mr. John Stephen, President

A nondenominational support agency of Baptist and Brethren tradition engaged in Christian education, childcare/orphanage programs, childrens programs, church construction, church planting and missionary education. Data from 2005.

Year Founded in US: 1984

Income for Overseas Min: $25,000.00

Gifts in Kind: $25,000.00

Personnel:
    Short-term less than 1 year: 2
    Non-US serving in own/other country: 80

Countries: India; Nepal

Project Mercy, Inc.

7011 Ardmore Ave.
Fort Wayne, IN 46809 USA
Phone: (260) 747-2559
Fax: (260) 478-1361
Web Site: www.projectmercy.org
Marta Gabre-Tsadick, Exec. Director

A nondenominational support agency of Evangelical tradition engaged in community development, agricultural programs,

KG—11 skills training and medical work. Data from 2005.

Purpose: "...providing aid, comfort and support to those in need anywhere in Africa...also participates to alleviate human suffering anywhere in the world in the name of Jesus Christ."

Year Founded in US: 1977

Income for Overseas Min: $1,178,079.00

Fully Supported US Personnel Overseas:
    Expecting to serve more than 4 years: 2
    Non-residential mission personnel: 2

Other personnel:
    Short-term less than 1 year: 119
    Home ministry & office staff in US: 7

Countries: Ethiopia 2

Providence Mission Homes, Inc.

PO Box 40727
Pasadena, CA 91114 USA
Phone: (626) 398-2487
Fax: (626) 398-2488
E-mail: providencehomes1@yahoo.com
Web Site: www.providencemissionhomes.com
Mr. John Pentecost, Director

A nondenominational specialized agency of Evangelical tradition engaged in furloughed missionary support.

Year Founded in US: 1972

Personnel:
    Home ministry & office staff in US: 1

Ramesh Richard Evangelism and Church Health

5500 W. Plano Pkwy., #100
Plano, TX 75093 USA
Phone: (972) 733-3402
Fax: (972) 733-3495
E-mail: info@rreach.org
Web Site: www.rreach.org
Dr. Ramesh Richard, President

A support agency engaged in training pastors, audio recording/distribution, broadcasting and evangelism.

Purpose: "...a global proclamation ministry, RREACH implements God's calling and gifting on Ramesh Richard to promote the Lord Jesus Christ worldwide."

Year Founded in US: 1987
Income for Overseas Min: $722,937.00
Personnel:
Home ministry & office staff in US: 6

Raul Zaldivar Ministries

3047 Marion St.
Elgin, IL 60124 USA
Phone: (847) 441-6861
Fax: (847) 628-6333
E-mail: ministerio@raulzaldivar.com
Web Site: www.raulzaldivar.com
Mr. Raul Zaldivar, President

An interdenominational service agency of Independent tradition engaged in evangelism, broadcasting, Christian education, theological education, TEE and leadership development.

Purpose: "...to mobilize individuals to evangelize the lost world and to develop educational and social ministries."

Year Founded in US: 1998

Fully Supported US Personnel Overseas:
Expecting to serve 1 to 4 years: 1
Non-residential mission personnel: 1

Other personnel:
Non-US serving in own/other country: 1
Home ministry & office staff in US: 4

Countries: Honduras

Ravi Zacharias International Ministries, Inc.

4725 Peachtree Corners Cir., Ste. 250
Norcross, GA 30092-2586 USA
Phone: (770) 449-6766
Fax: (770) 729-1729
E-mail: rzim@rzim.com
Web Site: www.rzim.org
Dr. Ravi Zacharias, President/CEO

An interdenominational specialized agency of Evangelical tradition engaged in evangelism, apologetics, discipleship, TEE, relief and/or rehabilitation and training.

Purpose: "...to support, expand, and enhance the preaching, teaching, and vision of Ravi Zacharias, distinctive in its strong evangelistic and apologetic foundation, intended to touch both the heart and the intellect of the thinkers and opinion-makers of society...to reach and challenge those

who shape the ideas of a culture with the credibility of the Gospel of Jesus Christ."
Year Founded in US: 1984
Income for Overseas Min: $2,300,000.00
Fully Supported US Personnel Overseas:
Non-residential mission personnel: 2
Other personnel:
Non-US serving in own/other country: 22
Home ministry & office staff in US: 41
Countries: Asia—General; Europe—General; Hong Kong; India; Middle East

RBC Ministries

3000 Kraft Ave. SE
Grand Rapids, MI 49512 USA
Phone: (616) 942-6770
Fax: (616) 957-5741
Web Site: www.rbc.org
Mr. Mart De Haan, President

A nondenominational service agency of Evangelical tradition engaged in literature production, literature distribution and broadcasting.

Purpose: "...to make the life-changing wisdom of the Bible understandable and accessible to all."

Year Founded in US: 1938
Income for Overseas Min: $8,600,000.00
Personnel:
Non-US serving in own/other country: 262
Home ministry & office staff in US: 270
Countries: Africa—General; Asia—General; Europe—General; Latin America—General; Singapore

Reach Ministries Intl.

PO Box 2060
Orange, CA 92859 USA
Phone: (562) 690-4252
Fax: (562) 690-5612
E-mail: reachministries@reachmin.com
Web Site: www.reachmin.com
Loring E. Tabor, CEO/President

A nondenominational sending agency of Evangelical tradition engaged in discipleship, Bible memorization, development, evangelism, leadership development and Bible translation. Data from 2005.

Purpose: "...to propagate the gospel of the Lord Jesus Christ and to promote aid and develop contextualized, holistic disciplemaking ministries in the Philippines and India with expansion to other countries and cultures as the Lord leads."

Year Founded in US: 1985

Income for Overseas Min: $126,236.00

Fully Supported US Personnel Overseas:
Expecting to serve more than 4 years: 7

Other personnel:
Non-US serving in own/other country: 2
Home ministry & office staff in US: 3

Countries: Hong Kong 1; India; Philippines 6

ReachAcross

PO Box 2047
Lexington, SC 29071-2047 USA

Phone: (803) 358-2330
Fax: (803) 358-2330
E-mail: ReachAcross@sc.rr.com
Web Site: www.reachacross.net
Associations: CrossGlobal Link

Dr. Herb Brasher, US Director

An interdenominational support agency of Evangelical tradition engaged in evangelism, church planting, discipleship, medical work, TESOL and Bible translation.

Purpose: "...to share the gospel with Muslims...to serve them in practical ways...to disciple them to follow Jesus."

Year Founded in US: 1951

Income for Overseas Min: $325,781.00

Fully Supported US Personnel Overseas:
Expecting to serve more than 4 years: 6
Non-residential mission personnel: 2

Other personnel:
Short-term less than 1 year: 3
Non-US serving in own/other country: 60
Home ministry & office staff in US: 3

Countries: Djibouti 4; Germany; Mali; Middle East 2; Pakistan; United Kingdom

ReachGlobal

(See ad on page 278)

901 E. 78th St.
Minneapolis, MN 55420 USA

Phone: (952) 854-1300
Fax: (952) 853-8474
Web Site: www.goreachglobal.com
Associations: The Mission Exchange

Rev. Timothy J. Addington

A denominational sending agency of Congregational tradition engaged in leadership development, business as mission, church planting, development, theological education and TEE. Countries of service data from 2005.

Purpose: "...to glorify God by multiplying healthy churches among all people."

Year Founded in US: 1887

Income for Overseas Min: $23,368,000.00

Fully Supported US Personnel Overseas:
Expecting to serve more than 4 years: 300
Expecting to serve 1 to 4 years: 76
Non-residential mission personnel: 10

Other personnel:
Short-term less than 1 year: 28
Non-US serving in own/other country: 71
Home ministry & office staff in US: 82

Countries: Austria 3; Belgium 12; Bosnia and Herzegovina 6; Brazil 5; Central African Republic 12; China; Colombia; Congo, Democratic Republic of; Costa Rica 7; Czech Republic 11; France 12; Germany 10; Honduras 2; Hong Kong 9; Hungary 10; India; Japan 19; Kenya 8; Macau; Malaysia; Mexico 10; Mongolia; Netherlands 4; Peru 11; Philippines 14; Poland 4; Portugal 4; Romania 16; Rwanda; Russia 16; Singapore; Slovakia 4; Spain 8; Sudan; Taiwan 1; Tanzania 9; Thailand 10; Turkey; Ukraine 8; United Kingdom 2; Unspecified Country 44; Uzbekistan; Venezuela 9

Reaching Indians Ministries International

(See ad on page 279)

PO Box 688
Round Lake Beach, IL 60073 USA

Phone: (847) 265-0630
Fax: (847) 265-0642
E-mail: ministry@rimi.org
Web Site: www.rimi.org

Saji Lukos, President

An interdenominational support agency of Fundamental and Independent tradition engaged in evangelism, childcare/orphanage programs, missionary education, theological education, support of national churches and support of national workers. Countries of Service data from 2005.

Purpose: "...to expand Christ's kingdom through evangelism and church planting,

YOU CAN HELP SEND

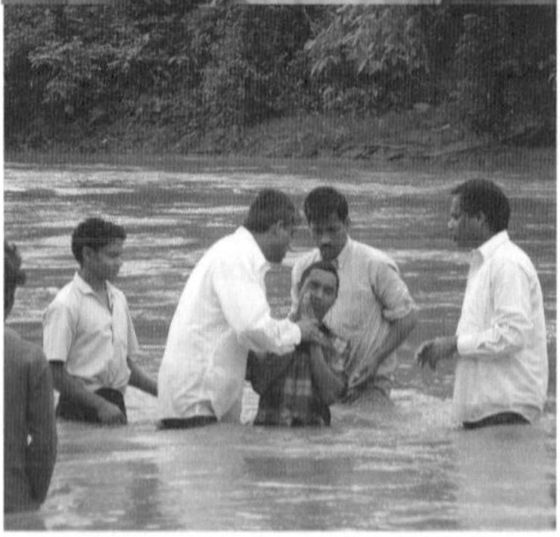

RIMI's main goal is raising up trained leaders throughout South Asia to go and reach their own people. To accomplish this, we have three program areas:

- Church Planting - 1,300 church planters
- Leadership Development - 650 leaders trained per year
- Compassion Services - 500 children in 16 Mercy Homes

Nearly 1/4 of the world's population lives in this area. Yet in many places, Christians make up less than 1% of the population.

To help send these leaders, or work alongside them in the mission field, contact RIMI and start making a difference today.

RIMI **Reaching Indians**
Ministries International
Church Planting, Leadership Development, Compassion

RIMI ✽ PO Box 688 ✽ Round Lake Beach, IL 60073
(847) 265-0630 ✽ ministry@RIMI.org

www.RIMI.org

which is further advanced by leadership development and compassion services."

Year Founded in US: 1993

Income for Overseas Min: $149,472.00

Personnel:
   Short-term less than 1 year: 20
   Non-US serving in own/other country: 810
   Home ministry & office staff in US: 6

Countries: India

Real Impact Missions, Inc.

PO Box 701792
Tulsa, OK 74170-1792 USA

Phone: (800) 774-6746
Fax: (918) 712-2528
E-mail: goinfo@realimpact.com
Web Site: www.realimpact.com

Mr. Scott Boss, President

A transdenominational service agency of Evangelical and Independent tradition engaged in short-term programs, development, evangelism, medical work, trafficking/slavery issues and youth programs.

Purpose: "...to mobilize, mentor, and manage missionaries for short-term missions projects around the world."

Year Founded in US: 1997

Income for Overseas Min: $430,000.00

Gifts in Kind: $10,000.00

Personnel:
   Short-term less than 1 year: 400
   Home ministry & office staff in US: 6

Reciprocal Ministries Intl.

5475 Lee St., Ste. 301
Lehigh Acres, FL 33971 USA

Phone: (877) 764-5439
Fax: (239) 368-8325
E-mail: dan.shoemaker@rminet.org
Web Site: www.rminet.org

Mr. Daniel Shoemaker, President

A nondenominational sending agency of Evangelical tradition engaged in cross-cultural partnership development, children at risk, development, Christian education, support of national churches and short-term programs.

Purpose: "...to see Christian laypersons ministering, through the vehicle of the Sister Church Program, to Christians in a

church of a different culture, and together with them, minister to each other's community."

Year Founded in US: 1988

Income for Overseas Min: $1,000,000.00

Fully Supported US Personnel Overseas:
   Expecting to serve more than 4 years: 2
   Expecting to serve 1 to 4 years: 1

Other personnel:
   Short-term less than 1 year: 176
   Non-US serving in own/other country: 20
   Home ministry & office staff in US: 5

Countries: Haiti 2

Reformation Translation Fellowship, Inc.

302 E. First St.
Bloomington, IN 47401 USA

Phone: (812) 339-1922
E-mail: Bill4rtf@gmail.com
Web Site: www.rtf-usa.com

Rev. J. Bruce Martin, Board President

An interdenominational service agency of Reformed tradition engaged in translation work.

Purpose: "...to translate, publish, and distribute Reformed literature in Chinese...to stimulate original Chinese Christian theological writing."

Year Founded in US: 1951

Income for Overseas Min: $44,385.00

Personnel:
   Home ministry & office staff in US: 1

Reformed Baptist Mission Services

402 East Louther St.
Carlisle, PA 17013 USA

Phone: (717) 249-7473
Fax: (717) 258-0614
E-mail: arbca@reformedbaptist.com
Web Site: www.reformedbaptist.com

Rev. Gordon Taylor, Coordinator

A mission service coordinating member churches to assist one another to send missionaries and plant churches worldwide. Data from 2005.

Purpose: "...to advance Christ's kingdom by providing an association in which churches of common confession may find mutual encouragement, assistance, edification and counsel, and to participate in cooperative efforts in church planting, foreign missions, ministerial training, publications and other endeavors deemed appropriate by the Association."

Year Founded in US: 1985

Income for Overseas Min: $674,213.00

Fully Supported US Personnel Overseas:
Expecting to serve more than 4 years: 3

Other personnel:
Non-US serving in own/other country: 22
Home ministry & office staff in US: 3

Countries: Argentina; Asia—General; Chile; Colombia; France; Ireland; Israel; Jamaica; Kenya; Switzerland; United Kingdom; Unspecified Country 3

Reformed Church in America, Gen. Synod Council, Mission Services

4500 60th St. SE
Grand Rapids, MI 49512 USA

Phone: (616) 698-7071
Fax: (616) 698-6606
Web Site: www.rca.org

Jhonny Alicea-Baez, Dir. of Global Mission

A denominational sending agency of Ecumenical and Evangelical tradition engaged in development, agricultural programs, TEE, theological education, justice and leadership development.

Purpose: "...to equip congregations for ministry—a thousand churches in a million ways doing one thing—following Christ in mission, in a lost and broken world so loved by God."

Year Founded in US: 1857

Income for Overseas Min: $7,419,607.00

Fully Supported US Personnel Overseas:
Expecting to serve more than 4 years: 35
Expecting to serve 1 to 4 years: 6

Other personnel:
Non-US serving in own/other country: 25
Home ministry & office staff in US: 13

Countries: Albania; Bahrain 3; Bangladesh; China 1; Croatia 2; Ecuador; Egypt; Ethiopia 5; Guatemala; Honduras; Hungary 2; India 2; Indonesia; Italy; Japan 6; Kenya 7; Korea, South; Malawi 2; Mexico; Myanmar/Burma; Nicaragua; Niger 3; Sudan 2; Taiwan

Reformed Episcopal Board of Foreign Missions

4142 Dayflower Dr.
Katy, TX 77449 USA

Phone: (800)732-3433
Fax: (281) 463-9575
E-mail: RoyalREC1@aol.com
Web Site: www.recus.org

Bishop Royal U. Grote, President

A denominational sending agency of Anglican tradition engaged in church planting, medical work and Bible translation. Data from 2005.

Year Founded in US: 1892

Income for Overseas Min: $220,000.00

Fully Supported US Personnel Overseas:
Expecting to serve more than 4 years: 3

Other personnel:
Short-term less than 1 year: 50
Non-US serving in own/other country: 15

Countries: Brazil 1; France 1; Germany 1; Liberia

Reformed Presbyterian Global Missions (RP Global Missions)

3004 Fifth Ave.
Beaver Falls, PA 15010-3671 USA

Phone: (412) 901-3553
E-mail: ServeChrist@rpglobalmissions.org
Web Site: www.rpglobalmissions.org

Mr. Matthew Filbert, Dev. & Communications

A denominational sending agency of Presbyterian and Reformed tradition engaged in church planting, broadcasting, discipleship, theological education and short-term programs.

Purpose: "...to give itself to the health, growth, and multiplication of the Reformed Presbyterian Church by establishing vigorous and truly Biblical, indigenous churches in other lands."

Year Founded in US: 1856

Fully Supported US Personnel Overseas:
Expecting to serve more than 4 years: 9

Other personnel:
Short-term less than 1 year: 75
Non-US serving in own/other country: 3
Home ministry & office staff in US: 1

Countries: Australia; Costa Rica; Cyprus

1; France; Japan 1; Sudan 7; Switzerland; Uganda; United Kingdom

Rehoboth Ministries, Inc.

333 Hilliard Dr.
Fayetteville, NC 28311 USA
Phone: (910) 630-3730
E-mail: pgiba3@aol.com
Rev. Pritchard Adams, III, President
A sending agency of Charismatic and Christian (Restoration Movement) tradition engaged in discipleship, broadcasting, Christian education and theological education.
Year Founded in US: 1985
Income for Overseas Min: $48,000.00
Fully Supported US Personnel Overseas:
   Expecting to serve more than 4 years: 2
Other personnel:
   Non-US serving in own/other country: 21
Countries: Haiti 2

Remnant Ministries, Inc.

PO Box 24398
Cleveland, OH 44124-0398 USA
Phone: (440) 943-7221
Fax: (440) 648-0219
E-mail: info@rmiforisrael.org
Web Site: www.rmiforisrael.org
Rev. Alan Wilson, Exec. Director
A nondenominational sending agency of Fundamental and Independent tradition engaged in Jewish evangelism, Bible distribution, discipleship and literature production. Data from 2005.
Purpose: "...to evangelize Jews in this present age...to reach the 'remnant according to the election of grace' Romans 11:5."
Year Founded in US: 1904
Income for Overseas Min: $100,000.00
Fully Supported US Personnel Overseas:
   Expecting to serve more than 4 years: 3
Other personnel:
   Home ministry & office staff in US: 2
Countries: Brazil 1; Israel 2

Resourcing Christian Education International

PO Box 4528
Wheaton, IL 60189 USA
Phone: (630) 580-5514

Fax: (630) 580-5757
E-mail: RCEIntl@aol.com
Web Site: www.rce-international.org
Mr. Brett K. Howard, President
A nondenominational support agency of Evangelical and Independent tradition engaged in international Christian education (K-12 type schools) church/school, evangelism and TESOL.
Purpose: "...to serve international Christian education ministries in their mission of providing exceptional educational opportunities with a biblical foundation and Christian worldview."
Year Founded in US: 2003
Income for Overseas Min: $3,238,754.00
Personnel:
   Non-US serving in own/other country: 150
   Home ministry & office staff in US: 2
Countries: Austria; Colombia; Czech Republic; Ecuador; Japan; Poland; Portugal; Spain; Russia; Ukraine

Rio Grande Bible Institute, Inc.

4300 S. US Hwy. 281
Edinburg, TX 78539-9650 USA
Phone: (956) 380-8100
Fax: (956) 380-8256
E-mail: rgbimail@riogrande.edu
Web Site: www.riogrande.edu
Associations: CrossGlobal Link
Dr. Lawrence B. Windle, President
A nondenominational service agency of Independent tradition engaged in theological education, broadcasting, correspondence courses, missionary education, leadership development and video/film production/distribution.
Purpose: "...exists to glorify God by serving the Hispanic church through equipping leaders, edifying believers, and evangelizing the lost."
Year Founded in US: 1946
Gifts in Kind: $125,400.00
Personnel:
   Short-term less than 1 year: 84
   Home ministry & office staff in US: 118

Ripe for Harvest, Inc.

2824 N. Power Rd. #113282
Mesa, AZ 85215 USA

Phone: (480) 373-9387
Fax: (480) 718-7379
E-mail: rfhphoenix@gmail.com
Web Site: www.ripeforharvest.org
Mr. Tim A. Smith, President

A nondenominational sending agency of Evangelical tradition engaged in evangelism, church planting, discipleship, tent-making and training.

Purpose: "...to conduct church services and related missions/ministries in obedience to the Great Commission as found in Matthew 28:18-20."

Year Founded in US: 1979

Income for Overseas Min: $1,300,000.00

Fully Supported US Personnel Overseas:
   Expecting to serve more than 4 years: 25
   Expecting to serve 1 to 4 years: 31

Other personnel:
   Non-US serving in own/other country: 2
   Home ministry & office staff in US: 8

Countries: Asia—General 2; Europe—General 3; Latin America—General 8; Mexico; South America—General 12

Rock the World Youth Mission Alliance

PO Box 43
Ambridge, PA 15003 USA
Phone: (724) 266-8876
Fax: (724) 266-5916
Web Site: www.rocktheworld.org
Mr. Whis Hays, Exec. Director

A nondenominational support agency of Episcopal and Evangelical tradition engaged in youth programs, theological education, evangelism, leadership development, mobilization for mission and short-term programs. Data from 2002.

Purpose: "...mobilize young people to make an impact for God."

Year Founded in US: 1989

Income for Overseas Min: $38,000.00

Fully Supported US Personnel Overseas:
   Non-residential mission personnel: 1

Other personnel:
   Short-term less than 1 year: 13
   Home ministry & office staff in US: 7

Countries: Belize; Honduras; Nepal; Peru

Rogma International, Inc.

PO Box 2008
Easley, SC 29641-2008 USA
Phone: (864) 855-2887
Fax: (864) 859-0100
E-mail: info@rogma.org
Web Site: www.rogma.org
Dr. John Vanden Akker, President

A service agency of Baptist and Fundamental tradition engaged in correspondence courses, discipleship and evangelism with 160 directors in 88 countries. Data from 2005.

Purpose: "...to share the Word with the world."

Year Founded in US: 1985

Income for Overseas Min: $42,500.00

Personnel:
   Home ministry & office staff in US: 1

Romanian Missionary Society

PO Box 527
Wheaton, IL 60189-0527 USA
Phone: (630) 665-6503
Fax: (630) 665-6538
E-mail: rms@rmsonline.org
Web Site: www.rmsonline.org
Dr. Livius T. Percy, President

An interdenominational sending agency of Baptist and Presbyterian tradition engaged in evangelism, broadcasting, childrens programs, theological education, literature production and support of national workers. Data from 2005.

Purpose: "...to support Christian projects and ministries in Romania."

Year Founded in US: 1968

Income for Overseas Min: $425,000.00

Fully Supported US Personnel Overseas:
   Non-residential mission personnel: 2

Other personnel:
   Short-term less than 1 year: 1
   Non-US serving in own/other country: 70
   Home ministry & office staff in US: 3

Countries: Romania

Rosedale Mennonite Missions

9920 Rosedale Milford Ctr. Rd.
Irwin, OH 43029 USA
Phone: (740) 857-1366
Fax: (866) 883-1367

E-mail: info@rmmoffice.org
Web Site: www.rosedalemennonitemis-sions.org

Mr. Joe Showalter, President

A denominational sending agency of Mennonite tradition engaged in church planting, business as mission, evangelism, short-term programs and tentmaking.

Purpose: "...to establish locally rooted and led, rapidly reproducing churches, prioritizing people groups, and locations that are least reached with the Good News."

Year Founded in US: 1919

Income for Overseas Min: $1,900,000.00

Fully Supported US Personnel Overseas:
   Expecting to serve more than 4 years: 25
   Non-residential mission personnel: 25

Other personnel:
   Short-term less than 1 year: 48
   Non-US serving in own/other country: 2
   Home ministry & office staff in US: 18

Countries: Africa—General 5; Albania 2; Asia—General 2; Bangladesh; Middle East 7; Spain 4; Thailand 5

RUN Ministries (Reaching Unreached Nations, Inc.)

PO Box 6543
Virginia Beach, VA 23456 USA

Phone: (757) 213-2053
Fax: (757) 420-5373
E-mail: run@runministries.org
Web Site: www.runministries.org
Associations: The Mission Exchange

Mr. Eric Watt, President

A nondenominational sending agency of Charismatic and Evangelical tradition engaged in church planting, Bible distribution, discipleship, evangelism, leadership development and Bible translation.

Purpose: "...to bring the revelation of God and His kingdom to unreached peoples."

Year Founded in US: 1990

Income for Overseas Min: $271,160.00

Fully Supported US Personnel Overseas:
   Expecting to serve 1 to 4 years: 2

Other personnel:
   Home ministry & office staff in US: 4

Countries: Malaysia

Russian Bible Society, Inc.

PO Box 6068
Asheville, NC 28816 USA

Phone: (828) 681-0370
Fax: (828) 681-0371
E-mail: russianbibles@bellsouth.net

Dr. Robert Doom, Director

An interdenominational specialized agency of Baptist and Fundamental tradition engaged in Bible distribution, literature distribution, literature production, Bible translation and translation work. Data from 2001.

Purpose: "...to continue providing the 'Synodal Translation' of the Russian Bible... and its translation into many of the minority languages [of Russia]."

Year Founded in US: 1944

Income for Overseas Min: $105,437.00

Personnel:
   Short-term less than 1 year: 10
   Home ministry & office staff in US: 1

Russian Christian Radio, Inc.

PO Box 1667
Estes Park, CO 80517 USA

Phone: (970) 586-8638
Fax: (970) 586-6374
E-mail: info@rcradio.net
Web Site: www.rcr.ru/eng

Mr. Mark Irwin, President/Chairman of Board

A specialized agency of Evangelical tradition engaged in broadcasting, audio recording/distribution, literature distribution and literature production.

Year Founded in US: 1970

Income for Overseas Min: $224,464.00

Fully Supported US Personnel Overseas:
   Expecting to serve more than 4 years: 2

Other personnel:
   Non-US serving in own/other country: 20
   Home ministry & office staff in US: 5

Countries: Russia 2

Salvation Army, U.S.A.

PO Box 269
Alexandria, VA 22313 USA

Phone: (703) 684-5500
Fax: (703) 684-3478
E-mail: usn_chief_secretary@usn.salvation-army.org

Web Site: www.salvationarmyusa.org
Associations: AERDO

Commissioner Israel L. Gaither, Natl. Commander

A denominational sending agency of Evangelical and Holiness tradition engaged in relief and/or rehabilitation, camping programs, childrens programs, evangelism, youth programs and disasters.

Purpose: "...to preach the Gospel of Jesus Christ and to meet human needs in His name without discrimination."

Year Founded in US: 1880

Income for Overseas Min: $30,375,318.00

Fully Supported US Personnel Overseas:
Expecting to serve more than 4 years: 12
Expecting to serve 1 to 4 years: 100
Non-residential mission personnel: 21

Other personnel:
Short-term less than 1 year: 479
Home ministry & office staff in US: 24

Countries: Argentina 2; Australia 1; Chile; Congo, Democratic Republic of; Costa Rica; Estonia; Georgia; Germany 2; Ghana; Guatemala; Haiti 1; Italy 2; Jamaica; Kenya 1; Liberia; Mexico; New Zealand; Papua New Guinea; Philippines; Poland; Portugal; Russia 2; Singapore 1; Spain; Switzerland; Uganda; Ukraine United Kingdom; Zambia

Samaritan's Purse International Relief
PO Box 3000
Boone, NC 28607 USA

Phone: (828) 262-1980
E-mail: info@samaritan.org
Web Site: www.samaritanspurse.org

Mr. Franklin Graham, President/CEO

A nondenominational specialized agency of Evangelical tradition engaged in relief and/or rehabilitation, childrens programs, development, evangelism and medical work.

Purpose: "...to provide spiritual and physical aid to hurting people around the world... to serve the church worldwide to promote the Gospel of the Lord Jesus Christ."

Year Founded in US: 1970

Income for Overseas Min: $304,169,762.00

Gifts in Kind: $159,250,958.00

Fully Supported US Personnel Overseas:

Expecting to serve more than 4 years: 5
Expecting to serve 1 to 4 years: 101
Other personnel:
Home ministry & office staff in US: 623

Countries: Bolivia; Cambodia; Congo, Democratic Republic of; Ecuador; Ethiopia 1; Honduras; Iraq; Kenya 2; Kosovo; Liberia; Mexico; Mongolia; Mozambique; Myanmar/Burma; Niger; Philippines; Sudan 2; Uganda; Vietnam

SAND Institutes International
693 Naoma Dr.
Crete, IL 60417 USA

Phone: (708) 367-1605
Fax: (708) 367-1605
E-mail: sand_ministries@yahoo.com
Web Site: www.sandinternational.org

Mr. Donald Sobkoviak, President

An interdenominational support agency of Independent tradition engaged in agricultural programs, development and training. SAND is an acronym for: Social Agriculture & New-life Development.

Purpose: "...to help train mission and development workers in the 'two-handed approach' to physical and spiritual development."

Year Founded in US: 1982

Personnel:
Short-term less than 1 year: 3

SAT-7 North America
PO Box 2770
Easton, MD 21601 USA

Phone: (410) 770-9804
Fax: (410) 770-9807
E-mail: usa@sat7.org
Web Site: www.sat7.org
Associations: The Mission Exchange

Mr. Paul Dilcher, Exec. Director

An interdenominational specialized agency of Evangelical tradition engaged in broadcasting, childrens programs, evangelism and funds transmission. Data from 2005.

Purpose: "...to provide the churches and Christians of the Middle East and North Africa with an opportunity to witness to Jesus Christ through inspirational, informative and educational television services."

Year Founded in US: 1997

Income for Overseas Min: $3,500,000.00

Personnel:
  Home ministry & office staff in US: 9

Scripture Union, USA
PO Box 215
Valley Forge, PA 19481 USA
Phone: (610) 935-2807
Fax: (610) 935-2809
E-mail: info@scriptureunion.org
Web Site: www.scriptureunion.org
Whitney T. Kuniholm, President

A service agency of Evangelical tradition engaged in literature distribution, childrens programs, discipleship, funds transmission, support of national workers and Bible engagement.

Purpose: "...to help children, young people, and their families know God's love, follow Jesus, and meet with Him daily in His Word."

Year Founded in US: 1959

Income for Overseas Min: $924,381.00

SEED International
PO Box 69
Merrifield, VA 22116-0069 USA
Phone: (703) 996-0717
Fax: (703) 996-0740
E-mail: email@seedusa.org
Web Site: www.seedusa.org
Associations: The Mission Exchange
Dr. Won Sang Lee, President

An interdenominational sending agency of Evangelical tradition engaged in church planting, business as mission, development, discipleship, Christian education and evangelism. Countries of service data from 2005.

Purpose: "...to fulfill the task of the Great Commission through assisting the local churches."

Year Founded in US: 1990

Income for Overseas Min: $2,500,000.00

Fully Supported US Personnel Overseas:
  Expecting to serve more than 4 years: 26
  Expecting to serve 1 to 4 years: 4
  Non-residential mission personnel: 100

Other personnel:
  Home ministry & office staff in US: 3

Countries: Brazil 2; Cambodia 1; Croatia 1; Czech Republic 1; Honduras; India 1; Japan

2; Kenya 1; Mexico 3; Philippines 1; Russia 1; Tanzania 1; Thailand 1; Uganda 1; Unspecified Country 9

Self-Help International
805 W. Bremer Ave.
Waverly, IA 50677 USA
Phone: (319) 352-4040
Fax: (319) 352-4040
E-mail: selfhelp@dybb.com
Web Site: www.selfhelpinternational.org
Merry L. Fredrick, Exec. Director

A nondenominational service agency of Ecumenical tradition engaged in agricultural programs, micro-credit for women, development, extension education and leadership development.

Purpose: "...to train small-scale farmers... improve and maintain their farming and transport methods; train people in developing countries...increase crop yields and improve nutrition...cooperate with others in the introduction of appropriate farming practices...and help the people of the United States understand the problems of life in developing countries."

Year Founded in US: 1959

Income for Overseas Min: $331,602.00

Gifts in Kind: $11,534.00

Personnel:
  Short-term less than 1 year: 10
  Non-US serving in own/other country: 10
  Home ministry & office staff in US: 3

Countries: Ghana; Nicaragua

SEND International USA
PO Box 513
Farmington, MI 48332 USA
Phone: (248) 477-4210
Fax: (248) 477-4232
E-mail: info@send.org
Web Site: www.send.org
Associations: CrossGlobal Link
Dr. Warren Janzen, Intl. Director

An interdenominational sending agency of Evangelical tradition engaged in church planting, discipleship, theological education, evangelism, leadership development and support of national churches.

Purpose: "...to mobilize God's people and

engage the unreached in order to establish reproducing churches."

Year Founded in US: 1947

Income for Overseas Min: $17,200,000.00

Fully Supported US Personnel Overseas:
Expecting to serve more than 4 years: 260
Expecting to serve 1 to 4 years: 6
Non-residential mission personnel: 4

Other personnel:
Short-term less than 1 year: 190
Non-US serving in own/other country: 62
Home ministry & office staff in US: 68

Countries: Asia—General; Bulgaria 14; China 7; Croatia 6; Czech Republic 7; Hungary 6; Japan 46; Kazakhstan 8; Kosovo 2; Macedonia 15; Philippines 29; Poland 11; Romania; Russia 32; Slovenia; Spain 13; Taiwan 14; Turkey 5; Ukraine 45

Sentinel Group, The

PO Box 6334
Lynnwood, WA 98036 USA

Phone: (800) 668-5657
Fax: (360) 805-2993
E-mail: info@sentinelgroup.org
Web Site: www.sentinelgroup.org

Mr. George K. Otis, Jr., President

A nondenominational support agency of Charismatic and Evangelical tradition engaged in video/DVD production/distribution, missions information service, mission-related research and training.

Purpose: "...to help the Church pray knowledgeably for end-time global evangelization and to enable communities to discover the pathway to genuine revival and societal transformation."

Year Founded in US: 1990

Income for Overseas Min: $509,000.00

Personnel:
Home ministry & office staff in US: 16

Servants in Faith & Technology (SIFAT)

2944 County Rd. 113
Lineville, AL 36266 USA

Phone: (256) 396-2015
Fax: (256) 396-2501
E-mail: info@sifat.org
Web Site: www.sifat.org

Mr. Thomas Corson, Exec. Director

An interdenominational service agency of Ecumenical and Evangelical tradition engaged in training in appropriate technologies & community development, camping programs, leadership development, missionary training and youth programs.

Purpose: "...to share God's love through service, education, and personal involvement with a needy world."

Year Founded in US: 1979

Income for Overseas Min: $1,400,000.00

Fully Supported US Personnel Overseas:
Expecting to serve more than 4 years: 5

Other personnel:
Short-term less than 1 year: 500
Non-US serving in own/other country: 35
Home ministry & office staff in US: 12

Countries: Bolivia; Ecuador 5

ServLife International

PO Box 20596
Indianapolis, IN 46220-0596 USA

Phone: (317) 544-0484
E-mail: info@servlife.org
Web Site: www.servlife.org

Mr. Joel Vestal, President

An interdenominational support agency of Evangelical tradition engaged in support of national workers, church planting, development, funds transmission and support of national churches. Data from 2001.

Year Founded in US: 1996

Seventh Day Baptist Missionary Society

19 Hillside Ave.
Ashaway, RI 02804 USA

Phone: (401) 596-4326
Fax: (401) 348-9494
E-mail: sdbmissoc@verizon.net
Web Site: www.sdbmissions.org

Mr. George Kirk Looper, Exec. Director

A denominational support agency of Baptist tradition engaged in association of missions, TEE, funds transmission, support of national churches, short-term programs and missionary training. Financial data from 2005.

Purpose: "...to coordinate and carry out... the message of salvation through faith in

Christ to all who will hear, so they may accept Him as Savior."

Year Founded in US: 1818

Income for Overseas Min: $58,000.00

Personnel:
Short-term less than 1 year: 2
Non-US serving in own/other country: 5

Countries: Finland; India; Malawi

Seventh-day Adventists, General Conference— Global Mission

12501 Old Columbia Pike
Silver Spring, MD 20904-6601 USA

Phone: (301) 680-6005
Fax: (301) 680-6090
Web Site: www.adventistmission.com

Dr. Jan Paulsen, President

A denominational sending agency of Adventist tradition engaged in evangelism, broadcasting, Christian education, literature production, medical work and mobilization for mission.

Purpose: "...to communicate to all peoples the everlasting Gospel of God's love as revealed in the life, death, resurrection, and high priestly ministry of Jesus Christ."

Year Founded in US: 1863

Income for Overseas Min: $53,959,359.00

Fully Supported US Personnel Overseas:
Expecting to serve more than 4 years: 331
Expecting to serve 1 to 4 years: 127

Other personnel:
Short-term less than 1 year: 348
Non-US serving in own/other country: 499

Countries: Afghanistan; Albania 2; Algeria; Angola; Antigua 2; Argentina; Armenia 1; Australia 3; Austria; Bangladesh; Bolivia; Botswana 2; Brazil; Burkina Faso; Cambodia 8; Cameroon 4; Chad 1; Chile 4; Colombia 1; Congo, Democratic Republic of 2; Costa Rica 2; Cote d'Ivoire; Cyprus 3; Denmark; Djibouti; Dominican Republic 2; Ecuador; Egypt 4; Equatorial Guinea 2; Ethiopia; France; French Guiana; French Polynesia; Gambia, The; Georgia 2; Germany; Ghana; Greece; Guam 50; Guinea-Bissau 2; Guyana 3; Haiti 2; Honduras 2; Hong Kong 14; India 8; Indonesia 4; Israel; Jamaica 12; Japan 3; Kazakhstan 2; Kenya 21; Korea, North 2; Korea, South 10; Kuwait; Laos; Lebanon; Lesotho 2; Liberia; Madagascar 2; Malawi 1; Mali; Marshall Islands 3; Mauritania; Mexico 12; Micronesia, Federated States of 2; Mongolia 2; Mozambique 1; Myanmar/Burma; Nepal 3; Netherlands Antilles 1; New Caledonia; Nicaragua; Niger; Nigeria 4; Oceania—General 2; Pakistan; Palau; Papua New Guinea; Paraguay; Peru; Philippines 22; Puerto Rico 8; Russia 6; Rwanda 6; Saint Vincent and the Grenadines 2; Sao Tome and Principe; Senegal; Sierra Leone; Singapore 2; Solomon Islands; South Africa 2; Spain; Sudan 6; Switzerland; Taiwan 8; Tanzania 4; Thailand 20; Togo 4; Trinidad and Tobago 4; Tunisia; Turkey 2; Uganda 2; Ukraine; United Arab Emirates 2; United Kingdom 6; Venezuela 2; Vietnam 1; Yemen 2; Zambia 2; Zimbabwe 3

Share International

207 N. Service Rd. E
Ruston, LA 71270 USA

Phone: (318) 513-2535
Fax: (318) 257-1998
E-mail: share123@bellsouth.net
Web Site: www.shareinternationalinc.com

Sammy Murimi, President

An interdenominational support agency of Evangelical tradition engaged in support of national workers, mobilization for mission, theological education, relief and/or rehabilitation, medical work, literacy work, evangelism and children at risk.

Purpose: "...challenging, training, sending, and supporting missionaries in partnership with the Church, with an initial emphasis on African nationals."

Year Founded in US: 1989

Countries: India; Kenya

Shelter for Life Intl., Inc.

7767 Elm Creek Blvd.
Maple Grove, MN 55369 USA

Phone: (763) 416-0441
Fax: (763) 416-0836
E-mail: rand@shelter.org
Web Site: www.shelter.org

Associations: AERDO

Mr. Randall Olson, President/CEO

A nondenominational specialized agency of Evangelical tradition engaged in development, agricultural programs, extension education, partnership development, short-term programs and training.

Purpose: "...to demonstrate God's love by enabling people affected by conflict and disaster to rebuild their communities and restore their lives."

Year Founded in US: 1989

Income for Overseas Min: $1,701,224.00

Gifts in Kind: $3,000.00

Fully Supported US Personnel Overseas:
Expecting to serve more than 4 years: 1
Expecting to serve 1 to 4 years: 17
Non-residential mission personnel: 4

Other personnel:
Short-term less than 1 year: 1
Non-US serving in own/other country: 18
Home ministry & office staff in US: 7

Countries: Afghanistan 1; Pakistan; Sudan

Shield of Faith Mission Intl.

PO Box 144
Bend, OR 97708 USA

Phone: (541) 382-7081
Fax: (541) 382-4471
E-mail: sfmi@sfmiusa.org
Web Site: www.sfmiusa.org

Mr. Web Loy, Vice President

A sending agency of Evangelical tradition engaged in evangelism, church planting, discipleship, missionary training and regional conferences for encouraging believers.

Purpose: "...to advance the Kingdom of God through the ministry of reconciliation by helping local churches grow in their mission awareness...to assist sending churches in training, placing and providing on-going support for their individual missionaries...to provide logistics support for each missionary and missionary team."

Year Founded in US: 1953

Fully Supported US Personnel Overseas:
Expecting to serve more than 4 years: 9
Expecting to serve 1 to 4 years: 8

Other personnel:
Short-term less than 1 year: 2
Home ministry & office staff in US: 2

Countries: Africa—General 3; Mexico 6

SIM USA, Inc.

PO Box 7900
Charlotte, NC 28241-7900 USA

Phone: (704) 588-4300
Fax: (704) 587-1518
E-mail: info@sim.org
Web Site: www.sim.org

Associations: The Mission Exchange

Dr. Steve Strauss, US Director

An interdenominational sending agency of Evangelical tradition engaged in church planting, development, theological education, TEE, medical work and mobilization for mission. Countries of service data from 2005.

Purpose: "...to glorify God by planting, strengthening, and partnering with churches around the world as we evangelize the unreached, minister to human need, disciple believers into churches, and equip churches to fulfill the Great Commission."

Year Founded in US: 1893

Fully Supported US Personnel Overseas:
Expecting to serve more than 4 years: 469
Expecting to serve 1 to 4 years: 50

Other personnel:
Short-term less than 1 year: 117
Home ministry & office staff in US: 288

Countries: Angola 7; Bangladesh 9; Benin 11; Bolivia 47; Botswana 5; Burkina Faso 9; Central African Republic 1; Chile 5; China; Cote d'Ivoire 2; Ecuador 5; Ethiopia 58; Ghana 12; Guatemala 2; Guinea 11; India 16; Italy 2; Kenya 21; Korea, South 2; Liberia 3; Malawi 15; Mozambique 8; Namibia 2; Niger 61; Nigeria 56; Paraguay 16; Peru 12; Senegal 13; South Africa 8; Switzerland 2; Tanzania 2; Thailand 5; Togo 2; Unspecified Country 12; Uruguay 6; Zambia 18; Zimbabwe 3

Slavic Gospel Association

6151 Commonwealth Dr.
Loves Park, IL 61111 USA

Phone: (815) 282-8900
Fax: (815) 282-8901
E-mail: info@sga.org
Web Site: www.sga.org

Associations: CrossGlobal Link

Dr. Robert W. Provost, President

An interdenominational support agency of Evangelical tradition engaged in theological education, Bible distribution, childrens programs, church planting, literature distribution and support of national workers.

Purpose: "...to help the evangelical churches make disciples of the people of the lands of Russia for our Lord and Savior, Jesus Christ, through prayer, strategic ministry, and financial assistance."

Year Founded in US: 1934

Personnel:
Home ministry & office staff in US: 31

Slavic Missionary Service, Inc.
PO Box 307
South River, NJ 08882 USA
Phone: (732) 873-8981
Fax: (732) 873-1625
E-mail: sms@smsinternational.org
Web Site: www.smsinternational.org
Rev. Alex Leonovich, Exec. Director

An interdenominational support agency of Baptist and Evangelical tradition engaged in support of national workers, broadcasting, church construction, church planting, funds transmission and support of national churches. Data from 2005.

Year Founded in US: 1933

Fully Supported US Personnel Overseas:
Non-residential mission personnel: 2

Other personnel:
Home ministry & office staff in US: 3

Society of St. Margaret
17 Highland Park St.
Boston, MA 02119-1436 USA
Phone: (617) 445-8961
Fax: (617) 445-7120
E-mail: ssmconvent@ssmbos.com
Web Site: www.ssmbos.com
Sister Carolyn Darr, Reverend Mother

A religious order of Episcopal tradition engaged in Christian education, childrens programs, development, leadership development, literacy work and support of national churches. Data from 2002.

Purpose: "...seeking to find Jesus present in the common life, and in ministries which concentrate on responding to the needs of the time."

Year Founded in US: 1873

Fully Supported US Personnel Overseas:
Expecting to serve more than 4 years: 2

Other personnel:
Non-US serving in own/other country: 2

Countries: Haiti 2

Son Shine Ministries Intl.
PO Box 456
Azle, TX 76098-0456 USA
Phone: (817) 444-3777
Fax: (817) 270-0199
Web Site: www.sonshineonline.org
Mr. David A. Shaffer, Director

An interdenominational sending agency of Baptist and Methodist tradition engaged in evangelism, missionary training, correspondence courses and training. Data is from 2003.

Year Founded in US: 1977

Personnel:
Home ministry & office staff in US: 6

Source of Light Ministries International, Inc.
1011 Mission Rd.
Madison, GA 30650 USA
Phone: (706) 342-0397
Fax: (706) 342-0724
E-mail: slm@sourcelight.org
Web Site: www.sourcelight.org
Associations: ANAM
Dr. William Shade, Gen. Director

An interdenominational sending agency of Baptist tradition engaged in correspondence courses, church planting, TEE, literature distribution, literature production and mobilization for mission.

Purpose: "...to bring people of every nation, language and ethnicity into a mature relationship with Jesus Christ and into fellowship with a local church family through disseminating Gospel literature, portions of Scripture and Bible correspondence courses into the hands of the multitudes in as many lands and languages as possible (Matt. 28:19-20)."

Year Founded in US: 1952

Income for Overseas Min: $2,036,347.00

Gifts in Kind: $2,500,000.00

Fully Supported US Personnel Overseas:
Expecting to serve more than 4 years: 10
Non-residential mission personnel: 1

Other personnel:
Non-US serving in own/other country: 47
Home ministry & office staff in US: 49

Countries: Argentina; Bolivia; Brazil; Chile; Congo, Democratic Republic of 2; Cote d'Ivoire; Eastern Europe—General; Ethiopia; Ghana; Guatemala 2; Guyana; Haiti 2; India; Jamaica 2; Japan; Kenya 2; Korea, South; Liberia; Mexico; Myanmar/Burma; Nigeria; Peru; Philippines; Romania; Singapore; South Africa; Togo; Uganda

South America Mission, Inc.

1021 Maxwell Mill Rd., Ste. B
Fort Mill, SC 29708 USA

Phone: (803) 802-8580
Fax: (803) 548-7955
E-mail: samusa@southamericamission.org
Web Site: www.southamericamission.org

Associations: CrossGlobal Link

Rev. W. Kirk Ogden, Jr., Exec. Director

A nondenominational sending agency of Evangelical tradition engaged in church planting, leadership development, aviation services, development, theological education and support of national churches.

Purpose: "...to build leaders to build churches."

Year Founded in US: 1914

Income for Overseas Min: $2,967,255.00

Gifts in Kind: $2,000.00

Fully Supported US Personnel Overseas:
Expecting to serve more than 4 years: 80
Expecting to serve 1 to 4 years: 11
Non-residential mission personnel: 2

Other personnel:
Short-term less than 1 year: 85
Non-US serving in own/other country: 2
Home ministry & office staff in US: 12

Countries: Bolivia 25; Brazil 18; Colombia 6; Paraguay 5; Peru 26

South American Missionary Society (USA)

PO Box 399
Ambridge, PA 15003 USA

Phone: (724) 266-0669
Fax: (724) 266-5681
E-mail: info@sams-usa.org
Web Site: www.sams-usa.org

Associations: The Mission Exchange

Mr. Stewart Wicker, President & Msn. Director

A transdenominational sending agency of Anglican tradition engaged in church planting, discipleship, Christian education, leadership development, medical work and short-term programs.

Purpose: "...to recruit, send, and support missionaries to be witnesses and make disciples for Jesus Christ in fellowship with the Episcopal/Anglican Church primarily in the Americas...to have missionaries share the Gospel, establish churches, and train nationals..."

Year Founded in US: 1976

Income for Overseas Min: $1,629,811.00

Fully Supported US Personnel Overseas:
Expecting to serve more than 4 years: 4

Countries: Uganda 4

Southern Baptist Convention International Mission Board

PO Box 6767
Richmond, VA 23230 USA

Phone: (804) 219-1209
Fax: (804) 254-8987
E-mail: dsteverson@imb.org
Web Site: www.imb.org

Associations: The Mission Exchange

Dr. Jerry Rankin, President

A denominational sending agency of Baptist tradition engaged in church planting, theological education, TEE, evangelism, leadership development and mission-related research.

Purpose: "...to make Jesus Christ known among all peoples."

Year Founded in US: 1845

Income for Overseas Min:
$256,036,000.00

Fully Supported US Personnel Overseas:
Expecting to serve more than 4 years: 4100
Expecting to serve 1 to 4 years: 1027

Countries: Unspecified Country 4100

Sowers International, The

26347 Governor Ave.
Harbor City, CA 90710-3617 USA

Phone: (310) 325-0950
Fax: (310) 325-9593
E-mail: gwynn@sower.org

Web Site: www.sower.org

Mr. Gwynn Lewis, Exec. Director

A transdenominational support agency of Evangelical tradition engaged in support of national workers, Bible distribution, evangelism, short-term programs and missionary training. Statistical data and countries of service from 2002.

Purpose: "...to sow the Word by raising up, equipping and sending out workers into the harvest."

Year Founded in US: 1993

Income for Overseas Min: $479,971.00

Fully Supported US Personnel Overseas:
  Expecting to serve more than 4 years: 1
  Non-residential mission personnel: 3

Other personnel:
  Short-term less than 1 year: 125
  Non-US serving in own/other country: 30
  Home ministry & office staff in US: 5

Countries: Brazil 1; China; Colombia; Paraguay 5; Peru 26

Spanish American Evangelistic Ministries

650 Linwood Dr.
El Paso, TX 79928 USA

Phone: (915) 852-2525
Fax: (915) 852-4747
E-mail: staff@saeministries.com
Web Site: www.saeministries.com

Mr. David A. Finch, Director

A denominational service agency of Christian (Restoration Movement) tradition engaged in Bible distribution, business as mission, correspondence courses, evangelism, literature distribution and literature production.

Purpose: "...to help evangelistic outreach worldwide...to provide a base and assist for new church evangelism...to offer short-term internship training...to develop a program of benevolence...to give a full accounting to all supporting churches."

Year Founded in US: 1964

Personnel:
  Home ministry & office staff in US: 2

Spanish World Ministries, Inc.

PO Box 542
Winona Lake, IN 46590 USA

Phone: (574) 267-8821
Fax: (574) 267-3524
E-mail: info@spanishworld.org
Web Site: www.spanishworld.org

Mr. Cornelius Rivera, Exec. Director

A nondenominational support agency of Fundamental tradition engaged in the production of radio broadcast in Spanish, audio recording/distribution, correspondence courses, literature distribution, providing medical supplies and support of national workers.

Purpose: "...to assist local churches in the Spanish speaking world to carry out the ministry of communicating the Gospel of the Lord Jesus Christ and making disciples."

Year Founded in US: 1959

Income for Overseas Min: $250,000.00

Fully Supported US Personnel Overseas:
  Expecting to serve more than 4 years: 16

Other personnel:
  Non-US serving in own/other country: 16
  Home ministry & office staff in US: 5

Countries: Argentina 1; Bolivia 1; Chile 1; Colombia 1; Cuba 1; Dominican Republic 1; Guatemala 1; Honduras 2; Mexico 1; Paraguay 1; Peru 1; Spain 2; Uruguay 1; Venezuela 1

Spiritual Growth Resources, Inc.

PO Box 2081
Gilroy, CA 95021-2081 USA

Phone: (408) 848-5608
Fax: (408) 848-4198
E-mail: SGR@sgrresources.org

Rev. Royal L. Peck, President

An interdenominational support agency of Evangelical tradition engaged in discipleship, evangelism and support of national workers.

Purpose: "...committed to a ministry of evangelistic outreach and discipleship training among persons who are identified as cultural Christians...to bring the Good News to Europe's post-Christian society."

Year Founded in US: 1984

Income for Overseas Min: $85,000.00

Fully Supported US Personnel Overseas:
  Non-residential mission personnel: 2

Other personnel:
  Non-US serving in own/other country: 8
  Home ministry & office staff in US: 1

Countries: Albania; Italy

Spiritual Overseers Service International

PO Box 5985
La Quinta, CA 92248 USA
Phone: (760) 345-0906
Fax: (760) 345-0906
E-mail: rfrazer1@mac.com
Web Site: www.sosinternational.us
Associations: The Mission Exchange

Dr. Richard J. Frazer, President

An interdenominational support agency of Evangelical tradition engaged in leadership development, childrens programs, support of national churches and training. Data from 2005.

Year Founded in US:

Income for Overseas Min: $100,000.00

Fully Supported US Personnel Overseas:
  Non-residential mission personnel: 7

Other personnel:
  Short-term less than 1 year: 3
  Non-US serving in own/other country: 1
  Home ministry & office staff in US: 3

Countries: India

Sports & Rec Plus

4121 Plank Rd., #433
Fredericksburg, VA 22407 USA
Phone: (571) 278-5987
Fax: (540) 854-6723
E-mail: sportsrecplus@cs.com
Web Site: www.sportsrecplus.org

Mr. Rick Mitchell, President

A denominational specialized agency of Baptist and Evangelical tradition engaged in sports program ministry, church planting, discipleship, evangelism, medical work and short-term programs.

Purpose: "...to help churches and mission organizations use sports and all forms of recreational activities for outreach, evangelism, church planting and church growth."

Year Founded in US: 1995

Income for Overseas Min: $10,500.00

Gifts in Kind: $1,200.00

Personnel:
  Short-term less than 1 year: 7
  Home ministry & office staff in US: 4

STEER, Inc.

PO Box 1236
Bismarck, ND 58502 USA
Phone: (701) 258-4911
Fax: (701) 258-7684
E-mail: ministry@steerinc.com
Web Site: www.steerinc.com

Mr. Keith Kost, Exec. Director

A nondenominational support agency of Evangelical tradition engaged in a three-way partnership program to help raise funds, agricultural programs and services for other agencies. Data from 2005.

Purpose: "...raising money to help existing missionary societies get the Gospel to the ends of the earth in the shortest possible time..."

Year Founded in US: 1957

Personnel:
  Home ministry & office staff in US: 6

STEM International

PO Box 386001
Minneapolis, MN 55438-6001 USA
Phone: (952) 996-1385
Fax: (952) 996-1384
E-mail: info@stemintl.org
Web Site: www.stemintl.org
Associations: The Mission Exchange

Rev. Roger P. Peterson, CEO/Founder

An interdenominational support agency of Christian (Restoration Movement) tradition engaged in evangelism, childrens programs, literature distribution, support of national workers, mobilization for mission and short-term programs. Countries of service data from 2005.

Purpose: "...to extend God's glory through strategic partnerships in short-term mission outreaches, training, and publications."

Year Founded in US: 1984

Income for Overseas Min: $372,047.00

Fully Supported US Personnel Overseas:
  Expecting to serve more than 4 years: 4
  Non-residential mission personnel: 2

Other personnel:

Short-term less than 1 year: 845
Home ministry & office staff in US: 26

Countries: Belize; Dominican Republic; Haiti 4; Honduras; Jamaica; Mexico; Paraguay; Trinidad and Tobago; Venezuela

Straightway Inc.

PO Box 74068
Romulus, MI 48174-0068 USA

Phone: (734) 946-0050
Fax: (734) 946-1419
E-mail: fshrum@straightway.com
Web Site: www.straightway.com

Mr. Daniel Gregg, President

A service agency engaged in transportation of cargo only.

Purpose: "...to provide a full range of quality air, marine and transportation services."

Year Founded in US: 1968

Supreme Task Intl., Inc.

PO Box 490245
Lawrenceville, GA 30049 USA

Phone: (678) 377-0179
Fax: (678) 377-0179
E-mail: supremetask@aol.com
Web Site: www.supremetask.org

Rev. Larry E. Derstine, CEO/President

An interdenominational support agency of Charismatic tradition engaged in discipleship, development, leadership development, literacy work, medical work and relief and/or rehabilitation.

Purpose: "...to train and aid nationals to reach North India with the Gospel."

Year Founded in US: 1989

Income for Overseas Min: $170,000.00

Fully Supported US Personnel Overseas:
  Expecting to serve more than 4 years: 2

Other personnel:
  Short-term less than 1 year: 10
  Non-US serving in own/other country: 30
  Home ministry & office staff in US: 2

Countries: India 2

Surfing the Nations

PO Box 29393
Honolulu, HI 96819 USA

Phone: (808) 843-2342
Fax: (808) 853-1174

E-mail: info@surfingthenations.com
Web Site: www.surfingthenations.com

Mr. Tom Bauer, Director

An interdenominational specialized agency of Charismatic tradition engaged in short-term programs, discipleship, evangelism, leadership development, relief and/or rehabilitation and youth programs. Data from 2005.

Purpose: "...to use the sport of surfing as a tool to communicate the Gospel locally and internationally."

Year Founded in US: 1998

Income for Overseas Min: $246,380.00

Fully Supported US Personnel Overseas:
  Non-residential mission personnel: 8

Other personnel:
  Short-term less than 1 year: 102
  Non-US serving in own/other country: 2
  Home ministry & office staff in US: 11

Countries: Bangladesh; Indonesia; Sri Lanka

Talking Bibles International

PO Box 906
Escondido, CA 92033 USA

Phone: (760) 745-8105
Fax: (760) 745-8150
E-mail: info@talkingbibles.org
Web Site: www.talkingbibles.org

Mr. Paul D. Hoekstra, Vice President

A nondenominational specialized agency of Reformed tradition engaged in audio recording/distribution, Bible distribution and leadership development. Countries of service data from 2005.

Purpose: "A Talking Bible in every language and village...A Talking Bible on Sunday in every church."

Year Founded in US: 1989

Income for Overseas Min: $456,093.00

Fully Supported US Personnel Overseas:
  Expecting to serve more than 4 years: 2

Other personnel:
  Short-term less than 1 year: 3
  Non-US serving in own/other country: 5
  Home ministry & office staff in US: 3

Countries: Africa—General; India; Unspecified Country 2

TCM International Institute

PO Box 24560
Indianapolis, IN 46224 USA
Phone: (317) 299-0333
Fax: (317) 290-8607
E-mail: tcm@tcmi.org
Web Site: www.tcmi.org
Dr. Tony Twist, President

A service agency of Christian (Restoration Movement) tradition engaged in theological education, benevolence and support of national churches in Eastern Europe. Data from 2005.

Purpose: "...to assist, disciple, encourage and equip Eastern and Central European Christians to reach their own people for Christ."

Year Founded in US: 1957

Income for Overseas Min: $2,274,432.00

Fully Supported US Personnel Overseas:
Expecting to serve more than 4 years: 4
Expecting to serve 1 to 4 years: 8
Non-residential mission personnel: 12

Other personnel:
Short-term less than 1 year: 200
Non-US serving in own/other country: 10
Home ministry & office staff in US: 6

Countries: Austria 4; Belarus; Bulgaria; Czech Republic; Estonia; Hungary; Moldova; Poland; Romania; Russia; Ukraine

TeachBeyond USA

PO Box 6248
Bloomingdale, IL 60108-6248 USA
E-mail: teachbeyond@teachbeyond.org
Web Site: www.teachbeyond.org
Associations: CrossGlobal Link
Dr. George Durance, President

A nondenominational sending agency of Evangelical tradition engaged in Christian education, business as mission, camping programs, evangelism, member care and mobilization for mission.

Purpose: "...to provide transformational education services to children and adults, regardless of gender, ethnicity, or religion, in order to promote holistic personal growth and enduring social benefit."

Year Founded in US: 1980

Income for Overseas Min: $1,623,684.00

Fully Supported US Personnel Overseas:
Expecting to serve more than 4 years: 18
Expecting to serve 1 to 4 years: 43

Other personnel:
Short-term less than 1 year: 23
Home ministry & office staff in US: 2

Countries: Brazil 2; Hungary; India; Switzerland; Germany 16

TEAM (The Evangelical Alliance Mission)

PO Box 969
Wheaton, IL 60187-0969 USA
Phone: (630) 653-5300
Fax: (630) 653-1826
E-mail: info@teamworld.org
Web Site: www.teamworld.org
Associations: CrossGlobal Link
Dr. Charles Davis, Intl. Director

An interdenominational sending agency of Evangelical tradition engaged in church planting, discipleship, theological education, evangelism, leadership development and medical work.

Purpose: "...to help churches send missionaries to establish reproducing churches among the nations to the glory of God."

Year Founded in US: 1890

Income for Overseas Min: $23,393,560.00

Fully Supported US Personnel Overseas:
Expecting to serve more than 4 years: 433

Other personnel:
Short-term less than 1 year: 148
Home ministry & office staff in US: 59

Countries: Asia—General 46; Australia 2; Austria 8; Brazil 6; Central Asia—General 4; Chad 20; Colombia 6; Costa Rica 2; Czech Republic 10; France 26; Germany 16; Honduras 2; Ireland 3; Italy 17; Japan 66; Java 2; Mexico 17; Middle East 24; Pakistan 27; Papua New Guinea 12; Peru 5; Philippines 9; Portugal 6; Russia 6; South Africa 22; Spain 44; Sri Lanka 1; Sweden 2; Taiwan 10; Thailand 7; Ukraine 5

Team Expansion, Inc.

4112 Old Routt Rd.
Louisville, KY 40299 USA
Phone: (502) 719-0007
Fax: (502) 719-0008
E-mail: info@teamexpansion.org

Web Site: www.teamexpansion.org

Mr. Doug K. Lucas, President

A nondenominational sending agency of Christian (Restoration Movement) tradition engaged in church planting, Christian education, support of national workers, mobilization for mission, short-term programs and Bible translation.

Purpose: "...to partner with local churches to send and sustain teams of interdependent missionaries to plant indigenous churches among unreached people groups worldwide."

Year Founded in US: 1978

Fully Supported US Personnel Overseas:
Expecting to serve more than 4 years: 175
Non-residential mission personnel: 237

Other personnel:
Short-term less than 1 year: 45
Home ministry & office staff in US: 56

Countries: Africa—General 22; Asia—General 22; Central Asia—General 13; Colombia 1; Ecuador 2; Europe—General 19; Ghana 3; Hungary 2; Ireland 2; Italy 17; Peru 8; Philippines 4; Romania 2; Spain 2; Taiwan 22; Tanzania 4; Thailand 4; Uganda 3; Ukraine 4; Venezuela 19

TEAMS for Medical Missions

PO Box 215
Macungie, PA 18062 USA
Phone: (610) 398-0070
Fax: (484) 221-9059
E-mail: t4mm@juno.com
Web Site: www.t4mm.org

Mr. Raymond Shive, Director

A nondenominational sending agency of Evangelical tradition engaged in medical work, childrens programs, evangelism, support of national churches and simple home construction.

Purpose: "...to strengthen Jamaican churches which will have the commitment, ability, and resources to make obedient disciples of Jesus Christ."

Year Founded in US: 1992

Income for Overseas Min: $416,806.00

Gifts in Kind: $172,669.00

Fully Supported US Personnel Overseas:
Expecting to serve more than 4 years: 5

Other personnel:

Short-term less than 1 year: 60
Home ministry & office staff in US: 2
Countries: Jamaica 5

Tech Serve International, Inc.

PO Box 598
Greenbrier, AR 72058 USA
Phone: (501) 679-2120
Fax: (501) 679-2017
E-mail: info@tech-serve.org
Web Site: www.techserve.org

Mr. Weston Syverson, President

A specialized agency engaged in utilities systems and construction, technical assistance, services for other agencies and supplying equipment.

Purpose: "...to support the technological needs of the modern missionary."

Year Founded in US: 1989

Fully Supported US Personnel Overseas:
Non-residential mission personnel: 4

Other personnel:
Short-term less than 1 year: 50
Home ministry & office staff in US: 5

Teen Mission, USA, Inc.

940 Holly Springs Dr.
Lexington, KY 40504 USA
Phone: (859) 278-3202
E-mail: tmusa@teenmission.org
Web Site: www.teenmission.org

Mr. Greg Herriford, Exec. Director

A nondenominational service agency of Christian (Restoration Movement) tradition engaged in short-term programs, church construction, development, evangelism, literature distribution and youth programs.

Purpose: "...to provide opportunities to see the larger world picture God sees, as they experience Him using their testimony to lead others to a saving relationship with Jesus."

Year Founded in US: 1970

Income for Overseas Min: $150,000.00

Personnel:
Short-term less than 1 year: 900
Home ministry & office staff in US: 3

Teen Missions Intl., Inc.

885 E. Hall Rd.
Merritt Island, FL 32953 USA

Phone: (321) 453-0350
Fax: (321) 452-7988
E-mail: info@teenmissions.net
Web Site: www.teenmissions.org

Mr. Robert M. Bland, Director

An interdenominational sending agency engaged in short-term programs, childrens programs, development, Christian education, missionary education, literacy work, services for other agencies, missionary training, training, video/film production/distribution, youth programs, children at risk, HIV/Aids and sports program ministry.

Purpose: "...to challenge, train, and disciple young people, exposing them to worldwide missions."

Year Founded in US: 1970

Income for Overseas Min: $2,926,115.00

Fully Supported US Personnel Overseas:
  Expecting to serve more than 4 years: 13
  Expecting to serve 1 to 4 years: 17
  Non-residential mission personnel: 14

Other personnel:
  Short-term less than 1 year: 800
  Non-US serving in own/other country: 173
  Home ministry & office staff in US: 40

Countries: Australia 4; Belize; Brazil 2; Cambodia; Cameroon 3; Ecuador; Honduras; India; Indonesia; Madagascar; Malawi; Mongolia; New Zealand; Philippines; Russia; South Africa; Tanzania 1; Uganda 1; Zambia 2; Zimbabwe

Tentmakers International

PO Box 30947
Seattle, WA 98113-0947 USA

Phone: (206) 781-3151
Fax: (206) 781-3182
E-mail: tentmakersinternational@gmail.com
Web Site: www.tentmakersinternational.com

Mr. Kenneth Smith, Dir. Finance

A nondenominational specialized agency of Ecumenical and Evangelical tradition engaged in tentmaking, business as mission, evangelism, missions information service and missionary training.

Purpose: "...to promote tentmaking worldwide and to provide training and resources for tentmakers and tentmaking organizations, including the exchange of ideas, information, and opportunities."

Year Founded in US: 1992

Personnel:
  Non-US serving in own/other country: 45
  Home ministry & office staff in US: 2

Countries: Cote d'Ivoire; Estonia; Finland; France; Gabon; Gambia, The; Germany; Ghana; Hungary; India; Indonesia; Israel; Kazakhstan; Kenya; Korea, South; Macedonia; Madagascar; Malaysia; Mali; Niger; Nigeria; New Zealand; Norway; Papua New Guinea; Philippines; Poland; Senegal; Serbia and Montenegro; Sierra Leone; Singapore; South Africa; Sri Lanka; Sudan; Sweden; Thailand; Togo; United Kingdom; Zambia; Zimbabwe

The Bodybuilders

PO Box 3556
Fayetteville, AR 72702 USA

Phone: (479) 587-9599
Fax: (479) 587-9901
E-mail: info@thebodybuilders.net
Web Site: www.thebodybuilders.net

Mr. Steve Shadrach, President

A nondenominational support agency of Evangelical tradition engaged in mobilization for mission, missionary education, management consulting/training and missionary training.

Year Founded in US: 2001

Personnel:
  Home ministry & office staff in US: 1

The Brethren Church, Inc.

524 College Ave.
Ashland, OH 44805 USA

Phone: (419) 289-1708
Fax: (419) 281-0450
E-mail: brethren@brethrenchurch.org
Web Site: www.brethrenchurch.org

Mr. Kenneth D. Hunn, Exec. Director

A denominational sending agency of Brethren tradition engaged in leadership development, childcare/orphanage programs, church planting, missionary education, theological education and support of national churches.

Purpose: "...to embrace a new day of transformed leadership, resulting in transformed congregations, whose mission is the transformation of their communities in the power of the Holy Spirit."

Year Founded in US: 1729

Income for Overseas Min: $730,000.00

Fully Supported US Personnel Overseas:
  Expecting to serve more than 4 years: 1
  Non-residential mission personnel: 1

Other personnel:
  Short-term less than 1 year: 100
  Non-US serving in own/other country: 168
  Home ministry & office staff in US: 7

Countries: Argentina; Chile; Colombia; India; Malaysia; Mexico 1; Paraguay; Peru; Philippines; Spain

The God's Story Project

PO Box 187
Hemet, CA 92546 USA

Phone: (951) 658-1619
Fax: (951) 658-9189
E-mail: info@gods-story.org
Web Site: www.gods-story.org

Dorothy A. Miller, Exec. Director

A transdenominational sending agency of Evangelical tradition engaged in video/film production/distribution, audio recording/distribution, church planting, evangelism, oral strategies and Bible storytelling/training..

Purpose: "...exists for the translation into, and production and distribution of the video, 'God's Story: From Creation to Eternity,' into world languages...and for training national instructors to tell Bible stories using an oral Bible study called 'Simply The Story.'"

Year Founded in US: 1996

Income for Overseas Min: $340,369.00

Fully Supported US Personnel Overseas:
  Non-residential mission personnel: 1

Other personnel:
  Short-term less than 1 year: 26
  Non-US serving in own/other country: 11

Countries: Ethiopia; India; Kenya; Myanmar/Burma; Nepal; Uganda; Zambia

The Gospel Furthering Fellowship

221 Hamilton Ave.
Myerstown, PA 17067 USA

Phone: (717) 866-1964
Fax: (717) 866-8527
E-mail: gff@comcast.net
Web Site: www.gffministries.com

Mr. Bruce P. Busch, Gen. Director

A sending agency of Baptist, Fundamental, and Independent tradition engaged in church planting, discipleship, theological education, evangelism and Bible translation.

Purpose: "...to initiate church planting movements among any unreached people groups...to offer short-term and summer opportunities to be directly involved in reaching unreached people groups...to go to any country if there are no other fundamental ministries trying to reach them and there is a team of people who feel God is leading them to go with GFF to get the job done."

Year Founded in US: 1935

Income for Overseas Min: $459,210.00

Gifts in Kind: $100.00

Fully Supported US Personnel Overseas:
  Expecting to serve more than 4 years: 18

Other personnel:
  Non-US serving in own/other country: 16
  Home ministry & office staff in US: 1

Countries: France 4; Indonesia 2; New Zealand 2; Spain 8; Tanzania 2

The Master's Mission, Inc.

PO Box 547
Robbinsville, NC 28771 USA

Phone: (828) 479-6873
Fax: (828) 479-2471
E-mail: info@mastersmission.org
Web Site: www.mastersmission.org

Rev. Paul Teasdale, Exec. Director, Emeritus

An interdenominational sending agency of Baptist tradition engaged in mobilization for mission, childcare/orphanage programs, church planting, development, missionary education, services for other agencies and missionary training. Countries of service data from 2005.

Purpose: "...in light of our Savior's commission to evangelize the world, we have undertaken in the power of God to equip His servants for preaching the Gospel and making disciples throughout the world with primary emphasis in establishing and developing churches in unreached areas."

Year Founded in US: 1979

Income for Overseas Min: $2,300,000.00

Gifts in Kind: $527.00

Fully Supported US Personnel Overseas:
  Expecting to serve more than 4 years: 26
Other personnel:
  Non-US serving in own/other country: 19
  Home ministry & office staff in US: 8
Countries: Congo, Democratic Republic of; Ecuador 2; India; Israel; Kazakhstan 2; Kenya 20; Nigeria; Romania 2; Uganda

The Mission Exchange

655 Village Square Dr. Ste. A
Stone Mountain, GA 30083 USA

Phone: (770) 457-6677
Fax: (770) 457-0037
E-mail: mjones@themissionexchange.org
Web Site: www.themissionexchange.org
Associations: The Mission Exchange

Rev. Steve Moore, President/CEO

A confederation of mission agencies which serves for the exchange of ideas and building of supportive relationships.

Purpose: "...to aid agencies and boards to work more efficiently, tapping into the rich resource of all our members so that the gifts God gives can be used most effectively in the task of world evangelization."

Year Founded in US: 1945

The Mission Society

PO Box 922637
Norcross, GA 30010 USA

Phone: (770) 446-1381
Fax: (770) 446-3044
E-mail: info@themissionsociety.org
Web Site: www.themissionsociety.org
Associations: The Mission Exchange

Dr. Philip R. Granger, President/CEO

An interdenominational sending agency of Methodist tradition engaged in support of national churches, children at risk, church planting, theological education, evangelism and leadership development. Countries of service data from 2005.

Purpose: "...to facilitate obedience to the Great Commission by the body of Christ."

Year Founded in US: 1984

Income for Overseas Min: $6,800,129.00

Fully Supported US Personnel Overseas:
  Expecting to serve more than 4 years: 46
  Expecting to serve 1 to 4 years: 30

Non-residential mission personnel: 4
Other personnel:
  Short-term less than 1 year: 12
  Home ministry & office staff in US: 31
Countries: China 3; Colombia; Costa Rica 2; France 6; Ghana 6; Hungary; India 2; Japan 2; Kazakhstan 6; Mexico 2; Paraguay 6; Peru 4; Philippines 2; Russia 4; Tanzania 1

The Waray-Waray Project

414 Highland Dr.
Bartlesville, OK 74003 USA

Phone: (918) 336-0750
Fax: (918) 336-3977
E-mail: mail.waray@yahoo.com
Web Site: www.waray.org

Mr. Gordon Clymer, Director

A nondenominational service agency of Christian (Restoration Movement) tradition engaged in church planting, broadcasting, evangelism, support of national workers, support of national churches and supplying equipment.

Purpose: "...to assist Filipino natives in evangelizing the Waray-Waray tribal group."

Year Founded in US: 1992

Income for Overseas Min: $16,475.00

Personnel:
  Non-US serving in own/other country: 11
Countries: Philippines

The Word for the World USA

PO Box 26363
Colorado Springs, CO 80936 USA

Phone: (719) 594-2052
Fax: (719) 594-4046
E-mail: info@twftw.org
Web Site: www.twftw.org

Veroni Kruger, President

A nondenominational sending agency of Evangelical tradition engaged in Bible translation, Bible distribution, linguistics, literacy work, support of national workers and training.

Purpose: "...to show the glory of God through transformed lives by the power of His Word in everyone's heart language."

Year Founded in US: 1997

Income for Overseas Min: $490,000.00

Gifts in Kind: $3,000.00

Fully Supported US Personnel Overseas:
  Expecting to serve more than 4 years: 4
Other personnel:
  Non-US serving in own/other country: 103
  Home ministry & office staff in US: 3
Countries: Congo, Democratic Republic of;
Ethiopia; India; Malawi; Slovakia 2; South
Africa; Tanzania; United Kingdom; Zambia
2; Zimbabwe

Things To Come Mission, Inc.
PO Box 127
Beech Grove, IN 46107 USA
Phone: (317) 783-0300
Fax: (435) 579-7862
E-mail: tcm@tcmusa.org
Web Site: www.tcmusa.org
Mr. Ben N. Anderson, Exec. Director
A nondenominational sending agency of
Evangelical and Dispensational tradition en-
gaged in church planting, theological ed-
ucation, evangelism, support of national
workers and short-term programs.
Purpose: "...to preach the Gospel of sal-
vation through faith in the shed blood of
Jesus Christ...to train believers for minis-
try and leadership, and to establish indige-
nous, local churches..."
Year Founded in US: 1955
Income for Overseas Min: $900,000.00
Fully Supported US Personnel Overseas:
  Expecting to serve more than 4 years: 5
  Expecting to serve 1 to 4 years: 2
Other personnel:
  Short-term less than 1 year: 30
  Non-US serving in own/other country: 119
  Home ministry & office staff in US: 6
Countries: Brazil 3; Cambodia; Indonesia;
Kenya; Middle East 2; Philippines; South Af-
rica; Thailand; Uganda; United Kingdom

TITUS International
1515 McBrien Rd.
Chattanooga, TN 37412 USA
Phone: (423) 867-7079
Fax: (423) 867-7263
E-mail: info@titusinternational.org
Web Site: www.titusinternational.org
Mr. Lowell David Marcum, President
A nondenominational service agency of

Baptist tradition engaged in support of na-
tional workers, camping programs, church
planting, discipleship and evangelism. Sta-
tistical data from 2005.
Purpose: "...to teach nationals to reach
their world for Christ."
Year Founded in US: 1984
Income for Overseas Min: $800,000.00
Fully Supported US Personnel Overseas:
  Expecting to serve more than 4 years: 16
  Non-residential mission personnel: 14
Other personnel:
  Short-term less than 1 year: 20
  Non-US serving in own/other country: 80
  Home ministry & office staff in US: 3
Countries: Austria 2; Azerbaijan; Czech Re-
public 2; France; Moldova 1; Philippines;
Romania 5; Russia; Ukraine 6

TMA Ministries Inc.
PO Box 49060
St. Petersburg, FL 33743 USA
Phone: (901) 301-1550
E-mail: TMAjl3@msn.com
Dr. John L. Langston III, President
A nondenominational service agency of
Evangelical tradition engaged in theologi-
cal education through overseas seminaries,
evangelism, technical assistance/architectu-
al services and training national pastors.
Purpose: "...to provide architectual assis-
tance to other overseas ministries...to evan-
gelize to the architectual global commu-
nity...to theologically educate and to train
national pastors and Christian workers."
Year Founded in US: 1982
Income for Overseas Min: $3,000.00
Gifts in Kind: $1,000.00
Fully Supported US Personnel Overseas:
  Expecting to serve more than 4 years: 6
  Expecting to serve 1 to 4 years: 4
  Non-residential mission personnel: 4
Other personnel:
  Non-US serving in own/other country: 10
Countries: Belize; Burkina Faso 2; Guyana
1; India 1; Mexico; Trinidad and Tobago 1;
United Kingdom 1

Touch the World Ministries, Inc.

1 Maple St.
Allendale, NJ 07401 USA
Phone: (201) 760-9925
Fax: (201) 760-9926
Web Site: www.touchtheworld.org
Mr. Greg Prairie, Chief Experience Officer

A nondenominational sending agency of Baptist tradition engaged in short-term programs, audio recording/distribution, Christian education, evangelism and missionary training.

Purpose: "...to introduce young people to Jesus Christ through various effective ministries, disciple them into the local body of assembled believers, and equip them to reach others with the Gospel."

Year Founded in US: 1991

Income for Overseas Min: $636,000.00

Fully Supported US Personnel Overseas:
  Non-residential mission personnel: 2

Other personnel:
  Home ministry & office staff in US: 5

Training Evangelistic Leadership (T.E.L.), Inc.

PO Box E
Denton, TX 76202 USA
Phone: (940) 765-1449
E-mail: development@tel-intl.org
Web Site: www.tel-intl.org
Mr. Sean Collins, Intl. Director

An interdenominational sending agency of Evangelical tradition engaged in evangelism, mass, Bible memorization, discipleship and support of national workers.

Purpose: "...to minister alongside existing national churches called to develop multinational gospel teams which major in evangelism, follow-up, and discipleship."

Year Founded in US: 1977

Income for Overseas Min: $655,905.00

Fully Supported US Personnel Overseas:
  Expecting to serve more than 4 years: 21
  Expecting to serve 1 to 4 years: 1

Other personnel:
  Short-term less than 1 year: 1
  Non-US serving in own/other country: 48
  Home ministry & office staff in US: 2

Countries: China 10; India 2; Indonesia 3; Philippines 4; Vietnam 2

Trans World Evangelism, Inc.

PO Box 1123
Norman, OK 73070-1123 USA
E-mail: info@transworldevangelism.com
Web Site: www.transworldevangelism.com
Apostle Paul J. Cunningham, CEO/President

An interdenominational sending agency engaged in theological education, audio recording/distribution, childcare/orphanage programs, discipleship, Christian education and TEE.

Purpose: "...to change nations through indigenous Bible colleges."

Year Founded in US: 1960

Income for Overseas Min: $180,000.00

Fully Supported US Personnel Overseas:
  Expecting to serve 1 to 4 years: 5
  Non-residential mission personnel: 4

Other personnel:
  Short-term less than 1 year: 6
  Home ministry & office staff in US: 1

Countries: Philippines

Tribes and Nations Outreach

PO Box 2174
Pasadena, CA 91102 USA
Phone: (626) 584-0383
Fax: (626) 582-0383
E-mail: tnousa@aol.com
Web Site: www.tribesandnationsoutreach.org
Arlene del Campo, Dev. Director

A nondenominational support agency of Charismatic and Pentecostal tradition engaged in training, agricultural programs, Bible distribution, church planting, medical work and short-term programs.

Purpose: "...to help build the body of Christ in Asia through training and other forms of encouragement."

Countries: Cambodia; China; Hong Kong; India; Indonesia; Laos; Macau; Myanmar/Burma; Nepal; Philippines; Thailand; Vietnam

Turkish World Outreach

508 Fruitvale Ct.
Grand Junction, CO 81504 USA

Phone: (970) 434-1942
Fax: (970) 434-1461
E-mail: info@two-fot.org
Web Site: www.two-fot.org
Mr. Steve Hagerman, US Director

A nondenominational support agency of Christian (Restoration Movement) tradition engaged in church planting, literature distribution, prayer mobilization, Bible distribution and evangelism.

Purpose: "...to multiply disciples through qualified laborers...to establish churches among the Turkish peoples and the cultures they touch."

Year Founded in US: 1969

Fully Supported US Personnel Overseas:
    Expecting to serve more than 4 years: 35
    Non-residential mission personnel: 6

Other personnel:
    Non-US serving in own/other country: 35
    Home ministry & office staff in US: 13

Countries: Germany 4; Turkey 31

TWR

PO Box 8700
Cary, NC 27512-8700 USA
Phone: (800) 456-7897
Fax: (919) 460-3702
E-mail: info@twr.org
Web Site: www.twr.org
Associations: CrossGlobal Link, AERDO
Mr. Lauren Libby, President/CEO

A nondenominational specialized agency of Evangelical tradition engaged in broadcasting, audio recording/distribution, correspondence courses, evangelism and technical assistance.

Purpose: "...to assist the Church to fulfill the command of Jesus Christ to make disciples of all peoples, and to do so by using and making available mass media..."

Year Founded in US: 1952

Income for Overseas Min: $20,560,000.00

Fully Supported US Personnel Overseas:
    Expecting to serve more than 4 years: 62
    Expecting to serve 1 to 4 years: 3

Countries: Austria 12; Benin 2; Cambodia 4; Germany 2; Guam 9; Netherlands 8; Netherlands Antilles 2; Singapore 4; Slovakia 2; South Africa 15; Swaziland 2

U.S. Center for World Mission

1605 E. Elizabeth St.
Pasadena, CA 91104-2921 USA
Phone: (626) 797-1111
Fax: (626) 398-2240
E-mail: personnel@uscwm.org
Web Site: www.uscwm.org
Associations: The Mission Exchange, CrossGlobal Link
Rev. Greg H. Parsons, Gen. Director

An interdenominational support agency of Evangelical tradition engaged in mobilization for mission, association of missions, discipleship, Christian education, missionary education, theological education and TEE. Countries of service data from 2005.

Purpose: "...to make the glory of God fully known, by advancing His Kingdom, by seeing all peoples on earth worship and obey God."

Year Founded in US: 1976

Income for Overseas Min: $250,000.00

Fully Supported US Personnel Overseas:
    Expecting to serve more than 4 years: 10
    Expecting to serve 1 to 4 years: 6
    Non-residential mission personnel: 5

Other personnel:
    Non-US serving in own/other country: 5

Countries: China; India 4; Korea, South 1; Mexico; Philippines 3; United Kingdom 2

Ukrainian Childrens Fund

1629 Pine Dr.
Grove, OK 74344 USA
Phone: (918) 791-1001
Fax: (918) 786-3874
E-mail: info@ukrainianchildrensfund.org
Web Site: www.ukrainianchildrensfund.org
Mr. David L. Tinney, Founder/President

A support agency of Evangelical tradition engaged in childcare/orphanage programs, childrens programs, providing medical supplies and relief and/or rehabilitation. Data from 2005.

Year Founded in US: 2001

Income for Overseas Min: $10,000.00

Personnel:
    Short-term less than 1 year: 20
    Non-US serving in own/other country: 2

Countries: Ukraine

United Board for Christian Higher Education in Asia

475 Riverside Dr. Rm. 1221
New York, NY 10115 USA
Phone: (212) 870-2600
Fax: (212) 870-2322
E-mail: info@unitedboard.org
Web Site: www.unitedboard.org
Patricia S. Stranahan, President

An interdenominational service agency of Ecumenical tradition engaged in leadership development, technical assistance and training. Activities from 2002.

Purpose: "...to contribute to higher education and to the exchange of resources in and with Asia for the pursuit of truth and knowledge...and full human development understood from the perspective of Christian faith."

Year Founded in US: 1932

Personnel:
   Home ministry & office staff in US: 11

United Church of Christ— Global Ministries

700 Prospect Ave. E.
Cleveland, OH 44115 USA
Phone: (216) 736-3201
Fax: (216) 736-3203
E-mail: wcm@ucc.org
Web Site: www.ucc.org
Rev. Cally Rogers-Witte, Co-Executive

A denominational sending agency of Christian (Restoration Movement) and Congregational tradition engaged in support of national churches, development, Christian education, theological education, leadership development and partnership development working in partnership with the Christian Church (Disciples of Christ) Global Ministries. Joint statistics found with Christian Church (Disciples of Christ) Global Ministries.

Year Founded in US: 1812

United Evangelical Churches

PO Box 1000
San Juan Bautista, CA 95045-1000 USA
Phone: (800) 595-4832
Fax: (831) 635-0909
E-mail: admin@uecol.org

Web Site: www.uecol.org
Mr. Robert B. Fort, Chairman/CEO

A service agency of Charismatic and Evangelical tradition engaged in missionary support, church planting, evangelism, member care and short-term programs.

Purpose: "...to serve God by serving those who serve."

Year Founded in US: 1958

Income for Overseas Min: $71,435.00

Fully Supported US Personnel Overseas:
   Expecting to serve more than 4 years: 3
   Non-residential mission personnel: 6

Other personnel:
   Short-term less than 1 year: 6
   Non-US serving in own/other country: 1
   Home ministry & office staff in US: 5

Countries: Bolivia 1; Philippines 2; Trinidad and Tobago

United Methodist Church, General Board of Global Ministries

475 Riverside Dr., Rm. 350
New York, NY 10115 USA
Phone: (800) 862-4246
Fax: (212) 870-3748
E-mail: info@gbgm-umc.org
Web Site: www.gbgm-umc.org
Associations: CWS
Edward W. Pup, Gen. Secretary

A denominational sending agency of Methodist tradition responding to program and personnel needs through relationships to partner churches and ecumenical organizations all over the world, including support of national churches, education, information service, relief and/or rehabilitation, short-term programs and missionary training. Data from 2005.

Year Founded in US: 1820

Income for Overseas Min: $91,200,000.00

Fully Supported US Personnel Overseas:
   Expecting to serve more than 4 years: 486

Other personnel:
   Short-term less than 1 year: 93
   Non-US serving in own/other country: 308

Countries: Unspecified Country 486

United Pentecostal Church Intl.—Compassion Services International

8855 Dunn Rd.
Hazelwood, MO 63042 USA
Phone: (314) 837-7300
Fax: (314) 837-2387
Web Site: www.upci.org

Bruce Howell, Foreign Missions Director

A denominational sending agency of Pentecostal and Apostolic tradition engaged in evangelism, church planting, discipleship, theological education, evangelism and leadership development. Data from 2005.

Year Founded in US: 1945

Fully Supported US Personnel Overseas:
Expecting to serve 1 to 4 years: 340
Non-residential mission personnel: 551

Other personnel:
Short-term less than 1 year: 300
Non-US serving in own/other country: 236
Home ministry & office staff in US: 35

Countries: Albania; American Samoa; Argentina; Armenia; Aruba; Australia; Austria; Azerbaijan; Bahamas, The; Bangladesh; Belarus; Belgium; Belize; Benin; Bhutan; Bolivia; Bosnia and Herzegovina; Botswana; Brazil; Bulgaria; Burkina Faso; Burundi; Cambodia; Cameroon; Caribbean—General; Cayman Islands; Central African Republic; Chile; China; Cote d'Ivoire; Colombia; Congo, Democratic Republic of; Costa Rica; Croatia; Cuba; Cyprus; Czech Republic; Dominican Republic; Ecuador; Egypt; El Salvador; Equatorial Guinea; Europe—General; Fiji; Finland; France; French Guiana; Gabon; Gambia, The; Georgia; Germany; Ghana; Greece; Grenada; Guam; Guatemala; Guyana; Haiti; Hong Kong; Honduras; Hungary; India; Indonesia; Israel; Italy; Jamaica; Japan; Jordan; Kazakhstan; Kenya; Korea, South; Laos; Latvia; Lebanon; Lesotho; Liberia; Lithuania; Macedonia; Madagascar; Malawi; Malaysia; Malta; Mauritius; Mexico; Micronesia, Federated States of; Middle East; Morocco; Mozambique; Myanmar/Burma; Namibia; Nepal; Netherlands; New Caledonia; New Zealand; Nicaragua; Niger; Nigeria; Norway; Oceania—General; Pakistan; Palestine; Panama; Papua New Guinea; Paraguay; Peru; Philippines; Poland; Portugal; Puerto Rico; Reunion; Romania; Russia; Rwanda; Samoa; Serbia and Montenegro; Seychelles; Sierra Leone; Singapore; Slovakia; Solomon Islands; South Africa; Spain; Sri Lanka; Sudan; Suriname; Swaziland; Sweden; Switzerland; Taiwan; Tanzania; Thailand; Togo; Tonga; Trinidad and Tobago; Turkey; Uganda; Ukraine; United Kingdom; Uruguay; Vanuatu; Venezuela; Vietnam; Zambia; Zimbabwe

United World Mission

9401B Southern Pine Blvd.
Charlotte, NC 28273-5596 USA
Phone: (704) 357-3355
Fax: (704) 357-6389
E-mail: info@uwm.org
Web Site: www.uwm.org
Associations: CrossGlobal Link

Dr. John Bernard, Exec. Director

A nondenominational sending agency of Evangelical tradition engaged in church planting, theological education, leadership development, support of national churches, partnership development and missionary training.

Purpose: "...to see the nations saturated with worshipping, serving, disciple-making churches that reproduce themselves and transform their societies for God's glory."

Year Founded in US: 1946

Income for Overseas Min: $7,260,015.00

Fully Supported US Personnel Overseas:
Expecting to serve more than 4 years: 70
Expecting to serve 1 to 4 years: 1
Non-residential mission personnel: 10

Other personnel:
Non-US serving in own/other country: 4
Home ministry & office staff in US: 3

Countries: Belgium 1; Central African Republic 2; Chile 2; China 4; Costa Rica 4; Croatia 2; Estonia 2; Greece 2; Hungary 3; India 6; Kazakhstan 4; Kenya 5; Mali 4; Nepal 4; Nicaragua 2; Russia 2; Senegal 9; Slovenia 4; Thailand 6; United Kingdom 2

University Bible Fellowship

6558 N. Artesian Ave.
Chicago, IL 60645 USA
Phone: (773) 338-1155
Fax: (773) 743-1554
Web Site: www.ubf.org

Associations: CrossGlobal Link

Dr. John Jun, Gen. Director

An interdenominational sending agency of Presbyterian and Reformed tradition engaged in evangelism, Bible memorization, discipleship, missionary education, leadership development, tentmaking and missionary training.

Purpose: "...therefore, go, and make disciples of all nations, baptizing them in the name of the Father and of the Son and of the Holy Spirit, and teaching them to obey everything I have commanded you..." (Matt. 28:18-20)

Year Founded in US: 1975

Income for Overseas Min: $1,130,000.00

Fully Supported US Personnel Overseas:
Expecting to serve more than 4 years: 4
Expecting to serve 1 to 4 years: 16
Non-residential mission personnel: 2

Other personnel:
Non-US serving in own/other country: 2
Home ministry & office staff in US: 75

Countries: Belize; China; Germany 1; Indonesia; Japan; Korea, South 1; Mongolia; Sudan; Taiwan; Turkey; Ukraine 2

UWEZO International, Inc.

PO Box 434
Hudson, WI 54016 USA

Phone: (715) 760-1882
E-mail: uwezo413@hotmail.com
Andrea Oreso, Exec. Director

A nondenominational specialized agency of Evangelical and Pentecostal tradition engaged in leadership development, support of national churches, partnership development, short-term programs, missionary training and training.

Purpose: "...to share the Good News of salvation to inmates, addicts, and their families through outreach ministries, so that they can live free in Christ..."

Year Founded in US: 2000

Personnel:
Home ministry & office staff in US: 1

Vellore Christian Medical College Board (USA), Inc.

475 Riverside Dr. Ste. 243
New York, NY 10115 USA

Phone: (212) 870-2640
Fax: (212) 870-2173
E-mail: usaboard@vellorecmc.org
Web Site: www.vellorecmc.org
Rev. Louis L. Knowles, President

An interdenominational specialized agency of Ecumenical tradition engaged in medical work, development, funds transmission, volunteer recruitment, providing medical supplies, supplying equipment and training. Activites from 2002.

Purpose: "...to provide a focus for excellence and integrity through the support of the wide range of programs of Vellore Christian Medical College and Hospital, Vellore, India."

Year Founded in US: 1948

Venture International

2405 E. Southern Ave. Ste. 6
Tempe, AZ 85282 USA

Phone: (480) 730-2710
E-mail: info@ventureint.org
Web Site: www.ventureint.org
Mr. Bruce Menser, President/CEO

An interdenominational service agency of Evangelical tradition engaged in development, disability assistance programs, support of national churches, partnership development, relief and/or rehabilitation. Data from 2005.

Purpose: "...serves as a bridge between those in need and those who want to help God's people in the Middle East; empowering and enhancing their work through strategic partnerships, emergency relief, small business creation and people development."

Year Founded in US: 1986

Personnel:
Non-US serving in own/other country: 51
Home ministry & office staff in US: 6

Countries: Egypt; Iraq; Israel; Jordan; Kyrgyzstan; Lebanon

Village Ministries Intl.

5350 S. Western Ave., Ste. 200
Oklahoma City, OK 73109 USA

Phone: (405) 634-4373
Fax: (405) 634-4465
E-mail: bobt@villageministries.org
Web Site: www.villageministries.org

Mr. Robert L. Thompson, CEO

A nondenominational service agency of Evangelical and Fundamental tradition engaged in discipleship, evangelism, literature distribution, training and translation work.

Purpose: "...to take both the Gospel and the teaching of God's Word to people of the world."

Year Founded in US: 1991

Income for Overseas Min: $360,000.00

Personnel:
 Short-term less than 1 year: 19
 Non-US serving in own/other country: 75
 Home ministry & office staff in US: 4

Countries: Belarus; Ghana; India; Myanmar/Burma; Nicaragua; Nigeria; Sri Lanka; Tanzania

Vineyard Church USA—Missions

112 Harvard Ave., #265
Claremont, CA 91711 USA
Phone: (909) 626-0773
E-mail: office@vineyardmissions.org
Web Site: www.vineyardmissions.org
Rev. Mark Fields, Missions Coordinator

A consortium of 8 different associations of Charismatic and Evangelical tradition engaged in church planting, evangelism, leadership development and support of national churches. There are approximately 380 Vineyard Churches outside the USA in 52 countries. The eight associations oversee the work being done in different areas of the world. Data from 2005.

Purpose: "...to equip the saints for the advancement of the Kingdom of God through evangelizing and church planting."

Year Founded in US: 1982

Virginia Mennonite Missions

901 Parkwood Dr.
Harrisonburg, VA 22802 USA
Phone: (540) 434-9727
Fax: (540) 434-7627
E-mail: info@vmmissions.org
Web Site: www.vmmissions.org
Mr. Loren E. Horst, President

A denominational sending agency of Mennonite tradition engaged in church planting, development, Christian education, evangelism and short-term programs.

Purpose: "...to invite people to faithful living in Jesus Christ by forming and enabling congregations and individuals to continue God's reconciling work in the world."

Year Founded in US: 1919

Income for Overseas Min: $1,100,000.00

Gifts in Kind: $4,000.00

Fully Supported US Personnel Overseas:
 Expecting to serve more than 4 years: 7
 Expecting to serve 1 to 4 years: 22

Other personnel:
 Short-term less than 1 year: 71
 Non-US serving in own/other country: 1
 Home ministry & office staff in US: 12

Countries: Asia—General; Belize; Eastern Europe—General 3; Italy 2; Jamaica; Latin America—General; Middle East; Trinidad and Tobago 2

Vision Beyond Borders

PO Box 6770
Sheridan, WY 82801 USA
Phone: (307) 672-5995
Fax: (307) 673-2694
E-mail: ptklein2003@yahoo.com
Web Site: www.vbbonline.org
Mr. Patrick Klein, Exec. Director

A service agency engaged in Bible distribution, childcare/orphanage programs, children at risk, support of national workers, relief and/or rehabilitation and trafficking/slavery issues.

Purpose: "...to help fulfill the Great Commission as stated by Jesus in Matthew 28:18-20 by meeting the spiritual and physical needs of people throughout the world."

Year Founded in US: 1994

Income for Overseas Min: $697,807.00

Gifts in Kind: $267,874.00

Personnel:
 Short-term less than 1 year: 50
 Home ministry & office staff in US: 5

visionSynergy

PO Box 232
Edmonds, WA 98026 USA
Phone: (425) 673-5644
Fax: (425) 775-8262
E-mail: info@visionsynergy.net

Web Site: www.visionsynergy.net

Associations: CrossGlobal Link, The Mission Exchange

Mr. Phillip W. Butler, Exec. Director

An interdenominational service agency of Evangelical tradition engaged in partnership development, extension education, leadership development, management consulting/training, services for other agencies and missionary training.

Purpose: "...to accelerate world evangelization among the neediest and most unreached by empowering the global Church's commitment to Kingdom collaboration."

Year Founded in US: 2003

Income for Overseas Min: $325,000.00

Personnel:
Home ministry & office staff in US: 1

Voice of the Martyrs, The

PO Box 443
Bartlesville, OK 74005-0443 USA

Phone: (877) 337-0302

Fax: (918) 338-0189

Web Site: www.persecution.com

Associations: CrossGlobal Link

Mr. Tom White, Exec. Director

A nondenominational support agency of Evangelical tradition engaged in Bible distribution, audio recording/distribution, broadcasting, literature distribution, providing medical supplies and support of national workers, working in 71 countries. Data from 2005.

Purpose: "...to serve the persecuted church through practical and spiritual assistance while leading Christians in the free world into fellowship with them."

Year Founded in US: 1967

Income for Overseas Min: $25,305,375.00

Gifts in Kind: $14,183,885.00

Personnel:
Home ministry & office staff in US: 111

Volunteers in Medical Missions

265 S. Cove Rd.
Seneca, SC 29672 USA

Phone: (864) 885-9023

Fax: (864) 885-9411

E-mail: missions@vimm.org

Web Site: www.vimm.org

Mr. Larry Secrest, Exec. Director

A nondenominational sending agency of Evangelical tradition engaged in medical work, development, evangelism and short-term programs.

Purpose: "...to minister to the physical and spiritual needs of children and adults in developing countries throughout the world and will provide opportunities for Christian medical professionals and other volunteers to experience missions first-hand."

Year Founded in US: 1986

Income for Overseas Min: $520,478.00

Fully Supported US Personnel Overseas:
Expecting to serve more than 4 years: 1

Other personnel:
Short-term less than 1 year: 230
Home ministry & office staff in US: 4

Countries: Afghanistan 1

Walk Thru the Bible Ministries, Inc.

4201 N. Peachtree Rd.
Atlanta, GA 30341 USA

Phone: (770) 458-9300

Fax: (770) 454-9313

Web Site: www.walkthru.org

Associations: The Mission Exchange

Mr. Chip Ingram, President

A nondenominational support agency of Evangelical tradition engaged in training, broadcasting, literature production, support of national churches and support of national workers. Data from 2005.

Purpose: "...to contribute to the spiritual growth of Christians worldwide through Bible teaching, tools, and training."

Year Founded in US: 1976

Income for Overseas Min: $1,951,167.00

Gifts in Kind: $382,136.00

Fully Supported US Personnel Overseas:
Non-residential mission personnel: 6

Other personnel:
Non-US serving in own/other country: 275
Home ministry & office staff in US: 47

Countries: Angola; Argentina; Armenia; Australia; Austria; Azerbaijan; Bahrain; Bangladesh; Belarus; Bhutan; Bolivia; Botswana; Brazil; Bulgaria; Cambodia; Cameroon; China; Colombia; Congo, Democratic Republic of; Costa Rica; Cuba; Dominican Republic; Ecuador; Egypt; El Salvador; Estonia; Ethiopia; Fiji; Georgia; Ghana; Guatemala; Haiti; Honduras; Hungary; India; Indonesia; Ireland; Iraq; Israel; Japan; Jordan; Kazakhstan; Kenya; Korea, South; Kuwait; Latvia; Lebanon; Lesotho; Liberia; Lithuania; Malawi; Malaysia; Mexico; Moldova; Mongolia; Morocco; Mozambique; Myanmar/Burma; Namibia; Nepal; Nigeria; Oman; Pakistan; Palestine; Peru; Philippines; Qatar; Romania; Russia; Saudi Arabia; Serbia and Montenegro; Sierra Leone; Singapore; South Africa; Sri Lanka; Sudan; Swaziland; Syria; Tanzania; Thailand; Togo; Tunisia; United Arab Emirates; Uganda; Ukraine; United Kingdom; Vietnam; Yemen; Zambia; Zimbabwe

Warm Blankets Orphan Care International

5105 Tollview Dr., Ste. 155
Rolling Meadows, IL 60008 USA

Phone: (847) 577-1070
Fax: (847) 577-1080
E-mail: advisor@warmblankets.org
Web Site: www.warmblankets.org
Associations: AERDO

Mr. Craig Muller, President/CEO

An interdenominational service agency of Evangelical, Pentecostal and Christian tradition engaged in childcare/orphanage programs, children at risk, church planting, discipleship, evangelism, leadership development and orphan rescue & care.

Purpose: "...dedicated to the rescue of orphans and widows through third world church planting and orphanage outreach."

Year Founded in US: 1999

Income for Overseas Min: $1,895,751.00

Gifts in Kind: $194,985.00

Fully Supported US Personnel Overseas:
  Expecting to serve more than 4 years: 2
  Non-residential mission personnel: 2

Other personnel:
  Short-term less than 1 year: 8
  Non-US serving in own/other country: 47
  Home ministry & office staff in US: 14

Countries: Cambodia 2; Congo, Demo-

cratic Republic of; Ethiopia; India; Indonesia; Kenya; Pakistan; Sudan; Tanzania; Thailand; Uganda

WayMakers International

PO Box 203131
Austin, TX 78720-3131 USA

Phone: (512) 419-7729
Fax: (512) 323-9066
E-mail: info@waymakers.org
Web Site: www.waymakers.org
Mr. Steve Hawthorne, Director

An interdenominational service agency of Evangelical tradition engaged in prayer mobilization, literature distribution, literature production and training.

Purpose: "...to impart vision and training for leaders of local movements of united prayer that will prepare communities for evangelization and spiritual awakening...vision and practical passion for the greater glory of Christ so people lead fruitful lives in God's global purpose."

Year Founded in US: 1994

Income for Overseas Min: $25,000.00

Personnel:
  Short-term less than 1 year: 2
  Home ministry & office staff in US: 5

Waymarks Radio Ministries International

PO Box 2324
Macon, GA 31203 USA

Phone: (478) 750-1422
E-mail: lorenwilson@juno.com
Web Site: www.waymarks.org
Mr. Loren H. Wilson, Radio Pastor

A specialized agency of Charismatic and Calvinist tradition engaged in broadcasting, radio and/or TV, audio recording/distribution, literature distribution, literature production and partnership development.

Year Founded in US: 1987

Income for Overseas Min: $500.00

Personnel:
  Short-term less than 1 year: 1
  Non-US serving in own/other country: 3
  Home ministry & office staff in US: 1

Countries: Malawi; Nigeria; Zimbabwe

WEC International

PO Box 1707
Fort Washington, PA 19034-8707 USA
Phone: (215) 646-2322
Fax: (215) 646-6202
E-mail: mailbox@wec-usa.org
Web Site: www.wec-usa.org
Associations: The Mission Exchange
Dr. Louis V. Sutton, Director

An interdenominational sending agency of Christian (Restoration Movement) tradition engaged in church planting, children at risk, evangelism, mission-related research, TESOL and tentmaking.

Purpose: "...to recruit, prepare, send, and care for missionaries...to mobilize USA Christians for missions in culturally relevant ways through church nurture, prayer, and providing missions resources."

Year Founded in US: 1939
Income for Overseas Min: $5,207,000.00
Fully Supported US Personnel Overseas:
   Expecting to serve more than 4 years: 159
   Expecting to serve 1 to 4 years: 2
Other personnel:
   Short-term less than 1 year: 12
Countries: Brazil 5; Chad 3; Cote d'Ivoire 1; El Salvador 2; Equatorial Guinea 4; France 2; Ghana 3; Italy 6; Mexico 24; New Zealand; Russia 4; Senegal 2; South Africa 2; Spain 9; Thailand 3; Togo 2; Tunisia 2; United Kingdom 15; Unspecified Country 70

Weiner Ministries Intl.

PO Box 1799
Gainesville, FL 32602 USA
Phone: (352) 375-4455
Fax: (352) 335-0080
Web Site: www.weinerministries.com
Mr. Robert Weiner, President

A nondenominational support agency of Charismatic tradition engaged in youth programs and training, discipleship, evangelism and mobilization for mission. Data from 2005.

Year Founded in US: 1991
Income for Overseas Min: $433,938.00
Fully Supported US Personnel Overseas:
   Expecting to serve more than 4 years: 1
Other personnel:

Home ministry & office staff in US: 4
Countries: Unspecified Country 1

Westminster Biblical Missions

PO Box 212
Rising Sun, MD 21911 USA
Phone: (530) 273-6280
Web Site: www.wbminc.org
Rev. Dennis E. Roe, Gen. Secretary

A transdenominational sending agency of Presbyterian tradition engaged in theological education, literature production and support of national churches. Financial figures from 1998. Countries of service data from 2001.

Purpose: "...planting and multiplying Reformed churches on the foreign field."
Year Founded in US: 1974
Income for Overseas Min: $375,000.00
Fully Supported US Personnel Overseas:
   Expecting to serve more than 4 years: 3
Other personnel:
   Non-US serving in own/other country: 51
   Home ministry & office staff in US: 3
Countries: Hungary 1; Korea, South 1; Mexico; Pakistan 1

White Fields, Inc.

PO Box 226
Stillwater, MN 55082 USA
Phone: (651) 430-0090
E-mail: prayerfacts@whitefields.org
Web Site: www.whitefields.org
Associations: CrossGlobal Link
Rev. Steve Wheeler, Exec. Director

A nondenominational service agency of Evangelical tradition engaged in church planting, support of national churches, partnership development and support of national workers.

Purpose: "...to provide collaborative start-up support to pastors planting local churches among their own people in other parts of the world."
Year Founded in US: 1955
Income for Overseas Min: $174,000.00
Personnel:
   Non-US serving in own/other country: 99
   Home ministry & office staff in US: 2

Countries: Argentina; Brazil; Ghana; Japan; Malawi; Myanmar/Burma; Paraguay; Philippines; Russia; South Africa; Zimbabwe

Wisconsin Evangelical Lutheran Synod, Board for World Missions

2929 N. Mayfair Rd.
Milwaukee, WI 53222 USA
Phone: (414) 256-3233
Fax: (414) 256-6480
E-mail: worldmissionsgroup@sab.wels.net
Web Site: www.wels.net

Rev. Daniel H. Koelpin, Administrator

A denominational sending agency of Lutheran tradition engaged in partnership development, broadcasting, church planting, correspondence courses, TEE, theological education, literature production, providing medical supplies and support of national churches.

Purpose: "...to make disciples throughout the world...using the Gospel to win the lost for Christ and to nurture believers for lives of Christian service..."

Year Founded in US: 1955
Income for Overseas Min: $10,886,785.00
Gifts in Kind: $1,000,000.00
Fully Supported US Personnel Overseas:
  Expecting to serve more than 4 years: 34
  Expecting to serve 1 to 4 years: 5
Other personnel:
  Home ministry & office staff in US: 8
Countries: Albania; Brazil 3; Bulgaria; Dominican Republic 1; Hong Kong 2; India 2; Indonesia 1; Japan 3; Malawi 7; Mexico 2; Russia 2; Taiwan 1; Thailand 2; Zambia 8

Women to the World, Inc.

PMB 581, Ste. 103
1860 Barnett Shoals Rd.
Athens, GA 30605 USA
Phone: (706) 548-0000
Fax: (706) 613-5110
E-mail: survival@womentotheworld.org
Web Site: www.womentotheworld.org

Doris Aldrich, President

A nondenominational specialized agency of Reformed tradition engaged in technical training & education in war areas for women, agricultural programs, childrens programs, evangelism, leadership development, literacy work, medical work, support of national workers, partnership development, relief and/or rehabilitation, services for other agencies, tentmaking, business as mission and trafficking/slavery issues.

Purpose: "...to improve the lives of disenfranchised women throughout the developing world."

Year Founded in US: 1985
Income for Overseas Min: $246,491.00
Gifts in Kind: $170,319.00
Fully Supported US Personnel Overseas:
  Non-residential mission personnel: 3
Other personnel:
  Short-term less than 1 year: 4
  Non-US serving in own/other country: 29
  Home ministry & office staff in US: 5
Countries: Afghanistan; Burkina Faso; Kenya

Word and Deed Ministries USA

PO Box 157
Hudsonville, MI 49426 USA
Phone: (616) 896-3160
Fax: (616) 896-9219
E-mail: usoffice@wordanddeed.org
Web Site: www.wordanddeed.org

Heidi Pronk, Exec. Director

An interdenominational service agency of Presbyterian and Reformed tradition engaged in relief and/or rehabilitation, childcare/orphanage programs, development, Christian education and medical work.

Purpose: "...to help meet the spiritual and physical needs of people irrespective of race, color, creed and class in accordance with Biblical principles."

Year Founded in US: 2000
Income for Overseas Min: $273,800.00
Fully Supported US Personnel Overseas:
  Non-residential mission personnel: 1
Other personnel:
  Short-term less than 1 year: 6
  Home ministry & office staff in US: 1

Word of Life Fellowship, Inc.—International Ministries

PO Box 600
Schroon Lake, NY 12870 USA

Phone: (518) 494-6000
Fax: (518) 494-6359
E-mail: IM@wol.org
Web Site: www.wol.org
Kris Stout, VP Intl. Ministries

A nondenominational sending agency of Baptist and Evangelical tradition engaged in camping programs, discipleship, theological education, evangelism, short-term programs and youth programs.

Purpose: "...to reach youth with the Gospel of Christ."

Year Founded in US: 1940
Income for Overseas Min: $17,237,620.00
Fully Supported US Personnel Overseas:
  Expecting to serve more than 4 years: 81
Other personnel:
  Short-term less than 1 year: 1319
  Non-US serving in own/other country: 1039
  Home ministry & office staff in US: 288

Countries: Argentina 12; Australia 3; Austria; Bahamas, The; Bermuda 2; Bolivia 1; Brazil 11; Bulgaria; Cayman Islands; Chile; Colombia; Costa Rica 1; Cuba; Czech Republic 4; Dominican Republic; Ecuador; El Salvador 1; France 2; Germany 4; Ghana; Guatemala; Honduras 1; Hungary 7; Italy; Japan 2; Kenya; Korea, South 10; Lithuania; Mexico; Netherlands Antilles; Nigeria 2; New Zealand; Panama 1; Papua New Guinea; Paraguay; Peru 1; Philippines 5; Poland 2; Portugal 1; Romania 1; Saint Martin; South Africa 3; Spain; Thailand 2; Uganda; Ukraine; United Kingdom 2; Uruguay; Venezuela

Word To Russia

PO Box 1521
West Sacramento, CA 95691 USA
Phone: (916) 372-4610
Fax: (916) 375-6770
E-mail: slopuga@sbcglobal.net
Web Site: www.wordtorussia.org
Sergey Lopuga, Exec. Director

A nondenominational support agency of Baptist and Evangelical tradition engaged in broadcasting, audio recording/distribution, camping programs, childcare/orphanage support, childrens radio/music programs and literature distribution to Russian-speaking immigrants, with outreach in the former Soviet Union and Ukraine. Emphasis is on

the children and youth. Data from 2005.
Year Founded in US: 1972
Income for Overseas Min: $95,000.00
Fully Supported US Personnel Overseas:
  Expecting to serve more than 4 years: 5
  Non-residential mission personnel: 1
Other personnel:
  Non-US serving in own/other country: 5
  Home ministry & office staff in US: 2
Countries: Russia 5

World Baptist Fellowship Mission Agency, Inc.

PO Box 13459
Arlington, TX 76094-0459 USA
Phone: (817) 274-7161
Fax: (817) 861-1992
E-mail: wbfraley@earthlink.net
Web Site: www.wbfi.net
Mr. Thomas M. Raley, Mission Director

A denominational sending agency of Baptist and Independent tradition engaged in church planting, Bible distribution and childcare/orphanage programs.

Purpose: "...from the cross, through the Church, to the world."

Year Founded in US: 1939
Income for Overseas Min: $5,985,096.00
Fully Supported US Personnel Overseas:
  Expecting to serve more than 4 years: 98
  Expecting to serve 1 to 4 years: 17
Other personnel:
  Non-US serving in own/other country: 5
  Home ministry & office staff in US: 5

Countries: Australia 2; Brazil 25; Cambodia 2; Chile 2; Colombia 2; Dominica 2; Dominican Republic 2; Ecuador 9; French Polynesia; Guatemala 2; Haiti 2; Honduras 4; Indonesia 5; Latvia 2; Mexico 19; Micronesia, Federated States of 4; Mozambique; New Zealand 2; Portugal 1; Spain 4; Thailand 1; Ukraine; United Kingdom 6; Unspecified Country

World Bible Translation Center

4028 Daley Ave. #201
North Richland Hills, TX 76180 USA
Phone: (817) 595-1664
Fax: (817) 589-7013

E-mail: tom@wbtc.com
Web Site: www.wbtc.com
Mr. Dale Randolph, CEO

A nondenominational specialized agency of Christian (Restoration Movement) tradition engaged in Bible translation and Bible distribution. Data from 2005.

Purpose: "...to translate and distribute faithful, easy-to-understand translations of the Scriptures in the world's major languages to lead people to Jesus and help believers grow in faith."

Year Founded in US: 1973

Personnel:
   Non-US serving in own/other country: 48
   Home ministry & office staff in US: 20

Countries: Bulgaria; China; Colombia; Croatia; Egypt; Hungary; India; Indonesia; Jordan; Myanmar/Burma; Romania; Russia; Serbia and Montenegro; Vietnam

World Christian Ministries

3995 William Ct.
Charlottesville, NC 22903 USA
Phone: (434) 296-5263
E-mail: John@worldchristianministries.org
Web Site: www.worldchristianministries.org
Mr. John Lindner, President/CEO

A transdenominational specialized agency of Evangelical tradition engaged in missions information service, support of national churches, support of national workers and partnership development.

Purpose: "...to provide a free e-mail newsletter emphasizing the struggle, passion, and achievements of indigenous missionary leaders for the purpose of stirring up interest in and support for indigenous ministries."

Year Founded in US: 2004

Income for Overseas Min: $6,128.00

Personnel:
   Home ministry & office staff in US: 1

World Christian Ministries Association

1015 Atlantic Blvd., Ste. 456
Jacksonville, FL 32233 USA
E-mail: drdanbriggs@wcma-usa.org
Web Site: www.wcma-usa.org

Dr. Daniel Briggs, Chairman

A support agency of Pentecostal and Apostolic tradition engaged in literature distribution, Bible distribution, correspondence courses, theological education, literature production and seed grants.

Year Founded in US: 2006

Income for Overseas Min: $370,500.00

Gifts in Kind: $369,075.00

World Christian Outreach, Inc.

28720 Alessandro Blvd.
Moreno Valley, CA 92555 USA
Phone: (951) 242-8795
Fax: (951) 924-1978
E-mail: herpickstantonxp@roadrunner.com
Web Site: www.wcous.org
Mr. Stanton R. Herpick, Founder/President

A nondenominational support agency of Evangelical tradition engaged in Christian education, childcare/orphanage programs, relief and/or rehabilitation and support of national workers.

Year Founded in US: 1976

Income for Overseas Min: $297,000.00

Fully Supported US Personnel Overseas:
   Expecting to serve 1 to 4 years: 1

Other personnel:
   Short-term less than 1 year: 37
   Non-US serving in own/other country: 15
   Home ministry & office staff in US: 1

Countries: Africa—General

World Compassion Terry Law Ministries

PO Box 92
Tulsa, OK 74101-0092 USA
Phone: (918) 492-2858
Fax: (918) 872-6132
Web Site: www.worldcompassion.tv
Mr. Terry Law, President/Founder

A transdenominational specialized agency of Charismatic and Independent tradition engaged in church planting, Bible distribution, discipleship, literature distribution, relief and/or rehabilitation and training.

Purpose: "...to take the message of Jesus Christ to nations that are hostile to the Gospel, working with local bodies of believers to support the spiritual and physical transformation of lives."

Year Founded in US: 1969

Income for Overseas Min: $1,810,982.00

Gifts in Kind: $124,168.00

Fully Supported US Personnel Overseas:
Non-residential mission personnel: 2

Other personnel:
Short-term less than 1 year: 4
Non-US serving in own/other country: 122
Home ministry & office staff in US: 12

Countries: Afghanistan; China; Iraq; Myanmar/Burma

World Concern

19303 Fremont Ave. N.
Seattle, WA 98133 USA

Phone: (800) 755-5022

Fax: (206) 546-7269

E-mail: info@worldconcern.org

Web Site: www.worldconcern.org

Associations: The Mission Exchange

Mr. David Eller, President

A nondenominational sending agency of Christian (Restoration Movement) tradition engaged in relief and/or rehabilitation, children at risk, development and HIV/Aids. Countries of service data from 2005.

Purpose: "...to relieve human suffering through disaster response and development programs in the name of Christ."

Year Founded in US: 1973

Income for Overseas Min: $48,818,000.00

Fully Supported US Personnel Overseas:
Expecting to serve more than 4 years: 13
Expecting to serve 1 to 4 years: 19
Non-residential mission personnel: 18

Other personnel:
Short-term less than 1 year: 1
Non-US serving in own/other country: 858
Home ministry & office staff in US: 26

Countries: Afghanistan 2; Africa—General; Asia—General; Bangladesh; Burkina Faso; Bolivia 1; Cambodia; Ethiopia 1; Haiti; Honduras 1; Kenya 3; Laos; Myanmar/Burma; Peru; Rwanda; Thailand 4; Uganda; Uzbekistan 1; Vietnam

World Gospel Mission

PO Box 948
Marion, IN 46952-0948 USA

Phone: (765) 664-7331

Fax: (765) 671-7230

E-mail: wgm@wgm.org

Web Site: www.wgm.org

Associations: The Mission Exchange

Dr. Hubert P. Harriman, President/CEO

An interdenominational sending agency of Evangelical tradition engaged in evangelism, church planting, Christian education, theological education, TEE and leadership development. Countries of service data from 2005.

Purpose: "...to serve God in holiness and righteousness, World Gospel Mission connects in ministry with churches worldwide to make disciples of Jesus Christ among all nations."

Year Founded in US: 1910

Income for Overseas Min: $12,498,657.00

Fully Supported US Personnel Overseas:
Expecting to serve more than 4 years: 177
Expecting to serve 1 to 4 years: 6
Non-residential mission personnel: 3

Other personnel:
Short-term less than 1 year: 1230
Non-US serving in own/other country: 3
Home ministry & office staff in US: 65

Countries: Argentina 8; Bolivia 37; Burundi; Dominica 4; Haiti; Honduras 29; Hungary 5; India 2; Japan 4; Kenya 46; Mexico 12; Papua New Guinea 5; Paraguay 4; Taiwan 2; Tanzania; Uganda 10; Ukraine 6; Unspecified Country 3

World Harvest—USA

301 E. Foothill Blvd. Ste. 201
Arcadia, CA 91006 USA

Phone: (626) 359-8500

Fax: (626) 359-8181

E-mail: contact@worldharvest.cc

Web Site: www.worldharvest.cc

Associations: AERDO

Mr. Daniel Hanafi, Vice Chair/Co-Founder

A support agency of Charismatic and Congregational tradition engaged in relief and/or rehabilitation, development/community, children at risk, childrens programs, extension education, theological education, leadership development and short-term programs.

Purpose: "...to impact the world through creative community, education and media services."

Year Founded in US: 1989
Income for Overseas Min: $705,843.00
Gifts in Kind: $175,318.00
Personnel:
   Non-US serving in own/other country: 45
   Home ministry & office staff in US: 8
Countries: Indonesia

World Harvest Mission
101 West Ave., Ste. #305
Jenkintown, PA 19046-2697 USA
Phone: (215) 885-1811
Fax: (215) 885-4762
E-mail: gwalsh@whm.org
Web Site: www.whm.org
Associations: The Mission Exchange
Mr. Bob Osborne, Exec. Director

A nondenominational sending agency of
Evangelical tradition engaged in church
planting, agricultural programs, develop-
ment, discipleship and evangelism. Coun-
tries of service data from 2005.
Purpose: "...to lay down our lives to pro-
claim the Kingdom of Jesus Christ through
preaching, healing, and equipping."
Year Founded in US: 1983
Income for Overseas Min: $7,223,760.00
Fully Supported US Personnel Overseas:
   Expecting to serve more than 4 years: 72
   Expecting to serve 1 to 4 years: 12
Other personnel:
   Short-term less than 1 year: 38
   Home ministry & office staff in US: 26
Countries: Chile 2; Czech Republic 2; Ger-
many 3; Hungary 2; India 2; Ireland 16;
Italy 2; Kenya 6; Netherlands 2; Romania
2; Spain 6; Uganda 11; Ukraine 2; United
Kingdom 14

World Harvest Now, Inc.
PO Box 911
Denton, TX 76202 USA
Phone: (940) 891-4400
Fax: (940) 484-6097
E-mail: officemanager@whn.org
Web Site: www.whn.org
Mr. W. Lamont Brown, President/Founder

A nondenominational sending agency of
Evangelical tradition engaged in church
planting, evangelism, leadership development, support of national churches and
missionary training. Activities from 2002.
Purpose: "...to facilitate the planting of
cell group churches among the least evangelized people in or near the 10/40 Window."
Year Founded in US: 1992

World Help
(See Ad on page 315)
PO Box 501
Forest, VA 24551 USA
Phone: (434) 525-4657
Fax: (434) 525-4727
E-mail: info@worldhelp.net
Web Site: www.worldhelp.net
Associations: The Mission Exchange
Dr. F. Vernon Brewer, President

A nondenominational support agency of
Evangelical tradition engaged in child advo-
cacy, Bible distribution, childrens programs,
church planting, leadership development
and relief and/or rehabilitation.
Purpose: "...to fulfill the Great Commission
and the Great Commandment through part-
nering, training, helping, and serving, espe-
cially in the unreached areas of the world."
Year Founded in US: 1992
Income for Overseas Min: $18,872,269.00
Gifts in Kind: $12,387,081.00
Personnel:
   Short-term less than 1 year: 128
   Home ministry & office staff in US: 69

World Horizons
2102 E. Main St.
Richmond, VA 23223 USA
Phone: (804) 225-5517
Fax: (804) 225-5517
E-mail: usinfo@worldhorizons.org
Web Site: www.worldhorizons.org
Mr. Andrew W. Fuller, Exec. Director

A support agency of Evangelical tradition
engaged in church planting, business as
mission, evangelism, support of national
churches, mobilization for mission and missionary training.
Purpose: "...to serve on behalf of souls
as yet unsaved; churches as yet unplant-
ed; missionaries as yet unsent...ministering

World*Help*

Help for Today . . . Hope for Tomorrow

**HUMANITARIAN
AID**

**CHILD
ADVOCACY**

**BIBLE
DISTRIBUTION**

**CHURCH
PLANTING**

World Help is a nonprofit, humanitarian organization uniquely qualified and strategically positioned to meet the spiritual and physical needs of hurting people around the world.

To learn how you can make a difference in the world, please call 800-541-6691, or visit our website at worldhelp.net.

P.O. Box 501   Forest, Virginia 24551
434-525-4657 phone   434-525-4727 fax   info@worldhelp.net e-mail   **worldhelp.net** website

through creative evangelism, church-planting and the establishment of a trained missionary presence..."

Year Founded in US: 1985
Income for Overseas Min: $847,000.00
Fully Supported US Personnel Overseas:
  Expecting to serve more than 4 years: 32
  Non-residential mission personnel: 7
Other personnel:
  Short-term less than 1 year: 7
  Non-US serving in own/other country: 7
  Home ministry & office staff in US: 2
Countries: Africa—General 13; Asia—General 3; Europe—General 10; Middle East 6

World Indigenous Missions

PO Box 310627
New Braunfels, TX 78131-0627 USA

Phone: (830) 629-0863
Fax: (830) 629-0357
E-mail: wim@worldim.com
Web Site: www.worldim.com
Mr. Charles E. Hall, President

An interdenominational sending agency of Charismatic and Evangelical tradition engaged in church planting, broadcasting, discipleship, evangelism, short-term programs and missionary training.
Purpose: "...to disciple the nations to reach the world."
Year Founded in US: 1982
Income for Overseas Min: $1,741,262.00
Fully Supported US Personnel Overseas:
  Expecting to serve more than 4 years: 79
  Expecting to serve 1 to 4 years: 6
  Non-residential mission personnel: 12
Other personnel:
  Short-term less than 1 year: 53
  Non-US serving in own/other country: 14
  Home ministry & office staff in US: 4
Countries: Asia—General 7; Bolivia 8; Hungary 2; Indonesia 4; Mexico 30; Middle East; Philippines 8; Russia 6; Spain 6; Thailand 4; Venezuela 4

World Link Ministries

PO Box 153026
Irving, TX 75015 USA

Phone: (972) 253-6800
Fax: (972) 253-6803

E-mail: wlmsefovan@aol.com
Web Site: www.worldlinkministries.org
Dr. Manny Fernandez, President

An interdenominational sending agency of Baptist and Evangelical tradition engaged in church planting, TEE, theological education, evangelism, leadership development and support of national workers.
Year Founded in US: 1994
Gifts in Kind: $30,000.00
Fully Supported US Personnel Overseas:
  Expecting to serve more than 4 years: 10
Other personnel:
  Non-US serving in own/other country: 720
Countries: Africa—General 2; Cuba; Equatorial Guinea; Italy 2; Mexico; Romania; Spain 6; Ukraine; Vietnam

World Mission Associates

600-C Eden Rd.
Lancaster, PA 17601 USA

Phone: (717) 299-1427
Fax: (717) 299-2943
E-mail: wmausa@wmausa.org
Web Site: www.wmausa.org
Mr. Glenn J. Schwartz, Exec. Director

A nondenominational service agency of Evangelical tradition engaged in seminars on overcoming dependency, leadership development, literature distribution, mission-related research and missionary training.
Year Founded in US: 1983
Income for Overseas Min: $130,000.00
Fully Supported US Personnel Overseas:
  Non-residential mission personnel: 3
Other personnel:
  Home ministry & office staff in US: 2

World Mission Prayer League

232 Clifton Ave.
Minneapolis, MN 55403 USA

Phone: (612) 871-6843
Fax: (612) 871-6844
E-mail: wmpl@wmpl.org
Web Site: www.wmpl.org
Associations: The Mission Exchange
Rev. Charles R. Lindquist, Gen. Director

A sending agency of Evangelical and Lutheran tradition engaged in leadership development, development, theological education, evangelism, medical work and youth programs.

Purpose: "...committed to know Christ, pray for the advance of His Kingdom, share the Gospel and ourselves with those who do not know Him, and encourage Christians everywhere in this global task."

Year Founded in US: 1937

Income for Overseas Min: $2,031,403.00

Fully Supported US Personnel Overseas:
Expecting to serve more than 4 years: 58
Expecting to serve 1 to 4 years: 4

Other personnel:
Short-term less than 1 year: 6
Non-US serving in own/other country: 11
Home ministry & office staff in US: 20

Countries: Asia—General 11; Bangladesh 8; Bolivia 6; Ecuador 3; Eritrea 1; India 1; Kenya 3; Mexico 6; Mongolia; Nepal 7; Pakistan 2; Peru 2; Philippines 5; Romania 2; Russia 1; Tanzania

World Mission, Inc.

2900 Wilson Ave., Ste. 110
Grandville, MI 49418 USA

Phone: (616) 534-5689
Fax: (616) 988-2613
E-mail: staff@worldmission.cc
Web Site: www.worldmission.cc

Mr. Greg Kelley, Director

A nondenominational support agency of Evangelical and Reformed tradition engaged in audio recording/distribution, evangelism, leadership development, support of national churches and short-term programs.

Year Founded in US: 1994

Income for Overseas Min: $265,900.00

Personnel:
Short-term less than 1 year: 2
Home ministry & office staff in US: 4

Countries: Congo, Democratic Republic of; India; Mexico; Myanmar/Burma; Nigeria

World Missionary Assistance Plan

1419 N. San Fernando Blvd.
Suite 200
Burbank, CA 91504-4194 USA

Phone: (818) 843-7233
Fax: (818) 845-5000

E-mail: wmap@world-map.com
Web Site: www.world-map.com

Rev. Frank R. Parrish, President

A transdenominational service agency of Charismatic and Evangelical tradition engaged in leadership development, theological education, literature distribution, literature production, training and translation work. Data from 2005.

Purpose: "...to make disciples of all nations by equipping indigenous church leaders in Third-World nations through biblically-based, Spirit-filled teaching resources and by sharing their triumphs with believers in Western nations."

Year Founded in US: 1964

Income for Overseas Min: $797,377.00

Personnel:
Short-term less than 1 year: 2
Home ministry & office staff in US: 8

World Missionary Press, Inc.

PO Box 120
New Paris, IN 46553 USA

Phone: (574) 831-2111
Fax: (574) 831-2161
E-mail: mailroom@wmpress.org
Web Site: www.wmpress.org

Mr. Jay E. Benson, President

An interdenominational Evangelical literature ministry producing topical Scripture booklets in 327 languages and Bible study booklets and New Testaments in a variety of languages for free distribution in 209 countries.

Purpose: "...to produce and ship as many Scripture booklets as possible in as many languages as possible for free distribution around the world."

Year Founded in US: 1961

Income for Overseas Min: $3,061,524.00

Gifts in Kind: $29,139.00

Personnel:
Home ministry & office staff in US: 48

World Missions & Evangelism, Inc.

PO Box 790
Benton, KY 42025 USA

Phone: (270) 527-8369 x131
Fax: (270) 527-2872

E-mail: life@christianfellowhip.org
Web Site: www.christianfellowship.org
Associations: The Mission Exchange
Dr. David T. Parish, President

A transdenominational sending agency of Evangelical tradition engaged in church planting, development, Christian education, funds transmission, leadership development and support of national workers. Data from 2005.

Income for Overseas Min: $812,913.00

Fully Supported US Personnel Overseas:
Expecting to serve more than 4 years: 42
Expecting to serve 1 to 4 years: 6
Non-residential mission personnel: 83

Other personnel:
Short-term less than 1 year: 3
Non-US serving in own/other country: 52
Home ministry & office staff in US: 4

Countries: Costa Rica; France 2; Guatemala; Honduras 4; Hungary 2; India; Jamaica 3; Kenya 10; Mexico 2; Niger 2; Romania 2; South Africa 2; Spain 2; Unspecified Country 10; Vietnam 1; Zimbabwe

World Missions
Far Corners, Inc.

8401 Jacksboro Hwy., Ste. 130
Lakeside, TX 76135 USA
Phone: (817) 237-3000
Fax: (817) 237-3387
E-mail: info@worldmissionsfarcorners.com
Web Site: www.worldmissionsfarcorners.com

Mr. Gary L. Bishop, President/CEO

A nondenominational sending agency of Evangelical tradition engaged in support of national churches, children at risk, church planting, discipleship, medical work and trafficking/slavery issues.

Purpose: "...a unique outreach carried on by missionaries and an army of national workers including medical work and preaching the Gospel on five continents."

Year Founded in US: 1958

Income for Overseas Min: $1,700,000.00

Fully Supported US Personnel Overseas:
Non-residential mission personnel: 1

Other personnel:
Non-US serving in own/other country: 406

Home ministry & office staff in US: 6
Countries: China; India; Kenya; Korea, South; Mexico; Nepal; Peru; Philippines; Thailand; United Kingdom

World Orphans

PO Box 1840
Castle Rock, CO 80104 USA
Phone: (720) 362-4881
Fax: (720) 362-4886
E-mail: info@worldorphans.org
Web Site: www.worldorphans.org
Mr. Paul Myhill, President/CEO

A specialized agency of Evangelical tradition engaged in childcare/orphanage, children at risk, HIV/Aids and support of national churches.

Purpose: "...to rescue millions of orphaned and abandoned children, to strengthen thousands of indigenous churches, and to impact hundreds of communities with the Gospel of Jesus Christ... through the cost-effective empowerment of church-based orphan prevention, rescue, care, and transition programs in the least-reached areas of the world."

Year Founded in US: 1993

Fully Supported US Personnel Overseas:
Expecting to serve more than 4 years: 7

Other personnel:
Non-US serving in own/other country: 1

Countries: Guatemala 2; Iraq 5; Kenya

World Outreach Intl.—US

615 E. 9800 South
Sandy, UT 84070 USA
Phone: (801) 599-3370
Web Site: www.wointl.com
Mr. Aaron Rudd, US Director

A nondenominational sending agency of Charismatic and Evangelical tradition engaged in church planting, childcare/orphanage programs, childrens programs, discipleship, evangelism and leadership development. Data from 2005.

Purpose: "...to impact least reached people groups with the Gospel of Jesus through raising leaders, evangelism, assisting emerging missions, children's ministry and humanitarian aid."

Year Founded in US: 1994

Fully Supported US Personnel Overseas:
Expecting to serve more than 4 years: 5
Expecting to serve 1 to 4 years: 2
Non-residential mission personnel: 2

Other personnel:
Short-term less than 1 year: 50
Home ministry & office staff in US: 10

Countries: Burkina Faso 1; Indonesia; Tanzania 2; Vanuatu 2;

World Partners USA
PO Box 9333
Fort Wayne, IN 46899 USA

Phone: (260) 747-2027
Fax: (260) 747-5331
E-mail: info@wpartners.org
Web Site: www.wpartners.org
Associations: The Mission Exchange
Mr. David Mann, Director

A denominational sending agency of Evangelical tradition engaged in leadership development, business as mission, church planting, development, discipleship, TEE, extension education, theological education, evangelism, HIV/Aids, linguistics, literacy work, support of national workers, support of national churches, partnership development, short-term programs, trafficking/slavery issues, Bible translation and translation work.

Purpose: "...to facilitate disciple-making movements thereby expanding the Church of Jesus Christ."

Year Founded in US: 1969

Income for Overseas Min: $4,283,354.00

Fully Supported US Personnel Overseas:
Expecting to serve 1 to 4 years: 68
Non-residential mission personnel: 2

Other personnel:
Short-term less than 1 year: 152
Home ministry & office staff in US: 8

Countries: Bulgaria; Cyprus; Ecuador; France; Guinea; Ireland; Portugal; Russia; Sierra Leone; South Africa; Spain; Thailand; Unspecified Country

World Reach, Inc.
PO Box 26155
Birmingham, AL 35260-6155 USA

Phone: (205) 979-2400

Fax: (205) 979-6289
E-mail: info@world-reach.org
Web Site: www.world-reach.org
Associations: CrossGlobal Link
Rev. Timothy Q. Prewitt, Gen. Director

A nondenominational sending agency of Evangelical tradition engaged in church planting, discipleship, evangelism, leadership development, relief and/or rehabilitation and short-term programs. Data from 2005.

Purpose: "...to reach the world with the gospel of Christ through the local church."

Year Founded in US: 1982

Income for Overseas Min: $1,243,927.00

Fully Supported US Personnel Overseas:
Expecting to serve more than 4 years: 13
Non-residential mission personnel: 1

Other personnel:
Short-term less than 1 year: 15
Non-US serving in own/other country: 41
Home ministry & office staff in US: 5

Countries: Albania; Colombia; El Salvador 4; Germany; Honduras 5; Kenya; Peru 2; Romania; Ukraine 2

World Relief
7 E. Baltimore St.
Baltimore, MD 21202 USA

Phone: (443) 451-1900
Fax: (410) 347-0840
Web Site: www.worldrelief.org
Associations: The Mission Exchange
Mr. Sammy T. Mah, President/CEO

A transdenominational sending agency of Christian (Restoration Movement) tradition engaged in relief and/or rehabilitation, development, agricultural programs, business as mission, children at risk, Christian education and HIV/Aids. Countries of service data from 2005.

Purpose: "...to work with, for, and from the Church to alleviate human suffering, poverty, and hunger worldwide in the name of Jesus Christ."

Year Founded in US: 1944

Income for Overseas Min: $28,300,000.00

Fully Supported US Personnel Overseas:
Expecting to serve more than 4 years: 10
Expecting to serve 1 to 4 years: 23

Other personnel:

Non-US serving in own/other country: 1196
Home ministry & office staff in US: 475

Countries: Burkina Faso; Burundi 4; Cambodia 2; China 1; Congo, Republic of the; Grenada; Haiti; India; Indonesia; Kenya; Kosovo; Liberia; Malawi 1; Mongolia; Mozambique; Nicaragua 1; Rwanda 1; Sierra Leone; Sudan; Zimbabwe

World Servants

7130 Portland Ave. S.
Richfield, MN 55423 USA

Phone: (612) 866-0010
Fax: (612) 866-0078
E-mail: info@worldservants.org
Web Site: www.worldservants.org

Mr. Tim Gibson, President

A nondenominational specialized agency of Friends tradition engaged in mobilization for mission, development, leadership development, partnership development, short-term programs and missionary training.

Purpose: "...to mobilize a global network of people to impact the world for Jesus Christ through responding to physical and spiritual needs."

Year Founded in US: 1986
Income for Overseas Min: $450,070.00
Gifts in Kind: $41,615.00

Personnel:
Short-term less than 1 year: 8
Non-US serving in own/other country: 11
Home ministry & office staff in US: 13

Countries: Brazil; Caribbean—General; Cuba; Ecuador; Haiti; Kenya; Kosovo; Mexico

World Team

1431 Stuckert Rd.
Warrington, PA 18976 USA

Phone: (215) 491-4900
Fax: (215) 491-4910
E-mail: wt-usa@worldteam.org
Web Site: www.worldteam.org
Associations: CrossGlobal Link

Rev. David Riddell, Intl. Director

A nondenominational sending agency of Evangelical tradition engaged in church planting, aviation services, discipleship, evangelism, missionary training and Bible translation.

Purpose: "...to glorify God by working together to establish reproducing churches focusing on unreached peoples of the world."

Year Founded in US: 1928
Income for Overseas Min: $8,549,000.00

Fully Supported US Personnel Overseas:
Expecting to serve more than 4 years: 145
Expecting to serve 1 to 4 years: 4
Non-residential mission personnel: 11

Other personnel:
Short-term less than 1 year: 15
Non-US serving in own/other country: 30
Home ministry & office staff in US: 34

Countries: Australia 1; Brazil 4; Cambodia 28; Cameroon 16; Chile 4; Dominican Republic 8; France 13; Greece 2; Guadeloupe 2; Haiti 3; Italy 7; Mexico 2; Moldova 2; Mozambique 2; Papua New Guinea 10; Peru 2; Philippines 12; Spain 5; Suriname 4; Taiwan 6; Trinidad and Tobago; United Kingdom 6; Unspecified Country 6

World Thrust Intl., Inc.

3545 Cruse Rd., Ste. 309A
Lawrenceville, GA 30044-3162 USA

Phone: (770) 923-5215
Fax: (770) 923-3933
E-mail: info@worldthrust.com
Web Site: www.worldthrust.com

Dr. Bill H. Boerop, Founder/President

A nondenominational equipping agency of Evangelical tradition engaged in mobilization, theological education, leadership development, mission-related research, services for other agencies and training. Countries of service are worldwide.

Purpose: "...to serve...as a catalyst to help mobilize the local church toward a more effective involvement in the evangelization of the world."

Year Founded in US: 1984
Income for Overseas Min: $102,645.00
Personnel:
Home ministry & office staff in US: 2

World Venture
(See ad on page 321)

1501 W. Mineral Ave.
Littleton, CO 80120-5612 USA

Phone: (720) 283-2000

Fax: (720) 283-9383
E-mail: info@worldventure.com
Web Site: www.worldventure.com
Associations: The Mission Exchange
Dr. Hans Finzel, President

A denominational sending agency of Baptist tradition engaged in leadership development, business as mission, church planting, discipleship, theological education and evangelism.

Purpose: "We see people of all nations transformed by Jesus Christ through partnership with His Church."

Year Founded in US: 1943

Income for Overseas Min: $29,529,039.00

Fully Supported US Personnel Overseas:
  Expecting to serve more than 4 years: 411
  Expecting to serve 1 to 4 years: 141

Other personnel:
  Home ministry & office staff in US: 73

Countries: Africa—General 2; Albania 6; Argentina 19; Asia—General 9; Austria 16; Belgium 4; Bolivia 2; Brazil 16; Cambodia; Central African Republic; Congo, Democratic Republic of 2; Costa Rica 2; Cote d'Ivoire 13; Czech Republic 2; Ecuador 4; Europe—General 4; France 16; Germany 5 Ghana 3; Guatemala; Guinea 3; Hong Kong 8; Hungary 2; India 4; Indonesia 11; Ireland 7; Italy 14; Japan 15; Jordan 4; Kenya 11; Lebanon 2; Lithuania 2; Macau 9; Madagascar 5; Mali 13; Mongolia 1; Mozambique 6; Myanmar/Burma; Netherlands; New Zealand 2; Pakistan 5; Philippines 20; Poland 10; Portugal 4; Romania 6; Russia 7; Rwanda 8; Senegal 27; Singapore 9; Slovenia 2; Spain 16; Sweden 2; Taiwan 14; Thailand 2; Uganda 14; Ukraine 8; United Kingdom 6; Uruguay 2; Venezuela 4; Zambia 1

World Vision International

800 W. Chestnut Ave.
Monrovia, CA 91016 USA

Phone: (626) 303-8811
Fax: (626) 301-7786
E-mail: worvis@wvi.org
Web Site: www.wvi.org
Associations: The Mission Exchange
Kevin Jenkins, President/CEO

The international coordination office for the regional and national offices and other entities of the World Vision Partnership engaged in development, children's programs, justice, relief/rehabilitation and technical assistance. North American personnel serving overseas, income for overseas ministries, and countries of activity included in World Vision (USA) and World Vision Canada.

Purpose: "...working with the poor and oppressed to promote human transformation, seek justice and bear witness to the good news of the Kingdom of God."

Year Founded in US: 1978

Personnel:
  Home ministry & office staff in US: 185

World Vision, Inc.

PO Box 9716
Federal Way, WA 98063-9716 USA

Phone: (253) 815-1000
Fax: (253) 815-3343
E-mail: info@worldvision.org
Web Site: www.worldvision.org
Associations: AERDO
Mr. Richard E. Stearns, President

An interdenominational service agency of Evangelical tradition engaged in Christian relief and/or rehabilitation, Christian development, agricultural programs, childcare/orphanage programs, justice and support of national churches.

Purpose: "...to follow our Lord and Savior Jesus Christ in working with the poor and oppressed to promote human transformation, seek justice, and bear witness to the Good News of the Kingdom of God."

Year Founded in US: 1950

Income for Overseas Min:
$892,000,000.00

Gifts in Kind: $206,000,000.00

Personnel:
  Home ministry & office staff in US: 1150

World Witness, The Board of Foreign Missions, Associate Reformed Presbyterian Church

One Cleveland St., Ste.220
Greenville, SC 29601 USA

Phone: (864) 233-5226
Fax: (864) 233-5326

E-mail: worldwitness@worldwitness.org
Web Site: www.worldwitness.org
Associations: The Mission Exchange
Rev. Frank Van Dalen, Exec. Director

A denominational sending agency of Presbyterian tradition engaged in church planting, childcare/orphanage programs, theological education, evangelism, medical work and support of national churches.

Purpose: "...to proclaim Christ as the only Savior and Lord through the means of evangelism, church planting, theological education, and works of compassion."

Year Founded in US: 1876

Income for Overseas Min: $4,355,123.00

Fully Supported US Personnel Overseas:
Expecting to serve more than 4 years: 17
Non-residential mission personnel: 8

Other personnel:
Short-term less than 1 year: 250
Home ministry & office staff in US: 9

Countries: Germany 4; Pakistan 5; Spain 2; Ukraine 2; United Kingdom 4

WorldServe Ministries

5795 Genesis Ct.
Frisco, TX 75034-4055 USA
Phone: (469) 633-9600
Fax: (469) 633-9604
E-mail: usoffice@worldserve.org
Web Site: www.worldserve.org
Dr. Tetsunao Yamamori, CEO

A nondenominational sending agency of Evangelical tradition engaged in church planting, Bible distribution, leadership development, literature production, support of national churches and training. Data from 2005.

Purpose: "...to equip indigenous believers in closed or restricted access countries with tools and resources to strategically fuel the fires of dynamic church growth."

Year Founded in US: 1992

Income for Overseas Min: $11,825,511.00

Gifts in Kind: $8,679,668.00

Fully Supported US Personnel Overseas:
Expecting to serve more than 4 years: 2
Non-residential mission personnel: 3

Other personnel:
Non-US serving in own/other country: 3

Home ministry & office staff in US: 7
Countries: China 1; Cuba; Ethiopia; India; Vietnam 1

WorldTeach

4201 N. Peachtree Rd
Atlanta, GA 30341 USA
Phone: (770) 458-9300
Fax: (770) 454-9313
E-mail: info@walkthru.org
Web Site: www.walkthru.org
Associations: The Mission Exchange
Chip Ingram, President/CEO

An interdenominational support agency of Evangelical tradition engaged in broadcasting, discipleship, Christian education, literature distribution, literature production and training. See Walk Thru the Bible for statistical information. Data from 2005.

Year Founded in US: 1976

Fully Supported US Personnel Overseas:
Non-residential mission personnel: 3

Worldwide Discipleship Assoc.

PO Box 142437
Fayetteville, GA 30214-6515 USA
Phone: (770) 460-6940
Fax: (770) 460-1339
E-mail: info@disciplebuilding.org
Web Site: www.disciplebuilding.org
Mr. Robert D. Dukes, President/Exec. Dir.

An interdenominational support agency of Evangelical tradition engaged in training, evangelism and missions information service. Data from 2002.

Year Founded in US: 1974

Income for Overseas Min: $98,416.00

Personnel:
Home ministry & office staff in US: 13

Worldwide Lab Improvement

3607 Gembrit Cir.
Kalamazoo, MI 49001 USA
Phone: (269) 323-8407
Fax: (269) 323-2030
E-mail: mail@wwlab.org
Web Site: www.wwlab.org
Mr. Edwin J. Bos, President

A service agency where staff and projects cross denominational lines to assist clinical labs.

Purpose: "...to serve Jesus Christ by providing mission hospitals, clinics, and short-term teams in developing countries with quality clinical laboratory equipment, supplies, consulting and on-site training at reasonable cost."

Year Founded in US: 1995

Income for Overseas Min: $241,567.00

Gifts in Kind: $23,259.00

Fully Supported US Personnel Overseas:
  Non-residential mission personnel: 1

Other personnel:
  Short-term less than 1 year: 4
  Home ministry & office staff in US: 2

Worldwide Medical-Dental Evangelical Mission

1615 Farrier Trail
Clearwater, FL 33765 USA

Phone: (727) 791-7299
Fax: (727) 797-2140
Web Site: www.mdemission.org

Dr. Shoukry Soliman, President

A specialized agency of Evangelical and Fundamental tradition engaged in medical work, Bible distribution, broadcasting, church planting and evangelism.

Purpose: "...to use our professions as dentists and physicians to spread the Gospel and bring the lost to Christ...to help the poor and needy...to plant churches."

Year Founded in US: 1998

Personnel:
  Short-term less than 1 year: 8

World-Wide Missions

PO Box 2300
Redlands, CA 92373 USA

Phone: (909) 793-2009
Fax: (909) 793-6880
E-mail: info@world-widemissions.org
Web Site: www.world-widemissions.org

Rev. Fred M. Johnson, President/CEO

A support agency of Evangelical tradition engaged in support of national workers, childcare/orphanage programs, church planting, Christian education, evangelism and funds transmission.

Purpose: "...to touch the suffering people of our world with the love of Jesus Christ, changing forever the lives of men, women, and children."

Year Founded in US: 1950

Income for Overseas Min: $11,396,421.00

Gifts in Kind: $10,376,549.00

Fully Supported US Personnel Overseas:
  Expecting to serve more than 4 years: 9
  Expecting to serve 1 to 4 years: 5
  Non-residential mission personnel: 13

Other personnel:
  Non-US serving in own/other country: 17
  Home ministry & office staff in US: 4

Countries: Bolivia; Brazil 6; Congo, Republic of the; France; India; Jordan; Kenya; Liberia; Macau 1; Mexico; Nepal 1; Papua New Guinea; Peru; Philippines; Turkey 1

Worldwide Tentmakers, Inc.

2435 East North St., Ste. 1108, PMB 363
Greenville, SC 29615 USA

Phone: (864) 370-0475
Fax: (864) 235-3369
E-mail: office@worldwidetentmakers.com
Web Site: www.worldwidetentmakers.com

Mr. David Nunnery, President

A service agency of Baptist tradition engaged in business as mission, management consulting/training, tentmaking and TESOL.

Purpose: "...committed to assisting local fundamentalist churches in the promotion, preparation, and placement of self-supporting witnesses worldwide."

Year Founded in US: 1987

Income for Overseas Min: $250,000.00

Fully Supported US Personnel Overseas:
  Expecting to serve more than 4 years: 4
  Expecting to serve 1 to 4 years: 5
  Non-residential mission personnel: 9

Other personnel:
  Non-US serving in own/other country: 9
  Home ministry & office staff in US: 2

Countries: Asia—General 2; United Kingdom 2

Wycliffe Associates

PO Box 620143
Orlando, FL 32682 USA

Phone: (800) 843-9673

E-mail: info@wycliffeassociates.org
Web Site: www.wycliffeassociates.org
Mr. Bruce Smith, CEO/President
A nondenominational service agency of Evangelical tradition engaged in international volunteer organization supporting Bible translators, mobilization for mission, services for other agencies, short-term programs and Bible translation.
Purpose: "...supports Wycliffe Bible Translators through programs and services that encourage and enable God's people to become involved in Bible translation by offering their prayers, skill, and resources to that life-changing work."
Year Founded in US: 1967
Income for Overseas Min: $11,992,503.00
Personnel:
   Short-term less than 1 year: 4100

Wycliffe Bible Translators, Inc.
PO Box 628200
Orlando, FL 32862-8200 USA
Phone: (407) 852-3600
Fax: (407) 852-3601
E-mail: Info_USA@wycliffe.org
Web Site: www.wycliffe.org
Associations: The Mission Exchange
Mr. Robert Creson, President/CEO
An interdenominational sending agency engaged in Bible translation, funds transmission, linguistics, literacy work and mobilization for mission.
Purpose: "...to see a Bible translation program in progress in every language still needing one by 2025."
Year Founded in US: 1934
Income for Overseas Min: $131,161,000.00
Fully Supported US Personnel Overseas:
Expecting to serve more than 4 years: 1,468
Other personnel:
   Short-term less than 1 year: 36
   Home ministry & office staff in US: 478
Countries: Australia 10; Bangladesh 3; Belgium 1; Belize 2; Benin 5; Brazil 35; Bulgaria 4; Burkina Faso 7; Cambodia 4; Cameroon 47; Central African Republic 6; Chad 9; Chile 2; Colombia 12; Congo, Democratic Republic of 3; Costa Rica 5; Cote d'Ivoire 2; Ecuador 10; Ethiopia 11; Finland 6; France 13; Germany 57; Ghana 1; Guatemala 9; Guyana 2; Honduras 2; India 2; Indonesia 95; Kenya 30; Malawi 2; Malaysia 22; Mali 4; Mexico 49; Mozambique 8; New Zealand 2; Niger 6; Nigeria 8; Northern Mariana Islands 2; Papua New Guinea 205; Paraguay 2; Peru 45; Philippines 119; Romania 1; Senegal 9; Singapore 10; Solomon Islands 4; South Africa 4; Spain 10; Sweden 2; Switzerland 8; Tanzania 20; Thailand 93; Togo 7; Trinidad and Tobago 1; Uganda 5; United Kingdom 12; Unspecified Country 405; Vanuatu 6; Vietnam 2

Young Life
PO Box 520
Colorado Springs, CO 80901 USA
Phone: (877) 438-9572
Fax: (719) 381-1750
E-mail: mat@sc.younglife.org
Web Site: www.younglife.org
Mr. Denny Rydberg, President
A nondenominational sending agency of Evangelical tradition engaged in youth programs, camping programs, discipleship and evangelism. Data from 2005.
Purpose: "...to introduce adolescents to Jesus Christ and help them grow in their faith."
Year Founded in US: 1940
Income for Overseas Min: $8,063,032.00
Fully Supported US Personnel Overseas:
   Expecting to serve more than 4 years: 39
   Expecting to serve 1 to 4 years: 47
Other personnel:
   Home ministry & office staff in US: 580
Countries: Africa—General 4; Asia—General 1; Caribbean—General 3; Europe—General 14; Latin America—General 10; Russia 1; United Kingdom 6

Youth Encounter
3490 Lexington Ave. N.
St. Paul, MN 55126 USA
Phone: (612) 287-8487
Fax: (651) 287-9689
E-mail: larry@youthencounter.org
Web Site: www.youthencounter.org
Rev. Dr. Larry Dean Johnson, President
A denominational and transdenominational specialized agency of Lutheran tradition engaged in youth programs.
Purpose: "...to strengthen Christian com-

munity ministries to, with, and through young people."

Year Founded in US: 1965
Income for Overseas Min: $300,000.00
Gifts in Kind: $80,000.00
Personnel:
  Short-term less than 1 year: 40
  Home ministry & office staff in US: 25

Youth for Christ Intl.

PO Box 4555
Englewood, CO 80155-4555 US
Phone: (303) 843-9000
Fax: (303) 843-6017
E-mail: info@yfci.org
Web Site: www.yfci.org
Mr. David Wraight, President/CEO

An interdenominational support agency of Evangelical tradition engaged in youth programs, discipleship, evangelism, leadership development and training.

Purpose: "...to see that every young person in every people group in every nation has the opportunity to make an informed decision to be a follower of Jesus Christ and become part of a local church...to participate in the body of Christ in responsible evangelism of youth, presenting them with the person, work and teachings of Christ and discipling them into a local church."

Year Founded in US: 1968
Personnel:
  Home ministry & office staff in US: 13

Youth for Christ/USA— World Outreach

PO Box 4478
Englewood, CO 80155 USA
Phone: (303) 843-9000
Fax: (303) 843-9002
E-mail: worldinfo@yfc.net
Web Site: www.yfc.org
Mr. Dan Wolgemuth, CEO

A nondenominational sending agency of Evangelical tradition engaged in youth evangelism and youth programs. Data from 2005.

Purpose: "...facilitate USA citizens to serve the YFC International movement in reaching youth in nearly 100 countries in the world."

Year Founded in US: 1945
Income for Overseas Min: $4,500,000.00
Fully Supported US Personnel Overseas:
  Expecting to serve more than 4 years: 92
  Non-residential mission personnel: 6
Other personnel:
  Short-term less than 1 year: 1400
  Home ministry & office staff in US: 19
Countries: Africa—General 2; Australia 2; Belgium 1; Bolivia 3; Brazil 2; Cayman Islands 1; Europe—General 8; France 2; Germany 9; Guinea-Bissau 6; Honduras 3; Ireland 1; Italy 4; Japan 1; Kenya 3; Middle East 6; New Zealand 3; Philippines 1; Portugal 2; Rwanda 4; Slovakia 1; South Africa 5; Spain 4; Switzerland 7; Thailand 2; Uganda 1; United Kingdom 8

Youth Ministry Intl. (YMI)

1300 Envoy Circle #1306
Louisville, KY 40299 USA
Phone: (502) 493-9530
Fax: (502) 493-9533
E-mail: info@ymionline.com
Web Site: www.ymionline.com
Dr. Randy Smith, President/Founder

A nondenominational sending agency of Evangelical tradition engaged in training youth workers for churches and youth ministry professors for evangelical schools, Christian education, extension education, leadership development, support of national workers, support of national churches and youth programs.

Purpose: "...to train national youth workers for local churches within people groups of the world."

Year Founded in US: 1990
Income for Overseas Min: $390,000.00
Fully Supported US Personnel Overseas:
  Expecting to serve more than 4 years: 14
  Non-residential mission personnel: 2
Other personnel:
  Short-term less than 1 year: 28
  Home ministry & office staff in US: 5
Countries: Kenya 4; Malaysia 2; Mexico 2; Ukraine 6

Youth With A Mission (YWAM)

PO Box 7206
Ventura, CA 93006 USA
Phone: (805) 642-5327
Fax: (805) 642-2588
E-mail: johndawsn@cs.com
Web Site: www.ywam.org
John Dawson, Intl. President

An interdenominational sending agency of Charismatic and Evangelical tradition engaged in youth programs, discipleship, evangelism, missionary training and relief and/or rehabilitation.

Year Founded in US: 1960

Fully Supported US Personnel Overseas:
  Expecting to serve 1 to 4 years: 1500

Other personnel:
  Short-term less than 1 year: 11325
  Non-US serving in own/other country: 6162

Countries: Africa—General; Asia—General; Australia; Europe—General; Latin America—General; Middle East; New Zealand; Oceania—General

YUGO Ministries (Youth Unlimited Gospel Outreach, Inc.)

PO Box 25
San Dimas, CA 91773 USA
Phone: (909) 592-6621
Fax: (909) 394-1210
E-mail: outreach@yugo.org
Web Site: www.yugo.org
Mr. Leonard K. Janssen, Exec. Director

An interdenominational sending agency of Evangelical tradition engaged in short-term programs, childcare/orphanage programs, evangelism, leadership development, mobilization for mission and home construction.

Purpose: "...to win the Mexican people to Christ...to teach them to disciple their neighbors...to challenge North American Christians with world missions."

Year Founded in US: 1964

Income for Overseas Min: $2,060,000.00

Gifts in Kind: $2,000.00

Fully Supported US Personnel Overseas:
  Expecting to serve more than 4 years: 36

Other personnel:
  Non-US serving in own/other country: 6
  Home ministry & office staff in US: 8

Countries: Mexico 36

Zion Evangelical Ministries of Africa (ZEMA)

PO Box 727
Zion, IL 60099 USA
Phone: (847) 872-7363
Fax: (847) 872-7363
E-mail: zema@zema.org
Web Site: www.zema.org
Associations: CrossGlobal Link
Dr. Mike McDowell, CEO

A nondenominational sending agency of Evangelical tradition engaged in theological education, Bible distribution, camping programs, Christian education, TEE and short-term programs.

Purpose: "...to know Christ and make Him known among the Ama Zion of Southern Africa."

Year Founded in US: 1907

Income for Overseas Min: $308,000.00

Fully Supported US Personnel Overseas:
  Expecting to serve more than 4 years: 12
  Expecting to serve 1 to 4 years: 3

Other personnel:
  Short-term less than 1 year: 100
  Non-US serving in own/other country: 18
  Home ministry & office staff in US: 3

Countries: Mozambique; South Africa 8; Swaziland 4

Chapter 3
Indices to U.S. Protestant Agencies

Many *Handbook* users find it valuable to locate agencies by particular categories of church tradition or ministry activity. This chapter provides the user with those indices. Agency responses on the *Mission Handbook* survey helped define the listed categories. The organizations in each category appear in alphabetical order by organization name.

Index by Church Tradition

If an agency needed more than one generic or denominational category to describe its traditional doctrinal and/or ecclesiastical stance, the agency may appear under as many as two of the given categories. We have arranged the list alphabetically by category and within each category by agency name. See question #8 of the survey (in Appendix C) for the actual wording of the question and the check-off list of choices.

Index by Ministry Activity

Almost all agencies are involved in several types of ministry activities. Each agency may be listed under as many as six primary categories of activity. We asked those with more than six primary activities to indicate the six activities toward which they had committed the largest amount of resources. We have divided the broad activities of education and evangelism into subcategories. For example, the evangelism category appears as "evangelism, mass" and "evangelism, student," and so on. See question #9 of the survey (in Appendix C) for the actual wording of the question and the check-off list of activities.

Agencies sometimes have written in new categories under the "other" choice in previous surveys. Some of these, if used often enough, may be included in the check-off list for the next edition's survey. Categories are occasionally dropped for lack of use. The most used categories have remained the same.

Church Tradition

Adventist
Advent Christian General Conf.
Adventist World Aviation
Seventh-day Adventists, General Conf.

Anglican
Anglican Frontier Missions
Christ for Children International
Episcopal Church USA
New Wineskins Missionary Network
Reformed Episcopal Bd. of Foreign Msns.
South American Missionary Society (USA)

Baptist
ABWE, Inc.
Advancing Native Missions
African Children's Mission, Inc.
African Leadership, Inc.
Amazon Outreach
American Baptist Chs. of the U.S.A.
AMG International
Anis Shorrosh Evangelistic Association
Aurora Mission, Inc.
Baptist Bible Fellowship International
Baptist Bible Translators Institute
Baptist International Evangelistic Ministries
Baptist International Missions, Inc. (BIMI)
Baptist International Outreach, Inc.
Baptist Medical & Dental Mission Intl., Inc.
Baptist Mid-Missions
Baptist Missionary Association of America
Baptist Missions to Forgotten Peoples
Brazil Gospel Fellowship Mission
Bridge Builders International
Calvary Evangelistic Mission, Inc.
Caribbean Baptist Mission Society
Christ to the Nations
Christian Missions Unlimited
Converge Worldwide
Cooperative Baptist Fellowship
CrossWorld
Envoy International
Eternal Hope in Haiti
EurAsian Baptist Mission
Evangelical Baptist Missions
Evangelize China Fellowship, Inc.
Final Frontiers Foundation, Inc.
Finishers Project
Free Will Baptist, Inc. Bd. of Intl. Msns.
Fundamental Baptist Msn. Trinidad/Tobago
Fundamental Baptist Missions International
General Assoc. of Regular Baptist Chs.
International Ministries
General Baptists International

Global Focus
Good Shepherd Ministries, Inc.
Gospel Mission of South America, Inc.
Greater Grace World Outreach
Have Christ Will Travel Ministries, Inc.
HBI Global Partners
Heart of the Bride Ministries
Independent Faith Mission, Inc.
Independent Gospel Missions
International Board of Jewish Missions, Inc.
International Partnership Ministries, Inc.
JARON Ministries International
Jewish Awareness Ministries, Inc.
Joshua Expeditions
Living Hope Ministries International, Inc.
Living Water International
Lott Carey Baptist Foreign Msn. Conv.
M/E International, Inc.
Macedonia World Baptist Missions, Inc.
Macedonian Missionary Service
Mission Nannys
Missions Door
Missions to Military, Inc.
Muslim Hope
National Baptist Convention of America
National Baptist Convention USA, Inc.
North American Baptist Conference
On The Go Ministries/Keith Cook Team
Open Door Baptist Missions
Outreach To Asia Nationals
Pan American Missions
Prakash Association, USA
Prayer Baptist Missions International, Inc.
Precept Ministries International
Progressive National Baptist Convention, Inc.
Project Christ International
Reformed Baptist Mission Services
Rogma International, Inc.
Romanian Missionary Society
Russian Bible Society, Inc.
Seventh Day Baptist Missionary Society
Slavic Missionary Service, Inc.
Son Shine Ministries International
Source of Light Ministries International, Inc.
Southern Baptist Convention Intl. Msn. Bd.
Sports & Rec Plus
The Gospel Furthering Fellowship
The Master's Mission, Inc.
TITUS International
Touch the World Ministries, Inc.
Word of Life Fellowship, Inc.
Word To Russia
World Baptist Fellowship Msn. Agency, Inc.
World Link Ministries
World Venture
Worldwide Tentmakers, Inc.

Brethren

Brethren in Christ World Missions
Christian Mission for the Deaf
Church of the Brethren
Forgotten Voices International
Global Ministries
GOGF Ministries
Grace and Truth, Inc.
Grace Brethren International Missions
The Brethren Church, Inc.

Charismatic

Abundant Life Association, Inc.
AF⁻ Ministries International, Inc.
Agape Gospel Mission
Apostolic Team Ministries, Intl.
Bethany International Ministries
Blessings International
Calvary Commission, Inc.
Calvary International
Celebrant Singers
Christ for India, Inc.
Christian Laymen's Missionary Evang. Assoc.
Christian Ministries International (CMI)
Christian Outreach International
Dawn Ministries, Inc.
DeNike Ministries
Elim Fellowship—International Ministries
Faith Christian Fellowship International
FOCAS
Foundation For His Ministry
Foursquare Missions International
Full Gospel Evangelistic Association
Full Gospel Fellowship of Chs. & Mins. Intl.
Globe International
Good News for India
Good Shepherd Ministries International
Helimission, Inc.—USA
In Motion Ministries
India Gospel Outreach, Inc.
International Gospel Outreach
Leadership Training International
Living Word Missions
Mahesh Chavda Ministries International
Messianic Jewish Movement Intl., Inc., The
Mission Catalyst International, Inc.
Missionary Revival Crusade
Missions To Japan, Inc.
New Life Advance International
New Way Missions
Open Bible Churches, Intl. Mins.
Pentecostal Assemblies of God of Am., Inc.
Precious Seed Ministries
Project AmaZon
Rehoboth Ministries, Inc.
RUN Ministries

Sentinel Group, The
Supreme Task International, Inc.
Surfing the Nations
Tribes and Nations Outreach
United Evangelical Churches
Vineyard Church USA—Missions
Waymarks Radio Ministries International
Weiner Ministries International
World Compassion Terry Law Ministries
World Harvest—USA
World Indigenous Missions
World Missionary Assistance Plan
World Outreach International—US
Youth With A Mission (YWAM)

Christian (Restoration Movement)

ACM International
African Mission Evangelism
Childspring International
Christian Aviation and Radio Mission
Christian Church (Disciples of Christ)
Christian Churches/Churches of Christ
Christian Relief Fund, The
Churches of Christ
CMF International
COMHINA
Continent of Great Cities
European Evangelistic Society
FAME
For God's Children International
Good News Productions International
Haitian Christian Outreach
Hisportic Christian Mission
IMA World Health
Key Communications
Kids for Christ International
Mission Services Association, Inc.
Missions Resource Network
Myanmar Christian Mission
Ninos de Mexico
Northwest Haiti Christian Mission
OC International, Inc.
Pass the Torch Ministries/Church of Acts
Pioneer Bible Translators
Spanish American Evangelistic Ministries
STEM International
TCM International Institute
Team Expansion, Inc.
Teen Mission, USA, Inc.
The Waray-Waray Project
Turkish World Outreach
United Church of Christ—Global Ministries
WEC International
World Bible Translation Center
World Concern
World Relief

Christian/Plymouth
Brethren Assemblies
Christian Missions in Many Lands, Inc.
Ireland Outreach International, Inc.

Congregational
Congregational Christian Churches
Conservative Congregational Christian Conf.
ReachGlobal

Ecumenical
American Waldensian Society
Asian Access
Beyond Borders
Bread for the World
Christian Cultural Development Foundation
Christian Dental Society
Christian Flights International
Christian Literacy Associates
Church World Service
Emmanuel International Mission
Engineering Ministries International (EMI)
Habitat for Humanity International
Intl. Foundation for EWHA Woman's University
International Students, Inc. (ISI)
Medical Teams International
Moravian Church in North America
Opportunity International
Overseas Ministries Study Center
Reformed Ch. in Am., Gen. Synod
Self-Help International
Servants in Faith & Technology (SIFAT)
Tentmakers International
United Bd. for Christian Higher Ed. in Asia
Vellore Christian Medical College Bd. (USA), Inc.

Episcopal
Colorado Haiti Project, Inc.
Rock the World Youth Mission Alliance
Society of St. Margaret

Evangelical
Action International Ministries, Inc.
ACTS International Ministries, Inc.
Advancing Indigenous Missions
Adventive Cross Cultural Initiatives—US
Adventures in Missions
Africa Inland Mission International, Inc.
Africa Inter-Mennonite Mission International
African Bible Colleges, Inc.
African Enterprise
African Leadership Development
Agathos Foundation
AIDS Family Fund, Inc.
AIMS (Accelerating Intl. Msn. Strategies)
Alberto Mottesi Evangelistic Association, Inc.
Alongside Ministries International

Alongside, Inc.
Amazon Focus, Inc.
Ambassadors for Christ International Ltd.
Ambassadors for Christ, Inc.
Am. Council of the Ramabai Mukti Msn., Inc.
American Evangelical Christian Churches
American Leprosy Missions, Inc.
American Missionary Fellowship
American Scripture Gift Mission, Inc.
AMOR Ministries
Arab World Ministries
Armenian Missionary Assoc. of Am., Inc.
Artists In Christian Testimony International
Asian Outreach U.S.A.
Association of Christian Schools Intl. (ACSI)
Audio Scripture Ministries
Avant Ministries
Awana International
Back to the Bible International
Barnabas International
BCM International
BEE World (Biblical Education by Extension)
Bible League, The
Bible Training Centre for Pastors
Bibles & Literature in French
Bibles For The World, Inc.
BILD International
Billy Graham Center, The
Blessing the Children International
Bright Hope International
Cadence International
Café 1040, Inc.
Caleb Resources
CAM International
Campus Crusade for Christ, Intl.
Caring for Others
Caring Partners International, Inc.
Carver International Missions, Inc.
Casa Viva
Catalyst Services
Cedar Lane Missionary Homes, Inc.
CEIFA Ministry International
Centers for Apologetics Research, The
Childcare Worldwide
Children of Promise International
Children's HopeChest
China Connection
China Ministries International
China Outreach Ministries, Inc.
ChinaSource
Chosen Mission Project
Chosen People Ministries
Christ Community Church
Christ for the City International
Christar
Christian Aid Mission
Christian and Missionary Alliance, The

Christian Associates International
Christian Broadcasting Network, Inc., The
Christian Fellowship Union, Inc.
Christian Involvement in Service (CIS)
Christian Literature International
Christian Medical & Dental Associations
Christian Pilots Association
Christian Reformed World Missions
Christian Resources International
Christian Union Churches of North America
ChristianCourses.Com
Christians In Action Missions International
Christ's Mandate for Missions
Church Leadership Dev. Intl.
Church Ministries International
Church Missions Link
Church of God (Seventh Day) Gen. Conf.
Church Resource Ministries (CRM)
Churches of God, General Conference
Churches Together
CLC Ministries International
CMTS Ministries, Inc.
ComCare International
Commission to Every Nation
Cook Communications Ministries Intl.
Crescent Project
Crisis Consulting International
CrossGlobal Link
CrossLink International
Crossover Communications International
CSI Ministries
CTI Music Ministries (Carpenter's Tools Intl.)
Cup of Cold Water Ministries
CWE
D & D Missionary Homes, Inc.
Dayspring International
Daystar U.S.
Deaf Missions, Inc.
Development Associates International (DAI)
Disciples International
DualReach
e3 Partners Ministry
East West Interknit
Eastern European Outreach, Inc.
East-West Ministries International
ECHO Cuba
Educational Resources & Referrals—China
Educational Services International (ESI)
Edwin L. Hodges Ministries
Empowering Lives International
endPoverty.org
Entrust
Equip International
Equipping the Saints
European Christian Mission Intl.—USA
Evangelical Covenant Church
Evangelical Friends Mission

Evangelical Mission Ministries, Inc.
Evangelical Presbyterian Church
Evangelism and Msns. Info. Service (EMIS)
Evangelism Explosion International
Evangelism Resources, Inc.
Every Child Ministries, Inc.
Every Home for Christ International
Face to Face International
Faith Missions International
FARMS International
Fellowship of Companies for Christ Intl.
Fellowship of Evangelical Churches
Fellowship Travel International
FLET University/Universidad FLET
Floresta USA, Inc.
Food for the Hungry, Inc.
For His Glory Evangelistic Ministries
Forward Edge International
FRIENDS in Action International
Friends of Israel Gospel Ministry, Inc.
Friendship International Ministries, Inc.
Frontiers
Gideons International, The
Global Adopt-A-People Network
Global Advance
Global Aid Network (GAiN USA)
Global Fellowship, Inc.
Global Harvest Ministries
Global Impact Services
Global Mapping International
Global Opportunities
Global Outreach International
Global Outreach Mission, Inc.
Global Recordings Network
Global Teams International, Inc.
Global Youth Ministry Network
Go Ye Fellowship
God Reports
Gospel for Asia, Inc.
Gospel Operation Intl. for Chinese Christians
Gospel Outbound
Gospel Outreach Ministries Intl.
Gospelink, Inc.
Grace Ministries International
Great Commission Center International
Great Commission Ministries, Inc.
Greater Europe Mission
Handclasp International, Inc.
Harvest International, Inc.
Harvest Mission to the Unreached
Harvesting In Spanish (HIS)
Health Emergent International Services
Heart to Heart Intl. Ministries (H2H)
Help for Christian Nationals, Inc.
Help for Haiti, Inc.
Helps International Ministries
Hermano Pablo Ministries

Proclaim! International, Inc.
Project Mercy, Inc.
Providence Mission Homes, Inc.
Ravi Zacharias International Ministries, Inc.
RBC Ministries
Reach Ministries International
ReachAcross
Real Impact Missions, Inc.
Reciprocal Ministries International
Resourcing Christian Education International
Ripe for Harvest, Inc.
Russian Christian Radio, Inc.
Salvation Army, U.S.A.
Samaritan's Purse International Relief
SAT-7 North America
Scripture Union, USA
SEED International
SEND International USA
ServLife International
Share International
Shelter for Life International, Inc.
Shield of Faith Mission International
SIM USA, Inc.
Slavic Gospel Association
South America Mission, Inc.
Sowers International, The
Spiritual Growth Resources, Inc.
Spiritual Overseers Service International
STEER, Inc.
TeachBeyond USA
TEAM (The Evangelical Alliance Mission)
TEAMS for Medical Missions
The Bodybuilders
The God's Story Project
The Word for the World USA
Things To Come Mission, Inc.
TMA Ministries, Inc.
Training Evangelistic Leadership (T.E.L.), Inc.
U.S. Center for World Mission
Ukrainian Childrens Fund
United World Mission
UWEZO International, Inc.
Venture International
Village Ministries International
visionSynergy
Voice of the Martyrs, The
Volunteers in Medical Missions
Walk Thru the Bible Ministries, Inc.
Warm Blankets Orphan Care International
WayMakers International
White Fields, Inc.
World Christian Ministries
World Christian Outreach, Inc.
World Gospel Mission
World Harvest Mission
World Harvest Now, Inc.
World Help

World Horizons
World Mission Associates
World Mission Prayer League
World Mission, Inc.
World Missionary Press, Inc.
World Missions & Evangelism, Inc.
World Missions Far Corners, Inc.
World Orphans
World Partners USA
World Reach, Inc.
World Team
World Thrust International, Inc.
World Vision, Inc.
WorldServe Ministries
WorldTeach
Worldwide Discipleship Assoc.
Worldwide Medical-Dental Evangelical Msn.
World-Wide Missions
Wycliffe Associates
Young Life
Youth for Christ International
Youth for Christ/USA—World Outreach
Youth Ministry International (YMI)
YUGO Ministries
Zion Evangelical Ministries of Africa (ZEMA)

Friends
Central Yearly Meeting of Friends Missions
Evangelical Friends Church Southwest
Friends United Meeting
World Servants

Fundamental
FOM (Fellowship of Missions)
Gospel Fellowship Association
Nehemiah Teams International
Reaching Indians Ministries International
Remnant Ministries, Inc.
Spanish World Ministries, Inc.

Holiness
Allegheny Wesleyan Methodist Connection
Church of God (Anderson, Ind.)
Church of God (Holiness)
Congregational Holiness Church
Evangelical Bible Mission
Evangelistic Faith Missions
Free Gospel Church, Inc.—Msns. Dept.
International Pentecostal Holiness Church
ISOH/IMPACT
Pentecostal Free Will Baptist Church, Inc.
Pillar of Fire Missions International

Independent
All About Orphans
ASSIST Ministries & ASSIST News Service
Biblical Ministries Worldwide

Wesleyan
Cornerstone International
Evangelical Congregational Church
Evangelical Methodist Church, Inc.
Global Partners/Wesleyan World Missions
GO InterNational
Men for Missions International

Ministry Activity

Adoption
All God's Children International
Holt International Children's Services, Inc.

Agricultural programs
Agathos Foundation
China Connection
Christian Flights International
Christian Reformed World Relief Committee
Church World Service
Congregational Christian Churches
Cooperative Baptist Fellowship
Discipleship Missions International
Empowering Lives International
Equip International
FARMS International
Floresta USA, Inc.
Food for the Hungry, Inc.
Frontiers
General Baptists International
Heifer Project International
Lutheran World Relief
Mennonite Central Committee (MCC)
Mercy Ships
Mission: Moving Mountains, Inc.
Mustard Seed International
Myanmar Christian Mission
Pilgrim
Prakash Association, USA
Project Mercy, Inc.
Reformed Ch. in Am., Gen. Synod Council
SAND Institutes International
Self-Help International
Shelter for Life International, Inc.
STEER, Inc.
Tribes and Nations Outreach
Women to the World, Inc.
World Harvest Mission
World Relief
World Vision, Inc.

Apologetics
Anis Shorrosh Evangelistic Association
Brethren in Christ World Missions
Caribbean Baptist Mission Society
Centers for Apologetics Research, The

Muslim Hope
Ravi Zacharias International Ministries, Inc.
Association of Missions
Abundant Life Association, Inc.
Congregational Christian Churches
CrossGlobal Link
Evangelical Friends Church Southwest
Faith Christian Fellowship International
FOM (Fellowship of Missions)
Full Gospel Evangelistic Association
Full Gospel Fellowship of Chs. & Mins. Intl.
Japanese Evangelical Missionary Society
Reformed Baptist Mission Services
Seventh Day Baptist Missionary Society
The Mission Exchange
U.S. Center for World Mission

Audio
Alberto Mottesi Evangelistic Association, Inc.
Anis Shorrosh Evangelistic Association
Assemblies of God World Missions
Audio Scripture Ministries
Celebrant Singers
Christian Aviation and Radio Mission
Edwin L. Hodges Ministries
Faith Comes By Hearing/Hosanna
Far East Broadcasting Company, Inc.
Friends of Israel Gospel Ministry, Inc.
Global Recordings Network
Hermano Pablo Ministries
Institute of Theological Studies
INTERCOMM, Inc.
JAARS, Inc.
Josue Yrion World Evangelism and Msns., Inc.
Key Communications
Missionary Revival Crusade
Overseas Radio & Television, Inc. (ORTV)
Ramesh Richard Evangelism and Ch. Health
Russian Christian Radio, Inc.
Spanish World Ministries, Inc.
Talking Bibles International
The God's Story Project
Touch the World Ministries, Inc.
Trans World Evangelism, Inc.
TWR
Voice of the Martyrs, The
Waymarks Radio Ministries International
Word To Russia
World Mission, Inc.

Aviation services
Adventist World Aviation
Christian Aviation and Radio Mission
Christian Pilots Association
Evangelical Congregational Church
Helimission, Inc.—USA

JAARS, Inc.
Mexico Medical Missions
Mission Aviation Fellowship
Mission Safety International
Missionaire International
Missionary Flights International
MMS Aviation (Missionary Maint. Svcs.)
South America Mission, Inc.
World Team

Bible distribution

Advancing Renewal Ministries, Inc.
African Bible Colleges, Inc.
African Methodist Episcopal Church
Ambassadors for Christ, Inc.
American Bible Society
Asian Outreach U.S.A.
Assemblies of God World Missions
Baptist International Evangelistic Ministries
Baptist International Missions, Inc. (BIMI)
Baptist Missionary Association of America
Bible League, The
Bibles & Literature in French
Bibles For The World, Inc.
CEIFA Ministry International
Central Yearly Meeting of Friends Missions
Children's Christian Concern Society
China Connection
China Ministries International
Christian Aid Ministries (CAM)
Christian Literature International
Christian Missions Unlimited
Christian Resources International
Church of God (Seventh Day) Gen. Conf.
Ch. of God of the Apostolic Faith, Inc., The
CLC Ministries International
Cook Communications Ministries Intl.
Door of Hope International
Edwin L. Hodges Ministries
Eternal Hope in Haiti
Evangel Bible Translators
Evangelical Bible Mission
Every Home for Christ International
Faith Comes By Hearing/Hosanna
Final Frontiers Foundation, Inc.
Fundamental Baptist Missions International
Galcom International USA, Inc.
Gideons International, The
Gospel Revival Ministries
Harvesting In Spanish (HIS)
India Evangelical Mission
India National Inland Mission
International Family Missions
Ireland Outreach International, Inc.
Kids for Christ International
Leadership Ministries Worldwide
Living Hope Ministries International, Inc.

Living Water International
Lutheran Bible Translators, Inc.
Macedonian Missionary Service
Mission International
Missionary Flights International
Missions To Japan, Inc.
New Life Advance International
New Way Missions
OneHope
Open Doors, USA
Outreach To Asia Nationals
Pan American Missions
Pentecostal Church of God—World Missions
Prayer Baptist Missions International, Inc.
Remnant Ministries, Inc.
RUN Ministries
Russian Bible Society, Inc.
Slavic Gospel Association
Sowers International, The
Spanish American Evangelistic Ministries
Talking Bibles International
The Word for the World USA
Tribes and Nations Outreach
Turkish World Outreach
Vision Beyond Borders
Voice of the Martyrs, The
World Baptist Fellowship Msn. Agency, Inc.
World Bible Translation Center
World Christian Ministries Association
World Compassion Terry Law Ministries
World Help
World Missionary Press, Inc.
WorldServe Ministries
Worldwide Medical-Dental Evangelical Msn.
Zion Evangelical Ministries of Africa (ZEMA)

Bible memorization

Awana International
Disciples International
Kids for Christ International
Missions To Japan, Inc.
Navigators, U.S. Intl. Msns. Group
Reach Ministries International
Training Evangelistic Leadership (T.E.L.), Inc.
University Bible Fellowship

Broadcasting, radio

African Bible Colleges, Inc.
Alberto Mottesi Evangelistic Association, Inc.
Anis Shorrosh Evangelistic Association
Assemblies of God World Missions
Avant Ministries
Back to the Bible International
Baptist Mid-Missions
Calvary Evangelistic Mission, Inc.
Celebrant Singers
Christian Aviation and Radio Mission

Christian Broadcasting Network Inc., The
Christian Laymen's Missionary Evang. Assoc.
Christian Union Churches of North America
Churches of Christ
Evangelistic Faith Missions
Evangelize China Fellowship, Inc.
Far East Broadcasting Company, Inc.
Foundation For His Ministry
Friends of Israel Gospel Ministry, Inc.
Global Outreach Mission, Inc.
GOGF Ministries
Good News Productions International
Gospel for Asia, Inc.
Greater Grace World Outreach
Have Christ Will Travel Ministries, Inc.
HCJB Global
Hermano Pablo Ministries
High Adventure Ministries/Voice of Hope
   Broadcasting Network
Impact International, Inc.
International Board of Jewish Missions, Inc.
International Cooperating Ministries (ICM)
Jewish Awareness Ministries, Inc.
Joni and Friends
Key Communications
Luis Palau Evangelistic Association
Lutheran Hour Ministries
Macedonia World Baptist Missions, Inc.
Macedonian Missionary Service
Middle East Media—USA
Missionary Revival Crusade
Missions To Japan, Inc.
National Religious Broadcasters
Precept Ministries International
Proclaim! International, Inc.
Ramesh Richard Evangelism and Ch. Health
Raul Zaldivar Ministries
RBC Ministries
Reformed Presbyterian Global Missions
Rehoboth Ministries, Inc.
Rio Grande Bible Institute, Inc.
Romanian Missionary Society
Russian Christian Radio, Inc.
SAT-7 North America
Seventh-day Adventists, General Conf.
Slavic Missionary Service, Inc.
Spanish World Ministries, Inc.
The Waray-Waray Project
TWR
Voice of the Martyrs, The
Walk Thru the Bible Ministries, Inc.
Waymarks Radio Ministries International
Wisconsin Evangelical Lutheran Synod
Word To Russia
World Indigenous Missions
WorldTeach
Worldwide Medical-Dental Evangelical Msn.

Business as Mission

ACM International
Africa Inland Mission International, Inc.
Agathos Foundation
Bethany International Ministries
Brethren in Christ World Missions
Café 1040, Inc.
Caribbean Baptist Mission Society
Church Resource Ministries (CRM)
CLC Ministries International
Crossover Communications International
Eastern Mennonite Missions
East-West Ministries International
Fellowship of Companies for Christ Intl.
Finishers Project
Frontiers
Global Opportunities
Global Teams International, Inc.
Gospel Outbound
Hope for the Hungry
HOPE International
Interserve USA
mPower
Paradigm Shift
Partners Worldwide
Pioneers USA
Project AmaZon
ReachGlobal
Rosedale Mennonite Missions
SEED International
Spanish American Evangelistic Ministries
TeachBeyond USA
Tentmakers International
Women to the World, Inc.
World Horizons
World Partners USA
World Relief
World Venture
Worldwide Tentmakers, Inc.

Camping programs

ABWE, Inc.
Action International Ministries, Inc.
American Missionary Fellowship
Avant Ministries
BCM International
Brazil Gospel Fellowship Mission
Christ Community Church
Christian Mission for the Deaf
Christian Union Churches of North America
Eastern European Outreach, Inc.
Engineering Ministries International (EMI)
EurAsian Baptist Mission
Fellowship International Mission
For God's Children International
Friendship International Ministries, Inc.
Gospel Fellowship Association

Have Christ Will Travel Ministries, Inc.
Heart to Heart Intl. Ministries (H2H)
Hope Haven International Ministries
International Messengers
Japanese Evangelical Missionary Society
Latin America Mission
Navigators, U.S. Intl. Msns. Group
Pentecostal Assemblies of God of Am., Inc.
Peter Deyneka Russian Ministries
Pioneer Clubs
Presbyterian Evangelistic Fellowship
Salvation Army, U.S.A.
Servants in Faith & Technology (SIFAT)
TeachBeyond USA
TITUS International
Word of Life Fellowship, Inc.
Word To Russia
Young Life
Zion Evangelical Ministries of Africa (ZEMA)

Childcare/orphanage
ACM International
Adventures in Missions
African Children's Mission, Inc.
African Leadership Development
African Leadership, Inc.
Agape Gospel Mission
Agathos Foundation
AIDS Family Fund, Inc.
All About Orphans
All God's Children International
Am. Council of the Ramabai Mukti Msn., Inc.
AMG International
Armenian Missionary Assoc. of Am., Inc.
Assemblies of God World Missions
Baptist Missionary Association of America
Bibles For The World, Inc.
Blessing the Children International
Calvary Commission, Inc.
Casa Viva
Childcare Worldwide
Children of Promise International
Children's Christian Concern Society
Children's Haven International
Children's HopeChest
China Connection
Christ for India, Inc.
Christ for the City International
Christ to the Nations
Christian Aid Ministries (CAM)
Christian Relief Fund, The
Christ's Mandate for Missions
Church of God (Cleveland, Tenn.)
Cities for Christ Worldwide (CCW)
CSI Ministries
Discipleship Missions International
Door of Hope International

Empowering Lives International
Eternal Hope in Haiti
Evangelistic Faith Missions
Evangelize China Fellowship, Inc.
Every Child Ministries, Inc.
Faith Missions International
Fellowship International Mission
Final Frontiers Foundation, Inc.
For God's Children International
Forward Edge International
Foundation For His Ministry
Friends United Meeting
General Baptists International
Global Outreach International
Good News for India
Gospel Outbound
Gospel Outreach Ministries Intl.
Gospelink, Inc.
Grace Ministries International
Greater Grace World Outreach
Harvest International, Inc.
Harvest Mission to the Unreached
Harvesting In Spanish (HIS)
Heart of the Bride Ministries
Heart to Heart Intl. Ministries (H2H)
Holt International Children's Services, Inc.
Hope for the Hungry
In Touch Mission International
Independent Gospel Missions
India Evangelical Mission
India Gospel League, NA
India National Inland Mission
India Partners
Intl. Christian Leprosy Mission, Inc. (USA)
International Crisis Aid
International Messengers
International Partnership Ministries, Inc.
International Street Kids Outreach Ministries
Kerus Global Education
Kids Alive International
Launch Out Ministries International
Living Hope Ministries International, Inc.
Macedonia World Baptist Missions, Inc.
Ministry to Educate and Equip, Intl.
Mission Nannys
Mission of Mercy
Mission to Children, Inc.
Mission To Unreached Peoples
Mission Without Borders International
Mustard Seed International
New Directions International, Inc.
New Hope International
New Hope Uganda Ministries
New Life Advance International
Ninos de Mexico
North American Baptist Conference
Northwest Haiti Christian Mission

Open Bible Churches, Intl. Mins.
ORPHANetwork
Outreach To Asia Nationals
Pan American Missions
Partners in Asian Missions
Pentecostal Assemblies of God of Am., Inc.
People International USA
Precious Seed Ministries
Presbyterian Mission International (PMI)
Project Christ International
Reaching Indians Ministries International
The Brethren Church, Inc.
The Master's Mission, Inc.
Trans World Evangelism, Inc.
Ukrainian Childrens Fund
Vision Beyond Borders
Warm Blankets Orphan Care International
Word and Deed Ministries USA
Word To Russia
World Baptist Fellowship Msn. Agency, Inc.
World Christian Outreach, Inc.
World Orphans
World Outreach International—US
World Vision, Inc.
World Witness
World-Wide Missions
YUGO Ministries

Children at risk

ACM International
Action International Ministries, Inc.
African Children's Mission, Inc.
AIDS Family Fund, Inc.
All God's Children International
American Bible Society
Assemblies of God World Missions
Beyond Borders
Casa Viva
CEIFA Ministry International
Childcare Worldwide
Children's HopeChest
Christ for Children International
Christ for the City International
Cities for Christ Worldwide (CCW)
COMHINA
Commission to Every Nation
Cup of Cold Water Ministries
Eastern European Outreach, Inc.
Evangelical Baptist Missions
Every Child Ministries, Inc.
Food for the Hungry, Inc.
Forgotten Voices International
Global Aid Network (GAiN USA)
Heart of the Bride Ministries
Heart to Heart Intl. Ministries (H2H)
Holt International Children's Services, Inc.
Hope for the Hungry

International Street Kids Outreach Ministries
International Teams, U.S.A.
Kerus Global Education
Kids Alive International
Kids for Christ International
Latin America Mission
Living Hope Ministries International, Inc.
Living Word Missions
Mission Generation, Inc.
Mission to Children, Inc.
Mission To Unreached Peoples
National Baptist Convention USA, Inc.
New Hope Uganda Ministries
North American Baptist Conference
ORPHANetwork
Partners International
Peter Deyneka Russian Ministries
Reciprocal Ministries International
Share International
Teen Missions International, Inc.
The Mission Society
Vision Beyond Borders
Warm Blankets Orphan Care International
WEC International
World Concern
World Harvest—USA
World Missions Far Corners, Inc.
World Orphans
World Relief

Childrens programs

Abundant Life Association, Inc.
African Children's Mission, Inc.
American Scripture Gift Mission Inc.
Assemblies of God World Missions
Awana International
Baptist International Outreach, Inc.
BCM International
Blessing the Children International
Bridge Builders International
Cadence International
Calvary International
Caring Partners International, Inc.
Carver International Missions, Inc.
CEIFA Ministry International
Child Evangelism Fellowship, Inc.
Children's International Lifeline
Children's Ministry International, Inc. (CMI)
China Service Ventures
Christ for Children International
Christian Reformed World Relief Committee
Compassion International, Inc.
Cornerstone International
Evangelical Methodist Church, Inc.
Every Child Ministries, Inc.
Faith Life Ministries, Inc.
Fellowship International Mission

FOCAS
Food for the Hungry, Inc.
For God's Children International
Global Action
GO InterNational
Gospel for Asia, Inc.
Have Christ Will Travel Ministries, Inc.
Heart of the Bride Ministries
Holt International Children's Services, Inc.
Hope for the Hungry
International Crisis Aid
International Messengers
ISOH/IMPACT
Kids Alive International
Kids for Christ International
Kidzana Ministries
Living Water Teaching
Mailbox Club International Inc., The
MAP International
Mexican Medical Ministries
Mission Generation, Inc.
Mission India
Mission of Mercy
Mission Possible Foundation, Inc.
Mission to Children, Inc.
Mission To Unreached Peoples
Missionary Ventures International
New Directions International, Inc.
New Hope Uganda Ministries
Operation Blessing Intl. Relief and Dev. Corp.
Operation Mobilization
Pioneer Clubs
Project Christ International
Romanian Missionary Society
Salvation Army, U.S.A.
Samaritan's Purse International Relief
SAT-7 North America
Scripture Union, USA
Slavic Gospel Association
Society of St. Margaret
Spiritual Overseers Service International
STEM International
TEAMS for Medical Missions
Teen Missions International, Inc.
Ukrainian Childrens Fund
Women to the World, Inc.
Word To Russia
World Harvest—USA
World Help
World Outreach International—US
World Vision International

Church construction

Allegheny Wesleyan Methodist Connection
Apostolic Christian Church Foundation, Inc.
Armenian Missionary Assoc. of Am., Inc.
Baptist International Evangelistic Ministries

Caribbean Baptist Mission Society
China Connection
Christ for India, Inc.
Christ for the Nations, Inc.
Christian Missions Unlimited
Christian Union Churches of North America
Church Ministries International
Church of God (Cleveland, Tenn.)
Ch. of God of the Apostolic Faith, Inc., The
Congregational Christian Churches
Congregational Holiness Church
CSI Ministries
CWE
DeNike Ministries
Evangelical Mission Ministries, Inc.
Evangelize China Fellowship, Inc.
Free Gospel Church, Inc.—Msns. Dept.
Free Will Baptist, Inc. Bd. of Intl. Msns.
Full Gospel Evangelistic Association
Global Outreach International
Gospel Revival Ministries
Harvest International, Inc.
International Messengers
Macedonian Missionary Service
Missionary Gospel Fellowship
Missionary TECH Team
Myanmar Christian Mission
Nehemiah Teams International
New Directions International, Inc.
Open Bible Churches, Intl. Mins.
Partners in Asian Missions
Pentecostal Church of God—World Missions
Pillar of Fire Missions International
Precious Seed Ministries
Project Christ International
Slavic Missionary Service, Inc.
Teen Mission, USA, Inc.

Church establishing/planting

Abundant Life Association, Inc.
ABWE, Inc.
ACM International
ACTS International Ministries, Inc.
Advancing Native Missions
Advancing Renewal Ministries, Inc.
Advent Christian General Conf.
AEGA Ministries International, Inc.
Africa Inland Mission International, Inc.
Africa Inter-Mennonite Mission International
African Mission Evangelism
Agape Gospel Mission
AIDS Family Fund, Inc.
AIMS (Accelerating Intl. Msn. Strategies)
American Association of Lutheran Churches
Am. Council of the Ramabai Mukti Msn., Inc.
American Missionary Fellowship
AMG International

Anglican Frontier Missions
Apostolic Team Ministries, Intl.
Arab World Ministries
Armenian Missionary Assoc. of Am., Inc.
Artists In Christian Testimony International
Asian Access
Asian Outreach U.S.A.
Assemblies of God World Missions
Aurora Mission, Inc.
Avant Ministries
Baptist Bible Fellowship International
Baptist International Evangelistic Ministries
Baptist International Missions, Inc. (BIMI)
Baptist International Outreach, Inc.
Baptist Medical & Dental Mission Intl., Inc.
Baptist Mid-Missions
Baptist Missionary Association of America
Baptist Missions to Forgotten Peoples
BCM International
Bethany International Ministries
Bible League, The
Biblical Ministries Worldwide
BILD International
Brazil Gospel Fellowship Mission
Brethren Assemblies
Brethren in Christ World Missions
Calvary International
CAM International
Caribbean Baptist Mission Society
CEIFA Ministry International
Central Yearly Meeting of Friends Missions
Children's International Lifeline
Chosen People Ministries
Christ Community Church
Christ for India, Inc.
Christ to the Nations
Christar
Christian Aid Mission
Christian and Missionary Alliance, The
Christian Associates International
Christian Churches/Churches of Christ
Christian Fellowship Union, Inc.
Christian Involvement in Service (CIS)
Christian Reformed World Missions
Christian Union Churches of North America
Christians In Action Missions International
Christ's Mandate for Missions
Church Leadership Dev. Intl.
Church Ministries International
Church Missions Link
Church of God (Cleveland, Tenn.)
Church of God (Holiness)
Church of God of Prophecy
Ch. of God of the Apostolic Faith, Inc., The
Church of the Nazarene, World Msn. Dept.
Church Planting International, Inc.
Church Resource Ministries (CRM)

Churches of Christ
Churches of God, General Conference
CityTeam Ministries—New Generations Intl.
CMF International
Commission to Every Nation
Congregational Methodist Missions
Continent of Great Cities
Converge Worldwide
Cornerstone International
Crossover Communications International
CrossWorld
Cumberland Presbyterian Ch. Bd. of Msns.
Dawn Ministries, Inc.
Dayspring International
DeNike Ministries
Discipleship Missions International
e3 Partners Ministry
Eastern Mennonite Missions
East-West Ministries International
Elim Fellowship—International Ministries
EurAsian Baptist Mission
European Christian Mission Intl.—USA
European Evangelistic Society
Evangel Bible Translators
Evangelical Baptist Missions
Evangelical Bible Mission
Evangelical Congregational Church
Evangelical Covenant Church
Evangelical Friends Church Southwest
Evangelical Friends Mission
Evangelical Methodist Church, Inc.
Evangelical Presbyterian Church
Evangelism Resources, Inc.
Evangelistic Faith Missions
Every Home for Christ International
Faith Christian Fellowship International
Fellowship International Mission
Fellowship of Evangelical Churches
Final Frontiers Foundation, Inc.
Foundation For His Ministry
Foursquare Missions International
Free Gospel Church, Inc.—Msns. Dept.
Free Methodist World Missions
Free Will Baptist, Inc. Bd. of Intl. Msns.
Frontiers
Full Gospel Evangelistic Association
Fundamental Baptist Msn. Trinidad/Tobago
Fundamental Baptist Missions International
Galcom International USA, Inc.
General Baptists International
Global Action
Global Fellowship, Inc.
Global Ministries
Global Outreach Mission, Inc.
Global Partners/Wesleyan World Missions
Global Teams International, Inc.
Globe International

GO InterNational
Go Ye Fellowship
GOGF Ministries
Good News for India
Gospel Fellowship Association
Gospel for Asia, Inc.
Gospel Mission of South America, Inc.
Gospel Operation Intl. for Chinese Christians
Gospel Outreach Ministries Intl.
Gospelink, Inc.
Grace Brethren International Missions
Grace Ministries International
Great Commission Ministries, Inc.
Greater Europe Mission
Greater Grace World Outreach
Haiti Lutheran Mission Society
Haitian Christian Outreach
Harvest Mission to the Unreached
Have Christ Will Travel Ministries, Inc.
HBI Global Partners
Heart of God Ministries
Helimission, Inc.—USA
Hellenic Ministries/USA
His Healing Helping Hands Intl. Mins.
Hisportic Christian Mission
Hope for the Hungry
I. N. Network USA
IFCA World Missions
Impact International, Inc.
Independent Faith Mission, Inc.
Independent Gospel Missions
India Gospel League, NA
India Gospel Outreach, Inc.
India National Inland Mission
InterAct Ministries
Intl. Christian Leprosy Mission, Inc. (USA)
International Cooperating Ministries (ICM)
International Partnership Ministries, Inc.
International Pentecostal Church of Christ
International Pentecostal Holiness Church
Ireland Outreach International Inc.
Italy for Christ, Inc.
Japanese Evangelization Center
Key Communications
Kids for Christ International
Liberty Corner Mission
Liebenzell Mission of USA, Inc.
Living Word Missions
Lutheran Brethren World Missions
Lutheran Church-Missouri Synod
Macedonia World Baptist Missions, Inc.
Macedonian Missionary Service
MBMS International
Men for Missions International
Mennonite Mission Network
Messianic Jewish Movement Intl., Inc., The
Mission Catalyst International, Inc.

Mission India
Mission International
Mission ONE, Inc.
Mission Possible Foundation, Inc.
Mission to the World (PCA), Inc.
Mission To Unreached Peoples
Mission: Moving Mountains, Inc.
Missionary Gospel Fellowship
Missionary Revival Crusade
Missionary Ventures International
Missions Door
Missions Resource Network
Morelli Ministries International, Inc.
Mustard Seed International
Myanmar Christian Mission
National Baptist Convention USA, Inc.
New Directions International, Inc.
New Life Advance International
New Mission Systems International
New Tribes Mission
Ninos de Mexico
North American Baptist Conference
Northwest Haiti Christian Mission
OC International, Inc.
OMF International
OMS International, Inc.
Open Bible Churches, Intl. Mins.
Open Door Baptist Missions
Operation Mobilization
Orthodox Presbyterian Church
Outreach To Asia Nationals
Pan American Missions
Partners in Asian Missions
Partners International
Pentecostal Assemblies of God of Am., Inc.
Pentecostal Church of God—World Missions
Pentecostal Free Will Baptist Church, Inc.
People International USA
Pioneers USA
Prayer Baptist Missions International, Inc.
Precious Seed Ministries
Presbyterian Mission International (PMI)
Presbyterian Missionary Union
Primitive Methodist Church in the USA
Project AmaZon
Project Christ International
ReachAcross
ReachGlobal
Reformed Baptist Mission Services
Reformed Episcopal Bd. of Foreign Msns.
Reformed Presbyterian Global Missions
Ripe for Harvest, Inc.
Rosedale Mennonite Missions
RUN Ministries
SEED International
SEND International USA
ServLife International

Shield of Faith Mission International
SIM USA, Inc.
Slavic Gospel Association
Slavic Missionary Service, Inc.
Source of Light Ministries International, Inc.
South America Mission, Inc.
South American Missionary Society (USA)
Southern Baptist Convention Intl. Msn. Bd.
Sports & Rec Plus
TEAM (The Evangelical Alliance Mission)
Team Expansion, Inc.
The Brethren Church, Inc.
The God's Story Project
The Gospel Furthering Fellowship
The Master's Mission, Inc.
The Mission Society
The Waray-Waray Project
Things To Come Mission, Inc.
TITUS International
Tribes and Nations Outreach
Turkish World Outreach
TWR
United Evangelical Churches
United Pentecostal Church Intl.
United World Mission
Vineyard Church USA—Missions
Virginia Mennonite Missions
Warm Blankets Orphan Care International
WEC International
White Fields, Inc.
Wisconsin Evangelical Lutheran Synod
World Baptist Fellowship Msn. Agency, Inc.
World Compassion Terry Law Ministries
World Gospel Mission
World Harvest Mission
World Harvest Now, Inc.
World Help
World Horizons
World Indigenous Missions
World Link Ministries
World Missions & Evangelism, Inc.
World Missions Far Corners, Inc.
World Outreach International—US
World Partners USA
World Reach, Inc.
World Team
World Venture
World Witness
WorldServe Ministries
Worldwide Medical-Dental Evangelical Msn.
World-Wide Missions

Correspondence courses
African Bible Colleges, Inc.
American Evangelical Christian Churches
Asian Outreach U.S.A.
Back to the Bible International

BCM International
Disciples International
Evangelical Mission Ministries, Inc.
Every Home for Christ International
FLET University/Universidad FLET
Global University
Good Shepherd Ministries International
Gospel Fellowship Association
Grace and Truth, Inc.
Institute of Theological Studies
Ireland Outreach International Inc.
Lutheran Hour Ministries
Macedonian Missionary Service
Mailbox Club International Inc., The
Missionary Revival Crusade
New Hope International
Open Air Campaigners—Overseas Ministries
Rio Grande Bible Institute, Inc.
Rogma International, Inc.
Son Shine Ministries International
Source of Light Ministries International, Inc.
Spanish American Evangelistic Ministries
Spanish World Ministries, Inc.
Wisconsin Evangelical Lutheran Synod
World Christian Ministries Association

Development, community
Abundant Life Association, Inc.
African Enterprise
African Leadership, Inc.
AIDS Family Fund, Inc.
All About Orphans
American Baptist Chs. of the U.S.A.
Am. Council of the Ramabai Mukti Msn., Inc.
American Leprosy Missions, Inc.
AMOR Ministries
Bright Hope International
Calvary International
China Service Ventures
Christian Blind Mission International
Christian Church (Disciples of Christ)
Christian Cultural Development Foundation
Christian Flights International
Christian Relief Fund, The
Church Resource Ministries (CRM)
Church World Service
Churches Together
CMF International
Colorado Haiti Project, Inc.
Commission to Every Nation
Compassion International, Inc.
Congregational Christian Churches
Congregational Methodist Missions
Converge Worldwide
Cooperative Baptist Fellowship
Discipleship Missions International
ECHO Cuba

Empowering Lives International
endPoverty.org
Engineering Ministries International (EMI)
Equip International
Evangelical Covenant Church
Evangelical Lutheran Church in America
Faith Missions International
FARMS International
Floresta USA, Inc.
Food for the Hungry, Inc.
Forgotten Voices International
Forward Edge International
FRIENDS in Action International
Friends of Israel Gospel Ministry, Inc.
Global Health Ministries
GO InterNational
Gospel Outreach Ministries Intl.
Gospel Revival Ministries
Grace Brethren International Missions
Habitat for Humanity International
Harvest
Health Emergent International Services
Heifer Project International
Help for Haiti, Inc.
His Healing Helping Hands Intl. Mins.
Hope for the Hungry
HOPE International
I. N. Network USA
IMA World Health
India Gospel League, NA
International Aid
International Crisis Aid
International Teams, U.S.A.
Interserve USA
ISOH/IMPACT
Kerus Global Education
Kids Alive International
Lifewater International, Inc.
LifeWind International
Living Hope Ministries International, Inc.
Luke Society, Inc., The
Lutheran Brethren World Missions
Lutheran World Relief
MAP International
MBMS International
Medical Missions Philippines, Inc.
Medical Teams International
Mennonite Central Committee (MCC)
Mercy Ships
Mexico Medical Missions
Ministries In Action
Mission of Mercy
Mission To Unreached Peoples
Mission Training and Resource Center
Mission: Moving Mountains, Inc.
New Life Advance International

New Mission Systems International
North American Baptist Conference
Northwest Haiti Christian Mission
OMF International
Operation Blessing Intl. Relief and Dev. Corp.
Operation Bootstrap Africa
Operation Mobilization
Operation Serve International
Opportunity International
Paradigm Shift
Partners in Christ International
Partners International
Partners Worldwide
Perimeter Church—Global Outreach
Pilgrim
Pioneer Bible Translators
Prakash Association, USA
Presbyterian Church (USA)
Presbyterian Mission International (PMI)
Project Mercy, Inc.
Reach Ministries International
ReachGlobal
Real Impact Missions, Inc.
Reciprocal Ministries International
Reformed Ch. in Am., Gen. Synod Council
Samaritan's Purse International Relief
SAND Institutes International
SEED International
Self-Help International
Servants in Faith & Technology (SIFAT)
ServLife International
Shelter for Life International, Inc.
SIM USA, Inc.
Society of St. Margaret
South America Mission, Inc.
Supreme Task International, Inc.
Teen Mission, USA, Inc.
Teen Missions International, Inc.
The Master's Mission, Inc.
United Church of Christ—Global Ministries
Vellore Christian Medical College Bd. (USA), Inc.
Venture International
Virginia Mennonite Missions
Volunteers in Medical Missions
Word and Deed Ministries USA
World Concern
World Harvest—USA
World Harvest Mission
World Mission Prayer League
World Missions & Evangelism, Inc.
World Partners USA
World Relief
World Servants
World Vision International
World Vision, Inc.

Disability assistance

Am. Council of the Ramabai Mukti Msn., Inc.
American Leprosy Missions, Inc.
Christian Blind Mission International
Deaf Missions Inc.
Foundation For His Ministry
Holt International Children's Services, Inc.
Hope Haven International Ministries
Intl. Christian Leprosy Mission, Inc. (USA)
Joni and Friends
Middle East Christian Outreach (MECO)
Northwest Haiti Christian Mission
Venture International

Discipleship

Abundant Life Association, Inc.
ABWE, Inc.
ACM International
Action International Ministries, Inc.
Africa Inland Mission International, Inc.
African Children's Mission, Inc.
African Leadership Development
Allegheny Wesleyan Methodist Connection
Alongside Ministries International
American Missionary Fellowship
Artists In Christian Testimony International
Association of Free Lutheran Congregations
Avant Ministries
Awana International
Back to the Bible International
Baptist International Missions, Inc. (BIMI)
Baptist International Outreach, Inc.
Baptist Medical & Dental Mission Intl., Inc.
Baptist Missionary Association of America
BEE World (Biblical Education by Extension)
Biblical Ministries Worldwide
BILD International
Brethren in Christ World Missions
Cadence International
Café 1040, Inc.
Campus Crusade for Christ, Intl.
Caring for Others
Centers for Apologetics Research, The
Children's HopeChest
Christ Community Church
Christ for Children International
Christar
Christian and Missionary Alliance, The
Christian Fellowship Union, Inc.
Christian Medical & Dental Associations
Christian Ministries International (CMI)
Church of God (Holiness)
Churches Together
CityTeam Ministries—New Generations Intl.
CMTS Ministries, Inc.
Connecting Businessmen to Christ, Inc.
Converge Worldwide

CrossWorld
Dawn Ministries, Inc.
Development Associates International (DAI)
Disciples International
Educational Resources & Referrals—China
Edwin L. Hodges Ministries
EQUIP International Ministries
Eternal Hope in Haiti
EurAsian Baptist Mission
European Christian Mission Intl.—USA
Evangelical Friends Mission
Evangelical Methodist Church, Inc.
Evangelical Presbyterian Church
Evangelism Explosion International
Faith Christian Fellowship International
Faith Life Ministries, Inc.
FARMS International
Fellowship International Mission
Fellowship of Companies for Christ Intl.
Fellowship of Evangelical Churches
Floresta USA, Inc.
Foundation For His Ministry
Foursquare Missions International
Free Will Baptist, Inc. Bd. of Intl. Msns.
Friendship International Ministries, Inc.
Global Advance
Global Ministries
Globe International
Go Ye Fellowship
Good Shepherd Ministries International
Gospel Operation Intl. for Chinese Christians
Grace Brethren International Missions
Great Commission Ministries, Inc.
Greater Europe Mission
Greater Grace World Outreach
Haitian Christian Outreach
HBI Global Partners
HCJB Global
Heart of the Bride Ministries
Hellenic Ministries/USA
India National Inland Mission
InterAct Ministries
International Family Missions
International Gospel Outreach
International Pentecostal Church of Christ
International Street Kids Outreach Ministries
International Students, Inc. (ISI)
International Teams, U.S.A.
InterVarsity Christian Fellowship/USA
Jewish Awareness Ministries, Inc.
Kids for Christ International
Kidzana Ministries
Liberty Corner Mission
Liebenzell Mission of USA, Inc.
Life in Messiah International
LifeWind International
Link Care Foundation

Living Word Missions
LOGOI Ministries
Luke Society, Inc., The
M/E International, Inc.
Mailbox Club International Inc., The
Messianic Jewish Movement Intl., Inc., The
Ministries In Action
Mission Catalyst International, Inc.
Mission International
Mission of Mercy
Mission Possible, Inc.
Mission To Unreached Peoples
Missionary Athletes International
Missionary Gospel Fellowship
Missionary Revival Crusade
Missions Door
Missions Resource Network
Missions To Japan, Inc.
Missions to Military, Inc.
Morelli Ministries International, Inc.
Navigators, U.S. Intl. Msns. Group
Nehemiah Teams International
Network of International Christian Schools
New Mission Systems International
New Way Missions
North American Baptist Conference
OMS International, Inc.
Open Bible Churches, Intl. Mins.
Paradigm Shift
Pass the Torch Ministries/Church of Acts
Pentecostal Assemblies of God of Am., Inc.
People International USA
Perimeter Church—Global Outreach
Pioneers USA
Prayer Baptist Missions International, Inc.
Precept Ministries International
Project AmaZon
Ravi Zacharias International Ministries, Inc.
Reach Ministries International
ReachAcross
Reformed Presbyterian Global Missions
Rehoboth Ministries, Inc.
Remnant Ministries, Inc.
Ripe for Harvest, Inc.
Rogma International, Inc.
RUN Ministries
Scripture Union, USA
SEED International
SEND International USA
Shield of Faith Mission International
South American Missionary Society (USA)
Spiritual Growth Resources, Inc.
Sports & Rec Plus
Supreme Task International, Inc.
Surfing the Nations
TEAM (The Evangelical Alliance Mission)
The Gospel Furthering Fellowship

TITUS International
Training Evangelistic Leadership (T.E.L.), Inc.
Trans World Evangelism, Inc.
TWR
U.S. Center for World Mission
United Pentecostal Church Intl.
University Bible Fellowship
Village Ministries International
Warm Blankets Orphan Care International
Weiner Ministries International
Word of Life Fellowship, Inc.
World Compassion Terry Law Ministries
World Harvest Mission
World Indigenous Missions
World Missions Far Corners, Inc.
World Outreach International—US
World Partners USA
World Reach, Inc.
World Team
World Venture
WorldTeach
Young Life
Youth for Christ International
Youth With A Mission (YWAM)

Education, church/school

Abundant Life Association, Inc.
African Bible Colleges, Inc.
Agape Gospel Mission
All About Orphans
Allegheny Wesleyan Methodist Connection
Am. Council of the Ramabai Mukti Msn., Inc.
Armenian Missionary Assoc. of Am., Inc.
Association of Christian Schools Intl. (ACSI)
Beyond Borders
Bibles For The World, Inc.
BILD International
Blessing the Children International
Brazil Gospel Fellowship Mission
CAM International
Carver International Missions, Inc.
Childcare Worldwide
Children's Christian Concern Society
Children's International Lifeline
Children's Ministry International, Inc. (CMI)
Christian Church (Disciples of Christ)
Christian Flights International
Christian Involvement in Service (CIS)
Christian Medical & Dental Associations
Christian Mission for the Deaf
Christian Reformed World Missions
ChristianCourses.Com
Church of God (Holiness)
Church of the Brethren
Church of the Nazarene, World Msn. Dept.
Churches of Christ
Churches of God, General Conference

Cities for Christ Worldwide (CCW)
Colorado Haiti Project, Inc.
Compassion International, Inc.
Congregational Holiness Church
CrossWorld
CSI Ministries
Cup of Cold Water Ministries
Daystar U.S.
Emmanuel International Mission
Empowering Lives International
Engineering Ministries International (EMI)
Entrust
Episcopal Church USA
EurAsian Baptist Mission
Evangelism Resources, Inc.
Evangelize China Fellowship, Inc.
Faith Christian Fellowship International
FLET University/Universidad FLET
FOCAS
Friends of Donetsk Christian University
Full Gospel Fellowship of Chs. & Mins. Intl.
Fundamental Baptist Missions International
Good Shepherd Ministries International
Grace Ministries International
Greater Grace World Outreach
Haiti Lutheran Mission Society
Haitian Christian Outreach
Harvest
Harvesting In Spanish (HIS)
Hope for the Hungry
I. N. Network USA
India Gospel League, NA
India Partners
Interaction International
International Child Care, USA
International Justice Mission
Joni and Friends
Joshua Expeditions
Kerus Global Education
Kids Alive International
Kids Around the World, Inc.
Kids for Christ International
Leadership Ministries Worldwide
Liebenzell Mission of USA, Inc.
Living Word Missions
Lutheran Church-Missouri Synod
Macedonia World Baptist Missions, Inc.
Middle East Christian Outreach (MECO)
Ministry to Educate and Equip, Intl.
Mission of Mercy
Mission Possible, Inc.
Mission Without Borders International
Moravian Church in North America
Mustard Seed International
National Baptist Convention of America
National Baptist Convention USA, Inc.
Network of International Christian Schools

New Hope Uganda Ministries
Northwest Haiti Christian Mission
Open Door Baptist Missions
Palm Missionary Ministries, Inc.
Pentecostal Free Will Baptist Church, Inc.
Peter Deyneka Russian Ministries
Pilgrim
Pillar of Fire Missions International
Primitive Methodist Church in the USA
Progressive National Baptist Convention, Inc.
Project Christ International
Project Mercy, Inc.
Raul Zaldivar Ministries
Reciprocal Ministries International
Rehoboth Ministries, Inc.
Resourcing Christian Education International
SEED International
Seventh-day Adventists, General Conf.
Society of St. Margaret
South American Missionary Society (USA)
TeachBeyond USA
Team Expansion, Inc.
Teen Missions International, Inc.
Touch the World Ministries, Inc.
Trans World Evangelism, Inc.
U.S. Center for World Mission
United Church of Christ—Global Ministries
Virginia Mennonite Missions
Word and Deed Ministries USA
World Christian Outreach, Inc.
World Gospel Mission
World Missions & Evangelism, Inc.
World Relief
WorldTeach
World-Wide Missions
Youth Ministry International (YMI)
Zion Evangelical Ministries of Africa (ZEMA)

Education, extension

American Evangelical Christian Churches
Association of Christian Schools Intl. (ACSI)
BEE World (Biblical Education by Extension)
Calvary Evangelistic Mission, Inc.
CrossGlobal Link
Crossover Communications International
Daystar U.S.
Discipleship Missions International
Eternal Hope in Haiti
Fellowship of Evangelical Churches
FLET University/Universidad FLET
Global University
Good Shepherd Ministries, Inc.
Handclasp International, Inc.
International Institute for Christian Studies
Joshua Expeditions
Liebenzell Mission of USA, Inc.
Lifewater International, Inc.

Ludhiana Christian Medical College Board
Mennonite Central Committee (MCC)
Mission Aviation Fellowship
Mission ONE, Inc.
Overseas Radio & Television, Inc. (ORTV)
Self-Help International
Shelter for Life International, Inc.
visionSynergy
World Harvest—USA
World Partners USA
Youth Ministry International (YMI)

Education, missionary
Abundant Life Association, Inc.
Baptist Bible Translators Institute
Baptist Missionary Association of America
Bethany International Ministries
Calvary Commission, Inc.
CEIFA Ministry International
Christ for the Nations, Inc.
Church of the Nazarene, World Msn. Dept.
COMHINA
Crescent Project
Entrust
Friends of Donetsk Christian University
Global University
Gospel Outbound
Heart of God Ministries
Hope for the Hungry
Jews for Jesus
Joshua Expeditions
Kids for Christ International
Missionaire International
Network of International Christian Schools
Overseas Ministries Study Center
Pentecostal Free Will Baptist Church, Inc.
Project Christ International
Reaching Indians Ministries International
Rio Grande Bible Institute, Inc.
Teen Missions International, Inc.
The Bodybuilders
The Brethren Church, Inc.
The Master's Mission, Inc.
U.S. Center for World Mission
United Methodist Church
University Bible Fellowship

Education, theological
ABWE, Inc.
Action International Ministries, Inc.
ACTS International Ministries, Inc.
Advancing Renewal Ministries, Inc.
Advent Christian General Conf.
Africa Inland Mission International, Inc.
Africa Inter-Mennonite Mission International
African Children's Mission, Inc.
African Leadership, Inc.

African Mission Evangelism
American Baptist Chs. of the U.S.A., Intl.
Armenian Missionary Assoc. of Am., Inc.
Asian Outreach U.S.A.
Association of Free Lutheran Congregations
Aurora Mission, Inc.
Baptist International Evangelistic Ministries
Baptist Mid-Missions
Baptist Missionary Association of America
BEE World (Biblical Education by Extension)
Bible Training Centre for Pastors
Bibles For The World, Inc.
BILD International
Brethren in Christ World Missions
CAM International
Carver International Missions, Inc.
Children's Christian Concern Society
China Ministries International
Chosen People Ministries
Christ for India, Inc.
Christ for the Nations, Inc.
Christ to the Nations
Christian and Missionary Alliance, The
Christian Church (Disciples of Christ)
Christian Fellowship Union, Inc.
Christian Ministries International (CMI)
ChristianCourses.Com
Christ's Mandate for Missions
Church of God (Anderson, Ind.)
Church of God (Cleveland, Tenn.)
Ch. of God of the Apostolic Faith, Inc., The
Church of the Nazarene, World Msn. Dept.
Church Planting International, Inc.
Converge Worldwide
CrossWorld
Daystar U.S.
DeNike Ministries
Development Associates International (DAI)
ECHO Cuba
Educational Resources & Referrals—China
Elim Fellowship—International Ministries
Emmanuel International Mission
Entrust
EurAsian Baptist Mission
European Christian Mission Intl.—USA
European Evangelistic Society
Evangelical Baptist Missions
Evangelical Methodist Church, Inc.
Evangelical Mission Ministries, Inc.
Evangelical Presbyterian Church
Evangelistic Faith Missions
Faith Christian Fellowship International
FLET University/Universidad FLET
Free Gospel Church, Inc.—Msns. Dept.
Friends of Donetsk Christian University
Friends of Israel Gospel Ministry, Inc.
Friends United Meeting

Global Advance
Global Partners/Wesleyan World Missions
Global University
Good News for India
Good Shepherd Ministries, Inc.
Gospel Fellowship Association
Gospel Mission of South America, Inc.
Gospel Outbound
Gospelink, Inc.
Grace Ministries International
Greater Grace World Outreach
Haiti Lutheran Mission Society
Haitian Christian Outreach
Harvest Mission to the Unreached
Help for Christian Nationals, Inc.
India National Inland Mission
Institute of Theological Studies
International Christian Ministries
International Gospel Outreach
International Institute for Christian Studies
International Partnership Ministries, Inc.
International Pentecostal Holiness Church
Ireland Outreach International Inc.
JARON Ministries International
Josue Yrion World Evangelism and Msns., Inc.
Latin America Mission
Liebenzell Mission of USA, Inc.
Living Water Teaching
LOGOI Ministries
Lott Carey Baptist Foreign Msn. Conv.
Lutheran Church-Missouri Synod
MAP International
Mennonite Mission Network
Ministry to Educate and Equip, Intl.
Mission Possible, Inc.
Mission to the World (PCA), Inc.
Missionary Gospel Fellowship
Muslim Hope
Myanmar Christian Mission
North American Baptist Conference
OC International, Inc.
OMS International, Inc.
On The Go Ministries/Keith Cook Team
Open Bible Churches, Intl. Mins.
Open Door Baptist Missions
Orthodox Presbyterian Church
Outreach To Asia Nationals
Overseas Council International
Pentecostal Free Will Baptist Church, Inc.
Perimeter Church—Global Outreach
Pillar of Fire Missions International
Precious Seed Ministries
Presbyterian Mission International (PMI)
Raul Zaldivar Ministries
ReachGlobal
Reaching Indians Ministries International
Reformed Baptist Mission Services

Reformed Ch. in Am., Gen. Synod Council
Reformed Presbyterian Global Missions
Rehoboth Ministries, Inc.
Rio Grande Bible Institute, Inc.
Rock the World Youth Mission Alliance
Romanian Missionary Society
SEND International USA
Share International
SIM USA, Inc.
Slavic Gospel Association
South America Mission, Inc.
Southern Baptist Convention Intl. Msn. Bd.
TCM International Institute
TEAM (The Evangelical Alliance Mission)
The Brethren Church, Inc.
The Gospel Furthering Fellowship
The Mission Society
Things To Come Mission, Inc.
TMA Ministries Inc.
Trans World Evangelism, Inc.
U.S. Center for World Mission
United Church of Christ—Global Ministries
United Pentecostal Church Intl.
United World Mission
Westminster Biblical Missions
Wisconsin Evangelical Lutheran Synod
Word of Life Fellowship, Inc.
World Christian Ministries Association
World Gospel Mission
World Harvest—USA
World Link Ministries
World Mission Prayer League
World Missionary Assistance Plan
World Partners USA
World Thrust International, Inc.
World Venture
World Witness
Zion Evangelical Ministries of Africa (ZEMA)

Education, theological by extension

ACM International
AEGA Ministries International, Inc.
Alberto Mottesi Evangelistic Association, Inc.
Arab World Ministries
BEE World (Biblical Education by Extension)
Brazil Gospel Fellowship Mission
Brethren in Christ World Missions
CEIFA Ministry International
ChristianCourses.Com
Church of God (Anderson, Ind.)
Church of God (Cleveland, Tenn.)
Church of the Brethren
Church of the Nazarene, World Msn. Dept.
Cornerstone International
East-West Ministries International
Evangelical Friends Church Southwest
Evangelical Friends Mission

FLET University/Universidad FLET
Friends of Donetsk Christian University
Global Partners/Wesleyan World Missions
Global University
Greater Europe Mission
Institute of Theological Studies
International Christian Ministries
Lutheran Church-Missouri Synod
Macedonia World Baptist Missions, Inc.
Middle East Christian Outreach (MECO)
Ministries In Action
Ministry to Educate and Equip, Intl.
Missions Door
Mustard Seed International
OMS International, Inc.
Open Bible Churches, Intl. Mins.
Partners in Christ International
Raul Zaldivar Ministries
Ravi Zacharias International Ministries, Inc.
ReachGlobal
Reformed Ch. in Am., Gen. Synod Council
Seventh Day Baptist Missionary Society
SIM USA, Inc.
Source of Light Ministries International, Inc.
Southern Baptist Convention Intl. Msn. Bd.
Trans World Evangelism, Inc.
U.S. Center for World Mission
Wisconsin Evangelical Lutheran Synod
World Gospel Mission
World Link Ministries
World Partners USA
Zion Evangelical Ministries of Africa (ZEMA)

Evangelism, mass
African Bible Colleges, Inc.
African Enterprise
African Methodist Episcopal Church
Agape Gospel Mission
Alberto Mottesi Evangelistic Association, Inc.
Allegheny Wesleyan Methodist Connection
Amazon Outreach
Anis Shorrosh Evangelistic Association
Apostolic Christian Church Foundation, Inc.
Baptist International Outreach, Inc.
Baptist Medical & Dental Mission Intl., Inc.
Billy Graham Center, The
Campus Crusade for Christ, Intl.
Caribbean Baptist Mission Society
CEIFA Ministry International
Celebrant Singers
Children's International Lifeline
Chosen People Ministries
Christ to the Nations
Christian Aid Mission
Christian Laymen's Missionary Evang. Assoc.
Church of God of Prophecy
Ch. of God of the Apostolic Faith, Inc., The

Church of the Nazarene, World Msn. Dept.
CMF International
Connecting Businessmen to Christ, Inc.
CTI Music Ministries (Carpenter's Tools Intl.)
Dayspring International
Discipleship Missions International
East-West Ministries International
Evangelical Lutheran Church in America
Evangelism Resources, Inc.
FOCAS
For His Glory Evangelistic Ministries
Friends of Donetsk Christian University
Friends of Israel Gospel Ministry, Inc.
Fundamental Baptist Msn. Trinidad/Tobago
Fundamental Baptist Missions International
Galcom International USA, Inc.
Global Action
Global Advance
Global Fellowship, Inc.
Global Recordings Network
GO InterNational
Good News Productions International
Gospel Outreach Ministries Intl.
Gospel Revival Ministries
Heart for Honduras
Hellenic Ministries/USA
Hermano Pablo Ministries
High Adventure Ministries/Voice of Hope
   Broadcasting Network
Impact International, Inc.
India Gospel League, NA
India Gospel Outreach, Inc.
India National Inland Mission
INTERCOMM, Inc.
Intl. Christian Leprosy Mission, Inc. (USA)
International Partnership Ministries, Inc.
Iranian Christians International
Italy for Christ, Inc.
Jews for Jesus
Joni and Friends
Josue Yrion World Evangelism and Msns., Inc.
Kids for Christ International
Living Word Missions
Luis Palau Evangelistic Association
Lutheran Hour Ministries
M/E International, Inc.
Mahesh Chavda Ministries International
Messianic Jewish Movement Intl., Inc., The
Mexican Medical Ministries
Middle East Media—USA
Middle Eastern Outreach
Ministries In Action
Mission Generation, Inc.
Mission to Children, Inc.
Morelli Ministries International, Inc.
Muslim Hope
National Baptist Convention of America

New Life Advance International
OMS International, Inc.
On The Go Ministries/Keith Cook Team
Open Air Campaigners—Overseas Ministries
Operation Mobilization
Outreach To Asia Nationals
Overseas Radio & Television, Inc. (ORTV)
Pentecostal Church of God—World Missions
Pioneer Bible Translators
Presbyterian Evangelistic Fellowship
Presbyterian Order for World Evangelization
Proclaim! International, Inc.
Progressive National Baptist Convention, Inc.
Project AmaZon
Raul Zaldivar Ministries
Rogma International, Inc.
Samaritan's Purse International Relief
SAT-7 North America
SEED International
Seventh-day Adventists, General Conf.
Son Shine Ministries International
Spiritual Growth Resources, Inc.
TeachBeyond USA
The Gospel Furthering Fellowship
Things To Come Mission, Inc.
TITUS International
Training Evangelistic Leadership (T.E.L.), Inc.
Turkish World Outreach
TWR
United Evangelical Churches
United Pentecostal Church Intl.
Weiner Ministries International
Women to the World, Inc.
World Reach, Inc.
Youth for Christ/USA—World Outreach
Youth With A Mission (YWAM)

Evangelism, personal and small group

ABWE, Inc.
Advancing Renewal Ministries, Inc.
Advent Christian General Conf.
Adventive Cross Cultural Initiatives—US
Africa Inland Mission International, Inc.
African Enterprise
Agape Gospel Mission
Alberto Mottesi Evangelistic Association, Inc.
Allegheny Wesleyan Methodist Connection
Alongside Ministries International
Amazon Outreach
Ambassadors for Christ International Ltd.
American Baptist Chs. of the U.S.A.
American Evangelical Christian Churches
American Scripture Gift Mission Inc.
AMG International
Anglican Frontier Missions
Anis Shorrosh Evangelistic Association
Artists In Christian Testimony International

Asian Access
Asian Outreach U.S.A.
Association of Free Lutheran Congregations
Awana International
Baptist International Missions, Inc. (BIMI)
Baptist Missionary Association of America
Baptist Missions to Forgotten Peoples
BCM International
Bethany International Ministries
Bible League, The
Biblical Ministries Worldwide
Blessing the Children International
Brazil Gospel Fellowship Mission
Cadence International
Calvary International
Campus Crusade for Christ, Intl.
Caring Partners International, Inc.
CEIFA Ministry International
Centers for Apologetics Research, The
Central Yearly Meeting of Friends Missions
Chosen People Ministries
Christ for Children International
Christ for the City International
Christ for the Nations, Inc.
Christar
Christian and Missionary Alliance, The
Christian Cultural Development Foundation
Christian Dental Society
Christian Involvement in Service (CIS)
Christian Laymen's Missionary Evang. Assoc.
Christian Medical & Dental Associations
Christian Missions Unlimited
Christian Outreach International
Christian Union Churches of North America
Christians In Action Missions International
Church of God (Cleveland, Tenn.)
Church of God (Holiness)
Church of God of Prophecy
Ch. of God of the Apostolic Faith, Inc., The
Church of the Nazarene, World Msn. Dept.
Congregational Methodist Missions
Connecting Businessmen to Christ, Inc.
Cornerstone International
Crescent Project
CrossWorld
Dayspring International
Disciples International
e3 Partners Ministry
East-West Ministries International
Educational Resources & Referrals—China
Elim Fellowship—International Ministries
Emmanuel International Mission
Empowering Lives International
Episcopal Church USA
Equip International
EurAsian Baptist Mission
European Christian Mission Intl.—USA

European Evangelistic Society
Evangelical Bible Mission
Evangelical Friends Mission
Evangelical Methodist Church, Inc.
Evangelical Mission Ministries, Inc.
Evangelical Presbyterian Church
Evangelism Explosion International
Evangelism Resources, Inc.
Evangelize China Fellowship, Inc.
Every Home for Christ International
FAME
Far East Broadcasting Company, Inc.
Fellowship of Companies for Christ Intl.
Fellowship of Evangelical Churches
For God's Children International
Foundation For His Ministry
Foursquare Missions International
Free Gospel Church, Inc.—Msns. Dept.
Free Methodist World Missions
Free Will Baptist, Inc. Bd. of Intl. Msns.
Friends of Donetsk Christian University
Friendship International Ministries, Inc.
Frontiers
Gideons International, The
Global Aid Network (GAiN USA)
Global Fellowship, Inc.
Global Ministries
Global Outreach Mission, Inc.
Global Partners/Wesleyan World Missions
Global Recordings Network
Global University
Globe International
Go Ye Fellowship
Good News for India
Good News Productions International
Good Shepherd Ministries, Inc.
Gospel Fellowship Association
Gospel Operation Intl. for Chinese Christians
Gospel Outbound
Gospelink, Inc.
Grace Brethren International Missions
Great Commission Ministries, Inc.
Greater Europe Mission
Greater Grace World Outreach
Harvest International, Inc.
Have Christ Will Travel Ministries, Inc.
Health Teams International
Heart to Heart Intl. Ministries (H2H)
Helimission, Inc.—USA
Hellenic Ministries/USA
Help for Christian Nationals, Inc.
His Healing Helping Hands Intl. Mins.
Hope for the Hungry
HOPE International
I. N. Network USA
Independent Faith Mission, Inc.
India Evangelical Mission

InterAct Ministries
International Board of Jewish Missions, Inc.
Intl. Christian Leprosy Mission, Inc. (USA)
International Family Missions
International Institute for Christian Studies
International Partnership Ministries, Inc.
International Pentecostal Church of Christ
International Students, Inc. (ISI)
InterVarsity Christian Fellowship/USA
Ireland Outreach International Inc.
ISOH/IMPACT
Italy for Christ, Inc.
Jewish Awareness Ministries, Inc.
Jews for Jesus
Liberty Corner Mission
Life in Messiah International
LifeWind International
Living Hope Ministries International, Inc.
Living Water International
Living Water Teaching
Luke Society, Inc., The
M/E International, Inc.
Macedonia World Baptist Missions, Inc.
Mailbox Club International Inc., The
MBMS International
Medical Missions Philippines, Inc.
Messianic Jewish Movement Intl., Inc., The
Middle Eastern Outreach
Mission Generation, Inc.
Mission India
Mission ONE, Inc.
Mission: Moving Mountains, Inc.
Missionary Athletes International
Missionary Gospel Fellowship
Missions To Japan, Inc.
Missions to Military, Inc.
National Baptist Convention of America
National Baptist Convention USA, Inc.
Navigators, U.S. Intl. Msns. Group
New Life Advance International
New Way Missions
Ninos de Mexico
OMF International
OMS International, Inc.
Open Air Campaigners—Overseas Ministries
Open Door Baptist Missions
Operation Mobilization
Orthodox Presbyterian Church
Palm Missionary Ministries, Inc.
Paradigm Shift
Partners in Asian Missions
Pentecostal Assemblies of God of Am., Inc.
Pentecostal Church of God—World Missions
People International USA
Pioneers USA
Prayer Baptist Missions International, Inc.
Presbyterian Evangelistic Fellowship

Presbyterian Mission International (PMI)
Presbyterian Missionary Union
Primitive Methodist Church in the USA
Proclaim! International, Inc.
Ramesh Richard Evangelism and Ch. Health
Reach Ministries International
ReachAcross
Reaching Indians Ministries International
Real Impact Missions, Inc.
Remnant Ministries, Inc.
Ripe for Harvest, Inc.
Romanian Missionary Society
Rosedale Mennonite Missions
RUN Ministries
Salvation Army, U.S.A.
Samaritan's Purse International Relief
SEND International USA
Share International
Shield of Faith Mission International
Son Shine Ministries International
Southern Baptist Convention Intl. Msn. Bd.
Sowers International, The
Spanish American Evangelistic Ministries
Sports & Rec Plus
STEM International
Surfing the Nations
TEAM (The Evangelical Alliance Mission)
TEAMS for Medical Missions
Tentmakers International
The God's Story Project
The Gospel Furthering Fellowship
The Mission Society
The Waray-Waray Project
Things To Come Mission, Inc.
TITUS International
TMA Ministries Inc.
Training Evangelistic Leadership (T.E.L.), Inc.
United Evangelical Churches
United Pentecostal Church Intl.
Village Ministries International
Vineyard Church USA—Missions
Virginia Mennonite Missions
Volunteers in Medical Missions
Warm Blankets Orphan Care International
WEC International
World Gospel Mission
World Harvest Mission
World Harvest Now, Inc.
World Horizons
World Indigenous Missions
World Link Ministries
World Mission Prayer League
World Mission, Inc.
World Outreach International—US
World Partners USA
World Team
World Venture

World Witness
Worldwide Medical-Dental Evangelical Msn.
World-Wide Missions
Young Life
Youth for Christ International
Youth for Christ/USA—World Outreach
Youth With A Mission (YWAM)
YUGO Ministries

Evangelism, student
Adventures in Missions
Alberto Mottesi Evangelistic Association, Inc.
Allegheny Wesleyan Methodist Connection
Cadence International
Calvary Commission, Inc.
Campus Crusade for Christ, Intl.
Carver International Missions, Inc.
Child Evangelism Fellowship, Inc.
Children of Promise International
Children's Ministry International, Inc. (CMI)
China Ministries International
China Outreach Ministries, Inc.
Christian Dental Society
Christian Laymen's Missionary Evang. Assoc.
Compassion International, Inc.
CTI Music Ministries (Carpenter's Tools Intl.)
Every Child Ministries, Inc.
Global Outreach International
Global Youth Ministry Network
Good Shepherd Ministries, Inc.
Great Commission Ministries, Inc.
Heart of the Bride Ministries
Hope for the Hungry
International Messengers
International Students, Inc. (ISI)
Italy for Christ, Inc.
Japanese Evangelical Missionary Society
Joshua Expeditions
Kids for Christ International
Liberty Corner Mission
Mission Generation, Inc.
Mission Possible, Inc.
Mission Without Borders International
Navigators, U.S. Intl. Msns. Group
Network of International Christian Schools
New Hope Uganda Ministries
OMF International
On The Go Ministries/Keith Cook Team
OneHope
Open Air Campaigners—Overseas Ministries
Proclaim! International, Inc.
Ravi Zacharias International Ministries, Inc.
Resourcing Christian Education International
Rock the World Youth Mission Alliance
Sowers International, The
TEAMS for Medical Missions
Teen Mission, USA, Inc.

Touch the World Ministries, Inc.
Training Evangelistic Leadership (T.E.L.), Inc.
University Bible Fellowship
Word of Life Fellowship, Inc.
Worldwide Discipleship Assoc.
Young Life
Youth for Christ International
Youth for Christ/USA—World Outreach

Funds transmission
Advancing Indigenous Missions
Advancing Native Missions
American Association of Lutheran Churches
American Waldensian Society
Apostolic Christian Church Foundation, Inc.
Artists In Christian Testimony International
Baptist International Outreach, Inc.
Children of Promise International
Christian Mission for the Deaf
Christian Missions in Many Lands, Inc.
Christ's Mandate for Missions
Church of God (Seventh Day) Gen. Conf.
Church Planting International, Inc.
Commission to Every Nation
Congregational Christian Churches
Dayspring International
East West Interknit
Elim Fellowship—International Ministries
Far East Broadcasting Company, Inc.
FARMS International
Final Frontiers Foundation, Inc.
Full Gospel Grace Fellowship
Fundamental Baptist Missions International
Globe International
God Reports
Gospel Revival Ministries
Hope for the Hungry
IFCA World Missions
International Child Care, USA
Intl. Foundation for EWHA Woman's University
Medical Missions Philippines, Inc.
Missions To Japan, Inc.
Opportunity International
SAT-7 North America
Scripture Union, USA
ServLife International
Seventh Day Baptist Missionary Society
Slavic Missionary Service, Inc.
Vellore Christian Medical College Bd. (USA), Inc.
World Missions & Evangelism, Inc.
World-Wide Missions
Wycliffe Bible Translators, Inc.

Furloughed missionary
Advent Christian General Conf.
Alongside, Inc.
Cedar Lane Missionary Homes, Inc.

CMTS Ministries, Inc.
D & D Missionary Homes, Inc.
Episcopal Church USA
Free Will Baptist, Inc. Bd. of Intl. Msns.
Interaction International
MATS International, Inc.
Mission Training International
Missionary Furlough Homes Foundation
Missionary Outreach Support Services
Missionary Retreat Fellowship, Inc.
National Baptist Convention USA, Inc.
Providence Mission Homes, Inc.

HIV/Aids
Action International Ministries, Inc.
African Leadership Development
African Leadership, Inc.
AIDS Family Fund, Inc.
American Bible Society
Children's HopeChest
Christian Reformed World Relief Committee
Christian Relief Fund, The
Church World Service
Churches Together
Eastern Mennonite Missions
endPoverty.org
Equip International
Evangelical Baptist Missions
Food for the Hungry, Inc.
Forgotten Voices International
Heart of the Bride Ministries
International Child Care, USA
International Institute for Christian Studies
Kerus Global Education
Kids Around the World, Inc.
Launch Out Ministries International
Lott Carey Baptist Foreign Msn. Conv.
Medical Teams International
National Baptist Convention USA, Inc.
Peter Deyneka Russian Ministries
Teen Missions International, Inc.
World Concern
World Orphans
World Partners USA
World Relief

Information services
American Waldensian Society
ASSIST Ministries & ASSIST News Service
Billy Graham Center, The
China Connection
Christian Missions in Many Lands, Inc.
Cities for Christ Worldwide (CCW)
Crisis Consulting International
CrossGlobal Link
Cumberland Presbyterian Ch. Bd. of Msns.
Door of Hope International

Envoy International
Equipping the Saints
Evangelism and Msns. Info. Service (EMIS)
Faith Christian Fellowship International
FOM (Fellowship of Missions)
General Assoc. of Regular Baptist Chs.
International Ministries
Global Focus
Global Impact Services
Global Mapping International
God Reports
Great Commission Center International
International Child Care, USA
Japanese Evangelization Center
LIGHT International, Inc.
Middle Eastern Outreach
Mission Data International
Mission Safety International
Mission Services Association, Inc.
Missionary Outreach Support Services
New Wineskins Missionary Network
Sentinel Group, The
Tentmakers International
United Methodist Church
World Christian Ministries
Worldwide Discipleship Assoc.

Justice & related
Bread for the World
Café 1040, Inc.
Casa Viva
Christian Cultural Development Foundation
Christian Reformed World Relief Committee
Church of the Brethren
Church World Service
Cooperative Baptist Fellowship
Dawn Ministries, Inc.
Equip International
Food for the Hungry, Inc.
Heart of God Ministries
Heifer Project International
International Justice Mission
International Street Kids Outreach Ministries
Iranian Christians International
Lutheran World Relief
Mennonite Central Committee (MCC)
Open Doors, USA
Progressive National Baptist Convention, Inc.
Reformed Ch. in Am., Gen. Synod Council
World Vision International
World Vision, Inc.

Leadership development
Abundant Life Association, Inc.
ACTS International Ministries, Inc.
Advancing Renewal Ministries, Inc.
Advent Christian General Conf.

AEGA Ministries International, Inc.
Africa Inter-Mennonite Mission International
African Bible Colleges, Inc.
African Enterprise
African Leadership Development
Agape Gospel Mission
AIDS Family Fund, Inc.
AIMS (Accelerating Intl. Msn. Strategies)
Alongside Ministries International
Amazon Focus, Inc.
American Baptist Chs. of the U.S.A.
American Waldensian Society
ARISE International Mission
Asian Access
Asian Outreach U.S.A.
Association of Christian Schools Intl. (ACSI)
Association of Free Lutheran Congregations
Aurora Mission, Inc.
Awana International
Baptist International Missions, Inc. (BIMI)
Barnabas International
BEE World (Biblical Education by Extension)
Beyond Borders
Biblical Ministries Worldwide
BILD International
Billy Graham Center, The
Brazil Gospel Fellowship Mission
Bridge Builders International
Bright Hope International
Café 1040, Inc.
Calvary International
Caring for Others
Carver International Missions, Inc.
Christ for the City International
Christian and Missionary Alliance, The
Christian Aviation and Radio Mission
Christian Blind Mission International
Christian Church (Disciples of Christ)
Christian Cultural Development Foundation
Christian Fellowship Union, Inc.
Christian Medical & Dental Associations
Christian Ministries International (CMI)
Christian Reformed World Missions
ChristianCourses.Com
Christ's Mandate for Missions
Church Leadership Dev. Intl.
Church Missions Link
Church of God (Anderson, Ind.)
Church of God of Prophecy
Church Planting International, Inc.
Church Resource Ministries (CRM)
Churches of God, General Conference
CMF International
Colorado Haiti Project, Inc.
COMHINA
Commission to Every Nation
Compassion International, Inc.

Orthodox Presbyterian Church
Overseas Council International
Paradigm Shift
Partners in Asian Missions
Partners in Christ International
Partners International
Pass the Torch Ministries/Church of Acts
Pentecostal Assemblies of God of Am., Inc.
People International USA
Perimeter Church—Global Outreach
Prakash Association, USA
Precept Ministries International
Precious Seed Ministries
Presbyterian Church (USA)
Presbyterian Missionary Union
Raul Zaldivar Ministries
Reach Ministries International
ReachGlobal
Reformed Ch. in Am., Gen. Synod Council
Rio Grande Bible Institute, Inc.
Rock the World Youth Mission Alliance
RUN Ministries
Self-Help International
SEND International USA
Servants in Faith & Technology (SIFAT)
Society of St. Margaret
South America Mission, Inc.
South American Missionary Society (USA)
Southern Baptist Convention Intl. Msn. Bd.
Spiritual Overseers Service International
Supreme Task International, Inc.
Surfing the Nations
Talking Bibles International
TEAM (The Evangelical Alliance Mission)
The Brethren Church, Inc.
The Mission Society
TWR
United Bd. for Christian Higher Ed. in Asia
United Church of Christ—Global Ministries
United Pentecostal Church Intl.
United World Mission
University Bible Fellowship
UWEZO International, Inc.
Vineyard Church USA—Missions
visionSynergy
Warm Blankets Orphan Care International
Women to the World, Inc.
World Gospel Mission
World Harvest—USA
World Harvest Now, Inc.
World Help
World Mission Associates
World Mission Prayer League
World Mission, Inc.
World Missionary Assistance Plan
World Missions & Evangelism, Inc.
World Outreach International—US

World Partners USA
World Reach, Inc.
World Servants
World Thrust International, Inc.
World Venture
WorldServe Ministries
Youth for Christ International
Youth Ministry International (YMI)
YUGO Ministries

Linguistics

Baptist Bible Translators Institute
Commission to Every Nation
Institute of Strategic Languages and Cultures
New Tribes Mission
Operation Serve International
The Word for the World USA
World Partners USA
Wycliffe Bible Translators, Inc.

Literacy

Abundant Life Association, Inc.
Beyond Borders
Bible League, The
Christian Literacy Associates
Christian Literature International
Christian Reformed World Relief Committee
Church World Service
Evangel Bible Translators
General Baptists International
Gospel Outreach Ministries Intl.
Ireland Outreach International Inc.
Literacy & Evangelism International
Lutheran Bible Translators, Inc.
Mission India
New Tribes Mission
Operation Serve International
Palm Missionary Ministries, Inc.
Pioneer Bible Translators
Share International
Society of St. Margaret
Supreme Task International, Inc.
Teen Missions International, Inc.
The Word for the World USA
Women to the World, Inc.
World Partners USA
Wycliffe Bible Translators, Inc.

Literature distribution

Action International Ministries, Inc.
Alberto Mottesi Evangelistic Association, Inc.
Ambassadors for Christ, Inc.
American Scripture Gift Mission Inc.
ARISE International Mission
Asian Outreach U.S.A.
Back to the Bible International
Baptist International Evangelistic Ministries

Bethany International Ministries
Bibles & Literature in French
Caleb Resources
CEIFA Ministry International
Child Evangelism Fellowship, Inc.
Chosen People Ministries
Christ for the Nations, Inc.
Christian Aid Ministries (CAM)
Christian Literature International
Christian Resources International
Christian Union Churches of North America
Church Leadership Dev. Intl.
Church of God (Seventh Day) Gen. Conf.
Ch. of God of the Apostolic Faith, Inc., The
Church of the Nazarene, World Msn. Dept.
CLC Ministries International
Cook Communications Ministries Intl.
Crescent Project
Dawn Ministries, Inc.
Disciples International
East West Interknit
Eastern European Outreach, Inc.
ECHO Cuba
Edwin L. Hodges Ministries
Equipping the Saints
Evangelical Bible Mission
Evangelical Mission Ministries, Inc.
Evangelism and Msns. Info. Service (EMIS)
Evangelism Resources, Inc.
Every Home for Christ International
Friends of Israel Gospel Ministry, Inc.
Full Gospel Grace Fellowship
Good Shepherd Ministries, Inc.
Gospel Revival Ministries
Harvesting In Spanish (HIS)
In Motion Ministries
International Board of Jewish Missions, Inc.
Iranian Christians International
Ireland Outreach International Inc.
Jewish Awareness Ministries, Inc.
Jews for Jesus
Key Communications
Life in Messiah International
Lutheran Bible Translators, Inc.
Lutheran Hour Ministries
Mailbox Club International Inc., The
Media Associates International
Middle Eastern Outreach
Mission International
Mission Possible Foundation, Inc.
Mission Without Borders International
Missions to Military, Inc.
Open Air Campaigners—Overseas Ministries
Open Doors, USA
Operation Mobilization
Overseas Ministries Study Center
Pentecostal Church of God—World Missions

Peter Deyneka Russian Ministries
Prayer Baptist Missions International, Inc.
Presbyterian Evangelistic Fellowship
RBC Ministries
Russian Bible Society, Inc.
Russian Christian Radio, Inc.
Scripture Union, USA
Slavic Gospel Association
Source of Light Ministries International, Inc.
Spanish American Evangelistic Ministries
Spanish World Ministries, Inc.
STEM International
Teen Mission, USA, Inc.
Turkish World Outreach
Village Ministries International
Voice of the Martyrs, The
WayMakers International
Waymarks Radio Ministries International
Word To Russia
World Christian Ministries Association
World Compassion Terry Law Ministries
World Mission Associates
World Missionary Assistance Plan
WorldTeach

Literature production

Alberto Mottesi Evangelistic Association, Inc.
Ambassadors for Christ, Inc.
Anis Shorrosh Evangelistic Association
Asian Outreach U.S.A.
Aurora Mission, Inc.
Back to the Bible International
Bibles & Literature in French
Caleb Resources
CEIFA Ministry International
Centers for Apologetics Research, The
Child Evangelism Fellowship, Inc.
Chosen People Ministries
Christ for the Nations, Inc.
Church of the Nazarene, World Msn. Dept.
CLC Ministries International
Cook Communications Ministries Intl.
Crescent Project
Edwin L. Hodges Ministries
Evangelism and Msns. Info. Service (EMIS)
Friends of Israel Gospel Ministry, Inc.
Friends United Meeting
Gospel Operation Intl. for Chinese Christians
Grace and Truth, Inc.
Grace Ministries International
Great Commission Center International
Iranian Christians International
Ireland Outreach International Inc.
JARON Ministries International
Jewish Awareness Ministries, Inc.
Kidzana Ministries
Leadership Ministries Worldwide

Literacy & Evangelism International
Lutheran Brethren World Missions
Lutheran Hour Ministries
Mahesh Chavda Ministries International
Media Associates International
Middle East Media—USA
Mission Possible Foundation, Inc.
Missionary TECH Team
Navigators, U.S. Intl. Msns. Group
Progressive National Baptist Convention, Inc.
RBC Ministries
Reformed Baptist Mission Services
Remnant Ministries, Inc.
Romanian Missionary Society
Russian Bible Society, Inc.
Russian Christian Radio, Inc.
Seventh-day Adventists, General Conf.
Source of Light Ministries International, Inc.
Spanish American Evangelistic Ministries
Walk Thru the Bible Ministries, Inc.
WayMakers International
Waymarks Radio Ministries International
Westminster Biblical Missions
Wisconsin Evangelical Lutheran Synod
World Christian Ministries Association
World Missionary Assistance Plan
World Missionary Press, Inc.
WorldServe Ministries
WorldTeach

Management

Association of Christian Schools Intl. (ACSI)
Caring for Others
Christian Ministries International (CMI)
Crisis Consulting International
Faith Life Ministries, Inc.
FARMS International
Fellowship of Companies for Christ Intl.
Global Health Ministries
Global Impact Services
Global Mapping International
Health Emergent International Services
International Steward
LifeWind International
LIGHT International, Inc.
Mission Training and Resource Center
Paraclete Mission Group, Inc.
Partners Worldwide
The Bodybuilders
visionSynergy
Worldwide Tentmakers, Inc.

Medical supplies

AEGA Ministries International, Inc.
African Methodist Episcopal Church
American Leprosy Missions, Inc.
Blessings International

Caribbean Baptist Mission Society
CEIFA Ministry International
Chosen Mission Project
Christ for India, Inc.
Christian Pilots Association
Ch. of God of the Apostolic Faith, Inc., The
Church of the Nazarene, World Msn. Dept.
Congregational Holiness Church
CrossLink International
Discipleship Missions International
Equipping the Saints
FAME
Global Aid Network (GAiN USA)
Global Health Ministries
Good Shepherd Ministries, Inc.
Harvest International, Inc.
Health Emergent International Services
His Healing Helping Hands Intl. Mins.
HIS Servants Ministries
IMA World Health
International Aid
ISOH/IMPACT
Ludhiana Christian Medical College Board
MAP International
Medical Teams International
Men for Missions International
Mexican Medical Ministries
Myanmar Christian Mission
National Baptist Convention of America
Spanish World Ministries, Inc.
Ukrainian Childrens Fund
Vellore Christian Medical College Bd. (USA), Inc.
Voice of the Martyrs, The
Wisconsin Evangelical Lutheran Synod

Medicine, incl. dental and public health

ABWE, Inc.
African Children's Mission, Inc.
Agathos Foundation
Amazon Outreach
American Baptist Chs. of the U.S.A.
American Leprosy Missions, Inc.
AMG International
Baptist Medical & Dental Mission Intl., Inc.
Baptist Mid-Missions
Blessing the Children International
Blessings International
Caring Partners International, Inc.
Childcare Worldwide
Children's International Lifeline
Childspring International
China Connection
China Service Ventures
Christian Aid Ministries (CAM)
Christian Dental Society
Christian Flights International
Christian Medical & Dental Associations

Church of the Nazarene, World Msn. Dept.
Churches of Christ
Churches of God, General Conference
Colorado Haiti Project, Inc.
ComCare International
Compassion International, Inc.
Converge Worldwide
CrossLink International
CSI Ministries
CWE
Empowering Lives International
Engineering Ministries International (EMI)
Eternal Hope in Haiti
Evangelistic Faith Missions
FAME
Flying Doctors of America
FOCAS
For Haiti with Love, Inc.
Forward Edge International
Foundation For His Ministry
Friends United Meeting
Global Health Ministries
Global Outreach International
Global Outreach Mission, Inc.
Good Shepherd Ministries, Inc.
Gospel Fellowship Association
Haiti Lutheran Mission Society
Haitian Christian Outreach
Harvesting In Spanish (HIS)
HCJB Global
Health Emergent International Services
Heart for Honduras
Heart to Heart Intl. Ministries (H2H)
His Healing Helping Hands Intl. Mins.
HIS Servants Ministries
IMA World Health
India Gospel League, NA
India Partners
International Crisis Aid
Interserve USA
Ireland Outreach International Inc.
Lifewater International, Inc.
Living Water Teaching
Lott Carey Baptist Foreign Msn. Conv.
Ludhiana Christian Medical College Board
Luke Society, Inc., The
Macedonian Missionary Service
Medical Ministry International
Medical Teams International
Mennonite Central Committee (MCC)
Mercy Ships
Mexican Medical Ministries
Mexico Medical Missions
Mission Possible, Inc.
Mission to the World (PCA), Inc.
Mission: Moving Mountains, Inc.
Missionary Gospel Fellowship

mPower
Mustard Seed International
National Baptist Convention of America
New Way Missions
Northwest Haiti Christian Mission
Operation Blessing Intl. Relief and Dev. Corp.
Operation Serve International
Orthodox Presbyterian Church
Overseas Insurance Consultants
Pilgrim
Presbyterian Church (USA)
Project AmaZon
Project Mercy, Inc.
ReachAcross
Real Impact Missions, Inc.
Reformed Episcopal Bd. of Foreign Msns.
Samaritan's Purse International Relief
Seventh-day Adventists, General Conf.
Share International
SIM USA, Inc.
South American Missionary Society (USA)
Sports & Rec Plus
Supreme Task International, Inc.
TEAM (The Evangelical Alliance Mission)
TEAMS for Medical Missions
Tribes and Nations Outreach
Vellore Christian Medical College Bd. (USA), Inc.
Volunteers in Medical Missions
Women to the World, Inc.
Word and Deed Ministries USA
World Mission Prayer League
World Missions Far Corners, Inc.
World Witness
Worldwide Medical-Dental Evangelical Msn.

Member care
Alongside, Inc.
American Association of Lutheran Churches
Barnabas International
Caring for Others
Cedar Lane Missionary Homes, Inc.
Christian Medical & Dental Associations
Church of God (Anderson, Ind.)
Church Resource Ministries (CRM)
Continent of Great Cities
Emmaus Road International
Evangelical Friends Church Southwest
Full Gospel Evangelistic Association
Global Opportunities
Global Teams International, Inc.
Interaction International
Interserve USA
Link Care Foundation
Missionary Outreach Support Services
Missions Resource Network
Narramore Christian Foundation
Paraclete Mission Group, Inc.

Reformed Baptist Mission Services
TeachBeyond USA
United Evangelical Churches

National church

ACTS International Ministries, Inc.
Advancing Indigenous Missions
Advancing Native Missions
Adventive Cross Cultural Initiatives—US
Africa Inter-Mennonite Mission International
AIDS Family Fund, Inc.
Alongside Ministries International
Amazon Focus, Inc.
Amazon Outreach
American Evangelical Christian Churches
AMOR Ministries
Aurora Mission, Inc.
Baptist Medical & Dental Mission Intl., Inc.
Barnabas International
Bibles For The World, Inc.
Blessing the Children International
Caring Partners International, Inc.
Casa Viva
Children's Christian Concern Society
Children's Ministry International, Inc. (CMI)
Christ for the City International
Christian Aid Mission
Christian Associates International
Christian Church (Disciples of Christ)
Christian Fellowship Union, Inc.
Christian Involvement in Service (CIS)
Christian Reformed World Missions
Christians In Action Missions International
Christ's Mandate for Missions
Church of God (Anderson, Ind.)
Church of God (Seventh Day) Gen. Conf.
Church of God of Prophecy
Church Planting International, Inc.
Church Resource Ministries (CRM)
Churches of Christ
Churches of God, General Conference
Churches Together
Conservative Congregational Christian Conf.
Continent of Great Cities
Cooperative Baptist Fellowship
Crossover Communications International
e3 Partners Ministry
Eastern Mennonite Missions
ECHO Cuba
Elim Fellowship—International Ministries
Emmanuel International Mission
Emmaus Road International
Empowering Lives International
Episcopal Church USA
Evangelical Congregational Church
Evangelical Covenant Church
Evangelical Friends Mission

Evangelical Mission Ministries, Inc.
Evangelical Presbyterian Church
Evangelistic Faith Missions
Faith Christian Fellowship International
Final Frontiers Foundation, Inc.
Forgotten Voices International
Foursquare Missions International
Free Gospel Church, Inc.—Msns. Dept.
Free Methodist World Missions
FRIENDS in Action International
Friends United Meeting
Full Gospel Evangelistic Association
Global Adopt-A-People Network
Global Advance
Global Ministries
Global Partners/Wesleyan World Missions
Global Youth Ministry Network
GOGF Ministries
Gospelink, Inc.
Grace Brethren International Missions
Harvest
HCJB Global
IFCA World Missions
In Motion Ministries
In Touch Mission International
International Cooperating Ministries (ICM)
International Pentecostal Church of Christ
International Pentecostal Holiness Church
International Teams, U.S.A.
Ireland Outreach International Inc.
Kidzana Ministries
Latin America Mission
Latin American Indian Ministries
Latin American Lutheran Mission
LOGOI Ministries
Lott Carey Baptist Foreign Msn. Conv.
Lutheran Church-Missouri Synod
Mahesh Chavda Ministries International
Mennonite Mission Network
Mexico Medical Missions
Middle East Christian Outreach (MECO)
Middle East Media—USA
Middle Eastern Outreach
Ministries In Action
Mission Aviation Fellowship
Mission ONE, Inc.
Mission to the World (PCA), Inc.
Missionary Ventures International
Missions Door
Morelli Ministries International, Inc.
New Directions International, Inc.
New Way Missions
Ninos de Mexico
OC International, Inc.
Open Doors, USA
Orthodox Presbyterian Church
Palm Missionary Ministries, Inc.

Paraclete Mission Group, Inc.
Partners in Christ International
Pass the Torch Ministries/Church of Acts
Pentecostal Church of God—World Missions
Pentecostal Free Will Baptist Church, Inc.
Perimeter Church—Global Outreach
Pioneer Bible Translators
Pioneers USA
Proclaim! International, Inc.
Reaching Indians Ministries International
Reciprocal Ministries International
SEND International USA
ServLife International
Seventh Day Baptist Missionary Society
Slavic Missionary Service, Inc.
Society of St. Margaret
South America Mission, Inc.
Spiritual Overseers Service International
TEAMS for Medical Missions
The Brethren Church, Inc.
The Mission Society
The Waray-Waray Project
United Church of Christ—Global Ministries
United Methodist Church
United World Mission
UWEZO International, Inc.
Venture International
Vineyard Church USA—Missions
Walk Thru the Bible Ministries, Inc.
Westminster Biblical Missions
White Fields, Inc.
Wisconsin Evangelical Lutheran Synod
World Christian Ministries
World Harvest Now, Inc.
World Horizons
World Mission, Inc.
World Missions Far Corners, Inc.
World Orphans
World Partners USA
World Vision, Inc.
World Witness
WorldServe Ministries
Youth Ministry International (YMI)

Other

Advancing Indigenous Missions
African Leadership, Inc.
AIMS (Accelerating Intl. Msn. Strategies)
Amazon Outreach
American Bible Society
Arab World Ministries
Artists In Christian Testimony International
BCM International
Bread for the World
Bright Hope International
Cadence International
Caring Partners International, Inc.

Carpenter's Brothers Family Travel
Celebrant Singers
Childcare Worldwide
Children's HopeChest
China Service Ventures
Christ for Children International
Christar
Christian Aid Mission
Church Missions Link
Church of the Brethren
Colorado Haiti Project, Inc.
Crisis Consulting International
D & D Missionary Homes, Inc.
Eastern European Outreach, Inc.
Educational Resources & Referrals—China
Emmanuel International Mission
endPoverty.org
Engineering Ministries International (EMI)
Faith Missions International
FAME
Fellowship Travel International
For Haiti with Love, Inc.
Free Methodist World Missions
Friends of Donetsk Christian University
Friends United Meeting
Full Gospel Fellowship of Chs. & Mins. Intl.
Global Aid Network (GAiN USA)
Global Fellowship, Inc.
Go Ye Fellowship
Good Neighbor Insurance, Inc.
Harvest
Harvest Mission to the Unreached
Health Teams International
Helimission, Inc.—USA
INTERCOMM, Inc.
International Child Care, USA
International Steward
Interserve USA
Iranian Christians International
Kids Around the World, Inc.
Kidzana Ministries
Living Water International
LOGOI Ministries
Luis Palau Evangelistic Association
Men for Missions International
Mercy Ships
Mexican Medical Ministries
Mission Nannys
Mission Possible, Inc.
Mission to Children, Inc.
Mission Training International
Mission Without Borders International
Missionary Expediters, Inc.
Missions to Military, Inc.
New Mission Systems International
Operation Bootstrap Africa
Operation Serve International

Overseas Insurance Consultants
Prakash Association, USA
Prayer Baptist Missions International, Inc.
Precept Ministries International
Resourcing Christian Education International
Salvation Army, U.S.A.
Scripture Union, USA
Self-Help International
Shield of Faith Mission International
Society of St. Margaret
Straightway Inc.
TEAMS for Medical Missions
Tech Serve International, Inc.
The God's Story Project
Turkish World Outreach
United Evangelical Churches
Venture International
Warm Blankets Orphan Care International
WayMakers International
Women to the World, Inc.
World Christian Ministries Association
World Help
World Mission Associates
Worldwide Lab Improvement
Wycliffe Associates
Youth Ministry International (YMI)
YUGO Ministries

Partnership development

Africa Inter-Mennonite Mission International
African Leadership Development
African Leadership, Inc.
African Methodist Episcopal Church
Agathos Foundation
Amazon Focus, Inc.
Ambassadors for Christ, Inc.
American Bible Society
American Waldensian Society
AMOR Ministries
Anglican Frontier Missions
ARISE International Mission
Awana International
BEE World (Biblical Education by Extension)
Bethany International Ministries
BILD International
Bridge Builders International
Bright Hope International
Catalyst Services
Child Evangelism Fellowship, Inc.
Childspring International
ChinaSource
Christ Community Church
Christian Church (Disciples of Christ)
Church Ministries International
Churches Together
CityTeam Ministries—New Generations Intl.
Colorado Haiti Project, Inc.

COMHINA
Congregational Methodist Missions
Cumberland Presbyterian Ch. Bd. of Msns.
DeNike Ministries
Development Associates International (DAI)
Emmaus Road International
endPoverty.org
Envoy International
Episcopal Church USA
Eternal Hope in Haiti
Evangelical Covenant Church
Evangelical Lutheran Church in America
Faith Christian Fellowship International
Free Methodist World Missions
FRIENDS in Action International
Global Health Ministries
Good News Productions International
Gospel Outbound
Habitat for Humanity International
HCJB Global
Heart for Honduras
IMA World Health
In Touch Mission International
India Partners
International Christian Ministries
International Family Missions
International Partnership Associates
International Partnership Ministries, Inc.
International Steward
Interserve USA
ISOH/IMPACT
Lifewater International, Inc.
LifeWind International
Living Water International
Lutheran Brethren World Missions
MAP International
Mennonite Mission Network
Middle East Christian Outreach (MECO)
Mission ONE, Inc.
Mission Safety International
Missions Resource Network
OC International, Inc.
Paraclete Mission Group, Inc.
Partners International
Partners Worldwide
Perimeter Church—Global Outreach
Presbyterian Church (USA)
Reciprocal Ministries International
Shelter for Life International, Inc.
STEER, Inc.
United Church of Christ—Global Ministries
United World Mission
UWEZO International, Inc.
Venture International
visionSynergy
Waymarks Radio Ministries International
White Fields, Inc.

Wisconsin Evangelical Lutheran Synod
Women to the World, Inc.
World Christian Ministries
World Partners USA
World Servants

Psychological counseling
Alongside, Inc.
Barnabas International
Caring for Others
Forgotten Voices International
Link Care Foundation
Mercy Ships
Missionary Outreach Support Services
Narramore Christian Foundation
Pilgrim

Purchasing services
CMTS Ministries, Inc.
Equipping the Saints
JAARS, Inc.
MATS International, Inc.

Recruiting/Mobilizing
Advancing Native Missions
Adventive Cross Cultural Initiatives—US
Adventures in Missions
AIMS (Accelerating Intl. Msn. Strategies)
Alongside Ministries International
Anglican Frontier Missions
ARISE International Mission
Artists In Christian Testimony International
Café 1040, Inc.
Caleb Resources
Catalyst Services
Children's HopeChest
Christian Missions Unlimited
Christian Reformed World Missions
Christians In Action Missions International
COMHINA
Continent of Great Cities
Cornerstone International
DualReach
e3 Partners Ministry
Emmaus Road International
Envoy International
European Christian Mission Intl.—USA
Finishers Project
Frontiers
Global Focus
Global Health Ministries
Global Teams International, Inc.
God Reports
Gospel Operation Intl. for Chinese Christians
Gospel Revival Ministries
Great Commission Center International
Great Commission Ministries, Inc.

Habitat for Humanity International
Heart of God Ministries
IFCA World Missions
In Motion Ministries
India Gospel Outreach, Inc.
International Family Missions
International Gospel Outreach
International Pentecostal Holiness Church
International Students, Inc. (ISI)
Kids for Christ International
Launch Out Ministries International
Life in Messiah International
MBMS International
Mission Data International
Missions Resource Network
Missions to Military, Inc.
Network of International Christian Schools
New Life Advance International
New Wineskins Missionary Network
OMF International
Pioneer Bible Translators
Presbyterian Church (USA)
Presbyterian Order for World Evangelization
Proclaim! International, Inc.
Rock the World Youth Mission Alliance
Seventh-day Adventists, General Conf.
Share International
SIM USA, Inc.
Source of Light Ministries International, Inc.
STEM International
TeachBeyond USA
Team Expansion, Inc.
The Bodybuilders
The Master's Mission, Inc.
Weiner Ministries International
World Horizons
World Servants
World Thrust International, Inc.
Wycliffe Associates
Wycliffe Bible Translators, Inc.
YUGO Ministries

Relief and/or rehabilitation
Adventive Cross Cultural Initiatives—US
African Enterprise
African Leadership, Inc.
Agathos Foundation
American Association of Lutheran Churches
American Leprosy Missions, Inc.
AMG International
AMOR Ministries
Apostolic Christian Church Foundation, Inc.
Armenian Missionary Assoc. of Am., Inc.
Baptist Mid-Missions
Baptist Missionary Association of America
Bright Hope International
Childcare Worldwide

Children's Christian Concern Society
Christian Aid Ministries (CAM)
Christian Blind Mission International
Christian Involvement in Service (CIS)
Christian Outreach International
Christian Reformed World Relief Committee
Christian Relief Fund, The
Church of the Nazarene, World Msn. Dept.
Church World Service
CityTeam Ministries—New Generations Intl.
Congregational Christian Churches
Cumberland Presbyterian Ch. Bd. of Msns.
Door of Hope International
Emmanuel International Mission
Engineering Ministries International (EMI)
Evangelical Lutheran Church in America
Evangelize China Fellowship, Inc.
Every Child Ministries, Inc.
For God's Children International
Forward Edge International
Global Aid Network (GAiN USA)
Global Outreach Mission, Inc.
Gospel Outreach Ministries Intl.
Habitat for Humanity International
Haiti Lutheran Mission Society
HBI Global Partners
Health Emergent International Services
Hellenic Ministries/USA
Help for Haiti, Inc.
High Adventure Ministries/Voice of Hope
   Broadcasting Network
His Healing Helping Hands Intl. Mins.
Hope for the Hungry
In Touch Mission International
International Aid
Intl. Christian Leprosy Mission, Inc. (USA)
International Crisis Aid
International Gospel Outreach
International Justice Mission
International Teams, U.S.A.
ISOH/IMPACT
Launch Out Ministries International
Living Water International
Ludhiana Christian Medical College Board
Lutheran World Relief
MAP International
Medical Teams International
Mennonite Central Committee (MCC)
Ministries In Action
Mission Without Borders International
Missionary Flights International
Missionary Outreach Support Services
Myanmar Christian Mission
New Hope Uganda Ministries
New Life Advance International
New Mission Systems International

Operation Blessing Intl. Relief and Dev. Corp.
Peter Deyneka Russian Ministries
Pilgrim
Precious Seed Ministries
Presbyterian Church (USA)
Ravi Zacharias International Ministries, Inc.
Salvation Army, U.S.A.
Samaritan's Purse International Relief
Share International
Supreme Task International, Inc.
Surfing the Nations
Ukrainian Childrens Fund
United Methodist Church
Venture International
Vision Beyond Borders
Women to the World, Inc.
Word and Deed Ministries USA
World Christian Outreach, Inc.
World Compassion Terry Law Ministries
World Concern
World Harvest—USA
World Help
World Reach, Inc.
World Relief
World Vision International
World Vision, Inc.
Youth With A Mission (YWAM)

Research

Anglican Frontier Missions
Billy Graham Center, The
Caleb Resources
Centers for Apologetics Research, The
ChinaSource
Church Missions Link
Dawn Ministries, Inc.
European Evangelistic Society
Evangelism and Msns. Info. Service (EMIS)
FOM (Fellowship of Missions)
Global Impact Services
Global Mapping International
Global Recordings Network
Good News Productions International
Gospel Outreach Ministries Intl.
Gospel Revival Ministries
Great Commission Center International
Handclasp International, Inc.
Japanese Evangelization Center
LIGHT International, Inc.
Mission Catalyst International, Inc.
OC International, Inc.
OneHope
Overseas Ministries Study Center
Presbyterian Order for World Evangelization
Sentinel Group, The
Southern Baptist Convention Intl. Msn. Bd.

WEC International
World Mission Associates
World Thrust International, Inc.

Services for other agencies
Alongside, Inc.
Caring for Others
Catalyst Services
Children's Haven International
Children's Ministry International, Inc. (CMI)
Church Ministries International
Cities for Christ Worldwide (CCW)
CMTS Ministries, Inc.
Crisis Consulting International
CrossGlobal Link
Engineering Ministries International (EMI)
Envoy International
Equipping the Saints
Finishers Project
FRIENDS in Action International
Full Gospel Evangelistic Association
Global Mapping International
Global Recordings Network
Handclasp International, Inc.
Harvest International, Inc.
Helimission, Inc.—USA
Help for Haiti, Inc.
Helps International Ministries
IMA World Health
Institute of Strategic Languages and Cultures
Interaction International
International Aid
Kerus Global Education
Literacy & Evangelism International
MATS International, Inc.
Mission Data International
Mission Safety International
Mission Training and Resource Center
Mission Training International
Missionaire International
Missionary TECH Team
MissionaryHealth.net
mPower
Muslim Hope
Nehemiah Teams International
Paraclete Mission Group, Inc.
Tech Serve International, Inc.
Teen Missions International, Inc.
The Master's Mission, Inc.
visionSynergy
Women to the World, Inc.
World Missionary Press, Inc.
World Thrust International, Inc.
Wycliffe Associates

Short-term programs
Advancing Native Missions

Adventive Cross Cultural Initiatives—US
Adventures in Missions
AEGA Ministries International, Inc.
All God's Children International
Alongside Ministries International
Amazon Outreach
Am. Council of the Ramabai Mukti Msn., Inc.
AMOR Ministries
Asian Outreach U.S.A.
Association of Christian Schools Intl. (ACSI)
Bibles & Literature in French
Calvary Commission, Inc.
Caring Partners International, Inc.
CEIFA Ministry International
Children's Haven International
Children's International Lifeline
Children's Ministry International, Inc. (CMI)
Chosen People Ministries
Christ Community Church
Christ for the City International
Christian Flights International
Christian Laymen's Missionary Evang. Assoc.
Christian Missions Unlimited
Christian Outreach International
Christians In Action Missions International
Church Missions Link
Church of the Nazarene, World Msn. Dept.
Churches of Christ
Congregational Methodist Missions
Conservative Congregational Christian Conf.
Cornerstone International
Crossover Communications International
CSI Ministries
CTI Music Ministries (Carpenter's Tools Intl.)
Cumberland Presbyterian Ch. Bd. of Msns.
Cup of Cold Water Ministries
DeNike Ministries
e3 Partners Ministry
Eastern European Outreach, Inc.
Eastern Mennonite Missions
ECHO Cuba
Educational Resources & Referrals—China
Empowering Lives International
Envoy International
Face to Face International
FAME
Fellowship Travel International
FOCAS
Forward Edge International
Free Will Baptist, Inc. Bd. of Intl. Msns.
Friendship International Ministries, Inc.
General Baptists International
Global Action
Global Aid Network (GAiN USA)
Global Outreach Mission, Inc.
GO InterNational
Gospel Operation Intl. for Chinese Christians

Gospel Outreach Ministries Intl.
Gospel Revival Ministries
Greater Europe Mission
Habitat for Humanity International
Harvest International, Inc.
Harvesting In Spanish (HIS)
Have Christ Will Travel Ministries, Inc.
HBI Global Partners
Heart for Honduras
Heart to Heart Intl. Ministries (H2H)
Hope for the Hungry
In Motion Ministries
Independent Faith Mission, Inc.
Independent Gospel Missions
India Partners
International Family Missions
International Messengers
International Pentecostal Holiness Church
InterVarsity Christian Fellowship/USA
Ireland Outreach International Inc.
Japanese Evangelical Missionary Society
JARON Ministries International
Jews for Jesus
Joni and Friends
Joshua Expeditions
Kids Alive International
Kids Around the World, Inc.
Latin America Mission
Latin American Lutheran Mission
Launch Out Ministries International
Life in Messiah International
Living Water International
Living Water Teaching
Macedonia World Baptist Missions, Inc.
Macedonian Missionary Service
Medical Teams International
Men for Missions International
Mennonite Mission Network
Mexican Medical Ministries
Ministries In Action
Missionary TECH Team
Missionary Ventures International
Moravian Church in North America
Mutual Faith Ministries Intl.
Nehemiah Teams International
New Way Missions
Ninos de Mexico
On The Go Ministries/Keith Cook Team
ORPHANetwork
Overseas Radio & Television, Inc. (ORTV)
Palm Missionary Ministries, Inc.
Presbyterian Missionary Union
Real Impact Missions, Inc.
Reciprocal Ministries International
Reformed Presbyterian Global Missions
Rock the World Youth Mission Alliance
Rosedale Mennonite Missions

Seventh Day Baptist Missionary Society
Shelter for Life International, Inc.
South American Missionary Society (USA)
Sowers International, The
Sports & Rec Plus
STEM International
Surfing the Nations
Team Expansion, Inc.
Teen Mission, USA, Inc.
Teen Missions International, Inc.
Things To Come Mission, Inc.
Touch the World Ministries, Inc.
Tribes and Nations Outreach
United Evangelical Churches
United Methodist Church
UWEZO International, Inc.
Virginia Mennonite Missions
Volunteers in Medical Missions
Word of Life Fellowship, Inc.
World Harvest—USA
World Indigenous Missions
World Mission, Inc.
World Partners USA
World Reach, Inc.
World Servants
Wycliffe Associates
YUGO Ministries
Zion Evangelical Ministries of Africa (ZEMA)

Sports program ministry

Christian Outreach International
Fellowship Travel International
International Cooperating Ministries (ICM)
Missionary Athletes International
Sports & Rec Plus
Teen Missions International, Inc.

Supplying equipment

Chosen Mission Project
Christian Aviation and Radio Mission
Christian Dental Society
Christian Flights International
CMTS Ministries, Inc.
ComCare International
Dayspring International
DeNike Ministries
East West Interknit
Equipping the Saints
Evangelical Bible Mission
FAME
FRIENDS in Action International
Global Recordings Network
Good Shepherd Ministries, Inc.
Gospel Revival Ministries
International Aid
JAARS, Inc.
M/E International, Inc.

MATS International, Inc.
mPower
Tech Serve International, Inc.
The Waray-Waray Project
Vellore Christian Medical College Bd. (USA), Inc.

Support of national

ACTS International Ministries, Inc.
Advancing Indigenous Missions
Advancing Native Missions
Advancing Renewal Ministries, Inc.
Advent Christian General Conf.
All About Orphans
Ambassadors for Christ International Ltd.
Am. Council of the Ramabai Mukti Msn., Inc.
AMG International
Apostolic Christian Church Foundation, Inc.
Arab World Ministries
Audio Scripture Ministries
Baptist International Evangelistic Ministries
Baptist International Outreach, Inc.
Bible League, The
Bibles For The World, Inc.
Calvary Commission, Inc.
Campus Crusade for Christ, Intl.
CEIFA Ministry International
Children of Promise International
China Ministries International
Christ Community Church
Christ for India, Inc.
Christ to the Nations
Christian Aid Mission
Christian Cultural Development Foundation
Christian Involvement in Service (CIS)
Christian Laymen's Missionary Evang. Assoc.
Christian Missions Unlimited
Christ's Mandate for Missions
Church Missions Link
Church of God (Holiness)
Church of God of Prophecy
Church of the Nazarene, World Msn. Dept.
Churches of God, General Conference
Congregational Holiness Church
Continent of Great Cities
Dayspring International
East West Interknit
Eastern European Outreach, Inc.
ECHO Cuba
European Christian Mission Intl.—USA
Faith Christian Fellowship International
Far East Broadcasting Company, Inc.
Final Frontiers Foundation, Inc.
Free Gospel Church, Inc.—Msns. Dept.
FRIENDS in Action International
Fundamental Baptist Msn. Trinidad/Tobago
Global Fellowship, Inc.
Global Outreach Mission, Inc.

Global Youth Ministry Network
Good News for India
Gospel for Asia, Inc.
Gospel Outreach Ministries Intl.
Gospel Revival Ministries
Gospelink, Inc.
Habitat for Humanity International
Haitian Christian Outreach
Harvest Mission to the Unreached
HBI Global Partners
I. N. Network USA
IFCA World Missions
In Motion Ministries
In Touch Mission International
Independent Gospel Missions
India Gospel Outreach, Inc.
International Child Care, USA
Kidzana Ministries
Latin American Indian Ministries
Latin American Lutheran Mission
LifeWind International
Luke Society, Inc., The
Mission Catalyst International, Inc.
Mission ONE, Inc.
Mission Without Borders International
Missionary Ventures International
Morelli Ministries International, Inc.
mPower
New Directions International, Inc.
New Hope International
Operation Serve International
Outreach To Asia Nationals
Palm Missionary Ministries, Inc.
Partners in Asian Missions
Partners International
Pass the Torch Ministries/Church of Acts
Pentecostal Church of God—World Missions
Pillar of Fire Missions International
Presbyterian Evangelistic Fellowship
Presbyterian Mission International (PMI)
Presbyterian Missionary Union
Reaching Indians Ministries International
Romanian Missionary Society
Scripture Union, USA
ServLife International
Share International
Slavic Gospel Association
Slavic Missionary Service, Inc.
Sowers International, The
Spanish World Ministries, Inc.
Spiritual Growth Resources, Inc.
STEM International
Team Expansion, Inc.
The Waray-Waray Project
The Word for the World USA
Things To Come Mission, Inc.
TITUS International

Training Evangelistic Leadership (T.E.L.), Inc.
Vision Beyond Borders
Voice of the Martyrs, The
Walk Thru the Bible Ministries, Inc.
White Fields, Inc.
Women to the World, Inc.
World Christian Ministries
World Christian Outreach, Inc.
World Missions & Evangelism, Inc.
World Partners USA
World-Wide Missions
Youth Ministry International (YMI)

Technical assistance
African Methodist Episcopal Church
American Leprosy Missions, Inc.
ARISE International Mission
Audio Scripture Ministries
Chosen Mission Project
Christian Aviation and Radio Mission
CMTS Ministries, Inc.
ComCare International
endPoverty.org
Engineering Ministries International (EMI)
FARMS International
Helps International Ministries
IMA World Health
JAARS, Inc.
Lifewater International, Inc.
Mennonite Central Committee (MCC)
Mission Aviation Fellowship
Missionary TECH Team
Tech Serve International, Inc.
TMA Ministries Inc.
United Bd. for Christian Higher Ed. in Asia
World Vision International

Tentmaking & related
Arab World Ministries
CMF International
Cooperative Baptist Fellowship
Educational Services International (ESI)
Frontiers
Global Opportunities
Go Ye Fellowship
Interserve USA
Mission Training and Resource Center
mPower
Pioneers USA
Ripe for Harvest, Inc.
Rosedale Mennonite Missions
Tentmakers International
University Bible Fellowship
WEC International
Women to the World, Inc.
Worldwide Tentmakers, Inc.

TESOL
Baptist Bible Translators Institute
Baptist Missionary Association of America
Christ Community Church
Christian Outreach International
Educational Services International (ESI)
Global Ministries
Greater Europe Mission
International Institute for Christian Studies
Kids for Christ International
Literacy & Evangelism International
Operation Serve International
Overseas Radio & Television, Inc. (ORTV)
ReachAcross
Resourcing Christian Education International
WEC International
Worldwide Tentmakers, Inc.

Trafficking/Slavery issues
American Baptist Chs. of the U.S.A.
Beyond Borders
Every Child Ministries, Inc.
Heart of God Ministries
India Partners
International Crisis Aid
International Justice Mission
International Street Kids Outreach Ministries
International Teams, U.S.A.
Launch Out Ministries International
Lott Carey Baptist Foreign Msn. Conv.
Real Impact Missions, Inc.
Vision Beyond Borders
Women to the World, Inc.
World Missions Far Corners, Inc.
World Partners USA

Training, other
ACTS International Ministries, Inc.
African Leadership, Inc.
Ambassadors for Christ International Ltd.
Asian Outreach U.S.A.
Audio Scripture Ministries
BCM International
Beyond Borders
Bible League, The
Billy Graham Center, The
Bridge Builders International
Caleb Resources
Campus Crusade for Christ, Intl.
Casa Viva
Centers for Apologetics Research, The
Child Evangelism Fellowship, Inc.
China Ministries International
Christian Ministries International (CMI)
Church Leadership Dev. Intl.
Church Ministries International
Church Missions Link

Ch. of God of the Apostolic Faith, Inc., The
Church Planting International, Inc.
CityTeam Ministries—New Generations Intl.
ComCare International
Connecting Businessmen to Christ, Inc.
Crescent Project
Crisis Consulting International
CrossGlobal Link
Dawn Ministries, Inc.
DeNike Ministries
Development Associates International (DAI)
endPoverty.org
Envoy International
Evangelism Explosion International
Every Home for Christ International
Fellowship of Companies for Christ Intl.
General Baptists International
Global Action
Global Advance
Global Harvest Ministries
Global Mapping International
Global Opportunities
Global Youth Ministry Network
GOGF Ministries
Good Shepherd Ministries International
Great Commission Center International
Heifer Project International
HOPE International
Independent Faith Mission, Inc.
Independent Gospel Missions
India Evangelical Mission
India Gospel Outreach, Inc.
International Aid
International Gospel Outreach
International Students, Inc. (ISI)
Italy for Christ, Inc.
Kerus Global Education
Kids Around the World, Inc.
Kidzana Ministries
Latin American Lutheran Mission
Leadership Ministries Worldwide
Life in Messiah International
Lifewater International, Inc.
Literacy & Evangelism International
Living Water International
Luis Palau Evangelistic Association
Media Associates International
Mennonite Central Committee (MCC)
Mercy Ships
Missionaire International
MMS Aviation (Missionary Maint. Svcs.)
Morelli Ministries International, Inc.
On The Go Ministries/Keith Cook Team
Open Air Campaigners—Overseas Ministries
Opportunity International
Paraclete Mission Group, Inc.
Partners in Christ International

Pass the Torch Ministries/Church of Acts
Prakash Association, USA
Precept Ministries International
Presbyterian Order for World Evangelization
Progressive National Baptist Convention, Inc.
Project AmaZon
Project Mercy, Inc.
Ramesh Richard Evangelism and Ch. Health
Ravi Zacharias International Ministries, Inc.
Ripe for Harvest, Inc.
SAND Institutes International
Sentinel Group, The
Servants in Faith & Technology (SIFAT)
Shelter for Life International, Inc.
Son Shine Ministries International
Spiritual Overseers Service International
TCM International Institute
Teen Missions International, Inc.
The Word for the World USA
TMA Ministries Inc.
Tribes and Nations Outreach
United Bd. for Christian Higher Ed. in Asia
UWEZO International, Inc.
Vellore Christian Medical College Bd. (USA), Inc.
Village Ministries International
Walk Thru the Bible Ministries, Inc.
WayMakers International
Weiner Ministries International
World Compassion Terry Law Ministries
World Missionary Assistance Plan
World Thrust International, Inc.
WorldServe Ministries
WorldTeach
Worldwide Discipleship Assoc.
Youth for Christ International
Youth Ministry International (YMI)

Training/Orientation,
Abundant Life Association, Inc.
Adventive Cross Cultural Initiatives—US
Adventures in Missions
African Enterprise
African Methodist Episcopal Church
AIMS (Accelerating Intl. Msn. Strategies)
Apostolic Team Ministries, Intl.
Baptist Bible Translators Institute
Bethany International Ministries
Café 1040, Inc.
Calvary Commission, Inc.
Calvary International
CEIFA Ministry International
China Ministries International
Christ to the Nations
Christian Aid Mission
Christian Churches/Churches of Christ
Christian Fellowship Union, Inc.
Christian Ministries International (CMI)

Christians In Action Missions International
Church of God (Anderson, Ind.)
Church of the Brethren
Church of the Nazarene, World Msn. Dept.
Continent of Great Cities
Crescent Project
Deaf Missions Inc.
Educational Resources & Referrals—China
Elim Fellowship—International Ministries
Emmaus Road International
Entrust
Equip International
Global Fellowship, Inc.
Global Outreach International
Globe International
Gospel for Asia, Inc.
Greater Grace World Outreach
Harvest
Harvest Mission to the Unreached
Heart of God Ministries
IFCA World Missions
In Motion Ministries
Institute of Strategic Languages and Cultures
Interaction International
International Board of Jewish Missions, Inc.
International Family Missions
International Messengers
InterVarsity Christian Fellowship/USA
Jewish Awareness Ministries, Inc.
Joni and Friends
Josue Yrion World Evangelism and Msns., Inc.
Kids for Christ International
Literacy & Evangelism International
Living Water Teaching
Ludhiana Christian Medical College Board
Macedonia World Baptist Missions, Inc.
MBMS International
Messianic Jewish Movement Intl., Inc., The
Middle East Media—USA
Middle Eastern Outreach
Mission Catalyst International, Inc.
Mission India
Mission Training and Resource Center
Mission Training International
Missions Resource Network
Missions to Military, Inc.
MMS Aviation (Missionary Maint. Svcs.)
Moravian Church in North America
Muslim Hope
New Wineskins Missionary Network
Ninos de Mexico
OC International, Inc.
Servants in Faith & Technology (SIFAT)
Seventh Day Baptist Missionary Society
Shield of Faith Mission International
Son Shine Ministries International
Sowers International, The

Teen Missions International, Inc.
Tentmakers International
The Bodybuilders
The Master's Mission, Inc.
Touch the World Ministries, Inc.
United Methodist Church
United World Mission
University Bible Fellowship
UWEZO International, Inc.
visionSynergy
World Harvest Now, Inc.
World Horizons
World Indigenous Missions
World Mission Associates
World Servants
World Team
Youth With A Mission (YWAM)

Translation, Bible

American Association of Lutheran Churches
American Bible Society
Baptist Mid-Missions
Bible League, The
Christian Literature International
Church of God (Holiness)
Commission to Every Nation
Door of Hope International
Evangel Bible Translators
Evangelical Congregational Church
Fundamental Baptist Missions International
Global Teams International, Inc.
Helimission, Inc.—USA
In Touch Mission International
Independent Faith Mission, Inc.
JAARS, Inc.
Liebenzell Mission of USA, Inc.
Lutheran Bible Translators, Inc.
Lutheran Brethren World Missions
M/E International, Inc.
New Tribes Mission
Operation Serve International
People International USA
Pioneer Bible Translators
Primitive Methodist Church in the USA
Reach Ministries International
ReachAcross
Reformed Episcopal Bd. of Foreign Msns.
RUN Ministries
Russian Bible Society, Inc.
Team Expansion, Inc.
The Gospel Furthering Fellowship
The Word for the World USA
World Bible Translation Center
World Partners USA
World Team
Wycliffe Associates

Translation, other
Evangel Bible Translators
Gospel Literature International (GLINT)
Leadership Ministries Worldwide
Living Word Missions
Lutheran Bible Translators, Inc.
M/E International, Inc.
Middle East Media—USA
New Hope International
Outreach To Asia Nationals
Precept Ministries International
Presbyterian Missionary Union
Reformation Translation Fellowship, Inc.
Russian Bible Society, Inc.
Village Ministries International
World Missionary Assistance Plan
World Partners USA
Urban Ministry
LIGHT International, Inc.

Video/Film
Alberto Mottesi Evangelistic Association, Inc.
Arab World Ministries
Caleb Resources
Christian Broadcasting Network Inc., The
Ch. of God of the Apostolic Faith, Inc., The
Church of the Nazarene, World Msn. Dept.
Evangelical Baptist Missions
Good News Productions International
Good Shepherd Ministries International
Habitat for Humanity International
Handclasp International, Inc.
Hermano Pablo Ministries
INTERCOMM, Inc.
International Board of Jewish Missions, Inc.
Josue Yrion World Evangelism and Msns., Inc.
Lutheran Hour Ministries
Middle East Christian Outreach (MECO)
Middle East Media—USA
OneHope
Overseas Radio & Television, Inc. (ORTV)
Rio Grande Bible Institute, Inc.
Sentinel Group, The
Teen Missions International, Inc.
The God's Story Project

Youth programs
Adventures in Missions
American Bible Society
American Missionary Fellowship
Cadence International
CEIFA Ministry International
China Service Ventures
Ch. of God of the Apostolic Faith, Inc., The
CTI Music Ministries (Carpenter's Tools Intl.)
Door of Hope International

Episcopal Church USA
Evangelism Explosion International
Faith Life Ministries, Inc.
Fellowship International Mission
For God's Children International
Friendship International Ministries, Inc.
Global Action
Global Youth Ministry Network
Good Shepherd Ministries International
Habitat for Humanity International
Harvest Mission to the Unreached
Hellenic Ministries/USA
Hope for the Hungry
International Pentecostal Church of Christ
Jews for Jesus
Joshua Expeditions
Kerus Global Education
Living Water Teaching
Lott Carey Baptist Foreign Msn. Conv.
MBMS International
Mission of Mercy
Mission to the World (PCA), Inc.
Missionaire International
Missionary Athletes International
Moravian Church in North America
New Hope International
New Mission Systems International
Pentecostal Free Will Baptist Church, Inc.
Prakash Association, USA
Presbyterian Evangelistic Fellowship
Progressive National Baptist Convention, Inc.
Real Impact Missions, Inc.
Rock the World Youth Mission Alliance
Salvation Army, U.S.A.
Servants in Faith & Technology (SIFAT)
Surfing the Nations
Teen Mission, USA, Inc.
Teen Missions International, Inc.
Weiner Ministries International
Word of Life Fellowship, Inc.
World Mission Prayer League
Young Life
Youth Encounter
Youth for Christ International
Youth for Christ/USA—World Outreach
Youth Ministry International (YMI)
Youth With A Mission (YWAM)

Chapter 4
Countries of Activity
for U.S. Protestant Agencies

In this chapter you will find the countries where agencies reported field personnel in answer to question #14 of the survey (see Appendix C). The few exceptions are agencies whose whole program supports (with funds raised in the U.S., but which may not be designated to specific personnel on a regular basis) churches or other initiatives in a country.

All countries are listed in alphabetical order according to the name most commonly recognized in North America. In a few cases we have listed a territory or other administrative district of a country because it is commonly viewed as a separate entity and mission agencies report it that way.

We have separated the personnel totals for all agencies into five categories. Under the "Personnel from U.S." heading, the term of expected service has been divided into three categories: 4+ years, 2-4 years, and 1-2 years for fully supported personnel. For non-U.S. personnel in the "Other Countries" heading, the categories are those who are citizens of that ministry country and those who are not citizens, and are fully or partially supported by funds raised in the U.S. by the associated agency. For example, a Korean with specific mission/ministry duties serving in Korea would be included in an agency's "citizens" column of the Korea section. A Korean serving in Russia would be listed in the "not citizen" column of the Russia section.

At the end of each country section, totals of each category for that country are given. Note that the totals for the "other countries" heading do not necessarily reflect all non-U.S. mission personnel who draw support from U.S. agencies. Some agencies give grants for ongoing institutions and other programs without specifying individual recipients. This may be in addition to U.S. mission personnel based in that country or the agency may not have U.S. personnel living in that country.

Note also that the totals will be minimum numbers only because of the bigger number of large agencies in this edition that reported their personnel only by general regions and not by specific countries. Their numbers are not included in this "countries of activity" section.

		Personnel from U.S.			Other Countries	
	First Year	1-2 yrs.	2-4 yrs.	4+ yrs.	Citizens	Non-Citizens

Afghanistan

	First Year	1-2 yrs.	2-4 yrs.	4+ yrs.	Citizens	Non-Citizens
Habitat for Humanity International		-	1	-	-	1
Health Emergent International Services	1999	2	10	2	-	1
HOPE International	2004	1	-	1	-	-
Interserve USA (International Service Fellowship)	1962	-	-	22	-	-
People International USA	1996	-	-	7	-	5
Precept Ministries International		-	-	-	-	2
Seventh-day Adventists, General Conference	1971	-	-	-	-	2
Shelter for Life International, Inc.	1998	11	3	1	8	7
Volunteers in Medical Missions		-	-	1	-	-
Women to the World, Inc.	2002	-	-	-	19	2
World Compassion Terry Law Ministries	2002	-	-	-	12	3
World Concern	1982	2	-	2	16	-
	Totals:	16	14	36	55	23

Africa—General

	First Year	1-2 yrs.	2-4 yrs.	4+ yrs.	Citizens	Non-Citizens
ABWE, Inc.	1966	-	19	79	-	-
Advancing Renewal Ministries, Inc.		-	-	2	-	2
Adventive Cross Cultural Initiatives—US	2009	-	4	-	-	-
African Leadership Development	1997	-	-	2	-	-
Arab World Ministries	1881	1	-	29	-	34
ARISE International Mission		-	-	-	4	
Artists In Christian Testimony International	2006	-	-	-	-	2
Baptist International Missions, Inc. (BIMI)	1960	-	-	2	-	-
Campus Crusade for Christ, Intl.		-	-	2	2	2
Children's Christian Concern Society	1998	-	-	-	-	-
Christar	2000	-	-	12	-	4
Christian and Missionary Alliance, The	1996	-	-	182	-	-
Christian Churches/Churches of Christ		-	-	4	-	-
Churches Together	2008	-	-	-	1	-
Cities for Christ Worldwide (CCW)	1963	-	-	2	-	-
Cooperative Baptist Fellowship—Global Missions	1996	-	-	6	-	
Dawn Ministries, Inc.		-	-	-	-	1
Eastern Mennonite Missions	1992	-	2	4	-	-
endPoverty.org	1985	-	-	-	1	-
Faith Christian Fellowship International		-	-	2	151	-
Faith Comes By Hearing/Hosanna	1994	-	-	4	-	-
Fellowship of Companies for Christ Intl. (FCCI)	2007	-	-	-	1	-
Final Frontiers Foundation, Inc.	1990	-	-	-	200	-
Gideons International, The		-	-	-	13	-
Global Partners/Wesleyan World Missions		2	5	-	-	-
Global Youth Ministry Network		-	-	-	2	-
Globe International	1993	-	-	2	-	-
Good News Productions International	1995	-	-	2	8	-
Heart of God Ministries	1998	-	-	-	65	-
International Cooperating Ministries (ICM)		-	-	-	-	-
Josue Yrion World Evangelism and Missions, Inc.	2001	-	-	-	2	-
Macedonia World Baptist Missions, Inc.	2007	-	-	5	-	-
Mennonite Central Committee (MCC)		-	-	153	-	-
Mercy Ships		300	100	50	15	75

	First Year	Personnel from U.S.			Other Countries	
		1-2 yrs.	2-4 yrs.	4+ yrs.	Citizens	Non-Citizens
Middle East Media—USA	1976	-	-	-	-	-
Mission Aviation Fellowship	1961	-	-	2	2	-
Morelli Ministries International, Inc.	1997	-	-	-	65	-
New Mission Systems International		-	16	10	6	20
New Tribes Mission		-	-	6	-	-
Operation Mobilization		5	2	13	-	4
Partners International	1989	-	-	-	200	-
Presbyterian Church (USA), Worldwide Ministries		-	85	80	-	-
Proclaim! International, Inc.	2004	-	-	1	-	1
RBC Ministries	1991	-	-	-	43	-
Rosedale Mennonite Missions	2007	-	-	5	-	-
Shield of Faith Mission International	1980	5	-	3	-	-
Talking Bibles International	2002	-	-	-	1	-
Team Expansion, Inc.	2001	-	-	22	-	-
World Christian Outreach, Inc.	1999	-	1	-	15	-
World Concern	1980	-	-	-	30	-
World Horizons	1981	-	-	13	-	1
World Link Ministries	1993	-	-	2	6	-
World Venture		-	-	2	-	-
Young Life		2	-	4	-	-
Youth for Christ/USA—World Outreach		-	-	2	-	-
Youth With A Mission (YWAM)		-	127	-	733	-
Totals:		315	361	709	1566	146

Albania

	First Year	1-2 yrs.	2-4 yrs.	4+ yrs.	Citizens	Non-Citizens
Alongside Ministries International	1994	1	-	6	3	4
BILD International		-	-	-	-	1
Brethren Assemblies		-	-	7	-	-
CAM International	2005	-	-	4	-	-
Campus Crusade for Christ, Intl.	1991	-	-	7	83	3
CEIFA Ministry International	1993	-	-	-	-	-
Child Evangelism Fellowship, Inc.	1992	-	-	1	-	-
Christar	1994	-	-	12	-	2
Christian Aid Mission		-	-	-	21	-
Church of God (Cleveland, Tenn.) World Missions	1993	-	2	-	-	2
Church of the Nazarene, World Msn. Dept.	1993	-	-	3	-	1
Churches of Christ	1992	-	-	17	-	-
Commission to Every Nation	2003	-	-	2	-	2
Eastern Mennonite Missions	1993	-	-	3	-	-
East-West Ministries International	1999	-	-	1	-	-
European Christian Mission International—USA		-	-	-	2	-
Every Home for Christ International	1992	-	-	-	-	-
Fellowship of Evangelical Churches—Intl. Mins.	1994	-	-	6	-	-
Foursquare Missions International	1996	-	-	2	-	-
Global Partners/Wesleyan World Missions	1993	-	2	-	-	-
Globe International	1995	-	-	6	-	-
Gospel Fellowship Association	1997	-	-	2	-	-
Greater Europe Mission	1992	-	-	2	-	-
Greater Grace World Outreach	1995	2	2	-	-	-
Intl. Pentecostal Holiness Ch. World Msns. Mins.	2001	-	2	-	2	-

	Personnel from U.S.				Other Countries	
	First Year	1-2 yrs.	2-4 yrs.	4+ yrs.	Citizens	Non-Citizens
International Teams, U.S.A.		1	-	4	-	2
LifeWind International	1995	-	-	2	3	-
Mission Possible Foundation, Inc.	1992	-	-	-	8	-
Mission To Unreached Peoples	2005	-	-	2	-	-
Mission Without Borders International		-	-	-	17	-
Operation Mobilization	1991	-	-	2	-	2
Partners International		-	-	1	-	-
Reformed Church in America, Gen. Synod	2000	-	1	-	-	-
Rosedale Mennonite Missions	2005	-	-	2	-	2
Seventh-day Adventists, General Conference	1992	-	-	2	-	-
Spiritual Growth Resources, Inc.	1994	-	-	-	4	1
United Pentecostal Church International		-	1	-	-	-
Wisconsin Evangelical Lutheran Synod	1996	-	1	-	-	-
World Reach, Inc.	1999	-	-	-	1	3
World Venture		-	-	6	-	-
Totals:		4	11	102	144	25

Algeria

Assemblies of God World Missions	2002	-	-	2	-	-
Christian Aid Mission	2005	-	-	-	6	-
Seventh-day Adventists, General Conference	1905	-	-	-	-	2
Totals:		-	-	2	6	2

American Samoa

Assemblies of God World Missions	1926	-	-	1	-	-
Baptist International Missions, Inc. (BIMI)		-	-	2	-	-
Church of the Nazarene, World Msn. Dept.	1958	-	-	-	-	-
Churches of Christ	1992	-	-	5	-	-
United Pentecostal Church International	1999	-	2	-	-	2
Totals:		-	2	8	-	2

Andorra

Elim Fellowship—International Ministries	1991	-	-	2	-	-
Totals:		-	-	2	-	-

Angola

Abundant Life Association, Inc.	1990	-	2	-	90	2
Africa Inland Mission International, Inc.	1997	-	-	2	-	-
African Leadership, Inc.	2002	-	-	-	1	-
American Leprosy Missions, Inc.	1948	-	-	-	-	1
Assemblies of God World Missions	1985	-	-	6	-	-
Campus Crusade for Christ, Intl.	1997	-	-	-	10	-
Child Evangelism Fellowship, Inc.	1993	-	-	-	1	-
Christian Church (Disciples of Christ)		-	1	-	-	-
Church of God of Prophecy—Global Outreach		-	-	-	2	-
Church of the Nazarene, World Msn. Dept.	1992	-	-	2	-	2
Every Child Ministries, Inc.	2007	-	-	-	-	1
Every Home for Christ International	1970	-	-	-	-	-
Living Water International		-	-	-	-	-
OneHope		-	-	-	-	-

	Personnel from U.S.				Other Countries	
	First Year	1-2 yrs.	2-4 yrs.	4+ yrs.	Citizens	Non-Citizens
Precept Ministries International		-	-	-	1	-
Seventh-day Adventists, General Conference	1924	-	-	-	-	2
SIM USA, Inc.	1914	2	-	7	-	-
Walk Thru the Bible Ministries, Inc.	2001	-	-	-	-	-
Totals:		2	3	17	105	8

Anguilla

	First Year	1-2 yrs.	2-4 yrs.	4+ yrs.	Citizens	Non-Citizens
Baptist International Missions, Inc. (BIMI)		-	-	2	-	-
Totals:		-	-	2	-	-

Antigua

	First Year	1-2 yrs.	2-4 yrs.	4+ yrs.	Citizens	Non-Citizens
Assemblies of God World Missions	1997	-	-	-	-	-
Awana International	1993	-	-	-	-	-
Baptist International Missions, Inc. (BIMI)		-	-	6	-	-
BCM International		-	-	1	-	-
Biblical Ministries Worldwide	2005	-	-	2	-	-
Church of the Nazarene, World Msn. Dept.	1973	-	-	-	-	-
Churches of Christ	1971	-	-	-	-	-
Global Outreach Mission, Inc.		-	-	1	-	-
Seventh-day Adventists, General Conference	1944	-	-	2	-	2
Totals:		-	-	12	-	2

Argentina

	First Year	1-2 yrs.	2-4 yrs.	4+ yrs.	Citizens	Non-Citizens
AMG International		-	-	-	2	-
Apostolic Christian Church Foundation, Inc.	1969	-	-	-	-	-
Assemblies of God World Missions	1910	6	-	26	-	-
Avant Ministries	1911	-	-	10	-	-
Awana International	1983	-	-	-	1	-
Baptist Bible Fellowship International	1959	-	-	19	-	-
Baptist International Missions, Inc. (BIMI)		-	-	4	-	-
Baptist International Outreach, Inc.	2009	2	-	-	-	-
Baptist Mid-Missions	1987	-	-	5	-	-
Baptist Missionary Association of America	1998	-	-	-	-	2
Biblical Ministries Worldwide	1979	-	-	12	-	-
Brethren Assemblies		-	-	6	-	-
Campus Crusade for Christ, Intl.	1963	14	-	6	41	1
Child Evangelism Fellowship, Inc.	1944	-	-	1	-	-
Chosen People Ministries	1952	-	-	-	1	-
Christian Aid Mission	1983	-	-	-	41	-
Christian Churches/Churches of Christ		-	-	4	4	-
Church of God of Prophecy—Global Outreach		-	-	-	3	2
Church of the Nazarene, World Msn. Dept.	1909	-	-	17	-	5
Churches of Christ	1957	-	-	4	-	-
Converge Worldwide	1957	-	-	8	-	-
Elim Fellowship—International Ministries	1956	-	-	1	-	-
Evangelical Baptist Missions		-	-	6	-	-
Evangelical Covenant Ch.—Covenant Wld. Msn.	2003	-	-	-	-	-
Evangelical Lutheran Church in America	1948	-	-	1	-	-
Evangelism Explosion International		-	-	-	-	2
Friends of Israel Gospel Ministry, Inc.	1970	-	-	-	2	-

	First Year	Personnel from U.S.			Other Countries	
		1-2 yrs.	2-4 yrs.	4+ yrs.	Citizens	Non-Citizens
Full Gospel Grace Fellowship	1940	-	-	-	3	-
Global Outreach International	2001	-	-	5	3	-
Globe International	2001	-	-	2	-	-
Go Ye Fellowship	1984	-	-	1	-	-
Gospel Fellowship Association	2005	-	-	2	-	-
Gospel Mission of South America, Inc.	1970	-	-	8	-	-
Grace Brethren International Missions	1909	-	6	7	-	-
Greater Grace World Outreach	1994	-	-	-	2	-
HCJB Global	1970	-	-	-	2	-
IFCA World Missions		-	-	-	1	-
Impact International, Inc.	1959	-	-	-	2	-
International Board of Jewish Missions, Inc.	1989	-	4	-	-	-
International Gospel Outreach	2003	-	-	2	2	-
Intl. Pentecostal Holiness Ch. World Msns. Mins.		-	-	-	-	-
International Teams, U.S.A.		-	-	-	-	2
Josue Yrion World Evangelism and Missions, Inc.	2003	-	-	-	1	-
Latin America Mission	1930	1	1	-	-	2
LifeWind International	1995	-	-	-	3	-
LOGOI Ministries	1972	-	-	-	1	-
Luis Palau Evangelistic Association	1978	-	-	2	2	-
Lutheran Church-Missouri Synod, World Mission	1902	-	-	1	-	-
Macedonia World Baptist Missions, Inc.	2002	-	-	4	-	-
Mennonite Mission Network	1917	-	2	6	10	-
Missionary Revival Crusade	1991	-	-	-	-	-
Navigators, U.S. International Missions Group		1	-	6	-	-
Network of International Christian Schools	1998	19	2	-	12	1
OC International, Inc.	1956	-	-	-	-	1
OneHope		-	-	-	-	-
Open Air Campaigners—Overseas Ministries	2008	-	-	-	2	-
Palm Missionary Ministries, Inc.	2006	-	-	-	-	2
Precept Ministries International		-	-	-	-	1
Reformed Baptist Mission Services		-	-	-	-	2
Salvation Army, U.S.A.	1890	-	4	2	-	-
Seventh-day Adventists, General Conference	1890	-	-	-	-	6
Source of Light Ministries International, Inc.	1999	-	-	-	2	-
Spanish World Ministries, Inc.		-	-	1	1	-
The Brethren Church, Inc.	1941	-	-	-	3	-
United Pentecostal Church International	1967	-	2	-	-	4
Walk Thru the Bible Ministries, Inc.	2001	-	-	-	-	-
White Fields, Inc.		-	-	-	12	-
Word of Life Fellowship, Inc.—Intl. Ministries	1971	-	-	12	213	-
World Gospel Mission	1970	-	-	8	-	-
World Venture	1947	-	-	19	-	-
Totals:		43	21	218	372	33

Armenia

	First Year	Personnel from U.S.			Other Countries	
Armenian Missionary Association of America, Inc.	1992	-	-	16	-	-
Assemblies of God World Missions	1999	-	-	5	-	-
Baptist Missionary Association of America	1994	-	-	-	22	-
Campus Crusade for Christ, Intl.	1993	-	-	-	30	-

	Personnel from U.S.				Other Countries	
	First Year	1-2 yrs.	2-4 yrs.	4+ yrs.	Citizens	Non-Citizens
Child Evangelism Fellowship, Inc.	1992	-	-	2	-	1
Church of the Nazarene, World Msn. Dept.	2002	-	-	-	-	-
Churches of Christ	1994	-	-	-	-	-
Evangelism Explosion International		-	-	-	-	3
Every Home for Christ International	1991	-	-	-	1	-
Macedonia World Baptist Missions, Inc.	2000	-	-	2	-	-
Medical Ministry International	1990	-	-	-	1	-
OneHope		-	-	-	-	-
Precept Ministries International		-	-	-	1	-
Seventh-day Adventists, General Conference	1990	-	-	1	-	1
United Pentecostal Church International		-	1	-	-	-
Walk Thru the Bible Ministries, Inc.	2000	-	-	-	1	-
Totals:		-	1	26	56	5

Aruba

	First Year	1-2 yrs.	2-4 yrs.	4+ yrs.	Citizens	Non-Citizens
Awana International		-	-	-	-	-
Church of God (Cleveland, Tenn.) World Missions	1968	-	-	2	-	-
Church of the Nazarene, World Msn. Dept.	2000	-	-	-	-	-
United Pentecostal Church International		-	2	-	-	3
Totals:		-	2	2	-	3

Asia—General

	First Year	1-2 yrs.	2-4 yrs.	4+ yrs.	Citizens	Non-Citizens
ABWE, Inc.	1970	-	45	141	-	-
ACM International	2004	-	2	-	-	-
Adventive Cross Cultural Initiatives—US	2007	-	-	1	-	2
Anglican Frontier Missions	1999	-	-	5	-	-
ARISE International Mission		-	-	-	5	-
Asian Access	2000	-	-	4	4	-
Assemblies of God World Missions	1926	52	-	122	-	-
Awana International		-	-	2	14	-
Baptist International Evangelistic Ministries		-	-	-	-	-
Baptist International Outreach, Inc.	2000	-	-	7	1	-
Baptist Mid-Missions	1988	-	-	7	-	-
BEE World (Biblical Education by Extension)	1994	-	-	7	2	-
Café 1040, Inc.	2008	1	1	-	-	-
Calvary International	1987	-	-	3	1	2
Campus Crusade for Christ, Intl.		141	-	163	2770	462
CEIFA Ministry International	1995	-	-	13	13	-
China Ministries International	1987	-	-	8	6	2
China Outreach Ministries, Inc.	2005	-	-	2	-	2
Christar	1994	-	-	11	-	4
Christian and Missionary Alliance, The		-	-	287	-	-
Christian Churches/Churches of Christ		-	-	6	2	-
Christian Outreach International	2000	-	1	-	1	-
Church of God (Anderson, Ind.), Global Msns.	1979	-	-	1	-	-
Church Resource Ministries (CRM)	1998	-	-	6	-	-
Cities for Christ Worldwide (CCW)	1985	-	-	2	-	-
CMF International	1999	-	2	9	-	-
Commission to Every Nation	2000	-	1	2	1	2
Compassion International, Inc.		3	1	2	-	-

	First Year	Personnel from U.S.			Other Countries	
		1-2 yrs.	2-4 yrs.	4+ yrs.	Citizens	Non-Citizens
Converge Worldwide		-	-	2	-	-
Cooperative Baptist Fellowship—Global Missions	1993	-	3	12	-	-
CrossWorld		-	-	16	-	-
Dawn Ministries, Inc.		-	-	-	1	-
Eastern Mennonite Missions	1957	-	-	4	-	-
Elim Fellowship—International Ministries		10	14	11	-	-
Evangelical Covenant Ch.—Covenant Wld. Msn.	2003	-	2	5	-	-
Every Home for Christ International	1972	-	-	-	3	-
Faith Comes By Hearing/Hosanna	1994	-	-	5	-	-
Fellowship of Companies for Christ Intl. (FCCI)	2007	-	-	-	1	-
Fellowship of Evangelical Churches—Intl. Mins.	1994	-	-	2	-	-
Final Frontiers Foundation, Inc.	1986	-	-	-	550	-
Free Methodist World Missions	1904	6	6	17	-	-
Gideons International, The		-	-	-	7	-
Global Action	1998	-	-	-	1	-
Global Fellowship, Inc.	2007	-	-	7	-	4
Global Youth Ministry Network		-	-	-	3	-
Go Ye Fellowship	2006	-	-	3	1	-
Gospel for Asia, Inc.	1979	-	-	-	9523	-
Greater Grace World Outreach	1987	-	-	-	8	3
Heifer Project International	1954	-	-	-	-	-
Hope for the Hungry	1981	-	-	2	-	-
India National Inland Mission		-	-	-	-	-
International Christian Leprosy Mission, Inc. (USA)	1954	-	-	-	-	-
International Cooperating Ministries (ICM)		-	-	-	-	-
International Street Kids Outreach Ministries	1998	1	-	-	164	-
InterVarsity Christian Fellowship/USA, Msns. Dept.		1	1	4	-	-
Literacy & Evangelism International	2004	-	-	-	2	-
Lutheran Church-Missouri Synod, World Mission		-	-	2	-	-
Macedonia World Baptist Missions, Inc.	1999	-	-	10	-	-
Mennonite Central Committee (MCC)		-	-	212	-	-
Mission Aviation Fellowship	1992	-	2	20	2	-
Mission Catalyst International, Inc.	2003	-	4	-	-	-
Mission ONE, Inc.		-	-	-	100	-
Missionary Athletes International	2008	-	1	-	-	-
Network of International Christian Schools	1999	21	11	6	9	6
New Mission Systems International		-	18	12	6	24
New Tribes Mission		-	-	42	-	-
OMF International	1865	26	-	126	-	152
Open Door Baptist Missions	2002	-	-	7	2	-
Operation Mobilization	1995	-	2	2	-	-
Outreach To Asia Nationals	1986	2	3	7	180	4
Partners in Asian Missions	1972	-	-	-	159	-
Pioneers USA		-	11	324	4	5
Presbyterian Church (USA), Worldwide Ministries		-	70	65	-	-
Presbyterian Missionary Union	2000	-	-	1	-	-
Ravi Zacharias International Ministries, Inc.	2004	-	-	-	1	3
RBC Ministries	1993	-	-	-	102	-
Reformed Baptist Mission Services		-	-	-	-	2
Ripe for Harvest, Inc.	1991	20	5	2	-	-

	First Year	Personnel from U.S.			Other Countries	
		1-2 yrs.	2-4 yrs.	4+ yrs.	Citizens	Non-Citizens
Rosedale Mennonite Missions	2000	-	-	2	-	-
SEND International USA	2008	-	-	-	-	2
TEAM (The Evangelical Alliance Mission)		-	-	46	-	-
Team Expansion, Inc.	1996	-	-	22	-	-
Virginia Mennonite Missions	2005	-	4	-	-	-
World Concern		-	-	-	30	-
World Horizons		-	-	3	-	1
World Indigenous Missions	1996	-	-	7	-	8
World Mission Prayer League		1	-	11	-	1
World Venture	1993	-	3	9	-	-
Worldwide Tentmakers, Inc.	2004	3	2	2	-	7
Young Life		4	1	1	-	-
Youth With A Mission (YWAM)		-	344		2694	-
Totals:		292	560	1842	16373	698

Australia

	First Year	1-2 yrs.	2-4 yrs.	4+ yrs.	Citizens	Non-Citizens
AMG International		-	-	-	-	2
Apostolic Christian Church Foundation, Inc.	1978	-	-	-	-	-
Asian Outreach U.S.A.		-	-	-	-	-
Awana International	1972	-	-	-	4	1
Baptist Bible Fellowship International	1968	-	-	30	-	-
Baptist International Missions, Inc. (BIMI)		-	-	31	-	-
Baptist Mid-Missions	1968	-	-	17	-	-
Biblical Ministries Worldwide	1981	-	-	6	-	-
BILD International		-	-	-	1	-
Calvary International	2008	-	-	-	-	-
Campus Crusade for Christ, Intl.	1967	10	-	10	126	3
Child Evangelism Fellowship, Inc.	1944	-	-	2	-	-
Chosen People Ministries	2000	-	-	-	8	-
Christian Aid Mission		-	-	-	38	-
Christian Churches/Churches of Christ		-	20		4	-
Church of God (Cleveland, Tenn.) World Missions	1976	2	2	-	-	4
Church of God of Prophecy—Global Outreach		-	-	2	1	-
Church of the Nazarene, World Msn. Dept.	1946	-	-	5	-	4
Church Resource Ministries (CRM)	1998	-	-	4	-	-
Churches of Christ	1845	-	-	12	-	-
Development Associates International (DAI)	2003	-	-	-	2	-
Eastern Mennonite Missions	1980	-	-	-	-	-
Elim Fellowship—International Ministries		-	-	1	-	-
Fellowship International Mission	1983	-	-	1	3	-
Foursquare Missions International	1954	-	-	2	-	-
Friends of Israel Gospel Ministry, Inc.	1991	-	-	-	4	-
Global Outreach Mission, Inc.	1994	-	-	2	-	-
Global Partners/Wesleyan World Missions	1945	-	5	-	-	2
Global Recordings Network		-	-	-	20	-
Gospel Fellowship Association	1973	-	-	6	-	-
Grace Ministries International	1976	-	4	-	-	-
Habitat for Humanity International	1988	-	1	-	1	-
HCJB Global	1950	-	-	4	-	2
IFCA World Missions		-	-	-	1	-

	First Year	Personnel from U.S. 1-2 yrs.	2-4 yrs.	4+ yrs.	Other Countries Citizens	Non-Citizens
International Board of Jewish Missions, Inc.	2004	-	-	-	1	2
Intl. Pentecostal Holiness Ch. World Msns. Mins.	1995	-	-	-	-	-
International Teams, U.S.A.		2	-	3	-	17
Josue Yrion World Evangelism and Missions, Inc.	2003	-	-	-	1	-
Macedonia World Baptist Missions, Inc.	2002	-	-	2	-	-
Mennonite Mission Network	2000	-	-	1	-	-
Middle East Christian Outreach (MECO)	1976	-	-	-	-	2
Mission to the World (PCA), Inc.	1984	1	1	20	-	-
Missions Resource Network	1845	-	-	6	-	-
Navigators, U.S. International Missions Group		1	-	6	-	-
New Tribes Mission	1958	-	-	2	-	-
OMS International, Inc.		-	-	-	-	3
Operation Mobilization		-	1	-	-	-
Precept Ministries International	1988	-	-	-	-	-
Presbyterian Church (USA), Worldwide Ministries		-	-	2	-	-
Presbyterian Missionary Union	2004	-	-	2	-	-
Reformed Presbyterian Global Missions		-	-	-	-	-
Salvation Army, U.S.A.	1881	-	5	1	-	-
Seventh-day Adventists, General Conference	1885	3	-	3	-	7
TEAM (The Evangelical Alliance Mission)		-	-	2	-	-
Teen Missions International, Inc.	1987	-	3	4	-	-
United Pentecostal Church International	1973	-	4	-	-	6
Walk Thru the Bible Ministries, Inc.	2002	-	-	-	-	-
Word of Life Fellowship, Inc.—Intl. Ministries	1970	-	-	3	4	1
World Baptist Fellowship Msn. Agency, Inc.	1998	2	-	2	-	-
World Team	1942	-	-	1	-	-
Wycliffe Bible Translators		-	-	10	-	-
Youth for Christ/USA—World Outreach		-	-	2	-	-
Youth With A Mission (YWAM)		-	218	-	-	-
Totals:		21	244	227	219	56

Austria

	First Year	1-2 yrs.	2-4 yrs.	4+ yrs.	Citizens	Non-Citizens
Assemblies of God World Missions	1967	10	-	13	-	-
Avant Ministries	1966	-	-	1	-	1
Baptist Bible Fellowship International	1984	-	-	4	-	-
Baptist International Missions, Inc. (BIMI)		-	-	2	-	-
BCM International		-	-	1	-	-
Biblical Ministries Worldwide	1964	-	-	2	-	-
Brethren Assemblies		-	-	7	-	-
Campus Crusade for Christ, Intl.	1974	-	-	-	-	2
Child Evangelism Fellowship, Inc.	1955	-	-	1	-	-
Christian Churches/Churches of Christ		-	2	6	9	-
Church of God (Cleveland, Tenn.) World Missions	1980	-	-	2	-	-
Churches of Christ	1953	-	-	12	-	-
CrossWorld	1984	-	-	2	-	-
European Christian Mission International—USA		-	-	2	-	4
Every Home for Christ International	1960	-	-	-	-	-
Global Outreach Mission, Inc.		-	-	1	-	-
Global Partners/Wesleyan World Missions		-	4	-	-	-
Go Ye Fellowship	2002	-	-	2	-	-

	Personnel from U.S.				Other Countries	
	First Year	1-2 yrs.	2-4 yrs.	4+ yrs.	Citizens	Non-Citizens
Gospel Fellowship Association	1997	1	-	7	-	-
Greater Europe Mission	1964	-	-	14	-	-
Greater Grace World Outreach	1984	-	2	-	2	1
International Teams, U.S.A.	1978	-	-	28	4	4
Mission to the World (PCA), Inc.	1991	-	-	2	-	-
Missions Resource Network	1953	-	-	8	-	-
Paraclete Mission Group, Inc.	2005	-	-	2	-	-
ReachGlobal	1971	-	-	3	-	-
Resourcing Christian Education International	2004	-	-	-	22	22
Seventh-day Adventists, General Conference	1902	1	-	-	-	-
TCM International Institute	1957	6	2	4	-	-
TEAM (The Evangelical Alliance Mission)		-	-	8	-	-
TITUS International	2005	-	-	2	-	-
TWR		-	-	12	-	-
United Pentecostal Church International	1971	-	2	-	-	1
Walk Thru the Bible Ministries, Inc.	2002	-	-	-	-	-
Word of Life Fellowship, Inc.—Intl. Ministries	1997	-	-	-	4	-
World Venture	1970	-	-	16	-	-
Totals:		18	12	164	41	35

Azerbaijan

Assemblies of God World Missions	1993	-	-	6	-	-
Baptist Missionary Association of America	1994	-	-	-	8	-
Church of God of Prophecy—Global Outreach		-	-	-	1	-
Evangel Bible Translators	1998	-	-	1	-	-
Greater Europe Mission		7	-	-	-	-
Greater Grace World Outreach	1991	-	-	-	8	-
Intl. Pentecostal Holiness Ch. World Msns. Mins.	2003	-	-	-	-	-
TITUS International		-	-	-	-	-
United Pentecostal Church International	2004	-	1	-	-	-
Walk Thru the Bible Ministries, Inc.	2002	-	-	-	-	-
Totals:		7	1	7	17	-

Azores

Baptist Bible Fellowship International	1993	-	-	2	-	-
Church of the Nazarene, World Msn. Dept.	1984	-	-	-	-	-
Totals:		-	-	2	-	-

Bahamas, The

					-	
American Baptist Chs. of the U.S.A., Intl. Mins.	2000	-	-	2	-	-
Assemblies of God World Missions	1942	-	-	2	-	-
Avant Ministries	1956	-	-	3	-	-
Awana International	1974	-	-	-	-	-
Baptist Bible Fellowship International	1999	-	-	2	-	-
Baptist International Missions, Inc. (BIMI)		-	-	5	-	-
Brethren Assemblies		-	-	10	-	-
Christ to the Nations	2001	-	-	4	4	-
Christian Churches/Churches of Christ		-	-	2	-	-
Church of the Nazarene, World Msn. Dept.	1971	-	-	-	-	-
Churches of Christ	1959	-	-	2	-	-

	Personnel from U.S.			Other Countries	
	First Year	1-2 yrs.	2-4 yrs.	4+ yrs.	Citizens	Non-Citizens

	First Year	1-2 yrs.	2-4 yrs.	4+ yrs.	Citizens	Non-Citizens
Macedonia World Baptist Missions, Inc.	2009	-	-	2	-	-
Missions Door	2008	-	-	1	1	-
Precept Ministries International	2001	-	-	-	2	-
United Pentecostal Church International		-	-	-	-	2
Word of Life Fellowship, Inc.—Intl. Ministries	2001	-	-	-	-	-
Totals:		-	-	35	7	2

Bahrain

	First Year	1-2 yrs.	2-4 yrs.	4+ yrs.	Citizens	Non-Citizens
Church of God (Cleveland, Tenn.) World Missions	1984	-	-	-	-	2
Interserve USA (International Service Fellowship)	1975	-	-	3	-	-
Reformed Church in America, Gen. Synod	1988	-	-	3	-	1
Walk Thru the Bible Ministries, Inc.	2002	-	-	-	-	-
Totals:		-	-	6	-	3

Bangladesh

	First Year	1-2 yrs.	2-4 yrs.	4+ yrs.	Citizens	Non-Citizens
AMG International		-	-	-	16	-
Assemblies of God World Missions	1949	2	-	8	-	-
Awana International	1984	-	-	1	10	-
Baptist Mid-Missions	1979	-	-	-	2	-
Campus Crusade for Christ, Intl.	1975	-	-	-	398	-
Children's Christian Concern Society	2008	-	-	-	-	-
Christian Aid Mission		-	-	-	90	-
Christian Churches/Churches of Christ		-	-	-	2	-
Christian Reformed World Missions	2001	-	2	-	-	-
Christian Reformed World Relief Committee	1972	-	-	1	-	-
Church of the Nazarene, World Msn. Dept.	1992	-	-	-	-	-
Churches of Christ	1962	-	-	1	-	-
Compassion International, Inc.	2004	-	-	1	33	-
Evangelical Friends Mission		-	-	-	-	-
Every Home for Christ International	1973	-	-	-	1	-
Food for the Hungry, Inc.	1972	-	-	-	-	-
Global Recordings Network		-	-	-	11	-
Habitat for Humanity International	1999	-	1	-	-	1
I. N. Network USA	1974	-	-	-	93	-
International Partnership Ministries, Inc.	2004	-	-	-	-	6
Interserve USA (International Service Fellowship)	1852	-	-	4	-	-
LifeWind International	1998	-	-	-	17	-
Mission to the World (PCA), Inc.		-	-	1	-	-
Reformed Church in America, Gen. Synod	1999	-	-	-	-	2
Rosedale Mennonite Missions		-	-	-	-	-
Seventh-day Adventists, General Conference	1906	-	-	-	-	8
SIM USA, Inc.	1958	2	-	9	-	-
Surfing the Nations	2004	-	-	-	1	-
United Pentecostal Church International	2004	-	2	-	-	-
Walk Thru the Bible Ministries, Inc.	2000	-	-	-	1	-
World Concern	1978	-	-	-	251	-
World Mission Prayer League	1972	-	1	8	1	2
Wycliffe Bible Translators		-	-	3	-	-
Totals:		4	6	37	927	19

	First Year	Personnel from U.S.			Other Countries	
		1-2 yrs.	2-4 yrs.	4+ yrs.	Citizens	Non-Citizens

Barbados

Baptist International Missions, Inc. (BIMI)		-	-	2	-	-
Campus Crusade for Christ, Intl.		1	-	-	-	-
Christian Churches/Churches of Christ		-	-	6	-	-
Church of God of Prophecy—Global Outreach		-	-	-	4	-
Church of the Nazarene, World Msn. Dept.	1926	-	-	-	-	-
Churches of Christ	1957	-	-	1	-	-
Global Outreach International	2005	-	-	2	-	-
IFCA World Missions		-	-	-	2	-
Intl. Pentecostal Holiness Ch. World Msns. Mins.		-	-	-	-	-
National Baptist Convention USA, Inc.	1975	-	-	-	1	-
Totals:		1	-	11	7	-

Belarus

Assemblies of God World Missions	1991	-	-	4	-	-
Awana International	1999	-	-	-	2	-
Baptist International Evangelistic Ministries		-	-	-	-	-
Baptist Missionary Association of America	1994	-	-	-	10	-
Campus Crusade for Christ, Intl.	1992	-	-	9	23	-
Christian Aid Mission		-	-	-	48	-
Christian Relief Fund, The	2005	-	-	-	1	-
Church of God of Prophecy—Global Outreach		-	-	-	2	2
Churches of Christ	1988	-	-	5	-	-
Full Gospel Grace Fellowship	1990	-	-	-	-	1
Greater Europe Mission		6	-	-	-	-
International Teams, U.S.A.		-	-	-	-	2
TCM International Institute		-	-	-	1	-
United Pentecostal Church International	1990	-	2	-	-	-
Village Ministries International	1993	-	-	-	2	-
Walk Thru the Bible Ministries, Inc.	2000	-	-	-	4	-
Totals:		6	2	18	93	5

Belgium

Assemblies of God World Missions	1969	10	-	20	-	-
Avant Ministries	1966	-	-	1	1	-
Baptist Bible Fellowship International	1962	-	-	6	-	-
BCM International		-	-	2	-	-
Bibles & Literature in French	1958	-	-	4	-	-
Brethren Assemblies		-	-	2	-	-
Campus Crusade for Christ, Intl.	2001	-	-	-	-	2
Child Evangelism Fellowship, Inc.	1955	-	-	2	3	-
Christian Associates International		-	-	-	-	-
Christian Churches/Churches of Christ		-	-	1	-	-
Church of God (Cleveland, Tenn.) World Missions	1973	-	-	5	-	-
Church of God of Prophecy—Global Outreach		-	-	-	1	-
Churches of Christ	1947	-	-	8	-	-
Cooperative Baptist Fellowship—Global Missions	1995	-	-	1	-	-
Development Associates International (DAI)	2001	-	-	-	2	-
European Christian Mission International—USA		-	1	-	2	-
Evangelical Baptist Missions		-	-	2	-	-

	Personnel from U.S.				Other Countries	
	First Year	1-2 yrs.	2-4 yrs.	4+ yrs.	Citizens	Non-Citizens
Evangelical Covenant Ch.—Covenant Wld. Msn.	2007	2	1	1	-	-
Evangelism Explosion International		-	-	-	-	2
Every Home for Christ International	1961	-	-	-	1	-
Faith Christian Fellowship International		-	-	1	1	-
Fellowship International Mission	1991	-	-	-	-	1
Free Methodist World Missions	2002	2	-	-	-	-
Global Outreach Mission, Inc.		-	-	2	-	-
Greater Europe Mission	1972	-	-	4	-	-
International Board of Jewish Missions, Inc.		-	-	1	1	-
Intl. Pentecostal Holiness Ch. World Msns. Mins.	1999	-	-	6	-	-
International Teams, U.S.A.		-	-	-	-	2
InterVarsity Christian Fellowship/USA, Msns. Dept.		-	2	-	-	-
Mission to the World (PCA), Inc.	2001	-	1	14	-	-
Operation Mobilization	1961	-	-	5	-	3
ReachGlobal	1977	2	-	12	-	-
United Pentecostal Church International		-	2	-	-	-
United World Mission		-	-	1	4	-
World Venture	1990	-	-	4	-	-
Wycliffe Bible Translators		-	-	1	-	-
Youth for Christ/USA—World Outreach		-	-	1	-	-
Totals:		16	7	107	16	10

Belize

Assemblies of God World Missions	1950	8	-	10	-	-
Avant Ministries	1955	-	-	-	2	-
Awana International		-	-	-	-	-
Baptist Bible Fellowship International	1979	-	-	6	-	-
Baptist International Outreach, Inc.	2009	-	-	2	-	-
Baptist Missionary Association of America	1990	-	-	-	2	-
BCM International		-	-	1	-	-
Brethren Assemblies		-	-	1	-	-
Calvary Commission, Inc.	1984	-	-	6	-	-
Child Evangelism Fellowship, Inc.	1997	-	-	2	-	-
Church of God (Anderson, Ind.), Global Msns.	1998	-	-	2	-	-
Church of God of Prophecy—Global Outreach		-	-	-	3	2
Church of the Nazarene, World Msn. Dept.	1934	-	-	-	-	-
Churches of Christ	1967	-	-	2	-	-
Commission to Every Nation	2008	-	-	2	-	2
Congregational Methodist Missions	2002	2	-	-	2	-
Converge Worldwide		-	-	4	-	-
Cooperative Baptist Fellowship—Global Missions	2008	2	-	-	-	-
Eastern Mennonite Missions	1960	-	-	-	-	-
Episcopal Church USA		17	9	42	-	-
Equip International	1999	-	-	2	2	-
Evangelical Congregational Church		-	-	1	-	-
Friends United Meeting		-	-	2	-	-
Full Gospel Grace Fellowship	1989	-	-	-	-	2
Global Outreach International	1991	-	-	11	-	-
Global Outreach Mission, Inc.		-	-	2	-	-
HIS Servants Ministries	2002	-	-	-	-	-

	Personnel from U.S.				Other Countries	
	First Year	1-2 yrs.	2-4 yrs.	4+ yrs.	Citizens	Non-Citizens
Intl. Pentecostal Holiness Ch. World Msns. Mins.	2000	-	-	2	-	-
LifeWind International	2003	-	-	-	-	-
Living Water Teaching		-	-	-	-	2
Mission to the World (PCA), Inc.	1996	-	8	5	-	-
Missionary Ventures International		-	-	2	-	-
Missions Door	1960	-	-	2	1	-
Rock the World Youth Mission Alliance		-	-	-	-	-
STEM International	1998	-	-	-	-	-
Teen Missions International, Inc.	2005	-	3	-	-	-
TMA Ministries Inc.	2007	-	2	-	-	2
United Pentecostal Church International	1984	-	3	-	-	3
University Bible Fellowship	2008	1	-	-	-	-
Virginia Mennonite Missions	2005	-	1	-	-	-
Wycliffe Bible Translators		-	-	2	-	
Totals:	30	26	111	12	13	

Benin

	First Year	1-2 yrs.	2-4 yrs.	4+ yrs.	Citizens	Non-Citizens
AEGA Ministries International, Inc.		-	-	-	-	1
Assemblies of God World Missions	1937	-	-	4	-	-
Awana International	1995	-	-	-	1	-
Baptist Missionary Association of America	2001	-	-	-	4	-
Campus Crusade for Christ, Intl.	1988	-	-	-	19	-
Child Evangelism Fellowship, Inc.	1987	-	-	-	2	-
Christian Aid Mission	1996	-	-	-	550	-
Church of God of Prophecy—Global Outreach		-	-	-	4	-
Church of the Nazarene, World Msn. Dept.	1998	-	-	6	-	-
Churches of Christ	1988	-	-	-	-	-
Evangel Bible Translators	1989	-	-	-	1	-
Evangelical Baptist Missions		-	-	2	-	-
Every Child Ministries, Inc.	2006	-	-	-	1	-
Fellowship International Mission	2006	-	-	2	-	-
Global Recordings Network		-	-	2	2	-
Greater Grace World Outreach	2003	-	-	-	-	2
Intl. Pentecostal Holiness Ch. World Msns. Mins.		-	-	-	-	-
Literacy & Evangelism International	2005	-	-	-	2	-
Mennonite Mission Network	1985	-	-	2	-	-
Mission ONE, Inc.		-	-	-	1	-
OneHope		-	-	-	-	-
SIM USA, Inc.	1946	-	-	11	-	-
TWR		-	-	2	-	-
United Pentecostal Church International	1988	-	2	-	-	4
Wycliffe Bible Translators		-	-	5	-	-
Totals:	-	2	36	587	7	

Bermuda

	First Year	1-2 yrs.	2-4 yrs.	4+ yrs.	Citizens	Non-Citizens
Church of God of Prophecy—Global Outreach		-	-	-	1	-
Word of Life Fellowship, Inc.—Intl. Ministries	1986	-	-	2	5	-
Totals:	-	-	2	6	-	

	First Year	Personnel from U.S.			Other Countries	
		1-2 yrs.	2-4 yrs.	4+ yrs.	Citizens	Non-Citizens
Bhutan						
Assemblies of God World Missions	1995	-	-	-	-	-
Christian Aid Mission		-	-	-	1	-
Evangelical Friends Mission		-	-	-	-	-
India Gospel Outreach, Inc.	1994	-	-	-	10	-
International Partnership Ministries, Inc.	2000	-	-	-	-	13
International Teams, U.S.A.		-	-	-	-	2
New Directions International, Inc.	1998	-	-	-	9	-
New Life Advance International		-	-	-	4	-
United Pentecostal Church International	2004	-	1	-	-	-
Walk Thru the Bible Ministries, Inc.	2002	-	-	-	1	-
Totals:		-	1	-	25	15
Bolivia						
American Baptist Chs. of the U.S.A., Intl. Mins.	1986	-	-	2	-	-
Assemblies of God World Missions	1946	4	-	12	-	-
Avant Ministries	1928	-	-	14	-	6
Awana International	1974	-	-	-	7	-
Baptist Bible Fellowship International	1978	-	-	6	-	-
Baptist International Missions, Inc. (BIMI)		-	-	10	-	-
Baptist Missionary Association of America	1967	-	-	-	13	-
BCM International		-	-	21	-	-
Bethany International Ministries	2001	-	-	6	-	-
Brethren Assemblies		-	-	19	-	-
Campus Crusade for Christ, Intl.	1965	-	-	4	16	-
Casa Viva	2009	-	-	-	1	-
Child Evangelism Fellowship, Inc.	1943	-	-	-	1	-
Children's Christian Concern Society	2003	-	-	-	-	-
Christ for the City International	2005	-	-	-	-	2
Christian Aid Mission	1988	-	-	-	22	-
Christ's Mandate for Missions	1985	-	-	-	6	-
Church of God (Anderson, Ind.), Global Msns.	1976	-	-	4	-	-
Church of God of Prophecy—Global Outreach		-	-	-	2	-
Church of the Nazarene, World Msn. Dept.	1945	-	-	2	-	-
Churches of Christ	1958	-	-	8	-	-
Commission to Every Nation	2002	-	2	-	-	2
Compassion International, Inc.	1975	-	-	-	55	-
Cup of Cold Water Ministries	1978	-	-	-	3	3
Equip International	1998	-	-	1	-	-
Evangelistic Faith Missions	1978	-	-	-	-	2
Fellowship International Mission	1998	-	-	2	-	-
Food for the Hungry, Inc.	1978	-	12	4	-	-
FRIENDS in Action International		-	-	-	-	-
Global Outreach Mission, Inc.		2	-	2	-	-
Global Recordings Network		-	-	2	1	1
Grace Ministries International	1954	-	5	-	-	-
Harvest		-	-	-	1	-
IFCA World Missions		-	-	-	1	-
International Justice Mission	2006	-	1	-	9	-
International Partnership Ministries, Inc.	2000	-	-	-	5	-

	First Year	1-2 yrs.	2-4 yrs.	4+ yrs.	Citizens	Non-Citizens
		Personnel from U.S.			**Other Countries**	
Intl. Pentecostal Holiness Ch. World Msns. Mins.		-	-	-	-	-
International Teams, U.S.A.		4	2	3	-	3
LeaderTreks	2003	15	-	-	-	-
Literacy & Evangelism International		-	-	-	-	-
LOGOI Ministries	1972	-	-	-	1	-
Luke Society, Inc., The	2004	-	-	-	-	-
Macedonia World Baptist Missions, Inc.	2004	-	-	2	-	-
MAP International	1989	-	-	-	36	2
Medical Ministry International	2002	-	-	-	7	1
Mennonite Mission Network	1974	-	-	-	-	1
Ministries In Action	2004	-	-	-	-	-
Mission Generation, Inc.	1995	-	-	2	55	-
Mission to Children, Inc.	2006	-	-	-	1	-
Mission to the World (PCA), Inc.		-	-	2	-	-
Missionary Ventures International	2002	-	-	4	-	-
Network of International Christian Schools	2003	8	6	1	6	2
New Tribes Mission	1942	-	-	59	-	-
Palm Missionary Ministries, Inc.	2006	-	-	1	-	3
Pioneers USA	1984	-	-	11	-	-
Precept Ministries International	1993	-	-	-	2	-
Presbyterian Missionary Union	2004	-	-	-	2	-
Samaritan's Purse International Relief	2008	3	-	-	-	-
Servants in Faith & Technology (SIFAT)	1979	-	-	-	30	-
Seventh-day Adventists, General Conference	1907	1	-	-	-	4
SIM USA, Inc.	1907	6	-	47	-	-
Source of Light Ministries International, Inc.	1993	-	-	-	2	-
South America Mission, Inc.	1922	4	-	25	-	-
Spanish World Ministries, Inc.		-	-	1	1	-
United Evangelical Churches	1967	-	-	1	-	-
United Pentecostal Church International	1974	-	4	-	-	4
Walk Thru the Bible Ministries, Inc.	2001	-	-	-	-	-
Word of Life Fellowship, Inc.—Intl. Ministries	1990	-	-	1	22	1
World Concern	1997	3	1	1	25	1
World Gospel Mission	1944	-	1	37	-	-
World Indigenous Missions	1985	-	-	8	-	-
World Mission Prayer League	1939	-	-	6	-	-
World Venture		-	6	2	-	-
World-Wide Missions	1962	-	1	-	-	-
Youth for Christ/USA—World Outreach		-	-	3	-	-
Totals:		50	41	336	333	38

Bosnia and Herzegovina

	First Year	1-2 yrs.	2-4 yrs.	4+ yrs.	Citizens	Non-Citizens
Assemblies of God World Missions	1992	1	-	2	-	-
Campus Crusade for Christ, Intl.	1994	5	-	-	1	2
Christian Churches/Churches of Christ		-	1	2	-	-
Ch. of the Brethren—Global Msn. Partnerships		2	-	-	-	-
Churches of Christ		-	-	2	-	-
CrossWorld	1996	-	-	4	-	-
Elim Fellowship—International Ministries	1987	-	-	1	-	-
European Christian Mission International—USA		-	-	2	-	-

	First Year	Personnel from U.S.			Other Countries	
		1-2 yrs.	2-4 yrs.	4+ yrs.	Citizens	Non-Citizens
Every Home for Christ International	1997	-	-	-	-	-
International Teams, U.S.A.		-	-	3	-	2
InterVarsity Christian Fellowship/USA, Msns. Dept.		-	3	-	-	-
LifeWind International	2004	-	-	-	-	-
Mission Without Borders International		-	-	-	10	-
Pioneers USA	1992	-	1	16	1	-
ReachGlobal	1997	-	-	6	-	-
United Pentecostal Church International		-	1	-	-	-
	Totals:	8	6	38	12	4

Botswana

	First Year	1-2 yrs.	2-4 yrs.	4+ yrs.	Citizens	Non-Citizens
Africa Inter-Mennonite Mission International	1975	2	-	3	-	4
African Leadership, Inc.	2008	-	-	-	1	-
Assemblies of God World Missions	1963	-	-	8	-	-
Awana International		-	-	-	-	-
Baptist Bible Fellowship International	2001	-	-	4	-	-
Baptist International Outreach, Inc.	1985	-	-	4	2	-
Baptist Mid-Missions	1999	-	-	2	-	-
Campus Crusade for Christ, Intl.	1993	-	-	-	7	4
Child Evangelism Fellowship, Inc.	1996	-	-	1	-	-
Christian Church (Disciples of Christ)		-	2	-	-	-
Church of God of Prophecy—Global Outreach		-	-	-	3	2
Church of the Nazarene, World Msn. Dept.	1984	-	-	1	-	-
Churches of Christ	1974	-	-	2	-	-
Habitat for Humanity International	1992	-	1	-	-	1
IFCA World Missions		-	-	-	1	-
Independent Faith Mission, Inc.	2007	-	-	2	-	-
International Gospel Outreach	2009	1	-	-	-	-
Intl. Pentecostal Holiness Ch. World Msns. Mins.		-	-	-	-	-
Launch Out Ministries International	2007	-	-	-	3	-
Lutheran Bible Translators, Inc.	1993	-	-	6	7	-
Mennonite Mission Network	1974	-	1	-	-	-
Seventh-day Adventists, General Conference	1921	-	-	2	-	10
SIM USA, Inc.	1973	2	-	5	-	-
United Pentecostal Church International	1980	-	2	-	-	2
Walk Thru the Bible Ministries, Inc.	1999	-	-	-	2	-
	Totals:	5	6	40	26	23

Brazil

	First Year	1-2 yrs.	2-4 yrs.	4+ yrs.	Citizens	Non-Citizens
Abundant Life Association, Inc.	1995	-	-	-	4	-
ABWE, Inc.	1939	-	23	60	-	-
Action International Ministries, Inc.	1991	-	-	11	2	-
Adventive Cross Cultural Initiatives—US	2009	2	-	-	-	-
Amazon Outreach		-	-	-	-	-
American Baptist Chs. of the U.S.A., Intl.Mins.	1999	-	-	4	-	-
American Leprosy Missions, Inc.	1935	-	-	1	-	-
AMG International		-	-	-	1	-
Apostolic Christian Church Foundation, Inc.	1961	-	-	-	-	-
Artists In Christian Testimony International	2001	-	-	3	2	1
Assemblies of God World Missions	1910	2	-	13	-	-

		Personnel from U.S.			Other Countries	
	First Year	1-2 yrs.	2-4 yrs.	4+ yrs.	Citizens	Non-Citizens
Association of Free Lutheran Congregations	1964	-	-	4	4	-
Avant Ministries	1911	-	-	18	2	-
Awana International	1975	-	-	2	11	-
Back to the Bible International	2000	-	-	-	6	-
Baptist Bible Fellowship International	1952	-	-	33	-	-
Baptist International Missions, Inc. (BIMI)		-	-	48	-	-
Baptist International Outreach, Inc.	1989	-	-	7	2	-
Baptist Mid-Missions	1935	-	-	139	1	-
Baptist Missionary Association of America	1950	-	-	-	13	-
BCM International		-	-	7	-	-
Bethany International Ministries	1963	-	-	15	-	-
Brazil Gospel Fellowship Mission	1945	-	1	44	-	-
Brethren Assemblies		-	-	9	-	-
Campus Crusade for Christ, Intl.	1968	15	-	9	120	-
Centers for Apologetics Research, The	1996	-	-	-	2	-
Child Evangelism Fellowship, Inc.	1941	-	-	-	-	2
Christian Aid Mission	1977	-	-	-	100	-
Christian Broadcasting Network Inc., The	2004	-	-	-	4	-
Christian Churches/Churches of Christ		1	4	28	6	-
Christian Ministries International (CMI)	1985	-	-	2	10	2
Christian Missions Unlimited	1973	-	-	-	-	-
Christians In Action Missions International	1960	-	-	2	-	-
Church of God (Cleveland, Tenn.) World Missions	1951	-	-	4	-	-
Church of God of Prophecy—Global Outreach		-	-	-	5	-
Ch. of the Brethren—Global Msn. Partnerships		2	2	-	-	-
Church of the Nazarene, World Msn. Dept.	1958	-	-	6	-	4
Churches of Christ	1956	-	-	97	-	-
Churches of God, General Conference	1994	-	-	4	-	-
CMF International	1957	-	-	-	3	-
Commission to Every Nation	2004	-	-	4	-	4
Compassion International, Inc.	1974	-	-	-	49	-
Converge Worldwide	1955	-	-	12	-	-
Cook Communications Ministries International	1995	-	-	-	-	-
Crossover Communications International	1996	-	-	3	-	-
CrossWorld	1931	1	-	35	-	8
Elim Fellowship—International Ministries		-	-	6	-	-
Emmanuel International Mission	1976	-	-	-	2	-
Equip International	1995	-	-	2	1	-
Evangelical Baptist Missions		-	-	3	1	-
Evangelical Congregational Church		-	-	2	-	-
Evangelical Covenant Ch.—Covenant Wld. Msn.	2006	-	-	2	-	-
Evangelical Lutheran Church in America	1958	-	-	2	-	-
Fellowship International Mission	1983	-	-	11	6	-
Food for the Hungry, Inc.	1997	-	2	-	-	-
Foursquare Missions International	1946	-	-	2	-	-
Free Methodist World Missions	1928	-	-	2	-	-
Free Will Baptist, Inc. Bd. of Intl. Missions	1958	-	1	16	-	-
Global Outreach International	2000	-	-	3	-	-
Global Outreach Mission, Inc.	1973	-	-	6	-	-
Global Partners/Wesleyan World Missions	1958	-	2	-	-	-

	Personnel from U.S.			Other Countries	
First Year	1-2 yrs.	2-4 yrs.	4+ yrs.	Citizens	Non-Citizens
Global Recordings Network		-	-	1	3	-
Go Ye Fellowship	1962	-	-	3	1	-
Gospel Fellowship Association	1965	-	-	4	-	-
Gospel Operation Intl. for Chinese Christians	1998	-	-	-	6	-
Grace Brethren International Missions	1949	-	-	6	-	-
Greater Grace World Outreach	2002	-	-	1	3	-
Habitat for Humanity International	1987	-	1	-	-	1
Harvest	2000	-	-	-	2	-
HCJB Global	1947	-	-	2	-	-
IFCA World Missions		-	-	-	1	-
International Gospel Outreach	2002	-	2	-	-	-
International Institute for Christian Studies	2003	-	-	3	1	2
International Pentecostal Church of Christ	1937	-	-	-	3	-
Intl. Pentecostal Holiness Ch. World Msns. Mins.		-	-	-	-	-
International Street Kids Outreach Ministries	1992	-	-	2	47	-
International Teams, U.S.A.		-	-	-	-	1
Jews for Jesus	2002	-	-	1	-	-
Josue Yrion World Evangelism and Missions, Inc.	1993	-	-	-	3	1
Latin America Mission	1973	-	-	8	1	7
Latin American Indian Ministries	1995	-	-	-	-	-
Launch Out Ministries International		-	-	-	-	-
LifeWind International	1999	-	-	-	3	-
Literacy & Evangelism International	2003	-	-	-	1	-
Living Water International		-	-	-	-	-
Living Water Teaching	2008	-	-	2	-	-
Macedonia World Baptist Missions, Inc.	1980	-	-	14	2	-
Mennonite Mission Network	1954	-	-	-	-	-
Ministries In Action	2002	-	-	-	-	-
Mission Aviation Fellowship	1956	-	4	-	-	-
Mission to the World (PCA), Inc.	1993	-	-	5	-	-
Missionary Revival Crusade		-	-	-	-	-
Navigators, U.S. International Missions Group		-	-	10	-	-
Network of International Christian Schools	1999	31	14	6	34	4
New Life Advance International	1984	-	-	1	-	-
New Tribes Mission	1946	-	1	119	358	-
N. Am. Baptist Conf.—Worldwide Outreach	1966	-	-	-	-	7
OC International, Inc.	1963	-	-	13	-	-
OMS International, Inc.	1950	-	-	6	-	1
OneHope		-	-	-	-	-
Open Air Campaigners—Overseas Ministries	1991	-	-	-	2	-
Pioneers USA		-	-	4	1	-
Precept Ministries International	2000	-	-	-	7	-
Presbyterian Mission International (PMI)	2002	-	-	-	2	-
Project AmaZon	1977	1	-	38	5	-
ReachGlobal	1986	-	1	5	-	-
Reformed Episcopal Bd. of Foreign Msns.		-	-	1	2	-
Remnant Ministries, Inc.	1956	-	-	1	-	-
SEED International	1995	-	-	2	-	-
Seventh-day Adventists, General Conference	1894	-	-	-	-	2
Source of Light Ministries International, Inc.	1982	-	-	-	1	-

	First Year	Personnel from U.S.			Other Countries	
		1-2 yrs.	2-4 yrs.	4+ yrs.	Citizens	Non-Citizens
South America Mission, Inc.	1914	-	-	18	-	-
Sowers International, The	2000	-	-	1	1	-
TeachBeyond USA	1970	-	-	2	-	-
TEAM (The Evangelical Alliance Mission)		-	-	6	-	-
Teen Missions International, Inc.	1995	-	3	2	2	-
Things To Come Mission, Inc.	1961	-	-	3	3	2
United Pentecostal Church International	1956	-	12	-	-	1
Walk Thru the Bible Ministries, Inc.	2003	-	-	-	2	-
WEC International	1957	-	-	5	-	-
White Fields, Inc.		-	-	-	7	-
Wisconsin Evangelical Lutheran Synod	1985	-	-	3	-	-
Word of Life Fellowship, Inc.—Intl. Ministries	1958	-	-	11	159	-
World Baptist Fellowship Msn. Agency, Inc.	1956	-	-	25	3	-
World Servants	1996	-	-	-	-	1
World Team	1957	-	-	4	-	-
World Venture	1946	3	5	16	-	-
World-Wide Missions	1965	1	-	6	-	-
Wycliffe Bible Translators, Inc.		-	-	35	-	-
Youth for Christ/USA—World Outreach	1950	-	-	2	-	-
	Totals:	59	78	1078	1023	51

Brunei

	First Year	1-2 yrs.	2-4 yrs.	4+ yrs.	Citizens	Non-Citizens
Greater Grace World Outreach	2007	-	-	-	2	1
	Totals:	-	-	-	2	1

Bulgaria

	First Year	1-2 yrs.	2-4 yrs.	4+ yrs.	Citizens	Non-Citizens
American Baptist Chs. of the U.S.A., Intl. Mins.	2001	-	-	2	-	-
AMG International		-	-	-	8	-
Assemblies of God World Missions	1926	2	-	4	-	-
Awana International		-	-	-	-	-
Baptist Bible Fellowship International	1995	-	-	2	-	-
Campus Crusade for Christ, Intl.	1991	-	-	4	42	-
Christian Aid Mission		-	-	-	15	-
Church of God (Anderson, Ind.), Global Msns.	1922	-	-	2	-	-
Church of God (Cleveland, Tenn.) World Missions	1982	-	-	1	-	1
Church of God of Prophecy—Global Outreach		-	-	-	4	-
Church of the Nazarene, World Msn. Dept.	1994	-	-	2	-	-
Churches of Christ	1990	-	-	5	-	-
Eastern Mennonite Missions	2006	-	-	2	-	-
Every Home for Christ International	1991	-	-	-	1	-
Free Methodist World Missions	2007	-	-	2	-	-
Greater Europe Mission		-	-	3	-	-
International Institute for Christian Studies		-	-	1	-	1
International Teams, U.S.A.		-	-	3	-	5
InterVarsity Christian Fellowship/USA, Msns. Dept.		-	1	-	-	-
ISOH/IMPACT	1992	-	-	1	-	-
Macedonia World Baptist Missions, Inc.	2001	-	-	2	-	-
Ministry to Educate and Equip, Intl. (MTEE)	1995	-	2	-	2	-
Mission Possible Foundation, Inc.	1991	-	-	-	8	-
Mission to the World (PCA), Inc.	1994	1	3	18	-	-

	Personnel from U.S.				Other Countries	
	First Year	1-2 yrs.	2-4 yrs.	4+ yrs.	Citizens	Non-Citizens
Mission Without Borders International		-	-	-	3	-
Navigators, U.S. International Missions Group		-	-	6	-	-
OC International, Inc.		-	-	4	-	-
OneHope		-	-	-	-	-
Precept Ministries International	1991	-	-	-	3	-
SEND International USA	1992	-	-	14	-	3
TCM International Institute		-	-	-	1	-
United Pentecostal Church International	1991	-	1	-	-	-
Walk Thru the Bible Ministries, Inc.	2003	-	-	-	-	-
Wisconsin Evangelical Lutheran Synod	1992	-	1	-	-	-
Word of Life Fellowship, Inc.—Intl. Ministries	2002	-	-	-	4	-
World Bible Translation Center		-	-	-	2	-
World Partners USA	2003	-	2	-	-	-
Wycliffe Bible Translators		-	-	4	-	-
Totals:		3	10	82	93	10

Burkina Faso

	First Year	1-2 yrs.	2-4 yrs.	4+ yrs.	Citizens	Non-Citizens
Africa Inter-Mennonite Mission International	1978	-	-	4	-	6
Assemblies of God World Missions	1919	-	-	7	-	-
Awana International	1997	-	-	-	-	-
Baptist Bible Fellowship International	1994	-	-	10	-	-
Baptist Missionary Association of America	1998	-	-	-	15	-
Calvary International	2003	-	-	3	-	3
Campus Crusade for Christ, Intl.	1991	-	-	2	17	-
Child Evangelism Fellowship, Inc.	1982	-	-	-	2	-
Christian Aid Mission	2008	-	-	-	20	-
Church of God of Prophecy—Global Outreach		-	-	-	2	-
Church of the Nazarene, World Msn. Dept.	1997	-	-	-	-	-
Churches of Christ	1986	-	-	8	-	-
CMF International	2007	-	-	4	-	-
Commission to Every Nation	2009	-	-	2	-	2
Compassion International, Inc.	2004	-	-	-	33	-
Evangelical Covenant Ch.—Covenant Wld. Msn.	1998	1	-	2	-	-
FRIENDS in Action International		-	2	-	-	-
Global Recordings Network		-	-	6	6	-
Greater Grace World Outreach	2001	-	-	-	28	-
Macedonia World Baptist Missions, Inc.	2003	-	-	2	-	-
Mennonite Mission Network	1976	1	-	-	1	2
OneHope		-	-	-	-	-
Seventh-day Adventists, General Conference	1972	-	-	-	-	4
SIM USA, Inc.	1930	1	-	9	-	-
TMA Ministries Inc.	2000	-	-	2	2	-
United Pentecostal Church International	1994	-	2	-	-	-
Women to the World, Inc.	1991	-	-	-	2	-
World Concern	2003	4	-	-	-	-
World Outreach International—US	2002	-	-	1	-	-
World Relief	1982	4	-	-	6	-
Wycliffe Bible Translators, Inc.		-	-	7	-	-
Totals:		11	4	69	134	17

	Personnel from U.S.				Other Countries	
	First Year	1-2 yrs.	2-4 yrs.	4+ yrs.	Citizens	Non-Citizens

Burundi

Assemblies of God World Missions	2002	-	-	4	-	-
Brethren Assemblies		-	-	2	-	-
Campus Crusade for Christ, Intl.	1980	-	-	-	22	-
Child Evangelism Fellowship, Inc.	1952	-	-	-	1	-
Christian Aid Mission	1997	-	-	-	150	-
Church of the Nazarene, World Msn. Dept.	1999	-	-	-	-	-
Every Home for Christ International	1982	-	-	-	1	-
Free Methodist World Missions	1935	-	-	2	-	-
Greater Grace World Outreach	2005	-	-	-	3	-
HOPE International	2008	-	-	-	-	1
Intl. Pentecostal Holiness Ch. World Msns. Mins.		-	-	-	-	-
Literacy & Evangelism International	2006	-	-	-	2	-
United Pentecostal Church International		-	4	-	-	-
World Gospel Mission		-	-	-	-	-
World Relief	1994	-	-	4	8	-
Totals:		-	4	12	187	1

Cambodia

Action International Ministries, Inc.	2003	-	-	4	-	-
Asian Outreach U.S.A.		-	-	-	-	-
Assemblies of God World Missions	1990	12	-	18	-	-
Baptist Bible Fellowship International	1997	-	-	4	-	-
Baptist International Missions, Inc. (BIMI)		-	-	8	-	-
Baptist International Outreach, Inc.	2004	-	-	2	-	-
Baptist Mid-Missions	1998	-	-	4	-	-
Baptist Missionary Association of America	2005	-	-	-	2	2
BCM International		-	-	2	-	-
Bethany International Ministries	1999	-	-	2	-	-
BILD International		-	-	-	3	-
Calvary International	2005	-	-	-	-	-
Campus Crusade for Christ, Intl.	1989	-	-	2	33	-
Christian Aid Mission		-	-	-	68	-
Christian Broadcasting Network Inc., The	2000	-	-	-	10	-
Church of the Nazarene, World Msn. Dept.	1992	-	-	2	-	2
Church Resource Ministries (CRM)	1995	-	3	6	-	-
Churches of Christ	1992	-	-	14	-	-
Commission to Every Nation	2008	-	2	-	-	2
Converge Worldwide		-	-	3	-	-
CrossWorld	2001	-	-	-	-	1
Eastern Mennonite Missions	1995	-	4	-	-	-
Evangelical Friends Church Southwest	1996	-	2	-	7	-
Every Home for Christ International	1993	-	-	-	1	-
Far East Broadcasting Company, Inc.	1993	-	-	-	26	-
Food for the Hungry, Inc.	1991	-	2	-	-	-
Foursquare Missions International	1995	-	-	2	-	-
Free Methodist World Missions	1994	-	-	2	-	-
Global Outreach International	2006	-	-	2	-	-
Global Partners/Wesleyan World Missions	1995	-	-	-	-	4
Gospel Fellowship Association	2000	-	-	4	-	-

	Personnel from U.S.				Other Countries	
	First Year	1-2 yrs.	2-4 yrs.	4+ yrs.	Citizens	Non-Citizens
Gospel Operation Intl. for Chinese Christians	1998	-	-	-	8	-
Grace Brethren International Missions	1998	-	4	4	11	-
Holt International Children's Services, Inc.		-	-	-	1	-
International Justice Mission	2000	-	3	-	13	1
International Teams, U.S.A.		-	-	6	-	5
Interserve USA (International Service Fellowship)	2005	-	-	1	-	-
LifeWind International	1998	-	-	-	3	-
Mission to the World (PCA), Inc.		-	3	7	-	-
Mission To Unreached Peoples	1989	-	-	16	2	-
Missions Door	2002	-	-	2	1	-
New Tribes Mission	2001	-	-	8	-	-
OMF International	1970	-	-	20	-	20
OneHope		-	-	-	-	-
Partners International	1993	-	-	2	164	-
Pioneers USA		-	1	4	-	-
Presbyterian Missionary Union	2006	-	-	1	-	-
Samaritan's Purse International Relief	2003	2	4	-	-	-
SEED International	2005	1	-	1	-	-
Seventh-day Adventists, General Conference	1991	-	-	8	-	2
Teen Missions International, Inc.	2003	-	2	-	2	2
Things To Come Mission, Inc.	2007	-	-	-	-	3
Tribes and Nations Outreach		-	-	-	-	-
TWR		-	-	4	-	-
United Pentecostal Church International		-	-	-	-	-
Walk Thru the Bible Ministries, Inc.	2002	-	-	-	-	-
Warm Blankets Orphan Care International	2000	-	-	2	22	-
World Baptist Fellowship Msn. Agency, Inc.	1996	-	-	2	-	-
World Concern	1991	-	-	-	-	2
World Relief	1989	-	-	2	318	3
World Team	1996	4	-	28	-	2
World Venture		-	2	-	-	-
Wycliffe Bible Translators		-	-	4	-	-
Totals:	19	32	203	695	51	

Cameroon

	First Year	1-2 yrs.	2-4 yrs.	4+ yrs.	Citizens	Non-Citizens
Assemblies of God World Missions	1976	1	-	8	-	-
Awana International	1992	-	-	-	-	1
Baptist Mid-Missions	2006	-	-	4	-	-
Campus Crusade for Christ, Intl.	1992	-	-	-	66	-
Child Evangelism Fellowship, Inc.	1995	-	-	-	2	-
Christian Aid Mission	2004	-	-	-	30	-
Christian Blind Mission International (CBM-US)	1982	-	1	-	-	-
Church of God of Prophecy—Global Outreach		-	-	-	5	-
Church of the Nazarene, World Msn. Dept.	1999	-	-	-	-	-
Churches of Christ	1963	-	-	3	-	-
Commission to Every Nation	1999	-	-	9	3	6
Converge Worldwide	1982	-	-	14	-	-
Evangelical Covenant Ch.—Covenant Wld. Msn.	1998	1	-	8	-	-
Evangelical Lutheran Church in America	1923	4	-	6	-	-
Global Outreach International	2002	-	-	2	-	-

	Personnel from U.S.				Other Countries	
	First Year	1-2 yrs.	2-4 yrs.	4+ yrs.	Citizens	Non-Citizens
Global Recordings Network		-	-	8	8	-
Gospel Fellowship Association	1987	2	-	16	-	-
Gospel Revival Ministries	1998	-	-	-	1	-
Grace Brethren International Missions	1991	-	-	3	-	-
International Gospel Outreach	1989	-	-	1	2	-
Intl. Pentecostal Holiness Ch. World Msns. Mins.		-	-	-	-	-
Lutheran Bible Translators, Inc.	1980	-	2	-	9	-
Lutheran Brethren World Missions	1918	-	-	-	-	-
Mailbox Club International Inc., The		-	-	-	1	-
Navigators, U.S. International Missions Group		-	-	4	-	-
N. Am. Baptist Conf.—Worldwide Outreach	1935	-	-	11	-	6
OneHope		-	-	-	-	-
Open Door Baptist Missions	2007	-	-	1	-	-
Seventh-day Adventists, General Conference	1928	1	-	4	-	5
Teen Missions International, Inc.	2001	-	-	3	3	-
United Pentecostal Church International	1971	-	2	-	-	2
Walk Thru the Bible Ministries, Inc.	2002	-	-	-	-	-
World Team	1985	-	-	16	-	9
Wycliffe Bible Translators, Inc.		-	-	47	-	-
Totals:		9	5	168	130	29

Cape Verde

	First Year	1-2 yrs.	2-4 yrs.	4+ yrs.	Citizens	Non-Citizens
Assemblies of God World Missions	1989	-	-	-	-	-
Baptist Missionary Association of America	1955	-	-	-	6	-
Church of the Nazarene, World Msn. Dept.	1901	-	-	-	-	-
Totals:		-	-	-	6	-

Caribbean—General

	First Year	1-2 yrs.	2-4 yrs.	4+ yrs.	Citizens	Non-Citizens
ABWE, Inc.	1990	-	17	20	-	-
Assemblies of God World Missions	1920	-	-	2	-	-
Calvary Evangelistic Mission, Inc.	1953	8	-	7	-	-
Christ to the Nations		-	-	2	2	-
Church of God (Cleveland, Tenn.) World Missions		-	-	2	-	-
Church of God of Prophecy—Global Outreach		-	-	-	7	-
Converge Worldwide		-	-	3	-	-
Evangelical Congregational Church		-	-	2	-	-
Final Frontiers Foundation, Inc.	1989	-	-	-	3	-
Global Partners/Wesleyan World Missions	1904	-	-	-	-	-
International Cooperating Ministries (ICM)		-	-	-	-	-
Macedonia World Baptist Missions, Inc.	2008	-	-	2	-	-
United Pentecostal Church International	1974	-	8	-	-	-
World Servants	1986	-	-	-	-	2
Young Life		-	2	3	-	-
Totals:		8	27	43	12	2

Caucasus

	First Year	1-2 yrs.	2-4 yrs.	4+ yrs.	Citizens	Non-Citizens
Operation Mobilization	1998	-	2	-	-	-
Totals:		-	2	-	-	-

Cayman Islands

	First Year	1-2 yrs.	2-4 yrs.	4+ yrs.	Citizens	Non-Citizens
Assemblies of God World Missions	1992	-	-	-	-	-

	First Year	Personnel from U.S.			Other Countries	
		1-2 yrs.	2-4 yrs.	4+ yrs.	Citizens	Non-Citizens
Awana International		-	-	-	-	-
Baptist International Missions, Inc. (BIMI)		-	-	6	-	-
Christian Churches/Churches of Christ		-	-	2	-	-
Ch. of God (Holiness), World Msn. Dept., Inc.	1970	2	-	-	-	-
United Pentecostal Church International		-	-	-	-	-
Word of Life Fellowship, Inc.—Intl. Ministries	2005	-	-	-	-	-
Youth for Christ/USA—World Outreach		-	-	1	-	-
Totals:		2	-	9	-	-

Central African Republic

	First Year	1-2 yrs.	2-4 yrs.	4+ yrs.	Citizens	Non-Citizens
Africa Inland Mission International, Inc.	1924	-	-	1	-	-
Assemblies of God World Missions	1997	-	-	-	-	-
Baptist Mid-Missions	1920	-	-	5	-	-
Campus Crusade for Christ, Intl.	1987	-	-	-	35	-
Church of God of Prophecy—Global Outreach		-	-	-	1	-
Churches of Christ	1990	-	-	-	-	-
Evangelical Covenant Ch.—Covenant Wld. Msn.	1998	-	-	3	-	-
Evangelical Lutheran Church in America	1974	1	-	1	-	1
Global Health Ministries	2008	-	-	-	-	1
Grace Brethren International Missions	1918	-	-	-	4	3
Living Water International		-	-	-	-	-
ReachGlobal	1997	1	-	12	-	-
SIM USA, Inc.	1990	-	-	1	-	-
United Pentecostal Church International	2000	-	2	-	-	-
United World Mission		-	-	2	-	-
World Venture		-	1	-	-	-
Wycliffe Bible Translators		-	-	6	-	-
Totals:		2	3	31	40	5

Central Asia—General

	First Year	1-2 yrs.	2-4 yrs.	4+ yrs.	Citizens	Non-Citizens
Assemblies of God World Missions		1	-	42	-	-
Campus Crusade for Christ, Intl.		52	-	60	383	81
Christian and Missionary Alliance, The		-	-	28	-	-
Church Leadership Dev. Intl.	2005	-	-	-	1	-
Church of God (Anderson, Ind.), Global Msns.	1909	-	3	1	-	-
CLC Ministries International	1997	-	-	1	-	-
Crossover Communications International	2006	-	-	2	17	-
CrossWorld		-	-	8	-	-
Dawn Ministries, Inc.		-	-	-	-	1
Eastern Mennonite Missions	2006	-	-	7	-	-
Faith Comes By Hearing/Hosanna	1990	-	-	1	-	-
Final Frontiers Foundation, Inc.	2004	-	-	-	15	-
Go Ye Fellowship	1993	-	-	2	-	2
Grace Brethren International Missions	1999	-	-	6	4	6
Lutheran Church-Missouri Synod, World Mission		-	-	2	-	-
Network of International Christian Schools	2003	38	20	6	3	6
Operation Mobilization	1995	7	6	17	-	6
Outreach To Asia Nationals	1987	2	4	-	4	-
TEAM (The Evangelical Alliance Mission)		-	-	4	-	-
Team Expansion, Inc.		-	-	13	-	-
Totals:		100	33	200	427	102

	First Year	1-2 yrs.	2-4 yrs.	4+ yrs.	Other Countries Citizens	Non-Citizens
Chad						
Africa Inland Mission International, Inc.	1986	-	-	5	-	10
Assemblies of God World Missions	1996	-	-	2	-	-
Awana International	2001	-	-	-	1	-
Baptist Mid-Missions	1925	-	-	7	-	-
BILD International		-	-	-	2	-
Brethren Assemblies		-	-	1	-	-
Campus Crusade for Christ, Intl.	1996	-	-	-	14	-
Child Evangelism Fellowship, Inc.	1997	-	-	-	1	1
Children's Christian Concern Society	2004	-	-	-	-	-
Christian Aid Mission	2003	-	-	-	6	-
Church of God of Prophecy—Global Outreach		-	-	-	1	-
Churches of Christ	1990	-	-	2	-	-
Global Recordings Network		-	-	5	5	-
Gospel Revival Ministries	1997	-	-	-	4	-
Grace Brethren International Missions	1966	-	2	-	4	-
International Partnership Ministries, Inc.	2000	-	-	-	9	-
Lutheran Brethren World Missions	1918	-	-	8	-	-
Pioneers USA		-	-	7	-	-
Seventh-day Adventists, General Conference	1870	-	-	1	-	1
TEAM (The Evangelical Alliance Mission)		-	-	20	-	-
WEC International	1962	-	-	3	-	-
Wycliffe Bible Translators, Inc.		-	-	9	-	-
Totals:		-	2	70	47	12
Chile						
American Baptist Chs. of the U.S.A., Intl.Mins.	1993	-	-	2	-	2
Assemblies of God World Missions	1941	-	-	16	-	-
Awana International	1986	-	-	-	-	-
Baptist Bible Fellowship International	1954	-	-	8	-	-
Baptist International Missions, Inc. (BIMI)		-	-	2	-	-
Baptist International Outreach, Inc.	2008	-	-	2	-	-
Baptist Mid-Missions	1992	-	-	4	-	-
Baptist Missionary Association of America	2007	-	-	1	-	-
Brethren Assemblies		-	-	4	-	-
Campus Crusade for Christ, Intl.	1963	-	-	2	4	4
Child Evangelism Fellowship, Inc.	1942	1	-	-	-	-
Christian Aid Mission	1998	-	-	-	16	-
Christian Church (Disciples of Christ)		-	1	-	-	-
Christian Churches/Churches of Christ		-	-	32	4	-
Church of God (Cleveland, Tenn.) World Missions	1954	-	-	3	-	-
Church of God of Prophecy—Global Outreach		-	-	-	1	-
Church of the Nazarene, World Msn. Dept.	1962	-	-	2	-	-
Churches of Christ	1958	-	-	9	-	-
CMF International	1988	-	-	8	1	-
Commission to Every Nation	2008	-	-	2	2	-
Eastern Mennonite Missions	2005	-	2	2	-	-
Evangelical Covenant Ch.—Covenant Wld. Msn.	1994	-	-	-	-	-
Free Methodist World Missions	1986	-	-	3	-	-
Friendship International Ministries, Inc.	2000	5	-	1	6	-

	Personnel from U.S.				Other Countries	
	First Year	1-2 yrs.	2-4 yrs.	4+ yrs.	Citizens	Non-Citizens
Global Outreach International	2001	-	-	1	-	-
Global Outreach Mission, Inc.		-	-	2	-	-
Global Partners/Wesleyan World Missions	1998	-	-	-	-	-
Gospel Mission of South America, Inc.	1923	-	-	10	-	-
Grace Brethren International Missions	2001	-	-	-	3	-
Greater Grace World Outreach	1985	-	-	-	2	-
IFCA World Missions		-	-	-	1	-
International Gospel Outreach	1973	-	-	-	2	-
International Partnership Ministries, Inc.	1999	-	-	-	16	-
Intl. Pentecostal Holiness Ch. World Msns. Mins.	1967	-	-	-	-	-
Latin America Mission		-	-	2	-	2
LOGOI Ministries	1972	-	-	-	2	-
Macedonia World Baptist Missions, Inc.	1998	-	-	10	2	-
Mission to the World (PCA), Inc.	1977	-	-	12	-	-
Navigators, U.S. International Missions Group		-	-	4	-	-
OneHope		-	-	-	-	-
Operation Mobilization		2	-	-	-	-
Precept Ministries International		-	-	-	-	1
Reformed Baptist Mission Services		-	-	-	2	-
Salvation Army, U.S.A.	1909	-	2	-	-	-
Seventh-day Adventists, General Conference	1895	-	-	4	-	4
SIM USA, Inc.	1988	-	-	5	-	-
Source of Light Ministries International, Inc.	1979	-	-	-	2	-
Spanish World Ministries, Inc.		-	-	1	1	-
The Brethren Church, Inc.	2007	-	-	-	1	-
United Pentecostal Church International	1964	-	2	-	-	-
United World Mission		-	-	2	-	-
Word of Life Fellowship, Inc.—Intl. Ministries	1976	-	-	-	22	-
World Baptist Fellowship Msn. Agency, Inc.	2004	-	-	2	-	-
World Harvest Mission	2000	-	-	2	-	-
World Team	1982	-	-	4	-	-
Wycliffe Bible Translators		-	-	2	-	-
Totals:		8	7	166	90	13

China

Advancing Renewal Ministries, Inc.		-	-	5	4	1
All God's Children International	1995	2	-	-	25	-
Ambassadors for Christ, Inc.	1963	-	-	-	-	-
American Baptist Chs. of the U.S.A., Intl. Mins.	1843	-	-	1	-	-
Artists In Christian Testimony International	2006	-	-	-	1	2
Asian Outreach U.S.A.		-	-	-	-	-
Baptist Missionary Association of America	1953	-	-	1	-	8
China Service Ventures	2007	1	1	3	2	-
ChinaSource	1995	-	-	1	-	-
Christar	1914	-	-	38	-	-
Christian Aid Mission		-	-	-	-	-
Christian Broadcasting Network Inc., The	1997	1	3	1	44	-
Christian Church (Disciples of Christ)		-	3	-	-	-
Christian Ministries International (CMI)	1987	-	-	2	2	4
Christian Reformed World Missions	1986	-	-	2	-	-

	First Year	Personnel from U.S. 1-2 yrs.	Personnel from U.S. 2-4 yrs.	Personnel from U.S. 4+ yrs.	Other Countries Citizens	Other Countries Non-Citizens
Church of God (Cleveland, Tenn.) World Missions	1937	-	-	6	-	-
Church of God of Prophecy—Global Outreach		-	-	2	-	-
Cook Communications Ministries International	1998	-	-	-	-	-
Cooperative Baptist Fellowship—Global Missions	1996	-	3	4	-	-
Eastern Mennonite Missions	1965	-	-	10	-	-
East-West Ministries International	1999	-	-	2	-	-
Educational Resources & Referrals—China (ERRC)	1986	21	16	8	-	2
Educational Services International (ESI)	1981	60	-	-	-	-
Evangelical Lutheran Church in America	1986	7	-	4	-	-
Fellowship International Mission	2003	-	-	1	-	-
Food for the Hungry, Inc.	1992	-	3	2	-	-
Global Mins., Ch. of the United Brethren in Christ		-	-	-	-	-
Global Outreach International	1992	-	-	13	-	-
Globe International	2003	-	-	2	-	-
Gospel Operation Intl. for Chinese Christians	1997	-	1	2	21	-
Habitat for Humanity International		-	2	-	-	2
Holt International Children's Services, Inc.		-	-	-	18	-
HOPE International	2000	-	-	1	-	1
International Partnership Ministries, Inc.	2005	-	-	-	-	5
International Students, Inc (ISI)	2009	2	-	-	-	-
Interserve USA (International Service Fellowship)	1870	-	-	16	-	-
Kids for Christ International	2006	-	-	-	-	-
Liebenzell Mission of USA, Inc.	1900	-	-	-	-	-
Literacy & Evangelism International		-	-	-	-	-
M/E International, Inc.	2003	-	-	-	-	-
Mennonite Mission Network	1911	-	-	2	-	2
Mission To Unreached Peoples	1986	-	-	30	-	2
Missions Door	2007	-	-	-	1	-
New Life Advance International		-	-	-	-	-
OMS International, Inc.	1999	-	-	3	-	2
OneHope		-	-	-	-	-
Orthodox Presbyterian Church	1994	4	2	4	-	-
Partners International	1943	-	-	-	422	-
Perimeter Church—Global Outreach		-	-	-	-	-
Precept Ministries International	1996	-	-	-	-	2
ReachGlobal	1887	-	-	-	5	-
Reformed Church in America, Gen. Synod	2000	-	-	1	1	-
SEND International USA	1988	1	2	7	6	4
SIM USA, Inc.	1997	3	-	-	-	-
Sowers International, The	1994	-	-	-	3	-
The Mission Society	1994	-	-	3	-	-
Training Evangelistic Leadership (T.E.L.), Inc.	1985	-	-	10	7	-
Tribes and Nations Outreach		-	-	-	-	-
U.S. Center for World Mission		2	-	-	-	-
United Pentecostal Church International		-	-	-	-	1
United World Mission		-	-	4	-	-
University Bible Fellowship	2005	2	2	-	-	-
Walk Thru the Bible Ministries, Inc.	2004	-	-	-	1	-
World Bible Translation Center		-	-	-	2	-
World Compassion Terry Law Ministries	1994	-	-	-	9	2

	First Year	Personnel from U.S. 1-2 yrs.	2-4 yrs.	4+ yrs.	Other Countries Citizens	Non-Citizens
World Missions Far Corners, Inc.	1988	-	-	-	2	-
World Relief		-	-	1	-	-
WorldServe Ministries		-	-	1	-	-
Totals:		106	38	193	576	40

CIS—General

	First Year	1-2 yrs.	2-4 yrs.	4+ yrs.	Citizens	Non-Citizens
Educational Services International (ESI)	1991	20	-	-	-	-
Pioneers USA	1993	-	-	5	-	-
Totals:		20	-	5	-	-

Colombia

	First Year	1-2 yrs.	2-4 yrs.	4+ yrs.	Citizens	Non-Citizens
Action International Ministries, Inc.	1992	-	-	2	3	-
Assemblies of God World Missions	1951	7	-	22	-	-
Awana International	1987	-	-	-	4	-
Baptist Bible Fellowship International	1971	-	1	4	-	-
Baptist Missionary Association of America	2007	-	-	1	1	-
Brethren Assemblies		-	-	13	-	-
Brethren in Christ World Missions		-	-	-	-	2
Calvary International	1984	-	-	-	-	-
Campus Crusade for Christ, Intl.	1963	-	-	-	21	-
Child Evangelism Fellowship, Inc.	1943	-	-	-	1	-
Christ for the City International	1988	-	1	2	2	2
Christian Aid Mission	1985	-	-	-	50	-
Christian Church (Disciples of Christ)		-	1	-	-	-
Christian Ministries International (CMI)	1997	-	-	2	1	4
Christians In Action Missions International	1969	-	-	2	4	-
Church of God (Anderson, Ind.), Global Msns.	1975	-	1	-	-	-
Church of God (Cleveland, Tenn.) World Missions	1954	-	-	3	-	-
Church of God of Prophecy—Global Outreach		-	-	-	3	-
Church of the Nazarene, World Msn. Dept.	1975	-	-	-	-	-
Churches of Christ	1958	-	-	2	-	-
Compassion International, Inc.	1976	-	-	-	53	-
Episcopal Church USA		-	-	-	-	-
Evangelical Covenant Ch.—Covenant Wld. Msn.	1968	-	-	3	-	-
Global Partners/Wesleyan World Missions	1943	-	-	-	-	-
Global Recordings Network		-	-	-	2	2
Hope for the Hungry	1979	-	-	1	-	-
I. N. Network USA	1994	-	-	-	8	-
IFCA World Missions	1965	-	-	-	1	-
Intl. Pentecostal Holiness Ch. World Msns. Mins.	1993	-	-	-	-	-
International Teams, U.S.A.		-	-	2	-	2
Latin America Mission	1953	1	4	8	2	11
LOGOI Ministries	1972	-	-	-	3	-
Luke Society, Inc., The	1998	-	-	-	-	-
Macedonia World Baptist Missions, Inc.	2002	-	-	2	1	-
Medical Ministry International	2004	-	-	-	1	-
Mennonite Mission Network	1931	-	2	2	2	-
Mission Generation, Inc.	2010	-	-	-	-	-
Mission to the World (PCA), Inc.	2002	-	1	4	-	-
Missionary Revival Crusade	1974	-	-	-	-	-

		Personnel from U.S.			Other Countries	
	First Year	1-2 yrs.	2-4 yrs.	4+ yrs.	Citizens	Non-Citizens
Missionary Ventures International	2001	-	-	2	-	-
New Tribes Mission	1944	-	1	20	35	-
OC International, Inc.		-	-	2	-	-
OMS International, Inc.	1943	-	-	6	-	2
OneHope		-	-	-	-	-
Palm Missionary Ministries, Inc.	1998	-	-	-	-	-
Pentecostal Assemblies of God of Am., Inc.		-	-	-	4	2
Pioneers USA		-	-	2	-	-
Precept Ministries International	1995	-	-	-	4	-
ReachGlobal	2002	-	-	-	-	-
Reformed Baptist Mission Services		-	-	-	-	2
Resourcing Christian Education International	2007	-	-	-	8	-
Seventh-day Adventists, General Conference	1921	-	-	1	-	3
South America Mission, Inc.	1934	-	-	6	-	-
Sowers International, The	1985	-	-	-	-	4
Spanish World Ministries, Inc.		-	-	1	1	-
TEAM (The Evangelical Alliance Mission)		-	-	6	-	-
Team Expansion, Inc.	1989	-	-	1	-	-
The Brethren Church, Inc.	1975	-	-	-	2	-
The Mission Society	1985	-	-	-	-	-
United Pentecostal Church International	1936	-	1	-	-	-
Walk Thru the Bible Ministries, Inc.	2000	-	-	-	-	-
Word of Life Fellowship, Inc.—Intl. Ministries	1980	-	-	-	1	1
World Baptist Fellowship Msn. Agency, Inc.	1966	-	-	2	-	-
World Bible Translation Center		-	-	-	2	-
World Reach, Inc.	2005	-	-	-	-	2
Wycliffe Bible Translators		-	-	12	-	-
Totals:		8	13	136	220	39

Congo, Democratic Republic of

Africa Inland Mission International, Inc.	1912	-	-	-	-	7
Africa Inter-Mennonite Mission International	1912	-	-	-	-	-
American Baptist Chs. of the U.S.A., Intl.Mins.	1884	-	-	11	-	-
American Leprosy Missions, Inc.	1906	-	-	-	1	-
Assemblies of God World Missions	1921	-	-	6	-	-
Baptist Bible Fellowship International	1957	-	-	1	-	-
Campus Crusade for Christ, Intl.	1979	-	-	-	166	12
Child Evangelism Fellowship, Inc.	1952	-	-	-	3	-
Christian Aid Mission	2005	-	-	-	25	-
Christian Mission for the Deaf	1990	-	-	2	-	-
Church of God of Prophecy—Global Outreach		-	-	-	20	-
Church of the Nazarene, World Msn. Dept.	1990	-	-	-	-	-
CrossWorld	1931	-	-	4	-	-
Elim Fellowship—International Ministries		-	-	1	-	-
Empowering Lives International	2001	-	-	-	36	-
Evangelical Covenant Ch.—Covenant Wld. Msn.	1937	-	-	1	-	-
Every Child Ministries, Inc.	1985	-	-	-	12	-
Food for the Hungry, Inc.	1994	-	-	-	-	-
Global Partners/Wesleyan World Missions	2003	-	-	-	-	-
Gospelink, Inc.		-	-	-	110	-

	First Year	Personnel from U.S. 1-2 yrs.	2-4 yrs.	4+ yrs.	Other Countries Citizens	Non-Citizens
Grace Ministries International	1928	-	4	-	-	-
Greater Grace World Outreach	2005	-	-	-	42	-
Habitat for Humanity International	1974	-	1	-	-	1
Harvest	2003	-	-	-	2	-
HOPE International	2004	-	3	1	-	1
Independent Faith Mission, Inc.	1961	-	-	-	6	-
International Christian Ministries	2001	-	-	-	4	-
Intl. Pentecostal Holiness Ch. World Msns. Mins.	1992	-	-	-	-	-
LifeWind International	1987	-	-	-	28	-
Mennonite Mission Network	1923	-	-	-	-	-
Mission Aviation Fellowship	1961	-	-	-	22	-
OneHope		-	-	-	-	-
ReachGlobal	1922	-	-	-	-	-
Salvation Army, U.S.A.	1934	-	1	-	-	-
Samaritan's Purse International Relief	1980	1	1	-	-	-
Seventh-day Adventists, General Conference	1965	-	-	2	-	12
Source of Light Ministries International, Inc.	2006	-	-	2	-	-
The Master's Mission, Inc.	1986	-	-	-	2	-
The Word for the World USA	2004	-	-	-	14	-
United Pentecostal Church International	1985	-	2	-	-	-
Walk Thru the Bible Ministries, Inc.	2002	-	-	-	2	-
Warm Blankets Orphan Care International	2002	-	-	-	3	-
World Mission, Inc.		-	-	-	-	-
World Venture	1946	-	-	2	-	-
Wycliffe Bible Translators, Inc.		-	-	3	-	-
Totals:		1	12	36	498	33

Congo, Republic of the

	First Year	1-2 yrs.	2-4 yrs.	4+ yrs.	Citizens	Non-Citizens
		-	-	-	-	-
African Enterprise	1994	-	-	-	5	-
African Leadership, Inc.	2004	-	-	-	1	-
Assemblies of God World Missions	1996	3	-	2	-	-
Campus Crusade for Christ, Intl.	1990	-	-	-	18	-
Christian Blind Mission International (CBM-US)	1991	-	1	-	-	-
Church of God of Prophecy—Global Outreach		-	-	-	2	-
Church of the Nazarene, World Msn. Dept.	1997	-	-	-	-	-
Global Outreach Mission, Inc.	1974	3	-	12	-	-
HOPE International	2009	-	-	-	-	1
World Relief	1994	-	1	-	26	-
World-Wide Missions	1961	-	-	-	-	2
Totals:		6	2	14	52	3

Cook Islands

	First Year	1-2 yrs.	2-4 yrs.	4+ yrs.	Citizens	Non-Citizens
Assemblies of God World Missions	1992	-	-	-	-	-
Churches of Christ	1987	-	-	-	-	-
Totals:		-	-	-	-	-

Costa Rica

	First Year	1-2 yrs.	2-4 yrs.	4+ yrs.	Citizens	Non-Citizens
American Baptist Chs. of the U.S.A., Intl. Mins.	1980	-	-	3	-	-
Assemblies of God World Missions	1943	7	-	21	-	-
Awana International	1985	-	-	2	2	-

		Personnel from U.S.			Other Countries	
	First Year	1-2 yrs.	2-4 yrs.	4+ yrs.	Citizens	Non-Citizens
Baptist Bible Fellowship International	1970	-	2	12	-	-
Baptist International Missions, Inc. (BIMI)		-	-	10	-	-
Baptist International Outreach, Inc.	1991	-	-	2	2	-
Baptist Missionary Association of America	1961	-	-	-	1	-
Bright Hope International	2000	-	-	-	1	-
Calvary International	1981	-	-	7	2	-
Campus Crusade for Christ, Intl.	1976	-	2	-	6	-
Casa Viva	2004	-	-	-	6	-
Children of Promise International		-	2	3	-	-
Christ for the City International	1985	1	3	7	20	18
Christian Broadcasting Network Inc., The	1998	-	-	-	8	1
Christian Reformed World Missions	1981	-	2	3	-	-
Church of God of Prophecy—Global Outreach		-	-	-	3	2
Church of the Nazarene, World Msn. Dept.	1964	-	-	11	-	5
Church Resource Ministries (CRM)	2006	-	2	-	-	-
Churches of Christ	1967	-	-	2	-	-
Commission to Every Nation	1998	-	1	8	1	7
Converge Worldwide		-	-	2	-	-
Engineering Ministries International (EMI)		1	-	4	-	-
Evangelical Lutheran Church in America	1998	1	-	1	-	1
Evangelistic Faith Missions	1982	-	-	-	-	2
Food for the Hungry, Inc.	1992	-	3	-	-	-
Foursquare Missions International	1953	-	-	2	-	-
Free Methodist World Missions	1990	-	-	2	-	-
Global Mins., Ch. of the United Brethren in Christ		-	-	-	-	-
Global Outreach International	2002	-	-	2	-	-
Global Outreach Mission, Inc.		1	-	9	-	-
Global Partners/Wesleyan World Missions	1995	-	-	-	-	-
Globe International	2006	1	-	-	-	-
Go Ye Fellowship	2000	-	-	-	-	-
Gospel Fellowship Association	1991	-	-	4	-	-
Grace Ministries International	1984	-	4	-	-	-
Habitat for Humanity International	1987	-	45	6	37	14
Hope for the Hungry	1982	-	-	2	-	-
Intl. Pentecostal Holiness Ch. World Msns. Mins.	1951	-	-	4	-	-
International Teams, U.S.A.	1993	5	-	15	7	11
Latin America Mission		3	-	38	3	38
LeaderTreks	2002	1	1	-	-	-
LifeWind International	1999	-	-	-	4	-
Macedonia World Baptist Missions, Inc.	2001	-	-	2	-	-
Mission Aviation Fellowship	1999	-	3	-	2	-
Mission Generation, Inc.	2010	-	-	-	-	-
Mission to Children, Inc.	1978	-	-	-	-	-
Mission to the World (PCA), Inc.		-	-	1	-	-
Missionary Ventures International	2001	-	-	1	-	-
Missions Door	1955	-	-	-	1	-
Mutual Faith Ministries Intl.	1992	-	-	1	-	-
Navigators, U.S. International Missions Group		-	-	1	-	-
Pentecostal Assemblies of God of Am., Inc.		-	-	-	-	-
Pentecostal Free Will Baptist Church, Inc.		-	-	-	1	-

	Personnel from U.S.				Other Countries	
	First Year	1-2 yrs.	2-4 yrs.	4+ yrs.	Citizens	Non-Citizens
Precept Ministries International	1994	-	-	-	3	-
ReachGlobal	2000	2	2	7	2	-
Reformed Presbyterian Global Missions		-	-	-	-	-
Salvation Army, U.S.A.	1907	-	2	-	-	-
Seventh-day Adventists, General Conference	1903	-	-	2	-	2
TEAM (The Evangelical Alliance Mission)		-	-	2	-	-
The Mission Society	1986	-	-	2	-	-
United Pentecostal Church International	1975	-	2	-	-	2
United World Mission		-	-	4	-	-
Walk Thru the Bible Ministries, Inc.	2004	-	-	-	-	-
Word of Life Fellowship, Inc.—Intl. Ministries	1986	-	-	1	6	-
World Missions & Evangelism, Inc.		-	3	-	-	-
World Venture		-	-	2	-	-
Wycliffe Bible Translators		-	-	5	-	-
Totals:		23	79	213	118	103

Cote d'Ivoire

	First Year	1-2 yrs.	2-4 yrs.	4+ yrs.	Citizens	Non-Citizens
AEGA Ministries International, Inc.		-	-	-	-	1
Assemblies of God World Missions	1927	-	-	-	-	-
Awana International	1988	-	-	-	-	-
Baptist Bible Fellowship International	1988	-	-	2	-	-
Baptist International Missions, Inc. (BIMI)		-	-	10	-	-
Baptist Mid-Missions	1974	-	-	7	-	-
Baptist Missionary Association of America	1999	-	-	-	38	-
Bright Hope International	2004	-	-	-	1	-
Campus Crusade for Christ, Intl.	1975	-	-	-	34	2
Child Evangelism Fellowship, Inc.	1976	-	-	-	4	-
Christian Aid Mission	1990	-	-	-	4	-
Christian Churches/Churches of Christ		-	-	6	-	-
Church of God (Anderson, Ind.), Global Msns.	1997	-	-	5	-	-
Church of God of Prophecy—Global Outreach		-	-	-	7	-
Church of the Nazarene, World Msn. Dept.	1987	-	-	10	-	6
Churches of Christ	1972	-	-	3	-	-
CityTeam Ministries—New Generations Intl.		-	-	-	2	-
CMF International	1998	-	1	6	-	-
Converge Worldwide		-	-	2	-	-
Development Associates International (DAI)	2001	-	-	-	1	-
Free Will Baptist, Inc. Bd. of Intl. Missions	1958	-	-	15	-	-
Greater Grace World Outreach	2000	-	-	-	58	-
International Partnership Ministries, Inc.	1999	-	-	-	13	-
Intl. Pentecostal Holiness Ch. World Msns. Mins.	1993	-	-	2	-	-
M/E International, Inc.	2009	-	-	-	-	-
MAP International	1993	-	-	-	23	-
Seventh-day Adventists, General Conference	1946	-	-	-	-	6
SIM USA, Inc.	1967	2	-	2	-	-
Source of Light Ministries International, Inc.	2001	-	-	-	1	-
Tentmakers International	2007	-	-	-	1	-
United Pentecostal Church International	1975	-	2	-	-	-
WEC International		-	-	1	-	-
World Venture	1947	-	3	13	-	-

	First Year	Personnel from U.S.			Other Countries	
		1-2 yrs.	2-4 yrs.	4+ yrs.	Citizens	Non-Citizens
Wycliffe Bible Translators		-	-	2	-	-
Totals:		2	6	86	187	15

Croatia

	First Year	1-2 yrs.	2-4 yrs.	4+ yrs.	Citizens	Non-Citizens
Action International Ministries, Inc.	2007	-	2	-	-	-
Assemblies of God World Missions	1992	-	-	6	-	-
Awana International		-	-	-	-	-
Baptist Bible Fellowship International	1997	-	-	2	-	-
Bethany International Ministries	1999	-	-	1	-	1
Biblical Ministries Worldwide		-	-	-	2	-
Campus Crusade for Christ, Intl.	1993	-	-	16	16	-
Child Evangelism Fellowship, Inc.	1989	-	-	2	2	-
Church of God (Cleveland, Tenn.) World Missions	1968	-	-	2	-	-
Church of the Nazarene, World Msn. Dept.	1999	-	-	1	-	-
Church Resource Ministries (CRM)	2004	-	-	4	-	-
Churches of Christ	1969	-	-	4	-	-
Every Home for Christ International	1993	-	-	-	-	-
Foursquare Missions International	1997	-	2	-	-	-
Global Partners/Wesleyan World Missions	1993	-	6	-	-	-
Greater Europe Mission	1974	-	-	8	-	-
Greater Grace World Outreach	2005	2	-	2	-	2
Intl. Pentecostal Holiness Ch. World Msns. Mins.	2003	-	-	-	-	-
InterVarsity Christian Fellowship/USA, Msns. Dept.		-	2	-	-	-
Pioneers USA	1992	-	-	8	1	1
Proclaim! International, Inc.	1987	-	2	-	2	-
Reformed Church in America, Gen. Synod	2006	-	-	2	-	-
SEED International	2000	-	-	1	-	-
SEND International USA	1997	-	-	6	-	-
United Pentecostal Church International		-	1	-	-	-
United World Mission		-	-	2	-	-
World Bible Translation Center		-	-	-	2	-
Totals:		2	15	67	25	4

Cuba

	First Year	1-2 yrs.	2-4 yrs.	4+ yrs.	Citizens	Non-Citizens
American Baptist Chs. of the U.S.A., Intl. Mins.	1898	-	-	1	-	-
AMG International		-	-	-	8	-
Assemblies of God World Missions	1920	-	-	-	-	-
Awana International		-	-	-	4	-
Baptist International Missions, Inc. (BIMI)		-	-	2	-	-
BCM International		-	-	1	-	-
Bright Hope International	2001	-	-	-	310	-
Calvary International	1992	-	-	-	1	-
Caring Partners International, Inc.	1997	-	-	-	2	-
Child Evangelism Fellowship, Inc.	1949	-	-	-	2	-
Christian Aid Mission	1995	-	-	-	400	-
Church of God of Prophecy—Global Outreach		-	-	-	4	-
Church of the Nazarene, World Msn. Dept.	1902	-	-	-	-	-
Churches of Christ	1937	-	-	-	-	-
ECHO Cuba	1994	-	-	-	12	-
Friends United Meeting		-	-	-	-	-

	First Year	Personnel from U.S. 1-2 yrs.	2-4 yrs.	4+ yrs.	Other Countries Citizens	Non-Citizens
HCJB Global	1992	-	-	2	-	-
International Gospel Outreach	1999	-	-	-	3	-
International Partnership Ministries, Inc.	1996	-	-	-	5	-
Intl. Pentecostal Holiness Ch. World Msns. Mins.		-	-	-	-	-
International Teams, U.S.A.		-	-	-	-	4
LifeWind International	2001	-	-	-	1	-
LOGOI Ministries	1972	-	-	-	4	-
New Life Advance International		-	-	-	-	-
OneHope		-	-	-	-	-
Precept Ministries International		-	-	-	1	-
Spanish World Ministries, Inc.		-	-	1	1	-
United Pentecostal Church International		-	2	-	-	-
Walk Thru the Bible Ministries, Inc.		-	-	-	1	-
Word of Life Fellowship, Inc.—Intl. Ministries	2001	-	-	-	4	-
World Link Ministries	2000	-	-	-	430	-
World Servants	1995	-	-	-	-	1
WorldServe Ministries		-	-	-	-	1
Totals:		-	2	7	1193	6

Cyprus

	First Year	1-2 yrs.	2-4 yrs.	4+ yrs.	Citizens	Non-Citizens
AMG International	1984	-	-	-	3	3
Assemblies of God World Missions	1984	-	-	-	-	-
Child Evangelism Fellowship, Inc.	1952	-	-	7	-	-
Church of God of Prophecy—Global Outreach		-	-	-	2	2
Church of the Nazarene, World Msn. Dept.	1985	-	-	2	-	-
Churches of Christ	1974	-	-	-	-	-
Commission to Every Nation	2002	-	4	-	-	4
Gospel Operation Intl. for Chinese Christians	2006	-	-	-	2	-
Interserve USA (International Service Fellowship)	2006	-	-	2	-	-
Macedonia World Baptist Missions, Inc.	1988	-	-	2	-	-
Middle East Christian Outreach (MECO)	1976	-	-	-	-	16
Reformed Presbyterian Global Missions	1888	-	-	1	-	-
Seventh-day Adventists, General Conference	1932	-	-	3	-	8
United Pentecostal Church International	1989	-	2	-	-	-
World Partners USA	1966	-	3	-	-	-
Totals:		-	9	17	7	33

Czech Republic

	First Year	1-2 yrs.	2-4 yrs.	4+ yrs.	Citizens	Non-Citizens
American Baptist Chs. of the U.S.A., Intl. Mins.	1995	-	-	-	-	2
Assemblies of God World Missions	1992	-	-	2	-	-
Avant Ministries	2008	-	-	4	-	4
Awana International	2000	-	-	-	1	-
Baptist International Missions, Inc. (BIMI)		-	-	2	-	-
Baptist Missionary Association of America	1992	-	-	-	1	-
Campus Crusade for Christ, Intl.	1981	3	-	7	13	-
Christian Aid Mission		-	-	-	9	-
Christian Associates International		-	-	-	-	-
Christian Churches/Churches of Christ		-	-	2	-	-
Church of God (Cleveland, Tenn.) World Missions	2001	1	-	2	-	2
Churches of Christ	1980	-	-	7	-	-

	First Year	Personnel from U.S. 1-2 yrs.	2-4 yrs.	4+ yrs.	Other Countries Citizens	Non-Citizens
Entrust	1979	-	2	2	-	-
Evangelical Covenant Ch.—Covenant Wld. Msn.	1999	-	-	2	-	-
Every Home for Christ International	1991	-	-	-	1	-
Faith Christian Fellowship International	1997	-	-	1	3	-
Global Partners/Wesleyan World Missions	1994	-	4	-	-	-
Grace Brethren International Missions	1994	-	-	2	2	-
Greater Europe Mission	1991	-	-	8	-	-
Greater Grace World Outreach	1991	-	-	-	2	-
HCJB Global	1992	-	-	2	2	-
I. N. Network USA	1993	-	-	-	6	-
International Institute for Christian Studies	1994	-	2	8	-	10
International Messengers	1994	-	-	-	2	-
International Teams, U.S.A.		-	-	3	-	-
Mission to the World (PCA), Inc.	1989	-	-	6	-	-
Missions Resource Network	1990	-	-	7	-	-
New Hope International	1971	-	-	-	2	-
Operation Mobilization	1991	-	-	1	-	1
Pioneers USA		-	-	2	-	-
Precept Ministries International		-	-	-	-	-
ReachGlobal	1991	1	2	11	-	-
Resourcing Christian Education International	2005	-	-	-	3	2
SEED International	2004	-	-	1	-	-
SEND International USA	1992	-	-	7	-	4
TCM International Institute		-	-	-	1	-
TEAM (The Evangelical Alliance Mission)		-	-	10	-	-
TITUS International	2006	-	-	2	-	-
United Pentecostal Church International	1995	-	2	-	-	-
Word of Life Fellowship, Inc.—Intl. Ministries	1997	-	-	4	4	1
World Harvest Mission	2004	-	-	2	-	-
World Venture	1993	-	4	2	-	-
	Totals:	5	16	109	52	26

Denmark

	First Year	1-2 yrs.	2-4 yrs.	4+ yrs.	Citizens	Non-Citizens
Assemblies of God World Missions	2000	1	-	-	-	-
Child Evangelism Fellowship, Inc.	1947	-	-	2	-	-
Church of the Nazarene, World Msn. Dept.	1960	-	-	-	-	-
Churches of Christ	1950	-	-	-	-	-
Evangelical Lutheran Church in America	1995	1	-	2	-	-
Seventh-day Adventists, General Conference	1877	1	-	-	-	-
	Totals:	3	-	4	-	-

Djibouti

	First Year	1-2 yrs.	2-4 yrs.	4+ yrs.	Citizens	Non-Citizens
ReachAcross	1969	-	-	4	-	4
Seventh-day Adventists, General Conference	1980	-	-	-	-	4
	Totals:	-	-	4	-	8

Dominica

	First Year	1-2 yrs.	2-4 yrs.	4+ yrs.	Citizens	Non-Citizens
Assemblies of God World Missions	1996	-	-	2	-	-
Awana International	1989	-	-	2	1	-
Christian Churches/Churches of Christ		-	-	5	15	-

	First Year	1-2 yrs.	2-4 yrs.	4+ yrs.	Citizens	Non-Citizens
		Personnel from U.S.			Other Countries	
Church of the Nazarene, World Msn. Dept.	1974	-	-	3	-	1
Churches of Christ	1966	-	-	-	-	-
Gospel Fellowship Association	1994	-	-	2	-	-
World Baptist Fellowship Msn. Agency, Inc.	1985	-	-	2	-	-
World Gospel Mission	1996	-	-	4	-	-
	Totals:	-	-	20	16	1

Dominican Republic

	First Year	1-2 yrs.	2-4 yrs.	4+ yrs.	Citizens	Non-Citizens
Adventures in Missions	1990	-	-	2	-	-
American Baptist Chs. of the U.S.A., Intl. Mins.	1980	-	-	1	-	1
Assemblies of God World Missions	1933	1	-	14	-	-
Awana International	1989	-	-	-	3	-
Baptist Bible Fellowship International	1996	-	-	6	-	-
Baptist Mid-Missions	1950	-	-	1	-	-
Baptist Missionary Association of America	1995	-	-	-	3	-
BCM International		-	-	2	-	-
Bethany International Ministries	1978	--	--	2	-	-
Brethren Assemblies		-	-	5	-	-
Campus Crusade for Christ, Intl.	1977	-	-	-	36	-
Christian Blind Mission International (CBM-US)	1985	1	-	-	-	-
Christian Churches/Churches of Christ		-	-	12	-	-
Christian Outreach International	2000	-	-	-	1	-
Christian Reformed World Missions	1979	-	1	8	-	-
Christian Reformed World Relief Committee	1983	-	-	1	-	-
Christian Relief Fund, The	1988	-	-	-	2	-
Christ's Mandate for Missions	2003	-	-	-	2	-
Ch. of the Brethren—Global Msn. Partnerships		2	1	2	-	-
Church of the Nazarene, World Msn. Dept.	1974	-	-	10	-	3
Churches of Christ	1963	-	-	6	-	-
Compassion International, Inc.	1970	-	-	-	51	-
CrossWorld	1949	-	-	8	-	-
Eastern Mennonite Missions	1976	-	-	-	-	-
Evangelical Covenant Ch.—Covenant Wld. Msn.	2006	-	1	-	-	-
Evangelistic Faith Missions	1981	2	-	-	-	-
Floresta USA, Inc.	1984	-	-	-	20	-
Food for the Hungry, Inc.	1979	-	3	-	1	-
Foursquare Missions International	1996	1	2	2	-	-
Global Outreach Mission, Inc.		-	-	2	-	-
Global Partners/Wesleyan World Missions	2001	-	2	-	-	-
Habitat for Humanity International	1987	-	1	-	-	1
Harvest	1981	-	-	-	2	-
International Partnership Ministries, Inc.	1999	-	-	-	8	-
Intl. Pentecostal Holiness Ch. World Msns. Mins.	1996	-	-	2	-	-
Kids Alive International	1989	1	12	10	130	-
LifeWind International	1988	-	-	-	4	-
Literacy & Evangelism International	2003	-	-	-	2	-
Medical Ministry International	1970	-	-	2	4	1
Ministries In Action	1995	-	-	-	1	-
Mission Generation, Inc.	2010	-	-	-	-	-
Mission Possible, Inc.	1992	-	-	-	33	-

	First Year	Personnel from U.S.			Other Countries	
		1-2 yrs.	2-4 yrs.	4+ yrs.	Citizens	Non-Citizens
Missionary Ventures International	1999	-	-	5	-	-
Missions Door	1981	-	-	-	5	1
New Way Missions	2000	-	-	-	-	-
OneHope		-	-	-	-	-
Pentecostal Free Will Baptist Church, Inc.		-	-	-	1	-
Primitive Methodist Church in the USA		-	-	-	-	-
Seventh-day Adventists, General Conference	1908	-	-	2	-	4
Spanish World Ministries, Inc.		-	-	1	1	-
STEM International	1994	-	-	-	-	-
United Pentecostal Church International	1965	-	4	-	-	2
Walk Thru the Bible Ministries, Inc.	2001	-	-	-	-	-
Wisconsin Evangelical Lutheran Synod	1993	-	-	1	-	-
Word of Life Fellowship, Inc.—Intl. Ministries	1994	-	-	-	9	-
World Baptist Fellowship Msn. Agency, Inc.	2004	-	-	2	-	-
World Team	1939	-	-	8	-	-
	Totals:	8	27	141	319	13

East Timor

Assemblies of God World Missions	2001	-	-	-	-	-
Campus Crusade for Christ, Intl.	2002	-	-	-	-	4
Christian Church (Disciples of Christ)		-	3	-	-	-
Church of the Nazarene, World Msn. Dept.	2001	-	-	2	-	-
LifeWind International	2003	-	-	-	-	-
	Totals:	-	3	2	-	4

Eastern Europe—General

Dawn Ministries, Inc.		-	-	-	-	1
Final Frontiers Foundation, Inc.	1992	-	-	-	25	-
Global Aid Network (GAiN USA))	1994	-	-	-	4	-
International Cooperating Ministries (ICM)		-	-	-	-	-
International Street Kids Outreach Ministries	1998	1	-	-	21	-
New Hope International	1971	3	-	3	-	-
Pioneers USA		-	-	8	-	1
Proclaim! International, Inc.	1987	-	-	-	-	1
Source of Light Ministries International, Inc.	1995	-	-	-	2	-
Virginia Mennonite Missions	1994	2	1	3	1	-
	Totals:	6	1	14	53	3

Ecuador

Action International Ministries, Inc.	1993	-	-	2	6	-
Adventive Cross Cultural Initiatives—US	2009	-	2	-	-	-
Assemblies of God World Missions	1962	7	-	27	-	-
Avant Ministries	1896	-	-	13	-	4
Awana International	1988	-	-	2	7	-
Back to the Bible International	1970	-	-	-	10	-
Baptist Bible Fellowship International	1975	-	-	13	-	-
Baptist International Missions, Inc. (BIMI)		-	-	4	-	-
Baptist Mid-Missions	1988	-	-	3	2	-
Biblical Ministries Worldwide		-	-	10	-	-
Brethren Assemblies		-	-	7	-	-

	Personnel from U.S.			Other Countries	
	First Year	1-2 yrs.	2-4 yrs.	4+ yrs.	Citizens	Non-Citizens
Calvary International	1985	-	-	-	-	-
Campus Crusade for Christ, Intl.	1965	-	-	-	21	-
Caring Partners International, Inc.	1998	-	-	-	2	-
Child Evangelism Fellowship, Inc.	1941	-	-	-	2	-
Christian Aid Mission	1997	-	-	-	31	-
Christian Blind Mission International (CBM-US)	1980	-	1	-	-	-
Christian Churches/Churches of Christ		-	4	4	-	-
Christian Reformed World Relief Committee	1983	-	-	2	-	-
Christian Relief Fund, The	1990	-	-	-	1	-
Christians In Action Missions International	1976	-	-	2	-	2
Church of God (Anderson, Ind.), Global Msns.	1986	-	-	4	-	-
Church of God (Cleveland, Tenn.) World Missions	1971	4	-	8	-	2
Church of God of Prophecy—Global Outreach		-	-	-	2	2
Church of the Nazarene, World Msn. Dept.	1972	-	-	6	-	-
Churches of Christ	1966	-	-	6	-	-
Commission to Every Nation	2006	-	2	8	2	6
Compassion International, Inc.	1974	-	-	-	53	-
CrossWorld	2000	-	-	11	-	-
Evangelical Covenant Ch.—Covenant Wld. Msn.	1947	4	-	2	-	-
Global Outreach International	1976	-	-	13	-	-
Global Partners/Wesleyan World Missions	2001	-	2	-	-	-
Global Recordings Network		-	-	2	-	2
Globe International	2006	-	-	2	-	-
Gospel Fellowship Association	2007	-	-	4	-	-
Greater Grace World Outreach	1985	-	-	3	2	1
Habitat for Humanity International	1998	-	1	-	-	1
HCJB Global	1931	2	-	91	110	21
IFCA World Missions		-	-	-	1	-
Intl. Pentecostal Holiness Ch. World Msns. Mins.	2002	-	-	2	2	-
International Teams, U.S.A.	1994	5	1	18	6	9
Latin America Mission		-	-	4	2	2
Liebenzell Mission of USA, Inc.	1989	-	-	5	-	-
LOGOI Ministries	1972	-	-	-	-	-
Luke Society, Inc., The	2002	-	-	-	-	-
Lutheran Bible Translators, Inc.	1984	-	-	-	2	-
MAP International	1988	-	-	-	17	-
Medical Ministry International	1990	-	-	-	3	-
Mennonite Mission Network	1969	-	2	-	-	2
Mission Aviation Fellowship	1948	3	8	-	-	-
Mission to the World (PCA), Inc.	1975	-	2	8	-	-
Missionary Ventures International		-	-	4	-	-
OMS International, Inc.	1952	-	-	7	-	8
OneHope		-	-	-	-	-
Open Air Campaigners—Overseas Ministries	2001	-	-	-	3	-
Palm Missionary Ministries, Inc.	1988	-	-	1	28	-
Precept Ministries International		-	-	-	2	-
Reformed Church in America, Gen. Synod		-	-	-	1	-
Resourcing Christian Education International	2005	-	-	-	31	10
Samaritan's Purse International Relief	2006	-	2	-	-	-
Servants in Faith & Technology (SIFAT)	1999	-	-	5	5	-

	First Year	Personnel from U.S. 1-2 yrs.	2-4 yrs.	4+ yrs.	Other Countries Citizens	Non-Citizens
Seventh-day Adventists, General Conference	1916	1	-	-	-	-
SIM USA, Inc.	1989	-	-	5	-	-
Team Expansion, Inc.	1990	-	-	2	-	-
Teen Missions International, Inc.	1997	-	-	-	-	2
The Master's Mission, Inc.	2003	-	-	2	-	-
United Pentecostal Church International	1964	-	1	-	-	-
Walk Thru the Bible Ministries, Inc.	2001	-	-	-	-	-
Word of Life Fellowship, Inc.—Intl. Ministries	1970	-	-	-	17	-
World Baptist Fellowship Msn. Agency, Inc.	1971	-	-	9	1	-
World Mission Prayer League	1951	-	-	3	-	1
World Partners USA	1945	-	4	-	-	-
World Servants	1988	-	-	-	-	1
World Venture	-	-	-	4	-	-
Wycliffe Bible Translators	-	-	-	10	-	-
Totals:	26	32	338	372	76

Egypt

	First Year	1-2 yrs.	2-4 yrs.	4+ yrs.	Citizens	Non-Citizens
Assemblies of God World Missions	1910	-	-	7	-	-
Awana International	1997	-	-	-	4	-
Baptist Missionary Association of America	1993	-	-	-	7	-
BCM International		-	-	10	-	-
Campus Crusade for Christ, Intl.	1972	-	-	3	140	-
Christian Aid Mission	1990	-	-	-	40	-
Christian Church (Disciples of Christ)		-	2	-	-	-
Church of God of Prophecy—Global Outreach		-	-	-	6	-
Church of the Nazarene, World Msn. Dept.	1986	-	-	-	-	-
Churches of Christ	1963	-	-	-	-	-
Development Associates International (DAI)	2002	-	-	-	1	-
Evangelical Lutheran Church in America	1967	-	2	2	-	-
Evangelistic Faith Missions	1905	2	-	-	-	-
Free Methodist World Missions	1899	-	-	2	-	-
Global Partners/Wesleyan World Missions	2004	-	-	-	-	-
Go Ye Fellowship	2008	-	-	1	-	-
I. N. Network USA	1997	-	-	-	2	-
International Christian Ministries	2003	-	-	-	4	-
Intl. Pentecostal Holiness Ch. World Msns. Mins.		-	-	-	-	-
Interserve USA (International Service Fellowship)	1951	-	-	2	-	-
Missionary Ventures International	1997	-	-	-	2	-
Operation Mobilization		-	2	7	-	-
Operation Serve International	1985	3	5	12	2	-
Precept Ministries International		-	-	-	-	-
Reformed Church in America, Gen. Synod	2001	-	-	-	2	-
Seventh-day Adventists, General Conference	1879	2	-	4	-	4
United Pentecostal Church International	1950	-	2	-	-	-
Venture International	1994	-	-	-	2	-
Walk Thru the Bible Ministries, Inc.	2001	-	-	-	4	-
World Bible Translation Center		-	-	-	2	-
Totals:	7	13	50	218	4

	First Year	Personnel from U.S.			Other Countries	
		1-2 yrs.	2-4 yrs.	4+ yrs.	Citizens	Non-Citizens

El Salvador

	First Year	1-2 yrs.	2-4 yrs.	4+ yrs.	Citizens	Non-Citizens
American Baptist Chs. of the U.S.A., Intl. Mins.	1911	-	-	-	-	2
Assemblies of God World Missions	1925	37	-	14	-	-
Awana International	1993	-	-	-	-	-
Baptist Bible Fellowship International	1976	-	-	2	-	-
Baptist International Missions, Inc. (BIMI)		-	-	4	-	-
Baptist Missionary Association of America	1970	-	-	-	6	-
Brethren Assemblies		-	-	6	-	-
Campus Crusade for Christ, Intl.	1966	-	-	2	13	-
Child Evangelism Fellowship, Inc.	1942	-	-	-	1	-
Children's Christian Concern Society	1991	-	-	-	-	-
Christian Reformed World Missions	1996	-	-	1	-	-
Christian Relief Fund, The	1990	-	-	-	1	-
Church of God of Prophecy—Global Outreach		-	-	-	4	-
Ch. of the Brethren—Global Msn. Partnerships		1	-	-	-	-
Church of the Nazarene, World Msn. Dept.	1964	-	-	-	-	-
Churches of Christ	1964	-	-	3	-	-
Commission to Every Nation	2004	-	-	2	1	1
Compassion International, Inc.	1977	-	-	-	51	-
Eastern Mennonite Missions	1980	-	-	-	-	-
Evangelical Lutheran Church in America	1985	1	1	-	-	-
Evangelistic Faith Missions	1964	-	-	-	-	-
Full Gospel Evangelistic Association	2000	-	1	2	-	-
Global Adopt-A-People Network	2003	-	-	-	-	-
Global Mins., Ch. of the United Brethren in Christ		-	-	-	-	-
Global Partners/Wesleyan World Missions	2002	-	-	-	-	-
Harvesting In Spanish (HIS)		-	-	3	-	3
Impact International, Inc.		-	-	-	2	-
Latin America Mission		-	-	2	-	2
LifeWind International	1984	-	-	-	6	-
Living Water International		-	-	-	-	-
Living Water Teaching	1985	-	-	3	-	-
Mission to Children, Inc.	1977	-	-	-	-	-
Missions Door	1996	-	-	-	1	-
Open Bible Churches, Intl. Mins.	1973	-	-	2	-	-
Pentecostal Assemblies of God of Am., Inc.		-	-	-	2	-
Precept Ministries International	1988	-	-	-	2	-
United Pentecostal Church International	1975	-	1	-	-	9
Walk Thru the Bible Ministries, Inc.	2000	-	-	-	-	-
WEC International		-	-	2	-	-
Word of Life Fellowship, Inc.—Intl. Ministries	1993	-	-	1	13	-
World Reach, Inc.	1996	-	-	4	3	-
Totals:		39	3	53	106	17

Equatorial Guinea

	First Year	1-2 yrs.	2-4 yrs.	4+ yrs.	Citizens	Non-Citizens
Assemblies of God World Missions	1987	4	-	7	-	-
Calvary International	2004	-	-	-	-	2
Christian Aid Mission	2004	-	-	-	6	-
Christian Churches/Churches of Christ		-	-	2	-	-
Church of the Nazarene, World Msn. Dept.	2002	-	-	-	-	-

	Personnel from U.S.			Other Countries	
	First Year	1-2 yrs.	2-4 yrs.	4+ yrs.	Citizens	Non-Citizens
Evangelical Covenant Ch.—Covenant Wld. Msn.	1999	-	-	2	-	-
Go Ye Fellowship	2004	-	-	-	-	-
Seventh-day Adventists, General Conference	1986	-	-	2	-	-
United Pentecostal Church International		-	2	-	-	-
WEC International	1933	-	-	4	-	-
World Link Ministries	2000	-	-	-	2	-
Totals:		4	2	17	8	2

Eritrea

Assemblies of God World Missions	1995	-	-	-	-	-
Christian Aid Mission	2009	-	-	-	20	-
Church of the Nazarene, World Msn. Dept.	1993	-	-	-	-	-
Evangelistic Faith Missions	1950	-	-	-	-	-
I. N. Network USA	1980	-	-	-	-	-
Orthodox Presbyterian Church	1944	-	-	4	-	-
World Mission Prayer League	1996	-	-	1	-	1
Totals:		-	-	5	20	1

Estonia

Alongside Ministries International	1998	-	-	2	1	1
Assemblies of God World Missions	2001	-	-	2	-	-
Baptist Bible Fellowship International	2008	-	-	2	-	-
Baptist International Missions, Inc. (BIMI)		-	-	2	-	-
Baptist Missionary Association of America	2009	-	-	1	-	-
Calvary International	1991	-	-	-	-	-
Campus Crusade for Christ, Intl.	1991	-	-	2	11	-
Child Evangelism Fellowship, Inc.	1989	-	-	-	1	-
Churches of Christ	1990	-	-	7	-	-
Converge Worldwide		-	-	2	-	-
Greater Europe Mission		17	-	-	-	-
Intl. Pentecostal Holiness Ch. World Msns. Mins.	2002	-	-	2	-	-
Precept Ministries International	1994	-	-	-	1	-
Salvation Army, U.S.A.	1927	-	4	-	-	-
TCM International Institute		-	-	-	1	-
Tentmakers International	2005	-	-	-	-	1
United World Mission		-	-	2	-	-
Walk Thru the Bible Ministries, Inc.	2001	-	-	-	-	-
Totals:		17	4	24	15	2

Ethiopia

African Enterprise	1995	-	-	-	3	-
African Leadership, Inc.	2001	-	-	-	1	-
Assemblies of God World Missions	1975	2	-	5	-	-
Baptist Bible Fellowship International	1960	-	-	15	-	-
Baptist International Outreach, Inc.	1985	-	-	28	26	-
Baptist Mid-Missions	1993	-	-	2	1	-
Blessing the Children International	2004	-	-	1	-	16
Bright Hope International	2004	-	-	-	7	-
Calvary International	2002	-	-	-	-	-
Campus Crusade for Christ, Intl.	1980	-	-	-	160	-

	First Year	Personnel from U.S. 1-2 yrs.	2-4 yrs.	4+ yrs.	Other Countries Citizens	Non-Citizens
Children's HopeChest	2008	-	-	-	5	-
Christian Churches/Churches of Christ		-	-	8	2	-
Christian Relief Fund, The	1991	-	-	-	-	-
Church of God of Prophecy—Global Outreach		-	-	-	9	-
Church of the Nazarene, World Msn. Dept.	1992	-	-	6	-	2
Churches of Christ	1961	-	-	-	-	-
CityTeam Ministries—New Generations Intl.		-	-	1	-	2
CMF International	1963	2	-	14	-	-
Compassion International, Inc.	1993	-	-	-	96	-
Converge Worldwide	1950	-	-	1	-	-
Eastern Mennonite Missions	1948	-	2	2	-	-
Equip International	1995	1	-	3	-	-
Evangelical Lutheran Church in America	1957	-	-	2	-	-
Evangelical Presbyterian Church—World Outreach	2002	-	-	4	-	-
Evangelistic Faith Missions	1961	-	-	-	-	-
Every Home for Christ International	1972	-	-	-	1	-
Food for the Hungry, Inc.	1984	-	-	-	-	-
Gospelink, Inc.		-	-	-	4	-
Harvest	1999	-	-	-	2	-
Helimission, Inc.—USA		-	-	-	-	4
Holt International Children's Services, Inc.		-	-	-	60	-
I. N. Network USA	1996	-	-	-	50	-
International Christian Ministries	2001	-	-	-	2	-
International Crisis Aid		-	-	-	5	-
International Gospel Outreach	2002	-	2	-	4	-
Intl. Pentecostal Holiness Ch. World Msns. Mins.	1995	-	-	-	-	-
LifeWind International	1993	-	-	-	4	-
Living Water International		-	-	-	-	-
Medical Ministry International	2004	1	-	-	-	-
Mission ONE, Inc.		-	-	-	37	-
Mission to the World (PCA), Inc.	1990	2	6	4	-	-
Mission Training and Resource Center	2005	-	-	-	2	-
Orthodox Presbyterian Church	1998	-	-	-	-	-
Pioneers USA		-	-	1	-	-
Project Mercy, Inc.	1977	-	-	2	-	-
Reformed Church in America, Gen. Synod	1981	-	-	5	1	-
Samaritan's Purse International Relief	2004	4	-	1	-	-
Seventh-day Adventists, General Conference	1907	-	-	-	-	15
SIM USA, Inc.	1927	10	-	58	-	-
Source of Light Ministries International, Inc.	2007	-	-	-	2	-
The God's Story Project	2004	-	-	-	-	1
The Word for the World USA	1995	-	-	-	37	-
Walk Thru the Bible Ministries, Inc.	2001	-	-	-	-	-
Warm Blankets Orphan Care International	2009	-	-	-	-	-
World Concern	1983	-	-	1	16	2
WorldServe Ministries		-	-	-	-	1
Wycliffe Bible Translators, Inc.		-	-	11	-	-
Totals:		22	10	175	537	43

	Personnel from U.S.			Other Countries	
	First Year	1-2 yrs.	2-4 yrs.	4+ yrs.	Citizens	Non-Citizens

Europe—General

	First Year	1-2 yrs.	2-4 yrs.	4+ yrs.	Citizens	Non-Citizens
ABWE, Inc.	1970	-	42	160	-	-
Arab World Ministries		-	-	6	11	2
Assemblies of God World Missions	1925	9	-	77	-	-
Campus Crusade for Christ, Intl.		4	-	11	9	-
Christian Aid Mission		-	-	-	9	-
Christian and Missionary Alliance, The		-	-	186	-	-
Church of God (Cleveland, Tenn.) World Missions		-	-	2	-	-
Cook Communications Ministries International	1991	-	-	-	-	-
Educational Services International (ESI)	1990	40	-	-	-	-
Fellowship of Companies for Christ Intl. (FCCI)	2005	-	-	-	1	-
Final Frontiers Foundation, Inc.	1992	-	-	-	25	-
Gideons International, The		-	-	-	21	-
Heifer Project International	1992	-	-	-	-	-
InterVarsity Christian Fellowship/USA, Msns. Dept.		-	-	5	-	-
Mennonite Central Committee (MCC)		-	-	26	-	-
New Mission Systems International		-	14	6	2	18
Operation Mobilization	1963	-	2	14	-	3
Presbyterian Church (USA), Worldwide Ministries		-	40	37	-	-
Ravi Zacharias International Ministries, Inc.	1998	-	-	-	8	-
RBC Ministries	1987	-	-	-	40	-
Ripe for Harvest, Inc.	1988	-	3	3	-	-
Team Expansion, Inc.	1997	-	-	19	-	-
United Pentecostal Church International		-	6	-	-	23
World Horizons		-	-	10	-	4
World Venture		-	-	4	-	-
Young Life		17	8	14	-	-
Youth for Christ/USA—World Outreach		-	-	8	-	-
Youth With A Mission (YWAM)		-	407	-	986	-
Totals:		70	522	588	1112	50

Fiji

	First Year	1-2 yrs.	2-4 yrs.	4+ yrs.	Citizens	Non-Citizens
Assemblies of God World Missions	1918	2	-	7	-	-
Awana International	1993	-	-	-	1	-
Baptist International Missions, Inc. (BIMI)		-	-	4	-	-
Biblical Ministries Worldwide	1990	-	-	6	9	-
Campus Crusade for Christ, Intl.	1974	-	-	-	11	5
Child Evangelism Fellowship, Inc.	1953	-	-	3	-	-
Church of God (Cleveland, Tenn.) World Missions	1990	-	-	2	-	-
Church of God of Prophecy—Global Outreach		-	-	-	3	-
Church of the Nazarene, World Msn. Dept.	1995	-	-	2	-	-
Churches of Christ	1961	-	-	3	-	-
Fellowship International Mission	1995	-	-	-	2	-
Habitat for Humanity International	1991	-	1	-	-	1
International Teams, U.S.A.		-	-	-	-	2
Medical Ministry International	2003	-	-	-	-	1
Pioneers USA		-	-	2	-	1
United Pentecostal Church International	1980	-	2	-	-	2
Walk Thru the Bible Ministries, Inc.	2002	-	-	-	-	-
Totals:		2	3	29	26	12

		Personnel from U.S.			Other Countries	
	First Year	1-2 yrs.	2-4 yrs.	4+ yrs.	Citizens	Non-Citizens

Finland

	First Year	1-2 yrs.	2-4 yrs.	4+ yrs.	Citizens	Non-Citizens
Assemblies of God World Missions	2000	-	-	2	-	-
Baptist Mid-Missions	1980	-	-	2	-	-
BCM International		-	-	2	-	-
Church of God of Prophecy—Global Outreach		-	-	-	1	-
Churches of Christ	1960	-	-	3	-	-
Far East Broadcasting Company, Inc.	1999	-	-	1	-	-
Greater Europe Mission		-	-	1	-	-
Greater Grace World Outreach	1975	-	-	-	16	2
International Gospel Outreach	2008	-	-	2	-	-
Mission Possible Foundation, Inc.	1985	-	-	-	-	-
Seventh Day Baptist Missionary Society	1960	-	-	-	1	-
Tentmakers International	1998	-	-	-	1	-
United Pentecostal Church International		-	-	-	-	4
Wycliffe Bible Translators		-	-	6	-	-
Totals:		-	-	19	19	6

France

	First Year	1-2 yrs.	2-4 yrs.	4+ yrs.	Citizens	Non-Citizens
Alongside Ministries International	1980	3	1	2	-	6
American Baptist Chs. of the U.S.A., Intl. Mins.	1832	-	-	1	-	-
Arab World Ministries		2	-	14	10	17
Artists In Christian Testimony International	2008	-	-	2	-	-
Assemblies of God World Missions	1952	2	-	13	-	-
Avant Ministries	1960	-	-	14	-	3
Awana International	1985	-	-	-	-	-
Baptist Bible Fellowship International	1970	-	-	8	-	-
Baptist International Missions, Inc. (BIMI)		-	-	8	-	-
Baptist Mid-Missions	1948	-	-	29	-	-
Baptist Missionary Association of America	1962	-	-	-	1	-
BCM International		-	-	6	-	-
Bethany International Ministries	1987	-	-	8	-	2
Bibles & Literature in French	2005	1	2	3	-	-
Biblical Ministries Worldwide	1996	-	-	8	-	-
BILD International		-	-	-	2	-
Brethren Assemblies		-	-	15	-	-
Campus Crusade for Christ, Intl.	1970	17	-	57	-	9
Child Evangelism Fellowship, Inc.	1949	-	-	2	-	-
Chosen People Ministries	1956	-	-	-	1	-
Christar	1988	-	-	13	-	2
Christian Associates International		-	-	-	-	-
Christian Churches/Churches of Christ		-	1	5	-	-
Christian Reformed World Missions	1989	-	-	2	-	-
Church of God (Cleveland, Tenn.) World Missions	1960	-	-	3	-	-
Church of God of Prophecy—Global Outreach		-	-	-	3	-
Ch. of the Brethren—Global Msn. Partnerships		1	-	-	-	-
Church of the Nazarene, World Msn. Dept.	1977	-	-	4	-	-
Churches of Christ	1945	-	-	8	-	-
Converge Worldwide	1989	-	-	5	-	-
CrossWorld	1962	-	-	25	-	2
European Christian Mission International—USA		-	-	1	-	2

	First Year	Personnel from U.S. 1-2 yrs.	Personnel from U.S. 2-4 yrs.	Personnel from U.S. 4+ yrs.	Other Countries Citizens	Other Countries Non-Citizens
Evangel Bible Translators	1978	-	-	2	-	-
Evangelical Baptist Missions		-	-	11	2	-
Evangelical Covenant Ch.—Covenant Wld. Msn.	1996	-	-	5	-	-
Every Home for Christ International	1964	-	-	-	1	-
Free Methodist World Missions	1994	-	-	2	-	-
Free Will Baptist, Inc. Bd. of Intl. Missions	1966	-	1	18	-	-
Friends of Israel Gospel Ministry, Inc.	1990	-	-	-	2	-
Global Aid Network (GAiN USA))	2008	-	-	-	-	2
Global Outreach Mission, Inc.	1946	1	-	38	-	-
Global Recordings Network		-	-	-	2	-
Go Ye Fellowship	2007	-	-	2	-	-
Grace Brethren International Missions	1951	1	2	13	3	-
Greater Europe Mission	1949	30	2	24	-	-
Greater Grace World Outreach	1981	-	-	-	8	-
HCJB Global	1943	-	-	-	2	-
International Board of Jewish Missions, Inc.	2000	-	-	4	-	4
Intl. Pentecostal Holiness Ch. World Msns. Mins.	1981	-	-	1	-	-
International Teams, U.S.A.		-	-	16	-	5
InterVarsity Christian Fellowship/USA, Msns. Dept.		-	1	2	-	-
Jews for Jesus	1992	-	-	1	-	-
Life in Messiah International	1998	-	-	3	3	-
Mennonite Mission Network	1953	-	-	3	-	-
Mission to the World (PCA), Inc.	1978	2	1	22	-	-
Missionary Revival Crusade	1983	-	-	-	-	-
Missions to Military, Inc.	1973	-	-	7	-	-
Navigators, U.S. International Missions Group		-	-	2	-	-
Open Door Baptist Missions	2008	-	-	1	-	-
Operation Mobilization	1961	-	1	2	-	2
Pioneers USA		-	-	9	-	-
Presbyterian Mission International (PMI)	2002	-	-	-	1	1
ReachGlobal	1988	-	2	12	-	-
Reformed Baptist Mission Services		-	-	-	-	2
Reformed Episcopal Bd. of Foreign Msns.		-	-	1	-	-
Reformed Presbyterian Global Missions		-	-	-	-	-
Seventh-day Adventists, General Conference	1876	-	-	-	-	2
TEAM (The Evangelical Alliance Mission)		-	-	26	-	-
Tentmakers International	1998	-	-	-	1	-
The Gospel Furthering Fellowship	2007	-	-	4	2	2
The Mission Society	1986	-	1	6	-	-
TITUS International		-	-	-	-	-
United Pentecostal Church International	1930	-	8	-	-	-
WEC International	1950	-	-	2	-	-
Word of Life Fellowship, Inc.—Intl. Ministries	1999	-	-	2	12	-
World Missions & Evangelism, Inc.		-	-	2	-	-
World Partners USA	1979	-	2	-	-	-
World Team	1980	-	-	13	-	2
World Venture	1962	2	3	16	-	-
World-Wide Missions		-	1	-	-	-
Wycliffe Bible Translators, Inc.		-	-	13	-	-
Youth for Christ/USA—World Outreach	1949	-	-	2	-	-

	Personnel from U.S.				Other Countries	
	First Year	1-2 yrs.	2-4 yrs.	4+ yrs.	Citizens	Non-Citizens
Totals:	62	29	543		56	65

French Guiana

Church of God of Prophecy—Global Outreach		-	-	-	1	-
Church of the Nazarene, World Msn. Dept.	1988	-	-	-	-	-
Seventh-day Adventists, General Conference	1946	-	-	-	-	2
United Pentecostal Church International	1991	-	2	-	-	-
Totals:	-		2	-	1	2

French Polynesia

Assemblies of God World Missions	1979	-	-	2	-	-
Baptist International Missions, Inc. (BIMI)		-	-	2	-	-
Churches of Christ		-	-	-	-	-
Seventh-day Adventists, General Conference	1891	-	-	-	-	2
World Baptist Fellowship Msn. Agency, Inc.	2008	2	-	-	-	-
Totals:	2		-	4	-	2

Gabon

Assemblies of God World Missions	2000	-	-	-	-	-
Campus Crusade for Christ, Intl.	1989	-	-	-	7	-
Christian Aid Mission	2009	-	-	-	2	-
Church of God of Prophecy—Global Outreach		-	-	-	2	-
Church of the Nazarene, World Msn. Dept.	1999	-	-	-	-	-
Churches of Christ	1990	-	-	-	-	-
Global Outreach Mission, Inc.		-	-	1	-	-
Global Recordings Network		-	-	2	2	-
Greater Grace World Outreach	2005	-	-	-	4	-
LifeWind International	1993	-	-	-	-	-
Missionary Ventures International		-	-	-	-	2
Tentmakers International	2007	-	-	-	1	-
United Pentecostal Church International	2001	-	2	-	-	-
Totals:	-		2	3	18	2

Gambia, The

Assemblies of God World Missions	1996	-	-	2	-	-
Child Evangelism Fellowship, Inc.	1986	-	-	2	-	-
Christian Aid Mission	1988	-	-	-	15	-
Church of God of Prophecy—Global Outreach		-	-	-	1	-
Churches of Christ	1964	-	-	-	-	-
Eastern Mennonite Missions	2005	-	1	2	-	-
International Gospel Outreach	1988	-	-	3	8	-
Living Word Missions	1996	-	-	-	2	-
Seventh-day Adventists, General Conference	1973	-	-	-	-	2
Tentmakers International	2007	-	-	-	1	-
United Pentecostal Church International	2003	-	2	-	-	-
Totals:	-		3	9	27	2

Georgia

Assemblies of God World Missions	1999	5	-	4	-	-
Baptist International Evangelistic Ministries		-	-	-	-	-
Baptist Missionary Association of America	1994	-	-	-	6	-

	Personnel from U.S.				Other Countries	
	First Year	1-2 yrs.	2-4 yrs.	4+ yrs.	Citizens	Non-Citizens
Church Leadership Dev. Intl.	1996	-	-	-	1	-
Churches of Christ	1995	-	-	-	-	-
Greater Europe Mission		3	-	-	-	-
International Gospel Outreach	2003	-	-	2	2	-
Salvation Army, U.S.A.	1993	-	2	-	-	-
Seventh-day Adventists, General Conference	1886	-	-	2	-	-
United Pentecostal Church International		-	-	-	-	2
Walk Thru the Bible Ministries, Inc.	2001	-	-	-	-	-
Totals:		8	2	8	9	2

Germany

	First Year	1-2 yrs.	2-4 yrs.	4+ yrs.	Citizens	Non-Citizens
Alongside Ministries International	1992	-	-	1	-	1
Artists In Christian Testimony International	2006	-	-	-	-	1
Assemblies of God World Missions	1948	9	-	40	-	-
Avant Ministries	1961	1	1	3	-	2
Awana International	1976	-	-	-	2	-
Baptist Bible Fellowship International	1970	-	-	17	-	-
Baptist International Missions, Inc. (BIMI)		-	-	30	-	-
Baptist Mid-Missions	1952	-	-	17	-	-
BCM International		-	-	9	-	-
Biblical Ministries Worldwide	1958	-	-	5	-	-
Brethren Assemblies		-	-	4	-	-
Cadence International	1973	3	9	25	-	-
Campus Crusade for Christ, Intl.	1966	16	-	29	-	10
Child Evangelism Fellowship, Inc.	1949	-	-	4	-	-
Chosen People Ministries	1992	-	-	-	24	-
Christar	2008	-	-	3	-	1
Christian Aid Mission		-	-	-	3	-
Christian Associates International	1996	-	-	-	-	-
Christian Churches/Churches of Christ		-	2	8	-	-
Christians In Action Missions International	1975	-	-	1	-	-
Church of God (Anderson, Ind.), Global Msns.	1901	-	-	3	-	-
Church of God (Cleveland, Tenn.) World Missions	1936	2	2	10	-	4
Church of God of Prophecy—Global Outreach		-	-	4	1	-
Ch. of the Brethren—Global Msn. Partnerships		1	-	-	-	-
Church of the Nazarene, World Msn. Dept.	1958	-	-	-	-	-
Churches of Christ	1947	-	-	10	-	-
CMF International	2008	-	-	6	-	
Commission to Every Nation	2007	-	2	-	-	2
Converge Worldwide		-	-	4	-	-
CrossWorld	1976	2	-	20	-	2
Eastern Mennonite Missions	1951	-	2	4	-	-
European Christian Mission International—USA		-	-	-	-	2
Evangelical Baptist Missions		-	-	9	-	-
Evangelical Covenant Ch.—Covenant Wld. Msn.	1991	-	-	-	-	-
Evangelical Lutheran Church in America	1972	3	-	6	-	-
Every Home for Christ International	1967	-	-	-	1	-
Faith Christian Fellowship International		-	-	1	11	-
Fellowship International Mission	1984	-	-	2	-	2
Global Mins., Ch. of the United Brethren in Christ		-	-	-	-	-

	Personnel from U.S.				Other Countries	
	First Year	1-2 yrs.	2-4 yrs.	4+ yrs.	Citizens	Non-Citizens
Global Outreach Mission, Inc.	1946	1	-	6	-	-
Global Partners/Wesleyan World Missions	1987	-	-	-	-	-
Global Recordings Network		-	-	-	3	-
Globe International	1987	-	-	2	-	-
Go Ye Fellowship	1980	-	2	2	-	-
Gospel Fellowship Association	1963	2	-	18	-	-
Grace Brethren International Missions	1969	-	-	2	2	-
Great Commission Ministries, Inc.		2	-	4	-	-
Greater Europe Mission	1954	30	6	73	-	-
Greater Grace World Outreach	1998	1	-	2	-	3
International Messengers	1996	-	1	-	2	-
Intl. Pentecostal Holiness Ch. World Msns. Mins.	1987	-	2	2	-	-
InterVarsity Christian Fellowship/USA, Msns. Dept.		-	1	-	-	-
Jews for Jesus		-	-	1	-	3
Liebenzell Mission of USA, Inc.	1994	-	-	3	-	-
Macedonia World Baptist Missions, Inc.	2005	-	-	2	-	-
Mennonite Mission Network	2002	-	2	2	-	-
Mission to the World (PCA), Inc.	1991	-	3	11	-	-
Navigators, U.S. International Missions Group		-	1	-	-	-
Network of International Christian Schools	2002	7	1	3	-	4
New Tribes Mission	1991	-	-	2	22	-
OC International, Inc.	1981	-	-	13	-	-
Prayer Baptist Missions International, Inc.	2004	-	-	2	-	-
Precept Ministries International	1992	-	-	1	1	1
Proclaim! International, Inc.	1997	-	-	10	-	-
ReachAcross		-	-	-	4	-
ReachGlobal	1958	1	-	10	-	-
Reformed Episcopal Bd. of Foreign Msns.		-	-	1	5	-
Salvation Army, U.S.A.	1886	-	2	2	-	-
Seventh-day Adventists, General Conference	1875	-	1	-	-	2
TeachBeyond USA	1955	4	37	16	-	-
TEAM (The Evangelical Alliance Mission)		-	-	16	-	-
Tentmakers International	1998	-	-	-	1	-
Turkish World Outreach	1988	-	-	4	3	1
TWR		-	-	2	-	-
United Pentecostal Church International	1960	-	4	-	-	-
University Bible Fellowship	1988	1	1	1	-	-
Word of Life Fellowship, Inc.—Intl. Ministries	1965	-	-	4	60	-
World Harvest Mission	1996	-	-	3	-	-
World Reach, Inc.	1998	-	-	-	2	-
World Venture	1981	-	10	5	-	-
World Witness	1991	-	-	4	-	-
Wycliffe Bible Translators		-	-	57	-	-
Youth for Christ/USA—World Outreach		-	-	9	-	-
Totals:		86	92	570	147	41

Ghana

	First Year	1-2 yrs.	2-4 yrs.	4+ yrs.	Citizens	Non-Citizens
AEGA Ministries International, Inc.		-	-	-	-	1
African Enterprise	1995	-	-	-	4	-
African Leadership, Inc.	2000	-	-	-	1	-

	First Year	Personnel from U.S.			Other Countries	
		1-2 yrs.	2-4 yrs.	4+ yrs.	Citizens	Non-Citizens
African Mission Evangelism	1966	-	-	6	10	-
Agape Gospel Mission		2	4	4	-	-
Allegheny Wesleyan Methodist Connection	1997	-	-	2	-	-
AMG International		-	-	-	2	-
Anis Shorrosh Evangelistic Association		-	-	-	-	-
Apostolic Christian Church Foundation, Inc.	1975	-	-	-	-	-
Artists In Christian Testimony International	2007	-	-	-	4	-
Assemblies of God World Missions	1930	-	-	8	-	-
Awana International	1984	-	-	-	5	-
Baptist International Missions, Inc. (BIMI)		-	-	8	-	-
Baptist Mid-Missions	1946	-	-	12	-	-
Baptist Missionary Association of America	1995	-	-	2	163	-
Bethany International Ministries	1995	-	-	2	-	2
Bright Hope International	2004	-	-	-	1	-
Calvary International	2004	-	-	-	-	2
Campus Crusade for Christ, Intl.	1969	-	-	1	86	6
Child Evangelism Fellowship, Inc.	1971	-	-	-	12	-
Christian Aid Mission	1990	-	-	-	10	-
Christian Broadcasting Network Inc., The	1999	-	-	-	2	-
Christian Churches/Churches of Christ		-	1	13	2	-
Christian Reformed World Relief Committee		1	-	-	-	-
Christians In Action Missions International	1994	-	-	-	2	-
Christ's Mandate for Missions	2002	-	-	5	-	-
Church of God (Cleveland, Tenn.) World Missions	1950	2	-	4	-	-
Ch. of God (Holiness), World Msn. Dept., Inc.	2008	-	2	-	-	-
Church of the Nazarene, World Msn. Dept.	1990	-	-	2	-	-
Churches of Christ	1958	-	-	4	-	-
Compassion International, Inc.	2005	-	-	1	40	-
Development Associates International (DAI)	1999	2	-	-	-	-
Evangel Bible Translators	1992	-	-	2	-	-
Evangelism Explosion International		-	-	-	-	2
Every Child Ministries, Inc.	1999	3	-	4	14	-
Every Home for Christ International	1976	-	-	-	-	-
Fellowship International Mission	2002	-	-	3	1	-
Global Outreach Mission, Inc.		-	-	1	-	-
Global Partners/Wesleyan World Missions	2004	-	-	-	-	-
Gospel Revival Ministries	1996	-	-	-	2	-
Greater Grace World Outreach	1986	-	-	2	152	-
Habitat for Humanity International	1987	-	1	-	1	-
Harvest	2001	-	-	-	1	-
HCJB Global	2005	-	-	2	1	-
Hope for the Hungry	1984	1	2	-	6	-
I. N. Network USA	1986	-	-	-	91	-
International Partnership Ministries, Inc.	1995	-	-	-	22	-
Intl. Pentecostal Holiness Ch. World Msns. Mins.	1992	-	-	2	-	-
Ireland Outreach International Inc.	1997	-	-	-	6	-
Kids Around the World, Inc.	1998	-	-	-	1	-
Literacy & Evangelism International	2006	-	-	-	2	-
Living Water International		-	-	-	-	-
Lutheran Bible Translators, Inc.	2000	-	-	5	3	-

	Personnel from U.S.			Other Countries	
	First Year	1-2 yrs.	2-4 yrs.	4+ yrs.	Citizens	Non-Citizens
M/E International, Inc.	2001	-	-	-	-	-
Medical Ministry International	1990	-	-	-	2	-
Mennonite Mission Network	1957	-	-	-	-	-
Mission ONE, Inc.		-	-	-	1	-
Mission: Moving Mountains, Inc.	2002	-	-	-	-	-
Mutual Faith Ministries Intl.		-	-	-	-	-
National Baptist Convention of America	1984	-	-	-	45	-
Navigators, U.S. International Missions Group		-	-	1	-	-
Network of International Christian Schools	2006	22	1	-	1	1
OneHope		-	-	-	-	-
Open Door Baptist Missions	2006	-	-	2	-	-
Partners International	1973	-	-	-	55	-
Salvation Army, U.S.A.	1922	-	2	-	-	-
Self-Help International	1990	-	-	-	5	-
Seventh-day Adventists, General Conference	1894	-	-	-	-	6
SIM USA, Inc.	1952	1	-	12	-	-
Source of Light Ministries International, Inc.	1995	-	-	-	2	-
Team Expansion, Inc.		-	-	3	-	-
Tentmakers International	1998	-	-	-	1	-
The Mission Society	1985	2	-	6	-	-
United Pentecostal Church International	1969	-	4	-	-	3
Village Ministries International	1994	-	-	-	5	-
Walk Thru the Bible Ministries, Inc.	2001	-	-	-	-	-
WEC International	1946	-	-	3	-	-
White Fields, Inc.		-	-	-	3	-
Word of Life Fellowship, Inc.—Intl. Ministries	2003	-	-	-	5	-
World Venture		-	1	3	-	-
Wycliffe Bible Translators, Inc.		-	-	1	-	-
Totals:		36	18	126	772	23

Greece

	First Year	1-2 yrs.	2-4 yrs.	4+ yrs.	Citizens	Non-Citizens
AMG International	1945	-	-	6	401	-
Assemblies of God World Missions	1935	4	-	4	-	-
Avant Ministries	1959	-	-	-	1	-
Baptist Bible Fellowship International	1993	-	2	2	-	-
BCM International		-	-	1	-	-
Brethren Assemblies		-	-	4	-	-
Campus Crusade for Christ, Intl.	1978	-	-	3	-	-
Child Evangelism Fellowship, Inc.	1971	-	-	2	2	-
Church of God (Cleveland, Tenn.) World Missions	1972	-	-	2	-	-
Church of God of Prophecy—Global Outreach		-	-	-	1	-
Church of the Nazarene, World Msn. Dept.	2002	-	-	-	-	-
Churches of Christ	1960	-	-	-	-	-
Cooperative Baptist Fellowship—Global Missions	2003	-	-	2	-	-
Entrust	2002	-	-	2	-	-
Fellowship International Mission	2002	-	-	-	2	-
Free Methodist World Missions	2000	-	-	2	-	-
Greater Europe Mission	1966	-	-	12	-	-
Hellenic Ministries/USA	1980	2	6	6	10	15
International Teams, U.S.A.	1984	-	-	9	4	11

	Personnel from U.S.				Other Countries	
	First Year	1-2 yrs.	2-4 yrs.	4+ yrs.	Citizens	Non-Citizens
Pioneers USA		-	-	2	-	1
Seventh-day Adventists, General Conference	1907	-	-	-	-	2
United Pentecostal Church International	1975	-	4	-	-	1
United World Mission		-	-	2	-	-
World Team		-	-	2	-	-
Totals:		6	12	63	421	30
Greenland						
Assemblies of God World Missions	1989	-	-	-	-	-
Totals:		-	-	-	-	-
Grenada						
Christian Churches/Churches of Christ		-	-	2	-	-
Church of the Nazarene, World Msn. Dept.	1977	-	-	-	-	-
Churches of Christ	1969	-	-	-	-	-
Foursquare Missions International	1987	-	-	1	-	-
Ministries In Action	1974	-	-	-	2	-
United Pentecostal Church International		-	-	-	-	2
World Relief		2	-	-	-	-
Totals:		2	-	3	2	2
Guadeloupe						
Baptist International Missions, Inc. (BIMI)		-	-	2	-	-
Christian Church (Disciples of Christ)		-	1	-	-	-
Church of the Nazarene, World Msn. Dept.	1986	-	-	-	-	-
Ministries In Action	2004	-	-	-	-	-
World Team	1947	-	-	2	-	-
Totals:		-	1	4	-	-
Guam						
Assemblies of God World Missions	1957	-	-	2	-	-
Awana International	1984	-	-	-	-	-
Baptist Bible Fellowship International	1975	-	-	2	-	-
Church of God (Anderson, Ind.), Global Msns.	1955	-	-	2	-	-
Church of the Nazarene, World Msn. Dept.	1971	-	-	2	-	-
Churches of Christ		-	-	-	-	-
Elim Fellowship—International Ministries	1991	-	-	2	-	-
Evangelical Covenant Ch.—Covenant Wld. Msn.	2006	-	4	-	-	-
Evangelical Lutheran Church in America	1961	-	-	2	-	-
Liebenzell Mission of USA, Inc.	1972	-	-	9	-	-
Mission to the World (PCA), Inc.	1996	-	-	2	-	-
Seventh-day Adventists, General Conference	1930	1	-	50	-	9
TWR		1	-	9	-	-
United Pentecostal Church International		-	-	-	-	2
Totals:		2	4	82	-	11
Guatemala						
Adventive Cross Cultural Initiatives—US	2008	-	-	-	-	-
All God's Children International	2000	1	-	-	130	1
AMG International	1978	2	4	2	460	-

	First Year	1-2 yrs.	2-4 yrs.	4+ yrs.	Citizens	Non-Citizens
		Personnel from U.S.			Other Countries	
Assemblies of God World Missions	1935	5	-	12	-	-
Avant Ministries		-	-	2	-	-
Awana International	1987	-	-	-	4	-
Baptist Bible Fellowship International	1975	-	-	5	-	-
Baptist International Missions, Inc. (BIMI)		-	-	2	-	-
Baptist Missionary Association of America	1964	-	-	1	5	-
BILD International		-	-	-	1	-
Brethren Assemblies		-	-	2	-	-
Calvary International	1987	2	-	11	6	-
CAM International	1899	-	-	56	2	-
Campus Crusade for Christ, Intl.	1963	-	-	-	40	-
Caring Partners International, Inc.	1994	-	-	-	4	-
Child Evangelism Fellowship, Inc.	1943	-	-	-	1	-
Children of Promise International		-	2	1	-	-
Children's Christian Concern Society	1968	-	-	-	-	-
Christian Aid Mission	1983	-	-	-	10	-
Christian Church (Disciples of Christ)		-	1	-	-	-
Christian Churches/Churches of Christ		-	-	2	2	-
Christian Relief Fund, The	1992	-	-	-	1	-
Christians In Action Missions International	1970	-	-	2	1	-
Christ's Mandate for Missions	1985	-	-	5	5	-
Church of God (Cleveland, Tenn.) World Missions	1934	-	-	2	-	-
Ch. of the Brethren—Global Msn. Partnerships	1980	2	-	-	-	-
Church of the Nazarene, World Msn. Dept.	1904	-	-	20	-	12
Church Resource Ministries (CRM)	2009	-	-	4	-	-
Churches of Christ	1958	-	-	6	-	-
Commission to Every Nation	1995	-	10	52	9	53
Compassion International, Inc.	1976	-	-	-	53	-
CrossWorld	2001	-	-	2	-	-
Eastern Mennonite Missions	1968	-	-	2	-	-
Evangel Bible Translators	1999	-	-	2	-	-
Evangelism Explosion International		-	-	-	-	2
Evangelistic Faith Missions	1960	2	-	-	-	-
Faith Christian Fellowship International	1991	-	-	1	12	-
Flying Doctors of Am. (Medical Mercy Msns., Inc.)	1990	-	-	-	-	-
Food for the Hungry, Inc.	1976	-	3	3	1	-
Global Mins., Ch. of the United Brethren in Christ		-	-	-	-	-
Global Outreach International	1998	-	-	1	-	-
Global Outreach Mission, Inc.		-	-	11	-	-
Global Partners/Wesleyan World Missions	1997	-	2	-	-	-
Globe International	1980	-	-	6	-	-
Gospel Outbound		-	-	-	-	-
HCJB Global	2003	-	-	2	-	-
Help for Christian Nationals, Inc.	1994	-	-	2	-	2
HIS Servants Ministries	2004	-	-	-	-	-
Holt International Children's Services, Inc.		-	-	-	1	-
Hope for the Hungry	1980	-	-	1	-	-
Hope Haven International Ministries	2008	-	-	1	10	-
Impact International, Inc.	1970	-	-	-	2	-
International Justice Mission	2005	-	-	-	10	-

	First Year	Personnel from U.S.			Other Countries	
		1-2 yrs.	2-4 yrs.	4+ yrs.	Citizens	Non-Citizens
International Partnership Ministries, Inc.	2002	-	-	-	4	-
Intl. Pentecostal Holiness Ch. World Msns. Mins.	1995	-	-	2	-	-
Kids Alive International	1993	1	3	3	27	-
LifeWind International	1983	-	-	-	21	-
Living Water International		-	-	-	-	-
Living Water Teaching	1979	1	1	5	4	-
Living Word Missions	2001	-	-	1	-	-
Luke Society, Inc., The	1996	-	-	-	-	-
Lutheran Bible Translators, Inc.	1996	-	-	10	5	-
Lutheran Church-Missouri Synod, World Mission	1947	-	-	1	-	-
Medical Teams International	2009	-	-	-	1	-
Mission Aviation Fellowship	1977	-	2	-	-	-
Missionary Ventures International	1985	-	-	8	4	-
Missions Door	1990	-	-	2	3	-
Mutual Faith Ministries Intl.	1993	-	-	2	-	-
Navigators, U.S. International Missions Group		1	-	1	-	-
New Life Advance International	1976	-	-	6	-	-
OC International, Inc.	1979	-	-	13	-	2
Pentecostal Assemblies of God of Am., Inc.		-	-	-	-	2
Pentecostal Free Will Baptist Church, Inc.		-	-	-	1	-
Precept Ministries International	1983	-	-	-	1	1
Primitive Methodist Church in the USA		-	-	-	-	-
Reformed Church in America, Gen. Synod	2001	-	-	-	1	-
Salvation Army, U.S.A.	1976	-	4	-	-	-
SIM USA, Inc.		-	-	2	-	-
Source of Light Ministries International, Inc.		-	-	2	-	-
Spanish World Ministries, Inc.		-	-	1	1	-
United Pentecostal Church International	1977	-	3	-	-	4
Walk Thru the Bible Ministries, Inc.	2000	-	-	-	-	-
Word of Life Fellowship, Inc.—Intl. Ministries	1998	-	-	-	16	-
World Baptist Fellowship Msn. Agency, Inc.	1966	-	-	2	-	-
World Missions & Evangelism, Inc.		-	2	-	-	-
World Orphans	2008	-	-	2	-	-
World Venture		-	2	-	-	-
Wycliffe Bible Translators		-	-	9	-	-
Totals:		17	39	293	859	79

Guinea

	First Year	1-2 yrs.	2-4 yrs.	4+ yrs.	Citizens	Non-Citizens
Baptist Missionary Association of America	2004	-	-	-	1	-
Campus Crusade for Christ, Intl.	1977	-	-	-	29	-
Child Evangelism Fellowship, Inc.	1992	-	-	-	1	-
Children's Christian Concern Society	1998	-	-	-	-	-
Christian Aid Mission	2008	-	-	-	1	-
Christian Churches/Churches of Christ		-	5	15	-	-
Christian Reformed World Missions	1984	2	-	13	-	-
Churches of Christ	1989	-	-	2	-	-
Global Recordings Network		-	-	2	2	-
International Gospel Outreach	1989	-	-	1	2	-
National Baptist Convention USA, Inc.	1990	-	-	2	23	-
New Tribes Mission	1988	-	-	35	-	-

	Personnel from U.S.				Other Countries	
	First Year	1-2 yrs.	2-4 yrs.	4+ yrs.	Citizens	Non-Citizens
Open Bible Churches, Intl. Mins.	1987	-	-	2	-	-
Pioneer Bible Translators	1988	-	-	27	-	1
Pioneers USA		-	-	2	-	-
SIM USA, Inc.	1986	-	-	11	-	-
World Partners USA	1995	-	6	-	-	-
World Venture	2003	-	1	3	-	-
Totals:		2	12	115	59	1

Guinea-Bissau

	First Year	1-2 yrs.	2-4 yrs.	4+ yrs.	Citizens	Non-Citizens
Abundant Life Association, Inc.	1990	-	-	-	2	-
Assemblies of God World Missions	1991	-	-	-	-	-
Campus Crusade for Christ, Intl.	1996	-	-	-	3	2
Christian Aid Mission	2003	-	-	-	25	-
Christians In Action Missions International	2002	-	-	-	-	4
Church of the Nazarene, World Msn. Dept.	2004	-	-	-	-	-
Eastern Mennonite Missions		-	-	-	-	-
Hisportic Christian Mission		-	-	-	-	1
International Gospel Outreach	1989	-	-	1	1	-
Precept Ministries International		-	-	-	-	-
Seventh-day Adventists, General Conference	1975	-	-	2	-	2
Youth for Christ/USA—World Outreach		-	-	6	-	-
Totals:		-	-	9	31	9

Guyana

	First Year	1-2 yrs.	2-4 yrs.	4+ yrs.	Citizens	Non-Citizens
Adventist World Aviation	2005	-	-	1	-	1
Assemblies of God World Missions	1953	-	-	-	-	-
Baptist Mid-Missions	1954	-	-	2	-	-
BCM International		-	-	4	-	-
Campus Crusade for Christ, Intl.	1977	-	-	-	8	-
Christ Community Church	1934	-	-	-	2	-
Christian Churches/Churches of Christ		-	-	-	2	-
Church of God of Prophecy—Global Outreach		-	-	-	2	-
Church of the Nazarene, World Msn. Dept.	1946	-	-	-	-	-
Churches of Christ	1970	-	-	14	-	-
CrossWorld	1949	-	-	6	-	-
Evangelical Lutheran Church in America	1914	-	-	2	-	-
Global Outreach International	1994	-	-	5	-	-
Global Partners/Wesleyan World Missions	1913	-	3	-	-	-
Greater Grace World Outreach	1998	-	-	-	2	-
IFCA World Missions	2002	-	-	2	4	-
Intl. Pentecostal Holiness Ch. World Msns. Mins.	1996	-	-	2	-	-
Lott Carey Baptist Foreign Msn. Conv.	1961	-	-	-	25	-
Macedonia World Baptist Missions, Inc.	1998	-	-	4	-	-
Prayer Baptist Missions International, Inc.	2009	-	-	2	-	-
Seventh-day Adventists, General Conference	1883	-	-	3	-	2
Source of Light Ministries International, Inc.	1960	-	-	-	1	-
TMA Ministries Inc.	1990	-	-	1	-	1
United Pentecostal Church International	1976	-	2	-	-	2
Wycliffe Bible Translators		-	-	2	-	-
Totals:		-	5	50	46	6

		Personnel from U.S.			Other Countries	
	First Year	1-2 yrs.	2-4 yrs.	4+ yrs.	Citizens	Non-Citizens

Haiti

	First Year	1-2 yrs.	2-4 yrs.	4+ yrs.	Citizens	Non-Citizens
Allegheny Wesleyan Methodist Connection	1968	3	-	5	-	-
American Baptist Chs. of the U.S.A., Intl.Mins.	1823	-	-	2	-	2
AMG International		-	-	-	25	-
Assemblies of God World Missions	1957	4	-	2	-	-
Awana International	2000	-	-	2	5	-
Baptist Bible Fellowship International	1982	-	-	3	-	-
Baptist International Missions, Inc. (BIMI)		-	-	6	-	-
Baptist Mid-Missions	1934	-	-	4	-	-
Beyond Borders	1993	1	-	-	10	-
Bright Hope International	1999	-	-	-	1	-
Campus Crusade for Christ, Intl.	1977	-	-	-	10	-
Caribbean Baptist Mission Society	1993	-	6	-	-	-
Child Evangelism Fellowship, Inc.	1946	-	-	2	1	-
Childcare Worldwide	1983	-	-	-	13	-
Children of Promise International		-	-	6	-	-
Children's Christian Concern Society	2009	-	-	-	-	-
Children's International Lifeline	1989	2	-	-	-	-
Christian Aid Ministries (CAM)	1988	3	4	11	38	-
Christian Church (Disciples of Christ)		-	2	-	-	-
Christian Churches/Churches of Christ		-	4	4	30	-
Christian Flights International	1977	-	1	1	100	-
Christian Reformed World Missions	1985	-	-	4	-	-
Christian Reformed World Relief Committee	1975	-	-	1	-	-
Christian Relief Fund, The	1998	-	-	-	2	-
Church of God (Anderson, Ind.), Global Msns.	1968	-	-	2	-	-
Church of God (Cleveland, Tenn.) World Missions	1933	1	-	2	-	-
Ch. of God (Holiness), World Msn. Dept., Inc.	1966	-	-	-	37	-
Church of God of Prophecy—Global Outreach		-	-	-	10	-
Ch. of the Brethren—Global Msn. Partnerships		-	-	-	-	-
Church of the Nazarene, World Msn. Dept.	1950	-	-	6	-	-
Churches of Christ	1989	-	-	4	-	-
Churches of God, General Conference	1967	-	-	4	-	-
Colorado Haiti Project, Inc.		-	-	-	23	-
Compassion International, Inc.	1968	-	-	-	71	-
Cooperative Baptist Fellowship—Global Missions	2005	-	-	2	-	-
CrossWorld	1943	-	-	13	-	1
CSI Ministries	1963	-	-	8	37	-
East-West Ministries International	2002	2	-	-	2	-
Elim Fellowship—International Ministries	1986	-	-	2	-	-
Emmanuel International Mission	1976	-	-	-	2	-
Eternal Hope in Haiti	1984	-	-	4	-	-
Evangelical Baptist Missions		-	-	-	2	-
Faith Missions International	1998	-	-	-	11	-
Fellowship International Mission	2006	-	-	2	-	-
Floresta USA, Inc.	1997	-	-	-	15	-
FOCAS	1986	-	-	-	8	-
For Haiti with Love, Inc.	1969	-	-	7	6	1
Free Methodist World Missions	1964	-	-	4	-	-
Global Outreach International	1988	-	-	8	-	-

	First Year	Personnel from U.S.			Other Countries	
		1-2 yrs.	2-4 yrs.	4+ yrs.	Citizens	Non-Citizens
Global Outreach Mission, Inc.		-	-	2	-	-
Global Partners/Wesleyan World Missions	1948	-	7	-	-	1
Globe International	2002	-	-	2	-	-
Good Shepherd Ministries, Inc.	1975	-	-	2	48	-
Haiti Lutheran Mission Society		-	-	-	75	-
Haitian Christian Outreach	1985	-	-	3	86	-
Harvest	1986	-	-	-	1	-
Harvest International, Inc.	1986	-	2	-	2	-
Have Christ Will Travel Ministries, Inc.	1966	-	-	-	30	-
Help for Haiti, Inc.	1995	-	-	-	1	2
Hope for the Hungry	1982	-	-	5	2	-
HOPE International	2006	2	-	-	1	-
International Partnership Ministries, Inc.	1982	-	-	-	31	-
Intl. Pentecostal Holiness Ch. World Msns. Mins.	1976	-	-	-	-	-
Kids Alive International	2003	-	-	2	10	2
LifeWind International	1981	-	-	-	8	2
Living Water International		-	-	-	-	-
Macedonia World Baptist Missions, Inc.	1985	-	-	1	-	-
Medical Ministry International	1990	1	-	-	-	-
Ministries In Action	1974	-	-	1	2	1
Mission Aviation Fellowship	1986	-	12	-	-	-
Mission Possible, Inc.	1974	-	-	-	171	-
Mission to the World (PCA), Inc.		-	-	2	-	-
Missionary Ventures International	1999	-	-	1	-	-
Missions Door	1992	-	-	-	3	-
National Baptist Convention of America	1975	-	-	-	25	-
New Directions International, Inc.	1969	-	-	-	3	-
New Life Advance International	1975	-	-	2	-	-
OMS International, Inc.	1958	-	1	10	-	6
OneHope		-	-	-	-	-
Open Door Baptist Missions	1994	-	-	6	-	-
Orthodox Presbyterian Church	2004	-	-	2	-	-
Progressive National Baptist Convention, Inc.	2005	-	-	-	-	-
Reciprocal Ministries International	1986	1	-	2	20	-
Rehoboth Ministries, Inc	1983	-	-	2	20	1
Salvation Army, U.S.A.	1950	-	2	1	-	-
Seventh-day Adventists, General Conference	1905	-	-	2	-	-
Society of St. Margaret	1927	-	-	2	2	-
Source of Light Ministries International, Inc.	1999	-	-	2	-	-
STEM International	1985	-	-	4	-	-
United Pentecostal Church International	1966	-	2	-	-	-
Walk Thru the Bible Ministries, Inc.	2005	-	-	-	-	-
World Baptist Fellowship Msn. Agency, Inc.	1980	-	-	2	-	-
World Concern	1995	-	-	-	120	-
World Gospel Mission	1962	-	-	-	-	-
World Relief	1987	-	-	-	18	1
World Servants	2002	-	-	-	-	2
World Team	1936	-	-	3	-	6
Totals:		20	43	182	1138	28

Honduras

	First Year	Personnel from U.S. 1-2 yrs.	2-4 yrs.	4+ yrs.	Other Countries Citizens	Non-Citizens
Action International Ministries, Inc.	2005	-	-	4	-	-
Assemblies of God World Missions	1940	10	-	11	-	-
Awana International	1987	-	-	2	4	-
Baptist Bible Fellowship International	1974	-	-	5	-	-
Baptist International Missions, Inc. (BIMI)		-	-	14	-	-
Baptist Medical & Dental Mission Intl., Inc.	1974	12	4	7	39	2
Baptist Mid-Missions	1959	-	-	10	-	-
Baptist Missionary Association of America	1976	-	-	-	14	-
Bethany International Ministries	2002	-	-	2	-	-
Biblical Ministries Worldwide	1949	-	-	5	1	-
Brethren Assemblies		-	-	9	-	-
Brethren in Christ World Missions	1989	-	-	2	-	-
Calvary International	1989	-	-	2	1	-
CAM International	1896	-	-	23	-	-
Campus Crusade for Christ, Intl.	1966	-	-	-	20	-
Children's Christian Concern Society	1985	-	-	-	-	-
Christian Aid Mission	1983	-	-	-	300	-
Christian Churches/Churches of Christ		2	-	19	2	-
Christian Outreach International	2009	-	-	-	1	-
Christian Reformed World Missions	1971	-	1	2	-	-
Christian Relief Fund, The	1984	-	-	-	4	-
Christians In Action Missions International	1978	-	-	1	-	2
Church of God (Cleveland, Tenn.) World Missions	1944	2	-	5	-	-
Church of God of the Apostolic Faith, Inc., The	1989	-	-	1	-	-
Ch. of the Brethren—Global Msn. Partnerships	1981	1	-	-	-	-
Church of the Nazarene, World Msn. Dept.	1970	-	-	-	-	-
Churches of Christ	1960	-	-	6	-	-
Commission to Every Nation	2004	-	-	-	1	1
Compassion International, Inc.	1974	-	-	-	51	-
Cup of Cold Water Ministries	2008	-	-	-	-	1
Eastern Mennonite Missions	1950	-	1	-	-	-
Evangelical Lutheran Church in America		1	-	-	-	-
Evangelistic Faith Missions	1968	4	-	-	-	-
Every Home for Christ International	1962	-	-	-	1	-
Flying Doctors of Am. (Medical Mercy Msns., Inc.)	1990	-	-	-	-	-
Full Gospel Evangelistic Association	1970	-	-	2	-	-
General Baptists International	1995	-	-	8	-	-
Global Mins., Ch. of the United Brethren in Christ		-	-	-	-	-
Global Outreach International	1990	-	-	11	-	-
Global Outreach Mission, Inc.		-	-	5	-	-
Global Partners/Wesleyan World Missions	1957	-	-	-	-	-
Globe International	1986	-	-	2	-	-
Harvest	1987	-	-	-	2	-
Heart for Honduras	1998	-	-	-	-	-
Impact International, Inc.	1970	-	-	-	4	-
International Gospel Outreach	1989	-	-	4	1	-
Intl. Pentecostal Holiness Ch. World Msns. Mins.	1993	-	-	2	2	-
International Teams, U.S.A.		-	-	2	-	-
ISOH/IMPACT	2004	-	-	1	-	-

	First Year	1-2 yrs.	2-4 yrs.	4+ yrs.	Citizens	Non-Citizens
		Personnel from U.S.			Other Countries	
Latin America Mission		-	3	5	-	8
LifeWind International	1999	-	-	-	3	-
Living Water International		-	-	-	-	-
Living Water Teaching	1983	-	-	3	-	-
Luke Society, Inc., The	1983	-	-	-	-	-
Macedonia World Baptist Missions, Inc.	2008	-	-	2	-	-
MAP International	2006	-	-	-	-	-
Medical Ministry International	1971	-	-	-	2	-
Mission to the World (PCA), Inc.	2001	-	4	-	-	-
Missionary Ventures International	1992	-	-	4	-	-
Missions Door	1951	-	-	2	12	-
Moravian Church in N. Am., Bd. of World Msn.	1994	-	-	-	2	-
OneHope		-	-	-	-	-
Pentecostal Assemblies of God of Am., Inc.		-	-	-	-	2
Pentecostal Free Will Baptist Church, Inc.		-	-	-	1	-
Precept Ministries International		-	-	-	-	1
Raul Zaldivar Ministries	2008	1	-	-	-	1
ReachGlobal	2002	-	5	2	-	-
Reformed Church in America, Gen. Synod	1995	-	-	-	3	-
Rock the World Youth Mission Alliance		-	-	-	-	-
Samaritan's Purse International Relief	2000	1	-	-	-	-
SEED International	2001	-	1	-	-	-
Seventh-day Adventists, General Conference	1891	-	-	2	-	2
Spanish World Ministries, Inc.		-	-	2	2	-
STEM International	1997	-	-	-	-	-
TEAM (The Evangelical Alliance Mission)		-	-	2	-	-
Teen Missions International, Inc.	1987	-	2	-	2	-
United Pentecostal Church International	1997	-	4	-	-	-
Walk Thru the Bible Ministries, Inc.	2002	-	-	-	4	-
Word of Life Fellowship, Inc.—Intl. Ministries	1998	-	-	1	10	-
World Baptist Fellowship Msn. Agency, Inc.	1968	-	-	4	-	-
World Concern	1998	-	-	1	-	1
World Gospel Mission	1944	-	-	29	-	-
World Missions & Evangelism, Inc.		-	-	4	-	-
World Reach, Inc.	1982	-	-	5	9	-
Youth for Christ/USA—World Outreach		-	-	3	-	-
Wycliffe Bible Translators		-	-	2	-	-
Totals:		34	25	240	498	21

Hong Kong

Asian Outreach U.S.A.		-	-	-	-	-
Awana International	1996	-	-	-	3	-
Baptist Bible Fellowship International	1969	-	-	6	-	-
Baptist International Missions, Inc. (BIMI)		-	-	2	-	-
Baptist Missionary Association of America	2004	-	-	-	-	1
Biblical Ministries Worldwide	1988	-	-	5	-	-
Brethren Assemblies		-	-	4	-	-
Campus Crusade for Christ, Intl.	1972	-	-	-	119	-
Child Evangelism Fellowship, Inc.	1948	-	-	1	-	2
Chosen People Ministries	2007	-	-	-	2	-

| | Personnel from U.S. | | | | Other Countries | |
	First Year	1-2 yrs.	2-4 yrs.	4+ yrs.	Citizens	Non-Citizens
Christian Broadcasting Network Inc., The	2004	-	1	-	11	-
Christian Church (Disciples of Christ)		-	2	-	-	-
Christian Churches/Churches of Christ		-	-	10	4	-
Christ's Mandate for Missions	2005	-	-	2	-	-
Church of God (Anderson, Ind.), Global Msns.	1987	-	-	2	-	-
Church of the Nazarene, World Msn. Dept.	1974	-	-	-	-	-
CLC Ministries International	1973	-	-	2	-	-
Eastern Mennonite Missions		-	-	-	-	-
Evangelical Lutheran Church in America	1890	1	-	6	2	-
Evangelize China Fellowship, Inc.		-	-	-	1	-
Habitat for Humanity International		-	2	-	-	2
Intl. Pentecostal Holiness Ch. World Msns. Mins.	1911	-	-	-	-	-
International Students, Inc (ISI)		-	-	-	2	-
Mission to the World (PCA), Inc.	1982	-	-	2	-	-
OMS International, Inc.	1954	-	-	5	-	1
Partners International	1950	-	-	-	2	-
Ravi Zacharias International Ministries, Inc.	2008	-	-	-	-	1
Reach Ministries International	1985	-	-	1	-	-
ReachGlobal	1987	-	-	9	-	-
Seventh-day Adventists, General Conference	1888	-	-	14	-	4
Tribes and Nations Outreach		-	-	-	-	-
United Pentecostal Church International	1976	-	2	-	-	-
Wisconsin Evangelical Lutheran Synod	1964	-	-	2	-	-
World Venture	1963	-	-	8	-	-
Totals:		1	7	81	146	11

Hungary

	First Year	1-2 yrs.	2-4 yrs.	4+ yrs.	Citizens	Non-Citizens
Artists In Christian Testimony International	2003	-	-	1	-	-
Assemblies of God World Missions	1926	-	-	6	-	-
Awana International	1993	-	-	-	5	-
Baptist Bible Fellowship International	1990	-	-	2	-	-
Baptist International Missions, Inc. (BIMI)		-	-	2	-	-
BCM International		-	-	2	-	-
Bethany International Ministries	1999	-	-	2	-	-
Brethren Assemblies		-	-	2	-	-
Campus Crusade for Christ, Intl.	1978	18	-	69	31	6
Centers for Apologetics Research, The	1998	-	-	-	2	-
Child Evangelism Fellowship, Inc.	1989	-	-	1	5	2
Christian Aid Mission		-	-	-	8	-
Christian Church (Disciples of Christ)		-	3	-	-	-
Christian Reformed World Missions	1990	-	-	5	-	-
Church of God of Prophecy—Global Outreach		-	-	-	1	-
Ch. of the Brethren—Global Msn. Partnerships		1	-	-	-	-
Church of the Nazarene, World Msn. Dept.	1996	-	-	-	-	-
Church Resource Ministries (CRM)	1987	-	-	6	-	-
Churches of Christ	1970	-	-	5	-	-
Cooperative Baptist Fellowship—Global Missions	1994	-	2	2	-	-
Entrust	1979	-	-	6	2	-
Every Home for Christ International	1992	-	-	-	-	-
Fellowship of Evangelical Chs.—Intl. Mins.	2000	-	-	2	-	-

	First Year	Personnel from U.S. 1-2 yrs.	2-4 yrs.	4+ yrs.	Other Countries Citizens	Non-Citizens
Free Methodist World Missions	1995	-	-	4	-	-
Friendship International Ministries, Inc.	1990	-	-	4	3	1
Greater Europe Mission	1996	-	-	4	-	-
Greater Grace World Outreach	1990	1	-	10	57	7
Habitat for Humanity International	1994	-	25	4	15	14
International Messengers	1992	-	1	2	9	1
Intl. Pentecostal Holiness Ch. World Msns. Mins.	1989	-	-	4	-	-
Ministry to Educate and Equip, Intl. (MTEE)	1995	-	4	-	1	-
Mission To Unreached Peoples	1996	-	-	3	-	-
Navigators, U.S. International Missions Group		1	1	3	-	-
New Hope International	1971	-	-	-	2	-
OMS International, Inc.	1992	-	-	8	-	1
Open Bible Churches, Intl. Mins.		-	-	2	-	-
Operation Mobilization		-	2	3	-	1
Pioneers USA	1992	-	1	16	-	-
Precept Ministries International		-	-	-	-	-
Presbyterian Mission International (PMI)	1999	-	-	-	2	1
ReachGlobal	1997	-	2	10	3	-
Reformed Church in America, Gen. Synod	2002	-	-	2	-	1
SEND International USA	1996	1	-	6	-	-
TCM International Institute		-	-	-	1	-
TeachBeyond USA		2	-	-	-	-
Team Expansion, Inc.		-	-	2	-	-
Tentmakers International	2005	-	-	-	1	-
The Mission Society	2001	2	-	-	-	-
United Pentecostal Church International		-	-	-	-	-
United World Mission		-	-	3	-	-
Walk Thru the Bible Ministries, Inc.	2000	-	-	-	-	-
Westminster Biblical Missions	1990	-	-	1	10	3
Word of Life Fellowship, Inc.—Intl. Ministries	1987	-	-	7	50	-
World Bible Translation Center		-	-	-	2	-
World Gospel Mission	1992	-	-	5	-	-
World Harvest Mission	1999	-	-	2	-	-
World Indigenous Missions	1997	-	-	2	-	-
World Missions & Evangelism, Inc.		-	-	2	-	-
World Venture	1990	-	-	2	-	-
Totals:		26	41	224	210	38

Iceland

Assemblies of God World Missions	1992	2	-	2	-	-
Baptist Bible Fellowship International	1982	-	-	2	-	-
Churches of Christ	1980	-	-	-	-	-
Greater Europe Mission	1985	-	-	2	-	-
Navigators, U.S. International Missions Group		-	-	2	-	-
Totals:		2	-	8	-	-

India

Action International Ministries, Inc.	1994	-	-	3	6	-
ACTS International Ministries, Inc.	2004	-	-	-	1	-
Advancing Renewal Ministries, Inc.		-	-	15	15	-

	Personnel from U.S.			Other Countries	
First Year	1-2 yrs.	2-4 yrs.	4+ yrs.	Citizens	Non-Citizens
Advent Christian Gen. Conf., Dept. of World Msns. 1882	1	-	-	-	-
AEGA Ministries International, Inc.	-	-	-	-	1
AIDS Family Fund, Inc. 2006	-	-	-	30	-
All About Orphans	-	-	-	-	-
American Baptist Chs. of the U.S.A., Intl.Mins. 1836	-	-	4	-	-
Am. Council of the Ramabai Mukti Msn., Inc. 1929	-	-	-	2	-
American Leprosy Missions, Inc. 1906	-	-	-	1	-
AMG International 1970	-	-	-	6400	-
Anis Shorrosh Evangelistic Association	-	-	35	-	-
Assemblies of God World Missions 1914	10	-	53	-	-
Audio Scripture Ministries 2005	-	-	1	1	-
Awana International 1991	-	-	-	22	1
Back to the Bible International 1970	-	-	-	46	-
Baptist International Missions, Inc. (BIMI)	-	-	7	-	-
Baptist Mid-Missions 1935	-	-	8	6	-
Baptist Missionary Association of America 1974	-	-	-	34	-
BCM International	-	-	211	-	-
Bibles For The World, Inc. 1972	-	-	-	400	-
BILD International	-	-	-	3	-
Brethren Assemblies	-	-	14	-	-
Bright Hope International 1990	-	-	-	5	-
Calvary International 1987	-	-	-	10	-
Campus Crusade for Christ, Intl. 1963	-	-	-	1721	2
CEIFA Ministry International 2006	-	-	2	2	-
Childcare Worldwide 1981	-	-	-	155	-
Christ for India, Inc. 1981	-	-	1	-	-
Christ to the Nations 1991	-	-	-	20	-
Christar 1930	-	-	26	-	10
Christian Aid Mission	-	-	-	-	-
Christian Broadcasting Network Inc., The 1997	-	1	-	151	-
Christian Church (Disciples of Christ)	-	2	-	-	-
Christian Churches/Churches of Christ	-	-	17	35	-
Christian Relief Fund, The 1974	-	-	-	12	-
Christians In Action Missions International 1977	-	-	-	8	-
Christ's Mandate for Missions 1978	-	-	-	190	-
Church Leadership Dev. Intl. 1996	-	-	-	3	-
Ch. of God (Holiness), World Msn. Dept., Inc. 2005	-	-	-	30	-
Church of God of Prophecy—Global Outreach	-	-	-	25	-
Church of the Nazarene, World Msn. Dept. 1898	-	-	-	-	-
Church Resource Ministries (CRM) 2004	-	-	1	-	-
Churches of Christ 1960	-	-	10	-	-
Commission to Every Nation 1999	-	-	-	-	1
Compassion International, Inc. 1968	-	-	-	129	-
Cook Communications Ministries International 1999	-	-	-	-	-
Cooperative Baptist Fellowship—Global Missions 2001	1	2	4	-	-
Dayspring International 1979	-	-	-	1000	-
Development Associates International (DAI) 2000	-	-	-	3	-
Eastern Mennonite Missions 2001	-	2	2	2	-
East-West Ministries International 2001	2	-	-	4	-
Engineering Ministries International (EMI) 1998	-	1	4	-	-

	First Year	Personnel from U.S. 1-2 yrs.	2-4 yrs.	4+ yrs.	Other Countries Citizens	Non-Citizens
Evangel Bible Translators	1978	-	-	6	28	-
Evangelical Covenant Ch.—Covenant Wld. Msn.	1999	-	-	-	-	-
Evangelical Friends Mission		-	-	-	-	-
Evangelical Lutheran Church in America	1842	-	-	1	-	-
Evangelism Explosion International		-	-	2	-	-
Evangelism Resources, Inc.	1990	-	-	-	2	-
Every Home for Christ International	1965	-	-	-	1	-
Faith Christian Fellowship International		-	-	2	24	-
Faith Life Ministries, Inc.	2008	-	-	-	-	-
Food for the Hungry, Inc.	1998	-	1	-	-	-
Foursquare Missions International		-	2	2	-	-
Free Gospel Church, Inc.—Missions Department	1935	-	-	-	2	-
Free Will Baptist, Inc. Bd. of Intl. Missions	1935	-	-	1	-	-
FRIENDS in Action International		-	-	-	-	-
Friends of Israel Gospel Ministry, Inc.	1969	-	-	-	2	-
General Baptists International	1982	-	-	-	1	-
Global Action	1998	-	-	-	10	-
Global Mins., Ch. of the United Brethren in Christ		-	-	-	-	-
Global Outreach International	1977	-	-	4	-	-
Global Outreach Mission, Inc.		1	-	8	-	-
Global Partners/Wesleyan World Missions	1910	-	-	-	-	-
Global Recordings Network		-	-	-	10	-
Globe International	1989	-	-	7	-	-
GOGF Ministries	2006	-	-	-	1	-
Good News for India	1987	-	-	-	350	-
Good News Productions International	1989	-	-	2	10	-
Gospel Outbound		-	-	-	-	-
Gospel Outreach Ministries Intl.	1988	-	-	-	250	-
Gospel Revival Ministries	1995	-	-	-	35	-
Gospelink, Inc.		-	-	-	46	-
Grace Ministries International	1969	-	2	-	-	-
Greater Grace World Outreach	1984	-	-	2	120	1
Habitat for Humanity International	1983	-	22	-	1	21
Harvest	1996	-	-	-	2	-
Harvest International, Inc.	2002	-	-	-	2	-
Harvest Mission to the Unreached		-	-	-	120	-
Have Christ Will Travel Ministries, Inc.	1989	-	-	-	27	-
HBI Global Partners	1984	-	-	-	595	-
Heart of God Ministries	1996	-	-	8	1	-
Help for Christian Nationals, Inc.	1996	-	-	1	1	-
His Healing Helping Hands Intl. Mins. (4 H.I.M.)	2007	-	-	-	1	-
Hope for the Hungry	1990	-	-	-	6	-
HOPE International		-	-	1	-	-
I. N. Network USA	1979	-	-	-	202	-
IFCA World Missions	1966	-	-	3	-	-
In Touch Mission International	2009	1	-	-	1	-
India Gospel League, NA	1948	-	-	-	908	-
India Gospel Outreach, Inc.	1984	-	-	1	2500	-
India National Inland Mission	1964	-	-	-	350	-
India Partners	2001	-	-	-	1	-

	First Year	Personnel from U.S.			Other Countries	
		1-2 yrs.	2-4 yrs.	4+ yrs.	Citizens	Non-Citizens
International Christian Leprosy Mission, Inc. (USA)	1960	-	-	-	2	-
International Gospel Outreach	1986	-	-	-	4	-
International Justice Mission	2000	-	6	-	82	1
International Partnership Ministries, Inc.	1983	-	-	-	108	-
International Pentecostal Church of Christ	1947	-	-	1	-	-
Intl. Pentecostal Holiness Ch. World Msns. Mins.	1911	-	-	2	-	-
Interserve USA (International Service Fellowship)	1852	-	-	8	-	-
Josue Yrion World Evangelism and Missions, Inc.	1997	-	-	-	13	-
LifeWind International	1982	-	-	-	38	-
Literacy & Evangelism International	2003	-	-	-	2	-
Living Water International		-	-	-	-	-
Lott Carey Baptist Foreign Msn. Conv.	1948	-	-	-	350	-
M/E International, Inc.	1985	-	-	-	-	-
Mailbox Club International Inc., The		-	-	-	1	-
Mennonite Mission Network	1899	-	-	-	-	-
Mission India	1981	-	-	-	2	-
Mission of Mercy	1954	-	-	1	1	-
Mission ONE, Inc.		-	-	-	68	-
Mission to Children, Inc.	1979	-	-	-	-	-
Mission to the World (PCA), Inc.	1973	-	-	10	-	-
Mission To Unreached Peoples	1987	-	-	12	3	1
Mustard Seed International	1998	-	-	-	-	-
New Directions International, Inc.	1985	-	-	-	25	-
New Life Advance International	1970	-	-	-	2	-
OC International, Inc.	1984	-	-	-	-	1
OMS International, Inc.	1941	-	-	1	-	1
OneHope		-	-	-	-	-
Open Air Campaigners—Overseas Ministries	1988	-	-	-	35	-
Operation Mobilization	1964	2	-	7	-	2
Partners in Christ International	2005	-	-	-	3	-
Partners International	1969	-	-	-	929	-
Perimeter Church—Global Outreach	1998	-	-	-	-	-
Pioneers USA		-	1	45	3	2
Prakash Association, USA	1968	-	-	-	40	-
Prayer Baptist Missions International, Inc.	1989	-	-	-	2	-
Precept Ministries International	2000	-	-	-	5	-
Presbyterian Mission International (PMI)	1989	-	-	-	8	-
Project Christ International	1985	-	-	-	75	-
Ravi Zacharias International Ministries, Inc.	1986	-	-	-	8	-
Reach Ministries International	1985	-	-	-	2	-
ReachGlobal	1995	-	-	-	33	-
Reaching Indians Ministries International	1993	-	-	-	810	-
Reformed Church in America, Gen. Synod	1990	-	-	2	1	-
SEED International	2000	-	-	1	-	-
Seventh Day Baptist Missionary Society	1950	-	-	-	1	-
Seventh-day Adventists, General Conference	1895	-	1	8	-	10
Share International		-	-	-	-	-
SIM USA, Inc.	1894	2	-	16	-	-
Source of Light Ministries International, Inc.	1978	-	-	-	6	-
Spiritual Overseers Service International	1985	-	-	-	1	-

	Personnel from U.S.				Other Countries	
	First Year	1-2 yrs.	2-4 yrs.	4+ yrs.	Citizens	Non-Citizens
Supreme Task International, Inc.	1989	-	-	2	30	-
Talking Bibles International	1997	-	-	-	4	-
TeachBeyond USA		-	-	-	-	-
Teen Missions International, Inc.	1982	-	-	-	12	-
Tentmakers International	1995	-	-	-	1	-
The Brethren Church, Inc.	1969	-	-	-	150	-
The God's Story Project	2000	-	-	-	1	-
The Master's Mission, Inc.	1993	-	-	-	2	-
The Mission Society	1995	-	-	2	-	-
The Word for the World USA	2008	-	-	-	-	2
TMA Ministries Inc.	1988	-	-	1	-	1
Training Evangelistic Leadership (T.E.L.), Inc.	1975	-	1	2	16	-
Tribes and Nations Outreach		-	-	-	-	-
U.S. Center for World Mission		-	2	4	-	-
United Pentecostal Church International	1909	-	1	-	-	3
United World Mission		-	-	6	-	-
Village Ministries International	2000	-	-	-	26	-
Walk Thru the Bible Ministries, Inc.	1998	-	-	-	21	-
Warm Blankets Orphan Care International	2004	-	-	-	3	-
Wisconsin Evangelical Lutheran Synod	1970	-	-	2	-	-
World Bible Translation Center		-	-	-	20	-
World Gospel Mission	1937	-	-	2	-	-
World Harvest Mission	1998	-	-	2	-	-
World Mission Prayer League	1941	-	-	1	1	-
World Mission, Inc.		-	-	-	-	-
World Missions & Evangelism, Inc.	1997	-	-	-	33	2
World Missions Far Corners, Inc.	1969	-	-	-	242	-
World Relief	2000	1	-	-	2	1
World Venture	1945	-	2	4	-	-
WorldServe Ministries		-	-	-	1	-
World-Wide Missions	1965	-	-	-	2	-
Wycliffe Bible Translators		-	-	2	-	-
Totals:		21	49	613	19312	64

Indonesia

AMG International	1975	-	-	-	493	-
Asian Outreach U.S.A.		-	-	-	-	-
Assemblies of God World Missions	1920	13	-	26	-	-
Back to the Bible International	2003	-	-	-	9	-
Baptist Bible Fellowship International	1972	-	-	4	-	-
Baptist International Missions, Inc. (BIMI)		-	-	2	-	-
Baptist Missionary Association of America	2007	-	-	-	2	1
BCM International		-	-	12	-	-
BILD International		-	-	-	1	-
Brethren Assemblies		-	-	3	-	-
Bright Hope International	2000	-	-	-	1	-
Calvary International	1999	-	-	-	-	-
Campus Crusade for Christ, Intl.	1968	-	-	2	445	4
Christ Community Church	2000	-	-	-	2	-
Christian Aid Mission		-	-	-	148	-

		Personnel from U.S.			Other Countries	
	First Year	1-2 yrs.	2-4 yrs.	4+ yrs.	Citizens	Non-Citizens
Christian Broadcasting Network Inc., The	1998	-	-	1	216	1
Christian Church (Disciples of Christ)		-	1	-	-	-
Christian Churches/Churches of Christ		-	-	15	-	-
Church of God (Anderson, Ind.), Global Msns.	1981	-	-	2	-	-
Church of God (Cleveland, Tenn.) World Missions	1967	-	-	2	-	-
Church of God of Prophecy—Global Outreach		-	-	-	2	-
Church of the Nazarene, World Msn. Dept.	1973	-	-	4	-	-
Churches of Christ	1967	-	-	6	-	-
CityTeam Ministries—New Generations Intl.		-	-	-	-	3
CMF International	1978	-	3	8	1	-
Compassion International, Inc.	1968	-	-	-	126	-
CrossWorld	1957	-	-	13	-	2
Eastern Mennonite Missions	1997	-	-	1	-	-
East-West Ministries International	2006	-	-	-	2	-
Evangelical Lutheran Church in America	1970	-	-	1	-	-
Evangelism Explosion International		-	-	-	-	10
Every Home for Christ International	1974	-	-	-	1	-
Far East Broadcasting Company, Inc.	1951	-	-	-	80	-
Global Partners/Wesleyan World Missions	1975	-	-	-	-	-
Global Recordings Network		-	-	-	6	-
Globe International	1989	-	-	2	-	-
Go Ye Fellowship	1988	-	-	1	1	-
Habitat for Humanity International		-	2	-	-	2
Helimission, Inc.—USA		-	-	-	-	8
Intl. Pentecostal Holiness Ch. World Msns. Mins.	1986	-	-	-	-	-
International Teams, U.S.A.		-	-	3	-	18
Interserve USA (International Service Fellowship)	2007	-	-	1	-	-
LifeWind International	1998	-	-	-	20	-
Macedonia World Baptist Missions, Inc.	1991	-	-	4	-	-
MAP International	2005	-	-	-	6	1
Medical Teams International	2005	-	-	-	-	1
Mission Aviation Fellowship	1952	5	3	70	-	-
Mission To Unreached Peoples	2002	-	-	4	-	-
Missionary Ventures International	2002	-	-	2	-	-
Mustard Seed International	1972	-	-	7	-	-
Network of International Christian Schools	1995	16	6	7	5	2
OMS International, Inc.	1971	-	-	9	-	6
OneHope		-	-	-	-	-
Partners International	1971	-	-	3	928	-
Reformed Church in America, Gen. Synod	2000	-	-	-	1	-
Seventh-day Adventists, General Conference	1900	-	-	4	-	2
Surfing the Nations	1998	-	-	-	-	-
Teen Missions International, Inc.	2000	-	-	-	38	2
Tentmakers International	1997	-	-	-	1	-
The Gospel Furthering Fellowship	2006	-	-	2	-	2
Things To Come Mission, Inc.	1973	-	-	-	20	-
Training Evangelistic Leadership (T.E.L.), Inc.	1976	-	-	3	8	-
Tribes and Nations Outreach		-	-	-	-	-
United Pentecostal Church International	1938	-	2	-	-	-
University Bible Fellowship	2008	1	-	-	-	-

		Personnel from U.S.			Other Countries	
	First Year	1-2 yrs.	2-4 yrs.	4+ yrs.	Citizens	Non-Citizens
Walk Thru the Bible Ministries, Inc.	2001	-	-	-	6	-
Warm Blankets Orphan Care International	2004	-	-	-	5	-
Wisconsin Evangelical Lutheran Synod	1969	-	-	1	-	-
World Baptist Fellowship Msn. Agency, Inc.	1966	-	-	5	-	-
World Bible Translation Center		-	-	-	4	-
World Harvest—USA	1989	-	-	-	45	-
World Indigenous Missions	1995	-	-	4	2	-
World Outreach International—US	2004	2	-	-	-	-
World Relief	2004	2	-	-	-	-
World Venture	1961	-	3	11	-	-
Wycliffe Bible Translators, Inc.		-	-	200	-	-
Totals:		39	20	340	2625	65

Iran

Baptist Missionary Association of America	2003	-	-	-	1	-
Churches of Christ	1970	-	-	-	-	-
Middle East Media—USA	1976	-	-	-	-	-
Partners International	2001	-	-	-	20	-
Precept Ministries International		-	-	-	-	-
Totals:		-	-	-	21	-

Iraq

Baptist Missionary Association of America	2003	-	-	-	1	-
Christian Aid Mission		-	-	-	25	-
International Partnership Ministries, Inc.	2001	-	-	-	2	-
Partners International	1989	-	-	-	125	-
Precept Ministries International		-	-	-	-	-
Samaritan's Purse International Relief	2003	-	1	-	-	-
Venture International	2003	-	-	-	25	-
Walk Thru the Bible Ministries, Inc.	2001	-	-	-	-	-
World Compassion Terry Law Ministries	2003	-	-	-	24	-
World Orphans	2007	-	-	5	-	-
Totals:		-	1	5	202	-

Ireland

Assemblies of God World Missions	1978	10	-	14	-	-
Baptist Bible Fellowship International	1977	-	-	3	-	-
Baptist International Missions, Inc. (BIMI)		-	-	14	-	-
Baptist Mid-Missions	1978	-	-	2	-	-
BCM International		-	-	6	-	-
Biblical Ministries Worldwide	1975	-	-	8	-	-
Brethren Assemblies		-	-	14	-	-
Christian Associates International		-	-	-	-	-
Christian Churches/Churches of Christ		1	-	6	-	-
Church of God (Cleveland, Tenn.) World Missions	1995	2	-	4	-	-
Ch. of the Brethren—Global Msn. Partnerships		5	-	-	-	-
Church of the Nazarene, World Msn. Dept.	1987	-	-	-	-	2
Churches of Christ	1967	-	-	2	-	-
Commission to Every Nation	2008	-	-	-	-	2
CrossWorld	1980	-	-	11	-	4

	First Year	Personnel from U.S. 1-2 yrs.	2-4 yrs.	4+ yrs.	Other Countries Citizens	Non-Citizens
Evangelical Friends Mission		-	-	-	-	-
Faith Christian Fellowship International		-	-	1	1	-
Global Outreach Mission, Inc.	1965	-	-	9	-	-
Grace Brethren International Missions	2003	-	-	4	-	-
Greater Europe Mission	1974	-	-	25	-	-
Greater Grace World Outreach	1997	-	-	1	1	2
International Gospel Outreach	2008	1	-	-	-	-
International Teams, U.S.A.		-	-	4	-	-
Ireland Outreach International Inc.	1970	-	3	10	-	3
Liebenzell Mission of USA, Inc.	2007	-	1	-	-	-
Macedonia World Baptist Missions, Inc.	2004	-	-	4	-	-
Mission to the World (PCA), Inc.	1995	1	-	4	-	-
Missionary Ventures International	1998	-	-	-	2	-
OMS International, Inc.	1996	-	-	1	-	1
Operation Mobilization		1	-	2	-	-
Prayer Baptist Missions International, Inc.	2008	2	-	-	-	-
Precept Ministries International	2002	-	-	-	4	-
Reformed Baptist Mission Services		-	-	-	2	-
TEAM (The Evangelical Alliance Mission)		-	-	3	-	-
Team Expansion, Inc.	1987	-	-	2	-	-
Walk Thru the Bible Ministries, Inc.	2000	-	-	-	-	-
World Harvest Mission	1986	-	-	16	-	-
World Partners USA	2003	-	6	-	-	-
World Venture	1993	-	3	7	-	-
Youth for Christ/USA—World Outreach		-	-	1	-	-
Totals:		23	13	178	10	14

Israel

	First Year	1-2 yrs.	2-4 yrs.	4+ yrs.	Citizens	Non-Citizens
Anis Shorrosh Evangelistic Association		-	-	40	-	-
Artists In Christian Testimony International	2008	-	-	-	-	2
Assemblies of God World Missions	1917	6	-	11	-	-
Child Evangelism Fellowship, Inc.	1951	-	-	2	2	-
Children's Christian Concern Society	2002	-	-	-	-	-
Chosen People Ministries	1952	-	-	-	15	-
Christian Aid Ministries (CAM)	2008	-	1	-	2	-
Christian Churches/Churches of Christ		-	-	2	1	-
Church of God of Prophecy—Global Outreach		-	-	-	-	2
Church of the Nazarene, World Msn. Dept.	1921	-	-	3	-	2
Churches of Christ	1960	-	-	-	-	-
East-West Ministries International	2008	2	-	-	-	-
Episcopal Church USA		-	-	-	-	-
Evangel Bible Translators	1998	-	-	1	-	-
Foursquare Missions International	1998	-	-	4	-	-
Friends of Israel Gospel Ministry, Inc.	1958	-	-	-	8	-
Globe International	2001	-	-	6	-	-
Go Ye Fellowship	2002	-	-	2	-	-
High Adventure Ministries	1979	-	-	-	3	-
Hope for the Hungry	1982	-	-	-	2	-
Independent Faith Mission, Inc.	2007	-	-	2	-	-
International Board of Jewish Missions, Inc.	1991	-	-	-	-	7

	Personnel from U.S.				Other Countries	
	First Year	1-2 yrs.	2-4 yrs.	4+ yrs.	Citizens	Non-Citizens
International Gospel Outreach	2008	1	-	-	-	-
International Teams, U.S.A.		-	-	2	-	2
Jewish Awareness Ministries, Inc.	2000	-	-	2	-	-
Jews for Jesus	1994	-	-	2	-	1
Life in Messiah International	1940	-	-	3	4	-
Mennonite Mission Network	1953	-	1	1	1	-
Messianic Jewish Movement Intl., Inc., The		-	-	-	7	-
Missionary Ventures International	1997	-	-	-	2	-
New Life Advance International		-	-	-	-	-
Operation Mobilization		5	3	-	-	5
Precept Ministries International	1995	-	-	-	4	-
Reformed Baptist Mission Services		-	-	-	2	-
Remnant Ministries, Inc.	2000	-	-	2	-	-
Seventh-day Adventists, General Conference	1898	-	-	-	-	4
Tentmakers International	2005	-	-	-	1	-
The Master's Mission, Inc.	1990	-	-	-	2	-
United Pentecostal Church International		-	2	-	-	4
Venture International	1989	-	-	-	3	-
Walk Thru the Bible Ministries, Inc.		-	-	-	-	-
Totals:		14	7	85	59	29

Italy

	First Year	1-2 yrs.	2-4 yrs.	4+ yrs.	Citizens	Non-Citizens
Adventive Cross Cultural Initiatives—US	2004	-	-	-	2	-
American Baptist Chs. of the U.S.A., Intl.Mins.	1872	-	-	2	-	-
AMG International	2002	-	-	2	-	-
Assemblies of God World Missions	1908	1	-	10	-	-
Aurora Mission, Inc.	1998	4	9	2	-	-
Avant Ministries	1950	-	-	20	2	-
Baptist Bible Fellowship International	1978	-	-	4	-	-
Baptist International Missions, Inc. (BIMI)		-	-	4	-	-
Baptist Mid-Missions	1951	-	-	6	-	-
BCM International		-	-	4	-	-
Biblical Ministries Worldwide	1962	-	-	4	-	-
Brethren Assemblies		-	-	8	-	-
Cadence International	1980	-	2	-	-	-
Campus Crusade for Christ, Intl.	1969	25	-	13	-	-
Christian Associates International		-	-	-	-	-
Christian Churches/Churches of Christ		-	-	14	6	-
Church of God (Cleveland, Tenn.) World Missions	1959	-	-	2	-	2
Church of the Nazarene, World Msn. Dept.	1948	-	-	2	-	-
Church Resource Ministries (CRM)	2009	-	-	2	-	-
Churches of Christ	1948	-	-	8	-	-
CLC Ministries International	1956	-	-	2	-	-
CrossWorld	1974	1	-	16	-	1
Evangelical Baptist Missions		-	-	4	-	-
Every Home for Christ International	1958	-	-	-	-	-
Fellowship International Mission	2006	-	-	2	-	-
Foursquare Missions International	1993	-	-	2	-	-
Globe International	2002	-	-	2	-	-
Gospel Fellowship Association	1983	-	-	2	-	-

		Personnel from U.S.			Other Countries	
	First Year	1-2 yrs.	2-4 yrs.	4+ yrs.	Citizens	Non-Citizens
Great Commission Ministries, Inc.		1	-	7	-	-
Greater Europe Mission	1956	-	-	10	-	-
Greater Grace World Outreach	2007	-	-	-	-	2
IFCA World Missions	1927	-	-	1	-	-
International Gospel Outreach	2006	-	-	4	-	-
Intl. Pentecostal Holiness Ch. World Msns. Mins.	1987	-	-	-	-	-
International Teams, U.S.A.		2	-	-	-	-
Italy for Christ, Inc.	1983	-	-	5	-	-
Mission to the World (PCA), Inc.	1988	-	-	2	-	-
Navigators, U.S. International Missions Group		-	-	4	-	-
Operation Mobilization	1962	1	3	4	-	-
Precept Ministries International	2007	-	-	-	2	-
Presbyterian Mission International (PMI)	2003	-	-	-	1	1
Reformed Church in America, Gen. Synod	2004	-	1	-	-	-
Salvation Army, U.S.A.	1887	-	1	2	-	-
SIM USA, Inc.	1979	-	-	2	-	-
Spiritual Growth Resources, Inc.	1984	-	-	-	3	-
TEAM (The Evangelical Alliance Mission)		-	-	17	-	-
Team Expansion, Inc.	2000	-	-	17	-	-
United Pentecostal Church International	1959	-	1	-	-	-
Virginia Mennonite Missions	1949	2	4	2	-	-
WEC International	1964	-	-	6	-	-
Word of Life Fellowship, Inc.—Intl. Ministries	1985	-	-	-	4	1
World Harvest Mission	2000	-	-	2	-	-
World Link Ministries	2005	-	-	2	7	-
World Team	1997	-	-	7	-	-
World Venture	1947	1	3	14	-	-
Youth for Christ/USA—World Outreach		-	-	4	-	-
Totals:		38	24	249	27	7

Jamaica

Assemblies of God World Missions	1936	5	-	10	-	-
Awana International	1997	-	-	-	3	-
Back to the Bible International	1958	-	-	-	3	-
Baptist Bible Fellowship International	1972	-	-	4	-	-
Baptist International Missions, Inc. (BIMI)		-	-	4	-	-
Baptist Mid-Missions	1939	-	-	1	-	-
BCM International		-	-	3	-	-
Brethren Assemblies		-	-	2	-	-
Calvary International	1985	-	-	-	1	-
Campus Crusade for Christ, Intl.	1990	2	-	-	3	-
Christian Churches/Churches of Christ		-	-	12	6	-
Christian Relief Fund, The	1999	-	-	-	1	-
Church of the Nazarene, World Msn. Dept.	1966	-	-	-	-	-
Churches of Christ	1857	-	-	2	-	-
CSI Ministries	1979	-	-	7	12	-
Evangelical Lutheran Church in America	1990	-	-	2	-	-
Faith Christian Fellowship International	1989	-	-	2	18	-
Friends United Meeting		-	-	-	-	-
Global Outreach Mission, Inc.		-	-	2	-	-

	First Year	1-2 yrs.	2-4 yrs.	4+ yrs.	Citizens	Non-Citizens
		Personnel from U.S.			Other Countries	
GOGF Ministries	1998	-	-	-	1	-
Greater Grace World Outreach	1995	-	-	-	2	-
Intl. Pentecostal Holiness Ch. World Msns. Mins.		-	-	-	-	-
Lott Carey Baptist Foreign Msn. Conv.	1995	-	-	-	10	-
Lutheran Church-Missouri Synod, World Mission	1993	-	-	2	-	-
Macedonia World Baptist Missions, Inc.	1984	-	-	2	-	-
Medical Ministry International	1970	-	-	-	1	-
Ministries In Action	1974	-	-	2	2	-
National Baptist Convention of America	1945	-	-	-	38	-
Open Air Campaigners—Overseas Ministries	1984	-	-	-	2	-
Progressive National Baptist Convention, Inc.		-	-	-	-	-
Reformed Baptist Mission Services		-	-	-	2	-
Salvation Army, U.S.A.	1887	-	8	-	-	-
Seventh-day Adventists, General Conference	1893	-	-	12	-	-
Source of Light Ministries International, Inc.	1952	-	-	2	1	-
STEM International	1985	-	-	-	-	-
TEAMS for Medical Missions	1992	-	-	5	-	-
United Pentecostal Church International	1930	-	-	-	-	-
Virginia Mennonite Missions	1955	-	2	-	-	-
World Missions & Evangelism, Inc.		-	-	3	-	-
Totals:		7	10	79	106	-

Japan

	First Year	1-2 yrs.	2-4 yrs.	4+ yrs.	Citizens	Non-Citizens
Advancing Renewal Ministries, Inc.		-	-	2	2	-
American Baptist Chs. of the U.S.A., Intl.Mins.	1872	-	-	9	-	-
Apostolic Christian Church Foundation, Inc.	1985	-	-	-	-	-
Artists In Christian Testimony International	2005	-	-	-	1	2
Asian Access	1967	1	6	22	14	3
Asian Outreach U.S.A.		-	-	-	-	-
Assemblies of God World Missions	1913	16	-	37	-	-
Awana International	1983	-	-	-	3	-
Back to the Bible International	2004	-	-	-	1	-
Baptist Bible Fellowship International	1950	-	-	23	-	-
Baptist International Missions, Inc. (BIMI)		-	-	45	-	-
Baptist Mid-Missions	1949	-	-	8	3	-
Baptist Missionary Association of America	1951	-	-	-	1	-
Bethany International Ministries	1985	-	1	2	-	6
Biblical Ministries Worldwide	1987	-	-	2	-	-
BILD International		-	-	-	-	-
Brethren Assemblies		-	-	11	-	-
Cadence International	1960	3	2	9	-	-
Campus Crusade for Christ, Intl.	1962	13	-	18	42	50
Child Evangelism Fellowship, Inc.	1948	-	-	-	-	2
Christ Community Church	1951	-	-	-	2	-
Christar	1950	-	-	13	-	-
Christian Church (Disciples of Christ)		-	3	-	-	-
Christian Churches/Churches of Christ		-	4	30	-	-
Christian Reformed World Missions	1951	-	2	12	-	-
Christians In Action Missions International	1957	-	-	-	-	6
Church of God (Anderson, Ind.), Global Msns.	1908	-	2	6	-	-

		Personnel from U.S.			Other Countries	
	First Year	1-2 yrs.	2-4 yrs.	4+ yrs.	Citizens	Non-Citizens
Church of God of Prophecy—Global Outreach		-	-	2	-	-
Ch. of the Brethren—Global Msn. Partnerships	1981	2	-	-	-	-
Church of the Nazarene, World Msn. Dept.	1905	-	-	2	-	-
Church Resource Ministries (CRM)	1998	-	-	4	-	-
Churches of Christ	1888	-		16	-	-
Converge Worldwide	1948	-	-	10	-	-
Equip International	1997	-	-	1	-	-
Evangelical Baptist Missions		-	-	4	-	-
Evangelical Covenant Ch.—Covenant Wld. Msn.	1949	-	-	10	-	-
Evangelical Lutheran Church in America	1892	-	13	13	2	-
Every Home for Christ International	1953	-	-	-	-	-
Fellowship International Mission	1975	-	-	1	2	3
Foursquare Missions International	1951	-	-	4	-	-
Free Will Baptist, Inc. Bd. of Intl. Missions	1954	-	4	10	-	-
Global Partners/Wesleyan World Missions	1949	-	-	-	-	-
Gospel Fellowship Association	1958	-	-	1	-	-
Grace Brethren International Missions	1984	-	2	2	2	-
Hope for the Hungry	1981	-	-	1	-	-
International Institute for Christian Studies	2004	-	-	1	-	1
Intl. Pentecostal Holiness Ch. World Msns. Mins.	1989	-	-	4	-	-
International Teams, U.S.A.		-	-	-	-	8
Japanese Evangelical Missionary Society	1953	2	3	2	1	-
Liberty Corner Mission	1951	-	-	1	-	6
Liebenzell Mission of USA, Inc.	1927	-	-	-	-	-
Life in Messiah International	1993	-	-	2	2	-
Lutheran Brethren World Missions	1949	-	-	4	-	-
Lutheran Church-Missouri Synod, World Mission	1948	-	9	7	-	-
Macedonia World Baptist Missions, Inc.	2005	-	-	2	-	-
Mennonite Mission Network	1949	-	-	3	-	-
Mission to the World (PCA), Inc.	1985	-	5	36	-	-
Mission To Unreached Peoples	1990	-	-	5	-	-
Navigators, U.S. International Missions Group		-	12	24	-	-
Network of International Christian Schools	2000	6	2	9	2	2
New Life Advance International		-	-	-	-	-
N. Am. Baptist Conf.—Worldwide Outreach	1951	-	-	9	-	-
OC International, Inc.	1985	-	-	2	-	-
OMF International	1950	2	-	25	-	27
OMS International, Inc.	1922	-	-	12	-	3
OneHope		-	-	-	-	-
Open Door Baptist Missions	2008	-	-	1	-	-
Orthodox Presbyterian Church	1938	-	-	6	-	-
Pioneers USA		-	-	8	1	-
Presbyterian Mission International (PMI)	1993	-	-	-	1	1
Project AmaZon	1987	-	-	2	-	-
ReachGlobal	1949	-	-	19	-	-
Reformed Church in America, Gen. Synod	1987	-	-	6	-	-
Reformed Presbyterian Global Missions	1954	-	-	1	3	-
Resourcing Christian Education International		-	-	-	16	4
SEED International	2003	-	-	2	-	-
SEND International USA	1948	-	-	46	-	6

	First Year	1-2 yrs.	2-4 yrs.	4+ yrs.	Citizens	Non-Citizens
		Personnel from U.S.			Other Countries	
Seventh-day Adventists, General Conference	1896	2	1	3	1	-
Source of Light Ministries International, Inc.	2000	-	-	-	2	-
TEAM (The Evangelical Alliance Mission)		-	-	66	-	-
The Mission Society	1997	-	-	2	-	-
United Pentecostal Church International	1900	-	8	-	-	4
University Bible Fellowship	2009	-	-	-	-	2
Walk Thru the Bible Ministries, Inc.	2002	-	-	-	1	-
White Fields, Inc.		-	-	-	7	-
Wisconsin Evangelical Lutheran Synod	1952	-	-	3	-	-
Word of Life Fellowship, Inc.—Intl. Ministries	1981	-	-	2	7	-
World Gospel Mission	1952	-	-	4	-	-
World Venture	1947	2	3	15	-	-
Youth for Christ/USA—World Outreach		-	-	1	-	-
Totals:		49	82	665	119	136

Java

	First Year	1-2 yrs.	2-4 yrs.	4+ yrs.	Citizens	Non-Citizens
TEAM (The Evangelical Alliance Mission)		-	-	2	-	-
Totals:		-	-	2	-	-

Jordan

	First Year	1-2 yrs.	2-4 yrs.	4+ yrs.	Citizens	Non-Citizens
	-					
Anis Shorrosh Evangelistic Association		-	-	40	-	-
Assemblies of God World Missions	1920	5	-	9	-	-
Avant Ministries		-	-	2	-	-
Calvary International	1992	-	-	-	-	-
Child Evangelism Fellowship, Inc.	1991	-	-	-	2	-
Christar	1990	-	-	13	5	-
Christian Aid Mission		-	-	-	77	-
Christian Blind Mission International (CBM-US)	1990	-	1	-	-	-
Church of the Nazarene, World Msn. Dept.	1950	-	-	3	-	-
Churches of Christ	1963	-	-	-	-	-
Global Outreach Mission, Inc.		-	-	3	-	-
Habitat for Humanity International	2002	-	1	-	-	1
Interserve USA (International Service Fellowship)	1951	-	-	4	-	-
Medical Ministry International	2005	-	-	-	-	1
Partners International	1997	-	-	3	173	-
United Pentecostal Church International	1955	-	2	-	-	-
Venture International	1998	-	-	-	2	-
Walk Thru the Bible Ministries, Inc.	2000	-	-	-	-	-
World Bible Translation Center		-	-	-	2	-
World Venture	1956	-	-	4	-	-
World-Wide Missions	1987	-	-	-	1	-
Totals:		5	4	81	262	2

Kazakhstan

	First Year	1-2 yrs.	2-4 yrs.	4+ yrs.	Citizens	Non-Citizens
Advancing Renewal Ministries, Inc.		-	-	4	4	-
All God's Children International		-	-	-	12	-
Assemblies of God World Missions	1991	1	-	2	-	-
Awana International	1992	-	-	-	1	-
Baptist International Evangelistic Ministries		-	-	-	-	-
Baptist Missionary Association of America	1994	-	-	-	11	-

	First Year	Personnel from U.S. 1-2 yrs.	2-4 yrs.	4+ yrs.	Other Countries Citizens	Non-Citizens
Christar	1991	-	-	8	-	2
Christian Aid Mission		-	-	-	31	-
Christian Broadcasting Network Inc., The	1995	-	-	-	2	-
Church of God of Prophecy—Global Outreach		-	-	-	1	-
Church of the Nazarene, World Msn. Dept.	1996	-	-	-	-	-
East-West Ministries International	1995	-	-	8	1	-
Evangelism Explosion International		-	-	-	-	2
Faith Life Ministries, Inc.	2002	-	-	-	-	-
Greater Grace World Outreach	2001	-	-	2	2	7
International Institute for Christian Studies		-	-	1	-	1
Mission To Unreached Peoples	2003	-	-	-	-	-
OMS International, Inc.	2003	-	-	1	-	1
People International USA	1991	-	-	6	-	5
SEND International USA	2006	-	-	8	-	-
Seventh-day Adventists, General Conference	1886	-	-	2	-	2
Tentmakers International	2005	-	-	-	1	-
The Master's Mission, Inc.	1993	-	-	2	-	-
The Mission Society	1993	3	6	6	-	-
United Pentecostal Church International		-	1	-	-	-
United World Mission		-	-	4	-	-
Walk Thru the Bible Ministries, Inc.		-	-	-	-	-
Totals:		4	7	54	66	20

Kenya

	First Year	1-2 yrs.	2-4 yrs.	4+ yrs.	Citizens	Non-Citizens
ACM International	1996	-	-	5	-	-
Adventures in Missions	1999	1	-	3	-	-
AEGA Ministries International, Inc.		-	-	-	-	1
Africa Inland Mission International, Inc.	1895	20	6	270	-	69
African Children's Mission, Inc.	1989	-	-	-	-	-
African Enterprise	1970	-	-	-	9	-
African Leadership, Inc.	2000	-	-	-	2	-
Artists In Christian Testimony International	2006	-	-	2	-	-
Assemblies of God World Missions	1967	4	-	32	-	-
Awana International	1992	-	-	-	4	-
Baptist Bible Fellowship International	1971	-	-	34	-	-
Baptist International Missions, Inc. (BIMI)		-	-	4	-	-
Baptist Mid-Missions	2006	-	-	2	2	-
Bethany International Ministries	1999	-	-	2	-	-
Brethren Assemblies		-	-	1	-	-
Bright Hope International	1990	-	-	-	5	-
Campus Crusade for Christ, Intl.	1972	2	-	6	132	-
Child Evangelism Fellowship, Inc.	1966	-	-	5	27	-
Childcare Worldwide	1984	-	-	-	60	-
Christian Aid Mission	1985	-	-	-	2000	-
Christian Blind Mission International (CBM-US)	1971	1	1	-	-	-
Christian Church (Disciples of Christ)		-	1	-	-	-
Christian Churches/Churches of Christ		2	3	35	8	-
Christian Reformed World Relief Committee	1983	-	-	1	-	-
Christian Relief Fund, The	1994	-	-	-	5	-
Church of God (Anderson, Ind.), Global Msns.	1922	-	2	7	-	-

		Personnel from U.S.			Other Countries	
	First Year	1-2 yrs.	2-4 yrs.	4+ yrs.	Citizens	Non-Citizens
Church of God (Cleveland, Tenn.) World Missions	1977	-	-	9	-	4
Church of God of Prophecy—Global Outreach		-	-	-	14	-
Church of the Nazarene, World Msn. Dept.	1984	-	-	20	-	-
Churches of Christ	1965	-	-	17	-	-
CMF International	1977	-	-	27	2	-
Commission to Every Nation	2009	-	-	-	-	2
Compassion International, Inc.	1980	-	-	-	79	-
Cooperative Baptist Fellowship—Global Missions	1999	-	-	2	-	-
CrossWorld		-	-	2	-	-
Daystar U.S.	1988	-	-	4	-	-
Eastern Mennonite Missions	1964	-	4	4	-	-
East-West Ministries International	2002	-	-	2	-	-
Elim Fellowship—International Ministries	1940	-	-	13	-	-
Empowering Lives International	1995	-	3	2	67	1
Entrust	2004	-	-	-	2	-
Equip International	1998	-	-	-	2	-
Evangel Bible Translators		-	-	-	2	-
Evangelical Congregational Church		-	-	5	-	-
Evangelical Covenant Ch.—Covenant Wld. Msn.	1998	-	-	-	-	-
Evangelical Lutheran Church in America	1969	-	-	4	-	1
Every Home for Christ International	1963	-	-	-	1	-
Faith Christian Fellowship International	1996	-	-	2	13	-
Faith Life Ministries, Inc.	2005	-	-	-	-	-
Fellowship International Mission	2000	-	-	2	-	-
Food for the Hungry, Inc.	1976	-	4	1	-	-
Friends United Meeting		1	1	1	1	-
Full Gospel Evangelistic Association	2000	-	-	1	2	-
Global Outreach International	2002	-	-	7	-	-
Global Partners/Wesleyan World Missions	1997	-	2	-	-	-
Global Recordings Network		-	-	6	6	-
Globe International	1987	-	-	2	-	-
Gospel Operation Intl. for Chinese Christians	2008	-	-	-	1	-
Greater Grace World Outreach	2005	-	-	-	15	-
Habitat for Humanity International	1985	-	1	-	-	1
Harvest	2001	-	-	-	3	-
Harvest International, Inc.	2005	-	2	-	-	-
Have Christ Will Travel Ministries, Inc.	2001	-	-	2	12	-
Heart of the Bride Ministries		2	-	-	-	-
HIS Servants Ministries	1995	-	-	-	-	-
Hope for the Hungry	1985	-	-	-	1	-
Independent Faith Mission, Inc.	1980	-	-	6	-	-
International Christian Ministries	1986	-	-	2	-	-
International Gospel Outreach	1986	-	-	4	6	2
International Justice Mission	2001	-	-	-	14	-
International Pentecostal Church of Christ	1940	2	1	3	-	-
Intl. Pentecostal Holiness Ch. World Msns. Mins.	1972	-	-	6	2	-
International Teams, U.S.A.		-	-	2	-	7
InterVarsity Christian Fellowship/USA, Msns. Dept.		-	-	1	-	-
Ireland Outreach International Inc.	2004	-	-	-	-	-
Kids Alive International	2000	-	-	-	68	1

	Personnel from U.S.			Other Countries	
First Year	1-2 yrs.	2-4 yrs.	4+ yrs.	Citizens	Non-Citizens
LifeWind International	1987	-	-	6	50	-
Living Hope Ministries International, Inc.	2001	-	-	-	-	-
Living Water International		-	-	-	-	-
Lott Carey Baptist Foreign Msn. Conv.	1985	-	-	-	50	-
Lutheran Church-Missouri Synod, World Mission	1999	-	-	2	-	-
M/E International, Inc.	2002	-	-	-	-	-
Macedonia World Baptist Missions, Inc.	2008	-	-	2	-	-
Mailbox Club International Inc., The		-	-	-	1	-
MAP International	1987	-	-	-	21	1
Mission ONE, Inc.		-	-	-	42	-
Mission to the World (PCA), Inc.	1977	-	-	2	-	-
Mission: Moving Mountains, Inc.	1985	-	-	16	13	6
Missions Door	1999	-	-	1	-	-
Moravian Church in N. Am., Bd. of World Msn.		-	-	-	-	-
Navigators, U.S. International Missions Group		-	-	2	-	-
Network of International Christian Schools	2003	23	5	2	3	4
New Directions International, Inc.	1984	-	-	-	21	-
OC International, Inc.	1985	-	-	6	-	-
OneHope		-	-	-	-	-
Orthodox Presbyterian Church	1980	-	-	-	-	-
Partners International	1972	-	-	-	65	-
Partners Worldwide		-	-	-	-	-
Pioneers USA		-	-	7	-	-
Prayer Baptist Missions International, Inc.		-	-	-	4	-
Precept Ministries International	1994	-	-	-	-	-
Presbyterian Mission International (PMI)	1989	-	-	-	1	1
Progressive National Baptist Convention, Inc.		-	-	-	-	-
ReachGlobal	1996	-	-	8	-	-
Reformed Baptist Mission Services		-	-	-	-	2
Reformed Church in America, Gen. Synod	1985	-	-	7	2	-
Salvation Army, U.S.A.	1921	-	4	1	-	-
Samaritan's Purse International Relief	1995	5	1	2	-	-
SEED International	2000	-	-	1	-	-
Seventh-day Adventists, General Conference	1906	-	-	21	-	31
Share International	1996	-	-	-	-	-
SIM USA, Inc.	1977	4	-	21	-	-
Source of Light Ministries International, Inc.	1991	-	-	2	1	-
Tentmakers International	2007	-	-	-	1	-
The God's Story Project	2005	-	-	-	3	-
The Master's Mission, Inc.	1979	-	-	20	2	2
Things To Come Mission, Inc.	1984	-	-	-	-	3
United Pentecostal Church International	1972	-	4	-	-	1
United World Mission		-	-	5	-	-
Walk Thru the Bible Ministries, Inc.	1999	-	-	-	2	-
Warm Blankets Orphan Care International	2007	-	-	-	4	-
Women to the World, Inc.	2005	-	-	-	6	-
Word of Life Fellowship, Inc.—Intl. Ministries	1970	-	-	-	41	-
World Concern	1984	3	1	3	66	-
World Gospel Mission	1932	-	-	46	-	-
World Harvest Mission	1990	-	-	6	-	-

	Personnel from U.S.				Other Countries	
	First Year	1-2 yrs.	2-4 yrs.	4+ yrs.	Citizens	Non-Citizens
World Mission Prayer League	1968	-	-	3	-	1
World Missions & Evangelism, Inc.		-	-	10	-	4
World Missions Far Corners, Inc.	1980	-	-	-	6	-
World Orphans	2008	-	-	-	1	-
World Reach, Inc.	1983	-	-	-	11	-
World Relief	1998	-	-	-	11	1
World Servants	1991	-	-	-	-	2
World Venture	1972	-	4	11	-	-
World-Wide Missions	1963	-	-	-	2	-
Wycliffe Bible Translators, Inc.		-	-	30	-	-
Youth for Christ/USA—World Outreach		-	-	3	-	-
Youth Ministry International (YMI)	1997	-	-	4	-	-
	Totals:	70	50	818	2997	148

Kiribati

Assemblies of God World Missions	1989	-	-	1	-	-
Churches of Christ	1993	-	-	-	-	-
LifeWind International	2004	-	-	-	-	-
	Totals:	-	-	1	-	

Korea, North

Calvary International	2004	-	-	-	1	-
Churches of Christ	1920	-	-	-	-	-
Seventh-day Adventists, General Conference		-	-	2	-	-
	Totals:	-	-	2	1	-

Korea, South

Assemblies of God World Missions	1928	2	-	4	-	-
Awana International	1983	-	-	-	7	-
Baptist Bible Fellowship International	1958	-	5	11	-	-
Baptist Missionary Association of America	1979	-	-	-	4	-
Brethren Assemblies		-	-	2	-	-
Cadence International	1975	-	-	4	-	-
Campus Crusade for Christ, Intl.	1958	-	-	-	827	1
Christian Churches/Churches of Christ		-	-	4	6	-
Christians In Action Missions International	1957	-	-	-	2	-
Church of God of Prophecy—Global Outreach		-	-	-	2	-
Church of the Nazarene, World Msn. Dept.	1948	-	-	6	-	-
Churches of Christ	1963	-	-	5	-	-
Evangelical Lutheran Church in America	1961	-	2	-	-	-
Evangelistic Faith Missions	1971	-	-	-	-	-
Faith Christian Fellowship International		-	-	1	1	-
Far East Broadcasting Company, Inc.	1976	-	-	1	150	-
Global Partners/Wesleyan World Missions	1982	-	-	-	-	-
Global Recordings Network		-	-	-	8	-
Go Ye Fellowship	1994	-	-	1	-	-
Gospel Fellowship Association	1967	1	-	4	-	-
Gospel Operation Intl. for Chinese Christians	2004	-	-	-	5	-
Greater Grace World Outreach	2002	1	1	3	-	-
Independent Faith Mission, Inc.	1992	-	-	2	-	-

	Personnel from U.S.			Other Countries	
	First Year	1-2 yrs.	2-4 yrs.	4+ yrs.	Citizens	Non-Citizens
International Gospel Outreach	1998	-	-	-	2	-
Intl. Pentecostal Holiness Ch. World Msns. Mins.		-	-	-	-	-
Macedonia World Baptist Missions, Inc.	2002	-	-	2	-	-
Mennonite Mission Network	1983	-	1	-	-	-
Mission to the World (PCA), Inc.		-	-	2	-	-
Mission To Unreached Peoples	2002	-	-	-	-	-
Network of International Christian Schools	1983	72	28	54	12	15
OMS International, Inc.	1907	-	-	2	-	-
Orthodox Presbyterian Church	1946	-	-	-	-	-
Precept Ministries International	1987	-	-	-	13	-
Reformed Church in America, Gen. Synod		-	-	-	1	-
Seventh-day Adventists, General Conference	1904	53	22	10	-	3
SIM USA, Inc.		-	-	2	-	-
Source of Light Ministries International, Inc.	1985	-	-	-	2	-
Tentmakers International	1994	-	-	-	1	-
U.S. Center for World Mission		-	-	1	-	1
United Pentecostal Church International	1985	-	1	-	-	-
University Bible Fellowship	1998	2	-	1	-	-
Walk Thru the Bible Ministries, Inc.	2000	-	-	-	4	-
Westminster Biblical Missions	1973	-	-	1	15	-
Word of Life Fellowship, Inc.—Intl. Ministries	1989	-	-	10	9	-
World Missions Far Corners, Inc.	2000	-	-	-	4	-
Totals:		131	60	133	1075	20

Kosovo

	First Year	1-2 yrs.	2-4 yrs.	4+ yrs.	Citizens	Non-Citizens
Assemblies of God World Missions	1999	4	-	4	-	-
Bethany International Ministries	1999	2	-	1	-	1
Christian Churches/Churches of Christ		-	-	2	1	-
Church of the Nazarene, World Msn. Dept.	2005	-	-	-	-	-
CrossWorld	2002	-	-	6	-	-
Eastern European Outreach, Inc.	1999	-	-	2	2	-
Eastern Mennonite Missions	2004	-	2	2	-	-
European Christian Mission International—USA		-	-	1	2	1
Every Home for Christ International	2004	-	-	-	-	-
Global Outreach Mission, Inc.		-	-	1	-	-
Greater Europe Mission	1974	-	1	2	-	-
International Teams, U.S.A.		-	-	2	-	-
LifeWind International	2003	-	-	-	-	-
Paraclete Mission Group, Inc.	2003	-	-	2	-	-
Pioneers USA		-	-	2	-	-
Samaritan's Purse International Relief	1999	1	-	-	-	-
SEND International USA	1999	-	-	2	-	-
World Relief	2000	-	1	-	14	-
World Servants	1999	-	-	-	-	1
Totals:		7	4	29	19	3

Kuwait

	First Year	1-2 yrs.	2-4 yrs.	4+ yrs.	Citizens	Non-Citizens
Seventh-day Adventists, General Conference	1978	-	-	-	-	2
Walk Thru the Bible Ministries, Inc.	2002	-	-	-	-	-
Totals:		-	-	-	-	2

		Personnel from U.S.			Other Countries	
	First Year	1-2 yrs.	2-4 yrs.	4+ yrs.	Citizens	Non-Citizens
Kyrgyzstan						
Assemblies of God World Missions	1995	4	-	10	-	-
Baptist International Evangelistic Ministries		-	-	-	-	-
Baptist Missionary Association of America	1994	-	-	-	5	-
Christian Aid Mission		-	-	-	8	-
Evangelism Explosion International		-	-	-	-	2
Gospel Operation Intl. for Chinese Christians	2001	-	-	2	-	-
Greater Grace World Outreach	1999	-	-	2	4	3
People International USA	1991	-	-	3	-	2
Venture International	1992	-	-	-	17	-
Totals:		4	-	17	34	7
Laos						
Advancing Renewal Ministries, Inc.		-	-	2	-	-
American Baptist Chs. of the U.S.A., Intl.Mins.	2000	-	-	2	-	-
Assemblies of God World Missions	1990	2	-	4	-	1
Baptist Missionary Association of America	2007	-	-	-	-	1
Christian Aid Mission		-	-	-	63	-
Christian Church (Disciples of Christ)		-	1	-	-	-
Christian Reformed World Relief Committee	1997	-	1	-	-	-
Churches of Christ	1991	-	-	4	-	-
Food for the Hungry, Inc.	1998	-	-	-	-	-
Globe International	2005	-	-	2	-	-
LifeWind International	2003	-	-	-	-	-
Seventh-day Adventists, General Conference	1919	-	-	-	-	2
Tribes and Nations Outreach		-	-	-	-	-
United Pentecostal Church International		-	-	-	-	-
World Concern	1990	-	-	-	29	1
Totals:		2	2	14	92	4
Latin America—General						
Assemblies of God World Missions	1910	3	-	81	-	-
Campus Crusade for Christ, Intl.		-	-	-	4	-
Christian and Missionary Alliance, The		-	-	144	-	-
Cook Communications Ministries International	1993	-	-	-	-	-
Dawn Ministries, Inc.		-	-	-	-	1
Faith Comes By Hearing/Hosanna	1987	-	-	4	-	-
Fellowship of Companies for Christ Intl. (FCCI)	2005	-	-	-	1	-
Final Frontiers Foundation, Inc.	1989	-	-	-	180	-
Gideons International, The		-	-	-	17	-
Global Action	1998	-	-	2	-	-
Global Youth Ministry Network		-	-	-	-	1
Heifer Project International	1944	-	-	-	-	-
Help for Christian Nationals, Inc.	1982	-	-	2	-	-
International Cooperating Ministries (ICM)		-	-	-	-	-
Luis Palau Evangelistic Association	1978	-	-	13	10	3
Mennonite Central Committee (MCC)		-	-	181	-	-
New Mission Systems International		-	14	6	2	18
Operation Mobilization		-	-	6	-	-
Presbyterian Church (USA), Worldwide Ministries		-	90	88	-	-

		Personnel from U.S.			Other Countries	
	First Year	1-2 yrs.	2-4 yrs.	4+ yrs.	Citizens	Non-Citizens
RBC Ministries	1985	-	-	-	47	-
Ripe for Harvest, Inc.	1985	1	2	8	-	-
Virginia Mennonite Missions	2007	2	-	-	-	-
Young Life		7	4	10	-	-
Youth With A Mission (YWAM)		-	303	-	1668	-
Totals:		13	413	545	1929	23

Latvia

Assemblies of God World Missions	1926	-	-	3	-	-
Awana International	2000	-	-	-	1	-
Baptist International Missions, Inc. (BIMI)		-	-	4	-	-
Bridge Builders International	1994	-	-	6	1	5
Calvary International	1989	-	-	1	1	-
Campus Crusade for Christ, Intl.	1991	-	-	8	19	-
Christian Associates International	1992	-	-	-	-	-
Churches of Christ	1991	-	-	-	-	-
Faith Life Ministries, Inc.	2002	-	-	-	-	-
Greater Europe Mission	1992	6	-	4	-	-
Mission to the World (PCA), Inc.		-	4	2	-	-
United Pentecostal Church International		-	-	-	-	4
Walk Thru the Bible Ministries, Inc.	2000	-	-	-	1	-
World Baptist Fellowship Msn. Agency, Inc.	1999	-	-	2	-	-
Totals:		6	4	30	23	9

Lebanon

American Baptist Chs. of the U.S.A., Intl.Mins.	1998	-	-	-	-	2
AMG International		-	-	-	4	-
Artists In Christian Testimony International	2006	-	-	-	-	1
Assemblies of God World Missions	1925	1	-	8	-	-
Baptist Missionary Association of America	1993	-	-	-	10	-
Campus Crusade for Christ, Intl.	1968	-	-	-	18	2
Christian Aid Mission		-	-	-	20	-
Church of the Nazarene, World Msn. Dept.	1950	-	-	2	-	-
Churches of Christ	1961	-	-	-	-	-
Evangelical Lutheran Church in America	1969	1	-	-	-	-
International Partnership Ministries, Inc.	1998	-	-	-	4	-
Kids Alive International	1948	-	4	-	22	4
Mennonite Mission Network	1967	-	2	-	-	-
Mutual Faith Ministries Intl.		-	-	-	-	-
Seventh-day Adventists, General Conference	1970	-	-	-	-	4
United Pentecostal Church International	1992	-	2	-	-	2
Venture International	1987	-	-	-	2	-
Walk Thru the Bible Ministries, Inc.	2002	-	-	-	-	-
World Venture	1993	-	3	2	-	-
Totals:		2	11	12	80	15

Lesotho

Africa Inland Mission International, Inc.	1986	-	-	3	-	11
Africa Inter-Mennonite Mission International	1972	-	-	-	-	-
Assemblies of God World Missions	1950	-	-	2	-	-

	Personnel from U.S.				Other Countries	
	First Year	1-2 yrs.	2-4 yrs.	4+ yrs.	Citizens	Non-Citizens
Campus Crusade for Christ, Intl.	1979	-	-	-	10	-
Christian Church (Disciples of Christ)		-	1	-	-	-
Church of the Nazarene, World Msn. Dept.	1993	-	-	2	-	-
Churches of Christ	1962	-	-	-	-	-
Every Home for Christ International	1985	-	-	-	1	-
Habitat for Humanity International	1986	-	1	-	-	1
Intl. Pentecostal Holiness Ch. World Msns. Mins.		-	-	-	-	-
Mission Aviation Fellowship	1980	-	-	13	-	-
National Baptist Convention USA, Inc.	1961	-	-	-	-	-
OneHope		-	-	-	-	-
Seventh-day Adventists, General Conference	1899	-	1	2	-	2
United Pentecostal Church International	1996	-	2	-	-	-
Walk Thru the Bible Ministries, Inc.	1999	-	-	-	1	-
Totals:		-	5	22	12	14

Liberia

	First Year	1-2 yrs.	2-4 yrs.	4+ yrs.	Citizens	Non-Citizens
African Leadership, Inc.	2003	-	-	-	1	-
Assemblies of God World Missions	1908	-	-	-	-	-
Awana International	1980	-	-	-	1	-
Baptist Mid-Missions	1938	-	-	2	-	-
Baptist Missionary Association of America	2000	-	-	-	33	-
Campus Crusade for Christ, Intl.	1979	-	-	-	26	-
Carver International Missions, Inc.	1955	1	-	5	3	-
Child Evangelism Fellowship, Inc.	1955	-	-	-	7	-
Childcare Worldwide	2003	-	-	-	-	-
Children's Christian Concern Society	1998	-	-	-	-	-
Christian Aid Ministries (CAM)	1995	1	6	3	40	-
Christian Aid Mission	1998	-	-	-	60	-
Christian Churches/Churches of Christ		-	-	2	-	-
Christian Relief Fund, The	1997	-	-	-	1	-
Church of God (Cleveland, Tenn.) World Missions	1974	-	-	-	-	4
Church of God of Prophecy—Global Outreach		-	-	-	6	-
Church of the Nazarene, World Msn. Dept.	1990	-	-	-	-	-
Churches of Christ	1850	-	-	-	-	-
Commission to Every Nation	2007	-	-	-	2	-
Development Associates International (DAI)		-	-	-	1	-
Equip International	1997	-	1	-	-	-
Evangel Bible Translators	1986	-	-	1	1	-
Evangelical Lutheran Church in America	1862	1	-	1	-	-
Every Home for Christ International	2001	-	-	-	1	-
Free Methodist World Missions	1996	-	-	2	-	-
Global Partners/Wesleyan World Missions	1978	-	-	-	-	-
Global Recordings Network		-	-	6	6	-
Greater Grace World Outreach	1987	-	-	-	37	-
Have Christ Will Travel Ministries, Inc.	1966	-	-	-	35	-
International Gospel Outreach	1988	-	-	1	-	-
International Partnership Ministries, Inc.	1997	-	-	-	21	-
Intl. Pentecostal Holiness Ch. World Msns. Mins.		-	-	-	-	-
Kids for Christ International	2009	-	-	-	-	-
Living Water International		-	-	-	-	-

	First Year	Personnel from U.S. 1-2 yrs.	2-4 yrs.	4+ yrs.	Other Countries Citizens	Non-Citizens
Lott Carey Baptist Foreign Msn. Conv.	1908	-	-	-	100	-
Lutheran Bible Translators, Inc.	1969	-	-	-	27	-
M/E International, Inc.	2002	-	-	-	-	-
Medical Teams International	2003	-	-	-	1	3
Missions Door	2003	-	-	-	3	-
Reformed Episcopal Bd. of Foreign Msns.		-	-	-	8	-
Salvation Army, U.S.A.	1988	-	2	-	-	-
Samaritan's Purse International Relief	2003	11	-	-	-	-
Seventh-day Adventists, General Conference	1927	-	-	-	-	2
SIM USA, Inc.	1952	1	-	3	-	-
Source of Light Ministries International, Inc.	1979	-	-	-	1	-
United Pentecostal Church International	1924	-	2	-	-	-
Walk Thru the Bible Ministries, Inc.	2004	-	-	-	1	-
World Relief	2000	-	-	-	-	1
World-Wide Missions	1961	-	-	-	4	-
Totals:		15	11	26	427	10

Libya

Christian Aid Mission	2005	-	-	-	13	-
Churches of Christ	1960	-	-	-	-	-
Totals:		-	-	-	13	-

Lithuania

Assemblies of God World Missions	1992	-	-	8	-	-
Baptist Bible Fellowship International	1991	-	-	2	-	-
Campus Crusade for Christ, Intl.	1991	-	-	5	9	-
Christ to the Nations	1989	-	-	-	6	2
Christian Relief Fund, The	1996	-	-	-	-	-
Churches of Christ	1991	-	-	6	-	-
Eastern Mennonite Missions	1994	-	-	2	-	-
Greater Grace World Outreach	1996	-	1	-	1	-
International Institute for Christian Studies	2003	-	2	1	-	3
Mennonite Mission Network	1995	-	-	3	-	-
Open Door Baptist Missions	1992	-	-	2	-	-
Pioneers USA		-	-	2	1	-
United Pentecostal Church International		-	-	-	-	7
Walk Thru the Bible Ministries, Inc.	2001	-	-	-	-	-
Word of Life Fellowship, Inc.—Intl. Ministries		-	-	-	-	1
World Venture	1997	-	4	2	-	-
Totals:		-	7	33	17	13

Luxembourg

Abundant Life Association, Inc.	2006	-	-	-	4	-
Assemblies of God World Missions	1981	-	-	2	-	-
Baptist Mid-Missions	1986	-	-	2	-	-
Biblical Ministries Worldwide	1972	-	-	2	-	-
Totals:		-	-	6	4	-

Macau

Campus Crusade for Christ, Intl.	1975	-	-	-	32	1

	First Year	Personnel from U.S.			Other Countries	
		1-2 yrs.	2-4 yrs.	4+ yrs.	Citizens	Non-Citizens
Child Evangelism Fellowship, Inc.	2000	-	-	-	1	-
Christians In Action Missions International	1973	-	-	1	1	-
Eastern Mennonite Missions		-	-	-	-	-
Global Mins., Ch. of the United Brethren in Christ		-	-	-	-	-
Lutheran Church-Missouri Synod, World Mission	1988	-	-	3	-	-
Mennonite Mission Network	1995	-	-	-	-	4
ReachGlobal	1993	-	-	-	-	-
Tribes and Nations Outreach		-	-	-	-	-
World Venture	1986	-	-	9	-	-
World-Wide Missions		-	-	1	-	-
	Totals:	-	-	14	34	5
Macedonia						
Assemblies of God World Missions	1991	-	-	2	-	-
Campus Crusade for Christ, Intl.	1996	8	-	4	7	2
Church of the Nazarene, World Msn. Dept.	2000	-	-	1	-	1
Cooperative Baptist Fellowship—Global Missions	1998	-	-	2	-	-
Macedonia World Baptist Missions, Inc.	2002	-	-	2	-	-
Mission To Unreached Peoples	2004	-	-	2	-	-
Precept Ministries International		-	-	-	-	-
SEND International USA	1993	-	-	15	-	-
Tentmakers International	2005	-	-	-	1	-
United Pentecostal Church International		-	1	-	-	-
	Totals:	8	1	28	8	3
Madagascar						
Africa Inland Mission International, Inc.	1979	-	-	4	-	22
Assemblies of God World Missions	1990	2	-	8	-	-
Campus Crusade for Christ, Intl.	1979	-	-	-	33	4
Child Evangelism Fellowship, Inc.	1988	-	-	-	19	-
Christian Blind Mission International (CBM-US)	1982	-	1	-	-	-
Church of the Nazarene, World Msn. Dept.	1993	-	-	4	-	-
Churches of Christ	1971	-	-	2	-	-
Evangelical Lutheran Church in America	1888	-	1	5	-	-
Every Home for Christ International	2000	-	-	-	1	-
Global Health Ministries	2007	-	-	-	1	-
Helimission, Inc.—USA		-	-	-	-	4
IFCA World Missions		-	-	-	1	-
OneHope		-	-	-	-	-
Seventh-day Adventists, General Conference	1926	-	-	2	-	15
Teen Missions International, Inc.	1997	-	-	-	15	-
Tentmakers International	2008	-	-	-	1	-
United Pentecostal Church International	1970	-	2	-	-	1
World Venture	1966	-	5	5	-	-
	Totals:	2	9	30	71	46
Malawi						
Action International Ministries, Inc.	2006	-	-	2	-	-
African Bible Colleges, Inc.	1988	8	4	14	25	-
African Enterprise	1982	-	-	-	6	-
African Leadership, Inc.	2001	-	-	-	2	-

	Personnel from U.S.				Other Countries	
	First Year	1-2 yrs.	2-4 yrs.	4+ yrs.	Citizens	Non-Citizens
Assemblies of God World Missions	1944	4	-	7	-	-
Awana International	1998	-	-	-	2	-
Baptist International Missions, Inc. (BIMI)		-	-	1	-	-
Brethren in Christ World Missions	1983	-	-	6	-	-
Bright Hope International	2004	-	-	-	1	-
Campus Crusade for Christ, Intl.	1979	-	-	-	10	-
Child Evangelism Fellowship, Inc.	1988	-	-	-	2	-
Christian Aid Mission	1986	-	-	-	30	-
Christian Reformed World Relief Committee	1989	-	-	2	-	-
Christian Relief Fund, The	1978	-	-	-	1	-
Church of God (Anderson, Ind.), Global Msns.	1992	-	-	1	-	-
Church of God of Prophecy—Global Outreach		-	-	-	1	-
Church of the Nazarene, World Msn. Dept.	1957	-	-	5	-	1
Churches of Christ	1906	-	-	2	-	-
Emmanuel International Mission	1976	-	-	1	1	8
Equip International	2009	-	-	1	-	-
EurAsian Baptist Mission	1999	-	-	-	3	2
Every Home for Christ International	1973	-	-	-	1	-
Faith Christian Fellowship International		-	-	2	5	-
Free Methodist World Missions	1973	-	-	2	-	-
Gospelink, Inc.		-	-	-	225	-
Grace Ministries International	2002	-	-	-	-	2
Habitat for Humanity International	1986	-	1	-	-	1
HCJB Global	2005	-	-	3	-	-
IFCA World Missions		-	-	-	1	-
Intl. Pentecostal Holiness Ch. World Msns. Mins.	1950	-	-	4	-	-
Launch Out Ministries International		-	-	-	-	-
Literacy & Evangelism International		-	-	-	-	-
Living Water International		-	-	-	-	-
National Baptist Convention USA, Inc.	1900	-	-	-	25	-
Reformed Church in America, Gen. Synod	1981	-	-	2	1	-
Seventh Day Baptist Missionary Society	1942	-	-	-	3	-
Seventh-day Adventists, General Conference	1902	1	-	1	-	12
SIM USA, Inc.	1900	-	-	15	-	-
Teen Missions International, Inc.	1988	-	2	-	25	2
The Word for the World USA	1994	-	-	-	11	-
United Pentecostal Church International		-	2	-	-	2
Walk Thru the Bible Ministries, Inc.	2001	-	-	-	-	-
Waymarks Radio Ministries International	2008	-	-	-	1	-
White Fields, Inc.		-	-	-	1	-
Wisconsin Evangelical Lutheran Synod	1963	-	-	7	-	-
World Relief	1988	-	-	1	86	-
Wycliffe Bible Translators		-	-	2	-	-
Totals:		13	9	81	469	30

Malaysia

Asian Outreach U.S.A.		-	-	-	-	-
Assemblies of God World Missions	1928	-	-	-	-	-
Awana International		-	-	-	-	-
Calvary International	1997	-	-	-	-	-

	First Year	Personnel from U.S. 1-2 yrs.	2-4 yrs.	4+ yrs.	Other Countries Citizens	Non-Citizens
Campus Crusade for Christ, Intl.	1968	-	-	-	96	-
Church of God (Cleveland, Tenn.) World Missions	1991	-	-	4	-	-
Church of God of Prophecy—Global Outreach		-	-	-	1	-
Churches of Christ	1950	-	-	3	-	-
Food for the Hungry, Inc.	2000	-	-	2	-	-
Foursquare Missions International	1984	-	-	-	-	-
Globe International	1983	-	-	2	-	-
Gospel Revival Ministries	1999	-	-	-	1	-
Intl. Pentecostal Holiness Ch. World Msns. Mins.	1995	-	-	-	-	-
LifeWind International	1999	-	-	-	-	-
Mission To Unreached Peoples	1995	-	-	-	-	-
Missionary Ventures International		-	-	-	-	2
OneHope		-	-	-	-	-
Partners International	1954	-	-	-	17	-
ReachGlobal	1963	-	-	-	-	-
RUN Ministries	2004	-	2	-	-	-
Tentmakers International	2004	-	-	-	1	-
The Brethren Church, Inc.	1972	-	-	-	1	-
United Pentecostal Church International	1975	-	1	-	-	-
Walk Thru the Bible Ministries, Inc.	2000	-	-	-	-	-
Wycliffe Bible Translators, Inc.		-	-	31	-	-
Youth Ministry International (YMI)	2003	-	-	2	-	-
Totals:		-	3	44	117	2

Maldives

Assemblies of God World Missions	1995	-	-	-	-	-
Totals:		-	-	-	-	-

Mali

Assemblies of God World Missions	1989	-	-	6	-	-
Avant Ministries	1919	-	-	2	-	6
Awana International	2003	-	-	-	-	-
Baptist Missionary Association of America	2001	-	-	-	1	-
Campus Crusade for Christ, Intl.	1972	-	-	-	50	-
Child Evangelism Fellowship, Inc.	1993	-	-	-	1	-
Christ for the City International	2004	-	-	-	-	1
Christian Aid Mission	2007	-	-	-	15	-
Christian Churches/Churches of Christ		-	-	2	-	-
Christian Reformed World Missions	1984	-	-	6	-	-
Christian Reformed World Relief Committee	1984	-	-	1	-	-
Churches of Christ	2001	-	-	-	-	-
Evangelical Baptist Missions		-	-	9	-	-
Macedonia World Baptist Missions, Inc.	2007	-	-	2	-	-
Partners International	2000	-	-	-	93	-
ReachAcross	1979	-	-	-	-	14
Seventh-day Adventists, General Conference	1982	-	-	-	-	2
Tentmakers International	2006	-	-	-	1	-
United World Mission		-	-	4	-	-
World Venture	1999	1	3	13	-	-
Wycliffe Bible Translators		-	-	4	-	-
Totals:		1	3	49	161	23

		Personnel from U.S.			Other Countries	
	First Year	1-2 yrs.	2-4 yrs.	4+ yrs.	Citizens	Non-Citizens
Malta						
Assemblies of God World Missions	1985	1	-	-	-	-
Baptist Mid-Missions	2005	-	-	2	-	-
Church of God of Prophecy—Global Outreach		-	-	-	-	1
Churches of Christ	1973	-	-	-	-	-
Greater Europe Mission		-	-	2	-	-
Intl. Pentecostal Holiness Ch. World Msns. Mins.	1988	-	-	-	-	-
Partners International	1997	-	-	-	2	-
United Pentecostal Church International	2002	-	2	-	-	-
Totals:		1	2	4	2	1
Marshall Islands						
Assemblies of God World Missions	1961	-	-	-	-	-
Churches of Christ	1990	-	-	-	-	-
Gospel Fellowship Association	1988	-	-	4	-	-
Independent Faith Mission, Inc.	2005	-	-	2	-	-
Missionary Ventures International	1999	-	-	2	-	-
Seventh-day Adventists, General Conference	1969	-	-	3	-	-
Totals:		-	-	11	-	-
Martinique						
Church of the Nazarene, World Msn. Dept.	1976	-	-	-	-	-
Totals:		-	-	-	-	-
Mauritania						
Baptist Missionary Association of America	2008	-	-	-	1	-
Christian Aid Mission	2004	-	-	-	40	-
Partners International	2006	-	-	-	15	-
Seventh-day Adventists, General Conference	1992	-	-	-	-	2
Totals:		-	-	-	56	2
Mauritius						
Assemblies of God World Missions	1967	-	-	2	-	-
Churches of Christ	1970	-	-	2	-	-
Intl. Pentecostal Holiness Ch. World Msns. Mins.		-	-	-	-	-
United Pentecostal Church International		-	2	-	-	-
Totals:		-	2	4	-	-
Mexico						
Action International Ministries, Inc.	1990	-	-	4	2	-
Adventures in Missions	1989	-	-	10	-	-
AEGA Ministries International, Inc.		-	-	-	-	1
American Baptist Chs. of the U.S.A., Intl.Mins.	1870	-	-	9	1	2
AMG International	1978	-	-	3	-	-
AMOR Ministries	1980	37	-	-	8	2
Apostolic Christian Church Foundation, Inc.	1972	-	-	-	-	-
Assemblies of God World Missions	1915	11	-	76	-	-
Association of Free Lutheran Congregations	1979	-	-	2	2	-
Avant Ministries	1956	-	-	5	-	4
Awana International	1985	-	-	-	5	-

	First Year	Personnel from U.S.			Other Countries	
		1-2 yrs.	2-4 yrs.	4+ yrs.	Citizens	Non-Citizens
Baptist Bible Fellowship International	1950	-	-	74	-	-
Baptist International Missions, Inc. (BIMI)		-	-	55	-	-
Baptist International Outreach, Inc.	1999	-	-	4	2	-
Baptist Mid-Missions	1960	-	-	11	-	-
Baptist Missionary Association of America	1950	-	-	4	32	-
BCM International		-	-	6	-	-
Bethany International Ministries	1972	2	3	10	72	-
Biblical Ministries Worldwide	1964	-	-	12	2	-
BILD International		-	-	-	-	-
Brethren Assemblies		-	-	44	-	-
Brethren in Christ World Missions	1993	-	-	2	-	-
Calvary Commission, Inc.	1980	-	-	10	-	-
Calvary International	1985	-	-	7	1	-
CAM International	1955	-	-	61	1	-
Campus Crusade for Christ, Intl.	1961	13	-	9	42	-
Child Evangelism Fellowship, Inc.	1939	-	-	1	1	-
Childcare Worldwide	1982	-	-	-	-	-
Children of Promise International		-	3	5	-	-
Children's Christian Concern Society	1996	-	-	-	-	-
Children's Haven International	1994	-	-	2	-	-
Christ for Children International	1992	1	1	5	3	-
Christ for the City International	1988	-	-	-	5	6
Christian Aid Mission	1982	-	-	-	14	-
Christian Broadcasting Network Inc., The	1998	-	-	-	4	-
Christian Church (Disciples of Christ)		-	2	-	-	-
Christian Churches/Churches of Christ		-	4	50	20	-
Christian Fellowship Union, Inc.	1944	-	-	2	-	-
Christian Outreach International	2000	-	-	-	1	-
Christian Reformed World Missions	1952	2	4	16	-	-
Christian Relief Fund, The	1999	-	-	-	1	-
Christians In Action Missions International	1957	-	-	-	2	-
Christ's Mandate for Missions	2004	-	-	5	5	-
Church of God (Cleveland, Tenn.) World Missions	1932	1	-	-	-	-
Church of God of the Apostolic Faith, Inc., The	1950	-	-	4	-	-
Ch. of the Brethren—Global Msn. Partnerships		-	1	-	-	-
Church of the Nazarene, World Msn. Dept.	1903	-	-	3	-	2
Churches of Christ	1880	-	-	40	-	-
CMF International	1980	2	1	16	-	-
CMTS Ministries, Inc.	1986	-	-	-	2	-
ComCare International	1997	-	-	2	2	-
Commission to Every Nation	1994	5	18	41	11	50
Compassion International, Inc.	1980	-	-	-	42	-
Congregational Methodist Missions	1965	-	-	2	2	-
Converge Worldwide	1955	-	-	10	-	-
Cooperative Baptist Fellowship—Global Missions	2008	2	-	-	-	-
CrossWorld	1971	-	-	10	-	2
DeNike Ministries	1992	-	-	1	-	-
Elim Fellowship—International Ministries	1962	2	-	13	-	-
Equip International	1996	-	-	2	-	-
Evangelical Baptist Missions		1	-	4	-	-

	First Year	Personnel from U.S. 1-2 yrs.	2-4 yrs.	4+ yrs.	Other Countries Citizens	Non-Citizens
Evangelical Covenant Ch.—Covenant Wld. Msn.	1946	4	2	12	-	-
Evangelical Friends Mission		-	-	-	-	-
Evangelical Lutheran Church in America	1956	1	-	2	1	-
Evangelical Methodist Church, Inc.	1946	-	-	5	-	-
Evangelical Mission Ministries, Inc.	1954	6	3	-	-	-
Evangelism Explosion International		-	-	-	-	2
Every Home for Christ International	1965	-	-	-	1	-
Faith Christian Fellowship International	1992	-	-	2	16	-
Fellowship International Mission	1988	1	-	13	1	-
Floresta USA, Inc.	1997	-	-	-	10	-
Flying Doctors of Am. (Medical Mercy Msns., Inc.)	1990	-	-	-	-	-
Foundation For His Ministry	1967	10	-	20	114	-
Foursquare Missions International	1943	-	-	4	-	-
Free Methodist World Missions	1917	-	2	8	-	-
FRIENDS in Action International		-	-	-	-	-
Full Gospel Evangelistic Association	1950	-	-	5	-	-
General Baptists International	2003	-	-	4	-	-
Global Adopt-A-People Network	2003	-	-	-	-	-
Global Outreach International	2000	-	-	9	-	-
Global Outreach Mission, Inc.		-	-	10	-	-
Global Partners/Wesleyan World Missions	1920	-	3	-	-	-
Global Recordings Network		-	-	2	6	-
Globe International	1985	1	-	11	-	-
Go Ye Fellowship	2005	-	-	4	-	-
Good News Productions International	1996	-	2	2	4	-
Gospel Fellowship Association	1967	2	-	9	-	-
Gospel Operation Intl. for Chinese Christians	2004	-	-	-	4	-
Grace Brethren International Missions	1951	-	-	2	4	-
Greater Grace World Outreach	1987	-	-	4	4	-
HIS Servants Ministries	2008	-	-	-	-	-
Impact International, Inc.	1970	-	-	-	4	-
Independent Faith Mission, Inc.	1993	-	-	2	-	-
International Board of Jewish Missions, Inc.		-	6	-	6	-
International Family Missions	1988	-	-	8	-	-
International Gospel Outreach	1986	-	-	4	-	-
International Institute for Christian Studies	2004	-	1	1	-	2
International Partnership Ministries, Inc.	1992	-	-	-	-	2
International Pentecostal Church of Christ	1952	-	-	1	2	-
Intl. Pentecostal Holiness Ch. World Msns. Mins.	1930	-	-	6	-	-
International Teams, U.S.A.		3	-	13	-	6
Josue Yrion World Evangelism and Missions, Inc.	2002	-	-	-	1	-
Latin America Mission	1952	9	2	25	4	32
Latin American Indian Ministries	1976	-	-	-	-	-
Latin American Lutheran Mission	1942	-	-	3	1	-
Life in Messiah International	1979	-	-	2	4	-
LifeWind International	1990	-	-	1	6	-
Living Water International		-	-	-	-	-
LOGOI Ministries	1972	-	-	-	2	-
Luke Society, Inc., The	2002	-	-	-	-	-
Macedonia World Baptist Missions, Inc.	1981	-	-	16	-	-

	First Year	Personnel from U.S. 1-2 yrs.	2-4 yrs.	4+ yrs.	Other Countries Citizens	Non-Citizens
Medical Ministry International	1970	-	-	-	1	1
Medical Teams International	1985	-	1	-	-	-
Mexican Medical Ministries	1963	-	-	13	8	3
Mexico Medical Missions	2001	-	-	-	10	35
Ministries In Action	2002	-	-	-	-	-
Mission Aviation Fellowship	1945	-	2	2	-	-
Mission to the World (PCA), Inc.	1977	3	9	49	-	-
Missionary Gospel Fellowship	1959	2	4	11	2	15
Missionary Revival Crusade	1949	-	-	-	-	-
Missionary Ventures International	1992	-	-	4	-	-
Missions Door	1951	-	-	2	9	-
Navigators, U.S. International Missions Group		-	-	8	-	-
New Life Advance International	1975	-	-	1	-	-
New Tribes Mission	1975	-	2	103	-	-
New Way Missions	1996	-	-	-	-	-
Ninos de Mexico	1967	-	3	6	25	-
N. Am. Baptist Conf.—Worldwide Outreach	1992	-	-	8	-	-
OC International, Inc.	1967	-	-	4	-	-
OMS International, Inc.	1990	-	-	9	-	2
OneHope		-	-	-	-	-
Open Air Campaigners—Overseas Ministries	2004	-	-	-	2	-
Open Bible Churches, Intl. Mins.	1965	-	-	8	-	-
Operation Mobilization	1957	1	-	2	-	-
Operation Serve International	1983	5	3	6	3	-
Palm Missionary Ministries, Inc.	2006	-	-	-	4	-
Pan American Missions	1960	-	-	2	-	-
Partners in Christ International	1986	-	-	1	7	-
Pentecostal Free Will Baptist Church, Inc.		-	-	-	1	-
Prayer Baptist Missions International, Inc.	1990	-	-	10	4	-
Precept Ministries International	1980	-	-	-	1	3
Precious Seed Ministries	1966	-	-	1	8	-
ReachGlobal	1987	-	-	10	-	-
Reformed Church in America, Gen. Synod	1967	-	1	-	2	-
Ripe for Harvest, Inc.		-	-	-	2	-
Salvation Army, U.S.A.	1937	-	12	-	-	-
Samaritan's Purse International Relief	2007	4	-	-	-	-
SEED International	1996	-	1	3	-	-
Seventh-day Adventists, General Conference	1893	1	-	12	-	22
Shield of Faith Mission International	1970	3	-	6	-	-
Source of Light Ministries International, Inc.	1962	-	-	-	2	-
Spanish World Ministries, Inc.		-	-	1	1	-
STEM International	2002	-	-	-	-	-
TEAM (The Evangelical Alliance Mission)		-	-	17	-	-
The Brethren Church, Inc.	1995	-	-	1	3	-
The Mission Society	1987	2	2	2	-	-
TMA Ministries Inc.	2006	-	2	-	-	2
U.S. Center for World Mission		-	-	-	-	2
United Pentecostal Church International		-	9	-	-	15
Walk Thru the Bible Ministries, Inc.	2000	-	-	-	4	-
WEC International		-	-	24	-	-

	Personnel from U.S.				Other Countries	
	First Year	1-2 yrs.	2-4 yrs.	4+ yrs.	Citizens	Non-Citizens
Westminster Biblical Missions	1991	-	-	-	1	2
Wisconsin Evangelical Lutheran Synod	1964	-	1	2	-	-
Word of Life Fellowship, Inc.—Intl. Ministries	1983	-	-	-	51	1
World Baptist Fellowship Msn. Agency, Inc.	1956	2	-	19	-	-
World Gospel Mission	1945	-	-	12	-	2
World Indigenous Missions	1982	-	-	30	-	-
World Link Ministries	2008	-	-	-	25	-
World Mission Prayer League	1945	-	-	6	-	-
World Mission, Inc.		-	-	-	-	-
World Missions & Evangelism, Inc.		-	-	2	-	-
World Missions Far Corners, Inc.	1958	-	-	-	20	-
World Servants	1987	-	-	-	-	1
World Team		-	-	2	-	-
World-Wide Missions		-	-	-	2	-
Wycliffe Bible Translators, Inc.		-	-	49	-	-
Youth Ministry International (YMI)	2000	-	-	2	-	-
YUGO Ministries	1964	-	-	36	5	1
Totals:	139	110	1348	683	220	

Micronesia, Federated States of

	First Year	1-2 yrs.	2-4 yrs.	4+ yrs.	Citizens	Non-Citizens
Baptist Mid-Missions	1981	-	-	5	2	-
Child Evangelism Fellowship, Inc.	1957	-	-	2	-	-
Church of the Nazarene, World Msn. Dept.	2000	-	-	-	-	-
Churches of Christ	1983	-	-	2	-	-
Conservative Congregational Christian Conference	1984	-	-	4	-	-
Independent Faith Mission, Inc.	1992	-	-	-	4	-
Liebenzell Mission of USA, Inc.	1906	-	-	-	-	-
Seventh-day Adventists, General Conference	1979	1	2	2	-	-
United Pentecostal Church International		-	2	-	-	-
World Baptist Fellowship Msn. Agency, Inc.	1998	-	-	4	-	-
Totals:	1	4	19	6	-	

Middle East

	First Year	1-2 yrs.	2-4 yrs.	4+ yrs.	Citizens	Non-Citizens
Anglican Frontier Missions	1999	-	-	4	-	4
Arab World Ministries		2	3	51	2	55
Assemblies of God World Missions	1910	6	-	21	-	-
Awana International	1979	-	-	-	7	1
Baptist International Outreach, Inc.	2008	-	-	2	-	-
Baptist Mid-Missions	1999	-	-	2	-	-
Café 1040, Inc.	2001	5	-	-	-	-
Christar	1992	-	-	15	-	2
Cooperative Baptist Fellowship—Global Missions	1994	-	-	7	-	-
Development Associates International (DAI)		-	-	-	1	-
Eastern Mennonite Missions	1953	-	-	3	1	-
Elim Fellowship—International Ministries		-	-	3	1	2
Entrust	2004	-	-	5	1	-
Faith Comes By Hearing/Hosanna	2008	-	-	1	-	-
Fellowship of Evangelical Chs.—Intl. Mins.	2007	-	-	2	-	-
Final Frontiers Foundation, Inc.	2004	-	-	-	10	-
Greater Grace World Outreach	1991	-	-	3	-	1

	Personnel from U.S.				Other Countries	
	First Year	1-2 yrs.	2-4 yrs.	4+ yrs.	Citizens	Non-Citizens
Heart of God Ministries	2005	-	-	5	-	-
InterVarsity Christian Fellowship/USA, Msns. Dept.		-	3	4	-	-
Mennonite Central Committee (MCC)		-	-	34	-	-
Mennonite Mission Network	2007	-	2	-	-	-
Middle East Christian Outreach (MECO)	1976	-	-	-	-	-
Middle East Media—USA	1976	-	-	-	-	-
Mission ONE, Inc.		-	-	-	9	-
OneHope		-	-	-	-	-
Open Door Baptist Missions	1997	-	-	5	-	-
Operation Mobilization		10	3	23	-	9
Pioneers USA		-	-	26	-	-
Ravi Zacharias International Ministries, Inc.	2007	-	-	-	1	-
ReachAcross	1951	-	-	2	-	27
Rosedale Mennonite Missions	1981	-	-	7	-	-
TEAM (The Evangelical Alliance Mission)		-	-	24	-	-
Things To Come Mission, Inc.	2000	-	-	2	-	-
United Pentecostal Church International	1992	-	2	-	-	2
Virginia Mennonite Missions	2004	1	1	-	-	-
World Horizons	1990	-	-	6	-	1
World Indigenous Missions	2001	-	6	-	-	-
Youth for Christ/USA—World Outreach		-	-	6	-	-
Youth With A Mission (YWAM)		-	48	-	11	-
Totals:		24	68	263	44	104

Moldova

Assemblies of God World Missions	1991	-	-	5	-	-
Awana International	1999	-	-	-	1	-
Baptist International Evangelistic Ministries		-	-	-	8	2
Baptist Missionary Association of America	1999	-	-	-	4	-
Campus Crusade for Christ, Intl.	1995	-	-	-	51	-
Child Evangelism Fellowship, Inc.	1995	-	-	1	-	-
Christian Aid Ministries (CAM)		-	3	-	-	-
Churches of Christ		-	-	-	-	-
Crossover Communications International	1995	-	-	-	37	-
Entrust	1979	-	-	1	-	-
EurAsian Baptist Mission	1992	-	-	-	2	7
Evangelism Explosion International		-	-	-	-	3
For God's Children International	1997	-	-	-	3	-
FRIENDS in Action International		-	-	-	-	-
Global Outreach International	2004	-	-	2	1	-
Greater Grace World Outreach	2005	1	-	-	-	2
Intl. Pentecostal Holiness Ch. World Msns. Mins.		-	-	-	-	-
InterVarsity Christian Fellowship/USA, Msns. Dept.		-	-	2	-	-
Ministry to Educate and Equip, Intl. (MTEE)	1998	-	4	-	2	-
Mission Without Borders International		-	-	-	65	-
New Hope International	1992	-	-	-	3	-
Pioneers USA		-	-	2	-	-
Precept Ministries International	1994	-	-	-	8	-
TCM International Institute		-	-	-	1	-
TITUS International	1995	-	-	1	45	-

	Personnel from U.S.				Other Countries	
	First Year	1-2 yrs.	2-4 yrs.	4+ yrs.	Citizens	Non-Citizens
Walk Thru the Bible Ministries, Inc.	2000	-	-	-	1	-
World Team		-	-	2	-	-
Totals:		1	7	16	232	14
Monaco						
CrossWorld		-	-	2	-	-
Totals:		-	-	2	-	-
Mongolia						
Asian Outreach U.S.A.		-	-	-	-	-
Assemblies of God World Missions	1993	2	-	10	-	-
Baptist Bible Fellowship International	2005	-	-	2	-	-
Baptist Missionary Association of America	2004	-	-	1	-	-
Christar	1992	-	-	1	-	-
Cup of Cold Water Ministries	1989	-	-	-	-	4
Evangelical Covenant Ch.—Covenant Wld. Msn.	2008	-	-	2	-	-
Every Home for Christ International	1997	-	-	-	1	-
Far East Broadcasting Company, Inc.	2001	-	-	-	6	-
Food for the Hungry, Inc.	1997	-	2	-	-	-
Global Partners/Wesleyan World Missions	1999	-	-	-	-	-
Gospel Operation Intl. for Chinese Christians	2008	1	-	-	-	-
Habitat for Humanity International	2000	-	1	-	-	1
Mennonite Mission Network	1993	-	-	4	-	2
Mission To Unreached Peoples	2003	-	-	2	-	-
ReachGlobal	1993	-	-	-	2	-
Samaritan's Purse International Relief	2005	3	-	-	-	-
Seventh-day Adventists, General Conference	1931	-	-	2	-	4
Teen Missions International, Inc.	1997	-	-	-	1	-
University Bible Fellowship	2008	1	-	-	-	-
Walk Thru the Bible Ministries, Inc.	2001	-	-	-	-	-
World Mission Prayer League	1993	-	-	-	-	2
World Relief	2002	-	1	-	-	-
World Venture	1996	-	1	1	-	-
Totals:		7	5	25	10	13
Morocco						
Christian Aid Mission	2005	-	-	-	30	-
Churches of Christ	1951	-	-	-	-	-
Educational Services International (ESI)	1999	33	-	-	-	-
Fellowship International Mission	1950	-	-	10	3	-
Greater Europe Mission		19	-	-	-	-
I. N. Network USA	1983	-	-	-	6	-
United Pentecostal Church International		-	1	-	-	2
Walk Thru the Bible Ministries, Inc.	2002	-	-	-	1	-
Totals:		52	1	10	40	2
Mozambique						
Abundant Life Association, Inc.	1990	-	-	-	50	-
Africa Inland Mission International, Inc.	1985	-	-	20	-	13
African Leadership, Inc.	2002	-	-	-	1	-

	Personnel from U.S.				Other Countries	
	First Year	1-2 yrs.	2-4 yrs.	4+ yrs.	Citizens	Non-Citizens
AMG International		-	-	-	2	-
Assemblies of God World Missions	1973	-	-	2	-	-
Awana International	1993	-	-	-	2	-
Baptist Mid-Missions	2005	-	-	2	-	-
BCM International		-	-	1	-	-
Brethren Assemblies		-	-	2	-	-
Bright Hope International	2004	-	-	-	-	2
Campus Crusade for Christ, Intl.	1990	-	-	-	14	2
Child Evangelism Fellowship, Inc.	1994	-	-	-	4	-
Christian Aid Mission	2003	-	-	-	100	-
Christian Churches/Churches of Christ		-	2	6	-	-
Church of God of Prophecy—Global Outreach		-	-	-	2	-
Church of the Nazarene, World Msn. Dept.	1922	-	-	9	-	3
Churches of Christ	1990	-	-	12	-	-
Commission to Every Nation	2005	1	-	4	-	5
Entrust	2004	-	-	-	2	-
Every Home for Christ International	1986	-	-	-	1	-
Food for the Hungry, Inc.	1987	-	-	-	-	-
Global Outreach International	2002	-	-	2	-	-
Global Partners/Wesleyan World Missions	1998	-	4	-	-	-
Global Recordings Network		-	-	-	-	2
Globe International	2000	-	-	2	-	-
Gospelink, Inc.		-	-	-	84	-
Greater Grace World Outreach	2003	-	-	-	3	-
Habitat for Humanity International	2000	-	1	-	-	1
Intl. Pentecostal Holiness Ch. World Msns. Mins.	1957	-	-	-	-	-
Launch Out Ministries International		-	-	-	-	-
LifeWind International	1999	-	-	-	-	-
Medical Teams International	2009	1	-	-	-	-
Mission Aviation Fellowship	1999	-	-	4	-	-
New Tribes Mission	2002	-	2	16	-	-
OC International, Inc.		-	-	2	-	4
OMS International, Inc.	1994	-	-	8	-	3
OneHope		-	-	-	-	-
Precept Ministries International		-	-	-	2	-
Samaritan's Purse International Relief	2000	4	-	-	-	-
Seventh-day Adventists, General Conference	1935	-	-	1	-	1
SIM USA, Inc.	1936	-	-	8	-	-
United Pentecostal Church International		-	2	-	-	-
Walk Thru the Bible Ministries, Inc.	1999	-	-	-	3	-
World Baptist Fellowship Msn. Agency, Inc.	2007	-	2	-	-	-
World Relief	1987	-	1	-	383	5
World Team		-	-	2	-	-
World Venture	2001	1	5	6	-	-
Wycliffe Bible Translators, Inc.		-	-	8	-	-
Zion Evangelical Ministries of Africa (ZEMA)	2008	-	-	-	-	4
Totals:		7	19	117	653	45

Myanmar/Burma

ACTS International Ministries, Inc.	1991	-	-	-	2	-

	Personnel from U.S.				Other Countries	
	First Year	1-2 yrs.	2-4 yrs.	4+ yrs.	Citizens	Non-Citizens
American Leprosy Missions, Inc.	1994	-	-	-	1	-
AMG International		1	-	-	4	-
Asian Outreach U.S.A.		-	-	-	-	-
Assemblies of God World Missions	1930	2	-	2	-	-
Baptist Missionary Association of America	1993	-	-	-	21	-
BCM International		-	-	7	-	-
BILD International		-	-	-	-	1
Campus Crusade for Christ, Intl.	1972	-	-	-	120	-
Christian Aid Mission		-	-	-	626	-
Christian Churches/Churches of Christ		-	-	-	8	-
Ch. of God (Holiness), World Msn. Dept., Inc.	2004	-	-	-	20	-
Church of the Nazarene, World Msn. Dept.	1984	-	-	-	-	-
Church Planting International, Inc.	1996	-	-	-	-	-
Churches of Christ	1960	-	-	-	-	-
Cook Communications Ministries International	2002	-	-	-	-	-
Evangel Bible Translators	2003	-	-	-	2	-
Every Home for Christ International	1981	-	-	-	1	-
Global Mins., Ch. of the United Brethren in Christ		-	-	-	-	-
Global Outreach International	2003	-	-	2	1	-
Global Outreach Mission, Inc.		-	-	5	-	-
Global Partners/Wesleyan World Missions	1997	-	-	-	-	-
Global Recordings Network		-	-	-	4	-
Good News Productions International	1999	-	-	-	2	-
Gospel Operation Intl. for Chinese Christians	2000	-	-	-	2	-
Gospel Outbound		-	-	-	-	-
Harvest		-	-	-	-	2
International Partnership Ministries, Inc.	1993	-	-	-	29	-
Intl. Pentecostal Holiness Ch. World Msns. Mins.		-	-	-	-	-
Josue Yrion World Evangelism and Missions, Inc.	2008	-	-	-	1	-
Kids for Christ International	2005	-	-	-	-	-
LifeWind International	2003	-	-	-	-	-
Myanmar Christian Mission	1996	-	-	-	-	-
Partners International	1978	-	-	-	153	-
Presbyterian Missionary Union	2005	-	-	-	2	-
Reformed Church in America, Gen. Synod	2004	-	-	-	1	-
Samaritan's Purse International Relief	2008	3	-	-	-	-
Seventh-day Adventists, General Conference	1919	-	-	-	-	2
Source of Light Ministries International, Inc.	2009	-	-	-	1	-
The God's Story Project	2003	-	-	-	2	-
Tribes and Nations Outreach		-	-	-	-	-
United Pentecostal Church International		-	-	-	-	-
Village Ministries International	2003	-	-	-	1	-
Walk Thru the Bible Ministries, Inc.	1999	-	-	-	2	-
White Fields, Inc.		-	-	-	9	-
World Bible Translation Center		-	-	-	2	-
World Compassion Terry Law Ministries	2003	-	-	-	72	-
World Concern	1994	-	-	-	94	-
World Mission, Inc.		-	-	-	-	-
World Venture		2	1	-	-	-
Totals:		8	1	16	1183	5

	First Year	Personnel from U.S. 1-2 yrs.	2-4 yrs.	4+ yrs.	Other Countries Citizens	Non-Citizens
N. Mariana Isls						
Baptist International Missions, Inc. (BIMI)		-	-	4	-	-
Church of the Nazarene, World Msn. Dept.	2000	-	-	-	-	-
Far East Broadcasting Company, Inc.	1974	-	-	4	3	-
General Baptists International	1947	-	-	2	-	-
Totals:		-	-	10	3	-
Namibia						
Africa Inland Mission International, Inc.	1981	4	-	13	-	15
Assemblies of God World Missions	1979	-	-	11	-	-
Campus Crusade for Christ, Intl.	1988	-	-	-	7	2
Child Evangelism Fellowship, Inc.	1994	-	-	3	1	-
Church of God of Prophecy—Global Outreach		-	-	-	-	1
Church of the Nazarene, World Msn. Dept.	1973	-	-	2	-	-
Churches of Christ	1960	-	-	-	-	-
Episcopal Church USA		-	-	-	-	-
Evangelical Lutheran Church in America	1983	6	-	1	-	-
Every Home for Christ International	1995	-	-	-	-	-
Living Water International		-	-	-	-	-
Lutheran Bible Translators, Inc.	1996	3	-	-	11	-
SIM USA, Inc.	1970	-	-	2	-	-
United Pentecostal Church International	1986	-	2	-	-	-
Walk Thru the Bible Ministries, Inc.	1999	-	-	-	2	-
Totals:		13	2	32	21	18
Nauru						
Assemblies of God World Missions	2000	-	-	-	-	-
Totals:		-	-	-	-	-
Nepal						
ACTS International Ministries, Inc.	2005	-	-	-	3	-
Advancing Renewal Ministries, Inc.		-	-	2	6	-
All God's Children International		-	-	-	3	-
American Baptist Chs. of the U.S.A., Intl.Mins.	1978	-	-	2	-	-
Asian Outreach U.S.A.		-	-	-	-	-
Awana International	1996	-	-	-	9	-
Back to the Bible International	2001	-	-	-	2	-
Baptist Bible Fellowship International	2004	-	-	2	-	-
Baptist International Missions, Inc. (BIMI)		-	-	2	-	-
BCM International		-	-	1	-	-
Calvary International	1996	-	-	1	-	1
Campus Crusade for Christ, Intl.	1975	-	-	-	249	-
CEIFA Ministry International	2006	-	-	2	2	-
Child Evangelism Fellowship, Inc.	1988	-	-	-	1	-
Christian Aid Mission		-	-	-	570	-
Church of the Nazarene, World Msn. Dept.	1998	-	-	-	-	-
Churches of Christ	1980	-	-	-	-	-
Development Associates International (DAI)		-	-	1	-	-
Evangel Bible Translators		-	-	-	2	1
Evangelical Friends Mission		-	-	-	-	-

	First Year	Personnel from U.S.			Other Countries	
		1-2 yrs.	2-4 yrs.	4+ yrs.	Citizens	Non-Citizens
Every Home for Christ International	1982	-	-	-	1	-
Fellowship International Mission	2003	-	-	2	-	-
Foursquare Missions International		-	-	2	-	-
Global Partners/Wesleyan World Missions	1950	-	-	-	-	2
Global Recordings Network		-	-	-	4	-
Globe International	2002	-	-	2	-	-
Greater Grace World Outreach	1997	-	-	-	4	-
Habitat for Humanity International	1997	-	1	-	-	1
Harvest		-	-	-	1	-
HBI Global Partners		-	-	-	10	-
Holt International Children's Services, Inc.		-	-	-	1	-
I. N. Network USA	1975	-	-	-	65	-
India Gospel Outreach, Inc.	1994	-	-	-	30	-
International Partnership Ministries, Inc.	1999	-	-	-	18	4
International Teams, U.S.A.		-	-	2	-	3
LifeWind International	1984	-	-	-	18	-
Mennonite Mission Network	1956	-	-	1	-	1
Mission ONE, Inc.		-	-	-	2	-
Mission To Unreached Peoples	1985	-	-	3	-	-
New Directions International, Inc.	1989	-	-	-	23	-
New Life Advance International		-	-	-	6	-
Operation Mobilization		6	1	2	-	2
Partners International	2007	-	-	-	10	-
Pass the Torch Ministries/Church of Acts	2006	-	-	-	2	-
Project Christ International	1985	-	-	-	5	-
Rock the World Youth Mission Alliance		-	-	-	-	-
Seventh-day Adventists, General Conference	1957	-	-	3	-	12
The God's Story Project	2003	-	-	-	2	-
Tribes and Nations Outreach		-	-	-	-	-
United Pentecostal Church International	1992	-	1	-	1	-
United World Mission		-	-	4	-	-
Walk Thru the Bible Ministries, Inc.	1999	-	-	-	2	-
World Mission Prayer League	1956	-	-	7	-	1
World Missions Far Corners, Inc.	1998	-	-	-	20	-
World-Wide Missions		-	-	1	1	-
Totals:		6	3	42	1073	28

Netherlands

	First Year	Personnel from U.S.			Other Countries	
Assemblies of God World Missions	1975	6	-	15	-	-
Baptist Bible Fellowship International	1979	-	-	6	-	-
Baptist Mid-Missions	1954	-	-	10	-	-
BCM International		-	-	11	-	-
Bethany International Ministries	2003	-	-	1	-	1
Biblical Ministries Worldwide	1958	-	-	2	-	-
Brethren Assemblies		-	-	2	-	-
Calvary International	1991	2	-	-	-	-
Campus Crusade for Christ, Intl.	1969	-	-	2	-	-
Christar	1989	-	-	5	-	-
Christian Associates International	1987	-	-	-	-	-
Ch. of the Brethren—Global Msn. Partnerships		1	-	-	-	-

	Personnel from U.S.				Other Countries	
	First Year	1-2 yrs.	2-4 yrs.	4+ yrs.	Citizens	Non-Citizens
Church of the Nazarene, World Msn. Dept.	1967	-	-	-	-	-
Churches of Christ	1946	-	-	-	-	-
Cooperative Baptist Fellowship—Global Missions	1996	-	-	2	-	-
European Christian Mission International—USA		-	-	-	-	2
Global Outreach Mission, Inc.		-	-	1	-	-
Global Recordings Network		-	-	-	1	-
Gospel Fellowship Association		-	-	2	-	-
Great Commission Ministries, Inc.	2002	6	-	9	-	-
Greater Europe Mission	1952	-	-	12	-	-
Intl. Pentecostal Holiness Ch. World Msns. Mins.	2003	-	-	2	-	-
International Teams, U.S.A.		-	-	-	-	6
Life in Messiah International	2005	-	-	1	1	-
New Tribes Mission	2000	-	-	-	6	-
Operation Mobilization		-	1	-	-	1
Presbyterian Mission International (PMI)	1999	-	-	-	2	-
ReachGlobal	1997	1	-	4	-	-
TWR		-	-	8	-	-
United Pentecostal Church International		-	2	-	-	7
World Harvest Mission	1989	-	-	2	-	-
World Venture	1985	-	5	-	-	-
	Totals:	16	8	97	10	17

Netherlands Antilles

Assemblies of God World Missions	1983	2	-	2	-	-
Awana International		-	-	-	-	-
Baptist Bible Fellowship International	2008	-	-	2	-	-
Child Evangelism Fellowship, Inc.		-	-	2	-	-
Church of God of Prophecy—Global Outreach		-	-	-	7	-
Global Outreach Mission, Inc.		-	-	1	-	-
Seventh-day Adventists, General Conference	1926	-	-	1	-	1
TWR		-	-	2	-	-
Word of Life Fellowship, Inc.—Intl. Ministries	1979	-	-	-	2	-
	Totals:	2	-	10	9	1

New Caledonia

Assemblies of God World Missions	1967	-	-	-	-	-
Baptist International Missions, Inc. (BIMI)		-	-	2	-	-
Seventh-day Adventists, General Conference	1925	-	-	-	-	2
United Pentecostal Church International	2002	-	2	-	-	-
	Totals:	-	2	2	-	2

New Zealand

Adventive Cross Cultural Initiatives—US	2009	-	-	-	4	-
Adventures in Missions	2004	1	-	2	-	-
Asian Outreach U.S.A.		-	-	-	-	-
Awana International		-	-	-	-	-
Baptist Bible Fellowship International	1971	-	-	12	-	-
Baptist International Missions, Inc. (BIMI)		-	-	6	-	-
Baptist Mid-Missions	1973	-	-	6	-	-
Biblical Ministries Worldwide	1967	-	-	2	-	-
Campus Crusade for Christ, Intl.	1972	13	-	17	49	-

	Personnel from U.S.				Other Countries	
	First Year	1-2 yrs.	2-4 yrs.	4+ yrs.	Citizens	Non-Citizens
Chosen People Ministries	2008	-	-	-	1	-
Christian Churches/Churches of Christ		-	-	8	-	-
Church of God (Anderson, Ind.), Global Msns.	1999	-	-	4	-	-
Church of God of Prophecy—Global Outreach		-	-	-	-	2
Church of the Nazarene, World Msn. Dept.	1952	-	-	-	-	-
Churches of Christ	1844	-	-	11	-	-
CrossWorld		-	-	-	1	-
Elim Fellowship—International Ministries	1964	-	-	-	-	-
Fellowship International Mission	1995	-	-	1	1	-
Global Partners/Wesleyan World Missions	2000	-	-	-	-	-
Gospel Fellowship Association	1998	-	-	2	-	-
International Teams, U.S.A.		-	-	2	-	4
Missions Resource Network	1844	-	-	6	-	-
Navigators, U.S. International Missions Group		-	1	4	-	-
Precept Ministries International	1990	-	-	-	2	1
Presbyterian Mission International (PMI)	2006	-	-	-	2	-
Salvation Army, U.S.A.	1883	-	2	-	-	-
Teen Missions International, Inc.	1990	-	-	-	2	-
Tentmakers International	1994	-	-	-	-	-
The Gospel Furthering Fellowship	2008	-	-	2	-	2
United Pentecostal Church International	1969	-	3	-	-	12
WEC International	1953	2	-	-	-	-
Word of Life Fellowship, Inc.—Intl. Ministries	1983	-	-	-	3	-
World Baptist Fellowship Msn. Agency, Inc.	1970	-	-	2	-	-
World Venture		-	-	2	-	-
Wycliffe Bible Translators		-	-	2	-	-
Youth for Christ/USA—World Outreach		-	-	3	-	-
Youth With A Mission (YWAM)		-	41	-	-	-
Totals:	16	47	94	65	21	

Nicaragua

	First Year	1-2 yrs.	2-4 yrs.	4+ yrs.	Citizens	Non-Citizens
American Baptist Chs. of the U.S.A., Intl. Mins.	1917	-	-	-	-	-
Assemblies of God World Missions	1912	5	-	24	-	-
Awana International	2001	-	-	-	2	1
Baptist Bible Fellowship International	1969	-	1	13	-	-
Baptist Medical & Dental Mission Intl., Inc.	1989	3	2	2	43	-
Baptist Missionary Association of America	1964	-	-	-	8	-
Brethren Assemblies		-	-	6	-	-
Campus Crusade for Christ, Intl.	1999	-	-	2	12	-
Children's Christian Concern Society	2000	-	-	-	-	-
Christ for the City International	2002	-	4	-	1	2
Christian Aid Ministries (CAM)	1988	-	10	-	1	20
Christian Medical & Dental Associations	2007	1	-	-	-	-
Christian Reformed World Missions	1996	-	2	2	-	-
Christian Relief Fund, The	1997	-	-	-	4	-
Church of God (Cleveland, Tenn.) World Missions	1950	2	-	-	-	-
Ch. of the Brethren—Global Msn. Partnerships		-	-	-	-	-
Church of the Nazarene, World Msn. Dept.	1937	-	-	-	-	-
Churches of Christ	1960	-	-	2	-	-
Commission to Every Nation	2000	-	-	2	-	2

	First Year	Personnel from U.S. 1-2 yrs.	2-4 yrs.	4+ yrs.	Other Countries Citizens	Non-Citizens
Compassion International, Inc.	2002	-	-	-	40	-
Equip International	1998	-	-	1	-	-
Every Home for Christ International	1965	-	-	-	1	-
Food for the Hungry, Inc.	1994	-	4	-	-	1
Forward Edge International	1985	1	-	-	1	-
FRIENDS in Action International	2005	2	-	-	-	-
Full Gospel Evangelistic Association	1960	-	-	2	-	-
Global Outreach International	2001	-	-	2	-	-
Global Partners/Wesleyan World Missions	1997	-	-	-	-	-
Globe International	1996	1	-	3	-	-
Habitat for Humanity International	1984	-	1	-	-	1
Intl. Pentecostal Holiness Ch. World Msns. Mins.	1994	-	-	1	-	-
International Teams, U.S.A.		-	-	-	-	1
LifeWind International	1999	-	-	-	3	-
Living Water International		-	-	-	-	-
Living Water Teaching	1986	-	-	-	2	-
Luke Society, Inc., The	2001	-	-	-	-	-
Mailbox Club International Inc., The		-	-	-	1	-
Medical Ministry International	2007	1	-	-	-	-
Mission to the World (PCA), Inc.	2002	-	-	2	-	-
Missionary Revival Crusade		-	-	-	-	-
Missionary Ventures International	1995	-	-	6	-	-
Missions Door	1997	-	-	-	1	-
National Baptist Convention USA, Inc.	1958	-	-	-	2	-
OneHope		-	-	-	-	-
Open Bible Churches, Intl. Mins.	2003	-	-	2	-	-
ORPHANetwork	2000	-	-	-	1	-
Partners in Christ International	2002	-	-	2	1	-
Pentecostal Assemblies of God of Am., Inc.		-	-	-	2	3
Pentecostal Free Will Baptist Church, Inc.		-	-	-	1	-
Prayer Baptist Missions International, Inc.	2002	-	-	2	-	-
Precept Ministries International		-	-	-	-	1
Precious Seed Ministries	1972	-	-	-	2	-
Reformed Church in America, Gen. Synod	1991	-	-	-	2	-
Self-Help International	1999	-	-	-	5	-
Seventh-day Adventists, General Conference	1928	1	-	-	-	2
United Pentecostal Church International	1971	-	2	-	-	1
United World Mission		-	-	2	-	-
Village Ministries International	2003	-	-	-	1	-
World Relief	1991	-	-	1	23	-
	Totals:	17	26	79	160	35

Niger

	First Year	1-2 yrs.	2-4 yrs.	4+ yrs.	Citizens	Non-Citizens
Assemblies of God World Missions	1991	1	-	4	-	-
Baptist International Missions, Inc. (BIMI)		-	-	2	-	-
Calvary International	2004	1	-	-	-	-
Campus Crusade for Christ, Intl.	1991	-	-	-	29	2
Child Evangelism Fellowship, Inc.	1994	-	-	-	1	-
Christian Aid Mission	2005	-	-	-	35	-
Christian Reformed World Relief Committee	1991	-	1	1	-	-

		Personnel from U.S.			Other Countries	
	First Year	1-2 yrs.	2-4 yrs.	4+ yrs.	Citizens	Non-Citizens
Christian Relief Fund, The	2005	-	-	-	-	-
Elim Fellowship—International Ministries	1991	2	-	4	-	-
Evangelical Baptist Missions		-	-	8	-	-
Fellowship International Mission	1950	-	-	1	-	1
Gospel Revival Ministries	1997	-	-	-	2	-
Greater Grace World Outreach	2007	-	-	-	-	2
LifeWind International	1997	-	-	-	-	-
OneHope		-	-	-	-	-
Partners International	2006	-	-	-	1	-
Reformed Church in America, Gen. Synod	2001	-	-	3	-	-
Samaritan's Purse International Relief	2005	1	-	-	-	-
Seventh-day Adventists, General Conference	1987	-	-	-	-	2
SIM USA, Inc.	1924	5	-	61	-	-
Tentmakers International	2008	-	-	-	1	-
United Pentecostal Church International	1999	-	2	-	-	-
World Missions & Evangelism, Inc.		-	-	2	-	-
Wycliffe Bible Translators, Inc.		-	-	6	-	-
Totals:		10	3	92	69	7

Nigeria

ACM International	1970	-	-	2	-	-
AEGA Ministries International, Inc.		-	-	-	-	1
African Leadership, Inc.	2007	-	-	-	1	-
Assemblies of God World Missions	1939	-	-	4	-	-
Awana International	1991	-	-	-	-	-
Baptist Bible Fellowship International	1987	-	-	2	-	-
Baptist International Missions, Inc. (BIMI)		-	-	6	-	-
Baptist International Outreach, Inc.	2001	-	-	5	4	-
Baptist Missionary Association of America	2000	-	-	-	11	-
BILD International		-	-	-	6	-
Brethren Assemblies		-	-	4	-	-
Calvary International	1992	-	-	-	17	-
Campus Crusade for Christ, Intl.	1969	1	-	4	378	5
Child Evangelism Fellowship, Inc.	1982	-	-	-	7	-
Christ to the Nations		-	-	-	4	-
Christian Aid Mission	1986	-	-	-	500	-
Christian Blind Mission International (CBM-US)	1997	-	1	-	-	-
Christian Broadcasting Network Inc., The	1997	-	-	-	20	-
Christian Churches/Churches of Christ		-	-	2	-	-
Christian Reformed World Missions	1940	2	3	22	-	-
Christian Reformed World Relief Committee	1969	-	-	1	-	-
Christian Relief Fund, The	1996	-	-	-	-	-
Christ's Mandate for Missions	2004	-	-	-	1	-
Church of God (Cleveland, Tenn.) World Missions	1951	2	-	-	-	-
Ch. of the Brethren—Global Msn. Partnerships		8	3	-	-	-
Church of the Nazarene, World Msn. Dept.	1977	-	-	-	-	4
Churches of Christ	1940	-	-	5	-	-
Converge Worldwide		-	-	4	-	-
Development Associates International (DAI)	1996	-	-	-	1	-
Elim Fellowship—International Ministries	1975	-	-	2	-	-

	Personnel from U.S.			Other Countries	
	First Year	1-2 yrs.	2-4 yrs.	4+ yrs.	Citizens	Non-Citizens

	First Year	1-2 yrs.	2-4 yrs.	4+ yrs.	Citizens	Non-Citizens
Entrust	2004	-	-	-	2	-
Equip International	1995	-	-	-	4	-
Evangelical Baptist Missions		-	-	-	2	-
Evangelical Covenant Ch.—Covenant Wld. Msn.	2007	-	1	-	-	-
Evangelical Lutheran Church in America	1913	-	-	1	-	-
Evangelical Presbyterian Church—World Outreach	2003	-	2	-	-	-
Evangelism Resources, Inc.	1991	-	2	-	-	-
Fellowship International Mission	1977	-	-	4	-	-
Food for the Hungry, Inc.	2000	-	2	-	-	-
Foursquare Missions International	1955	-	-	2	-	-
Free Methodist World Missions	1989	-	-	1	-	-
Global Recordings Network		-	-	12	12	-
Gospel Revival Ministries	1990	-	-	-	8	-
Greater Grace World Outreach	2007	-	-	-	-	2
International Christian Ministries	2002	-	-	-	4	-
International Institute for Christian Studies	1988	-	2	4	1	5
Intl. Pentecostal Holiness Ch. World Msns. Mins.	1950	-	-	-	-	-
Ireland Outreach International Inc.	1994	-	-	-	9	-
Liebenzell Mission of USA, Inc.	2005	-	-	1	-	-
LifeWind International	2003	-	-	-	-	-
Living Water International		-	-	-	-	-
Lott Carey Baptist Foreign Msn. Conv.	1965	-	-	-	100	-
Lutheran Bible Translators, Inc.	2003	-	-	2	3	-
Lutheran Church-Missouri Synod, World Mission	1936	-	-	2	-	-
M/E International, Inc.	2002	-	-	-	-	-
Mennonite Mission Network	1959	-	-	-	-	-
Mission ONE, Inc.		-	-	-	1	-
Mission: Moving Mountains, Inc.	2002	-	-	-	-	-
Missionary Ventures International	1990	-	-	-	2	-
Mutual Faith Ministries Intl.		-	-	-	-	-
Navigators, U.S. International Missions Group		-	-	2	-	-
N. Am. Baptist Conf.—Worldwide Outreach	1939	2	-	-	-	2
OneHope		-	-	-	-	-
Pentecostal Free Will Baptist Church, Inc.		-	-	-	1	-
Seventh-day Adventists, General Conference	1914	1	1	4	-	2
SIM USA, Inc.	1893	6	-	56	-	-
Source of Light Ministries International, Inc.	2004	-	-	-	2	-
Tentmakers International	2007	-	-	-	1	-
The Master's Mission, Inc.	1987	-	-	-	5	-
United Pentecostal Church International	1970	-	4	-	-	5
Village Ministries International	1991	-	-	-	32	-
Walk Thru the Bible Ministries, Inc.	2000	-	-	-	4	-
Waymarks Radio Ministries International	1999	-	-	-	1	-
Word of Life Fellowship, Inc.—Intl. Ministries	2000	-	-	2	13	-
World Mission, Inc.		-	-	-	-	-
Wycliffe Bible Translators, Inc.		-	-	8	-	-
Totals:		22	21	164	1157	26

Northern Mariana Islands

	First Year	1-2 yrs.	2-4 yrs.	4+ yrs.	Citizens	Non-Citizens
Churches of Christ		-	-	2	-	-

		Personnel from U.S.			Other Countries	
	First Year	1-2 yrs.	2-4 yrs.	4+ yrs.	Citizens	Non-Citizens
Wycliffe Bible Translators		-	-	2	-	-
Totals:		-	-	4	-	-

Norway

Baptist International Missions, Inc. (BIMI)			-	2	-	-
Churches of Christ	1960	-	-	-	-	-
Intl. Pentecostal Holiness Ch. World Msns. Mins.	1992	-	-	2	-	-
International Teams, U.S.A.		-	-	-	-	2
Navigators, U.S. International Missions Group		-	-	2	-	-
Tentmakers International	1994	-	-	-	3	-
United Pentecostal Church International		-	2	-	-	3
Totals:			2	6	3	5

Oceania—General

Assemblies of God World Missions	1972	2	-	9	-	-
Final Frontiers Foundation, Inc.	2001	-	-	-	2	-
Seventh-day Adventists, General Conference	1930	1	-	2	-	-
United Pentecostal Church International	2004	-	2	-	-	-
Youth With A Mission (YWAM)		-	12	-	70	-
Totals:		3	14	11	72	-

Oman

Interserve USA (International Service Fellowship)	1951	-	-	1	-	-
Walk Thru the Bible Ministries, Inc.	2002	-	-	-	-	-
Totals:		-	-	1	-	-

Pakistan

AEGA Ministries International, Inc.		-	-	-	-	1
Baptist Bible Fellowship International	1959	-	-	4	-	-
BILD International		-	-	-	-	-
Campus Crusade for Christ, Intl.	1960	-	-	-	83	-
Child Evangelism Fellowship, Inc.	1955	-	-	-	1	-
Christ to the Nations	2004	-	-	-	2	-
Christar	1953	-	-	4	-	-
Christian Aid Mission		-	-	-	450	-
Christian Blind Mission International (CBM-US)	1982	-	1	-	-	-
Christian Churches/Churches of Christ		-	-	-	2	-
Church of God (Cleveland, Tenn.) World Missions	1972	1	-	-	-	-
Church of God of Prophecy—Global Outreach		-	-	-	2	-
Church of the Nazarene, World Msn. Dept.	1996	-	-	-	-	-
Churches of Christ	1960	-	-	-	-	-
Full Gospel Evangelistic Association	2003	3	-	-	-	-
Global Partners/Wesleyan World Missions	1992	-	-	-	-	-
Global Recordings Network		-	-	-	10	-
Gospel Revival Ministries	2006	-	-	-	2	-
Greater Grace World Outreach	2007	-	-	-	16	-
Interserve USA (International Service Fellowship)	1852	-	-	11	1	-
Key Communications	1977	-	-	-	1	-
Literacy & Evangelism International		-	-	-	-	-
Mission ONE, Inc.		-	-	-	54	-
ReachAcross	1980	-	-	-	-	5

	Personnel from U.S.			Other Countries	
	First Year	1-2 yrs.	2-4 yrs.	4+ yrs.	Citizens	Non-Citizens
Seventh-day Adventists, General Conference	1914	1	-	-	-	4
Shelter for Life International, Inc.	1979	1	-	-	1	-
TEAM (The Evangelical Alliance Mission)		-	-	27	-	-
United Pentecostal Church International	1971	-	2	-	-	-
Walk Thru the Bible Ministries, Inc.	2002	-	-	-	-	-
Warm Blankets Orphan Care International	2008	-	-	-	1	-
Westminster Biblical Missions	1973	-	-	1	20	-
World Mission Prayer League	1946	-	-	2	-	-
World Venture	1954	-	-	5	-	-
World Witness	1906	-	-	5	-	-
Totals:		6	3	59	646	10

Palau

Assemblies of God World Missions	1983	-	-	2	-	-
Biblical Ministries Worldwide		-	-	4	-	-
Church of the Nazarene, World Msn. Dept.	1995	-	-	-	-	-
Liebenzell Mission of USA, Inc.	1929	-	-	1	-	-
Seventh-day Adventists, General Conference	1930	1	-	-	-	-
Totals:		1	-	7	-	-

Palestine

Anis Shorrosh Evangelistic Association		-	-	40	-	-
Christ Community Church	1928	-	-	-	6	-
Christian Aid Mission		-	-	-	26	-
Christian Church (Disciples of Christ)		-	3	-	-	-
Evangelical Lutheran Church in America	1967	2	2	-	-	-
Friends United Meeting		-	1	-	-	-
Mission Generation, Inc.	2010	-	-	-	-	-
United Pentecostal Church International		-	2	-	-	-
Walk Thru the Bible Ministries, Inc.	2002	-	-	-	-	-
Totals:		2	8	40	32	-

Panama

American Baptist Chs. of the U.S.A., Intl.Mins.	2001	-	-	-	-	1
Assemblies of God World Missions	1967	-	-	8	-	-
Avant Ministries	1953	-	-	3	1	-
Baptist Bible Fellowship International	1976	-	-	6	-	-
Baptist International Missions, Inc. (BIMI)		-	-	2	-	-
Baptist Missionary Association of America	2006	-	-	-	-	1
Campus Crusade for Christ, Intl.	1965	-	-	2	16	-
Children's Christian Concern Society	1995	-	-	-	-	-
Christian Churches/Churches of Christ		2	-	2	-	-
Church of God (Cleveland, Tenn.) World Missions	1935	-	-	2	-	-
Church of God of Prophecy—Global Outreach		-	-	-	2	2
Church of the Nazarene, World Msn. Dept.	1953	-	-	-	-	-
Churches of Christ	1963	-	-	4	-	-
Foursquare Missions International		-	-	2	-	-
Free Will Baptist, Inc. Bd. of Intl. Missions	1971	-	-	8	-	-
Global Partners/Wesleyan World Missions	1997	-	-	-	-	-
Gospel Fellowship Association	2002	-	-	2	-	-

	First Year	Personnel from U.S. 1-2 yrs.	2-4 yrs.	4+ yrs.	Other Countries Citizens	Non-Citizens
Intl. Pentecostal Holiness Ch. World Msns. Mins.	1988	-	-	2	-	-
LifeWind International	2003	-	-	-	-	-
Living Water Teaching	2001	-	-	-	-	2
Lutheran Church-Missouri Synod, World Mission	1941	-	-	6	-	-
Mission to the World (PCA), Inc.		-	-	2	-	-
Missions Door	2003	-	-	-	-	1
National Baptist Convention of America	1969	-	-	-	4	-
New Tribes Mission	1953	-	-	9	-	-
Pentecostal Assemblies of God of Am., Inc.		-	-	-	-	2
Precept Ministries International		-	-	-	-	1
United Pentecostal Church International	1980	-	2	-	-	1
Word of Life Fellowship, Inc.—Intl. Ministries	1988	-	-	1	16	-
Totals:		2	2	61	39	11

Papua New Guinea

	First Year	1-2 yrs.	2-4 yrs.	4+ yrs.	Citizens	Non-Citizens
Apostolic Christian Church Foundation, Inc.	1961	-	-	-	-	-
Assemblies of God World Missions	2000	-	-	-	-	-
Awana International	1991	-	-	-	1	-
Baptist Bible Fellowship International	1961	-	-	6	-	-
Baptist International Missions, Inc. (BIMI)		-	-	4	-	-
Baptist Mid-Missions	2006	-	-	2	-	-
Brethren Assemblies		-	-	8	-	-
Bright Hope International	2000	-	-	-	1	-
Campus Crusade for Christ, Intl.	1978	-	-	-	5	-
Christian Aid Mission		-	-	-	64	-
Christian Blind Mission International (CBM-US)	1988	-	2	-	-	-
Christian Churches/Churches of Christ		-	6	30	-	-
Church of the Nazarene, World Msn. Dept.	1955	-	-	28	-	1
Churches of Christ	1971	-	-	9	-	-
Evangel Bible Translators		-	-	2	-	-
Evangelical Congregational Church		-	-	5	-	-
Evangelical Lutheran Church in America	1886	-	-	2	-	1
Evangelism Explosion International		-	-	-	-	10
Foursquare Missions International	1956	-	-	2	-	-
FRIENDS in Action International	1995	-	2	-	-	-
Global Partners/Wesleyan World Missions	1961	-	4	-	-	2
Global Recordings Network		-	-	-	2	-
Gospel Fellowship Association	1997	5	-	13	-	-
HCJB Global	2005	-	-	2	-	-
Kids Alive International	1992	1	-	-	68	-
Liebenzell Mission of USA, Inc.	1906	-	-	-	-	-
LifeWind International	2003	-	-	-	2	2
Lutheran Bible Translators, Inc.	1998	-	-	2	-	-
Lutheran Church-Missouri Synod, World Mission	1948	-	-	1	-	-
Mission to the World (PCA), Inc.	1987	-	1	2	-	-
Mustard Seed International	1974	-	-	-	-	-
New Life Advance International		-	-	-	-	-
New Tribes Mission	1950	-	32	266	-	-
Pioneer Bible Translators	1977	-	-	33	-	-
Pioneers USA	1980	-	-	10	-	-

	First Year	1-2 yrs.	2-4 yrs.	4+ yrs.	Citizens	Non-Citizens
		Personnel from U.S.			Other Countries	
Primitive Methodist Church in the USA		-	-	-	-	-
Salvation Army, U.S.A.	1956	-	2	-	-	-
Seventh-day Adventists, General Conference	1908	-	-	-	-	22
TEAM (The Evangelical Alliance Mission)		-	-	12	-	-
Tentmakers International	2000	-	-	-	1	-
United Pentecostal Church International	1973	-	-	-	-	3
Word of Life Fellowship, Inc.—Intl. Ministries	2000	-	-	-	4	-
World Gospel Mission	1996	-	-	5	-	-
World Team		-	-	10	-	7
World-Wide Missions	1975	-	-	-	1	-
Wycliffe Bible Translators		-	-	205	-	-
Totals:		6	49	659	149	48

Paraguay

	First Year	1-2 yrs.	2-4 yrs.	4+ yrs.	Citizens	Non-Citizens
Apostolic Christian Church Foundation, Inc.	1978	-	-	-	-	-
Assemblies of God World Missions	1944	2	-	14	-	-
Awana International	1985	-	-	-	-	-
Baptist Bible Fellowship International	1980	-	-	2	-	-
Baptist International Missions, Inc. (BIMI)		-	-	2	-	-
Bethany International Ministries	2001	2	-	-	-	-
BILD International		-	-	-	-	-
Brethren Assemblies		-	-	14	-	-
Campus Crusade for Christ, Intl.	1966	-	-	-	11	-
Children's Christian Concern Society	2008	-	-	-	-	-
Christian Aid Mission	1984	-	-	-	24	-
Church of God (Anderson, Ind.), Global Msns.	1974	-	-	2	-	-
Church of God (Cleveland, Tenn.) World Missions	1954	-	-	2	-	-
Church of God of Prophecy—Global Outreach		-	-	-	4	-
Church of the Nazarene, World Msn. Dept.	1980	-	-	-	-	4
Churches of Christ	1965	-	-	8	-	-
Elim Fellowship—International Ministries		1	-	1	-	-
Foursquare Missions International	1986	-	-	2	-	-
Full Gospel Grace Fellowship	1940	-	-	-	2	-
Global Outreach Mission, Inc.		-	-	4	-	-
Intl. Pentecostal Holiness Ch. World Msns. Mins.		-	-	-	2	-
InterVarsity Christian Fellowship/USA, Msns. Dept.		-	-	2	-	-
Latin America Mission		-	2	4	-	6
LifeWind International	2003	-	-	-	-	-
Living Water Teaching	1990	-	-	2	-	-
Luke Society, Inc., The	2001	-	-	-	-	-
Mission Generation, Inc.	2009	-	-	-	3	2
Missionary Ventures International	2002	-	-	2	-	-
New Tribes Mission	1946	-	2	47	-	-
Open Air Campaigners—Overseas Ministries	1991	-	-	-	8	-
Seventh-day Adventists, General Conference	1900	-	-	-	-	2
SIM USA, Inc.	1987	1	-	16	-	-
South America Mission, Inc.	1991	-	-	5	-	-
Spanish World Ministries, Inc.		-	-	1	1	-
STEM International	1994	-	-	-	-	-
The Brethren Church, Inc.	1989	-	-	-	1	-

	First Year	1-2 yrs.	2-4 yrs.	4+ yrs.	Other Countries Citizens	Non-Citizens
			Personnel from U.S.		Other Countries	

	First Year	1-2 yrs.	2-4 yrs.	4+ yrs.	Citizens	Non-Citizens
The Mission Society	1988	3	2	6	-	-
United Pentecostal Church International	1973	-	2	-	-	6
White Fields, Inc.		-	-	-	6	-
Word of Life Fellowship, Inc.—Intl. Ministries	1979	-	-	-	13	-
World Gospel Mission	1986	-	-	4	-	1
Wycliffe Bible Translators		-	-	2	-	-
	Totals:	9	8	142	75	21

Peru

	First Year	1-2 yrs.	2-4 yrs.	4+ yrs.	Citizens	Non-Citizens
Allegheny Wesleyan Methodist Connection	1972	-	-	5	-	-
Amazon Focus, Inc.	1995	-	-	2	10	-
AMG International		-	-	-	6	-
Assemblies of God World Missions	1919	2	-	12	-	-
Awana International	1987	-	-	-	3	-
Baptist Bible Fellowship International	1958	-	-	19	-	-
Baptist International Missions, Inc. (BIMI)		-	-	13	-	-
Baptist International Outreach, Inc.	1994	-	-	4	-	-
Baptist Mid-Missions	1937	-	-	33	1	-
Baptist Missionary Association of America	1999	-	-	1	2	-
BCM International		-	-	44	-	-
BILD International		-	-	-	1	-
Brethren Assemblies		-	-	22	-	-
Calvary International	1986	-	-	1	1	-
Campus Crusade for Christ, Intl.	1964	-	-	-	1	3
Child Evangelism Fellowship, Inc.	1946	-	-	-	1	-
Childcare Worldwide	1984	-	-	-	-	-
Christ for the City International	1989	1	-	1	1	1
Christian Aid Mission	1980	-	-	-	451	-
Christians In Action Missions International	1979	-	-	-	-	2
Church of God (Cleveland, Tenn.) World Missions	1947	-	-	2	-	-
Church of God of Prophecy—Global Outreach		-	-	-	2	-
Church of the Nazarene, World Msn. Dept.	1914	-	-	8	-	-
Churches of Christ	1958	-	-	13	-	-
Commission to Every Nation	2004	-	6	4	-	10
Compassion International, Inc.	1977	-	-	-	62	-
Cooperative Baptist Fellowship—Global Missions	2008	2	-	-	-	-
Eastern Mennonite Missions	1986	-	2	6	-	-
Elim Fellowship—International Ministries	1964	-	-	1	-	-
Faith Life Ministries, Inc.	2001	-	-	-	-	-
Flying Doctors of Am. (Medical Mercy Msns., Inc.)	1990	-	-	-	-	-
Food for the Hungry, Inc.	1982	2	8	-	3	-
Free Methodist World Missions	1993	-	-	4	-	-
Global Outreach International	2005	-	-	2	-	-
Global Outreach Mission, Inc.		-	-	4	-	-
Global Partners/Wesleyan World Missions	1903	-	2	-	-	-
Global Recordings Network		-	-	-	-	3
Gospel Operation Intl. for Chinese Christians	2002	-	-	-	2	-
Greater Grace World Outreach	2003	1	5	2	-	2
Harvest	1997	-	-	-	1	-
Impact International, Inc.		-	-	-	2	-

	First Year	Personnel from U.S. 1-2 yrs.	2-4 yrs.	4+ yrs.	Other Countries Citizens	Non-Citizens
International Board of Jewish Missions, Inc.		1	-	-	-	1
International Partnership Ministries, Inc.	1996	-	-	-	25	-
Intl. Pentecostal Holiness Ch. World Msns. Mins.	1996	-	-	2	2	-
Josue Yrion World Evangelism and Missions, Inc.	1997	-	-	-	1	-
Kids Alive International	1993	-	3	5	23	3
Kids Around the World, Inc.		-	-	-	1	-
Latin America Mission		2	-	6	4	4
Latin American Indian Ministries	1996	-	-	-	-	-
LifeWind International	1999	-	-	-	1	-
Literacy & Evangelism International	1995	-	-	2	-	-
Living Water International		-	-	-	-	-
LOGOI Ministries	1972	-	-	-	2	-
Luke Society, Inc., The	1988	-	-	-	-	-
Macedonia World Baptist Missions, Inc.	1995	-	-	15	-	-
Medical Ministry International	1999	1	-	-	7	-
Ministries In Action	2005	-	-	-	-	-
Mission Generation, Inc.	2010	-	-	-	-	-
Mission to the World (PCA), Inc.	1987	2	10	34	-	-
Missionary Ventures International	1999	-	-	8	1	-
Network of International Christian Schools	2001	16	3	7	9	-
New Way Missions	2006	-	-	-	-	-
OneHope		-	-	-	-	-
Open Door Baptist Missions	2007	-	-	2	-	-
Pentecostal Free Will Baptist Church, Inc.		-	-	-	1	-
Pioneers USA	1997	-	-	15	1	-
Precept Ministries International	1992	-	-	-	5	-
Proclaim! International, Inc.	2004	-	-	-	1	-
ReachGlobal	1975	2	-	11	3	-
Rock the World Youth Mission Alliance		-	-	-	-	-
Seventh-day Adventists, General Conference	1898	5	-	-	-	-
SIM USA, Inc.	1965	1	-	12	-	-
Source of Light Ministries International, Inc.	1975	-	-	-	2	-
South America Mission, Inc.	1921	7	-	26	2	-
Spanish World Ministries, Inc.		-	-	1	1	-
TEAM (The Evangelical Alliance Mission)		-	-	5	-	-
Team Expansion, Inc.		-	-	8	-	-
The Brethren Church, Inc.	1992	-	-	-	2	-
The Mission Society	1997	2	2	4	-	-
United Pentecostal Church International	1962	-	4	-	-	-
Walk Thru the Bible Ministries, Inc.	2000	-	-	-	-	-
Word of Life Fellowship, Inc.—Intl. Ministries	1986	-	-	1	18	1
World Concern	1987	-	-	-	6	-
World Mission Prayer League	1985	-	-	2	-	-
World Missions Far Corners, Inc.	1978	-	-	-	71	-
World Reach, Inc.	1998	-	-	2	3	1
World Team	1941	-	-	2	-	-
World-Wide Missions		-	-	-	2	-
Wycliffe Bible Translators, Inc.		-	-	45	-	-
Totals:		47	45	418	744	31

	Personnel from U.S.				Other Countries	
	First Year	1-2 yrs.	2-4 yrs.	4+ yrs.	Citizens	Non-Citizens

Philippines

	First Year	1-2 yrs.	2-4 yrs.	4+ yrs.	Citizens	Non-Citizens
ACM International	1998	-	-	2	-	-
Action International Ministries, Inc.	1974	-	-	23	5	-
Advent Christian Gen. Conf., Dept. of World Msns.	1953	-	-	5	-	-
Adventist World Aviation	2002	1	1	1	-	-
AEGA Ministries International, Inc.		-	-	-	-	1
All About Orphans		-	-	-	-	-
American Leprosy Missions, Inc.	1953	-	-	-	2	1
AMG International	1979	-	-	-	312	-
Asian Outreach U.S.A.		-	-	-	-	-
Assemblies of God World Missions	1926	19	-	53	-	-
Association of Christian Schools Intl. (ACSI)	1998	-	-	1	-	-
Awana International	1982	-	-	-	6	-
Back to the Bible International	1957	-	-	-	20	-
Baptist Bible Fellowship International	1950	-	14	42	-	-
Baptist International Missions, Inc. (BIMI)		-	-	35	-	-
Baptist International Outreach, Inc.	1998	-	-	7	4	-
Baptist Missionary Association of America	1974	-	-	4	93	-
BCM International		-	-	89	-	-
Bethany International Ministries	1982	-	-	6	-	-
Biblical Ministries Worldwide		-	-	2	-	-
Brethren Assemblies		-	-	14	-	-
Bright Hope International	2004	-	-	-	3	-
Calvary International	1987	2	-	14	7	-
Campus Crusade for Christ, Intl.	1965	-	-	21	148	-
Child Evangelism Fellowship, Inc.	1952	-	-	-	15	-
Childcare Worldwide	1996	-	-	-	-	-
Christ Community Church	1947	-	-	-	123	-
Christ to the Nations	1992	-	-	-	8	-
Christar	1954	-	-	17	-	5
Christian Aid Mission		-	-	-	1671	-
Christian Aviation and Radio Mission	1995	-	-	-	4	-
Christian Blind Mission International (CBM-US)	1982	1	-	-	-	-
Christian Broadcasting Network Inc., The	1976	-	-	-	129	-
Christian Churches/Churches of Christ		-	-	40	10	-
Christian Cultural Development Foundation	1985	-	-	2	4	2
Christian Reformed World Missions	1961	-	2	10	-	-
Christians In Action Missions International	1977	-	-	-	-	2
Christ's Mandate for Missions	1995	-	-	-	75	-
Church of God (Cleveland, Tenn.) World Missions	1947	-	-	16	-	8
Church of God of Prophecy—Global Outreach		-	-	-	6	-
Church of the Nazarene, World Msn. Dept.	1946	-	-	22	-	2
Churches of Christ	1920	-	-	18	-	-
Commission to Every Nation	1997	-	2	8	1	9
Compassion International, Inc.	1972	-	-	-	78	-
Converge Worldwide	1949	-	-	17	-	-
CrossWorld	1985	-	-	5	-	-
Eastern Mennonite Missions	1971	-	-	-	-	-
Elim Fellowship—International Ministries	1997	-	-	2	-	-

	First Year	Personnel from U.S. 1-2 yrs.	2-4 yrs.	4+ yrs.	Other Countries Citizens	Non-Citizens
Emmanuel International Mission	1976	-	-	1	4	4
Evangelical Covenant Ch.—Covenant Wld. Msn.	1998	-	-	-	-	-
Evangelical Friends Mission		-	-	-	-	-
Evangelize China Fellowship, Inc.		-	-	-	1	-
Every Home for Christ International	1960	-	-	-	1	-
Faith Life Ministries, Inc.	2001	-	-	-	-	-
Far East Broadcasting Company, Inc.	1948	-	-	7	200	-
Food for the Hungry, Inc.	1982	-	3	1	-	-
Free Gospel Church, Inc.—Missions Department	1920	-	2	-	35	-
Free Methodist World Missions	1949	-	2	4	-	-
General Baptists International	1957	-	-	6	-	-
Global Adopt-A-People Network	1995	-	-	9	-	-
Global Outreach International	2000	-	-	2	-	-
Global Partners/Wesleyan World Missions	1932	-	4	-	-	-
Global Recordings Network		-	-	-	3	-
Globe International	1986	-	-	2	-	-
Go Ye Fellowship	2000	-	-	-	2	-
Good News Productions International	1995	-	-	1	4	-
Gospel Fellowship Association	1978	6	-	15	-	-
Gospel Revival Ministries		-	-	-	1	-
Grace Brethren International Missions	1984	-	-	2	7	-
Great Commission Ministries, Inc.		-	-	-	1	-
Greater Grace World Outreach	1997	-	-	1	2	1
Habitat for Humanity International	1986	-	4	-	3	1
Harvest	2001	-	-	-	2	-
Help for Christian Nationals, Inc.	2000	-	-	-	-	2
I. N. Network USA	1977	-	-	-	71	-
IFCA World Missions		-	-	-	1	-
Independent Faith Mission, Inc.	1993	-	-	2	-	-
International Christian Leprosy Mission, Inc. (USA)	1951	-	-	-	4	-
International Gospel Outreach	1998	-	-	2	4	-
International Justice Mission	2000	-	4	-	55	-
International Partnership Ministries, Inc.	2001	-	-	-	13	-
International Pentecostal Church of Christ	1982	-	-	2	-	-
Intl. Pentecostal Holiness Ch. World Msns. Mins.	1975	-	-	6	-	-
International Teams, U.S.A.	1981	-	4	2	32	152
Kids for Christ International	2007	-	-	-	4	-
LifeWind International	1975	-	-	-	38	-
Literacy & Evangelism International	1999	-	-	2	-	-
Medical Ministry International	1990	-	-	-	1	-
Medical Missions Philippines, Inc.		-	-	-	-	-
Mission to Children, Inc.	1978	-	-	-	-	-
Mission to the World (PCA), Inc.	1991	-	-	8	-	-
Mission To Unreached Peoples	1987	-	-	4	2	-
Missionary Ventures International	2000	-	-	2	4	-
Mutual Faith Ministries Intl.		-	-	-	-	-
Navigators, U.S. International Missions Group		-	-	10	-	-
New Life Advance International	2000	1	-	-	-	-
New Tribes Mission	1951	-	5	66	-	-
OC International, Inc.	1952	-	-	18	-	-

		Personnel from U.S.			Other Countries	
	First Year	1-2 yrs.	2-4 yrs.	4+ yrs.	Citizens	Non-Citizens
OMF International	1950	3	-	17	-	20
OMS International, Inc.	1982	-	-	6	-	1
OneHope		-	-	-	-	-
Partners International	1968	-	-	-	23	-
Pass the Torch Ministries/Church of Acts	1987	-	-	-	3	-
Pentecostal Free Will Baptist Church, Inc.		-	-	2	-	-
Precept Ministries International	1996	-	-	-	2	-
Presbyterian Mission International (PMI)	2000	-	-	-	2	-
Reach Ministries International	1968	-	-	6	-	-
ReachGlobal	1951	2	-	14	3	-
Salvation Army, U.S.A.	1937	-	2	-	-	-
Samaritan's Purse International Relief	1999	1	-	-	-	-
SEED International	2003	-	-	1	-	-
SEND International USA	1947	-	-	29	2	3
Seventh-day Adventists, General Conference	1906	-	-	22	-	31
Source of Light Ministries International, Inc.	1980	-	-	-	3	-
Sowers International, The	1993	-	-	-	8	-
TEAM (The Evangelical Alliance Mission)		-	-	9	-	-
Team Expansion, Inc.		-	-	4	-	-
Teen Missions International, Inc.	1983	-	-	-	8	-
Tentmakers International	1996	-	-	-	1	-
The Brethren Church, Inc.	2003	-	-	-	4	-
The Mission Society	1988	-	-	2	-	-
The Waray-Waray Project	1992	-	-	-	11	-
Things To Come Mission, Inc.	1958	-	-	-	80	-
TITUS International		-	-	-	-	-
Training Evangelistic Leadership (T.E.L.), Inc.	1977	-	-	4	12	-
Trans World Evangelism, Inc.	2007	3	2	-	-	-
Tribes and Nations Outreach		-	-	-	-	-
U.S. Center for World Mission		2	-	3	-	2
United Evangelical Churches	1970	-	-	2	-	-
United Pentecostal Church International	1957	-	8	-	-	5
Walk Thru the Bible Ministries, Inc.	2000	-	-	-	68	-
White Fields, Inc.		-	-	-	43	-
Word of Life Fellowship, Inc.—Intl. Ministries	1973	-	-	5	71	-
World Indigenous Missions	1989	-	-	8	-	-
World Mission Prayer League	1984	-	-	5	-	-
World Missions Far Corners, Inc.	1990	-	-	-	4	-
World Team	1981	-	-	12	-	-
World Venture	1948	-	5	20	-	-
World-Wide Missions	1971	-	2	-	-	-
Wycliffe Bible Translators, Inc.	1960	-	-	119	-	-
Youth for Christ/USA—World Outreach		-	-	1	-	-
	Totals:	41	66	942	3567	252

Poland

Assemblies of God World Missions	1925	-	-	8	-	-
Avant Ministries	2004	-	-	9	-	1
Baptist Bible Fellowship International	2001	-	-	2	-	-
Baptist International Missions, Inc. (BIMI)		-	-	2	-	-

	First Year	1-2 yrs.	2-4 yrs.	4+ yrs.	Citizens	Non-Citizens
		Personnel from U.S.			**Other Countries**	
BCM International		-	-	2	-	-
Brethren Assemblies		-	-	6	-	-
Campus Crusade for Christ, Intl.	1977	2	-	-	97	-
Child Evangelism Fellowship, Inc.	1989	-	-	-	2	-
Christian Aid Mission		-	-	-	2	-
Christian Associates International		-	-	-	-	-
Christian Church (Disciples of Christ)		-	2	-	-	-
Christian Churches/Churches of Christ		-	-	2	60	-
Church of the Nazarene, World Msn. Dept.	1999	-	-	-	-	-
Church Resource Ministries (CRM)	1995	-	-	2	-	-
Churches of Christ	1981	-	-	2	-	-
Commission to Every Nation	1999	-	-	2	1	1
Elim Fellowship—International Ministries	1997	-	-	2	1	-
Friends of Israel Gospel Ministry, Inc.	1961	-	-	-	8	-
Global Mins., Ch. of the United Brethren in Christ		-	-	-	-	-
Global Outreach International	1997	-	-	2	-	-
Great Commission Ministries, Inc.	2002	-	-	2	1	-
Greater Europe Mission	1993	6	1	5	-	-
Greater Grace World Outreach	1985	-	-	-	6	-
In Touch Mission International	1984	-	-	5	9	-
International Messengers	1991	-	-	12	15	1
Literacy & Evangelism International		-	-	-	-	-
Lutheran Church-Missouri Synod, World Mission	1943	-	-	3	-	-
Mailbox Club International Inc., The		-	-	-	2	-
Mission To Unreached Peoples	1989	-	-	4	-	-
Pioneers USA		-	-	6	-	-
Precept Ministries International		-	-	-	-	-
ReachGlobal	1993	-	-	4	-	-
Resourcing Christian Education International	2005	-	-	-	1	-
Salvation Army, U.S.A.	2005	-	2	-	-	-
SEND International USA	1991	-	1	11	-	4
TCM International Institute		-	-	-	1	-
Tentmakers International	2005	-	-	-	1	-
United Pentecostal Church International		-	2	-	-	3
Word of Life Fellowship, Inc.—Intl. Ministries	1987	-	-	2	5	-
World Venture	1988	-	4	10	-	-
Totals:		8	12	105	212	10

Portugal

	First Year	1-2 yrs.	2-4 yrs.	4+ yrs.	Citizens	Non-Citizens
Abundant Life Association, Inc.	1989	-	-	-	60	-
Assemblies of God World Missions	1972	-	-	9	-	-
Baptist Bible Fellowship International	1987	-	-	12	-	-
Baptist Missionary Association of America	1954	-	-	-	7	-
BILD International		-	-	-	1	-
Brethren Assemblies		-	-	3	-	-
Campus Crusade for Christ, Intl.	1975	-	-	-	-	6
Christian Associates International	1997	-	-	-	-	-
Christian Churches/Churches of Christ		-	-	4	-	-
Church of God of Prophecy—Global Outreach		-	-	-	1	-
Church of the Nazarene, World Msn. Dept.	1973	-	-	3	-	1

	First Year	Personnel from U.S. 1-2 yrs.	2-4 yrs.	4+ yrs.	Other Countries Citizens	Non-Citizens
Church Planting International, Inc.	1989	-	-	-	-	-
Churches of Christ	1969	-	-	2	-	-
European Christian Mission International—USA		-	-	-	-	2
Grace Brethren International Missions	1990	-	-	4	2	-
Greater Europe Mission	1971	1	-	8	-	-
Greater Grace World Outreach	1999	-	-	1	-	-
Intl. Pentecostal Holiness Ch. World Msns. Mins.	2001	-	-	2	-	-
Macedonia World Baptist Missions, Inc.	2008	-	-	2	-	-
Mission to the World (PCA), Inc.		-	-	3	-	-
Precept Ministries International		-	-	-	-	-
ReachGlobal	1994	-	-	4	-	-
Resourcing Christian Education International	2006	-	-	-	4	-
Salvation Army, U.S.A.	1971	-	1	-	-	-
TEAM (The Evangelical Alliance Mission)		-	-	6	-	-
United Pentecostal Church International	1972	-	4	-	-	-
Word of Life Fellowship, Inc.—Intl. Ministries	1976	-	-	1	8	2
World Baptist Fellowship Msn. Agency, Inc.	2003	-	-	1	-	-
World Partners USA	1991	-	2	-	-	-
World Venture	1945	-	-	4	-	-
Youth for Christ/USA—World Outreach	1996	-	-	2	-	-
Totals:	1	7	71		83	11

Puerto Rico

	First Year	1-2 yrs.	2-4 yrs.	4+ yrs.	Citizens	Non-Citizens
Awana International	1986	-	-	-	-	1
Baptist Bible Fellowship International	1955	-	-	3	-	-
Baptist International Missions, Inc. (BIMI)		-	-	13	-	-
Baptist Mid-Missions	1959	-	-	2	-	-
Baptist Missionary Association of America	1994	-	-	1	2	-
Biblical Ministries Worldwide	1986	-	-	2	-	-
Brethren Assemblies		-	-	2	-	-
Christian Churches/Churches of Christ		-	-	5	5	-
Church of the Nazarene, World Msn. Dept.	1944	-	-	1	-	1
Churches of Christ		-	-	-	-	-
Foursquare Missions International		-	-	2	-	-
Global Partners/Wesleyan World Missions	1952	-	2	-	-	-
Gospel Fellowship Association	1963	-	-	2	-	-
Grace Ministries International	1961	-	8	-	-	-
Greater Grace World Outreach	2007	-	2	-	-	2
International Partnership Ministries, Inc.	1999	-	-	-	2	-
Lutheran Church-Missouri Synod	1993	-	-	8	-	-
Macedonia World Baptist Missions, Inc.	1974	-	-	9	-	-
Ministries In Action	2005	-	-	2	-	-
Mission to the World (PCA), Inc.		-	-	4	-	-
Open Door Baptist Missions	1995	-	-	2	-	-
Pentecostal Free Will Baptist Church, Inc.		-	-	-	1	-
Seventh-day Adventists, General Conference	1901	-	-	8	-	-
United Pentecostal Church International	1964	-	2	-	-	-
Totals:	-	14	66		10	4

	First Year	Personnel from U.S.			Other Countries	
		1-2 yrs.	2-4 yrs.	4+ yrs.	Citizens	Non-Citizens

Qatar

Walk Thru the Bible Ministries, Inc.	2003	-	-	-	-	-
Totals:		-	-	-	-	-

Reunion

Church of the Nazarene, World Msn. Dept.	2003	-	-	1	-	1
United Pentecostal Church International	1999	-	2	-	-	-
Totals:		-	2	1	-	1

Romania

AMG International	1992	-	-	-	48	-
Assemblies of God World Missions	1951	14	-	10	-	-
Awana International	1991	-	-	-	8	-
Baptist Bible Fellowship International	1990	-	-	9	-	-
Baptist International Evangelistic Ministries		-	-	-	16	-
Baptist International Missions, Inc. (BIMI)		-	-	12	-	-
Baptist Mid-Missions	1993	-	-	13	-	-
Baptist Missionary Association of America	1998	-	-	-	13	-
Brethren Assemblies		-	-	4	-	-
Calvary Commission, Inc.	1990	3	4	2	-	-
Campus Crusade for Christ, Intl.	1980	1	-	8	153	-
CEIFA Ministry International	1990	-	-	1	-	1
Christian Aid Ministries (CAM)	1981	-	13	-	20	134
Christian Associates International		-	-	-	-	-
Christian Relief Fund, The	1991	-	-	-	-	-
Church of God (Cleveland, Tenn.) World Missions	1922	2	-	2	-	-
Church of God of Prophecy—Global Outreach		-	-	-	1	-
Church of the Nazarene, World Msn. Dept.	1992	-	-	1	-	-
Church Resource Ministries (CRM)	1990	-	-	3	-	-
Churches of Christ	1964	-	-	8	-	-
Commission to Every Nation	2001	-	1	2	1	2
CrossWorld	1991	-	-	2	2	-
Entrust	1979	-	-	7	1	-
European Christian Mission International—USA		-	-	-	5	-
Evangelical Baptist Missions		-	-	3	1	-
Food for the Hungry, Inc.	1991	-	6	4	-	-
For God's Children International	1995	-	1	-	4	-
Free Methodist World Missions	2006	2	2	2	-	-
Friendship International Ministries, Inc.	1995	2	-	2	3	1
Global Outreach International	1988	-	-	14	2	2
Global Outreach Mission, Inc.		-	-	2	-	-
Greater Europe Mission	1993	-	1	16	-	-
Greater Grace World Outreach	1991	4	-	-	2	-
Harvest International, Inc.	2005	2	2	-	-	-
Heart to Heart Intl. Ministries (H2H)	1994	-	-	11	9	-
Hope Haven International Ministries		-	-	-	4	-
I. N. Network USA	1992	-	-	-	11	-
In Touch Mission International	1967	-	-	-	6	-
International Gospel Outreach	2005	-	4	-	-	-
International Institute for Christian Studies	1991	-	-	1	-	1

	First Year	Personnel from U.S.			Other Countries	
		1-2 yrs.	2-4 yrs.	4+ yrs.	Citizens	Non-Citizens
International Messengers	1996	-	-	7	12	-
Intl. Pentecostal Holiness Ch. World Msns. Mins.	1996	-	-	2	-	-
International Teams, U.S.A.		3	-	6	-	13
InterVarsity Christian Fellowship/USA, Msns. Dept.		-	-	3	-	-
LifeWind International	1992	-	-	-	3	-
Living Water International		-	-	-	-	-
Macedonia World Baptist Missions, Inc.	2004	-	-	2	-	-
Mission to the World (PCA), Inc.	2001	2	2	7	-	-
Mission Without Borders International		-	-	-	39	-
New Hope International	1971	-	-	-	9	-
OC International, Inc.	1996	-	-	11	-	-
OneHope		-	-	-	-	-
Operation Mobilization		2	-	-	-	-
Prayer Baptist Missions International, Inc.	2003	-	-	2	-	-
Precept Ministries International		-	-	-	12	-
ReachGlobal	1991	-	6	16	-	-
Romanian Missionary Society	1968	-	-	-	70	-
SEND International USA	1993	-	-	-	-	2
Source of Light Ministries International, Inc.	1992	-	-	-	2	-
TCM International Institute		-	-	-	1	-
Team Expansion, Inc.		-	-	2	-	-
The Master's Mission, Inc.	1999	-	-	2	2	-
TITUS International	1999	-	-	5	20	-
United Pentecostal Church International	1995	-	2	-	-	1
Walk Thru the Bible Ministries, Inc.	2000	-	-	-	2	-
Word of Life Fellowship, Inc.—Intl. Ministries	1993	-	-	1	27	1
World Bible Translation Center		-	-	-	2	-
World Harvest Mission	2003	-	-	2	-	-
World Link Ministries	2002	-	-	-	70	-
World Mission Prayer League	1994	-	-	2	-	-
World Missions & Evangelism, Inc.		-	-	2	-	-
World Reach, Inc.	1998	-	-	-	-	2
World Venture	1991	-	-	6	-	-
Wycliffe Bible Translators		-	-	1	-	-
Totals:		37	44	218	581	160

Russia

	First Year	Personnel from U.S.			Other Countries	
All About Orphans		-	-	-	-	-
Artists In Christian Testimony International	2004	-	-	-	-	1
Assemblies of God World Missions	1990	7	-	41	-	-
Awana International	1996	-	-	-	17	-
Baptist Bible Fellowship International	1993	-	-	10	-	-
Baptist International Evangelistic Ministries		-	-	3	40	2
Baptist International Missions, Inc. (BIMI)		-	-	16	-	-
Baptist International Outreach, Inc.	2009	-	-	2	-	-
Baptist Mid-Missions	1992	-	-	4	-	-
Baptist Missionary Association of America	1994	-	-	-	12	-
BCM International		-	-	4	-	-
Calvary International	1990	2	-	2	-	-
Campus Crusade for Christ, Intl.	1991	36	-	65	160	34

	First Year	Personnel from U.S. 1-2 yrs.	2-4 yrs.	4+ yrs.	Other Countries Citizens	Non-Citizens
Centers for Apologetics Research, The	1993	-	-	-	3	-
Child Evangelism Fellowship, Inc.	1989	-	-	-	2	2
Children's HopeChest	1994	-	-	1	145	-
Chosen People Ministries	2008	-	-	-	1	-
Christian Aid Mission		-	-	-	192	-
Christian Associates International	1993	-	-	-	-	-
Christian Broadcasting Network Inc., The	1992	-	-	-	8	-
Christian Churches/Churches of Christ		2	4	16	6	-
Christian Involvement in Service (CIS)	2004	-	-	-	13	-
Christian Ministries International (CMI)	1998	-	-	-	1	-
Christian Reformed World Missions	1994	-	-	1	-	-
Church of God (Anderson, Ind.), Global Msns.	1902	-	-	2	-	-
Church of God (Cleveland, Tenn.) World Missions	1992	-	-	6	-	2
Church of God of Prophecy—Global Outreach		-	-	-	3	2
Church of the Nazarene, World Msn. Dept.	1992	-	-	7	-	-
Church Resource Ministries (CRM)	1990	-	-	6	-	-
Churches of Christ	1952	-	-	3	-	-
Development Associates International (DAI)	2001	-	-	-	3	-
Eastern European Outreach, Inc.	1990	-	-	-	8	-
East-West Ministries International	1993	-	11	2	-	-
Entrust	1979	-	-	3	1	-
Evangelical Baptist Missions		-	-	1	2	-
Evangelical Covenant Ch.—Covenant Wld. Msn.	1993	-	-	2	-	-
Evangelical Lutheran Church in America	1994	1	-	1	-	-
Evangelism Explosion International		-	-	-	-	10
Every Home for Christ International	1991	-	-	-	-	-
Faith Christian Fellowship International		-	-	1	1	-
Far East Broadcasting Company, Inc.	1992	-	-	-	50	-
Free Will Baptist, Inc. Bd. of Intl. Missions	1999	-	-	2	-	-
Friends of Israel Gospel Ministry, Inc.	1994	-	-	-	4	-
Full Gospel Evangelistic Association	2002	-	2	-	-	-
Global Outreach Mission, Inc.		-	-	5	-	-
Global Partners/Wesleyan World Missions	1993	-	8	-	-	-
Global Recordings Network		-	-	2	5	-
Globe International	1995	-	-	2	-	-
Gospelink, Inc.		-	-	-	37	-
Grace Brethren International Missions	1994	-	2	-	-	-
Greater Europe Mission	1995	-	-	1	-	-
Greater Grace World Outreach	1990	-	-	-	9	7
Help for Christian Nationals, Inc.	1996	-	-	-	2	-
InterAct Ministries	1991	-	2	9	-	-
International Gospel Outreach	1992	-	-	4	-	-
International Teams, U.S.A.		-	-	4	-	5
LifeWind International	2004	-	-	-	2	-
Lutheran Church-Missouri Synod, World Mission	1992	-	-	5	-	-
Mailbox Club International Inc., The		-	-	-	2	-
Mission Possible Foundation, Inc.	1990	-	-	-	28	-
Mission To Unreached Peoples	1993	-	-	2	-	-
Missionary Ventures International	1994	-	-	-	2	-
OMS International, Inc.	1993	-	1	5	-	8

	Personnel from U.S.				Other Countries	
	First Year	1-2 yrs.	2-4 yrs.	4+ yrs.	Citizens	Non-Citizens
OneHope		-	-	-	-	-
Open Air Campaigners—Overseas Ministries	2003	-	-	-	2	-
Operation Mobilization	1991	-	1	-	-	-
Perimeter Church—Global Outreach	1985	-	-	-	-	-
Prayer Baptist Missions International, Inc.	2003	-	-	2	-	-
Precept Ministries International	1994	-	-	-	3	-
ReachGlobal	1993	2	2	16	10	-
Resourcing Christian Education International	2005	-	-	-	11	-
Russian Christian Radio, Inc.	1992	-	-	2	20	-
Salvation Army, U.S.A.	1913	-	4	2	-	-
SEED International	2004	-	-	1	-	-
SEND International USA	1992	-	-	32	-	6
Seventh-day Adventists, General Conference	1886	-	-	6	-	14
TCM International Institute		-	-	-	1	-
TEAM (The Evangelical Alliance Mission)		-	-	6	-	-
Teen Missions International, Inc.	2006	-	-	-	-	-
The Mission Society	1995	1	-	4	-	-
TITUS International		-	-	-	-	-
United Pentecostal Church International	1990	-	7	-	-	5
United World Mission		-	-	2	-	-
Walk Thru the Bible Ministries, Inc.	2000	-	-	-	21	-
WEC International		-	-	4	-	-
White Fields, Inc.		-	-	-	2	-
Wisconsin Evangelical Lutheran Synod	1991	-	2	2	-	-
Word To Russia		-	-	5	5	-
World Bible Translation Center		-	-	-	2	-
World Indigenous Missions	1990	-	-	6	-	-
World Mission Prayer League	2005	-	-	1	-	-
World Partners USA	1994	-	4	-	-	-
World Venture	1992	-	-	7	-	-
Young Life		-	-	1	-	-
Totals:	51	50	339	836	98	

Rwanda

Action International Ministries, Inc.	2006	-	-	4	-	-
Africa Inland Mission International, Inc.	2006	1	-	-	-	6
African Enterprise	1988	-	-	-	10	-
African Leadership, Inc.	2002	-	-	-	1	-
Assemblies of God World Missions	1993	-	-	8	-	-
Campus Crusade for Christ, Intl.	1980	-	-	-	30	-
Church of God of Prophecy—Global Outreach		-	-	-	6	-
Church of the Nazarene, World Msn. Dept.	1990	-	-	-	-	-
Churches of Christ	2002	-	-	16	-	-
Commission to Every Nation	2009	-	1	-	-	1
Compassion International, Inc.	1980	-	-	2	66	-
Evangelical Friends Mission		-	-	-	-	-
Every Home for Christ International	1994	-	-	-	1	-
Food for the Hungry, Inc.	1994	-	-	-	-	-
Foursquare Missions International	2005	-	-	2	-	-
Free Methodist World Missions	1942	-	2	1	-	-

	First Year	1-2 yrs.	2-4 yrs.	4+ yrs.	Citizens	Non-Citizens
		Personnel from U.S.			**Other Countries**	
Global Outreach International	1994	-	-	2	-	-
Go Ye Fellowship	1999	-	-	2	-	-
Greater Grace World Outreach	2005	-	-	-	15	-
Harvest	2000	-	-	-	2	-
HOPE International	2005	1	-	-	-	1
International Gospel Outreach	1999	-	-	-	1	-
International Justice Mission	2007	-	-	-	14	2
Intl. Pentecostal Holiness Ch. World Msns. Mins.		-	-	-	-	-
International Teams, U.S.A.		-	-	-	-	2
Living Water International		-	-	-	-	-
Missions Resource Network	2005	-	-	6	-	-
ReachGlobal	1994	-	-	-	-	-
Seventh-day Adventists, General Conference	1920	-	-	6	-	9
United Pentecostal Church International	1999	-	2	-	-	-
World Concern	1995	-	-	-	2	-
World Relief	1994	3	2	1	165	1
World Venture	1965	1	1	8	-	-
Youth for Christ/USA—World Outreach		-	-	4	-	-
Totals:		6	8	62	313	22

Saint Kitts and Nevis

	First Year	1-2 yrs.	2-4 yrs.	4+ yrs.	Citizens	Non-Citizens
Baptist International Missions, Inc. (BIMI)		-	-	2	-	-
Church of the Nazarene, World Msn. Dept.	1983	-	-	-	-	-
Totals:		-	-	2	-	-

Saint Lucia

	First Year	1-2 yrs.	2-4 yrs.	4+ yrs.	Citizens	Non-Citizens
Assemblies of God World Missions	1996	-	-	2	-	-
Church of the Nazarene, World Msn. Dept.	1972	-	-	-	-	-
Churches of Christ	1968	-	-	-	-	-
Macedonia World Baptist Missions, Inc.	1996	-	-	4	-	-
Ministries In Action	2005	-	-	-	-	-
Prayer Baptist Missions International, Inc.	2000	-	-	2	-	-
Totals:		-	-	8	-	-

Saint Martin

	First Year	1-2 yrs.	2-4 yrs.	4+ yrs.	Citizens	Non-Citizens
Ministries In Action	2003	-	-	-	-	-
Word of Life Fellowship, Inc.—Intl. Ministries		-	-	-	-	-
Totals:		-	-	-	-	-

Saint Vincent and the Grenadines

	First Year	1-2 yrs.	2-4 yrs.	4+ yrs.	Citizens	Non-Citizens
Baptist Bible Fellowship International	2006	-	-	2	-	-
Baptist Mid-Missions	1946	-	-	6	-	-
BCM International		-	-	2	-	-
Church of the Nazarene, World Msn. Dept.	1975	-	-	-	-	-
Churches of Christ	1965	-	-	-	-	-
Independent Faith Mission, Inc.	2008	-	-	-	2	-
Ministries In Action	1974	-	-	-	2	-
Seventh-day Adventists, General Conference	1889	-	-	2	-	-
Totals:		-	-	12	4	-

	Personnel from U.S.				Other Countries	
	First Year	1-2 yrs.	2-4 yrs.	4+ yrs.	Citizens	Non-Citizens
Samoa						
Church of God of Prophecy—Global Outreach		-	-	2	-	-
Church of the Nazarene, World Msn. Dept.	1964	-	-	-	-	-
Churches of Christ		-	-	-	-	-
United Pentecostal Church International	1999	-	2	-	-	-
Totals:		-	2	2	-	-
Sao Tome and Principe						
Abundant Life Association, Inc.	1990	-	-	-	1	-
Church of the Nazarene, World Msn. Dept.	1997	-	-	2	-	-
Seventh-day Adventists, General Conference	1938	-	-	-	-	2
Totals:		-	-	2	1	2
Saudi Arabia						
Churches of Christ	1960	-	-	-	-	-
Walk Thru the Bible Ministries, Inc.	2003	-	-	-	-	-
Totals:		-	-	-	-	-
Senegal						
Africa Inland Mission International, Inc.	2002	-	-	2	-	-
Africa Inter-Mennonite Mission International	1996	5	2	-	-	-
Assemblies of God World Missions	1956	-	-	7	-	-
Awana International	1997	-	-	-	-	-
Baptist International Missions, Inc. (BIMI)		-	-	4	-	-
Brethren Assemblies		-	-	5	-	-
Campus Crusade for Christ, Intl.	1985	-	-	1	20	-
Christian Aid Mission	1996	-	-	-	100	-
Christian Broadcasting Network Inc., The	2004	-	-	2	1	-
Christian Reformed World Relief Committee	1991	-	-	1	-	-
Church of God of Prophecy—Global Outreach		-	-	-	1	-
Church of the Nazarene, World Msn. Dept.	1988	-	-	2	-	-
Churches of Christ	1971	-	-	-	-	-
Converge Worldwide		-	-	8	-	-
Evangelical Lutheran Church in America	1976	-	-	7	-	3
Fellowship International Mission	2000	-	-	2	-	-
Global Recordings Network		-	-	-	2	-
Habitat for Humanity International	2003	-	1	-	-	1
Heart of God Ministries	2001	-	-	12	-	-
International Gospel Outreach	1989	-	-	1	1	-
Mennonite Mission Network	1998	-	-	2	1	1
Mission: Moving Mountains, Inc.	1995	-	-	10	-	2
New Tribes Mission	1954	-	-	30	-	-
Partners International	2000	-	-	-	66	-
Pioneers USA	1991	-	-	9	-	1
Seventh-day Adventists, General Conference	1952	-	-	-	-	2
SIM USA, Inc.	1984	-	-	13	-	-
Tentmakers International	2007	-	-	-	1	-
United World Mission		-	-	9	-	-
WEC International	1936	-	-	2	-	-
World Venture	1962	-	5	27	-	-

		Personnel from U.S.			Other Countries	
	First Year	1-2 yrs.	2-4 yrs.	4+ yrs.	Citizens	Non-Citizens
Wycliffe Bible Translators		-	-	9	-	-
Totals:		5	8	165	193	10

Serbia and Montenegro

Assemblies of God World Missions	1993	-	-	4	-	-
Brethren Assemblies		-	-	2	-	-
Campus Crusade for Christ, Intl.	1979	-	-	-	15	6
Child Evangelism Fellowship, Inc.	1989	-	-	2	4	-
Ch. of the Brethren—Global Msn. Partnerships		-	-	-	-	-
Churches of Christ	1985	-	-	2	-	-
European Christian Mission International—USA		-	-	-	2	-
Global Action	1999	-	-	-	-	1
Greater Europe Mission		-	-	4	-	-
Precept Ministries International	1994	-	-	-	2	-
Tentmakers International	2005	-	-	-	1	-
United Pentecostal Church International		-	1	-	-	-
Walk Thru the Bible Ministries, Inc.	2002	-	-	-	-	-
World Bible Translation Center		-	-	-	2	-
Totals:		-	1	14	26	7

Seychelles

Churches of Christ	1980	-	-	-	-	-
Intl. Pentecostal Holiness Ch. World Msns. Mins.		-	-	-	-	-
United Pentecostal Church International	1988	-	2	-	-	-
Totals:		-	2	-	-	-

Sierra Leone

African Leadership, Inc.	2002	-	-	-	1	-
Assemblies of God World Missions	1920	-	-	4	-	-
Baptist Bible Fellowship International	1997	-	-	2	-	-
Baptist Missionary Association of America	2003	-	-	-	1	-
Brethren Assemblies		-	-	2	-	-
Campus Crusade for Christ, Intl.	1981	-	-	-	27	-
Children's Christian Concern Society	2005	-	-	-	-	-
Christian Aid Mission	1988	-	-	-	15	-
Christian Reformed World Relief Committee	1979	-	1	-	-	-
Christians In Action Missions International	1976	-	-	-	2	-
Church of God of Prophecy—Global Outreach		-	-	-	8	-
Church of the Nazarene, World Msn. Dept.	2004	-	-	2	-	-
Churches of Christ	1966	-	-	-	-	-
CityTeam Ministries—New Generations Intl.		-	-	-	2	-
Episcopal Church USA		-	-	-	-	-
Every Home for Christ International	1993	-	-	-	1	-
Free Gospel Church, Inc.—Missions Department	1928	-	-	-	22	-
Global Mins., Ch. of the United Brethren in Christ		-	-	-	-	-
Global Outreach Mission, Inc.		-	-	4	-	-
Global Partners/Wesleyan World Missions	1889	-	-	-	-	-
Global Recordings Network		-	-	12	12	-
His Healing Helping Hands Intl. Mins. (4 H.I.M.)	2005	-	-	-	7	-
International Christian Ministries	2001	-	-	-	2	1

	First Year	Personnel from U.S. 1-2 yrs.	2-4 yrs.	4+ yrs.	Other Countries Citizens	Non-Citizens
International Gospel Outreach	1990	-	-	1	2	-
Intl. Pentecostal Holiness Ch. World Msns. Mins.		-	-	-	-	-
LifeWind International	2001	-	-	-	1	-
Living Water International		-	-	-	-	-
Living Word Missions	1996	-	-	-	2	-
Lutheran Bible Translators, Inc.	1974	-	-	-	24	-
M/E International, Inc.	2009	-	-	-	-	-
National Baptist Convention USA, Inc.	1950	-	-	-	51	-
OneHope		-	-	-	-	-
Seventh-day Adventists, General Conference	1905	-	-	-	-	2
Tentmakers International	2007	-	-	-	1	-
United Pentecostal Church International	1975	-	2	-	-	-
Walk Thru the Bible Ministries, Inc.	2001	-	-	-	-	-
World Partners USA	1945	-	1	-	-	-
World Relief	1994	1	1	-	27	1
	Totals:	1	5	27	208	4

Singapore

	First Year	1-2 yrs.	2-4 yrs.	4+ yrs.	Citizens	Non-Citizens
Advancing Native Missions	2008	1	-	-	-	-
Asian Access	2009	-	-	2	2	-
Asian Outreach U.S.A.		-	-	-	-	-
Assemblies of God World Missions	1926	-	-	10	-	-
Awana International	1984	-	-	-	1	-
Baptist Bible Fellowship International	1970	-	-	4	-	-
Baptist International Missions, Inc. (BIMI)		-	-	3	-	-
BCM International		-	-	1	-	-
Calvary International		-	-	-	-	-
Campus Crusade for Christ, Intl.	1969	-	-	41	-	-
Child Evangelism Fellowship, Inc.	1970	-	-	-	2	-
Christian Broadcasting Network Inc., The	1996	-	-	-	3	-
Christian Churches/Churches of Christ		-	-	4	-	-
Church of God (Anderson, Ind.), Global Msns.	1979	-	-	2	-	-
Church of God (Cleveland, Tenn.) World Missions	1989	-	-	2	-	2
Church Resource Ministries (CRM)	2000	-	-	4	-	-
Churches of Christ	1955	-	-	3	-	-
Converge Worldwide		-	-	2	-	-
Evangelical Lutheran Church in America	1966	-	-	1	-	-
Faith Christian Fellowship International		-	-	1	6	-
Foursquare Missions International		-	-	2	-	-
Global Fellowship, Inc.	2007	-	-	1	-	2
Global Recordings Network		-	-	-	2	-
Good News Productions International		-	-	2	2	-
Habitat for Humanity International		-	15	3	9	9
HCJB Global	2002	-	-	6	4	4
Intl. Pentecostal Holiness Ch. World Msns. Mins.	1987	-	-	6	-	-
Mission to the World (PCA), Inc.		-	-	2	-	-
Missionary Ventures International		-	-	1	-	-
Network of International Christian Schools	1995	34	10	15	3	13
New Tribes Mission	1994	-	-	2	-	-
OC International, Inc.	1970	-	-	6	-	-

	Personnel from U.S.				Other Countries	
	First Year	1-2 yrs.	2-4 yrs.	4+ yrs.	Citizens	Non-Citizens
OMF International	1950	-	-	3	-	3
Partners International		-	-	2	-	-
Precept Ministries International	1988	-	-	-	4	-
RBC Ministries	1991	-	-	-	30	-
ReachGlobal	1957	-	-	-	-	-
Salvation Army, U.S.A.	1935	-	2	1	-	-
Seventh-day Adventists, General Conference	1904	-	-	2	-	5
Source of Light Ministries International, Inc.	2000	-	-	-	2	-
Tentmakers International	1998	-	-	-	1	-
TWR		-	-	4	-	-
United Pentecostal Church International	1981	-	2	-	-	-
Walk Thru the Bible Ministries, Inc.	1998	-	-	-	7	-
World Venture	1983	-	2	9	-	-
Wycliffe Bible Translators, Inc.		-	-	10	-	-
Totals:		**35**	**31**	**157**	**78**	**38**

Slovakia

Assemblies of God World Missions	1960	1	-	3	-	-
Awana International	2002	-	-	-	1	-
Baptist Bible Fellowship International	1998	-	-	2	-	-
Baptist International Missions, Inc. (BIMI)		-	-	4	-	-
Baptist Mid-Missions	1992	-	-	2	-	-
Campus Crusade for Christ, Intl.	1992	12	-	9	14	-
Child Evangelism Fellowship, Inc.	1989	-	-	-	2	-
Ch. of the Brethren—Global Msn. Partnerships		-	-	-	-	-
Churches of Christ	1990	-	-	2	-	-
Cooperative Baptist Fellowship—Global Missions	1996	-	-	2	-	-
CrossWorld	1991	-	-	2	-	-
Entrust	1979	1	-	2	1	-
Evangelical Lutheran Church in America	1991	-	5	2	-	-
Free Methodist World Missions		-	-	2	-	-
Global Outreach International	2000	-	-	1	-	-
Go Ye Fellowship	2002	-	-	2	-	-
Greater Europe Mission	1992	-	-	2	-	-
I. N. Network USA	1993	-	-	-	6	-
International Messengers	1994	-	1	3	-	1
Mission to the World (PCA), Inc.		3	2	11	-	-
New Hope International	1971	-	-	-	3	-
Pioneers USA		-	-	2	-	-
Precept Ministries International	1991	-	-	-	1	-
ReachGlobal	1993	-	-	4	-	-
The Word for the World USA	2003	-	-	2	-	-
TWR		-	-	2	-	-
United Pentecostal Church International	1930	-	2	-	-	2
Youth for Christ/USA—World Outreach		-	-	1	-	-
Totals:		**17**	**10**	**62**	**28**	**3**

Slovenia

Assemblies of God World Missions	1933	-	-	2	-	-
Avant Ministries	2009	-	-	6	-	-

	First Year	1-2 yrs.	2-4 yrs.	4+ yrs.	Other Countries Citizens	Other Countries Non-Citizens
Baptist Bible Fellowship International	2005	-	-	2	-	-
Bethany International Ministries	1992	-	-	2	-	2
Campus Crusade for Christ, Intl.	1994	-	-	3	3	-
Child Evangelism Fellowship, Inc.	1997	-	-	-	2	2
Church of the Nazarene, World Msn. Dept.		-	-	1	-	-
Greater Europe Mission		-	1	-	-	-
Partners in Christ International	2004	-	-	-	2	-
Pioneers USA		-	-	2	-	-
SEND International USA	1997	-	-	-	-	3
United World Mission		-	-	4	-	-
World Venture	1991	-	-	2	-	-
Totals:		-	1	24	7	7

Solomon Islands

	First Year	1-2 yrs.	2-4 yrs.	4+ yrs.	Citizens	Non-Citizens
Assemblies of God World Missions	1977	-	-	4	-	-
Campus Crusade for Christ, Intl.	1975	-	-	-	4	-
Church of the Nazarene, World Msn. Dept.	1992	-	-	2	-	-
Churches of Christ	1970	-	-	-	-	-
Global Recordings Network		-	-	-	2	-
LifeWind International	2004	-	-	-	-	-
Seventh-day Adventists, General Conference	1914	-	-	-	-	4
United Pentecostal Church International	1991	-	2	-	-	-
Wycliffe Bible Translators		-	-	4	-	-
Totals:		-	2	10	6	4

Somalia

	First Year	1-2 yrs.	2-4 yrs.	4+ yrs.	Citizens	Non-Citizens
Global Mins., Ch. of the United Brethren in Christ		-	-	-	-	-
Greater Grace World Outreach	2003	-	-	-	6	-
Totals:		-	-	-	6	-

South Africa

	First Year	1-2 yrs.	2-4 yrs.	4+ yrs.	Citizens	Non-Citizens
ACM International	1996	-	-	2	-	-
Africa Inter-Mennonite Mission International	1982	-	-	-	-	2
African Enterprise	1962	-	-	-	16	-
African Leadership, Inc.	2001	-	-	-	4	1
American Baptist Chs. of the U.S.A., Intl.Mins.	1990	-	-	2	-	-
Anis Shorrosh Evangelistic Association		-	-	-	-	-
Asian Outreach U.S.A.		-	-	-	-	-
Assemblies of God World Missions	1917	13	-	44	-	-
Awana International	1971	-	-	-	5	-
Baptist Bible Fellowship International	1980	-	-	10	-	-
Baptist International Missions, Inc. (BIMI)		-	-	19	-	-
Baptist International Outreach, Inc.	1994	-	-	6	2	-
BCM International		-	-	4	-	-
Biblical Ministries Worldwide	1976	-	-	11	6	-
Brethren Assemblies		-	-	7	-	-
Calvary International	1995	-	-	2	-	-
Campus Crusade for Christ, Intl.	1971	3	-	6	112	10
Child Evangelism Fellowship, Inc.	1947	-	-	3	4	-
Christ Community Church	1904	-	3	8	10	2

	First Year	Personnel from U.S. 1-2 yrs.	2-4 yrs.	4+ yrs.	Other Countries Citizens	Non-Citizens
Christian Aid Mission	1954	-	-	-	15	-
Christian Broadcasting Network Inc., The	1997	-	-	-	3	-
Christian Church (Disciples of Christ)		-	4	-	-	-
Christian Churches/Churches of Christ		-	3	32	4	-
Church of God (Cleveland, Tenn.) World Missions	1951	-	-	1	-	1
Church of God of Prophecy—Global Outreach		-	-	-	20	-
Church of the Nazarene, World Msn. Dept.	1919	-	-	30	-	7
Church Resource Ministries (CRM)	2001	2	2	4	-	-
Churches of Christ	1900	-	-	17	-	-
CityTeam Ministries—New Generations Intl.		-	-	-	2	-
Commission to Every Nation	2002	1	-	1	-	2
Cooperative Baptist Fellowship—Global Missions	1999	-	-	4	-	-
CrossWorld	1979	-	-	1	-	-
Development Associates International (DAI)	2001	-	-	-	1	-
Emmanuel International Mission	2002	-	-	-	-	2
Entrust	2004	-	-	-	2	-
Evangelical Baptist Missions		-	-	16	2	-
Evangelical Covenant Ch.—Covenant Wld. Msn.	1999	-	-	-	-	-
Evangelical Lutheran Church in America	1844	1	-	1	1	-
Every Home for Christ International	1965	-	-	-	-	-
Faith Christian Fellowship International	1994	-	-	1	2	-
Foursquare Missions International	1928	-	-	4	-	-
Global Partners/Wesleyan World Missions	1901	-	10	-	-	2
Global Recordings Network		-	-	-	3	-
Globe International	2000	1	-	2	-	-
Gospel Fellowship Association	1988	-	-	2	-	-
Greater Grace World Outreach	2001	-	-	2	2	-
Habitat for Humanity International	1987	-	20	4	14	10
HCJB Global	1999	-	-	1	-	-
Hope for the Hungry	1980	-	-	-	2	-
IFCA World Missions	1989	-	-	2	-	-
In Touch Mission International	1977	-	-	2	6	-
Independent Faith Mission, Inc.	1983	-	-	12	-	-
International Board of Jewish Missions, Inc.	2000	-	-	-	2	-
International Christian Ministries	2002	-	-	-	4	-
Intl. Pentecostal Holiness Ch. World Msns. Mins.	1911	-	-	19	-	-
Launch Out Ministries International	2005	-	-	-	3	1
LeaderTreks	2000	-	1	-	-	-
LifeWind International	2003	-	-	-	-	-
Lott Carey Baptist Foreign Msn. Conv.	1995	-	-	-	75	-
Macedonia World Baptist Missions, Inc.	2005	-	-	4	-	-
Mailbox Club International Inc., The		-	-	-	3	-
Mennonite Mission Network	1982	-	-	4	-	-
Mission to the World (PCA), Inc.	1997	-	2	24	-	-
Missionary Ventures International		-	-	-	1	2
National Baptist Convention USA, Inc.	1894	1	-	-	1	-
Navigators, U.S. International Missions Group		-	-	4	-	-
OC International, Inc.	1986	-	-	14	-	2
OMS International, Inc.		-	-	-	-	1
OneHope		-	-	-	-	-

	First Year	Personnel from U.S. 1-2 yrs.	2-4 yrs.	4+ yrs.	Other Countries Citizens	Non-Citizens
Open Door Baptist Missions	2003	-	-	6	-	-
Operation Mobilization		7	-	6	-	2
Paradigm Shift	2009	6	-	-	-	-
Precept Ministries International	1990	-	-	-	17	-
Progressive National Baptist Convention, Inc.	2000	-	-	-	-	-
Seventh-day Adventists, General Conference	1887	-	-	2	-	15
SIM USA, Inc.	1889	-	-	8	-	-
Source of Light Ministries International, Inc.	2003	-	-	-	1	-
TEAM (The Evangelical Alliance Mission)		-	-	22	-	-
Teen Missions International, Inc.	1985	-	2	-	2	1
Tentmakers International	1994	-	-	-	3	-
The Word for the World USA	1981	-	-	-	6	-
Things To Come Mission, Inc.	1989	-	-	-	-	2
TWR		2	-	15	-	-
United Pentecostal Church International	1948	-	8	-	-	2
Walk Thru the Bible Ministries, Inc.	1999	-	-	-	44	-
WEC International	1955	-	-	2	-	-
White Fields, Inc.		-	-	-	6	-
Word of Life Fellowship, Inc.—Intl. Ministries	1998	-	-	3	1	-
World Missions & Evangelism, Inc.	2003	1	-	2	13	-
World Partners USA	1999	-	1	-	-	-
Wycliffe Bible Translators		-	-	4	-	-
Youth for Christ/USA—World Outreach	1977	-	-	5	-	-
Zion Evangelical Ministries of Africa (ZEMA)	1907	-	3	8	10	2
Totals:		38	59	415	430	69

South America—General

	First Year	1-2 yrs.	2-4 yrs.	4+ yrs.	Citizens	Non-Citizens
ABWE, Inc.	1939	-	29	70	-	-
Church of God (Cleveland, Tenn.) World Missions		-	-	2	-	-
Impact International, Inc.		-	-	4	-	-
International Cooperating Ministries (ICM)		-	-	-	-	-
Ripe for Harvest, Inc.	1987	-	-	12	-	-
Totals:		-	29	88	-	-

South Pacific

	First Year	1-2 yrs.	2-4 yrs.	4+ yrs.	Citizens	Non-Citizens
Baptist Bible Fellowship International	1957	-	-	4	-	-
Evangelical Baptist Missions		-	-	2	-	-
Totals:		-	-	6	-	-

Spain

	First Year	1-2 yrs.	2-4 yrs.	4+ yrs.	Citizens	Non-Citizens
Action International Ministries, Inc.	2003	-	-	3	-	-
AMG International	1989	-	-	1	2	4
Assemblies of God World Missions	1932	22	-	46	-	-
Avant Ministries	1966	3	-	30	-	12
Awana International	1984	-	-	-	-	-
Baptist Bible Fellowship International	1970	-	1	14	-	-
Baptist International Missions, Inc. (BIMI)		-	-	7	-	-
Baptist Mid-Missions	1979	-	-	8	-	-
BCM International		-	-	5	-	-
Bethany International Ministries	1992	-	-	2	-	-

		Personnel from U.S.			Other Countries	
	First Year	1-2 yrs.	2-4 yrs.	4+ yrs.	Citizens	Non-Citizens
Biblical Ministries Worldwide	1958	-	-	4	-	-
Brethren Assemblies		-	-	11	-	-
Brethren in Christ World Missions	1988	-	-	3	-	-
Cadence International	1974	-	2	-	-	-
CAM International	1971	-	-	14	-	-
Campus Crusade for Christ, Intl.	1970	12	-	30	-	25
Christ for the City International	1994	-	-	2	-	-
Christian Associates International	1992	-	-	-	-	-
Christian Churches/Churches of Christ		-	-	1	-	-
Christian Fellowship Union, Inc.	1999	-	-	2	-	-
Christ's Mandate for Missions	1980	-	-	-	1	-
Church of God (Cleveland, Tenn.) World Missions	1937	-	-	4	-	9
Church of God of Prophecy—Global Outreach		-	-	-	2	-
Church of the Nazarene, World Msn. Dept.	1981	-	-	-	-	-
Church Resource Ministries (CRM)	2009	-	-	3	-	-
Churches of Christ	1964	-	-	-	-	-
CMF International	2004	2	3	4	-	-
Commission to Every Nation	2006	-	-	2	2	-
Converge Worldwide		-	-	4	-	-
Cooperative Baptist Fellowship—Global Missions	2006	-	2	-	-	-
CrossWorld	1985	-	-	4	-	-
East-West Ministries International	1998	-	-	2	-	-
Episcopal Church USA		-	-	-	-	-
Equip International	2004	-	-	1	1	-
European Christian Mission International—USA		-	-	7	10	5
Evangelical Congregational Church		-	-	4	-	-
Evangelical Covenant Ch.—Covenant Wld. Msn.	1996	2	2	4	-	-
Evangelical Methodist Church, Inc.	2004	-	-	-	-	1
Fellowship of Evangelical Chs.—Intl. Mins.	2008	-	-	2	-	-
Foursquare Missions International	1975	-	-	2	-	-
Free Methodist World Missions	2005	-	-	4	-	-
Free Will Baptist, Inc. Bd. of Intl. Missions	1974	1	2	9	-	-
Global Outreach Mission, Inc.		1	-	-	-	-
Gospel Fellowship Association	1978	-	-	4	-	-
Grace Brethren International Missions	1984	-	-	2	-	2
Greater Europe Mission	1960	12	-	12	-	-
HCJB Global	1997	-	-	1	-	5
Help for Christian Nationals, Inc.	1990	-	-	2	-	-
International Partnership Ministries, Inc.	2000	-	-	-	2	-
Intl. Pentecostal Holiness Ch. World Msns. Mins.	1988	-	-	4	-	-
International Teams, U.S.A.		2	1	6	-	1
InterVarsity Christian Fellowship/USA,Msns. Dept.		-	1	-	-	-
Josue Yrion World Evangelism and Missions, Inc.	2004	-	-	-	1	-
Latin America Mission		-	-	4	-	4
Liebenzell Mission of USA, Inc.	1996	-	-	-	-	-
Macedonia World Baptist Missions, Inc.	2004	-	-	6	-	-
Mennonite Mission Network	1972	-	-	3	1	-
Mission to the World (PCA), Inc.	1983	-	5	8	-	-
Missionary Revival Crusade	1969	-	-	-	-	-
Navigators, U.S. International Missions Group		-	-	8	-	-

	Personnel from U.S.				Other Countries	
	First Year	1-2 yrs.	2-4 yrs.	4+ yrs.	Citizens	Non-Citizens
OC International, Inc.	1995	-	-	13	-	-
OMS International, Inc.	1972	-	-	11	-	3
OneHope		-	-	-	-	-
Open Door Baptist Missions	1999	-	-	4	2	-
Operation Mobilization	1961	-	-	3	-	1
Palm Missionary Ministries, Inc.	2001	-	-	-	-	2
Pioneers USA		-	-	1	-	-
Primitive Methodist Church in the USA		-	-	-	-	-
Proclaim! International, Inc.	2004	-	-	2	-	-
ReachGlobal	1994	-	4	8	-	-
Resourcing Christian Education International	2007	-	-	-	3	4
Rosedale Mennonite Missions	2008	-	-	4	-	-
Salvation Army, U.S.A.	1971	-	5	-	-	-
SEND International USA	1987	-	-	13	-	6
Seventh-day Adventists, General Conference	1903	1	-	-	-	-
Spanish World Ministries, Inc.		-	-	2	2	-
TEAM (The Evangelical Alliance Mission)		-	-	44	-	-
Team Expansion, Inc.		-	-	2	-	-
The Brethren Church, Inc.	2005	-	-	-	1	-
The Gospel Furthering Fellowship	1994	-	-	8	7	1
United Pentecostal Church International		-	6	-	-	8
WEC International	1968	-	-	9	-	-
Word of Life Fellowship, Inc.—Intl. Ministries	1976	-	-	-	4	2
World Baptist Fellowship Msn. Agency, Inc.	1958	-	-	4	-	-
World Harvest Mission	1998	-	5	6	-	-
World Indigenous Missions	1993	-	-	6	-	-
World Link Ministries	1985	-	-	6	30	-
World Missions & Evangelism, Inc.		-	-	2	-	-
World Partners USA	1985	-	6	-	-	-
World Team	1972	-	-	5	-	-
World Venture	1984	-	11	16	-	-
World Witness		-	-	2	-	-
Wycliffe Bible Translators		-	-	10	-	-
Youth for Christ/USA—World Outreach	1982	-	-	4	-	-
Totals:		58	56	484	71	95

Sri Lanka

	First Year	1-2 yrs.	2-4 yrs.	4+ yrs.	Citizens	Non-Citizens
Adventive Cross Cultural Initiatives—US		-	-	-	-	-
Assemblies of God World Missions	1923	-	-	6	-	-
Awana International	1992	-	-	-	-	-
Back to the Bible International	1955	-	-	-	34	-
BCM International		-	-	2	-	-
Campus Crusade for Christ, Intl.	1967	-	-	-	34	-
Childcare Worldwide	1990	-	-	-	-	-
Christian Aid Mission		-	-	-	40	-
Church of God of Prophecy—Global Outreach		-	-	-	1	-
Church of the Nazarene, World Msn. Dept.	2000	-	-	-	-	-
Churches of Christ	1960	-	-	-	-	-
Every Home for Christ International	1970	-	-	-	1	-
Faith Christian Fellowship International		-	-	1	2	-

		Personnel from U.S.			Other Countries	
	First Year	1-2 yrs.	2-4 yrs.	4+ yrs.	Citizens	Non-Citizens
Global Partners/Wesleyan World Missions	1993	-	-	-	-	-
Globe International	1984	-	-	2	-	-
Gospel Revival Ministries	2006	-	-	-	2	-
Habitat for Humanity International	1994	-	1	-	-	1
Hope for the Hungry	1982	-	-	-	3	-
I. N. Network USA	1976	-	-	-	29	-
Intl. Pentecostal Holiness Ch. World Msns. Mins.	-	-	-	-	-	-
Medical Teams International	2005	2	2	-	-	-
Partners International	2005	-	-	-	70	-
Surfing the Nations	1999	-	-	-	1	-
TEAM (The Evangelical Alliance Mission)		-	-	1	-	-
Tentmakers International	1996	-	-	-	1	-
United Pentecostal Church International	1949	-	2	-	-	3
Village Ministries International	1997	-	-	-	7	-
Walk Thru the Bible Ministries, Inc.	1999	-	-	-	2	-
	Totals:	2	5	12	227	4

Sudan

Africa Inland Mission International, Inc.	1949	-	9	8	-	8
African Leadership, Inc.	2004	-	-	-	1	-
Baptist Missionary Association of America	2008	-	-	-	2	-
Christar	2007	-	2	-	-	-
Christian Aid Mission	2003	-	-	-	15	-
Church of God of Prophecy—Global Outreach		-	-	-	2	-
Ch. of the Brethren—Global Msn. Partnerships		-	-	-	-	-
Church of the Nazarene, World Msn. Dept.	1999	-	-	-	-	-
Churches of Christ	2008	-	-	2	-	-
Elim Fellowship—International Ministries		-	-	2	-	-
Empowering Lives International	2005	-	-	-	12	-
Evangelical Covenant Ch.—Covenant Wld. Msn.	1998	-	1	-	-	-
Global Outreach International	2004	-	-	1	-	-
Gospel Revival Ministries	1997	-	-	-	1	-
Greater Grace World Outreach	2003	-	-	-	2	-
In Touch Mission International	1998	-	-	-	2	-
International Gospel Outreach	2002	-	2	-	1	-
Intl. Pentecostal Holiness Ch. World Msns. Mins.	2003	-	-	-	-	-
Kids Alive International	2006	-	-	-	26	-
LifeWind International	2003	-	-	-	-	-
Living Water International		-	-	-	-	-
M/E International, Inc.	2009	-	-	-	-	-
Mission ONE, Inc.		-	-	-	42	-
Mustard Seed International		-	-	-	-	-
Partners International	1973	-	-	-	210	-
ReachGlobal	1997	-	-	-	-	-
Reformed Church in America, Gen. Synod	2005	-	-	2	1	-
Reformed Presbyterian Global Missions	2003	-	-	7	-	-
Samaritan's Purse International Relief	1997	25	14	2	-	-
Seventh-day Adventists, General Conference	1978	-	-	6	-	2
Shelter for Life International, Inc.	2007	2	-	-	-	2
Tentmakers International	2007	-	-	-	1	-

		Personnel from U.S.			Other Countries	
	First Year	1-2 yrs.	2-4 yrs.	4+ yrs.	Citizens	Non-Citizens
United Pentecostal Church International	2004	-	2	-	-	-
University Bible Fellowship	2006	-	2	-	-	-
Walk Thru the Bible Ministries, Inc.	2001	-	-	-	1	-
Warm Blankets Orphan Care International	2007	-	-	-	4	-
World Relief	1999	3	-	-	90	3
Totals:	30	32	30	413	15

Suriname

Assemblies of God World Missions	1959	-	-	2	-	-
Awana International		-	-	-	-	-
BCM International		-	-	4	-	-
Biblical Ministries Worldwide		-	-	2	-	-
Campus Crusade for Christ, Intl.	1979	-	-	-	7	2
Child Evangelism Fellowship, Inc.	1973	-	-	-	-	1
Church of God of Prophecy—Global Outreach		-	-	-	1	-
Church of the Nazarene, World Msn. Dept.	1984	-	-	-	-	-
Churches of Christ	1989	-	-	-	-	-
Commission to Every Nation	2006	1	-	2	2	1
Global Partners/Wesleyan World Missions	1945	-	3	-	-	-
Independent Faith Mission, Inc.	1966	-	-	7	-	-
Network of International Christian Schools	1998	12	4	-	1	4
Orthodox Presbyterian Church	1987	-	-	2	-	-
United Pentecostal Church International	2003	-	2	-	-	2
World Team	1957	-	-	4	-	--
Totals:	13	9	23	11	10

Swaziland

Adventures in Missions	2004	1	-	6	-	-
Assemblies of God World Missions	1985	-	-	10	-	-
Awana International		-	-	-	-	-
BCM International		-	-	2	-	-
Campus Crusade for Christ, Intl.	1973	-	-	-	8	-
Children's HopeChest	2006	-	-	-	6	2
Church of God of Prophecy—Global Outreach		-	-	-	4	-
Church of the Nazarene, World Msn. Dept.	1910	-	-	1	-	-
Churches of Christ	1966	-	-	6	-	-
Every Home for Christ International	1961	-	-	-	-	-
Greater Grace World Outreach	1999	-	-	-	3	-
Intl. Pentecostal Holiness Ch. World Msns. Mins.		-	-	-	-	-
Launch Out Ministries International	2005	-	-	-	1	2
National Baptist Convention USA, Inc.	1971	1	-	-	27	-
OneHope		-	-	-	-	-
TWR		-	-	2	-	-
United Pentecostal Church International	1982	-	2	-	-	-
Walk Thru the Bible Ministries, Inc.	2000	-	-	-	2	-
Zion Evangelical Ministries of Africa (ZEMA)	2006	-	-	4	-	2
Totals:	2	2	31	51	6

Sweden

Baptist Bible Fellowship International	1985	-	-	2	-	-

	Personnel from U.S.				Other Countries	
	First Year	1-2 yrs.	2-4 yrs.	4+ yrs.	Citizens	Non-Citizens
Biblical Ministries Worldwide		-	-	4	-	-
Campus Crusade for Christ, Intl.	1972	11	-	-	-	7
Christian Associates International		-	-	-	-	-
Churches of Christ	1957	-	-	-	-	-
Commission to Every Nation	2007	-	2	-	-	1
CrossWorld	1984	-	-	2	-	-
Elim Fellowship—International Ministries	1990	-	-	2	-	-
Evangelical Baptist Missions		-	-	1	1	-
Evangelical Covenant Ch.—Covenant Wld. Msn.	2007	-	1	-	-	-
Fellowship International Mission	1977	-	-	3	-	-
Greater Europe Mission	1955	-	-	8	-	-
Greater Grace World Outreach	1976	-	-	-	4	2
Mennonite Mission Network	1983	-	-	-	-	-
Mission Possible Foundation, Inc.	2000	-	-	-	-	-
Mission to the World (PCA), Inc.	1999	-	-	2	-	-
Operation Mobilization		2	-	1	-	1
TEAM (The Evangelical Alliance Mission)		-	-	2	-	-
Tentmakers International	1998	-	-	-	1	-
United Pentecostal Church International		-	-	-	-	2
World Venture		-	-	2	-	-
Wycliffe Bible Translators		-	-	2	-	-
Totals:		13	3	31	6	13

Switzerland

	First Year	1-2 yrs.	2-4 yrs.	4+ yrs.	Citizens	Non-Citizens
Assemblies of God World Missions	1967	-	-	-	-	-
Baptist International Missions, Inc. (BIMI)		-	-	2	-	-
Campus Crusade for Christ, Intl.		-	-	-	-	2
Child Evangelism Fellowship, Inc.	1950	-	-	6	-	4
Christian Associates International		-	-	-	-	-
Ch. of the Brethren—Global Msn. Partnerships		-	-	-	-	-
Church of the Nazarene, World Msn. Dept.	1978	-	-	19	-	9
Churches of Christ	1959	-	-	6	-	-
CrossWorld	2005	-	-	4	-	-
Global Outreach Mission, Inc.		-	-	1	-	-
Global Recordings Network		-	-	-	6	-
Greater Grace World Outreach	1994	-	-	-	2	1
HCJB Global	1983	-	-	-	2	-
Literacy & Evangelism International	2005	-	-	-	1	-
Reformed Baptist Mission Services		-	-	-	2	-
Reformed Presbyterian Global Missions		-	-	-	-	-
Salvation Army, U.S.A.	1882	-	2	-	-	-
Seventh-day Adventists, General Conference	1870	-	-	-	-	2
SIM USA, Inc.		-	-	2	-	-
TeachBeyond USA		-	-	-	-	-
United Pentecostal Church International		-	2	-	-	2
Wycliffe Bible Translators		-	-	8	-	-
Youth for Christ/USA—World Outreach		-	-	7	-	-
Totals:		-	4	55	13	20

	Personnel from U.S.				Other Countries	
	First Year	1-2 yrs.	2-4 yrs.	4+ yrs.	Citizens	Non-Citizens
Syria						
Assemblies of God World Missions	1999	-	-	-	-	-
Baptist Missionary Association of America	1993	-	-	-	6	-
Christian Aid Mission		-	-	-	14	-
Church of the Nazarene, World Msn. Dept.	1920	-	-	-	-	-
Precept Ministries International		-	-	-	-	-
Walk Thru the Bible Ministries, Inc.	2001	-	-	-	-	-
Totals:		-	-	-	20	-
Taiwan						
Asian Outreach U.S.A.		-	-	-	-	-
Assemblies of God World Missions	1948	-	-	8	-	-
Awana International	2000	-	-	2	4	-
Baptist Bible Fellowship International	1950	-	-	10	-	-
Baptist Mid-Missions	1972	-	-	2	-	-
Baptist Missionary Association of America	1953	-	-	-	2	-
Campus Crusade for Christ, Intl.	1964	-	-	-	109	4
Child Evangelism Fellowship, Inc.	1951	-	2	2	-	-
Christian Churches/Churches of Christ		-	2	21	-	-
Church of the Nazarene, World Msn. Dept.	1956	-	-	-	-	-
Episcopal Church USA		-	-	-	-	-
Evangelical Covenant Ch.—Covenant Wld. Msn.	1952	-	-	2	-	-
Foursquare Missions International	1988	-	-	2	-	-
Free Methodist World Missions	1952	-	-	4	-	-
Globe International	2000	-	-	2	-	-
Great Commission Ministries, Inc.		-	2	-	-	-
Heart of God Ministries	1995	-	-	3	-	-
Hope for the Hungry	2003	-	-	2	-	-
International Gospel Outreach	2004	-	-	2	-	-
International Partnership Ministries, Inc.	2002	-	-	1	1	-
International Teams, U.S.A.		-	-	-	-	7
Kids Alive International	1971	-	-	2	-	-
Liberty Corner Mission	1952	-	-	2	-	3
Lutheran Brethren World Missions	1951	-	-	6	-	-
Lutheran Church-Missouri Synod, World Mission	1951	-	-	9	-	-
Macedonia World Baptist Missions, Inc.	1985	-	-	2	-	-
Mission to the World (PCA), Inc.	1977	-	1	12	-	-
Mission To Unreached Peoples	1989	-	-	2	-	-
Mustard Seed International	1948	-	-	-	-	-
Navigators, U.S. International Missions Group		-	-	4	-	-
OC International, Inc.	1951	-	-	5	-	-
OMF International	1950	-	29	-	-	29
OMS International, Inc.	1950	-	-	5	-	2
OneHope		-	-	-	-	-
Open Door Baptist Missions	2005	-	-	1	-	1
Overseas Radio & Television, Inc. (ORTV)	1961	-	-	-	220	5
Partners International	1959	-	-	-	96	-
Precept Ministries International	1990	-	-	1	2	-
ReachGlobal	1994	-	-	1	-	-
Reformed Church in America, Gen. Synod	1970	-	3	-	-	-

	First Year	Personnel from U.S. 1-2 yrs.	2-4 yrs.	4+ yrs.	Other Countries Citizens	Non-Citizens
SEND International USA	1966	-	-	14	-	6
Seventh-day Adventists, General Conference	1902	2	1	8	-	1
Sowers International, The	1995	-	-	-	4	-
TEAM (The Evangelical Alliance Mission)		-	-	10	-	-
Team Expansion, Inc.	1996	-	-	22	-	-
United Pentecostal Church International		-	4	-	-	-
University Bible Fellowship	2008	2	-	-	-	-
Wisconsin Evangelical Lutheran Synod	1968	-	-	1	-	-
World Gospel Mission	1953	-	-	2	-	-
World Team	1999	-	-	6	-	-
World Venture	1952	-	-	14	-	-
	Totals:	4	15	221	438	58

Tajikistan

	First Year	1-2 yrs.	2-4 yrs.	4+ yrs.	Citizens	Non-Citizens
Assemblies of God World Missions	1997	1	-	7	-	-
Baptist International Evangelistic Ministries		-	-	-	-	-
Baptist Missionary Association of America	1994	-	-	-	5	-
Food for the Hungry, Inc.	1996	-	-	-	-	-
Foursquare Missions International		-	-	2	-	-
Greater Grace World Outreach	2005	-	-	-	-	6
Health Emergent International Services	1997	-	-	2	-	-
Interserve USA (International Service Fellowship)	1993	-	-	3	-	-
ISOH/IMPACT	1996	-	-	2	-	-
Partners International	2008	-	-	-	2	-
People International USA	1994	1	-	2	-	10
Precept Ministries International		-	-	-	1	-
	Totals:	2	-	18	8	16

Tanzania

	First Year	1-2 yrs.	2-4 yrs.	4+ yrs.	Citizens	Non-Citizens
ACM International	2004	-	-	4	-	-
Africa Inland Mission International, Inc.	1909	3	4	39	-	34
African Enterprise	1970	-	-	-	8	-
African Leadership, Inc.	2002	-	-	-	2	-
Artists In Christian Testimony International	2006	-	-	-	-	2
Assemblies of God World Missions	1940	4	-	10	-	-
Awana International		-	-	-	-	-
Baptist Bible Fellowship International	1988	-	-	10	-	-
Baptist International Missions, Inc. (BIMI)		-	-	6	-	-
Brethren Assemblies		-	-	2	-	-
Calvary International	2005	-	-	6	-	-
Campus Crusade for Christ, Intl.	1977	-	-	-	53	2
Christian Aid Mission	1990	-	-	-	80	-
Christian Blind Mission International (CBM-US)	1971	-	1	1	-	-
Christian Churches/Churches of Christ		-	-	21	-	-
Church of God (Anderson, Ind.), Global Msns.	1959	-	2	4	-	-
Church of God of Prophecy—Global Outreach		-	-	-	7	-
Church of the Nazarene, World Msn. Dept.	1990	-	-	-	-	2
Churches of Christ	1962	-	-	29	-	-
CMF International	1999	-	1	9	-	-
Commission to Every Nation	2009	-	2	-	-	2

		Personnel from U.S.			Other Countries	
	First Year	1-2 yrs.	2-4 yrs.	4+ yrs.	Citizens	Non-Citizens
Compassion International, Inc.	1999	-	-	-	65	-
Eastern Mennonite Missions	1934	-	-	1	-	-
Elim Fellowship—International Ministries	1955	-	3	6	-	-
Emmanuel International Mission	1976	1	-	-	-	2
Empowering Lives International	2000	-	-	-	6	-
Evangelical Lutheran Church in America	1924	1	2	19	-	-
Every Home for Christ International	1970	-	-	-	1	-
Floresta USA, Inc.	2004	-	-	-	2	-
Global Recordings Network		-	-	-	2	-
Go Ye Fellowship	2004	-	-	1	1	-
Gospelink, Inc.		-	-	-	193	-
Grace Ministries International	1952	-	13	-	-	-
Greater Grace World Outreach	1999	-	-	-	9	-
Habitat for Humanity International	1986	-	3	-	-	3
I. N. Network USA	1997	-	-	-	21	-
International Christian Ministries	1994	2	-	-	2	4
International Gospel Outreach	1999	-	-	2	2	-
Intl. Pentecostal Holiness Ch. World Msns. Mins.	1996	-	-	4	-	-
Launch Out Ministries International	2006	-	-	-	5	-
LifeWind International	1987	-	-	-	3	-
Living Water International		-	-	-	-	-
MAP International	1994	-	-	-	-	-
Mission ONE, Inc.		-	-	-	2	-
Moravian Church in N. Am., Bd. of World Msn.	2003	-	-	-	-	2
OneHope		-	-	-	-	-
Perimeter Church—Global Outreach		-	-	-	-	-
Pioneer Bible Translators	1997	-	-	6	-	1
Progressive National Baptist Convention, Inc.	2008	-	-	-	-	-
ReachGlobal	1993	1	2	9	-	-
SEED International	2003	-	-	1	-	-
Seventh-day Adventists, General Conference	1903	-	-	4	-	7
SIM USA, Inc.	1990	-	-	2	-	-
Team Expansion, Inc.	1994	-	-	4	-	-
Teen Missions International, Inc.	2000	-	-	1	2	-
The Gospel Furthering Fellowship	1949	-	-	2	-	-
The Mission Society	2000	-	2	1	-	-
The Word for the World USA	2004	-	-	-	26	2
United Pentecostal Church International	1980	-	4	-	-	1
Village Ministries International	2007	-	-	-	1	-
Walk Thru the Bible Ministries, Inc.	2000	-	-	-	2	-
Warm Blankets Orphan Care International	2009	-	-	-	-	-
World Gospel Mission	1985	-	-	-	-	-
World Mission Prayer League	2008	-	2	-	-	-
World Outreach International—US	1986	-	-	2	-	-
Wycliffe Bible Translators		-	-	20	-	-
Totals:		12	41	226	495	64

Thailand

American Baptist Chs. of the U.S.A., Intl. Mins.	1833	-	-	15	-	2
AMG International	1976	-	-	-	76	13

	Personnel from U.S.			Other Countries	
	First Year	1-2 yrs.	2-4 yrs.	4+ yrs.	Citizens	Non-Citizens

	First Year	1-2 yrs.	2-4 yrs.	4+ yrs.	Citizens	Non-Citizens
Asian Outreach U.S.A.		-	-	-	-	-
Assemblies of God World Missions	1968	13	-	19	-	-
Baptist Bible Fellowship International	1983	-	-	4	-	-
Baptist International Missions, Inc. (BIMI)		-	-	2	-	-
Baptist Mid-Missions	1998	-	-	9	-	-
Baptist Missionary Association of America	2006	-	-	-	1	-
Bethany International Ministries	1999	-	1	1	-	1
Bright Hope International	2000	-	-	-	4	-
Cadence International	1967	-	-	4	-	-
Calvary International	1988	-	-	3	-	2
Campus Crusade for Christ, Intl.	1971	2	-	8	116	3
Child Evangelism Fellowship, Inc.	1957	-	-	-	1	-
Childcare Worldwide	1996	-	-	-	-	-
Children's Christian Concern Society	2008	-	-	-	-	-
Christian Aid Mission		-	-	-	123	-
Christian Blind Mission International (CBM-US)	1982	1	-	-	-	-
Christian Broadcasting Network Inc., The	1999	1	-	1	47	3
Christian Church (Disciples of Christ)		-	1	-	-	-
Christian Churches/Churches of Christ		2	-	41	12	-
Christian Ministries International (CMI)	1990	-	-	1	1	2
Christ's Mandate for Missions	2003	-	-	-	2	-
Church of God (Anderson, Ind.), Global Msns.	1975	-	-	2	-	-
Church of God of Prophecy—Global Outreach		-	-	-	2	-
Church of the Nazarene, World Msn. Dept.	1989	-	-	6	-	3
Churches of Christ	1958	-	-	12	-	-
CMF International	1994	-	1	8	-	-
Commission to Every Nation	2001	-	-	4	-	4
Compassion International, Inc.	1970	1	-	-	58	-
Converge Worldwide	1990	-	-	8	-	-
Cup of Cold Water Ministries	2005	-	-	-	-	2
Eastern Mennonite Missions	1990	-	-	3	-	-
Evangelical Congregational Church		-	-	3	-	-
Evangelical Covenant Ch.—Covenant Wld. Msn.	1971	-	-	8	-	-
Evangelical Lutheran Church in America	1975	-	-	-	-	2
Every Home for Christ International	1971	-	-	-	1	-
Fellowship International Mission	2006	-	-	2	-	-
Food for the Hungry, Inc.	2004	-	2	2	-	-
Foursquare Missions International	1987	-	2	2	-	-
Free Methodist World Missions	2000	-	-	2	-	-
Global Mins., Ch. of the United Brethren in Christ		-	-	-	-	-
Global Outreach Mission, Inc.		-	-	-	2	-
Global Partners/Wesleyan World Missions	2003	-	2	-	-	-
Global Recordings Network		-	-	4	8	-
Globe International	1992	-	-	6	-	-
Good News Productions International	1998	-	-	4	-	2
Gospel Operation Intl. for Chinese Christians	2002	-	2	1	2	-
Grace Brethren International Missions	2005	-	2	4	-	-
Greater Grace World Outreach	1989	-	-	3	1	2
Habitat for Humanity International	1998	-	21	5	14	12
HIS Servants Ministries	2001	-	-	-	-	-

	Personnel from U.S.				Other Countries	
	First Year	1-2 yrs.	2-4 yrs.	4+ yrs.	Citizens	Non-Citizens
International Justice Mission	2000	-	-	-	9	-
Intl. Pentecostal Holiness Ch. World Msns. Mins.	1988	-	-	4	-	-
International Teams, U.S.A.		-	-	-	-	9
Kids for Christ International	2002	-	-	-	1	-
Launch Out Ministries International	2008	2	-	-	-	-
LifeWind International	1999	-	-	-	2	-
Mennonite Mission Network	1967	-	-	-	-	2
Mission ONE, Inc.		-	-	-	47	-
Mission to the World (PCA), Inc.	2000	-	2	8	-	-
Mission To Unreached Peoples	1988	-	-	27	-	-
Missionary Ventures International		-	-	2	-	-
New Life Advance International	1989	-	-	2	-	-
New Tribes Mission	1951	-	2	36	-	-
OMF International	1950	-	-	22	-	22
OneHope		-	-	-	-	-
Partners International	1955	-	-	-	43	-
Pass the Torch Ministries/Church of Acts	1987	-	-	-	3	-
Perimeter Church—Global Outreach		-	-	-	-	-
Pioneers USA	1985	1	-	44	1	1
Presbyterian Mission International (PMI)	2000	-	-	-	2	-
ReachGlobal	1996	1	-	10	2	-
Rosedale Mennonite Missions	2004	-	-	5	-	-
SEED International	2003	-	-	1	-	-
Seventh-day Adventists, General Conference	1919	9	4	20	1	19
SIM USA, Inc.	2005	-	-	5	-	-
Sowers International, The	1999	-	-	-	-	10
TEAM (The Evangelical Alliance Mission)		-	-	7	-	-
Team Expansion, Inc.		-	-	4	-	-
Tentmakers International	2000	-	-	-	-	1
Things To Come Mission, Inc.	2008	2	-	-	-	2
Tribes and Nations Outreach		-	-	-	-	-
United Pentecostal Church International	1968	-	6	-	-	-
United World Mission		-	-	6	-	-
Walk Thru the Bible Ministries, Inc.	2001	-	-	-	-	-
Warm Blankets Orphan Care International	2002	-	-	-	1	-
WEC International	1947	-	-	3	-	-
Wisconsin Evangelical Lutheran Synod	1993	-	-	2	-	-
Word of Life Fellowship, Inc.—Intl. Ministries		-	-	2	1	-
World Baptist Fellowship Msn. Agency, Inc.	1988	-	-	1	1	-
World Concern	1980	-	2	4	15	-
World Indigenous Missions	1999	-	-	4	-	4
World Missions Far Corners, Inc.	2001	-	-	-	35	-
World Partners USA	1992	-	2	-	-	-
World Venture		-	2	2	-	-
Wycliffe Bible Translators		-	-	93	-	-
Youth for Christ/USA—World Outreach		-	-	2	-	-
Totals:		35	54	515	633	123

Togo

Assemblies of God World Missions	1937	2	-	11	-	-

	Personnel from U.S.				Other Countries	
	First Year	1-2 yrs.	2-4 yrs.	4+ yrs.	Citizens	Non-Citizens
Awana International	1986	-	-	-	1	-
Baptist International Missions, Inc. (BIMI)		-	-	8	-	-
Baptist Missionary Association of America	1999	-	-	-	11	-
Campus Crusade for Christ, Intl.	1979	-	-	-	33	-
Child Evangelism Fellowship, Inc.		-	-	-	1	-
Christian Aid Mission	1995	-	-	-	230	-
Christian Blind Mission International (CBM-US)	1980	-	1	-	-	-
Church of God of Prophecy—Global Outreach		-	-	-	2	-
Church of the Nazarene, World Msn. Dept.	1998	-	-	-	-	-
Churches of Christ	1970	-	-	10	-	-
Compassion International, Inc.	2008	-	-	-	11	-
Development Associates International (DAI)		-	-	-	1	-
Every Child Ministries, Inc.	2006	-	-	-	1	-
Global Recordings Network		-	-	-	7	-
Greater Grace World Outreach	1990	-	-	-	47	-
His Healing Helping Hands Intl. Mins. (4 H.I.M.)	2003	-	-	-	3	-
International Partnership Ministries, Inc.	1994	-	-	-	16	-
Intl. Pentecostal Holiness Ch. World Msns. Mins.	1993	-	-	-	-	-
Ireland Outreach International Inc.	2000	-	-	-	-	-
Literacy & Evangelism International		-	-	-	-	-
Lutheran Bible Translators, Inc.	1996	-	-	-	3	-
Lutheran Church-Missouri Synod, World Mission	1980	-	-	2	-	-
M/E International, Inc.	2009	-	-	-	-	-
Mission ONE, Inc.		-	-	-	1	-
OneHope		-	-	-	-	-
Seventh-day Adventists, General Conference	1964	-	-	4	-	2
SIM USA, Inc.	1997	-	-	2	-	-
Source of Light Ministries International, Inc.	1998	-	-	-	2	-
Tentmakers International	2007	-	-	-	1	-
United Pentecostal Church International	1972	-	2	-	-	-
Walk Thru the Bible Ministries, Inc.	2002	-	-	-	-	-
WEC International		-	-	2	-	-
Wycliffe Bible Translators		-	-	7	-	-
Totals:	2	3	46	371	2	

Tonga

	First Year	1-2 yrs.	2-4 yrs.	4+ yrs.	Citizens	Non-Citizens
Assemblies of God World Missions	1975	3	-	6	-	-
Campus Crusade for Christ, Intl.	1974	-	-	-	2	-
Church of the Nazarene, World Msn. Dept.	2000	-	-	-	-	-
Churches of Christ	1991	-	-	-	-	-
United Pentecostal Church International		-	2	-	-	1
Totals:	3	2	6	2	1	

Trinidad and Tobago

	First Year	1-2 yrs.	2-4 yrs.	4+ yrs.	Citizens	Non-Citizens
Assemblies of God World Missions	1945	-	-	2	-	-
Awana International	1997	-	-	-	-	-
Back to the Bible International	1996	-	-	-	1	-
Baptist International Missions, Inc. (BIMI)		-	-	9	-	-
BCM International		-	-	1	-	-
Campus Crusade for Christ, Intl.	1977	-	-	-	13	-

	Personnel from U.S.				Other Countries	
	First Year	1-2 yrs.	2-4 yrs.	4+ yrs.	Citizens	Non-Citizens
Church of God of Prophecy—Global Outreach		-	-	-	7	-
Church of the Nazarene, World Msn. Dept.	1926	-	-	-	-	4
Churches of Christ	1947	-	-	4	-	-
Commission to Every Nation	2008	-	-	4	-	4
Fundamental Baptist Msn. Trinidad/Tobago		-	-	-	-	-
Independent Faith Mission, Inc.	2004	-	-	-	2	-
Intl. Pentecostal Holiness Ch. World Msns. Mins.	1983	-	-	-	-	-
Mission to the World (PCA), Inc.		-	-	2	-	-
Seventh-day Adventists, General Conference	1893	-	-	4	-	3
STEM International	1986	-	-	-	-	-
TMA Ministries Inc.	1989	-	-	1	-	1
United Evangelical Churches	1981	-	-	-	1	-
United Pentecostal Church International		-	2	-	-	-
Virginia Mennonite Missions	1971	-	2	2	-	-
World Team	1953	-	-	-	-	4
Wycliffe Bible Translators		-	-	1	-	-
Totals:		-	4	30	24	16

Tunisia

	First Year	1-2 yrs.	2-4 yrs.	4+ yrs.	Citizens	Non-Citizens
Awana International		-	-	-	-	-
Churches of Christ	2009	-	-	2	-	-
Seventh-day Adventists, General Conference	1928	-	-	-	-	2
Walk Thru the Bible Ministries, Inc.	2002	-	-	-	-	-
WEC International		-	-	2	-	-
Totals:		-	-	4	-	2

Turkey

	First Year	1-2 yrs.	2-4 yrs.	4+ yrs.	Citizens	Non-Citizens
AMG International	1977	-	-	-	2	-
Calvary International	1991	-	-	-	-	-
Christar	1974	-	-	37	-	1
Christian Church (Disciples of Christ)		-	3	-	-	-
Churches of Christ	1960	-	-	4	-	-
Crossover Communications International	2002	-	-	4	-	-
Faith Christian Fellowship International		-	-	1	3	-
Gospel Operation Intl. for Chinese Christians	2005	-	-	-	2	-
Greater Grace World Outreach	2005	5	-	-	-	7
International Gospel Outreach	2007	-	-	2	-	-
Intl. Pentecostal Holiness Ch. World Msns. Mins.	2001	-	-	-	6	-
International Teams, U.S.A.		-	-	3	-	1
Interserve USA (International Service Fellowship)	1985	-	-	15	1	-
Josue Yrion World Evangelism and Missions, Inc.	2008	-	-	-	1	-
Middle East Media—USA	1976	-	-	-	-	-
Mission To Unreached Peoples	2002	-	-	8	-	-
New Life Advance International	1994	-	-	2	-	-
Operation Mobilization	1961	1	2	8	-	2
Partners International	2001	-	-	-	14	-
People International USA	1984	1	-	7	-	15
ReachGlobal	1994	-	-	-	-	-
SEND International USA	2001	-	-	5	-	-
Seventh-day Adventists, General Conference	1889	-	-	2	-	2

	Personnel from U.S.			Other Countries	
	First Year	1-2 yrs.	2-4 yrs.	4+ yrs.	Citizens	Non-Citizens

	First Year	1-2 yrs.	2-4 yrs.	4+ yrs.	Citizens	Non-Citizens
Turkish World Outreach	1989	-	-	31	4	27
United Pentecostal Church International		-	4	-	-	5
University Bible Fellowship	2007	1	-	-	-	-
World-Wide Missions	1970	-	-	1	-	-
Totals:		8	9	130	33	60

Turkmenistan

	First Year	1-2 yrs.	2-4 yrs.	4+ yrs.	Citizens	Non-Citizens
Assemblies of God World Missions	1996	-	-	-	-	-
Baptist International Evangelistic Ministries		-	-	-	-	-
Baptist Missionary Association of America	1995	-	-	-	3	-
Evangelism Explosion International		-	-	-	-	2
Greater Grace World Outreach	1995	-	-	-	2	-
Totals:		-	-	-	5	2

Turks and Caicos Islands

	First Year	1-2 yrs.	2-4 yrs.	4+ yrs.	Citizens	Non-Citizens
Baptist International Missions, Inc. (BIMI)		-	-	1	-	-
Totals:		-	-	1	-	-

Tuvalu

	First Year	1-2 yrs.	2-4 yrs.	4+ yrs.	Citizens	Non-Citizens
Churches of Christ	1989	-	-	-	-	-
Totals:		-	-	-	-	-

Uganda

	First Year	1-2 yrs.	2-4 yrs.	4+ yrs.	Citizens	Non-Citizens
Action International Ministries, Inc.	2002	-	-	6	-	-
Africa Inland Mission International, Inc.	1918	3	-	17	-	24
African Bible Colleges, Inc.	1975	-	-	-	-	-
African Children's Mission, Inc.	1989	-	-	2	-	-
African Enterprise	1970	-	-	-	7	-
African Leadership, Inc.	2001	-	-	-	1	-
AMG International		-	-	-	18	-
Anglican Frontier Missions	2004	-	2	-	-	2
Assemblies of God World Missions	1979	-	-	-	-	-
Association of Free Lutheran Congregations	2006	-	-	2	2	-
Awana International	1997	-	-	-	3	-
Baptist Bible Fellowship International	1986	-	-	2	-	-
Baptist International Missions, Inc. (BIMI)		-	-	36	-	-
Brethren Assemblies		-	-	3	-	-
Bright Hope International	2004	-	-	-	5	-
Campus Crusade for Christ, Intl.	1971	-	-	2	132	-
Child Evangelism Fellowship, Inc.	1965	-	-	-	2	-
Childcare Worldwide	1985	-	-	-	47	-
Children's HopeChest	2008	-	-	-	4	-
Christ to the Nations	1998	-	-	-	2	-
Christian Aid Mission	1986	-	-	-	60	-
Christian Blind Mission International (CBM-US)	1978	-	2	-	-	-
Christian Reformed World Relief Committee	1982	-	1	-	-	-
Christian Relief Fund, The	1995	-	-	-	2	-
Church of God (Anderson, Ind.), Global Msns.	1983	-	-	3	-	-
Church of God of Prophecy—Global Outreach		-	-	-	4	-
Church of the Nazarene, World Msn. Dept.	1988	-	-	2	-	-

		Personnel from U.S.			Other Countries	
	First Year	1-2 yrs.	2-4 yrs.	4+ yrs.	Citizens	Non-Citizens
Church Planting International, Inc.	1983	-	-	-	-	-
Churches of Christ	1969	-	-	24	-	-
Commission to Every Nation	2004	-	1	-	-	1
Compassion International, Inc.	1980	-	-	-	86	-
Cooperative Baptist Fellowship—Global Missions	2007	-	2	-	-	-
Development Associates International (DAI)	2002	-	-	-	2	-
Discipleship Missions International	1986	-	-	-	3	-
Emmanuel International Mission	1976	-	-	-	-	4
Engineering Ministries International (EMI)	2003	3	1	2	-	-
Equip International	2009	-	-	2	-	-
Every Child Ministries, Inc.	2006	2	2	-	9	-
Every Home for Christ International	1970	-	-	-	1	-
Faith Life Ministries, Inc.	2008	-	-	-	-	-
Fellowship International Mission	1989	-	-	-	2	-
Foursquare Missions International	1997	-	-	4	-	-
Global Outreach International	1984	-	-	22	-	-
Go Ye Fellowship	2008	-	1	-	-	-
Gospel Outbound	2008	-	-	1	-	-
Greater Grace World Outreach	1996	-	-	-	47	-
Habitat for Humanity International	1984	-	1	-	-	1
Harvest International, Inc.	1996	-	2	-	2	-
Heart of the Bride Ministries		2	-	-	-	-
Hope for the Hungry	2002	-	-	2	-	-
I. N. Network USA	1994	-	-	-	74	-
In Touch Mission International		-	-	1	-	2
International Christian Ministries	1988	-	-	-	6	-
International Gospel Outreach	2003	-	-	2	2	-
International Institute for Christian Studies		-	2	-	-	2
International Justice Mission	2002	-	1	-	13	-
Intl. Pentecostal Holiness Ch. World Msns. Mins.	2002	-	-	2	-	-
International Teams, U.S.A.		-	-	-	-	5
LifeWind International	1990	-	-	2	8	-
Living Water International		-	-	-	-	-
Mailbox Club International Inc., The		-	-	-	2	-
MAP International	2006	-	-	-	4	-
Medical Teams International	2005	-	-	-	2	-
Mission Aviation Fellowship	1961	-	-	6	-	-
Mission ONE, Inc.		-	-	-	2	-
Mission to the World (PCA), Inc.	1983	-	2	10	-	-
Mission: Moving Mountains, Inc.	1982	-	-	-	6	-
Missionary Ventures International	2002	-	-	-	-	2
New Hope Uganda Ministries	1988	-	-	20	-	-
OneHope		-	-	-	-	-
Open Door Baptist Missions	2005	-	-	2	-	-
Orthodox Presbyterian Church	1995	2	3	8	-	-
Partners Worldwide		-	-	-	-	-
Reformed Presbyterian Global Missions		-	-	-	-	-
Salvation Army, U.S.A.	1931	-	2	-	-	-
Samaritan's Purse International Relief	1999	4	1	-	-	-
SEED International	1999	-	-	1	-	-

	First Year	1-2 yrs.	2-4 yrs.	4+ yrs.	Citizens	Non-Citizens
		Personnel from U.S.			**Other Countries**	
Seventh-day Adventists, General Conference	1926	-	-	2	-	8
Source of Light Ministries International, Inc.	1998	-	-	-	2	-
South American Missionary Society (USA)	2004	-	-	4	-	-
Team Expansion, Inc.		-	-	3	-	-
Teen Missions International, Inc.	1992	-	-	1	20	-
The God's Story Project	2008	-	-	-	1	-
The Master's Mission, Inc.	1998	-	-	-	2	-
Things To Come Mission, Inc.	2004	-	-	-	-	2
United Pentecostal Church International	1970	-	2	-	-	-
Walk Thru the Bible Ministries, Inc.	1999	-	-	-	3	-
Warm Blankets Orphan Care International	2004	-	-	-	4	-
Word of Life Fellowship, Inc.—Intl. Ministries	2002	-	-	-	46	3
World Concern	1985	-	-	-	-	1
World Gospel Mission	1992	-	5	10	-	-
World Harvest Mission	1984	-	3	11	-	-
World Venture	1961	1	8	14	-	-
Wycliffe Bible Translators		-	-	5	-	-
Youth for Christ/USA—World Outreach		-	-	1	-	-
Totals:		17	44	237	638	57

Ukraine

	First Year	1-2 yrs.	2-4 yrs.	4+ yrs.	Citizens	Non-Citizens
All About Orphans		-	-	-	-	-
Assemblies of God World Missions	1993	7	-	23	-	-
Association of Christian Schools Intl. (ACSI)	1992	-	-	2	-	-
Awana International	1992	-	-	-	13	-
Baptist Bible Fellowship International	1993	-	-	2	-	-
Baptist International Evangelistic Ministries		-	-	-	25	-
Baptist International Missions, Inc. (BIMI)		-	-	13	-	-
Baptist Missionary Association of America	1994	-	-	2	9	-
BCM International		-	-	25	-	-
Calvary International	1992	-	-	2	-	-
Campus Crusade for Christ, Intl.	1991	1	-	13	95	6
Centers for Apologetics Research, The	1998	-	-	-	1	-
Child Evangelism Fellowship, Inc.	1989	-	-	-	6	-
Chosen People Ministries	1997	-	-	-	1	-
Christ to the Nations	1991	-	-	2	2	-
Christian Aid Ministries (CAM)	2001	-	6	2	10	-
Christian Aid Mission		-	-	-	505	-
Christian Broadcasting Network Inc., The	1991	-	2	1	180	-
Christian Churches/Churches of Christ		-	-	30	8	-
Christian Involvement in Service (CIS)	2004	-	-	-	6	-
Christian Ministries International (CMI)	1992	-	-	-	1	-
Christian Outreach International	1995	1	-	-	3	1
Christian Relief Fund, The	1997	-	-	-	2	-
Church Leadership Dev. Intl.	1994	-	-	-	2	-
Church of God (Cleveland, Tenn.) World Missions	1992	-	-	3	-	2
Ch. of God (Holiness), World Msn. Dept., Inc.	1996	-	-	2	-	-
Church of God of Prophecy—Global Outreach		-	-	3	16	-
Church of the Nazarene, World Msn. Dept.	1992	-	-	-	-	-
Churches of Christ	1952	-	-	10	-	-

	First Year	Personnel from U.S.			Other Countries	
		1-2 yrs.	2-4 yrs.	4+ yrs.	Citizens	Non-Citizens
CMF International	1994	-	-	11	-	-
Commission to Every Nation	2005	-	-	2	1	1
Converge Worldwide		-	-	2	-	-
Cooperative Baptist Fellowship—Global Missions	2002	-	-	2	-	-
CrossWorld		-	-	6	-	-
Eastern European Outreach, Inc.	1991	-	1	-	28	-
Evangelical Congregational Church		-	-	1	-	-
Evangelism Explosion International		-	-	-	-	10
Every Home for Christ International	1991	-	-	-	1	-
Free Methodist World Missions	1999	-	-	3	-	-
Friends of Donetsk Christian University (DCU)	1991	-	2	5	45	5
Global Action	2001	-	-	1	8	1
Global Outreach International	2000	-	-	5	-	-
Global Outreach Mission, Inc.		-	-	2	-	-
Globe International	2000	-	-	2	-	-
Good News Productions International	1997	-	-	2	2	-
Gospel Operation Intl. for Chinese Christians	2005	-	-	-	1	-
Gospelink, Inc.		-	-	-	75	-
Great Commission Ministries, Inc.		7	-	10	3	-
Greater Europe Mission	1993	36	-	6	-	-
Greater Grace World Outreach	1991	-	-	-	14	-
Harvest International, Inc.	1996	-	1	-	4	-
Holt International Children's Services, Inc.		-	-	-	8	-
HOPE International	1998	-	-	-	1	-
IFCA World Missions		-	-	-	1	-
International Board of Jewish Missions, Inc.	2000	-	2	-	-	2
International Messengers	2000	-	1	-	-	4
Intl. Pentecostal Holiness Ch. World Msns. Mins.	1990	-	-	-	9	-
International Teams, U.S.A.		-	-	9	-	3
InterVarsity Christian Fellowship/USA, Msns. Dept.		-	-	3	-	-
LifeWind International	1992	-	-	-	4	2
Mennonite Mission Network	1996	-	-	1	-	-
Ministry to Educate and Equip, Intl. (MTEE)	1996	-	4	-	9	-
Mission Possible Foundation, Inc.	1990	-	-	-	8	-
Mission to the World (PCA), Inc.	1993	2	9	21	-	-
Mission To Unreached Peoples	2004	-	-	2	-	-
Mission Without Borders International		-	-	-	75	-
Missionary Athletes International	2005	-	-	1	-	-
Missions Resource Network	1952	-	-	6	-	-
Missions to Military, Inc.	1998	-	2	-	2	-
New Hope International	1971	-	-	-	15	-
New Life Advance International		-	-	-	-	-
OMS International, Inc.	2003	-	-	4	-	4
OneHope		-	-	-	-	-
Open Air Campaigners—Overseas Ministries	2001	-	-	-	2	-
Open Bible Churches, Intl. Mins.		-	-	1	-	-
Operation Mobilization		3	-	-	-	-
Pioneer Bible Translators	1999	-	-	4	-	1
Precept Ministries International	1994	-	-	-	5	-
Presbyterian Mission International (PMI)	2004	-	-	-	-	2

	First Year	Personnel from U.S.			Other Countries	
		1-2 yrs.	2-4 yrs.	4+ yrs.	Citizens	Non-Citizens
ReachGlobal	1993	-	2	8	8	-
Resourcing Christian Education International	2005	-	-	-	9	-
Salvation Army, U.S.A.	1993	-	3	-	-	5
SEND International USA	1991	-	1	45	-	-
Seventh-day Adventists, General Conference	1886	2	-	-	-	-
TCM International Institute		-	-	-	1	-
TEAM (The Evangelical Alliance Mission)		-	-	5	-	-
Team Expansion, Inc.	1991	-	-	4	-	-
TITUS International	1993	-	-	6	15	-
Ukrainian Childrens Fund	1995	-	-	-	2	-
United Pentecostal Church International		-	1	-	-	-
University Bible Fellowship	2004	-	-	2	-	-
Walk Thru the Bible Ministries, Inc.	1998	-	-	-	26	3
Word of Life Fellowship, Inc.—Intl. Ministries	1992	-	-	-	20	-
World Baptist Fellowship Msn. Agency, Inc.	2000	1	-	-	-	-
World Gospel Mission	1997	-	-	6	-	-
World Harvest Mission	1999	-	-	2	-	-
World Link Ministries	2002	-	-	-	50	-
World Reach, Inc.	1991	-	-	2	4	-
World Venture	1992	-	1	8	-	-
World Witness		-	-	2	-	-
Youth Ministry International (YMI)	1998	-	-	6	-	-
Totals:		60	38	343	1341	52

United Arab Emirates

	First Year	1-2 yrs.	2-4 yrs.	4+ yrs.	Citizens	Non-Citizens
Evangelical Baptist Missions		-	-	-	2	-
Gospel Operation Intl. for Chinese Christians	2006	3	-	-	1	-
Interserve USA (International Service Fellowship)	1951	-	-	2	-	-
On The Go Ministries/Keith Coot Team	1974	-	2	4	2	-
Seventh-day Adventists, General Conference	1987	-	-	2	-	-
Walk Thru the Bible Ministries, Inc.	2002	-	-	-	-	-
Totals:		3	2	8	5	-

United Kingdom

	First Year	1-2 yrs.	2-4 yrs.	4+ yrs.	Citizens	Non-Citizens
ACM International	1998	-	-	2	-	-
Adventures in Missions	2005	1	1	2	-	-
Alongside Ministries International	1980	2	-	2	-	1
American Baptist Chs. of the U.S.A., Intl.Mins.	2006	-	-	-	-	1
Arab World Ministries		2	-	6	12	1
Artists In Christian Testimony International	2005	-	-	-	-	2
Asian Outreach U.S.A.		-	-	-	-	-
Assemblies of God World Missions	2001	4	-	15	-	-
Avant Ministries	1963	-	-	2	-	-
Awana International	1993	-	-	-	1	-
Baptist Bible Fellowship International	1971	-	3	48	-	-
Baptist International Missions, Inc. (BIMI)		-	-	39	-	-
Baptist Mid-Missions	1972	-	-	11	-	-
Baptist Missionary Association of America	2009	-	-	1	-	-
BCM International		-	-	13	-	-
Biblical Ministries Worldwide	1968	-	-	15	-	-

		Personnel from U.S.			Other Countries	
	First Year	1-2 yrs.	2-4 yrs.	4+ yrs.	Citizens	Non-Citizens
Cadence International						
Calvary International	1990	-	-	2	-	-
Campus Crusade for Christ, Intl.	1987	-	-	-	-	-
Chosen People Ministries	1967	13	-	17	-	2
Christar	1953	-	-	-	1	-
Christian Associates International	1966	-	-	7	-	1
Christian Broadcasting Network Inc., The		-	-	-	-	-
Christian Churches/Churches of Christ	1997	-	-	-	4	1
Christians In Action Missions International		-	6	20	-	-
Church of God (Cleveland, Tenn.) World Missions	1965	-	-	2	-	-
Church of the Nazarene, World Msn. Dept.	1955	-	-	-	-	2
Church Resource Ministries (CRM)	1909	-	-	-	-	-
Churches of Christ	2004	-	1	16	-	-
CMF International	1850	-	-	12	-	-
CrossWorld	1989	2	2	16	-	-
Development Associates International (DAI)		-	-	2	-	-
Eastern Mennonite Missions		-	-	-	1	-
Elim Fellowship—International Ministries	1994	-	-	2	-	-
Engineering Ministries International (EMI)	1979	-	-	2	-	-
European Christian Mission International—USA		-	-	-	-	1
Far East Broadcasting Company, Inc.		-	-	-	5	-
Fellowship International Mission	1995	-	-	1	-	1
Fellowship of Evangelical Chs.—Intl. Mins.	1993	-	-	2	-	-
Free Methodist World Missions	2000	-	-	3	-	-
Friends of Israel Gospel Ministry, Inc.	1971	-	-	1	-	-
Global Outreach International	2000	-	-	-	-	2
Global Outreach Mission, Inc.	2000	-	-	5	-	-
Global Partners/Wesleyan World Missions		-	-	9	-	-
Global Recordings Network	1990	-	-	-	-	-
Globe International		-	-	-	2	-
Go Ye Fellowship	1994	-	-	10	-	-
Gospel Fellowship Association	2008	-	-	1	1	-
Grace Brethren International Missions	1972	1	-	17	-	-
Greater Europe Mission	1982	-	-	5	-	-
Greater Grace World Outreach	1970	10	-	2	-	-
Habitat for Humanity International	1975	-	-	1	4	5
HCJB Global	1994	-	1	-	1	-
Intl. Pentecostal Holiness Ch. World Msns. Mins.	1950	-	-	2	6	-
International Trans, U.S.A.	1978	-	-	8	-	-
InterVarsity Christian Fellowship/USA, Msns. Dept.		-	1	13	-	15
JosueYrion World Evangelism and Missions, Inc.		1	-	-	-	-
Luis Palau Evangelistic Association	2000	-	-	-	-	1
Macedonia World Baptist Missions, Inc.	1978	-	-	3	3	-
Mennonite Mission Network	2008	-	-	2	-	-
Mission to World (PCA), Inc.	1952	-	-	-	-	2
Missionary Ventures International	1990	-	7	28	-	-
Navigators, U.S. International Missions Group	1990	-	-	2	-	-
New Tribes Mission		2	-	2	-	-
OC International, Inc.	1958	-	1	6	-	-
OMS International, Inc.	2000	-	-	4	-	-
		-	-	-	-	7

	Personnel from U.S.				Other Countries	
	First Year	1-2 yrs.	2-4 yrs.	4+ yrs.	Citizens	Non-Citizens
OneHope		-	-	-	-	-
Open Door Baptist Missions	2006	-	-	1	-	-
Operation Mobilization	1961	13	5	21	-	14
Pioneers USA		-	-	6	-	-
Precept Ministries International	1998	-	-	-	11	-
Progressive National Baptist Convention, Inc.		-	-	-	-	-
ReachAcross	1951	-	-	-	4	2
ReachGlobal	1993	-	2	2	-	-
Reformed Baptist Mission Services		-	-	-	-	2
Reformed Presbyterian Global Missions		-	-	-	-	-
Salvation Army, U.S.A.	1865	-	15	-	-	-
Seventh-day Adventists, General Conference	1902	-	-	6	1	13
Tentmakers International	1994	-	-	-	4	-
The Word for the World USA	2005	-	-	-	1	-
Things To Come Mission, Inc.	1973	-	-	-	2	-
TMA Ministries Inc.	1986	-	-	1	-	1
U.S. Center for World Mission		-	-	2	-	-
United Pentecostal Church International		-	6	-	-	14
United World Mission		-	1	2	-	-
Walk Thru the Bible Ministries, Inc.	2003	-	-	-	4	-
WEC International	1913	-	-	15	-	-
Word of Life Fellowship, Inc.—Intl. Ministries	1980	-	-	2	3	-
World Baptist Fellowship Msn. Agency, Inc.	1996	-	2	6	-	-
World Harvest Mission	1994	3	1	14	-	-
World Missions Far Corners, Inc.	1985	-	-	-	2	-
World Team	1986	-	-	6	-	-
World Venture	1998	-	2	6	-	-
World Witness	2002	-	-	4	-	-
Worldwide Tentmakers, Inc.	1989	-	-	2	-	2
Wycliffe Bible Translators, Inc.		-	-	12	-	-
Young Life		2	-	6	-	-
Youth for Christ/USA—World Outreach	1983	-	-	8	-	-
Totals:	56	59	503	73	100	
Totals:	-	-	2	-	2	

Unspecified Country

	First Year	1-2 yrs.	2-4 yrs.	4+ yrs.	Citizens	Non-Citizens
ABWE, Inc.	1995	-	11	69	-	-
Advancing Renewal Ministries, Inc.		-	-	2	-	-
Africa Inland Mission International, Inc.		7	7	66	-	40
American Baptist Chs. of the U.S.A., Intl.Mins.	2001	-	-	5	-	-
Arab World Ministries		-	-	2	-	4
Assemblies of God World Missions		28	-	68	-	-
Avant Ministries	2005	-	-	-	-	-
Baptist Bible Fellowship International		-	2	52	-	-
Baptist Missions to Forgotten Peoples		-	-	125	-	-
Bethany International Ministries		-	-	25	-	9
Bible League, The		-	-	-	500	-
Brethren Assemblies		-	-	41	-	-
Brethren in Christ World Missions		-	-	18	-	1

	First Year	Personnel from U.S.			Other Countries	
		1-2 yrs.	2-4 yrs.	4+ yrs.	Citizens	Non-Citizens
Caring for Others	2002	-	-	2	-	-
Christian and Missionary Alliance, The		-	-	61	-	-
Christian Churches/Churches of Christ		20	10	160	120	-
Church of God (Cleveland, Tenn.) World Missions		-	-	18	-	-
Church of the Nazarene, World Msn. Dept.		-	-	10	-	6
Churches of Christ		-	-	15	-	-
Congregational Christian Churches		-	-	-	22	-
Dawn Ministries, Inc.		-	-	-	2	-
Evangelical Baptist Missions		-	-	14	-	-
Evangelical Friends Mission		-	-	-	-	-
Evangelistic Faith Missions		-	4	-	-	-
Foursquare Missions International		-	4	-	-	-
Frontiers	1982	-	-	288	-	9
General Baptists International		7	-	-	-	-
Global Advance		-	-	8	-	-
Global Partners/Wesleyan World Missions		-	19	-	-	-
Global Youth Ministry Network	1997	-	-	1	-	-
Gospel Fellowship Association	2005	14	-	4	-	-
International Institute for Christian Studies		-	-	8	1	7
Intl. Pentecostal Holiness Ch. World Msns. Mins.		1	-	5	8	-
International Teams, U.S.A.		2	-	23	-	71
LifeWind International		-	-	2	27	4
Lutheran Hour Ministries		-	-	1	290	-
Middle East Christian Outreach (MECO)		-	2	4	-	32
Middle East Media—USA		-	-	2	80	9
Mission to the World (PCA), Inc.		2	30	70	-	-
Navigators, U.S. International Missions Group		10	2	179	-	-
OC International, Inc.		-	-	70	-	7
OMS International, Inc.		-	-	-	-	5
Open Bible Churches, Intl. Mins.		-	-	4	-	-
Operation Mobilization	1970	37	8	21	-	6
Presbyterian Church (USA), Worldwide Ministries		-	100	78	-	-
ReachGlobal		8	17	44	-	-
Reformed Baptist Mission Services		-	-	3	-	-
SEED International		1	-	9	-	-
SIM USA, Inc.		-	-	12	-	-
Southern Baptist Conv. Intl. Msn. Bd.	1845	-	1027	4100	-	-
Talking Bibles International	1989	-	-	2	-	-
United Methodist Ch., General Bd. of Global Mins.		-	-	486	298	10
WEC International		-	-	70	-	-
Weiner Ministries International	1991	-	-	1	-	-
World Baptist Fellowship Msn. Agency, Inc.	2007	4	2	-	-	-
World Gospel Mission		-	-	3	-	-
World Missions & Evangelism, Inc.		-	-	10	-	-
World Partners USA		-	29	-	-	-
World Team		-	-	6	-	-
Wycliffe Bible Translators, Inc.		-	-	405	-	-
Totals:		141	1274	6672	1348	220

	First Year	Personnel from U.S. 1-2 yrs.	2-4 yrs.	4+ yrs.	Other Countries Citizens	Non-Citizens

Uruguay

	First Year	1-2 yrs.	2-4 yrs.	4+ yrs.	Citizens	Non-Citizens
Assemblies of God World Missions	1946	-	-	10	-	-
Awana International		-	-	-	-	-
Baptist Bible Fellowship International	1958	-	-	2	-	-
Baptist Missionary Association of America	1964	-	-	-	4	-
Biblical Ministries Worldwide	1967	-	-	9	2	-
CAM International	2009	-	-	4	-	-
Campus Crusade for Christ, Intl.	1966	-	-	-	3	-
Children's Christian Concern Society	2009	-	-	-	-	-
Christian Aid Mission	1983	-	-	-	7	-
Church of God of Prophecy—Global Outreach		-	-	-	4	-
Church of the Nazarene, World Msn. Dept.	1949	-	-	-	-	-
Churches of Christ	1952	-	-	-	-	-
Converge Worldwide	1991	-	-	2	-	-
Every Home for Christ International	1978	-	-	-	1	-
Free Will Baptist, Inc. Bd. of Intl. Missions	1961	1	-	5	-	-
Gospel Mission of South America, Inc.	1970	-	-	6	-	-
Grace Ministries International	1983	-	2	-	-	-
IFCA World Missions		-	-	-	1	-
International Board of Jewish Missions, Inc.	1952	-	-	3	2	1
International Partnership Ministries, Inc.	1999	-	-	-	3	3
International Pentecostal Church of Christ	1997	-	-	-	1	-
Intl. Pentecostal Holiness Ch. World Msns. Mins.	2004	-	-	-	-	-
LifeWind International	1999	-	-	-	1	-
LOGOI Ministries	1972	-	-	-	1	-
Mailbox Club International Inc., The		-	-	-	1	-
OMS International, Inc.	2002	-	-	6	-	1
SIM USA, Inc.	1995	-	-	6	-	-
Spanish World Ministries, Inc.		-	-	1	1	-
United Pentecostal Church International	1932	-	2	-	-	-
Word of Life Fellowship, Inc.—Intl. Ministries	1976	-	-	-	3	1
World Venture	1995	-	-	2	-	-
Totals:		1	4	56	35	6

Uzbekistan

	First Year	1-2 yrs.	2-4 yrs.	4+ yrs.	Citizens	Non-Citizens
Assemblies of God World Missions	1996	-	-	4	-	-
Baptist International Evangelistic Ministries		-	-	-	-	-
Baptist Missionary Association of America	1994	-	-	-	9	-
Christian Aid Mission		-	-	-	28	-
Evangelism Explosion International		-	-	-	-	2
Food for the Hungry, Inc.	2004	-	1	-	-	-
Greater Grace World Outreach	1999	-	-	-	4	-
Interserve USA (International Service Fellowship)	2007	-	-	2	-	-
Operation Mobilization		5	1	1	-	-
People International USA	1991	-	-	12	-	28
Precept Ministries International	1994	-	-	-	1	-
ReachGlobal	1995	-	-	-	-	-
World Concern	1993	2	-	1	136	-
Totals:		7	2	20	178	30

	First Year	Personnel from U.S. 1-2 yrs.	2-4 yrs.	4+ yrs.	Other Countries Citizens	Non-Citizens
Vanuatu						
Assemblies of God World Missions	1967	3	-	4	-	-
Baptist Bible Fellowship International	1999	-	-	2	-	-
Biblical Ministries Worldwide		-	-	9	-	-
Church of the Nazarene, World Msn. Dept.	2001	-	-	2	-	-
Churches of Christ	1979	-	-	3	-	-
FRIENDS in Action International	2003	-	-	-	-	-
Global Recordings Network		-	-	-	-	2
United Pentecostal Church International	1970	-	5	-	-	-
World Outreach International—US	1995	-	-	2	-	-
Wycliffe Bible Translators		-	-	6	-	-
	Totals:	3	5	28	-	2
Venezuela						
Assemblies of God World Missions	1919	2	-	14	-	-
Awana International	1986	-	-	-	10	-
Baptist International Missions, Inc. (BIMI)		-	-	18	-	-
Baptist International Outreach, Inc.	2008	-	-	2	-	-
Baptist Mid-Missions	1924	-	-	7	-	-
Brethren Assemblies		-	-	1	-	-
Calvary International	1995	-	-	-	-	-
Campus Crusade for Christ, Intl.	1971	12	-	3	47	-
Children of Promise International		-	1	1	-	-
Children's Christian Concern Society	1991	-	-	-	-	-
Christian Church (Disciples of Christ)		-	1	-	-	-
Christian Churches/Churches of Christ		-	-	15	-	-
Church of God (Cleveland, Tenn.) World Missions	1966	-	-	3	-	2
Church of God of Prophecy—Global Outreach		-	-	-	3	1
Church of the Nazarene, World Msn. Dept.	1982	-	-	6	-	-
Church Resource Ministries (CRM)	1992	-	3	2	-	-
Churches of Christ	1957	-	-	3	-	-
Eastern Mennonite Missions	1979	-	-	-	-	-
Fellowship International Mission	1990	-	-	5	-	-
Fellowship of Evangelical Chs.—Intl. Mins.	1980	-	-	3	-	-
Free Methodist World Missions	1984	1	-	-	-	-
Global Partners/Wesleyan World Missions	2001	-	-	-	-	-
Harvest	1989	-	-	-	1	-
IFCA World Missions		-	-	-	1	-
Impact International, Inc.		-	-	-	2	-
International Board of Jewish Missions, Inc.	1996	2	-	-	-	2
International Pentecostal Church of Christ		-	-	-	1	-
Intl. Pentecostal Holiness Ch. World Msns. Mins.		-	-	-	-	-
Latin America Mission		-	-	1	-	1
LifeWind International	1995	-	-	-	5	-
LOGOI Ministries	1972	-	-	-	3	-
Lutheran Church-Missouri Synod, World Mission	1951	-	-	3	-	-
Macedonia World Baptist Missions, Inc.	2002	-	-	6	2	2
Network of International Christian Schools	2006	9	2	-	5	1
OneHope		-	-	-	-	-
Pentecostal Assemblies of God of Am., Inc.		-	-	-	2	-

	Personnel from U.S.				Other Countries	
	First Year	1-2 yrs.	2-4 yrs.	4+ yrs.	Citizens	Non-Citizens
Pentecostal Free Will Baptist Church, Inc.		-	-	-	1	-
Precept Ministries International	1998	-	-	-	-	-
ReachGlobal	1920	1	2	9	-	-
Seventh-day Adventists, General Conference	1910	-	-	2	-	-
Spanish World Ministries, Inc.		-	-	1	1	-
STEM International	2002	-	-	-	-	-
Team Expansion, Inc.	1987	-	-	19	-	-
United Pentecostal Church International	1956	-	4	-	-	-
Word of Life Fellowship, Inc.—Intl. Ministries	1979	-	-	-	5	4
World Indigenous Missions	1999	-	-	4	-	-
World Venture	1986	-	-	4	-	-
Totals:		27	13	132	89	13

Vietnam

	First Year	1-2 yrs.	2-4 yrs.	4+ yrs.	Citizens	Non-Citizens
All God's Children International		-	-	-	10	-
Asian Outreach U.S.A.		-	-	-	-	-
Assemblies of God World Missions	1971	3	-	4	-	-
Baptist Missionary Association of America	2008	-	-	-	-	1
Christian Aid Mission		-	-	-	289	-
Church of God (Cleveland, Tenn.) World Missions	1995	1	-	-	-	-
Ch. of the Brethren—Global Msn. Partnerships		-	-	1	-	-
Churches of Christ	1962	-	-	-	-	-
Cook Communications Ministries International	1999	-	-	-	-	-
Educational Services International (ESI)	2002	12	-	-	-	-
Elim Fellowship—International Ministries		-	-	2	-	-
Global Outreach International	2003	-	-	2	-	-
Globe International	2002	-	-	2	-	-
Gospelink, Inc.		-	-	-	10	-
Habitat for Humanity International		-	1	-	-	1
Holt International Children's Services, Inc.		-	-	-	13	-
Hope Haven International Ministries		-	-	-	2	-
I. N. Network USA	1991	-	-	-	57	-
Intl. Pentecostal Holiness Ch. World Msns. Mins.		-	-	-	-	-
LifeWind International	1999	-	-	-	4	-
Mission To Unreached Peoples	1997	-	-	2	-	-
Partners International	1991	-	-	-	380	-
Samaritan's Purse International Relief	2000	-	4	-	-	-
Seventh-day Adventists, General Conference	1937	-	-	1	-	1
Training Evangelistic Leadership (T.E.L.), Inc.	1991	-	-	2	4	1
Tribes and Nations Outreach		-	-	-	-	-
United Pentecostal Church International		-	-	-	-	-
Walk Thru the Bible Ministries, Inc.	2000	-	-	-	-	-
World Bible Translation Center		-	-	-	2	-
World Concern	1989	1	-	-	14	-
World Link Ministries	2008	-	-	-	100	-
World Missions & Evangelism, Inc.		-	-	1	-	-
WorldServe Ministries		-	-	1	-	-
Wycliffe Bible Translators		-	-	2	-	-
Totals:		17	5	20	885	4

	Personnel from U.S.			Other Countries	
First Year	1-2 yrs.	2-4 yrs.	4+ yrs.	Citizens	Non-Citizens

Virgin Islands

Awana International	2000	-	-	-	-	-
Baptist International Missions, Inc. (BIMI)		-	-	2	-	-
Church of God of Prophecy—Global Outreach		-	-	-	5	-
Church of the Nazarene, World Msn. Dept.	1944	-	-	-	-	-
National Baptist Convention of America	1978	-	-	-	6	-
Totals:		-	-	2	11	-

Western Europe–General

Dawn Ministries, Inc.		-	-	-	-	1
Totals:		-	-	-	-	1

Western Sahara

Christian Aid Mission	2005	-	-	-	20	-
Totals:		-	-	-	20	-

Yemen

Assemblies of God World Missions	2002	-	-	2	-	-
Interserve USA (International Service Fellowship)		-	-	5	-	-
Seventh-day Adventists, General Conference	1994	-	-	2	-	-
Walk Thru the Bible Ministries, Inc.	2002	-	-	-	-	-
Totals:		-	-	9	-	-

Zambia

Action International Ministries, Inc.	2002	-	-	11	2	-
Adventive Cross Cultural Initiatives—US		-	-	-	-	-
African Leadership, Inc.	2003	-	-	-	1	-
Agathos Foundation	2004	5	-	1	6	-
American Baptist Chs. of the U.S.A., Intl.Mins.	2006	-	-	2	-	-
Assemblies of God World Missions	1987	2	-	8	-	-
Awana International	1984	-	-	-	2	-
Baptist Bible Fellowship International	1989	-	2	16	-	-
Baptist International Missions, Inc. (BIMI)		-	-	2	-	-
Baptist International Outreach, Inc.	1985	-	-	24	20	-
Baptist Mid-Missions	1990	-	-	15	-	-
BCM International		-	-	2	-	-
Brethren Assemblies		-	-	25	-	-
Brethren in Christ World Missions	1906	-	-	2	-	-
Campus Crusade for Christ, Intl.	1975	-	-	-	61	1
Child Evangelism Fellowship, Inc.	1970	-	-	-	3	-
Christian Aid Mission	1999	-	-	-	5	-
Christian Relief Fund, The	2004	-	-	-	1	-
Church of God (Cleveland, Tenn.) World Missions	1965	-	-	3	-	-
Church of God of Prophecy—Global Outreach		-	-	-	2	-
Church of the Nazarene, World Msn. Dept.	1961	-	-	4	-	-
Churches of Christ	1910	-	-	12	-	-
Commission to Every Nation	2008	-	-	2	-	2
Evangelical Baptist Missions		-	-	2	-	-
Forgotten Voices International	2004	-	-	-	1	-
Global Partners/Wesleyan World Missions	1930	-	4	-	-	-

	Personnel from U.S.				Other Countries	
	First Year	1-2 yrs.	2-4 yrs.	4+ yrs.	Citizens	Non-Citizens
Gospel Fellowship Association	2005	1	-	11	-	-
Gospelink, Inc.		-	-	-	238	-
Grace Ministries International	1998	2	10	-	-	-
Greater Grace World Outreach	2004	2	1	2	2	3
Heart of the Bride Ministries		3	-	-	-	-
I. N. Network USA	1985	-	-	-	12	-
In Touch Mission International	1995	-	-	2	4	-
Independent Faith Mission, Inc.	1997	-	-	7	-	-
International Justice Mission	2004	-	-	-	11	-
International Partnership Ministries, Inc.	2002	-	-	2	-	-
Intl. Pentecostal Holiness Ch. World Msns. Mins.	1950	-	2	-	-	-
International Teams, U.S.A.		-	-	-	-	2
Ireland Outreach International Inc.	2004	-	-	-	1	-
Kids Alive International	2001	-	1	-	58	-
Launch Out Ministries International	2005	-	-	-	5	-
Liebenzell Mission of USA, Inc.	1985	-	-	1	-	-
LifeWind International	1999	-	-	-	-	-
Living Water International		-	-	-	-	-
Mission to the World (PCA), Inc.	2002	-	-	2	-	-
Missionary Ventures International	2000	-	-	2	-	2
Navigators, U.S. International Missions Group		-	-	2	-	-
Pioneers USA		-	-	2	1	-
Salvation Army, U.S.A.	1922	-	1	-	-	-
Seventh-day Adventists, General Conference	1905	-	-	2	-	8
SIM USA, Inc.	1910	1	-	18	-	-
Teen Missions International, Inc.	1993	-	-	2	30	-
Tentmakers International	2008	-	-	-	1	-
The God's Story Project	2002	-	-	-	1	-
The Word for the World USA	2004	-	-	2	2	-
United Pentecostal Church International	1980	-	2	-	-	-
Walk Thru the Bible Ministries, Inc.	1999	-	-	-	8	-
Wisconsin Evangelical Lutheran Synod	1953	-	-	8	-	-
World Venture		-	-	1	-	-
Totals:		16	23	197	478	18

Zimbabwe

	First Year	1-2 yrs.	2-4 yrs.	4+ yrs.	Citizens	Non-Citizens
African Enterprise	1980	-	-	-	5	-
African Leadership, Inc.	2001	-	-	-	1	-
Assemblies of God World Missions	1968	-	-	6	-	-
Awana International	1983	-	-	-	6	-
Brethren in Christ World Missions	1898	-	-	2	-	-
Campus Crusade for Christ, Intl.	1978	-	-	8	67	12
Child Evangelism Fellowship, Inc.	1951	-	-	-	2	-
Christian Aid Mission	1954	-	-	-	15	-
Christian Church (Disciples of Christ)		-	2	-	-	-
Christian Churches/Churches of Christ		-	-	34	14	-
Christian Relief Fund, The	2004	-	-	-	-	-
Church of God of Prophecy—Global Outreach		-	-	-	7	-
Church of the Nazarene, World Msn. Dept.	1963	-	-	-	-	2
Churches of Christ	1902	-	-	2	-	-

	First Year	Personnel from U.S. 1-2 yrs.	2-4 yrs.	4+ yrs.	Other Countries Citizens	Non-Citizens
Faith Christian Fellowship International	1987	-	-	1	3	-
Fellowship of Evangelical Chs.—Intl. Mins.	2009	-	-	1	-	-
Forgotten Voices International	2004	-	-	-	2	-
Global Recordings Network		-	-	-	1	2
Gospelink, Inc.		-	-	-	91	-
Harvest International, Inc.	2008	-	-	-	-	2
Hope for the Hungry	1983	-	-	-	2	-
Independent Faith Mission, Inc.	1990	-	-	3	-	-
Intl. Pentecostal Holiness Ch. World Msns. Mins.	1950	-	-	-	-	-
Lott Carey Baptist Foreign Msn. Conv.	1998	-	-	-	20	-
Mission Training and Resource Center	2001	-	-	-	1	1
Seventh-day Adventists, General Conference	1894	-	-	3	-	12
SIM USA, Inc.	1887	-	-	3	-	-
Teen Missions International, Inc.	1986	-	-	-	-	-
Tentmakers International	2008	-	-	-	1	-
The Word for the World USA	1984	-	-	-	2	-
United Pentecostal Church International	1968	-	2	-	-	1
Walk Thru the Bible Ministries, Inc.	1999	-	-	-	6	-
Waymarks Radio Ministries International		-	-	-	1	-
White Fields, Inc.		-	-	-	3	-
World Missions & Evangelism, Inc.		-	-	-	-	-
World Relief	2003	-	-	-	2	-
Totals:	-	4	63	252	32	

Chapter 5
Canadian Protestant Agencies

This chapter contains the basic information for Canadian Protestant agencies engaged in Christian ministries outside Canada and the U.S. It includes agencies that directly support the work of such ministries or the work of overseas national churches/workers. The agencies supplied the information. The survey used to gather the information is reproduced in the appendix.

The *Handbook* covers an agency's overseas ministry and support activities; it does not cover its mission work in Canada. Agencies with both overseas and Canadian mission ministries, however, were asked to include Canada-based ministry personnel in the total that appears in the "home ministry and office staff" line of the "Other Personnel" section. Each agency will have at least seven of the basic categories of information listed below, with others included as applicable.

Agency Name

Agencies are listed alphabetically. If the article "the" is in an agency's name, it will appear at the end of the name so the agency is in the most commonly referenced alphabetical order. Rare exceptions occur where the Christian public commonly uses the article "the" as the first word in the agency's name. Agencies that have changed their name since the previous *Handbook* have their prior name listed also, with a cross-reference to the current or new name. A subdivision of a larger organization may be listed separately if it is organized to also serve the larger mission community rather than just its parent organization.

Telephone and Fax Numbers

Area codes are in parentheses. Since area codes change rapidly, some may have changed since time of publication.

Email Address

The Internet format and standards for capitalization are used. In some cases, agencies have a general email address. Others have supplied an individual person's address within the organization. In cases where only a web address is given, it generally means a web page provides access to an email address that can be directed to the relevant department or person.

Web Address

The Internet format and standards for capitalization are used. Most agencies have a web address; however, a few have chosen not to list it for security reasons.

Postal Mailing Address

A post office box number usually appears whenever the agency has one. Exceptions occur when the agency prefers the street address.

Chief Executive Officer

In a few cases where there are multiple primary contacts, or due to agency preference, two officers may be listed.

Short Descriptive Paragraph

A brief description appears based upon the denominational orientation and primary activities information supplied by the agency. Additional specific information, such as name changes, mergers, or other unique aspects may also be included.

Purpose Statement

Purpose statements are included when available. Some of the statements are concise and shown in their entirety, straight from the agency or its promotional material. For most, however, common or similar phrases such as "exists for the purpose of" are replaced by ellipses to present a more concise statement.

Year Founded in Canada

This date is the year the agency or overseas mission component of a larger organization was founded or incorporated in Canada. In some cases, the denomination or organization may have existed earlier in another country. For some organizations, the founding date of the missionary-sending component may be later than the founding of the larger organization. For organizations that have experienced mergers, the founding date is generally that of the oldest component involved in the merger.

Income for Overseas Ministries

This is the part of an agency's overall income used or budgeted for ministry activities outside Canada and the U.S. or in activities that directly facilitate overseas ministries. "NA" indicates that income in this sense is not applicable, and usually applies to specialized service agencies or agencies whose income is reported under a sister or parent organization. "NR" indicates that the agency did not report income for overseas ministries, but may make this information available upon request.

Gifts-in-Kind

If applicable, this is the portion of the income received in the form of donated gifts-in-kind commodities and/or services used for overseas ministries. Please note that some agencies do not include gifts-in-kind as part of their financial audit process, so the value of such gifts may not be included in their income for overseas ministries.

Fully Supported Canadian Personnel Overseas

Not all agencies have overseas personnel in the following categories, so the above heading will not always appear. If applicable, the following lines will appear with the appropriate numbers:

"Expecting to serve more than four years" for persons from Canada who are fully supported by the agency

"Expecting to serve one up to four years" for persons from Canada who are fully supported by the agency

"Nonresidential mission personnel" for fully supported Canadian mission personnel not residing in the country or countries of their ministry, but assigned to work and travel overseas at least twelve weeks per year on operational aspects of the overseas ministry

Other Personnel

If applicable for the agency, the following lines will appear:

"Non-Canadian serving in own/other country" for persons with either citizenship in their country of service or another non-Canadian country, who are fully or partially supported from Canada. Such individuals are not included in the specific numbers for individual countries listed under the "Countries" heading at the bottom of many entries.

"Bivocational/Tentmaker from Canada" for persons sponsored or supervised by the agency, but who support themselves partially or fully through nonchurch/ non-mission vocations and live overseas for the purpose of Christian witness and/or encouraging believers.

"Short-term less than one year from Canada" for persons who went on overseas projects or mission trips that lasted at least one year through the agency, either fully or partially supported, or raising their own support.

"Home Ministry and office staff in Canada" for persons assigned to ministry and/ or office duties in Canada either as full-time or part-time paid staff/associates.

Countries

These are the countries where the agency sends Canadian personnel or regularly supports national or other non-Canadian personnel. Following the name of the country is the number of Canadian personnel with terms of service of four years or more. In some cases, a continent or other general region is shown instead of a country. This may be due to several reasons, such as mission personnel whose ministry covers several countries.

Where an agency's work is maintained by nationals of countries other than Canada or the U.S., or by personnel serving less than four years, the country of activity may be listed without a number. Refer to the chapter entitled "Countries of Activity for Canadian Protestant Agencies" for more detailed country personnel totals. "Unspecified Country" may also be listed for security reasons.

ABWE Canada (Across Borders for World Evangelism)
980 Adelaide St. S., Ste. #34
LONDON, ON N6E 1R3 CAN
Phone: (519) 690-1009
Fax: (519) 690-1618
E-mail: office@abwecanada.org
Web Site: www.abwe.ca

Rev. David W. Smith, President

A sending agency of Baptist and Evangelical tradition engaged in church planting, discipleship, theological education, evangelism, funds transmission and partnership development.

Purpose: "...to assist local churches to achieve their Canadian and international mission objectives."

Year founded in CAN: 1967

Income for Overseas Min: $1,600,000.00

Fully Supported CAN Personnel Overseas:
Expecting to serve more than 4 years: 30
Expecting to serve 1 to 4 years: 3
Non-residential mission personnel: 4

Other personnel:
Short-term less than 1 year: 68
Home ministry & office staff in CAN: 6

Countries: Africa—General 2; Asia—General 1; Brazil 4; Croatia 2; Europe—General 3; Liberia 1; Middle East 2; Portugal 3; Romania 2; Togo 4; Trinidad and Tobago 2; Ukraine 2; United Kingdom 2

Action International Ministries—Canada
3015 A 21st St. NE
CALGARY, AB T2E 7T1 CAN
Phone: (403) 204-1421
Fax: (403) 204-1501
E-mail: info@actioncanada.net
Web Site: www.actioncanada.net

Dr. Wayne Whitbourne, Canadian Director

An interdenominational sending agency of Evangelical tradition engaged in training, camping programs, childcare/orphanage programs, discipleship, leadership development, literature distribution and urban ministry to the poor. Data from 2005.

Purpose: "...networks with local churches, national organizations and other mission agencies to reach people for Christ (evangelism), train them in Christian living (discipleship) and assist them in their physical and economic needs (development)."

Year founded in CAN: 1980

Income for Overseas Min: $1,383,914.00

Fully Supported CAN Personnel Overseas:
Expecting to serve more than 4 years: 17
Expecting to serve 1 to 4 years: 2
Non-residential mission personnel: 1

Other personnel:
Short-term less than 1 year: 36
Non-CAN serving in own/other country: 11
Home ministry & office staff in CAN: 2

Countries: Brazil 2; Colombia 4; Ecuador 2; Honduras; India 2; New Zealand; Philippines 5; Ukraine 1; Zambia 1

Adventist Development and Relief Agency Canada (ADRA Canada)
115 Clarence Biesenthal Drive
OSHAWA, ON L1K 2H5 CAN
Phone: (905) 433-8004
Fax: (905) 723-1903
E-mail: info@adra.ca
Web Site: www.adra.ca

Mr. Ronald Kuhn, Exec. Director

A service agency of Adventist tradition engaged in development, agricultural programs, medical work, relief and/or rehabilitation, children at risk and HIV/Aids.

Purpose: "...to work with people in poverty and distress to create just and positive change through empowering partnerships and responsible action."

Year founded in CAN: 1985

Income for Overseas Min: $3,899,496.00

Personnel:
Home ministry & office staff in CAN: 15

Adventive Cross Cultural Initiatives
89 Auriga Dr.
NEPEAN, ON K2E 7Z2 CAN
Phone: (613) 298-1546
Fax: (613) 225-7455
E-mail: lauren@adventive.ca
Web Site: www.adventive.ca

Lauren Carrion, Canadian Natl. Director

A nondenominational support agency of Evangelical tradition engaged in leadership development, Bible distribution, church planting, discipleship, support of national churches and partnership development.

Purpose: "...to attract, equip, send, and serve the vision of passionate, effective leaders and teams who are focused on cross-culturally advancing the Kingdom of Christ."

Year founded in CAN: 1991

Income for Overseas Min: $189,000.00

Personnel:
Short-term less than 1 year: 3

Africa Community Technical Service (ACTS)
PO Box 1515
COMOX, BC V9M 8A2 CAN
Phone: (250) 339-1212
Fax: (250) 339-1300
E-mail: moore@acts.ca
Web Site: www.acts.ca

Mr. David Moore, Exec. Director

A transdenominational support agency of Orthodox and Biblical Christian tradition engaged in technical assistance (rural water supply of Africa), agricultural programs, development, HIV/Aids, relief and/or rehabilitation and short-term programs.

Purpose: "...to provide community development assistance and skills training to the people of Africa in cooperation with the local church and other grassroots organizations...to carry out our mission under the authority of Scripture, seeking in all we do to glorify our Lord Jesus Christ."

Year founded in CAN: 1972

Income for Overseas Min: $1,400,000.00

Gifts in Kind: $16,100.00

Fully Supported CAN Personnel Overseas:
Expecting to serve more than 4 years: 2
Non-residential mission personnel: 1

Other personnel:
Short-term less than 1 year: 15
Non-CAN serving in own/other country: 29
Home ministry & office staff in CAN: 5

Countries: Uganda 2

Africa Inland Mission International (Canada)
1641 Victoria Park Ave.
SCARBOROUGH, ON M1R 1P8 CAN
Phone: (416) 751-6077
Fax: (416) 751-3467
E-mail: general.can@aimint.net
Web Site: www.aimint.org/can
Associations: CrossGlobal Link

Mr. John P. Brown, Canadian Director

A nondenominational sending agency of Evangelical tradition engaged in church planting, leadership development, aviation services, discipleship, Christian education and medical work.

Purpose: "...to have Christ centered churches among all African peoples."

Year founded in CAN: 1953

Income for Overseas Min: $3,762,000.00

Fully Supported CAN Personnel Overseas:
Expecting to serve more than 4 years: 29
Expecting to serve 1 to 4 years: 32

Other personnel:
Short-term less than 1 year: 60
Home ministry & office staff in CAN: 11

Countries: Congo, Democratic Republic of 2; Kenya 18; Lesotho; Madagascar; Namibia; Oceania—General; South Africa; Sudan 2; Tanzania 5; Uganda 2

African Enterprise Association of Canada
4509 W. 11th Ave.
VANCOUVER, BC V6R 2M5 CAN
Phone: (604) 228-0930
Fax: (604) 228-0936
E-mail: aecanada@africanenterprise.com
Web Site: www.africanenterprise.com

Mr. David Richardson, Exec. Director/CEO

An interdenominational support agency of Evangelical and Independent tradition engaged in partnership development, evangelism, justice, management consulting/training, support of national workers and short-term programs.

Purpose: "...to build partnerships for urban outreach in Africa and Canada."

Year founded in CAN: 1964

Income for Overseas Min: $157,400.00

Fully Supported CAN Personnel Overseas:
Expecting to serve more than 4 years: 3
Non-residential mission personnel: 6
Other personnel:
Short-term less than 1 year: 3
Non-CAN serving in own/other country: 3
Home ministry & office staff in CAN: 4
Countries: Africa—General 3

Apostolic Church in Canada, The

220 Adelaide St. N.
LONDON, ON N6B 3H4 CAN
Phone: (519) 438-7036
Fax: (519) 438-5800
E-mail: cheryl@newlifecentre.com
Web Site: www.newlifecentre.com
Mr. D. Karl Thomas, President

A denominational support agency of Charismatic and Apostolic tradition engaged in member care, discipleship and support of national churches.
Purpose: "...to establish a network of churches in apostolic relationship and reap a harvest through church planting."
Year founded in CAN: 1940
Personnel:
Home ministry & office staff in CAN: 13
Countries: Brazil; India; Jamaica

Apostolic Church of Pentecost of Canada, Inc.

#119—2340 Pegasus Way NE
CALGARY, AB T2E 8M5 CAN
Phone: (403) 273-5777
Fax: (403) 273-8102
E-mail: acop@acop.ca
Web Site: www.acop.ca
Rev. Wes Mills, MCL, President

A denominational sending agency of Baptist and Pentecostal tradition engaged in church planting, discipleship, HIV/Aids, leadership development, support of national churches and relief and/or rehabilitation.
Purpose: "...is engaged in community transformation through developing effective leaders and healthy churches."
Year founded in CAN: 1921
Income for Overseas Min: $1,655,000.00
Fully Supported CAN Personnel Overseas:

Expecting to serve more than 4 years: 24
Other personnel:
Non-CAN serving in own/other country: 1
Home ministry & office staff in CAN: 6
Countries: Burkina Faso 1; Bolivia 2; Brazil 2;
El Salvador 2; Estonia 2; France 2; Ireland 2;
Malawi 2; Mexico 2; Taiwan 2; Tanzania 2;
Trinidad and Tobago 1; Zambia 2; Zimbabwe

Arab World Ministries (Canada)

PO Box 3398
CAMBRIDGE, ON N3H 4T3 CAN
Phone: (519) 624-6170
Fax: (519) 624-6576
E-mail: info@awmcanada.org
Web Site: www.awm.org
Mr. Amal Gendi, Exec. Director

An interdenominational sending agency of Evangelical tradition engaged in mobilization for mission, business as mission, church planting, evangelism, short-term programs and missionary training.
Purpose: "...to exalt Jesus Christ through word and deed, making disciples and establishing mature, multiplying churches among Muslims of the Arab world wherever they reside."
Year founded in CAN: 1967
Income for Overseas Min: $1,101,075.00
Fully Supported CAN Personnel Overseas:
Expecting to serve more than 4 years: 22
Residential mission personnel: 1
Other personnel:
Non-CAN serving in own/other country: 17
Home ministry & office staff in CAN: 17
Countries: Africa—General 9; France 4;
Middle East 9

Arms of Jesus Children's Mission, Inc., The

PO Box 10
PICKERING, ON L1V 2R2 CAN
Phone: (905) 831-3646
Fax: (905) 831-3661
E-mail: aojchildmis@rogers.com
Web Site: www.armsofjesus.org
Associations: CCRDA
Dr. Sam Martin, Founder/Director

An interdenominational and transdenominational service agency of Baptist and Evangelical tradition engaged in childrens programs, children at risk, development, Christian education, relief and/or rehabilitation and short-term programs.

Year founded in CAN: 1990

Fully Supported CAN Personnel Overseas:
Expecting to serve 1 to 4 years: 2

Other personnel:
Short-term less than 1 year: 122
Non-CAN serving in own/other country: 54
Home ministry & office staff in CAN: 8

Countries: Africa—General; Central African Republic; Dominican Republic; Guatemala; Haiti; Kenya; Namibia

Asian Outreach Intl. Canada
PO Box 42052
VANCOUVER, BC V6P 6S6 CAN
Phone: (604) 272-1789
Fax: (888) 669-0985
E-mail: info@asianoutreach.ca
Web Site: www.asianoutreach.ca
Associations: CCRDA

Mr. Patrick Elaschuk, Reg. Msn. Director, N. A.

A nondenominational support agency engaged in missions, Bible distribution, church planting, development, leadership development, literacy work and missionary training.

Year founded in CAN: 1989

Income for Overseas Min: $356,478.00

Fully Supported CAN Personnel Overseas:
Expecting to serve more than 4 years: 1

Other personnel:
Non-CAN serving in own/other country: 38
Home ministry & office staff in CAN: 2

Countries: Asia—General; Central Asia—General 1

Avant Ministries Canada
2121 Henderson Hwy.
WINNIPEG, MB R2G 1P8 CAN
Phone: (204) 338-7831
Fax: (204) 339-3321
E-mail: AMC@avmi.org
Web Site: www.avantministries.org
Associations: CrossGlobal Link

Mr. Grant Morrison, Canadian Director

An interdenominational sending agency of

Baptist and Mennonite tradition engaged in church planting, broadcasting, children at risk and youth programs.

Purpose: "...to glorify God by helping others enjoy His presence through planting and developing new churches in unreached areas of the world."

Year founded in CAN: 1949

Income for Overseas Min: $2,026,282.00

Fully Supported CAN Personnel Overseas:
Expecting to serve more than 4 years: 35

Other personnel:
Short-term less than 1 year: 10
Home ministry & office staff in CAN: 17

Countries: Austria 1; Bolivia 6; Brazil 2; Czech Republic 4; Ecuador 4; Germany 2; Mali 4; Mexico 4; Spain 8;

Back to the Bible Canada
PO Box 700
CHATHAM, ON N7M 5K7 CAN
Phone: (519) 351-6930
Fax: (519) 351-5795
E-mail: bttb@backtothebible.ca
Web Site: www.backtothebible.ca

Mr. Bob Beasley, CEO

An interdenominational service agency of Evangelical tradition engaged in broadcasting, audio recording/distribution and literacy work.

Purpose: "...to lead people into a dynamic relationship with God."

Year founded in CAN: 1964

Income for Overseas Min: $233,543.00

Personnel:
Home ministry & office staff in CAN: 7

Baptist General Conference of Canada Global Ministries (BGCC Global Ministries)
#205 15824 131 Ave.
EDMONTON, AB T5V 1J4 CAN
Phone: (780) 438-9127
Fax: (780) 435-2478
E-mail: office@bgc.ca
Web Site: www.bgc.ca

Jamey McDonald, Exec. Director

A denominational sending agency of Baptist tradition engaged in church planting, theological education, evangelism and member care. The mission agency of the Baptist General Conference of Canada. Countries of service data from 2005.

Purpose: "...to plant and grow worship, caring and reproducing churches globally."

Year founded in CAN: 1981

Income for Overseas Min: $553,515.00

Fully Supported CAN Personnel Overseas:
   Expecting to serve more than 4 years: 6
   Expecting to serve 1 to 4 years: 1

Other personnel:
   Home ministry & office staff in CAN: 5

Countries: Asia—General 2; Ethiopia; Philippines 2; Portugal 1; Tanzania 1

Barry Moore Ministries, Inc.

PO Box 9100
LONDON, ON N6E 3P3 CAN
Phone: (519) 661-0205
Fax: (519) 661-0206
E-mail: bmoore@odyssey.on.ca
Web Site: www.bmoore.on.ca

Rev. John Laari, Exec. Director

An interdenominational support agency of Evangelical tradition engaged in evangelism.

Purpose: "...to go to the small, out-of-the-way places where seldom, if ever before, a united outreach for Christ has been held."

Year founded in CAN: 1960

Income for Overseas Min: $196,806.00

Fully Supported CAN Personnel Overseas:
   Non-residential mission personnel: 2

Other personnel:
   Short-term less than 1 year: 8
   Non-CAN serving in own/other country: 10
   Home ministry & office staff in CAN: 3

Countries: Europe—General; India; Malawi; South Africa; South America—General; Tanzania

BCM Intl. (Canada), Inc.

685 Main St. East
HAMILTON, ON L8M 1K4 CAN
Phone: (905) 549-9810
Fax: (905) 549-7664
E-mail: mission@bcmintl.ca
Web Site: www.bcmintl.ca
Associations: CrossGlobal Link

Mr. William Ricketts, Exec. Director

A nondenominational support agency of Evangelical tradition engaged in evangelism, camping programs, childrens programs, church planting, correspondence courses and training.

Purpose: "...to make disciples of all age groups for the Lord Jesus Christ through evangelism, teaching, and training so that churches are established and the Church strengthened."

Year founded in CAN: 1941

Personnel:
   Short-term less than 1 year: 1
   Non-CAN serving in own/other country: 4
   Home ministry & office staff in CAN: 1

Countries: Italy; Netherlands; Spain

Bible Holiness Movement, The

PO Box 223, Postal Stn. A
VANCOUVER, BC V6C 2M3 CAN
Phone: (250) 492-3376

Wesley H. Wakefield, Bishop-General

A denominational support agency of Holiness and Wesleyan tradition engaged in evangelism, Bible distribution, church planting, literature distribution, literature production and trafficking/slavery issues.

Purpose: "...to establish, conduct and maintain worldwide missionary work; to spread Scriptural holiness, vital Christianity and practical Godliness through a proper qualified ministry."

Year founded in CAN: 1949

Income for Overseas Min: $26,945.00

Gifts in Kind: $2,300.00

Personnel:
   Non-CAN serving in own/other country: 100

Countries: Ghana; India; Kenya; Korea, South; Malawi; Nigeria; Philippines; Tanzania; Zambia

Bible League of Canada, The

PO Box 5037
BURLINGTON, ON L7R 3Y8 CAN
Phone: (905) 319-9500
Fax: (905) 319-0484
E-mail: ministry@bibleleague.ca
Web Site: www.bibleleague.ca

Mr. Dick L. Kranendonk, President

A specialized agency of Evangelical and Reformed tradition engaged in Bible distribution, childrens programs, church planting, discipleship, literacy work and literature distribution.

Purpose: "...to provide Scriptures and training worldwide, so that people prepared by the Holy Spirit will be brought into fellowship with Christ and His Church."

Year founded in CAN: 1943

Income for Overseas Min: $4,368,550.00

Fully Supported CAN Personnel Overseas:
Non-residential mission personnel: 2

Other personnel:
Short-term less than 1 year: 18
Non-CAN serving in own/other country: 5
Home ministry & office staff in CAN: 18

Countries: Africa—General; Asia—General; Eastern Europe—General; Latin America—General

BLF Canada

256 Marc-Aurele-Fortin
LACHUTE, PQ J8H 3W7 CAN
Phone: (450) 562-7859
E-mail: toeblake@sympatico.ca
Rev. Toe-Blake Roy, Canadian Director

An interdenominational support agency of Evangelical tradition engaged in literature production, Bible distribution, discipleship, evangelism, literature distribution and short-term programs.

Purpose: "...to provide French literature to the French world at an affordable cost."

Year founded in CAN: 2001

Brethren in Christ World Missions—Canada

2700 Bristol Circle
OAKVILLE, ON L6H 6E1 CAN
Phone: (905) 339-2335
Fax: (905) 337-2120
E-mail: bicwm@bellnet.ca
Web Site: www.bic-church.org/wm
Marsha Sider, Interim Chair—Wld. Msns. Team

A denominational sending agency of Brethren and Evangelical tradition engaged in church planting, apologetics, theological education, evangelism, leadership development and support of national churches.

Purpose: "...to extend the Kingdom of God as we labor cross-culturally with oth-

er believers...to evangelize, disciple, serve, and plant churches...to challenge the BIC church to accomplish the Great Commission with prayers, personnel, and finance."

Year founded in CAN: 1967

Income for Overseas Min: $245,716.00

Personnel:
Short-term less than 1 year: 54
Home ministry & office staff in CAN: 2

Countries: Colombia; Cuba; Honduras; India; Japan; Malawi; Mexico; Middle East; Mozambique; Nepal; Nicaragua; Spain; Thailand; United Kingdom; Venezuela; Zambia; Zimbabwe

CAM International of Canada

PO Box 71034
Maplehurst Postal Outlet
BURLINGTON, ON L7T4J8 CAN
Phone: (905) 689-2473
E-mail: lljjhower@aol.com
Web Site: www.caminternational.org
Associations: CrossGlobal Link
Mr. Larry Hower, Asst. to the President

A nondenominational sending agency of Baptist tradition engaged in church planting, camping programs, discipleship, theological education, TEE and evangelism.

Purpose: "...to partner with the Hispanic world to help fulfill the Great Commission."

Year founded in CAN: 1965

Income for Overseas Min: $262,000.00

Fully Supported CAN Personnel Overseas:
Expecting to serve more than 4 years: 2
Expecting to serve 1 to 4 years: 2

Other personnel:
Short-term less than 1 year: 14
Home ministry & office staff in CAN: 1

Countries: Mexico 2

Canadian Assemblies of God, General Conference

PO Marquette #37315
MONTREAL, PQ H2E 3B5 CAN
Phone: (514) 279-1100
Fax: (514) 279-1131
E-mail: info@caogonline.org
Web Site: www.caogonline.org
Rev. Elio Marrocco, Superintendent

A denominational support agency of Pentecostal tradition engaged in support of national churches, association of missions, leadership development and youth programs.

Year founded in CAN: 1912
Income for Overseas Min: $85,867.00
Personnel:
Home ministry & office staff in CAN: 1

Canadian Baptist Ministries
7185 Millcreek Dr.
MISSISSAUGA, ON L5N 5R4 CAN
Phone: (905) 821-3533
Fax: (905) 826-3441
E-mail: administration@cbmin.org
Web Site: www.cbmin.org
Mrs. Brenda Halk, President

A denominational sending agency of Baptist tradition engaged in leadership development, church planting, development and discipleship.

Purpose: "...to unite, encourage, and enable Canadian Baptist Churches in their national and international endeavors to fulfill the Great Commandment and the Great Commission of our Lord Jesus Christ, in the power of the Holy Spirit, proclaiming the Gospel and showing the love of God in word and deed."

Year founded in CAN: 1912

Fully Supported CAN Personnel Overseas:
Expecting to serve more than 4 years: 22

Other personnel:
Short-term less than 1 year: 327
Non-CAN serving in own/other country: 10
Home ministry & office staff in CAN: 33

Countries: Angola 1; Argentina 1; Bolivia 3; Brazil 2; China; El Salvador; Europe—General 1; India; Indonesia 3; Kenya 5; Lebanon 2; Middle East 2; Rwanda 2;

Canadian Bible Society/La Societe Biblique Canadienne
10 Carnforth Rd.
TORONTO, ON M4A 1S4 CAN
Phone: (416) 757-4171
Fax: (416) 757-3376
E-mail: donorenq@biblesociety.ca
Web Site: www.biblesociety.ca
Mr. Ted Seres, Nat. Director

An interconfessional support agency of Ecumenical tradition engaged in Bible distribution, linguistics, literature distribution, literature production, support of national churches and Bible translation. Data from 2005.

Purpose: "...to promote and encourage, without doctrinal note or comment, the translation, publication, distribution and use of the Scriptures throughout Canada and Bermuda, and to cooperate with the United Bible Societies in its worldwide work."

Year founded in CAN: 1904
Income for Overseas Min: $2,694,000.00
Personnel:
Home ministry & office staff in CAN: 120

Canadian Churches' Forum for Global Ministries
47 Queen's Park Cresc. East
TORONTO, ON M5S 2C3 CAN
Phone: (416) 924-9351
Fax: (416) 978-7821
E-mail: director@ccforum.ca
Web Site: www.ccforum.ca
Jonathan Schmidt & Alice Schuda, Co-Directors

An Ecumenical service agency of Anglican, Lutheran, Methodist and Presbyterian tradition engaged in missionary training, literature production, support of national churches and short-term programs.

Purpose: "...a Christian agency through which Canadian churches reflect and work together on global mission issues and are challenged to prophetic global witness through programs of education, training and dialogue."

Year founded in CAN: 1921
Personnel:
Home ministry & office staff in CAN: 3

Canadian National Baptist Convention (CNBC)
100 Convention Way
COCHRANE, AB T4C 2G2 CAN
Phone: (403) 932-5688
Fax: (403) 932-4937
E-mail: office@cnbc.ca
Web Site: www.cnbc.ca
Rev. Gerald Taillon, Natl. Min. Leader

A denominational sending agency of Baptist tradition engaged in church planting, discipleship, evangelism, support of national churches, partnership development and mobilization for mission.

Purpose: "...churches in covenant giving ourselves away to advance the Kingdom of God."

Year founded in CAN: 1985

Income for Overseas Min: $362,462.00

Fully Supported CAN Personnel Overseas:
Expecting to serve more than 4 years: 6
Non-residential mission personnel: 26

Other personnel:
Non-CAN serving in own/other country: 26
Home ministry & office staff in CAN: 21

Countries: Africa—General; Asia—General 2; Botswana; Central Asia—General; Croatia; Europe—General 2; Germany; Mexico; Middle East 2; Niger

Canadian South America Mission

336 Speedvale Ave. West, Unit H
GUELPH, ON N1H7M7 CAN

Phone: (866) 443-2250

Web Site: www.southamericamission.org

Associations: CrossGlobal Link

Rev. William K. Ogden, Exec. Director

A nondenominational sending agency of Evangelical tradition engaged in church leadership development, aviation services, church planting and development.

Purpose: "...building leaders to build churches."

Year founded in CAN: 1983

Income for Overseas Min: $158,590.00

Fully Supported CAN Personnel Overseas:
Expecting to serve more than 4 years: 3
Expecting to serve 1 to 4 years: 2

Other personnel:
Non-CAN serving in own/other country: 6
Home ministry & office staff in CAN: 1

Countries: Bolivia 2; Brazil; Peru 1

Child Evangelism Fellowship of Canada

PO Box 165 Station Main
WINNIPEG, MB R3C 2G9 CAN

Phone: (204) 943-2774

Fax: (204) 943-9967

E-mail: info@cefcanada.org

Web Site: www.cefcanada.org

Mr. Jerry Hanson, Natl. Director

A nondenominational sending agency of Evangelical tradition engaged in evangelism, childrens programs, discipleship, member care, missionary training and training.

Purpose: "...to evangelize children, disciple them in the Word of God, and establish them in a Bible-believing church."

Year founded in CAN: 1938

Income for Overseas Min: $569,097.00

Fully Supported CAN Personnel Overseas:
Expecting to serve more than 4 years: 9

Other personnel:
Short-term less than 1 year: 1
Home ministry & office staff in CAN: 4

Countries: Asia—General 2; Bolivia 1; Brazil 2; Caribbean—General 1; Japan 2; Nicaragua 1

Chosen People Ministries (Canada)

PO Box 897, Station B
TORONTO, ON M3A 2V6 CAN

Phone: (416) 250-0177

Fax: (416) 250-9235

E-mail: info@chosenpeople.ca

Web Site: www.chosenpeople.ca

Associations: CrossGlobal Link

Rev. Joseph Gray, Director

An interdenominational service agency of Evangelical and Messianic tradition engaged in evangelism, church planting and discipleship.

Purpose: "...to share the Gospel with Jewish people and help others do the same."

Year founded in CAN: 1940

Income for Overseas Min: $32,400.00

Personnel:
Short-term less than 1 year: 10
Home ministry & office staff in CAN: 8

Christar Canada

PO Box 20164
ST. CATHARINES, ON L2M 7W7 CAN

Phone: (905) 646-0228

Fax: (905) 646-8707

E-mail: christar@on.aibn.com

Web Site: www.christar.org

Associations: CrossGlobal Link

Marty Frisk, Director

A sending agency of Evangelical tradition engaged in church planting, evangelism and tentmaking.

Purpose: "...to proclaim the gospel and establish local indigenous churches, primarily among least-reached Asian communities worldwide."

Year founded in CAN: 1949

Income for Overseas Min: $600,000.00

Fully Supported CAN Personnel Overseas:
 Expecting to serve 1 to 4 years: 21

Other personnel:
 Short-term less than 1 year: 10
 Home ministry & office staff in CAN: 4

Countries: Albania; Asia—General; France; United Kingdom

Christian Aid for Under-Assisted Societies Everywhere (CAUSE Canada)

PO Box 8100
CANMORE, AB T1W 2T8 CAN

Phone: (403) 678-3332
Fax: (403) 678-8869
E-mail: info@cause.ca
Web Site: www.cause.ca
Associations: CCRDA

Beverley Carrick, Exec. Director

A nondenominational sending agency of Ecumenical and Evangelical tradition engaged in development, children at risk, justice, leadership development, literacy work and relief and/or rehabilitation.

Purpose: "...inspired by our faith in Christ and the inherent dignity of every person, CAUSE Canada seeks to alleviate poverty and injustice through long-term partnerships that empower communities to improve their quality of life."

Year founded in CAN: 1984

Income for Overseas Min: $1,209,294.00

Fully Supported CAN Personnel Overseas:
 Expecting to serve 1 to 4 years: 5

Other personnel:
 Short-term less than 1 year: 20
 Non-CAN serving in own/other country: 80
 Home ministry & office staff in CAN: 8

Countries: Guatemala; Honduras; Sierra Leone

Christian and Missionary Alliance in Canada, The

30 Carrier Dr., Ste. 100
TORONTO, ON M9W 5T7 CAN

Phone: (416) 674-7878
Fax: (416) 674-0808
E-mail: info@cmacan.org
Web Site: www.cmacan.org

Dr. Franklin Pyles, President

A denominational sending agency of Evangelical tradition engaged in church planting, business as mission, theological education, evangelism, leadership development and tentmaking.

Purpose: "...a movement of churches transformed by Christ, transforming Canada and the world."

Year founded in CAN: 1981

Income for Overseas Min: $9,200,000.00

Fully Supported CAN Personnel Overseas:
 Expecting to serve more than 4 years: 175
 Expecting to serve 1 to 4 years: 9
 Non-residential mission personnel: 199

Other personnel:
 Home ministry & office staff in CAN: 28

Countries: Africa—General 11; Asia—General 12; Cambodia 6; Congo, Republic of the 3; Ecuador 5; France 3; Germany 6; Guatemala 2; Guinea 6; Hungary 4; Indonesia 10; Japan 8; Laos; Malaysia 9; Mexico 12; Middle East 26; Netherlands 1; Niger 10; Panama 2; Philippines 1; Poland 4; Russia 2; Senegal 1; Serbia and Montenegro 2; Spain 1; Taiwan 6; Thailand 4; Venezuela 5; Unspecified Country 13

Christian Blind Mission International—Canada

3844 Stouffville Rd.
PO Box 800
STOUFFVILLE, ON L4A 7Z9 CAN

Phone: (905) 640-6464
Fax: (905) 640-4332
E-mail: cbmi@cbmicanada.org
Web Site: www.cbmicanada.org

Mr. David McComiskey, Exec. Director

A nondenominational medical and rehabilitational agency engaged in the cure, prevention and care of disabling afflictions, including the training of nationals. Data from 2005.

Purpose: "...to rescue and restore people trapped in poverty by disability."
Year founded in CAN: 1978
Income for Overseas Min: $8,540,527.00
Gifts in Kind: $1,616,361.00
Personnel:
  Home ministry & office staff in CAN: 31

Christian Reformed World Relief Committee of Canada
PO Box 5070STN LCD
BURLINGTON, ON L7R 3Y8 CAN
Phone: (905) 336-2920
Fax: (905) 336-8344
E-mail: imutoigo@crwrc.org
Web Site: www.crwrc.org
Associations: AERDO, CCRDA
Ida Mutoigo, Dir. Canada
A denominational service agency of Reformed tradition engaged in development, HIV/Aids, justice, leadership development, relief and/or rehabilitation and education with volunteer opportunities regarding global hunger."
Purpose: "...to engage God's people in redeeming resources and developing gifts in collaborative acts of love, mercy, justice, and compassion."
Year founded in CAN: 1962
Income for Overseas Min: $19,455,537.00
Fully Supported CAN Personnel Overseas:
  Expecting to serve more than 4 years: 12
  Expecting to serve 1 to 4 years: 2
Other personnel:
  Short-term less than 1 year: 122
  Non-CAN serving in own/other country: 28
Countries: Bangladesh 1; Cambodia 2; Dominican Republic; Ecuador; Haiti; Honduras; Kenya 1; Malawi; Mali 3; Mozambique; Nicaragua 1; Niger; Nigeria 2; Philippines; Sierra Leone; Tanzania; Uganda; Zambia 2

Christian Studies International of Canada
13607-109 Ave.
EDMONTON, AB T5M 2G8 CAN
Phone: (780) 452-2715
E-mail: csidesk@telus.net
Web Site: www.christianstudiesinternational.ca

Dr. Henk W. H. Van Andel, Exec. Director
A transdenominational service agency of Evangelical tradition engaged in teaching as mission (university level), Christian education, leadership development and tent-making.
Purpose: "...to recruit and support Christian professors to teach in public universities overseas, with the objective to provide students with an education rooted in a Biblical worldview, preparing them to be Godly servant leaders in their home country."
Year founded in CAN: 1995
Income for Overseas Min: $252,000.00
Fully Supported CAN Personnel Overseas:
  Expecting to serve more than 4 years: 1
  Expecting to serve 1 to 4 years: 1
Other personnel:
  Short-term less than 1 year: 5
  Home ministry & office staff in CAN: 2
Countries: China 1; Nigeria

Church of God (Anderson, IN) —Canadian Bd. of Missions
4717—56th St.
CAMROSE, AB T4V 2C4 CAN
Phone: (780) 672-0772
Fax: (780) 672-6888
E-mail: wcdncog@telus.net
Web Site: www.chog.ca
Rev. Ken Wiedrick, Exec. Director
A support agency of Holiness and Wesleyan tradition engaged in church planting, church construction, funds transmission, leadership development and providing congregational services to local congregations.
Purpose: "...focused on developing dynamic congregational life, effective leadership and church planting."
Year founded in CAN: 1905
Income for Overseas Min: $427,780.00
Fully Supported CAN Personnel Overseas:
  Non-residential mission personnel: 7
Other personnel:
  Short-term less than 1 year: 20
  Home ministry & office staff in CAN: 3
Countries: Brazil; Guam; Malawi; Mozambique; Uganda; Zambia

Commission to Every Nation—Canada

1371 Lesperance Rd
WINDSOR, ON N8N 1Y2 CAN
Phone: (519) 735-8620
Fax: (519) 735-0007
E-mail: canada@cten.org
Web Site: www.cten.org
Mr. Rick Spencer, President

An interdenominational sending agency of Evangelical and Independent tradition engaged in missionary education and support of national workers.

Purpose: "...to partner with churches to help Christians become personally involved in fulfilling the Great Commission to every nation."

Year founded in CAN: 2006
Income for Overseas Min: $97,056.00
Fully Supported CAN Personnel Overseas:
Expecting to serve more than 4 years: 2
Expecting to serve 1 to 4 years: 10
Non-residential mission personnel: 12
Other personnel:
Non-CAN serving in own/other country: 13
Countries: Cameroon 2; Costa Rica; Ecuador; Guatemala

Compasio

PO Box 77015
OTTAWA, ON K1S 5N2 CAN
Phone: (613) 686-5535
Fax: (866) 610-8850
E-mail: info@compasio.org
Web Site: www.compasio.org
Mr. Allan Brown, Exec. Director

A service agency engaged in trafficking/slavery issues, children at risk, development, justice, psychological counseling and relief and/or rehabilitation.

Purpose: "...to see a need, to feel compassion, and to act with practical love."

Year founded in CAN: 2006
Income for Overseas Min: $50,000.00
Fully Supported CAN Personnel Overseas:
Expecting to serve more than 4 years: 2
Other personnel:
Non-CAN serving in own/other country: 12
Home ministry & office staff in CAN: 1
Countries: Thailand 2

Compassion Canada

985 Adelaide St. S
LONDON, ON N6E 4A3 CAN
Phone: (519) 668-0224
Fax: (519) 685-1107
E-mail: info@compassion.ca
Web Site: www.compassion.ca
Associations: AERDO
Dr. Barry Slauenwhite, CEO

A service agency of Evangelical tradition engaged in holistic child development, children at risk, discipleship, leadership development and partnership development.

Purpose: "...exists as an advocate for children to release them from their spiritual, economic, social and physical poverty and enable them to become fulfilled, Christian adults, in response to the Great Commission."

Year founded in CAN: 1963
Personnel:
Home ministry & office staff in CAN: 60

Crossroads Christian Communications Inc. (ERDF)

PO Box 5100
BURLINGTON, ON L7R 4M2 CAN
Phone: (905) 332-6400
Fax: (905) 332-1880
E-mail: dshelley@crossroads.ca
Web Site: www.crossroads.ca
Associations: CCRDA
Mr. Doug McKenzie, Exec. VP

A nondenominational service agency of Evangelical and Pentecostal tradition engaged in broadcasting, agricultural programs, development, funds transmission, relief and/or rehabilitation and supplying equipment. Financial data from 2005.

Year founded in CAN: 1977
Income for Overseas Min: $2,680,897.00
Gifts in Kind: $41,507.00
Personnel:
Home ministry & office staff in CAN: 155
Countries: Haiti; India; Kenya; Uganda; Ukraine; Zambia

CrossWorld Canada

1020 Matheson Blvd. E., #11
MISSISSAUGA, ON L4W 4J9 CAN
Phone: (905) 238-0904

Fax: (905) 629-8439
E-mail: info.canada@crossworld.org
Web Site: www.crossworld.org
Associations: CrossGlobal Link

Mr. Dave Koning, Interim Director

An interdenominational sending agency of Baptist and Evangelical tradition engaged in discipleship, business as mission, church planting, leadership development, support of national churches and short-term programs.

Purpose: "...to mobilize teams to make disciples and train leaders which will result in movements of reproducing churches among the unreached."

Year founded in CAN: 1931

Income for Overseas Min: $1,008,726.00

Fully Supported CAN Personnel Overseas:
  Expecting to serve more than 4 years: 13
  Expecting to serve 1 to 4 years: 2
  Non-residential mission personnel: 1

Other personnel:
  Short-term less than 1 year: 20
  Non-CAN serving in own/other country: 3
  Home ministry & office staff in CAN: 2

Countries: Brazil 6; Haiti 1; Ireland 3; Italy 1; Senegal 2

CSM Canada International (Christian Salvage Mission)

120 Lansing Dr., Unit #3
HAMILTON, ON L8W 3A1 CAN

Phone: (905) 574-3334
E-mail: info@csmcanada.org

Rev. Donald C. Ralph, President

A nondenominational support agency of Evangelical and Fundamental tradition engaged in Bible distribution, services for other agencies, supplying equipment and video/film production/distribution.

Purpose: "...to supply Bibles and evangelical materials to Christian pastors and students around the world."

Year founded in CAN: 1994

Income for Overseas Min: $40,000.00

Personnel:
  Home ministry & office staff in CAN: 1

EMAS Canada

PO Box 820
STOUFFVILLE, ON L4A 7Z9 CAN

Phone: (905) 642-4661
Fax: (905) 640-2186
E-mail: info@emascanada.rog
Web Site: www.emascanada.org

Mr. Michael Wills, Exec. Director

A transdenominational specialized agency of Evangelical tradition engaged in medical work, development, extension education and short-term programs.

Purpose: "...to reveal Christ's love by working with national groups and to provide assistance in healing and teaching."

Year founded in CAN: 1948

Income for Overseas Min: $1,611,035.00

Gifts in Kind: $84,823.00

Personnel:
  Short-term less than 1 year: 341
  Home ministry & office staff in CAN: 2

Countries: Angola; Cambodia; China; Cuba; Ecuador; Haiti; Hong Kong; Malawi; Philippines; Romania; Russia; Vietnam

Emmanuel Intl. Canada

PO Box 4050
STOUFFVILLE, ON L4A 8B6 CAN

Phone: (905) 640-2111
Fax: (905) 640-2186
E-mail: info@eicanada.org
Web Site: www.eicanada.org
Associations: CCRDA

Mr. Richard McGowan, Interim Exec. Director

An interdenominational sending agency of Evangelical tradition engaged in development, discipleship, TEE, leadership development, partnership development and relief and/or rehabilitation.

Purpose: "...to encourage, strengthen, and assist churches worldwide to meet the spiritual and physical needs of the poor in accordance with the holy Scriptures."

Year founded in CAN: 1975

Income for Overseas Min: $1,848,353.00

Personnel:
  Non-CAN serving in own/other country: 25
  Home ministry & office staff in CAN: 9

Countries: Africa—General; Brazil; Haiti; Malawi; Philippines; South Africa; Tanzania; Uganda; United Kingdom

Equip, Canada

PO Box 683
DUNCAN, BC V9L 3Y1 CAN
Phone: (250) 743-7171
Fax: (250) 743-7171
Web Site: www.equipinternational.com
Associations: AERDO

Rev. Barrie G. Flitcroft, Gen. Director

An interdenominational sending agency of
Evangelical tradition engaged in development, community and/or other, agricultural
programs, childcare/orphanage programs,
children at risk, justice and medical work.

Purpose: "...to prepare, send, and support evangelical missionaries to assist the
Church around the world to be responsive
to the poor, sensitive to the Holy Spirit, focused on personal evangelism, and practi-
cally engaged in strengthening the Body of
Christ."

Year founded in CAN: 1997

Income for Overseas Min: $155,313.00

Fully Supported CAN Personnel Overseas:
Expecting to serve more than 4 years: 6
Non-residential mission personnel: 6

Other personnel:
Home ministry & office staff in CAN: 3

Countries: Liberia 2; Nigeria 2; Uganda 2

ERDO—Emergency Relief and Development

2450 Milltower Ct.
MISSISSAUGA, ON L7L 5X3 CAN
Phone: (905) 542-7400
Fax: (905) 542-0377
E-mail: info@erdo.ca
Web Site: www.erdo.ca
Associations: CCRDA

Rev. Kelvin Honsinger, Exec. Director

A denominational support agency of Pentecostal tradition engaged in relief and/or rehabilitation, agricultural programs, child-
care/orphanage programs, children at risk,
development, HIV/Aids, justice and food aid.

Purpose: "...to respond to human need
where there is poverty, hunger, disaster and
injustice, on behalf of the Pentecostal Assemblies of Canada."

Year founded in CAN: 1983

Income for Overseas Min: $4,810,000.00

Fully Supported CAN Personnel Overseas:
Non-residential mission personnel: 1

Other personnel:
Short-term less than 1 year: 1
Home ministry & office staff in CAN: 6

ERRC Educational Society

6200 McKay Ave.
Box 141-592
BURNABY, BC V5H 4M9 CAN
Phone: (778) 322-5411
Fax: (604) 431-7980
E-mail: errc_canada@hotmail.com
Web Site: www.errchina.com

Dr. Ward Gasque, President

A transdenominational specialized agency
of Evangelical and Reformed tradition engaged in cross-cultural education, training/
orientation, discipleship, theological education, evangelism, leadership development
and short-term programs.

Purpose: "...to offer educational services
and academic resources to China...to send
teachers, professionals, and academics to
serve in educational institutions...to conduct
local and international culturally relevant
long-term programs, short-term seminars,
conferences, and events of an educational nature consistent with the key values endorsed by the board."

Year founded in CAN: 1987

Income for Overseas Min: $252,188.00

Gifts in Kind: $18,501.00

Fully Supported CAN Personnel Overseas:
Expecting to serve 1 to 4 years: 1
Non-residential mission personnel: 4

Other personnel:
Short-term less than 1 year: 8
Non-CAN serving in own/other country: 46
Home ministry & office staff in CAN: 3

Countries: China

Evangelical Christian Church in Canada, The

410-125 Lincoln Rd.
WATERLOO, ON N2J 2N9 CAN
Phone: (519) 880-9110
Fax: (519) 880-9110
E-mail: cecc@rogers.com
Web Site: www.cecconline.com

Dr. David Patrick Lavigne, Bishop

A denominational sending agency of Christian (Restoration Movement), Evangelical, and Holiness tradition engaged in training, church planting, correspondence courses, TEE and support of national workers.

Year founded in CAN: 1944

Gifts in Kind: $75,000.00

Fully Supported CAN Personnel Overseas:
Expecting to serve more than 4 years: 5
Non-residential mission personnel: 1

Other personnel:
Short-term less than 1 year: 1
Non-CAN serving in own/other country: 5
Home ministry & office staff in CAN: 3

Countries: Africa—General 1; China 1; India 1; Russia 1; South America—General 1

Evangelical Covenant Church of Canada

PO Box 34025
RPO Fort Richmond
WINNIPEG, MB R3T 5T5 CAN

Phone: (204) 269-3437
Fax: (204) 269-3584
E-mail: messengr@escape.ca
Web Site: www.canadacovenantchurch.org

Mr. Jeffrey Anderson, Superintendent

A denominational conference of Covenantal and Evangelical tradition engaged in denominational funds transmission and mission mobilization for evangelism and church planting. Data from 2005.

Year founded in CAN: 1904

Income for Overseas Min: $52,280.00

Personnel:
Home ministry & office staff in CAN: 3

Evangelical Free Church of Canada Mission

PO Box 850
Langley Stn. LCD 1
LANGLEY, BC V3A 8S6 CAN

Phone: (604) 513-2183
Fax: (604) 888-3108
E-mail: info@efccm.org
Web Site: www.efccm.org

Associations: The Mission Exchange

Mr. Rich Peachey, Personnel Director

A denominational sending agency of Evangelical tradition engaged in church planting, broadcasting, development, support of national churches, TESOL and short-term programs.

Purpose: "...exists to serve in the birth and growth of healthy churches internationally."

Year founded in CAN: 1976

Income for Overseas Min: $3,700,000.00

Fully Supported CAN Personnel Overseas:
Expecting to serve more than 4 years: 33
Expecting to serve 1 to 4 years: 29
Non-residential mission personnel: 7

Other personnel:
Short-term less than 1 year: 65
Non-CAN serving in own/other country: 6
Home ministry & office staff in CAN: 6

Countries: Asia—General 6; Bolivia 4; Central Asia—General 2; Congo, Democratic Republic of; Cuba; Ecuador 2; Germany; Haiti; Hungary 4; Japan 2; Lithuania; Mexico 2; Panama 2; Rwanda; Thailand 2; Venezuela 2; Ukraine 5

Evangelical Lutheran Church in Canada—Global Mission

302—393 Portage Ave.
WINNIPEG, MB R3B 3H6 CAN

Phone: (204) 984-9150
Fax: (204) 984-9185
E-mail: sjohnson@elcic.ca
Web Site: www.elcic.ca/Global-Mission

Rev. Susan C. Johnson, National Bishop

The national mission office of a Lutheran denomination engaged in support of overseas partner churches, missions in Canada and campus ministry. Countries of service and activities data from 2002.

Purpose: "...to share the Gospel of Jesus Christ with people in Canada and around the world through the proclamation of the Word, the celebration of the Sacraments and through service in Christ's name."

Year founded in CAN: 1985

Fully Supported CAN Personnel Overseas:
Expecting to serve more than 4 years: 5
Expecting to serve 1 to 4 years: 6

Other personnel:
Home ministry & office staff in CAN: 1

Countries: Argentina; Cameroon 2; Colombia; El Salvador 1; Guyana; Hong Kong; Jordan; Papua New Guinea 1; Peru 1; Slovakia; Thailand

Evangelical Mennonite Conference, Bd. of Missions

440 Main St.
STEINBACH, MB R5G IZ5 CAN
Phone: (204) 326-6401
Fax: (204) 326-1613
E-mail: info@emconf.ca
Web Site: www.emconf.ca
Associations: The Mission Exchange, CrossGlobal Link

Mr. Tim Dyck, Gen. Secretary

A denominational sending agency of Evangelical and Mennonite tradition engaged in church planting, discipleship, evangelism, leadership development and support of national churches.

Year founded in CAN: 1953
Income for Overseas Min: $1,053,973.00
Fully Supported CAN Personnel Overseas:
　Expecting to serve more than 4 years: 23
　Expecting to serve 1 to 4 years: 4
　Non-residential mission personnel: 4
Other personnel:
　Short-term less than 1 year: 20
　Home ministry & office staff in CAN: 10
Countries: Burkina Faso 2; Mexico 7; Paraguay 14

Evangelical Mennonite Mission Conference

757 St. Anne's Road
WINNIPEG, MB R2N 4G6 CAN
Phone: (204) 253-7929
Fax: (204) 256-7384
E-mail: info@emmc.ca
Web Site: www.emmc.ca

Mr. Jacob Friesen, Exec. Director

A denominational sending agency of Mennonite tradition engaged in support of national churches, church planting, association of missions, leadership development and partnership development.

Purpose: "...to inspire and facilitate local outreach and global mission."

Year founded in CAN: 1959
Income for Overseas Min: $619,000.00
Fully Supported CAN Personnel Overseas:
　Expecting to serve more than 4 years: 10
　Expecting to serve 1 to 4 years: 3
Other personnel:

Home ministry & office staff in CAN: 6
Countries: Belize 2; Bolivia 8; Mexico

Evangelical Missionary Church of Canada, World Partners

4031 Brentwood Rd. NW
CALGARY, AB T2L 1L1 CAN
Phone: (403) 250-2759
Fax: (403) 291-4720
E-mail: wp@emcc.ca
Web Site: www.emcc.ca

Sandra Tjart, Director

A denominational sending agency of Evangelical tradition engaged in discipleship, church planting, correspondence courses, development, evangelism, medical work, relief and/or rehabilitation, short-term programs and Bible translation. Data from 2005.

Purpose: "...to promote and provide opportunities for churches and individuals to participate in intentional, holistic ministry by sharing spiritual, human and material resources in cross-cultural and/or global contexts."

Year founded in CAN: 1998
Fully Supported CAN Personnel Overseas:
　Expecting to serve more than 4 years: 8
　Expecting to serve 1 to 4 years: 20
　Non-residential mission personnel: 1
Other personnel:
　Short-term less than 1 year: 10
　Non-CAN serving in own/other country: 1
　Home ministry & office staff in CAN: 4
Countries: Brazil; Cuba; El Salvador; Haiti; Hungary; Ireland; Mexico 6; Nigeria; Portugal 2; Romania; Spain; Tanzania;

Evangelical Tract Distributors

PO Box 146
EDMONTON, AB T5J 2G9 CAN
Phone: (780) 477-1538
Fax: (780) 477-3795
E-mail: etdsupport@evangelicaltract.com
Web Site: www.evangelicaltract.com

Mr. John Harder, President

An interdenominational specialized agency of Evangelical tradition engaged in literature distribution, literature production and evangelism.

Purpose: "...to proclaim the Gospel of Jesus Christ and His message of salvation in as many languages as possible primarily by the printing of Gospel literature and any other appropriate media."

Year founded in CAN: 1935

Income for Overseas Min: $550,000.00

Personnel:
Home ministry & office staff in CAN: 7

FAIR (Fellowship Agency for International Relief)
PO Box 457
GUELPH, ON N1H 6K9 CAN
Phone: (519) 821-4830
Fax: (519) 821-9829
E-mail: international@fellowship.ca
Web Site: www.febinternational.ca

Dr. John Kaiser, President

A denominational support agency of Baptist tradition engaged in relief and/or rehabilitation. The relief arm of FEBInternational.

Year founded in CAN: 1974

Income for Overseas Min: $180,741.00

Personnel:
Home ministry & office staff in CAN: 1

Far East Broadcasting Associates of Canada (FEB Canada)
PO Box 457
GUELPH, ON N1H 6K9 CAN
Phone: (519) 821-4830
Fax: (519) 821-9829
E-mail: international@fellowship.ca
Web Site: www.febinternational.ca

Mr. Dan Baetz, Director

A denominational sending agency of Baptist and Evangelical tradition engaged in church planting, discipleship, evangelism, leadership development, medical work and relief and/or rehabilitation.

Purpose: "...to develop reproducing churches among strategic populations and to facilitate humanitarian development."

Year founded in CAN: 1963

Income for Overseas Min: $2,729,335.00

Fully Supported CAN Personnel Overseas:
Expecting to serve more than 4 years: 50
Expecting to serve 1 to 4 years: 15

Other personnel:
Short-term less than 1 year: 6

Non-CAN serving in own/other country: 6
Home ministry & office staff in CAN: 7

Countries: Bulgaria; Cambodia; Chile 2; Colombia 4; France 8; Honduras; India; Indonesia 2; Italy 2; Japan 6; Kazakhstan 2; Kenya 6; Mexico 4; Middle East; Netherlands; Pakistan 6; Philippines; Poland 3; Spain 2; Venezuela 3

Fellowship of Companies for Christ International Canada
27 Waubeek St.
PARRY SOUND, ON P2A 1C1 CAN
Phone: (705) 746-1521
E-mail: jsfcci@vianet.ca
Web Site: www.fcci.org

Mr. Jonathon Shaw, VP of Intl. Ministry

A specialized agency of Evangelical tradition engaged in business as mission, discipleship, evangelism, leadership development, management consulting/training and training. For statistical information see the US listing for Fellowship of Companies for Christ International.

Purpose: "...to equip and encourage Christian business leaders to operate their businesses and conduct their personal lives in accordance with biblical principles."

FH Canada
1-31741 Peardonville Rd
ABBOTSFORD, BC V2T 1L2 CAN
Phone: (604) 853-4262
Fax: (604) 853-4332
E-mail: info@fhcanada.org
Web Site: www.fhcanada.org

Mr. Ben Hoogendoorn, President/CEO

A nondenominational service agency engaged in development, Christian education, leadership development, providing medical supplies, partnership development and relief and/or rehabilitation. Statistical information from 2005.

Purpose: "...to serve a suffering world by sending appropriate people, ideas and resources to needy communities influencing society to become advocates for the poor and empowering the Christian community with a Biblical view of poverty, social action and injustice."

Year founded in CAN: 1988

Income for Overseas Min: $40,874,000.00
Gifts in Kind: $37,883,000.00
Fully Supported CAN Personnel Overseas:
  Expecting to serve more than 4 years: 5
  Expecting to serve 1 to 4 years: 12
  Non-residential mission personnel: 1
Other personnel:
  Short-term less than 1 year: 24
  Non-CAN serving in own/other country: 1
  Home ministry & office staff in CAN: 26
Countries: Bolivia 2; Brazil; Cambodia; Ethiopia; Indonesia; Peru; Romania; Thailand 2; Uganda 1

Finishers Canada

PO Box 223
ORILLIA, ON L3V 6J3 CAN
Phone: (705) 238-8671
E-mail: info@finisherscanada.ca
Web Site: www.finisherscanada.ca
Mr. Ronald Aitken, Exec. Director

A support agency of Evangelical tradition engaged in mobilizing mature Christian adults to missionary activities, mobilization for mission, association of missions and services for other agencies.

Purpose: "...to recruit and assist mature Christian adults by helping them use their skills and/or resources to carry out Christian missionary activities on behalf of Canadian Evangelical Christian Charities."

Year founded in CAN: 2003
Personnel:
  Home ministry & office staff in CAN: 1

FRIENDS in Action International—Canada

PO Box 21066 RPO
ORANGEVILLE, ON L9W 4S7 CAN
Phone: (519) 942-0144
E-mail: FIA-CAN@fiaintl.org
Web Site: www.fiaintl.org
Mr. Roger Wingfield, Board Chairman

A support agency of Baptist tradition engaged in services for other agencies, agricultural programs, church planting, development and support of national workers.

Purpose: "...to assist missionary groups and individuals around the world with similar purposes in helping to lighten their loads

in some way...to enable them to continue in their work of reaching the unreached."
Year founded in CAN: 1999
Income for Overseas Min: $478,138.00
Fully Supported CAN Personnel Overseas:
  Expecting to serve more than 4 years: 3
  Expecting to serve 1 to 4 years: 1
Other personnel:
  Short-term less than 1 year: 24
  Home ministry & office staff in CAN: 1
Countries: Burkina Faso 1; Papua New Guinea 2

Frontiers Canada

PO Box 99
EDMONTON, AB T5J 2H7 CAN
Phone: (780) 421-9090
Fax: (780) 421-9292
E-mail: info@frontiers.ca
Web Site: www.frontiers.ca
Associations: CrossGlobal Link
Rev. Nelson Wolf, Canadian Director

An interdenominational sending agency of Evangelical tradition engaged in church planting, development, Christian education, medical work, mobilization for mission and tentmaking. Financial data from 2005.

Purpose: "...with love and respect, inviting all Muslims to follow Jesus."
Year founded in CAN: 1984
Income for Overseas Min: $998,546.00
Fully Supported CAN Personnel Overseas:
  Expecting to serve more than 4 years: 37
Other personnel:
  Non-CAN serving in own/other country: 2
Countries: Africa—General 6; Asia—General 10; Central Asia—General 9; Europe—General 4; Middle East 8

Fundamental Baptist Mission of Trinidad and Tobago (Canada)

25 Clearwater Street
STEINBACH, MB R5G 2J8 CAN
Phone: (204) 320-1304
E-mail: married1988@gmail.com
Mr. Garry Francis, Acting Chair/Treasurer

A support agency of Baptist and Independent tradition engaged in church planting, broadcasting, camping programs, theological education, funds transmission, literature distribution, missionary training and youth programs.

Year founded in CAN: 1990
Gifts in Kind: $800.00
Personnel:
  Non-CAN serving in own/other country: 1
Countries: Trinidad and Tobago

Galcom International, Inc.
115 Nebo Rd.
HAMILTON, ON L8W 2E1 CAN

Phone: (905) 574-4626
Fax: (905) 574-4633
E-mail: galcom@galcom.org
Web Site: www.galcom.org
Associations: CrossGlobal Link
Rev. Allan T. McGuirl, Intl. Director
An interdenominational support agency of Evangelical tradition engaged in designing, building and distributing high-tech communications equipment for other agencies used in evangelism and other ministries in 102 countries.
Purpose: "...to provide durable technical equipment for communicating the Gospel worldwide."
Year founded in CAN: 1989
Income for Overseas Min: $270,000.00
Personnel:
  Home ministry & office staff in CAN: 16

Gateway Training for Cross-cultural Service
21233—32nd Avenue
LANGLEY, BC V2Z 2E7 CAN

Phone: (604) 530-4283
Fax: (604) 530-7192
E-mail: registrar@gatewaytraining.org
Web Site: www.gatewaytraining.org
Mr. Ike Agawin, Director
An interdenominational specialized agency of Evangelical tradition engaged in missionary training and missionary education. A division of WEC International.
Year founded in CAN: 1995
Personnel:
  Home ministry & office staff in CAN: 9

Global Aid Network, Inc.— Canada
20385—64 Ave.
LANGLEY, BC V2Y 1N5 CAN

Phone: (604) 514-2026
Fax: (604) 514-2121
E-mail: info@globalaid.net
Web Site: www.globalaid.net
Mr. William Blaney, Chief Exec. Officer
A sending agency of Evangelical tradition engaged in development, childcare/orphanage programs, church planting, psychological counseling and relief and/or rehabilitation.
Purpose: "...to demonstrate the love of God in word and deed to hurting and needy people around the world through relief and development projects."
Year founded in CAN: 1998
Income for Overseas Min: $2,015,693.00
Gifts in Kind: $193,410.00
Fully Supported CAN Personnel Overseas:
  Expecting to serve more than 4 years: 25
  Expecting to serve 1 to 4 years: 25
Other personnel:
  Short-term less than 1 year: 34
  Home ministry & office staff in CAN: 2
Countries: Africa—General 25

Global Outreach Mission Inc.,Canada
PO Box 1210
ST. CATHARINES, ON L2R 7A7 CAN

Phone: (905) 684-1401
Fax: (905) 684-3069
E-mail: glmiss@on.aibn.com
Web Site: www.missiongo.org
Associations: CrossGlobal Link
Mr. Brian M. Albrecht, President
A nondenominational sending agency of Evangelical and Independent tradition engaged in church planting, broadcasting, evangelism, medical work, support of national workers, mobilization for mission and short-term programs. Personnel data not reported.
Purpose: "...to share the Gospel...to plant and encourage His church...to help those who are hurting physically and to serve in every area of Christian development."
Year founded in CAN: 1943

Income for Overseas Min: $1,176,212.00

Fully Supported CAN Personnel Overseas:
Expecting to serve more than 4 years: 40
Expecting to serve 1 to 4 years: 1

Countries: Belgium 1; Brazil 1; Congo, Republic of the 1; France 6; Guatemala 4; Hong Kong 1; India 17; Ireland 4; Kazakhstan 2; Romania 1; United Kingdom 2

Global Recordings Network Canada

Unit 6, 120 Lancing Dr.
HAMILTON, ON L8W 3A1 CAN

Phone: (905) 574-8220
Fax: (905) 574-6843
E-mail: ca@globalrecordings.net
Web Site: www.globalrecordings.net/ca
Associations: CrossGlobal Link

Mr. David Elliott, Natl. Director

A nondenominational specialized agency of Evangelical tradition engaged in audio recording/distribution, evangelism, support of national workers, evangelism and translation work.

Purpose: "...to glorify God by producing recorded Bible teaching materials for people to hear the story of Jesus in their heart language."

Year founded in CAN: 1969

Income for Overseas Min: $70,899.00

Fully Supported CAN Personnel Overseas:
Non-residential mission personnel: 2

Other personnel:
Short-term less than 1 year: 17
Non-CAN serving in own/other country: 4
Home ministry & office staff in CAN: 5

Countries: Kenya

Gospel for Asia

245 King St. E.
STONEY CREEK, ON L8G 1L9 CAN

Phone: (905) 662-2101
Fax: (905) 662-8447
E-mail: infocanada@gfa.org
Web Site: www.gfa.org

Pastor Pat Emerick, Canadian Director

An interdenominational support agency of Evangelical tradition engaged in support of national workers totaling approximately 16,000 native missionaries, Bible distribution, broadcasting, church planting, evangelism and literature production.

Year founded in CAN: 1984

Personnel:
Home ministry & office staff in CAN: 13

Countries: Bangladesh; Bhutan; Cambodia; China; India; Laos; Myanmar/Burma; Nepal; Sri Lanka; Thailand

Gospel Mission of South America of Canada

PO Box 150
ST. CHARLES, ON P0M 2W0 CAN

Phone: (705) 967-1262
E-mail: canada@gmsa.org
Web Site: www.gmsa.org

Rev. John Kenyon, Chairperson

A sending agency of Baptist tradition engaged in church planting, discipleship, evangelism, furloughed missionary support and support of national churches.

Purpose: "...to glorify God by serving sending churches as we help their missionaries establish reproducing churches in Latin America through evangelism, discipleship, and leadership development."

Year founded in CAN: 1965

Income for Overseas Min: $103,203.00

Fully Supported CAN Personnel Overseas:
Expecting to serve more than 4 years: 3

Other personnel:
Short-term less than 1 year: 2
Non-CAN serving in own/other country: 5

Countries: Argentina 1; Chile 2

Gospel Operation International for Chinese Christians Canada, Inc.

63 Silver Star Blvd., Unit C17
TORONTO, ON M1V 5E5 CAN

Phone: (416) 756-2111
Fax: (416) 756-2188
E-mail: gointl@goic.ca
Web Site: www.gointl.org

Rev. Peter Chan, CAN Director

An interdenominational sending agency of Evangelical tradition engaged in mobilization for mission, church planting, furloughed missionary support, missions information service, short-term programs and missionary training.

Purpose: "...focuses in sending missionaries to establish indigenous missions and churches among all peoples. All ministries, functions, and activities must relate to or support this goal."

Year founded in CAN: 1997

Income for Overseas Min: $500,759.00

Fully Supported CAN Personnel Overseas:
Expecting to serve more than 4 years: 2
Expecting to serve 1 to 4 years: 5

Other personnel:
Short-term less than 1 year: 39
Non-CAN serving in own/other country: 3
Home ministry & office staff in CAN: 2

Countries: Brazil; Cambodia; Korea, South; Mexico 2; Myanmar/Burma; Peru; Thailand;

Greater Europe Mission (Canada)

100 Ontario St.
OSHAWA, ON L1G 4Z1 CAN

Phone: (905) 728-8222
Fax: (905) 728-8958
E-mail: gemcanada@gemission.com
Web Site: www.gemission.org
Associations: CrossGlobal Link

Mr. Howard Moore, Canadian Director

An interdenominational sending agency of Evangelical tradition engaged in church planting, camping programs, Christian education and evangelism.

Purpose: "...to disciple all peoples of Europe through rapidly reproducing churches."

Year founded in CAN: 1960

Income for Overseas Min: $1,173,436.00

Fully Supported CAN Personnel Overseas:
Expecting to serve more than 4 years: 17
Expecting to serve 1 to 4 years: 3

Other personnel:
Short-term less than 1 year: 62
Home ministry & office staff in CAN: 6

Countries: Croatia 2; Germany 4; Hungary 3; Ireland; Latvia 4; Luxembourg 2; Portugal 2

Habitat for Humanity Canada

40 Albert St.
WATERLOO, ON N2L 3S2 CAN

Phone: (519) 885-4565

Fax: (519) 885-5225
E-mail: habitat@habitat.ca
Web Site: www.habitat.ca
Associations: CCRDA

Mr. Stewart Hardacre, President/COO

A nondenominational specialized agency of Ecumenical tradition engaged in affordable housing, development, relief and/or rehabilitation and short-term programs.

Purpose: "...to mobilize volunteers and community partners in building affordable housing and promoting homeownership as a means to breaking the cycle of poverty."

Year founded in CAN: 1985

Income for Overseas Min: $2,355,678.00

Personnel:
Short-term less than 1 year: 1387
Home ministry & office staff in CAN: 30

Haiti Arise—Canada

PO Box 85267, Albert Park PO
CALGARY, AB T2A 7R7 CAN

Phone: (403) 272-6493
E-mail: info@haitiarise.org
Web Site: www.haitiarise.org

Mr. James Roberts, Vice President

A nondenominational sending agency of Charismatic tradition engaged in technical/trade college education, agricultural programs, church planting, theological education, providing medical clinics & supplies and TESOL.

Purpose: "...to educate and relieve poverty in Haiti."

Income for Overseas Min: $211,000.00

Fully Supported CAN Personnel Overseas:
Expecting to serve more than 4 years: 2

Other personnel:
Short-term less than 1 year: 157

Countries: Haiti 2

HCJB Global—Canada

3-44 Saltsman Dr.
CAMBRIDGE, ON N3H 4R7 CAN

Phone: (519) 650-5444
Fax: (519) 650-0547
E-mail: canada@hcjb.org
Web Site: www.hcjbglobal.org
Associations: CrossGlobal Link

Mr. Ian Leaver, Dir. Canada

An interdenominational support agency of Evangelical and Fundamental tradition engaged in broadcasting, discipleship, Christian education, medical work, partnership development and training.

Purpose: "...to empower dynamic media and healthcare ministries that declare and demonstrate Jesus Christ."

Year founded in CAN: 1952

Income for Overseas Min: $1,400,000.00

Fully Supported CAN Personnel Overseas:
 Expecting to serve more than 4 years: 11

Other personnel:
 Short-term less than 1 year: 3
 Non-CAN serving in own/other country: 4
 Home ministry & office staff in CAN: 9

Countries: Ecuador 9; Singapore 2

Health Partners International of Canada

955 St. Jean Blvd., Ste. 100
POINTE-CLAIRE, PQ H4H 2N2 CAN
Phone: (514) 695-0007
Fax: (514) 695-8528
E-mail: info@hpicanada.ca
Web Site: www.hpicanada.ca

Mr. Glen Shepherd, President/CEO

A nondenominational specialized agency engaged in providing medical supplies, development, relief and/or rehabilitation and services for other agencies.

Purpose: "...a Canadian charitable humanitarian organization that provides free medical aid without discrimination for the world's most needy by operating through partnership and the motivation of Christian love."

Year founded in CAN: 1986

Hellenic Ministries/Canada

PO Box 141
CHILLIWACK, BC V2P 6H7 CAN
Phone: (604) 792-8750
Fax: (604) 792-1410
E-mail: tdeby@hmnet.org.gr
Web Site: www.hellenicministries.com

Associations: CrossGlobal Link

Mr. Trevor Eby, Exec. Director

A nondenominational sending agency of Independent tradition engaged in discipleship, Bible distribution, camping programs, church planting, evangelism and justice.

Year founded in CAN: 2001

Fully Supported CAN Personnel Overseas:
 Expecting to serve 1 to 4 years: 4

Countries: Greece

High Adventure Gospel Communication Ministries

PO Box 425, Station E
TORONTO, ON M6H 4E3 CAN
Phone: (905) 898-5447
Fax: (905) 898-2500
E-mail: admin@hagcm.org
Web Site: www.biblevoice.org

Mr. Don McLaughlin, President

A nondenominational support agency of Evangelical tradition engaged in broadcasting, Bible distribution, evangelism, literacy work, literature distribution and providing medical supplies.

Purpose: "...exists to proclaim God's Word to those who have never heard the Gospel of Jesus Christ as well as to facilitate spiritual growth for listeners."

Year founded in CAN: 1979

Income for Overseas Min: $1,200,000.00

Personnel:
 Short-term less than 1 year: 20
 Non-CAN serving in own/other country: 10
 Home ministry & office staff in CAN: 6

Countries: Liberia; Uganda

Hope Haven Canada Mins.

18362 94th Ave.
SURREY, BC V4N 4A6 CAN
Phone: (604) 882-1412
E-mail: hopehavencanada@hotmail.com
Web Site: www.hopehaveninternational.org

Mr. Ralph Terpstra, President

An interdenominational service agency of Mennonite and Reformed tradition engaged in providing medical supplies, disability assistance programs, Christian education, relief and/or rehabilitation, supplying equipment and youth programs.

Purpose: "...to unleash the potential in people through work and life skills so that they may enjoy a productive life in their community."

Year founded in CAN: 2003

Income for Overseas Min: $24,640.00
Personnel:
  Short-term less than 1 year: 7

HOPE International Development Agency

214 Sixth Street
NEW WESTMINSTER, BC V3L 3A2 CAN
Phone: (604) 525-5481
Fax: (604) 525-3471
E-mail: hope@hope-international.com
Web Site: www.hope-international.com
Associations: AERDO
Mr. David S. McKenzie, Exec. Director

A nondenominational service agency engaged in development, agricultural programs, leadership development, relief and/or rehabilitation and training. Use data from 2005.

Purpose: "...supports water resource development, agriculture, health care, education and micro-enterprise projects in Africa, South Asia, Southeast Asia, Central and Latin America. We provide volunteer opportunities for people with skills in the above areas. We also offer short-term serving and learning opportunities for students and young North Americans in various countries."

Year founded in CAN: 1975
Income for Overseas Min: $18,000,000.00
Gifts in Kind: $15,000,000.00
Fully Supported CAN Personnel Overseas:
  Expecting to serve 1 to 4 years: 1
  Non-residential mission personnel: 1
Other personnel:
  Short-term less than 1 year: 6
  Non-CAN serving in own/other country: 23
  Home ministry & office staff in CAN: 10
Countries: Afghanistan; Cambodia; Ethiopia; South Africa

Hungry for Life International

45950 Alexander Ave.
CHILLIWACK, BC V2P 1L5 CAN
Phone: (604) 703-0223
Fax: (866) 255-8498
E-mail: info@hungryforlife.org
Web Site: www.hungryforlife.org
Mr. Dave Blundell, Exec. Director

A specialized agency engaged in development, partnership development, relief and/or rehabilitation and to help churches plan short-term programs.

Purpose: "...to facilitate opportunities for people to know the power and presence of Jesus Christ through worship and world-wide compassion."

Year founded in CAN: 2003
Personnel:
  Home ministry & office staff in CAN: 20

I. N. (International Needs) Network Canada

115 First St., Ste. 243
COLLINGWOOD, ON L9Y 4W3 CAN
Phone: (705) 446-3540
Fax: (705) 446-3546
E-mail: inc@innetwork.ca
Web Site: www.innetwork.ca
Mr. David Marshall, Exec. Director

A service agency of Evangelical tradition engaged in support of national workers, childcare/orphanage programs, development, HIV/Aids, justice and partnership development.

Purpose: "...to link Canadian Christians and churches with overseas ministries of INC that seek to integrate evangelism, discipleship, and fulfillment of human needs through effective development."

Year founded in CAN: 1975
Income for Overseas Min: $2,476,141.00
Personnel:
  Short-term less than 1 year: 6
  Non-CAN serving in own/other country: 3688
  Home ministry & office staff in CAN: 10
Countries: Bangladesh; Colombia; Cuba; Czech Republic; Dominican Republic; Egypt; Ghana; India; Nepal; Philippines; Romania; Sri Lanka; Tanzania; Turkey; Uganda; Vietnam; Zambia

InterAct Ministries of Canada

PO Box 60029
STRATHMORE, AB T1P 0C2 CAN
Phone: (403) 934-3322
Fax: (403) 450-8240
E-mail: canada@interactministries.org
Web Site: www.interactministries.org
Associations: CrossGlobal Link

Mr. Dan Mayerle, Canada Field Director

A nondenominational service agency of Evangelical tradition engaged in church planting, discipleship, evangelism, support of national churches, short-term programs and training.

Purpose: "...to glorify God by fulfilling the Great Commission among unreached people groups. The vision is to see a culturally relevant church transforming every community in the North Pacific Crescent."

Year founded in CAN: 1967

Income for Overseas Min: $146,863.00

Personnel:
  Home ministry & office staff in CAN: 3

Intercede International
201 Stanton St.
FORT ERIE, ON L2A 3N8 CAN
Phone: (905) 871-1773
Fax: (905) 871-5165
E-mail: friends@intercedenow.ca
Web Site: www.intercedenow.ca

Mr. James S. Eagles, President

A nondenominational support agency of Evangelical tradition engaged in support of national workers, childcare/orphanage programs, missions information service, support of national churches and relief and/or rehabilitation.

Purpose: "...to establish, encourage and stengthen an indigenous New Testament witness for our Lord Jesus Christ among all nations, by providing material and spiritual aid to Christians who are impoverished or persecuted; and to encourage Christian witness and ministry to the international community in Canada."

Year founded in CAN: 1953

Income for Overseas Min: $1,350,000.00

Gifts in Kind: $46,385.00

Personnel:
  Short-term less than 1 year: 4
  Non-CAN serving in own/other country: 64
  Home ministry & office staff in CAN: 10

Countries: China; Haiti; India; Indonesia; Jordan; Kenya; Liberia; Myanmar/Burma; Nepal; Nigeria; Pakistan; Philippines; Senegal; Sudan; Thailand; Turkey; Vietnam; Ukraine

International Child Care (Canada), Inc.
500 Alden Rd., Ste. 210
MARKHAM, ON L3R 5H5 CAN
Phone: (905) 752-0501
Fax: (905) 415-0460
E-mail: canada@intlchildcare.org
Web Site: www.intlchildcare.org
Associations: CCRDA

Mr. Peter Montgomery, Natl. Director

An interdenominational sending agency of Evangelical tradition engaged in childcare/orphanage programs, childrens programs, development, disability assistance programs, medical work and short-term programs. Countries of service data from 2005.

Purpose: "...to respond to Jesus Christ through caring service by sharing and promoting health and wholeness to those in need, especially children."

Year founded in CAN: 1978

Fully Supported CAN Personnel Overseas:
  Expecting to serve more than 4 years: 2
  Expecting to serve 1 to 4 years: 4

Countries: Dominican Republic; Haiti 2

International Christian Ministries Canada (ICM)
#304 19978—72 Ave.
LANGLEY, BC V2Y 1R7 CAN
Phone: (604) 575-8686
E-mail: icmcanada@cs.com
Web Site: www.icmcanada.org

Mr. Phil Jeske, President

An interdenominational sending agency of Evangelical tradition engaged in leadership development, extension education, theological education, literature production, support of national churches and mentoring/coaching.

Purpose: "...to serve the Church by discipling and equipping its leaders."

Year founded in CAN: 1989

Fully Supported CAN Personnel Overseas:
  Expecting to serve more than 4 years: 14
  Expecting to serve 1 to 4 years: 2
  Non-residential mission personnel: 4

Other personnel:
  Non-CAN serving in own/other country: 14
  Home ministry & office staff in CAN: 4

Countries: Africa—General 8; Eastern Europe—General 2; Latin America—General 2; Russia 2

International Russian Radio/TV (IRR/TV)

PO Box 75297
WHITE ROCK, BC V4B 5L4 CAN
Phone: (604) 542-1986
E-mail: info_irrtv@irrtv.org
Web Site: www.irrtv.org
Mr. John Haukka, COO

An interdenominational sending agency of Evangelical and Pentecostal tradition engaged in video/film production/distribution, association of missions, broadcasting, Christian education, evangelism and leadership development.

Purpose: "...to win, build, train and send."
Year founded in CAN: 1986
Income for Overseas Min: $501,764.00
Personnel:
Non-CAN serving in own/other country: 48
Countries: Israel; Russia; Ukraine

International Teams, Canada (Evangelical Intl, Crusades Canada, Inc.)

1 Union St.
ELMIRA, ON N3B 3J9 CAN
Phone: (519) 669-8844
Fax: (519) 669-5644
E-mail: canada@iteams.org
Web Site: www.iteams.ca
Mr. Neil Ostrander, President

A sending agency of Brethren tradition engaged in compassionate evangelism, childrens programs, church planting and youth programs. Data from 2005.

Purpose: "...engages in authentic partnerships with local churches and other missions to mobilize teams of people around the world to compassionate evangelism and training next generation leaders."
Year founded in CAN: 1959
Income for Overseas Min: $1,094,000.00
Gifts in Kind: $1,000.00
Fully Supported CAN Personnel Overseas:
Expecting to serve more than 4 years: 10
Expecting to serve 1 to 4 years: 3
Non-residential mission personnel: 3

Other personnel:
Short-term less than 1 year: 98
Home ministry & office staff in CAN: 16
Countries: Austria 2; Bolivia 1; Costa Rica 2; Ecuador; Greece; Rwanda 2; Unspecified Country 3

InterServe Canada (Intl. Service Fellowship)

10 Huntingdale Blvd.
TORONTO, ON M1W 2S5 CAN
Phone: (416) 499-7511
Fax: (416) 499-4472
E-mail: info@interservecanada.org
Web Site: www.interservecanada.org
Associations: CrossGlobal Link
Rev. David Sparrow, Natl. Exec. Director

A sending agency of Evangelical tradition engaged in mobilization for mission, business as mission, development, medical work, services for other agencies and tentmaking.

Purpose: "...to make Christ known where He is least known among the neediest peoples in Asia and the Arab world."
Year founded in CAN: 1903
Income for Overseas Min: $1,600,000.00
Fully Supported CAN Personnel Overseas:
Expecting to serve more than 4 years: 36
Expecting to serve 1 to 4 years: 21
Non-residential mission personnel: 8
Other personnel:
Home ministry & office staff in CAN: 6
Countries: Africa—General; Asia—General; Central Asia—General 32; Middle East 4; United Kingdom

Inter-Varsity Christian Fellowship of Canada

64 Prince Andrew Pl.
TORONTO, ON M3C 2H4 CAN
Phone: (416) 443-1170
Fax: (416) 443-1499
E-mail: inquiries@ivcf.ca
Web Site: www.ivcf.ca
Ms. Geri Rodman, President

A nondenominational support agency of Evangelical tradition engaged in campus ministry, camping programs, evangelism and youth programs.

Purpose: "...to be shaped by God's Word

and led by the Holy Spirit, the purpose of Inter-Varsity Christian Fellowship of Canada is the transformation of youth, students, and graduates into fully committed followers of Jesus Christ."

Year founded in CAN: 1928

Income for Overseas Min: $1,361,000.00

Gifts in Kind: $64,547.00

Personnel:
   Home ministry & office staff in CAN: 178

Countries: Azerbaijan; China; France; Kazakhstan; Ukraine

Into All The World

51 Bond Ct.
GUELPH, ON N1H 8N6 CAN

Phone: (519) 763-6147
Fax: (519) 763-1491
E-mail: bill@iatw.ca
Web Site: www.iatw.ca

Rev. Bill Lewis, Exec. Director

A transdenominational sending agency of Charismatic and Congregational tradition engaged in church planting, childcare/orphanage programs, evangelism, leadership development, support of national workers and short-term programs.

Purpose: "...a mission enabling agency that works with individuals and churches and denominations to partner with them to bring the good news of Jesus Christ and His salvation to all tribes and nations."

Year founded in CAN: 1981

Income for Overseas Min: $560,000.00

Fully Supported CAN Personnel Overseas:
   Expecting to serve more than 4 years: 15
   Expecting to serve 1 to 4 years: 2
   Non-residential mission personnel: 2

Other personnel:
   Short-term less than 1 year: 15
   Home ministry & office staff in CAN: 3

Countries: Belize 1; Bolivia 2; Dominican Republic 1; Ethiopia 2; Kenya 2; Papua New Guinea; Peru; South Africa 4; Tanzania 2; Uganda 1

Jusqu'aux Extremites de la Terre (JET)

29 Pied-de-Roi
LAC-BEAUPORT, PQ G3B 1N7 CAN

Phone: (418) 849-3179
E-mail: jeffettonda@yahoo.fr

Mr. Jeff Street, Sec./Director

A nondenominational service agency of Evangelical tradition engaged in short-term programs, leadership development, support of national workers, mobilization for mission and youth programs.

Purpose: "...to help French churches become involved in world missions."

Year founded in CAN: 2002

Income for Overseas Min: $45,000.00

Personnel:
   Short-term less than 1 year: 15
   Home ministry & office staff in CAN: 2

Latin America Mission (Canada) Inc.

3075 Ridgeway Dr., Unit 14
MISSISSAUGA, ON L5L 5M6 CAN

Phone: (905) 569-0001
Fax: (866) 470-6680
E-mail: info@lamcanada.ca
Web Site: www.lamcanada.ca

Mr. Carluci Dos Santos, Exec. Director

An interdenominational sending agency of Evangelical tradition engaged in mobilization for mission, camping programs, childcare/orphanage programs, church planting, development and support of national workers.

Purpose: "...an international evangelical community of men and women who, motivated by their love for the Lord Jesus Christ and in obedience to His commands, partner with Canadian and Latin churches and institutions in the task of building the Church of Jesus Christ in the Latin world."

Year founded in CAN: 1961

Income for Overseas Min: $611,828.00

Gifts in Kind: $3,762.00

Fully Supported CAN Personnel Overseas:
   Expecting to serve more than 4 years: 11
   Expecting to serve 1 to 4 years: 2

Other personnel:
   Short-term less than 1 year: 18
   Non-CAN serving in own/other country: 6
   Home ministry & office staff in CAN: 2

Countries: Brazil 2; Colombia 2; Costa Rica 4; Honduras 2; Mexico 1

Leprosy Mission Canada, The
100 Mural Street, Ste. 100
RICHMOND HILL, ON L4B 1J3 CAN
Phone: (905) 886-2885
Fax: (905) 886-2887
E-mail: info@leprosy.ca
Web Site: www.leprosy.ca
Rev. Peter A. Derrick, Exec. Director
An interdenominational service agency
of Congregational and Evangelical tradi-
tion engaged in hospitals and leprosy care,
development, Christian education, funds
transmission, support of national workers
and relief and/or rehabilitation. Data from
2005.
Year founded in CAN: 1892
Income for Overseas Min: $3,416,028.00
Gifts in Kind: $181,921.00
Fully Supported CAN Personnel Overseas:
Expecting to serve 1 to 4 years: 2
Non-residential mission personnel: 3
Other personnel:
Home ministry & office staff in CAN: 20
Countries: Nigeria

Liebenzell Mission of Canada
RR #1
MOFFAT, ON L0P 1J0 CAN
Phone: (519) 822-9748
E-mail: mission@liebenzell.ca
Web Site: www.liebenzell.ca
Associations: CrossGlobal Link
Rev. Jakob Koch, Exec. Director
An interdenominational sending agency of
Evangelical tradition engaged in support of
national churches, discipleship, funds trans-
mission, mobilization for mission, mission-
ary training and local ministry retreats.
Purpose: "...to glorify God by bringing the
saving knowledge of Jesus Christ to people
around the world, in the power of the Holy
Spirit through fervent prayer."
Year founded in CAN: 1966
Income for Overseas Min: $148,313.00
Fully Supported CAN Personnel Overseas:
Expecting to serve more than 4 years: 4
Expecting to serve 1 to 4 years: 2
Non-residential mission personnel: 5
Other personnel:
Short-term less than 1 year: 5

Non-CAN serving in own/other country: 5
Home ministry & office staff in CAN: 3
Countries: Bangladesh 1; Ecuador; France;
Kyrgyzstan; Malawi; Micronesia, Federat-
ed States of; Papua New Guinea 2; Russia;
Spain 1; Zambia

Link International Ministries
PO Box 32
NEW WESTMINSTER, BC V3L 4X9 CAN
Phone: (604) 707-0222
E-mail: linkinternationalministries@hot-
mail.com
Web Site: www.linkinternational.org
Rev. Paul C. Ndukwe, CEO
An interdenominational support agency of
Evangelical and Pentecostal tradition en-
gaged in leadership development, child-
care/orphanage programs, church planting,
development, providing medical supplies
and support of national workers.
Purpose: "...to make sure that all human-
ity, regardless of ethnicity or social status,
are helped, empowered with the resourc-
es available to us, to become what they are
created to be."
Year founded in CAN: 1988
Income for Overseas Min: $7,000.00
Fully Supported CAN Personnel Overseas:
Non-residential mission personnel: 6
Other personnel:
Short-term less than 1 year: 1
Non-CAN serving in own/other country: 27
Countries: Belgium; Cote d'Ivoire; Kenya;
Nigeria

MBMS International
302-32025 George Ferguson Way
ABBOTSFORD, BC V2T2K7 CAN
Phone: (604) 859-6267
Fax: (604) 859-6422
E-mail: mbmsi@mbmsi.org
Web Site: www.mbmsi.org
Associations: The Mission Exchange
Dr. Randy Friesen, Gen. Director
A denominational sending agency of Men-
nonite tradition engaged in church plant-
ing, development, evangelism, recruiting/
mobilizing, training and youth programs.
MBMS is a bi-national organization and sta-

tistics cannot be separated into U.S. and Canadian. U.S. statistics are included in this Canadian listing.

Purpose: "...to transform lives in mission."

Year founded in CAN: 1878

Income for Overseas Min: $4,947,000.00

Fully Supported CAN Personnel Overseas:
Expecting to serve more than 4 years: 68
Expecting to serve 1 to 4 years: 5
Non-residential mission personnel: 6

Other personnel:
Short-term less than 1 year: 518
Non-CAN serving in own/other country: 18
Home ministry & office staff in CAN: 38

Countries: Africa—General 4; Angola; Asia—General 4; Austria 2; Brazil 8; Burkina Faso 4; Central Asia—General 2; Colombia; Congo, Democratic Republic of 1; France 2; Germany 5; India 8; Japan 2; Lithuania 1; Mexico 8; Middle East 4; Panama; Paraguay; Peru 3; Philippines 1; Portugal 2; Russia 1; South Africa; Thailand 6; Ukraine; Uruguay; Venezuela

Medical Ministry Canada, Inc.

PO Box 56086
STONEY CREEK, ON L8G 5C9 CAN
Phone: (905) 524-3544
Fax: (905) 664-8386
E-mail: mmican@mmint.org
Web Site: www.mmint.org
Leanne H. Skinner, Director

An interdenominational service agency engaged in medical work, discipleship, providing medical supplies, short-term programs and training.

Purpose: "...to serve Jesus Christ by providing spiritual and physical health care in this world of need."

Year founded in CAN: 1968

Income for Overseas Min: $1,400,000.00

Fully Supported CAN Personnel Overseas:
Non-residential mission personnel: 1

Other personnel:
Short-term less than 1 year: 3
Non-CAN serving in own/other country: 14

Countries: Bolivia; Dominican Republic; Ecuador; Haiti; Jordan; Peru

Mennonite Central Committee Canada

134 Plaza Dr.
WINNIPEG, MB R3T 5K9 CAN
Phone: (204) 261-6381
Fax: (204) 269-9875
E-mail: canada@mennonitecc.ca
Web Site: www.mcc.org/canada
Mr. Don Peters, Exec. Director

A transdenominational service agency of Mennonite tradition engaged in development, agricultural programs, justice, partnership development and relief and/or rehabilitation. Data from 2005.

Year founded in CAN: 1963

Income for Overseas Min: $32,529,651.00

Gifts in Kind: $12,519,107.00

Fully Supported CAN Personnel Overseas:
Non-residential mission personnel: 5

Other personnel:
Short-term less than 1 year: 29
Non-CAN serving in own/other country: 606
Home ministry & office staff in CAN: 198

Countries: Africa—General; Bangladesh; Bolivia; Brazil; Cambodia; China; Colombia; Congo, Democratic Republic of; Egypt; El Salvador; Ethiopia; Europe—General; Guatemala; Haiti; Honduras; Hong Kong; India; Indonesia; Iran; Iraq; Jamaica; Jordan; Kenya; Korea, South; Laos; Lebanon; Mexico; Mozambique; Nepal; Nicaragua; Nigeria; Palestine; Philippines; Rwanda; Russia; Somalia; South Africa; Sri Lanka; Sudan; Syria; Tanzania; Thailand; Uganda; Vietnam; Zambia; Zimbabwe

Mennonite Economic Development Associates (MEDA)

155 Frobisher Dr., Ste. I-106
WATERLOO, ON N2V 2E1 CAN
Phone: (800) 665-7026
Fax: (519) 725-9083
E-mail: meda@meda.org
Web Site: www.meda.org
Mr. Allan Sauder, President

A denominational service agency of Mennonite tradition engaged in development, agricultural programs, management consulting/training, technical assistance and investment fund development..

Purpose: "...that all people may experience God's love and unleash their potential to earn a livelihood, provide for families and enrich their communities."
Year founded in CAN: 1953
Income for Overseas Min: $14,894,263.00
Personnel:
Non-CAN serving in own/other country: 186
Home ministry & office staff in CAN: 8
Countries: Afghanistan; Ethiopia; Nicaragua; Pakistan; Peru; Tajikistan; Tanzania; Zambia

Mennonite Mission Health Association
568 Campbell St.
WINNIPEG, MB R3N 1C1 CAN
Phone: (204) 489-2812
Fax: (204) 489-2812
E-mail: paulsfd@mts.net
Web Site: www.mennonitemha.org
Associations: CCRDA
Dr. Ferdinand Pauls, President

An interdenominational support agency of Mennonite tradition engaged in medical work, HIV/Aids and providing medical supplies.
Purpose: "...a non-profit charitable organization of Christian health and business professionals and others, serving God by providing resources and services to Mennonite health care facilities in low resource countries."
Year founded in CAN: 2001
Income for Overseas Min: $53,942.00
Personnel:
Home ministry & office staff in CAN: 1
Countries: Congo, Democratic Republic of; India; Paraguay; Zimbabwe

Mercy Ships Canada
5-3318 Oak Street
VICTORIA, BC V8X 1R1 CAN
Phone: (250) 381-2160
Fax: (250) 381-2170
E-mail: msca@mercyships.org
Web Site: www.mercyships.ca
Mr. Tim Maloney, Natl. Director

A nondenominational service agency engaged in medical work, development and leadership development.
Purpose: "...to follow the example of Jesus by bringing hope and healing to the world's forgotten poor."
Year founded in CAN: 1989
Income for Overseas Min: $458,000.00
Personnel:
Home ministry & office staff in CAN: 5

Mission Aviation Fellowship of Canada (MAFC)
PO Box 368
GUELPH, ON N1H 6K5 CAN
Phone: (519) 821-3914
Fax: (519) 823-1650
E-mail: info@mafc.org
Web Site: www.mafc.org
Mr. Mark Outerbridge, President/CEO

A nondenominational specialized agency of Evangelical tradition engaged in aviation services.
Purpose: "...to share God's love through aviation and technology."
Year founded in CAN: 1972
Income for Overseas Min: $3,732,455.00
Fully Supported CAN Personnel Overseas:
Expecting to serve more than 4 years: 32
Expecting to serve 1 to 4 years: 9
Non-residential mission personnel: 44
Other personnel:
Home ministry & office staff in CAN: 20
Countries: Angola 2; Australia 3; Botswana 2; Central Asia—General 1; Chad; Haiti 1; Indonesia 7; Kenya 2; Laos 1; Lesotho 1; Madagascar 1; Mongolia 1; Papua New Guinea 7; Uganda 2; Zambia 1

Mission of Mercy Canada
4104-97 St.
EDMONTON, AB T6E 5Y6 CAN
Phone: (780) 485-9995
Fax: (780) 485-9980
E-mail: info@missionofmercy.ca
Web Site: www.missionofmercy.ca
Mr. Dale Reesor, Exec. Director

An interdenominational service agency of Pentecostal tradition engaged in constructing churches & children's homes, extension education, childrens programs, partnership development and relief and/or rehabilitation.

Purpose: "...to help meet the physical and spiritual needs of the hurting children and adults of North and East India by feeding, housing, educating, and providing health and wellness care...to see the children of India who live in poverty, experience transformation and wholeness through God's love."

Year founded in CAN: 1978
Income for Overseas Min: $2,134,000.00
Fully Supported CAN Personnel Overseas:
   Expecting to serve 1 to 4 years: 4
Other personnel:
   Home ministry & office staff in CAN: 4
Countries: India

Mission Possible Canada

PO Box 40121
LONDON, ON N5W 5Z5 CAN
Phone: (519) 285-2644
Fax: (519) 285-2644
E-mail: missionpossible@odyssey.on.ca
Web Site: www.ourmissionispossible.org
Mr. Heath Gillam, Chairman

A nondenominational support agency of Evangelical tradition engaged in Christian education, discipleship, evangelism and leadership development. Operates via a joint ministry agreement with Mission Possible, USA.

Purpose: "...to equip Christ-centered leaders for the Kingdom through spiritual, character, educational and vocational development."

Year founded in CAN: 1994
Income for Overseas Min: $156,000.00
Gifts in Kind: $24,000.00
Personnel:
   Short-term less than 1 year: 5

Mission Without Borders Canada

PO Box 2007
ABBOTSFORD, BC V2T 3T8 CAN
Phone: (604) 855-9126
Fax: (604) 855-9136
E-mail: dfraser@mwbi.org
Web Site: www.mwbca.org
Mr. Doug Fraser, Natl. Manager

A nondenominational service agency of Evangelical tradition engaged in childcare/orphanage programs, camping programs, children at risk, development, discipleship and providing medical supplies.

Purpose: "...to serve the physical, emotional, and spiritual needs of those suffering the effects of poverty and oppression... to involve those we serve by recognizing the dignity of the individual...to help build capacity for self-sufficiency...to serve people without regard to their religion or ethnic background."

Year founded in CAN: 1992
Income for Overseas Min: $1,055,546.00
Gifts in Kind: $501,690.00
Personnel:
   Home ministry & office staff in CAN: 3

Missionary Internship Canada, Inc. (MissionPREP)

PO Box 92204
TORONTO, ON M1W 3Y9 CAN
Phone: (416) 840-5488
E-mail: info@missionprep.ca
Web Site: www.missionprep.ca
Mr. Dan Davies, Exec. Director

An interdenominational specialized agency of Evangelical tradition engaged in missionary training.

Purpose: "...to enhance the long-term effectiveness and reduce the attrition rates of cross-cultural workers by providing interactive learning experiences in a multi-cultural context. These programs will be affordable and accessible in Canada, and will allow participants to develop knowledge and skills in adaptability, Christian witness, and service in new cultural settings."

Year founded in CAN: 1989
Personnel:
   Home ministry & office staff in CAN: 3

Missionary Ventures Canada

336 Speedvale Ave. W.
GUELPH, ON N1H 7M7 CAN
Phone: (519) 824-9380
Fax: (519) 824-9452
E-mail: mvcanada@mvcanada.org
Web Site: www.mvcanada.org
Mr. John Verdone, Exec. Director

An interdenominational service agency of Evangelical tradition engaged in short-term programs, evangelism, development, medical work, providing medical supplies and church construction. Data from 2005.

Purpose: "...to encourage and support indigenous missions...through personal involvement, financial sponsorship, and ministry development."

Year founded in CAN: 1991

MSC Canada
101 Amber St., Unit 16
MARKHAM, ON L3R 3B2 CAN
Phone: (905) 947-0468
Fax: (905) 947-0352
E-mail: msc@msccanada.org
Web Site: www.msccanada.org
Mr. Kevin Shantz, Exec. Director

A service agency of Brethren tradition engaged in funds transmission, church planting, evangelism, providing medical supplies, short-term programs and Bible translation.

Purpose: "...to encourage and support service for the Lord by assembly-commended workers, in compliance with scriptural guidelines, government legislation, and agreements with other organizations with which MSC is associated."

Year founded in CAN: 1940
Income for Overseas Min: $6,000,000.00
Personnel:
    Short-term less than 1 year: 40
    Home ministry & office staff in CAN: 6

Mustard Seed Mission Canada, Inc.
#226—1885 Clements Rd.
PICKERING, ON L1W 3V4 CAN
Phone: (905) 427-5189
Fax: (905) 427-0334
E-mail: mustardseed@canada.com
Web Site: www.mustardseedcanada.org
Mr. John W. Irwin, President

A nondenominational service agency engaged in Christian education, missionary education, evangelism, leadership development and support of national workers.

Purpose: "...to bear witness to the Lord Jesus Christ through education, skills training, medical assistance, basic improvement in living conditions, evangelistic outreach, and discipleship training among the indigenous people whom it serves."

Year founded in CAN: 1967
Income for Overseas Min: $207,665.00

Navigators of Canada, The
PO Box 27070
LONDON, ON N5X 3X5 CAN
Phone: (519) 660-8300
Fax: (519) 660-4922
E-mail: navscanada@navigators.ca
Web Site: www.navigators.ca
Mr. Eric E. Stolte, President

An interdenominational sending agency of Evangelical tradition engaged in discipleship, Bible memorization, evangelism and leadership development.

Purpose: "...to advance the Gospel of Jesus and His Kingdom into the nations through spiritual generations of labourers living and discipling among the lost."

Year founded in CAN: 1960
Income for Overseas Min: $900,000.00
Fully Supported CAN Personnel Overseas:
    Expecting to serve more than 4 years: 17
    Expecting to serve 1 to 4 years: 2
Other personnel:
    Short-term less than 1 year: 40
    Home ministry & office staff in CAN: 12
Countries: Africa—General 3; Asia—General 2; Chile 2; Hungary 2; Indonesia 2; Slovakia 2; Thailand 2; Turkey 2

Nazarene Compassion Ministries Canada
20 Regan Rd., Unit 9
BRAMPTON, ON N4L 1W5 CAN
Phone: (888) 808-7490
Web Site: www.ncmc.ca
Associations: CCRDA
Dr. Clair MacMillan, CEO

A denominational support agency of Holiness tradition engaged in children at risk, HIV/Aids, leadership development, providing medical supplies, medical work and relief and/or rehabilitation.

Income for Overseas Min: $275,000.00

New Tribes Mission of Canada

313363 Hwy. 6 S.
DURHAM, ON N0G 1R0 CAN
Phone: (519) 369-2622
Fax: (519) 369-5828
E-mail: ntmc@ntmc.ca
Web Site: www.ntmc.ca

A nondenominational sending agency of Evangelical tradition engaged in church planting (encompasses literacy, linguistics, teaching, etc.), discipleship, linguistics, missionary training, Bible translation and translation work.

Purpose: "...to assist the ministry of the local church through the mobilizing, equipping, and coordinating of believers to evangelize unreached people groups, translate Scripture, and see indigenous New Testament churches established."

Year founded in CAN: 1950
Income for Overseas Min: $5,100,000.00
Gifts in Kind: $40,000.00
Fully Supported CAN Personnel Overseas:
   Expecting to serve more than 4 years: 126
   Expecting to serve 1 to 4 years: 5
Other personnel:
   Short-term less than 1 year: 4
   Home ministry & office staff in CAN: 60
Countries: Africa—General 14; Asia—General 39; Latin America—General 31; Oceania—General 41; United Kingdom 1

OMF International—Canada

5155 Spectrum Way, Bldg. 21
MISSISSAUGA, ON L4W 5A1 CAN
Phone: (905) 568-9971
Fax: (905) 568-9974
E-mail: omfcanada@omf.ca
Web Site: www.omf.ca
Associations: CrossGlobal Link
Richard Konieczny, Natl. Director

A nondenominational sending agency of Evangelical tradition engaged in church planting, development, theological education, evangelism, support of national churches and relief and/or rehabilitation.

Purpose: "...to glorify God by the urgent evangelization of East Asia's people..."

Year founded in CAN: 1888

Income for Overseas Min: $1,849,136.00
Fully Supported CAN Personnel Overseas:
   Expecting to serve more than 4 years: 71
   Expecting to serve 1 to 4 years: 7
   Non-residential mission personnel: 2
Other personnel:
   Short-term less than 1 year: 35
   Non-CAN serving in own/other country: 2
   Home ministry & office staff in CAN: 6
Countries: Asia—General 23; Cambodia 3; Indonesia 6; Japan 6; Malaysia 2; New Zealand; Philippines 9; Singapore 4; Thailand 18; United Kingdom

OMS International—Canada

293 Wellington St. N., # 132
HAMILTON, ON L8L 8E7 CAN
Phone: (905) 522-1605
Fax: (905) 522-2849
E-mail: mail@omscanada.org
Web Site: www.omscanada.org
Mr. Gordon Morley, Exec. Director

An interdenominational sending agency of Methodist and Wesleyan tradition engaged in church planting, broadcasting, theological education, evangelism, support of national workers and support of national churches. Data from 2005.

Year founded in CAN: 1948
Income for Overseas Min: $1,000,000.00
Fully Supported CAN Personnel Overseas:
   Expecting to serve more than 4 years: 13
   Expecting to serve 1 to 4 years: 4
Other personnel:
   Short-term less than 1 year: 16
   Home ministry & office staff in CAN: 6
Countries: Asia—General 4; Haiti 8; Hungary 1

Open Doors with Brother Andrew Canada

8-19 Brownridge Rd.
HALTON HILLS, ON L7G 0C6 CAN
Phone: (905) 636-0944
Fax: (905) 636-0946
E-mail: opendoorsca@od.org
Web Site: www.opendoorsca.org
Rev. Paul W. Johnson, Exec. Director

A transdenominational support agency of Evangelical tradition engaged in Bible distribution, theological education, literature distribution, literature production, support of national churches and training.

Purpose: "...to serve persecuted Christians worldwide."

Year founded in CAN: 1977

Operation Mobilization Canada (Send the Light)
84 West St.
PORT COLBORNE, ON L3K 4C8 CAN

Phone: (905) 835-2546
Fax: (905) 835-2533
E-mail: info@cdn.om.org
Web Site: www.omcanada.org
Mr. Harvey Thiessen, Field Leader

A sending agency of Evangelical tradition engaged in short-term programs, broadcasting, business as mission, mobilization for mission, missionary training and training. Financial & countries of service data from 2005.

Purpose: "...to motivate, develop, and equip people for world evangelization, and to strengthen and help plant churches, especially among the unreached in the Middle East, South and Central Asia, and Europe."

Year founded in CAN: 1957

Income for Overseas Min: $2,200,000.00

Fully Supported CAN Personnel Overseas:
Expecting to serve more than 4 years: 31
Expecting to serve 1 to 4 years: 47

Other personnel:
Short-term less than 1 year: 150

Countries: Afghanistan 3; Africa—General 5; Asia—General 3; Austria; Bosnia and Herzegovina; Central Asia—General 2; France 1; India 1; Middle East 6; Myanmar/Burma; Nepal; Pakistan 1; Sweden; Switzerland; Uruguay 2; Unspecified Country 3; Western Europe—General 4

Opportunity Intl. Canada
295 The West Mall, Ste. 504
TORONTO, ON M9C 4Z4 CAN

Phone: (416) 444-2448
E-mail: info@opportunityinternational.ca
Web Site: www.opportunityinternational.ca
Paula A. Curtis, President/CEO

A service agency engaged in justice, business as mission, discipleship, HIV/Aids and training.

Purpose: "...to provide opportunities for people in chronic poverty to improve their lives."

Year founded in CAN: 1997

Income for Overseas Min: $2,979,892.00

Personnel:
Short-term less than 1 year: 8
Home ministry & office staff in CAN: 7

Outreach Canada
2—7201 72nd St.
DELTA, BC V4G 1M5 CAN

Phone: (604) 952-0050
Fax: (604) 952-4650
E-mail: contact@outreach.ca
Web Site: www.outreach.ca
Rev. Craig Kraft, Exec. Director

An interdenominational support agency of Evangelical tradition engaged in church planting, leadership development, management consulting/training, support of national churches, mobilization for mission and mission-related research.

Purpose: "...to encourage and serve local churches, evangelical Christian denominations, para-church and market-place organizations, and all believers in their efforts in fulfilling our Lord's Great Commission in Canada and abroad...to help these organizations develop godly, effective leaders so they may set and reach the goals of God for their respective ministries."

Year founded in CAN: 1977

Income for Overseas Min: $169,000.00

Fully Supported CAN Personnel Overseas:
Expecting to serve more than 4 years: 4
Expecting to serve 1 to 4 years: 2

Other personnel:
Short-term less than 1 year: 5
Home ministry & office staff in CAN: 28

Countries: Europe—General 2; Russia 2; South Africa

Partners Intl. Canada
56—8500 Torbram Rd.
BRAMPTON, ON L6T 5C6 CAN

Phone: (905) 458-1202
Fax: (905) 458-4339

E-mail: brentm@partnersinternational.ca
Web Site: www.partnersinternational.ca
Mr. R. Brent Mitchell, President

A nondenominational support agency of Evangelical tradition engaged in support of national workers, childcare/orphanage programs, church planting, development, theological education and partnership development.

Purpose: "...to bring Canadians into partnership with indigenous Christian ministries to advance the Kingdom of God."

Year founded in CAN: 1960

Income for Overseas Min: $3,840,000.00

Fully Supported CAN Personnel Overseas:
Expecting to serve 1 to 4 years: 1
Non-residential mission personnel: 3

Other personnel:
Short-term less than 1 year: 80
Non-CAN serving in own/other country: 1
Home ministry & office staff in CAN: 17

Countries: Bangladesh; Bhutan; Bolivia; Brazil; China; Cuba; India; Indonesia; Lebanon; Myanmar/Burma; Nepal; Nigeria; Pakistan; Peru; Senegal; South Africa; Thailand

Pentecostal Assemblies of Canada, The

2450 Milltower Ct.
MISSISSAUGA, ON L5N 5Z6 CAN
Phone: (905) 542-7400
Fax: (905) 542-0377
E-mail: info@paoc.org
Web Site: www.paoc.org
Mr. Murray Cornelius, Asst. Supt. of Intl. Msns.

A denominational sending agency of Pentecostal tradition engaged in church planting, childcare/orphanage programs, discipleship, theological education, leadership development and support of national churches.

Purpose: "...to make disciples everywhere by the proclamation and practice of the Gospel of Jesus Christ in the power of the Holy Spirit; to establish local congregations and train spiritual leaders."

Year founded in CAN: 1919

Income for Overseas Min: $19,000,000.00

Gifts in Kind: $400,000.00

Fully Supported CAN Personnel Overseas:

Expecting to serve more than 4 years: 195
Expecting to serve 1 to 4 years: 26
Non-residential mission personnel: 10

Other personnel:
Non-CAN serving in own/other country: 6
Home ministry & office staff in CAN: 12

Countries: Africa—General 4; Armenia 2; Asia—General 25; Brazil 6; Cambodia 2; Central Asia—General 2; Congo, Democratic Republic of 2; Dominican Republic 2; El Salvador 2; Estonia 2; Ethiopia 4; Germany 2; Guatemala 4; Guinea 2; Haiti 2; Honduras 2; Israel 2; Jamaica 2; Japan 2; Kenya 14; Kyrgyzstan 2; Malawi 6; Middle East 9; Mozambique 8; Panama 2; Philippines 1; Russia 4; Romania 5; Rwanda 2; Senegal 11; Slovakia 7; South Africa 4; Switzerland 2; Tanzania 6; Thailand 13; Trinidad and Tobago; Uganda 9; Ukraine 4; United Kingdom 2; Zambia 5; Zimbabwe 8

People Intl.—Canada

PO Box 356
TILLSONBURG, ON N4G 4H8 CAN
Phone: (519) 688-3499
Fax: (519) 842-4172
E-mail: info@peopleintl.org
Web Site: www.peopleintlcanada.org
Mr. Doug Humphrey, Acting Director

An interdenominational support agency of Baptist, Christian/Plymouth Brethren and Charismatic tradition engaged in church planting, discipleship and missionary training.

Purpose: "...to see churches established that proclaim the Good News among the Muslim peoples of Central Asia and model true Christian living on the example of Jesus Christ."

Year founded in CAN: 2004

Fully Supported CAN Personnel Overseas:
Expecting to serve 1 to 4 years: 1
Non-residential mission personnel: 1

Countries: Turkey

Pioneers Canada

51 Byron Ave.
DORCHESTER, ON N0L 1G1 CAN
Phone: (519) 268-8778
Fax: (519) 268-2787
E-mail: info@pioneers.ca
Web Site: www.pioneers.ca

Associations: CrossGlobal Link

Mr. Donnie Scearce, Exec. Director/CEO

An interdenominational sending agency of Evangelical tradition engaged in church planting, mobilization for mission and short-term programs.

Purpose: "...to mobilize teams to glorify God among unreached peoples by initiating church planting movements in partnership with the local church."

Year founded in CAN: 1994

Income for Overseas Min: $1,800,000.00

Fully Supported CAN Personnel Overseas:
Expecting to serve more than 4 years: 40

Other personnel:
Home ministry & office staff in CAN: 25

Countries: Bolivia 2; Brazil 2; Bulgaria 1; Cambodia 2; China 15; India 4; Japan 1; Kosovo 2; Pakistan 1; Peru 2; Sudan 4; Syria 3; Turkey 1

Power to Change

20385—64 Ave.
LANGLEY, BC V2Y 1N5 CAN
Phone: (604) 514-2000
Fax: (604) 514-2002
E-mail: info@powertochange.org
Web Site: www.powertochange.org

Mr. Leonard Buhler, President

A nondenominational sending agency engaged in evangelism, discipleship, providing medical supplies, mobilization for mission and sports program ministry.

Purpose: "...helping to fulfill the Great Commission in Canada and around the world, by developing movements of Evangelism and Discipleship."

Year founded in CAN: 1966

Income for Overseas Min: $9,527,477.00

Gifts in Kind: $795,406.00

Fully Supported CAN Personnel Overseas:
Expecting to serve more than 4 years: 23
Expecting to serve 1 to 4 years: 21

Other personnel:
Short-term less than 1 year: 530
Home ministry & office staff in CAN: 150

Countries: Africa—General 2; Asia—General 12; India 2; Japan 2; Panama; Philippines 2; Russia 1; South Africa 2; United Kingdom

Presbyterian Church in Canada—Life and Mission Agency

50 Wynford Dr.
TORONTO, ON M3C 1J7 CAN
Phone: (416) 441-1111
Fax: (416) 441-2825
Web Site: www.presbycan.ca

Rev./Dr. Richard Fee, Gen. Secretary—L & MA

A denominational sending agency of Presbyterian and Reformed tradition engaged in support of national churches, development, leadership development, relief and/or rehabilitation, short-term programs and missionary training.

Purpose: "...to assist one another in evangelism and in the nurturing and building up of Christ's body, the Church...serving the communities where God has placed us, working for a new day of freedom and justice for God's people everywhere, and working in the confidence that God will bring all things together in Christ, the Lord of the Church and the Lord over all creation."

Year founded in CAN: 1875

Income for Overseas Min: $4,559,917.00

Fully Supported CAN Personnel Overseas:
Expecting to serve more than 4 years: 13
Expecting to serve 1 to 4 years: 4
Non-residential mission personnel: 1

Other personnel:
Short-term less than 1 year: 219
Home ministry & office staff in CAN: 15

Countries: Grenada; Guatemala; Hungary 1; Kenya 1; Malawi 4; Nicaragua 2; Nigeria 1; Romania 1; Taiwan 1; Ukraine 2

Project AmaZon Canada Society

PO Box 601
CRANBROOK, BC V1C 4J2 CAN
Phone: (250) 919-4142
Web Site: www.projectamazon.org

The Canadian partner of Project AmaZon in the US. See Project AmaZon for statistical information.

ReachAcross

PO Box 88520
SURREY, BC V3W 0X1 CAN

Phone: (604) 596-7937
Fax: (604) 596-7926
E-mail: info.ca@reachacross.net
Web Site: www.reachacross.net
Associations: CrossGlobal Link

Mr. Perry Zelman, CAN Director

A nondenominational support agency of Evangelical tradition engaged in TESOL, development, literacy work, medical work, tentmaking and Bible translation.

Purpose: "...to share the Gospel with Muslims...to serve them in practical ways...to disciple them to follow Jesus."

Income for Overseas Min: $249,000.00

Fully Supported CAN Personnel Overseas:
  Expecting to serve more than 4 years: 8
  Expecting to serve 1 to 4 years: 2
  Non-residential mission personnel: 2

Other personnel:
  Short-term less than 1 year: 4
  Non-CAN serving in own/other country: 31
  Home ministry & office staff in CAN: 2

Countries: Africa—General; Mali; Middle East 8; Pakistan

reSource Leadership Intl. for Theological Education

#200—5726 Minoru Blvd.
RICHMOND, BC V6X 2A9 CAN
Phone: (604) 270-6045
Fax: (604) 270-6046
E-mail: administrator@resourceleadership.com
Web Site: www.resourceleadership.com

Dr. Gordon T. Smith, President

An interdenominational support agency of Evangelical tradition engaged in theological education and library & program development.

Purpose: "...to resource sustainable theological education in the developing world."

Year founded in CAN: 1979

Income for Overseas Min: $269,664.00

Fully Supported CAN Personnel Overseas:
  Non-residential mission personnel: 1

Other personnel:
  Home ministry & office staff in CAN: 1

Salvation Army—Canada and Bermuda Territory, the

2 Overlea Blvd.
TORONTO, ON M4H 1P4 CAN
Phone: (416) 425-2111
Fax: (416) 422-6201
E-mail: donor_questions@can.salvationarmy.org
Web Site: www.salvationarmy.ca

Commissioner M. Christine MacMillan, Territorial Commander

A denominational sending agency of Evangelical and Wesleyan tradition engaged in relief and/or rehabilitation, camping programs, childcare/orphanage programs, childrens programs, church planting, development, Christian education, evangelism, leadership development and medical work. Data from 2005.

Year founded in CAN: 1884

Income for Overseas Min: $10,000,000.00

Fully Supported CAN Personnel Overseas:
  Expecting to serve more than 4 years: 22
  Expecting to serve 1 to 4 years: 16
  Non-residential mission personnel: 2

Other personnel:
  Short-term less than 1 year: 123

Countries: Africa—General 11; Argentina 1; Australia; Bangladesh 1; Caribbean—General; Chile 1; France; Germany 4; Pakistan; Papua New Guinea; Russia; Spain 2; United Kingdom 2

Samaritan's Purse—Canada

20 Hopewell Way NE
CALGARY, AB T3J 5H5 CAN
Phone: (800) 663-6500
Fax: (403) 250-6567
E-mail: canada@samaritan.org
Web Site: www.samaritanspurse.ca
Associations: CCRDA

Mr. Fred Weiss, Exec. Director

A nondenominational service agency of Evangelical tradition engaged in relief, development, HIV/Aids, medical work, partnership development and short-term programs.

Purpose: "...to provide spiritual and physical aid to hurting people around the world...to meet the needs of people who are victims of war, poverty, natural disasters, disease, and famine with the purpose of sharing the Good News of God's love through His Son, Jesus Christ...to serve the Church worldwide to promote the Gospel of the Lord Jesus Christ."

Year founded in CAN: 1973

Income for Overseas Min: $39,457,964.00

Gifts in Kind: $26,736,672.00

Fully Supported CAN Personnel Overseas:
Non-residential mission personnel: 10

Other personnel:
Short-term less than 1 year: 496
Home ministry & office staff in CAN: 73

Countries: Afghanistan; Cambodia; Hong Kong; Jordan; Kosovo Liberia; Myanmar/Burma; Nepal; Niger; Sudan; Thailand; Vietnam

SEND Intl. of Canada
1—22423 Jefferies Rd. RR5
KOMOKA, ON N0L 1R0 CAN
Phone: (519) 657-6775
Fax: (519) 657-7027
E-mail: info@sendcanada.org
Web Site: www.send.org/canada
Associations: CrossGlobal Link

Rev. Rob Magwood, Canadian Director

An interdenominational sending agency of Evangelical tradition engaged in church planting, evangelism, leadership development, support of national churches, short-term programs and discipleship.

Purpose: "...to start churches...to evangelize the unreached...to nurture disciples...to develop leaders."

Year founded in CAN: 1963

Income for Overseas Min: $2,319,719.00

Gifts in Kind: $8,306.00

Fully Supported CAN Personnel Overseas:
Expecting to serve more than 4 years: 21
Expecting to serve 1 to 4 years: 12

Other personnel:
Short-term less than 1 year: 47
Home ministry & office staff in CAN: 14

Countries: Asia—General 2; Bulgaria; Croatia; Czech Republic; Hungary; Japan 2; Kazakhstan; Macedonia 3; Philippines 5; Poland; Russia 5; Slovenia; Spain; Taiwan; Ukraine 4

SGM Canada
PO Box 609
ORILLIA, ON L3V 6K8 CAN
Phone: (705) 325-1002
E-mail: canada@sgmlifewords.com
Web Site: www.sgmlifewords.com
Mr. Lawson Murray, Natl. Director

A support agency engaged in Bible engagement & advocacy, Bible distribution, literature distribution, literature production, partnership development and mission-related research.

Purpose: "...to connect Canadians with the Bible and each other."

Year founded in CAN: 1916

Personnel:
Home ministry & office staff in CAN: 7

SIM Canada
10 Huntingdale Blvd.
SCARBOROUGH, ON M1W 2S5 CAN
Phone: (416) 497-2424
Fax: (416) 497-2444
E-mail: info@sim.ca
Web Site: www.sim.ca
Associations: CrossGlobal Link

Rev. Gregg Bryce, Exec. Director

An interdenominational sending agency of Evangelical tradition engaged in church planting, development, theological education, HIV/Aids, medical work and support of national churches.

Purpose: "...will be engaged interculturally and connected globally to declare and demonstrate the Gospel among all nations in our local and global neighborhoods."

Year founded in CAN: 1893

Income for Overseas Min: $9,247,067.00

Gifts in Kind: $20,000.00

Fully Supported CAN Personnel Overseas:
Expecting to serve more than 4 years: 104
Expecting to serve 1 to 4 years: 24
Non-residential mission personnel: 1

Other personnel:
Short-term less than 1 year: 193
Non-CAN serving in own/other country: 3
Home ministry & office staff in CAN: 64

Countries: Angola 6; Asia—General 6; Benin 7; Bolivia 7; Botswana 1; Burkina Faso 9; Chile 2; Ethiopia 15; Ghana 5; Niger 13;

Nigeria 10; Paraguay 2; Senegal 2; South Africa 7; Sudan 1; Zambia 11

Slavic Gospel Association— Canada

55 Fleming Dr., Ste. #26
CAMBRIDGE, ON N1T 2A9 CAN
Phone: (519) 621-3553
Fax: (519) 621-7571
E-mail: canada@sga.org
Web Site: www.sgacanada.ca
Associations: CrossGlobal Link
Rev. Allan W. Vincent, Exec. Director

An interdenominational support agency of Baptist and Evangelical tradition engaged in church planting, Bible distribution, child-care/orphanage programs, theological education, literature production and support of national workers.

Purpose: "...to serve the churches that Christ is building in Russia."

Year founded in CAN: 1947

Income for Overseas Min: $596,937.00

Fully Supported CAN Personnel Overseas:
Expecting to serve more than 4 years: 1

Other personnel:
Short-term less than 1 year: 12
Home ministry & office staff in CAN: 3

Countries: Ukraine 1

South American Missionary Society in Canada

PO Box 21082
BARRIE, ON L4M 6J1 CAN
Phone: (705) 728-7151
Fax: (705) 726-6716
E-mail: office@samscanada.ca
Web Site: www.samscanada.ca
Dr. Trevor Smith, Chair

A denominational sending agency of Anglican and Evangelical tradition engaged in mobilization for mission, evangelism, leadership development and support of national workers.

Purpose: "...to find and send those whom God is calling to the mission field, and to widen and deepen the missionary vision of Canadian Anglicans."

Year founded in CAN: 1979

Income for Overseas Min: $9,980,000.00

Personnel:
Short-term less than 1 year: 2
Home ministry & office staff in CAN: 3

TeachBeyond

2121 Henderson Hwy.
WINNIPEG, MB R2G 1P8 CAN
Phone: (204) 334-0055
Fax: (204) 339-3321
E-mail: jtm@janzteam.org
Web Site: www.teachbeyond.org
Associations: CrossGlobal Link
Mr. Jack Stenekes, Exec. Director

A nondenominational sending agency of Evangelical tradition engaged in Christian education, business as mission, camping programs, evangelism, member care and mobilization for mission.

Purpose: "...to provide transformational education services to children and adults regardless of gender, ethnicity, or religion in order to promote holistic personal growth and enduring social benefit."

Year founded in CAN: 1955

Income for Overseas Min: $1,646,862.00

Fully Supported CAN Personnel Overseas:
Expecting to serve more than 4 years: 36
Expecting to serve 1 to 4 years: 14

Other personnel:
Short-term less than 1 year: 34
Non-CAN serving in own/other country: 3
Home ministry & office staff in CAN: 9

Countries: Belarus; Bolivia; Brazil; Germany 33; Malaysia 1; Mexico; Moldova 2; Paraguay; Switzerland

TEAM of Canada (The Evangelical Alliance Mission of Canada)

2635—32nd St. SW
CALGARY, AB T3E 2R8 CAN
Phone: (800) 295-4160
Fax: (403) 207-6025
E-mail: team@teamcanada.org
Web Site: www.teamcanada.org
Associations: CrossGlobal Link
Mr. Lorne W. Strom, Canadian Director

An interdenominational sending agency of Evangelical tradition engaged in church planting, development, discipleship, evangelism, medical work, short-term programs and TESOL.

Purpose: "...to help churches send missionaries to establish reproducing churches among the nations to the glory of God."
Year founded in CAN: 1945
Fully Supported CAN Personnel Overseas:
 Expecting to serve more than 4 years: 35
 Expecting to serve 1 to 4 years: 8
Other personnel:
 Short-term less than 1 year: 40
 Home ministry & office staff in CAN: 11
Countries: Asia—General 5; Central Asia—General 5; Chad 2; Czech Republic 2; France 1; India 1; Italy 3; Japan 8; Middle East; Peru 3; South Africa 2; Spain 2; Zimbabwe 1

Teen Missions in Canada, Inc.
PO Box 415
OUTLOOK, SK S0L 2N0 CAN
Phone: (306) 867-9293
E-mail: info@teenmissions.ca
Web Site: www.teenmissions.ca
Shirley Charron, Treasurer

An interdenominational support agency of Ecumenical tradition engaged in youth programs, short-term programs, association of missions, discipleship, evangelism and mobilization for mission.

Purpose: "...to provide an opportunity for spiritual growth, to instill a missionary vision, and bring people into a relationship with Jesus, publicly, privately, and through local churches."
Year founded in CAN: 1980
Income for Overseas Min: $200,000.00
Fully Supported CAN Personnel Overseas:
 Non-residential mission personnel: 6
Other personnel:
 Short-term less than 1 year: 50

The Free Methodist Church in Canada
4315 Village Centre Court
MISSISSAUGA, ON L4Z 1S2 CAN
Phone: (905) 848-2600
Fax: (905) 848-2603
Web Site: www.fmc-canada.org
Bishop Keith Elford, Bishop

A denominational sending agency of Evan-

gelical and Methodist tradition engaged in church planting, development, leadership development, support of national churches and partnership development.

Purpose: "...to establish healthy churches within the reach of all people in Canada and beyond."
Year founded in CAN: 1889
Income for Overseas Min: $520,000.00
Fully Supported CAN Personnel Overseas:
 Expecting to serve more than 4 years: 6
 Non-residential mission personnel: 1
Other personnel:
 Short-term less than 1 year: 90
 Non-CAN serving in own/other country: 2
 Home ministry & office staff in CAN: 1
Countries: Cambodia; Congo, Democratic Republic of 1; Kenya 1; Niger 2; Sri Lanka 2

The Master's Foundation
1290 Eglinton Ave. E, Ste. 5
MISSISSAUGA, ON L4W 1K8 CAN
Phone: (905) 602-1350
E-mail: sgw@globalserve.net
Web Site: www.mastersfoundation.org
Mr. Stanley G. Watrich, President

An interdenominational support agency of Evangelical and Pentecostal tradition engaged in childcare/orphanage programs, Bible distribution, broadcasting, church construction, relief and/or rehabilitation and short-term programs.

Year founded in CAN: 1983
Income for Overseas Min: $447,601.00
Gifts in Kind: $260,000.00
Personnel:
 Short-term less than 1 year: 11
 Non-CAN serving in own/other country: 9
Countries: Ukraine

The Mission to Children
PO Box 51143
RPO Beddington
CALGARY, AB T3K 3V9 CAN
Phone: (877) 766-2400
Fax: (760) 839-1620
E-mail: info@missiontochildren.org
Web Site: www.missiontochildren.org
Dr. John Garmo, President

A nondenominational specialized agency of

Evangelical tradition engaged in children at risk, childcare/orphanage programs, childrens programs, evangelism and character education/training/development.

Purpose: "...to care for and cultivate Christ-like character in children, especially those at risk."

Year founded in CAN: 1963

Income for Overseas Min: $352,348.00

Countries: Costa Rica; El Salvador; India; Philippines

The Wellspring Foundation for Education

Unit 72, 21579 88B Ave.
LANGLEY, BC V1M 2X4 CAN

Phone: (604) 592-5062
E-mail: info@thewellspringfoundation.com
Web Site: www.thewellspringfoundation.com

Associations: CCRDA

Mr. Richard Taylor, Exec. Director

A nondenominational support agency of Evangelical tradition engaged in building schools and empowering teachers in Rwanda, development, Christian education, management consulting/training and training.

Purpose: "...to establish high quality Christian values based education in Rwanda that will produce creative, capable, and principled leaders to serve within all sectors of society."

Year founded in CAN: 2004

Income for Overseas Min: $500,000.00

Fully Supported CAN Personnel Overseas:
   Expecting to serve more than 4 years: 2
   Expecting to serve 1 to 4 years: 1

Other personnel:
   Short-term less than 1 year: 50
   Non-CAN serving in own/other country: 23
   Home ministry & office staff in CAN: 4

Countries: Rwanda 2

Trans World Radio Canada

PO Box 25324
LONDON, ON N6G 3W2 CAN

Phone: (888) 672-6510
Fax: (519) 672-6512
E-mail: info@twrcanada.org
Web Site: www.twrcanada.org

Associations: CrossGlobal Link

Mr. Ray Alary, President

A nondenominational specialized agency engaged in broadcasting, discipleship, evangelism, leadership development, member care and support of national workers.

Year founded in CAN: 1973

Income for Overseas Min: $1,255,794.00

Fully Supported CAN Personnel Overseas:
   Expecting to serve more than 4 years: 10
   Non-residential mission personnel: 1

Other personnel:
   Short-term less than 1 year: 5
   Non-CAN serving in own/other country: 10
   Home ministry & office staff in CAN: 7

Countries: Austria 3; Eastern Europe—General; Malaysia 1; Middle East 1; Netherlands 2; South Africa 3

Ukrainian Children's Christian Fund

10340 Freshwater Dr.
RICHMOND, BC V7E 4H7 CAN

Phone: (604) 278-0692
Fax: (604) 279-9080
E-mail: pcf.lapka@shaw.ca

Olga O. Lapka, President

A nondenominational service agency of Baptist and Christian/Plymouth Brethren tradition engaged in childcare/orphanage programs, Bible distribution, childrens programs, literature distribution and relief and/or rehabilitation. Financial data from 2005.

Year founded in CAN: 1976

Income for Overseas Min: $72,000.00

Countries: Ukraine

United Church of Canada, Justice, Global & Ecumenical Relations

3250 Bloor St. W.
TORONTO, ON M5M 1K8 CAN

Phone: (416) 231-5931
Fax: (416) 231-3103
E-mail: info@united-church.ca
Web Site: www.united-church.ca

Nora Sanders

A denominational sending agency of the Union of Presbyterian, Methodist, Congregationalist, & United Brethren tradition engaged in justice, development, theological education, leadership development, support of national churches and partnership development.

Year founded in CAN: 1925

Income for Overseas Min: $5,000,000.00

Fully Supported CAN Personnel Overseas:
Expecting to serve more than 4 years: 11
Expecting to serve 1 to 4 years: 6
Non-residential mission personnel: 20

Other personnel:
Short-term less than 1 year: 20
Home ministry & office staff in CAN: 20

Countries: Brazil; China 2; Israel; Japan 4; Korea, South 1; Mozambique 2; Palestine; Peru 1; Switzerland; Zambia 1

Venture Teams International

#3A 3023 21 St. NE
CALGARY, AB T2E 7T1 CAN

Phone: (403) 777-2970
Fax: (403) 777-2973
E-mail: info@vti.ca
Web Site: www.vti.ca

Mr. Mark Sorell, Exec. Director

An interdenominational service agency of Evangelical tradition engaged in discipleship, childrens programs, church planting, evangelism, short-term programs and youth programs.

Purpose: "...to mentor, equip, and inspire followers of Christ for purposeful global and community service."

Year founded in CAN: 1979

Income for Overseas Min: $97,631.00

Gifts in Kind: $1,702.00

Fully Supported CAN Personnel Overseas:
Non-residential mission personnel: 28

Other personnel:
Short-term less than 1 year: 103
Home ministry & office staff in CAN: 3

Visionledd

PO Box 460
BURLINGTON, ON L7R 3Y3 CAN

Phone: (905) 319-8834
Fax: (905) 332-6655
E-mail: info@visionledd.com
Web Site: www.visionledd.com

Associations: CCRDA

Mr. Jim Cantelon, Founder/President

An interdenominational support agency of Pentecostal tradition engaged in HIV/Aids, development, justice, partnership development, mobilization for mission and missionary training.

Purpose: "...to build the capacity of church and community leaders to be the hands and feet of Jesus, in practical and relevant ways, for those infected and affected by HIV/Aids."

Year founded in CAN: 1999

Personnel:
Home ministry & office staff in CAN: 7

Countries: Malawi

Voice of the Martyrs, Inc., The

PO Box 117, Port Credit
MISSISSAUGA, ON L5G 4L5 CAN

Phone: (905) 670-9721
Fax: (905) 670-0246
E-mail: thevoice@persecution.net
Web Site: www.persecution.net

Mr. Glenn M. Penner, CEO

A nondenominational support agency of Evangelical tradition engaged in persecution ministries, missions information service, justice, literature distribution, relief and/or rehabilitation and training.

Purpose: "...to glorify God by serving His persecuted Church."

Year founded in CAN: 1969

Income for Overseas Min: $1,645,818.00

Fully Supported CAN Personnel Overseas:
Non-residential mission personnel: 2

Other personnel:
Home ministry & office staff in CAN: 11

WEC International (Canada)

37 Aberdeen Ave.
HAMILTON, ON L8P 2N6 CAN

Phone: (905) 529-0166
Fax: (905) 529-0630
E-mail: info@wec-canada.org
Web Site: www.wec-canada.org

An interdenominational sending agency of Evangelical tradition engaged in church planting, children at risk, Christian education, medical work, missionary training and drug/alcohol rehabilitation.

Purpose: "...to glorify God by forming viable churches among the unreached peoples of Canada and the world through imparting missionary vision and recruiting, training, sending and supporting those called of God."

Year founded in CAN: 1936

Income for Overseas Min: $1,800,000.00

Gifts in Kind: $5,500.00

Fully Supported CAN Personnel Overseas:
  Expecting to serve more than 4 years: 50
  Expecting to serve 1 to 4 years: 1

Other personnel:
  Short-term less than 1 year: 9
  Non-CAN serving in own/other country: 63
  Home ministry & office staff in CAN: 19

Countries: Africa—General; Asia—General 10; Brazil 1; Cambodia 1; Central Asia—General 4; Chad; Congo, Democratic Republic of 2; Cote d'Ivoire; Equatorial Guinea 4; Fiji 2; France 2; Gambia, The 2; Guinea-Bissau; Greece; Indonesia 2; Mexico 2; Middle East 8; Russia; Senegal 1; South Africa 2; Spain 3; Thailand 1; United Kingdom 2; Venezuela; Zimbabwe 1

Western Tract Mission, Inc.

401 33rd St. W.
SASKATOON, SK S7L 0V5 CAN

Phone: (306) 244-0446
E-mail: wtm@sasktel.net
Web Site: www.westerntractmission.org

Mr. Arnold Stobbe, Director

A nondenominational service agency of Evangelical tradition engaged in correspondence courses, evangelism and literature distribution. Personnel data from 2005.

Year founded in CAN: 1941
Personnel:
  Home ministry & office staff in CAN: 6

White Fields Missionary Society

PO Box 242
EDMONTON, AB T5J 2J1 CAN

Phone: (780) 483-5750
Web Site: www.whitefields.org

Mr. Stephen Lonetti, General Director

A service agency of Evangelical tradition engaged in church planting and evangelism. Countries of service and personnel information included in White Fields, Inc. (USA).

Purpose: "...to provide collaborative start-up support to pastors and churches among their own people in other parts of the world."

Year founded in CAN: 1955

Income for Overseas Min: $227,252.00

Word & Deed Ministries Canada, Inc.

PO Box 20100
ST. THOMAS, ON N5P 4H4 CAN

Phone: (519) 633-2333
Fax: (519) 633-7181
E-mail: office@wordanddeed.org
Web Site: www.wordanddeed.org

Associations: CCRDA

Mr. Bernie Pennings, Exec. Director

An interdenominational service agency of Presbyterian and Reformed tradition engaged in education/development, Christian education, agricultural programs, childcare/orphanage programs, theological education, medical work and relief and/or rehabilitation.

Purpose: "...to improve the spiritual and physical needs of people in the developing world in accordance with Biblical principals."

Year founded in CAN: 1994

Income for Overseas Min: $2,170,000.00

Personnel:
  Home ministry & office staff in CAN: 4

World Compassion Society

PO Box 1415
MEDICINE HAT, AB T1A 7N3 CAN

Phone: (403) 526-8229
Web Site: www.worldcompassion.tv

Mr. Terry Law, Founder

A transdenominational specialized agency of Charismatic and Independent tradition engaged in church planting, Bible distribution, discipleship, literature distribution, relief and/or rehabilitation and training. See World Compassion Terry Law Ministries for statistical information.

Purpose: "...to take the message of Jesus Christ to nations that are hostile to the Gospel, working with local bodies of believers to support the spiritual and physical transformation of lives."

Year founded in CAN: 1969

World Hope Canada

PO Box 21082
OTTAWA, ON K1S 5N1 CAN
Phone: (877) 482-1499
Fax: (613) 730-0655
E-mail: contact@worldhope.ca
Web Site: www.worldhope.ca
Associations: CCRDA

Mr. Clint Curle, Exec. Director

A service agency of Wesleyan tradition engaged in trafficking/slavery issues, children at risk, development, partnership development and relief and/or rehabilitation.

Purpose: "...a faith based relief and development organization which seeks to bring hope and healing to a hurting world."

Year founded in CAN: 2000

Income for Overseas Min: $479,791.00

Gifts in Kind: $1,410.00

Fully Supported CAN Personnel Overseas:
Expecting to serve more than 4 years: 2

Other personnel:
Short-term less than 1 year: 75
Non-CAN serving in own/other country: 12
Home ministry & office staff in CAN: 2

Countries: Niger; Sierra Leone; Ukraine 2

World Mission Prayer League

5408 49th Ave.
CAMROSE, AB T4V 0N7 CAN
Phone: (780) 672-0464
Fax: (780) 672-0464
E-mail: wmplcdn@cable-lynx.net
Web Site: www.wmpl.org
Associations: The Mission Exchange

Rev. Charles R. Lingquist, Gen.Director

A denominational sending agency of Lutheran tradition engaged in leadership development, development, theological education, evangelism, medical work and youth programs. For statistical data see U.S. listing.

Purpose: "...committed to know Christ, pray for the advance of His Kingdom, share the Gospel and ourselves with those who do not know Him, and encourage Christians everywhere in this global task."

Year founded in CAN: 1951

World Relief Canada

#310—600 Alden Rd.
MARKHAM, ON L3R 0E7 CAN
Phone: (905) 415-8181
Fax: (905) 415-0287
E-mail: worldrelief@wrcanada.org
Web Site: www.wrcanada.org

Mr. Laurie Cook, CEO/President

An interdenominational specialized agency of Evangelical tradition engaged in relief and/or rehabilitation, development and partnership development.

Purpose: "...to respond to the relief and developmental needs of the world's poor in the name of Jesus Christ through our global network of Christian organizations in partnership with the Canadian and overseas Church."

Year founded in CAN: 1982

Income for Overseas Min: $4,785,382.00

Fully Supported CAN Personnel Overseas:
Expecting to serve more than 4 years: 2

Other personnel:
Home ministry & office staff in CAN: 13

Countries: Bangladesh; Burundi; Cambodia; China; Congo, Democratic Republic of; Ethiopia; India; Kenya 2; Liberia; Rwanda; Sudan; Tanzania; Vietnam

World Team Canada

7575 Danbro Cres.
MISSISSAUGA, ON L5N 6P9 CAN
Phone: (905) 821-6300
Fax: (905) 821-6325
E-mail: wt-canada@worldteam.org
Web Site: www.worldteam.org
Associations: CrossGlobal Link

Mr. Bill Allan, Exec. Director

An interdenominational sending agency of Evangelical tradition engaged in church planting, TEE, evangelism, leadership development, partnership development and Bible translation.

Purpose: "...to glorify God by working together to establish reproducing churches focusing on unreached peoples of the world."

Income for Overseas Min: $1,215,000.00

Fully Supported CAN Personnel Overseas:
Expecting to serve more than 4 years: 30
Expecting to serve 1 to 4 years: 1

Non-residential mission personnel: 1

Other personnel:
Short-term less than 1 year: 25
Non-CAN serving in own/other country: 1
Home ministry & office staff in CAN: 4

Countries: Asia—General 6; Cambodia
2; Cameroon 4; Central African Republic;
Cuba 2; Haiti 2; Italy 2; Papua New Guinea
4; Peru 4; Spain 2; Ukraine 2

World Vision Canada

1 World Dr.
MISSISSAUGA, ON L5T 2Y4 CAN
Phone: (905) 565-6100
Fax: (905) 696-2162
E-mail: info@worldvision.ca
Web Site: www.worldvision.ca
Mr. Dave Toycen, President/CEO

A transdenominational service agency of
Evangelical tradition engaged in development, childrens programs, relief and/or rehabilitation, training and youth programs.
Countries of service data from 2005.

Purpose: "...an international partnership
of Christians...working with the poor and
oppressed to promote human transformation, seek justice, and bear witness to the
good news of the Kingdom of God...moti-
vated by God's love for all people regardless of race, religion, gender or ethnicity."

Year founded in CAN: 1954

Income for Overseas Min:
$306,600,000.00

Gifts in Kind: $72,100,000.00

Fully Supported CAN Personnel Overseas:
Non-residential mission personnel: 10

Other personnel:
Home ministry & office staff in CAN: 552

Countries: Cambodia; Congo, Democratic
Republic of; Mali; Senegal; Uganda

WorldServe Ministries Canada

1301 Johnson Rd.
WHITE ROCK, BC V4B 3Z3 CAN
Phone: (604) 531-3955
Fax: (604) 531-9168
E-mail: caoffice@worldserve.org
Web Site: www.worldserve.org
Ken Leggatt, President

A transdenominational support agency of
Evangelical tradition engaged in Bible distribution, church planting, evangelism, support of national workers, support of national churches and Bible translation. Data from
2005.

Purpose: "...to serve and equip the
Church worldwide."

Year founded in CAN: 1976

Income for Overseas Min: $3,960,000.00

Personnel:
Home ministry & office staff in CAN: 7

Wycliffe Bible Translators of Canada, Inc.

4316—10 St. NE
CALGARY, AB T2E 6K3 CAN
Phone: (403) 250-5411
Fax: (403) 250-2623
Web Site: www.wycliffe.ca
Mr. David H. Ohlson, Exec. Director

An interdenominational sending agency of
Evangelical tradition engaged in Bible translation, Bible distribution, development, linguistics, literacy work and translation work.

Purpose: "...to empower indigenous people worldwide for spiritual, personal and social growth through Bible translation and
other language-related ministries."

Year founded in CAN: 1951

Income for Overseas Min: $11,808,452.00

Gifts in Kind: $80,000.00

Fully Supported CAN Personnel Overseas:
Expecting to serve more than 4 years: 239

Other personnel:
Home ministry & office staff in CAN: 12

Countries: Africa—General 5; Asia—General
11; Austria 1; Burkina Faso 7; Brazil 3; Cameroon 21; Central Asia—General 45; Chad 1;
Congo, Democratic Republic of 6; Ethiopia
3; Ghana 3; Kenya 3; Latin America—General 19; Mali 2; Mexico 9; Mozambique 6;
Netherlands 2; Nigeria 4; Papua New Guinea 23; Philippines 21; Senegal 3; South Pacific 14; Tanzania 5; Togo 1; United Kingdom 5; Unspecified Country 16

Young Life of Canada

#120—9440 202nd St.
LANGLEY, BC V1M 4A6 CAN

Phone: (604) 881-6023
Fax: (604) 881-0204
E-mail: national@younglife.ca
Web Site: www.younglife.ca
Mr. Don Crompton, Natl. Director

A nondenominational support agency of Evangelical tradition engaged in youth programs, camping programs and discipleship.
Purpose: "...loving teenagers in their world encouraging them to know Jesus Christ."
Year founded in CAN: 1954
Personnel:
   Home ministry & office staff in CAN: 8

Youth for Christ, Canada
PO Box 93008
LANGLEY, BC V3A 8H2 CAN
Phone: (604) 595-2498
Fax: (604) 595-2473
E-mail: info@yfccanada.org
Web Site: www.yfccanada.org
Mr. Dave Brereton, Natl. Director

A nondenominational support agency of Evangelical tradition engaged in evangelism, training, children at risk and youth programs.
Purpose: "...to reach young people everywhere, working together with the local church and other like-minded partners to raise up life-long followers of Jesus who lead by godliness in lifestyle, devotion to the Word of God and prayer, passion for sharing the love of Christ, and commitment to social involvement."
Year founded in CAN: 1972
Fully Supported CAN Personnel Overseas:
   Expecting to serve more than 4 years: 2
   Expecting to serve 1 to 4 years: 2
Other personnel:
   Short-term less than 1 year: 58
   Home ministry & office staff in CAN: 413
Countries: Argentina 2; United Kingdom 2

Youth with a Mission Canada, Inc.
PO Box 57100
VANCOUVER, BC V5K 5G6 CAN
Phone: (604) 436-4433
Fax: (604) 436-4466

E-mail: revpaul@telus.net
Web Site: www.ywamcanada.ca
Mr. Paul Martinson, Chair Canadian Leadership Team

An interdenominational sending agency of Charismatic and Evangelical tradition engaged in discipleship, evangelism, mobilization for mission, short-term programs and missionary training.
Purpose: "...to know God and to make Him known."
Year founded in CAN: 1978
Income for Overseas Min: $6,000,000.00
Fully Supported CAN Personnel Overseas:
   Non-residential mission personnel: 13
Other personnel:
   Home ministry & office staff in CAN: 305

YUGO Canada Ministries
PO Box 231
ST. ALBERT, AB T8N 1N3 CAN
Phone: (780) 461-0891
Fax: (780) 961-7690
E-mail: yugominstries@cruzinternet.com
Web Site: www.yugo.org
Mr. Dwight Pritchard, Chairman of Board of Directors

An interdenominational sending agency of Baptist tradition engaged in short-term mission trips for youth & adults, childcare/orphanage programs, church planting, evangelism, support of national churches and support of national workers.
Year founded in CAN: 2004
Income for Overseas Min: $243,563.00
Fully Supported CAN Personnel Overseas:
   Expecting to serve more than 4 years: 6
   Expecting to serve 1 to 4 years: 4
Other personnel:
   Short-term less than 1 year: 345
   Non-CAN serving in own/other country: 1
   Home ministry & office staff in CAN: 1
Countries: Mexico 6

Chapter 6
Indices to Canadian Protestant Agencies

M any *Handbook* users find it valuable to locate agencies by particular categories of church tradition or ministry activity. This chapter provides the user with those indices. Agency responses on the *Mission Handbook* survey helped define the listed categories. The organizations in each *category* appear in alphabetical order by organization name.

Index by Church Tradition

If an agency needed more than one generic or denominational category to describe its traditional doctrinal and/or ecclesiastical stance, the agency may appear under as many as two of the given categories. We have arranged the list alphabetically by category and within each category by agency name. See question #8 of the survey (in Appendix D) for the actual working of the question and the check-off list of choices.

Index by Ministry Activity

Almost all agencies are involved in several types of ministry activities. Each agency may be listed under as many as six primary categories of activity. We asked those with more than six primary activities to indicate the six activities toward which they had committed the largest amount of resources. We have divided the broad activities of education and evangelism into subcategories. For example, the evangelism category appears as "evangelism, mass" and "evangelism, student," and so on. See question #9 of the survey (in Appendix D) for the actual wording of the question and the check-off list of activities.

Agencies sometimes have written in new categories under the "other" choice in previous surveys. Some of these, if used often enough, may be included in the check-off list for the next edition's survey. Categories are occasionally dropped for lack of use. The most used categories have remained the same.

Church Tradition

Adventist
Adventist Dev. and Relief Agency Canada

Anglican
Canadian Churches' Forum for Global Mins.
So. American Missionary Society in Canada

Baptist
ABWE Canada
Apostolic Church of Pentecost of Can., Inc.
Arms of Jesus Children's Mission, Inc., The
Avant Ministries Canada
Baptist General Conf. of Canada Global Mins.
CAM International of Canada
Canadian Baptist Ministries
Canadian National Baptist Convention
CrossWorld Canada
FAIR (Fellowship Agency for Intl. Relief)
Far East Broadcasting Associates of Canada
FRIENDS in Action International—Canada
Fundamental Baptist Msn., Trinidad/Tobago
Gospel Mission of South America of Canada
People International—Canada
Slavic Gospel Association—Canada
Ukrainian Children's Christian Fund
YUGO Canada Ministries

Brethren
Brethren in Christ World Missions—Canada
International Teams, Canada
MSC Canada

Charismatic
Apostolic Church in Canada, The
Haiti Arise—Canada
Into All The World
Project AmaZon Canada Society
World Compassion Society
Youth with a Mission Canada, Inc.

Christian (Restoration Movement)
Evangelical Christian Church in Canada,The

Christian/Plymouth
Brethren Assemblies (Canada)

Congregational
Leprosy Mission Canada, The

Ecumenical
Canadian Bible Society/La Societe Biblique
    Canadienne
Christian Aid for Under-Assisted Societies
    Everywhere (CAUSE Canada)

Habitat for Humanity Canada
Teen Missions in Canada, Inc.

Evangelical
Action International Ministries—Canada
Adventive Cross Cultural Initiatives
Africa Inland Mission International (Canada)
African Enterprise Association of Canada
Arab World Ministries (Canada)
Back to the Bible Canada
Barry Moore Ministries, Inc.
BCM International (Canada), Inc.
Bible League of Canada, The
BLF Canada
Canadian South America Mission
Child Evangelism Fellowship of Canada
Chosen People Ministries (Canada)
Christar Canada
Christian and Missionary Alliance in Can., The
Christian Blind Mission Intl.—Canada
Christian Studies International of Canada
Commission to Every Nation—Canada
Compassion Canada
Crossroads Christian Communications, Inc.
CSM Canada Intl. (Christian Salvage Msn.)
EMAS Canada
Emmanuel International Canada
Equip, Canada
ERRC Educational Society
Evangelical Covenant Church of Canada
Evangelical Free Church of Canada Mission
Evangelical Mennonite Conf., Board of Msns.
Evangelical Missionary Church of Canada
Evangelical Tract Distributors
Fellowship of Companies for Christ Intl. Can.
Finishers Canada
Frontiers Canada
Galcom International, Inc.
Gateway Training for Cross-cultural Service
Global Aid Network, Inc.—Canada
Global Outreach Mission, Inc.,Canada
Global Recordings Network Canada
Gospel for Asia
Gospel Operation International for Chinese
    Christians Canada, Inc.
Greater Europe Mission (Canada)
HCJB Global—Canada
High Adventure Gospel Communication Mins.
HOPE International Development Agency
I. N. (Intl. Needs) Network Canada
InterAct Ministries of Canada
Intercede International
International Child Care (Canada), Inc.
International Christian Ministries Canada
International Russian Radio/TV (IRR/TV)
InterServe Canada (Intl. Service Fellowship)

Inter-Varsity Christian Fellowship of Canada
Jusqu'aux Extremites de la Terre (JET)
Latin America Mission (Canada), Inc.
Liebenzell Mission of Canada
Link International Ministries
Mission Aviation Fellowship of Canada
Mission Possible Canada
Mission Without Borders Canada
Missionary Internship Canada, Inc.
Missionary Ventures Canada
Navigators of Canada, The
New Tribes Mission of Canada
OMF International—Canada
Open Doors with Brother Andrew Canada
Operation Mobilization Canada
Outreach Canada
Partners International Canada
Pioneers Canada
ReachAcross
reSource Leadership International for
    Theological Education
Salvation Army—Can./Bermuda Territory
Samaritan's Purse—Canada
SEND International of Canada
SIM Canada
TeachBeyond
TEAM of Canada
The Free Methodist Church in Canada
The Master's Foundation
The Mission to Children
The Wellspring Foundation for Education
Venture Teams International
Voice of the Martyrs, Inc., The
WEC International (Canada)
Western Tract Mission, Inc.
White Fields Missionary Society
World Relief Canada
World Team Canada
World Vision Canada
WorldServe Ministries Canada
Wycliffe Bible Translators of Canada, Inc.
Young Life of Canada
Youth for Christ, Canada

Holiness
Bible Holiness Movement, The
Ch. of God (Anderson, Ind.)—Can. Bd. of Msns.
Nazarene Compassion Ministries Canada

Independent
Hellenic Ministries/Canada

Lutheran
Evangelical Lutheran Church in Canada
    Global Mission
World Mission Prayer League

Mennonite
Evangelical Mennonite Mission Conference
Hope Haven Canada Ministries
MBMS International
Mennonite Central Committee Canada
Mennonite Economic Dev. Assoc. (MEDA)
Mennonite Mission Health Association

Methodist
OMS International—Canada

Pentecostal
Canadian Assemblies of God, General Conf.
ERDO—Emergency Relief and Development
Mission of Mercy Canada
Pentecostal Assemblies of Canada, The
Visionledd

Presbyterian
Presbyterian Church in Canada—Life and
    Mission Agency
Word & Deed Ministries Canada, Inc.

Reformed
Christian Reformed World Relief Committee
    of Canada

Wesleyan
World Hope Canada

Ministry Activity

Agricultural programs
Adventist Dev. and Relief Agency Canada
Africa Community Technical Service (ACTS)
Crossroads Christian Communications, Inc.
Equip, Canada
ERDO—Emergency Relief and Development
FRIENDS in Action International—Canada
Haiti Arise—Canada
HOPE International Development Agency
Mennonite Central Committee Canada
Mennonite Economic Dev. Associates
Word & Deed Ministries Canada, Inc.

Apologetics
Brethren in Christ World Missions—Canada
    Association of Missions
Canadian Assemblies of God, General Conf.
Evangelical Mennonite Mission Conference
Finishers Canada
International Russian Radio/TV (IRR/TV)
Teen Missions in Canada, Inc.

Audio
Back to the Bible Canada

Global Recordings Network Canada

Aviation services
Africa Inland Mission International (Canada)
Canadian South America Mission
Mission Aviation Fellowship of Canada

Bible distribution
Adventive Cross Cultural Initiatives
Asian Outreach International Canada
Bible Holiness Movement, The
Bible League of Canada, The
BLF Canada
Canadian Bible Society/La Societe Biblique Canadienne
CSM Canada Intl. (Christian Salvage Msn.)
Gospel for Asia
Hellenic Ministries/Canada
High Adventure Gospel Communication Mins.
Open Doors with Brother Andrew Canada
SGM Canada
Slavic Gospel Association— Canada
The Master's Foundation
Ukrainian Children's Christian Fund
World Compassion Society
WorldServe Ministries Canada
Wycliffe Bible Translators of Canada, Inc.

Bible memorization
Navigators of Canada, The

Broadcasting, radio
Avant Ministries Canada
Back to the Bible Canada
Crossroads Christian Communications, Inc.
Evangelical Free Church of Canada Mission
Fundamental Baptist Mission
Galcom International, Inc.
Global Outreach Mission, Inc., Canada
Gospel for Asia
HCJB Global—Canada
High Adventure Gospel Communication Mins.
International Russian Radio/TV (IRR/TV)
OMS International—Canada
Operation Mobilization Canada
The Master's Foundation
Trans World Radio Canada

Business as Mission
Arab World Ministries (Canada)
Christian and Missionary Alliance in Can.
CrossWorld Canada
Fellowship of Companies for Christ Intl. Can.
InterServe Canada (Intl. Service Fellowship)
Operation Mobilization Canada
Opportunity International Canada
TeachBeyond

Camping programs
Action International Ministries—Canada
BCM International (Canada), Inc.
CAM International of Canada
Fundamental Baptist Mission of Trinidad and Tobago (Canada)
Greater Europe Mission (Canada)
Hellenic Ministries/Canada
Inter-Varsity Christian Fellowship of Canada
Latin America Mission (Canada), Inc.
Mission Without Borders Canada
Salvation Army—Can./Bermuda Territory
TeachBeyond
Young Life of Canada

Childcare/orphanage
Action International Ministries—Canada
Equip, Canada
ERDO—Emergency Relief and Development
Global Aid Network, Inc.—Canada
I. N. (International Needs) Network Canada
Intercede International
International Child Care (Canada), Inc.
Into All The World
Latin America Mission (Canada), Inc.
Link International Ministries
Mission Without Borders Canada
Partners International Canada
Pentecostal Assemblies of Canada, The
Salvation Army—Can./Bermuda Territory
Slavic Gospel Association— Canada
The Master's Foundation
The Mission to Children
Ukrainian Children's Christian Fund
Word & Deed Ministries Canada, Inc.
YUGO Canada Ministries

Children at risk
Adventist Dev. and Relief Agency Canada
Arms of Jesus Children's Mission, Inc., The
Avant Ministries Canada
Christian Aid for Under-Assisted Societies Everywhere (CAUSE Canada)
Compasio
Compassion Canada
Equip, Canada
ERDO—Emergency Relief and Development
Mission Without Borders Canada
Nazarene Compassion Ministries Canada
The Mission to Children
WEC International (Canada)
World Hope Canada
Youth for Christ, Canada

Childrens programs
Arms of Jesus Children's Mission, Inc., The

BCM International (Canada), Inc.
Bible League of Canada, The
Child Evangelism Fellowship of Canada
International Child Care (Canada), Inc.
International Teams, Canada (Evangelical
    International Crusades Canada, Inc.)
Mission of Mercy Canada
Salvation Army—Can./Bermuda Territory
The Mission to Children
Ukrainian Children's Christian Fund
Venture Teams International
World Vision Canada

Church construction
Ch. of God (Anderson, Ind.)—Can. Bd. of Msns.
Missionary Ventures Canada
The Master's Foundation

Church establishing/planting
ABWE Canada
Adventive Cross Cultural Initiatives
Africa Inland Mission International (Canada)
Apostolic Ch. of Pentecost of Can., Inc.
Arab World Ministries (Canada)
Asian Outreach International Canada
Avant Ministries Canada
Baptist General Conf. of Canada Global Mins.
BCM International (Canada), Inc.
Bible Holiness Movement, The
Bible League of Canada, The
Brethren Assemblies (Canada)
Brethren in Christ World Missions—Canada
CAM International of Canada
Canadian Baptist Ministries
Canadian National Baptist Convention
Canadian South America Mission
Chosen People Ministries (Canada)
Christar Canada
Christian and Missionary Alliance in Can.
Ch. of God (Anderson, Ind.)—Can. Bd. of Msns.
CrossWorld Canada
Evangelical Christian Church in Canada,The
Evangelical Covenant Church of Canada
Evangelical Free Church of Canada Mission
Evangelical Mennonite Conf., Bd. of Msns.
Evangelical Mennonite Mission Conference
Evangelical Missionary Church of Canada
Far East Broadcasting Associates of Canada
FRIENDS in Action International—Canada
Frontiers Canada
Fundamental Baptist Mission of Trinidad and
    Tobago (Canada)
Global Aid Network, Inc.—Canada
Global Outreach Mission, Inc., Canada
Gospel for Asia
Gospel Mission of South America of Canada

Gospel Operation International for Chinese-
    Christians Canada, Inc.
Greater Europe Mission (Canada)
Haiti Arise—Canada
Hellenic Ministries/Canada
InterAct Ministries of Canada
International Teams, Canada (Evangelical
    International Crusades Canada, Inc.)
Into All The World
Latin America Mission (Canada), Inc.
Link International Ministries
MBMS International
Mission of Mercy Canada
MSC Canada
New Tribes Mission of Canada
OMF International—Canada
OMS International—Canada
Outreach Canada
Partners International Canada
Pentecostal Assemblies of Canada, The
People International—Canada
Pioneers Canada
Salvation Army—Can./Bermuda Territory
SEND International of Canada
SIM Canada
Slavic Gospel Association— Canada
TEAM of Canada
The Free Methodist Church in Canada
Venture Teams International
WEC International (Canada)
White Fields Missionary Society
World Compassion Society
World Team Canada
WorldServe Ministries Canada
YUGO Canada Ministries

Correspondence courses
BCM International (Canada), Inc.
Evangelical Christian Church in Canada,The
Evangelical Missionary Church of Canada
Western Tract Mission, Inc.

Development, community
Adventist Dev. and Relief Agency Canada
Africa Community Technical Service (ACTS)
Arms of Jesus Children's Mission, Inc., The
Asian Outreach International Canada
Canadian Baptist Ministries
Canadian South America Mission
Christian Aid for Under-Assisted Societies
    Everywhere (CAUSE Canada)
Christian Blind Mission Intl.—Canada
Christian Reformed World Relief Committee
    of Canada
Compasio
Crossroads Christian Communications, Inc.

EMAS Canada
Emmanuel International Canada
Equip, Canada
ERDO—Emergency Relief and Development
Evangelical Free Church of Canada Mission
Evangelical Missionary Church of Canada
FH Canada
FRIENDS in Action International—Canada
Frontiers Canada
Global Aid Network, Inc.—Canada
Habitat for Humanity Canada
Health Partners International of Canada
HOPE International Development Agency
Hungry for Life International
I. N. (International Needs) Network Canada
International Child Care (Canada), Inc.
InterServe Canada (Intl. Service Fellowship)
Latin America Mission (Canada), Inc.
Leprosy Mission Canada, The
Link International Ministries
MBMS International
Mennonite Central Committee Canada
Mennonite Economic Dev. Associates
Mercy Ships Canada
Mission Without Borders Canada
Missionary Ventures Canada
OMF International—Canada
Partners International Canada
Presbyterian Church in Canada
ReachAcross
Salvation Army—Can./Bermuda Territory
Samaritan's Purse—Canada
SIM Canada
TEAM of Canada
The Free Methodist Church in Canada
The Wellspring Foundation for Education
United Church of Canada
Visionledd
World Hope Canada
World Mission Prayer League
World Relief Canada
World Vision Canada
Wycliffe Bible Translators of Canada, Inc.

Disability assistance
Christian Blind Mission Intl.—Canada
Hope Haven Canada Ministries
International Child Care (Canada), Inc.

Discipleship
ABWE Canada
Action International Ministries—Canada
Adventive Cross Cultural Initiatives
Africa Inland Mission International (Canada)
Apostolic Church in Canada, The
Apostolic Ch. of Pentecost of Can., Inc.

Bible League of Canada, The
BLF Canada
CAM International of Canada
Canadian Baptist Ministries
Canadian National Baptist Convention
Child Evangelism Fellowship of Canada
Chosen People Ministries (Canada)
Compassion Canada
CrossWorld Canada
Emmanuel International Canada
ERRC Educational Society
Evangelical Mennonite Conf., Bd. of Msns.
Evangelical Missionary Church of Canada
Far East Broadcasting Associates of Canada
Fellowship of Companies for Christ Intl. Can.
Gospel Mission of South America of Canada
HCJB Global—Canada
Hellenic Ministries/Canada
InterAct Ministries of Canada
Liebenzell Mission of Canada
Medical Ministry Canada, Inc.
Mission Possible Canada
Mission Without Borders Canada
Navigators of Canada, The
New Tribes Mission of Canada
Opportunity International Canada
Pentecostal Assemblies of Canada, The
People International—Canada
Power to Change
SEND International of Canada
TEAM of Canada
Teen Missions in Canada, Inc.
Trans World Radio Canada
Venture Teams International
World Compassion Society
Young Life of Canada
Youth with a Mission Canada, Inc.

Education, church/sch.
Africa Inland Mission International (Canada)
Arms of Jesus Children's Mission, Inc., The
Christian Studies International of Canada
Evangelical Covenant Church of Canada
FH Canada
Frontiers Canada
Greater Europe Mission (Canada)
HCJB Global—Canada
Hope Haven Canada Ministries
International Russian Radio/TV (IRR/TV)
Leprosy Mission Canada, The
Mission Possible Canada
Mustard Seed Mission Canada, Inc.
Salvation Army—Can./Bermuda Territory
TeachBeyond
The Wellspring Foundation for Education
WEC International (Canada)
Word & Deed Ministries Canada, Inc.

Education, extension
EMAS Canada
International Christian Ministries Canada
Mission of Mercy Canada

Education, missionary
Commission to Every Nation—Canada
Gateway Training for Cross-cultural Service
Mustard Seed Mission Canada, Inc.

Education, theological
ABWE Canada
Baptist General Conf. of Canada Global Mins.
Brethren in Christ World Missions—Canada
CAM International of Canada
Christian and Missionary Alliance in Can.
ERRC Educational Society
Evangelical Lutheran Church in Canada
Fundamental Baptist Mission of Trinidad and
   Tobago (Canada)
Haiti Arise—Canada
International Christian Ministries Canada
OMF International—Canada
OMS International—Canada
Open Doors with Brother Andrew Canada
Partners International Canada
Pentecostal Assemblies of Canada, The
reSource Leadership International for Theo-
   logical

Education
SIM Canada
Slavic Gospel Association—Canada
United Church of Canada
Word & Deed Ministries Canada, Inc.
World Mission Prayer League

Education, theological by
CAM International of Canada
Emmanuel International Canada
Evangelical Christian Church in Canada,The
Mission Possible Canada
World Team Canada

Evangelism, mass
Barry Moore Ministries, Inc.
Canadian National Baptist Convention
Evangelical Lutheran Church in Canada
Evangelical Missionary Church of Canada
Evangelical Tract Distributors
Galcom International, Inc.
Global Recordings Network Canada
Gospel for Asia
Gospel Mission of South America of Canada
High Adventure Gospel Communication Mins.
International Russian Radio/TV (IRR/TV)

International Teams, Canada (Evangelical In-
   ternational Crusades Canada, Inc.)
OMS International—Canada
Power to Change
Salvation Army—Can./Bermuda Territory
TeachBeyond
The Mission to Children
Trans World Radio Canada
Venture Teams International
Western Tract Mission, Inc.
Youth with a Mission Canada, Inc.

Evangelism, personal and small group
ABWE Canada
African Enterprise Association of Canada
Arab World Ministries (Canada)
Baptist General Conf. of Canada Global Mins.
BCM International (Canada), Inc.
Bible Holiness Movement, The
BLF Canada
Brethren in Christ World Missions—Canada
CAM International of Canada
Canadian National Baptist Convention
Child Evangelism Fellowship of Canada
Chosen People Ministries (Canada)
Christar Canada
Christian and Missionary Alliance in Can.
ERRC Educational Society
Evangelical Covenant Church of Canada
Evangelical Mennonite Conf., Bd. of Msns.
Evangelical Missionary Church of Canada
Far East Broadcasting Associates of Canada
Fellowship of Companies for Christ Intl. Can.
Global Outreach Mission, Inc., Canada
Global Recordings Network Canada
Greater Europe Mission (Canada)
Hellenic Ministries/Canada
Into All The World
MBMS International
Missionary Ventures Canada
MSC Canada
Navigators of Canada, The
OMF International—Canada
Salvation Army—Can./Bermuda Territory
SEND International of Canada
South Am. Missionary Society in Canada
TEAM of Canada
Teen Missions in Canada, Inc.
White Fields Missionary Society
World Mission Prayer League
World Team Canada
WorldServe Ministries Canada
Youth for Christ, Canada
Youth with a Mission Canada, Inc.
YUGO Canada Ministries

Evangelism, student
InterAct Ministries of Canada
Inter-Varsity Christian Fellowship of Canada
Mission Possible Canada
Mustard Seed Mission Canada, Inc.
Power to Change
Youth for Christ, Canada

Funds transmission
ABWE Canada
Ch. of God (Anderson, Ind.)—Can. Bd. of Msns.
Crossroads Christian Communications, Inc.
Evangelical Lutheran Church in Canada
Fundamental Baptist Mission of Trinidad and
  Tobago (Canada)
Leprosy Mission Canada, The
Liebenzell Mission of Canada
MSC Canada

Furloughed missionary
Gospel Mission of South America of Canada
Gospel Operation International for Chinese
  Christians Canada, Inc

HIV/Aids
Adventist Dev. and Relief Agency Canada
Africa Community Technical Service (ACTS)
Apostolic Ch. of Pentecost of Can., Inc.
Christian Reformed World Relief Committee
  of Canada
ERDO—Emergency Relief and Development
I. N. (International Needs) Network Canada
Mennonite Mission Health Association
Nazarene Compassion Ministries Canada
Opportunity International Canada
Samaritan's Purse—Canada
SIM Canada
Visionledd

Information services
Gospel Operation International for Chinese-
  Christians Canada, Inc
Intercede International
Voice of the Martyrs, Inc., The

Justice & related
African Enterprise Association of Canada
Christian Aid for Under-Assisted Societies Ev-
  erywhere (CAUSE Canada)
Christian Reformed World Relief Committee
  of Canada
Compasio
Equip, Canada
ERDO—Emergency Relief and Development
Hellenic Ministries/Canada
I. N. (International Needs) Network Canada
Mennonite Central Committee Canada

Opportunity International Canada
United Church of Canada
Visionledd
Voice of the Martyrs, Inc., The

Leadership development
Action International Ministries—Canada
Adventive Cross Cultural Initiatives
Africa Inland Mission International (Canada)
Apostolic Ch. of Pentecost of Can., Inc.
Asian Outreach International Canada
Brethren in Christ World Missions—Canada
Canadian Assemblies of God, General Conf.
Canadian Baptist Ministries
Canadian South America Mission
Christian Aid for Under-Assisted Societies Ev-
  erywhere (CAUSE Canada)
Christian and Missionary Alliance in Can.
Christian Reformed World Relief Committee
  of Canada
Christian Studies International of Canada
Ch. of God (Anderson, Ind.)—Can. Bd. of Msns.
Compassion Canada
CrossWorld Canada
Emmanuel International Canada
ERRC Educational Society
Evangelical Mennonite Conf., Bd. of Msns.
Evangelical Mennonite Mission Conference
Far East Broadcasting Associates of Canada
Fellowship of Companies for Christ Intl. Can.
FH Canada
HOPE International Development Agency
International Christian Ministries Canada
International Russian Radio/TV (IRR/TV)
Into All The World
Jusqu'aux Extremites de la Terre (JET)
Link International Ministries
Mercy Ships Canada
Mission Possible Canada
Mustard Seed Mission Canada, Inc.
Navigators of Canada, The
Nazarene Compassion Ministries Canada
Outreach Canada
Pentecostal Assemblies of Canada, The
Presbyterian Church in Canada
Salvation Army—Can./Bermuda Territory
SEND International of Canada
South Am. Missionary Society in Canada
The Free Methodist Church in Canada
Trans World Radio Canada
United Church of Canada
World Mission Prayer League
World Team Canada

Linguistics
Canadian Bible Society / La Societe Biblique
  Canadienne

New Tribes Mission of Canada
Wycliffe Bible Translators of Canada, Inc.

Literacy

Asian Outreach International Canada
Back to the Bible Canada
Bible League of Canada, The
Christian Aid for Under-Assisted Societies Everywhere (CAUSE Canada)
High Adventure Gospel Communication Mins.
ReachAcross
Wycliffe Bible Translators of Canada, Inc.

Literature distribution

Action International Ministries—Canada
Bible Holiness Movement, The
Bible League of Canada, The
BLF Canada
Canadian Bible Society/La Societe Biblique Canadienne
Evangelical tract distributors
Fundamental Baptist Mission of Trinidad and Tobago (Canada)
High Adventure Gospel Communication Mins.
Open Doors with Brother Andrew Canada
SGM Canada
Ukrainian Children's Christian Fund
Voice of the Martyrs, Inc., The
Western Tract Mission, Inc.
World Compassion Society

Literature production

Bible Holiness Movement, The
BLF Canada
Canadian Bible Society/La Societe Biblique Canadienne
Canadian Churches' Forum for Global Mins.
Evangelical Tract Distributors
Gospel for Asia
International Christian Ministries Canada
Open Doors with Brother Andrew Canada
SGM Canada
Slavic Gospel Association—Canada

Management

African Enterprise Association of Canada
Fellowship of Companies for Christ Intl. Can.
Mennonite Economic Dev. Associates
Outreach Canada
The Wellspring Foundation for Education
Medical supplies
Canadian National Baptist Convention
FH Canada
Haiti Arise—Canada
Health Partners International of Canada
High Adventure Gospel Communication Mins.

Hope Haven Canada Ministries
Link International Ministries
Medical Ministry Canada, Inc.
Mennonite Mission Health Association
Mission Without Borders Canada
Missionary Ventures Canada
MSC Canada
Nazarene Compassion Ministries Canada
Power to Change

Medicine, incl. dental and public health

Adventist Dev. and Relief Agency Canada
Africa Inland Mission International (Canada)
Canadian National Baptist Convention
Christian Blind Mission Intl.—Canada
EMAS Canada
Equip, Canada
Evangelical Lutheran Church in Canada
Evangelical Missionary Church of Canada
Far East Broadcasting Associates of Canada
Frontiers Canada
Global Outreach Mission Inc., Canada
HCJB Global—Canada
International Child Care (Canada), Inc.
InterServe Canada (Intl. Service Fellowship)
Leprosy Mission Canada, The
Medical Ministry Canada, Inc.
Mennonite Mission Health Association
Mercy Ships Canada
Missionary Ventures Canada
Nazarene Compassion Ministries Canada
ReachAcross
Salvation Army—Can./Bermuda Territory
Samaritan's Purse—Canada
SIM Canada
TEAM of Canada
WEC International (Canada)
Word & Deed Ministries Canada, Inc.
World Mission Prayer League

Member care

Apostolic Church in Canada, The
Baptist General Conference of Canada Global Ministries (BGCC Global Ministries)
Child Evangelism Fellowship of Canada
TeachBeyond
Trans World Radio Canada

National church

Adventive Cross Cultural Initiatives
Apostolic Church in Canada, The
Apostolic Ch. of Pentecost of Can., Inc.
Brethren in Christ World Missions—Canada
Canadian Assemblies of God, General Conf.
Canadian Bible Society/La Societe Biblique Canadienne

Canadian Churches' Forum for Global Mins.
CrossWorld Canada
Evangelical Free Church of Canada Mission
Evangelical Lutheran Church in Canada
  Global Mission
Evangelical Mennonite Conf., Bd. of Msns.
Evangelical Mennonite Mission Conference
Gospel Mission of South America of Canada
InterAct Ministries of Canada
Intercede International
International Christian Ministries Canada
Liebenzell Mission of Canada
OMF International—Canada
OMS International—Canada
Open Doors with Brother Andrew Canada
Outreach Canada
Pentecostal Assemblies of Canada, The
Presbyterian Church in Canada
SEND International of Canada
SIM Canada
The Free Methodist Church in Canada
United Church of Canada
WorldServe Ministries Canada
YUGO Canada Ministries

Other

Asian Outreach International Canada
Christian Reformed World Relief Committee
  of Canada
Christian Studies International of Canada
Ch. of God (Anderson, Ind.)—Can. Bd. of Msns.
Compassion Canada
ERDO—Emergency Relief and Development
ERRC Educational Society
Evangelical Lutheran Church in Canada
Finishers Canada
Habitat for Humanity Canada
Haiti Arise—Canada
International Christian Ministries Canada
Inter-Varsity Christian Fellowship of Canada
Liebenzell Mission of Canada
Mennonite Economic Dev. Associates
Mission of Mercy Canada
reSource Leadership International for Theo-
  logical Education
SGM Canada
The Mission to Children
The Wellspring Foundation for Education
Voice of the Martyrs, Inc., The
WEC International (Canada)
Word & Deed Ministries Canada, Inc.
World Vision Canada
YUGO Canada Ministries

Partnership development

ABWE Canada
Adventive Cross Cultural Initiatives

African Enterprise Association of Canada
Christian Blind Mission Intl.—Canada
Compassion Canada
Emmanuel International Canada
Evangelical Mennonite Mission Conference
FH Canada
HCJB Global—Canada
Hungry for Life International
I. N. (International Needs) Network Canada
Mennonite Central Committee Canada
Mission of Mercy Canada
Partners International Canada
Samaritan's Purse—Canada
SGM Canada
The Free Methodist Church in Canada
United Church of Canada
Visionledd
World Hope Canada
World Relief Canada
World Team Canada

Psychological counseling

Christian Blind Mission Intl.—Canada
Compasio
Global Aid Network, Inc.—Canada

Recruiting/Mobilizing

Arab World Ministries (Canada)
Evangelical Covenant Church of Canada
Finishers Canada
Frontiers Canada
Global Outreach Mission Inc., Canada
Gospel Operation International for Chinese
  Christians Canada, Inc.
InterServe Canada (Intl. Service Fellowship)
Jusqu'aux Extremites de la Terre (JET)
Latin America Mission (Canada) Inc.
Liebenzell Mission of Canada
MBMS International
Operation Mobilization Canada
Outreach Canada
Pioneers Canada
Power to Change
South Am. Missionary Society in Canada
TeachBeyond
Teen Missions in Canada, Inc.
Visionledd
Youth with a Mission Canada, Inc.

Relief and/or rehabilitation

Adventist Dev. and Relief Agency Canada
Africa Community Technical Service (ACTS)
Apostolic Ch. of Pentecost of Can., Inc.
Arms of Jesus Children's Mission, Inc., The
Christian Aid for Under-Assisted Societies Ev-
  erywhere (CAUSE Canada)

Christian Blind Mission Intl.—Canada
Christian Reformed World Relief Committee
 of Canada
Compasio
Crossroads Christian Communications Inc.
Emmanuel International Canada
ERDO—Emergency Relief and Development
Evangelical Missionary Church of Canada
FAIR (Fellowship Agency for Intl. Relief)
Far East Broadcasting Associates of Canada
FH Canada
Global Aid Network, Inc.—Canada
Habitat for Humanity Canada
Health Partners International of Canada
Hope Haven Canada Ministries
HOPE International Development Agency
Hungry for Life International
Intercede International
Leprosy Mission Canada, The
Mennonite Central Committee Canada
Mission of Mercy Canada
Nazarene Compassion Ministries Canada
OMF International—Canada
Presbyterian Church in Canada
Salvation Army—Can./Bermuda Territory
Samaritan's Purse—Canada
The Master's Foundation
Ukrainian Children's Christian Fund
Voice of the Martyrs, Inc., The
Word & Deed Ministries Canada, Inc.
World Compassion Society
World Hope Canada
World Relief Canada
World Vision Canada

Research
Outreach Canada
SGM Canada

Services for other agencies
CSM Canada Intl. (Christian Salvage Msn.)
Finishers Canada
FRIENDS in Action International—Canada
Health Partners International of Canada
InterServe Canada (Intl. Service Fellowship)

Short-term programs
Africa Community Technical Service (ACTS)
African Enterprise Association of Canada
Arab World Ministries (Canada)
Arms of Jesus Children's Mission, Inc., The
BLF Canada
Canadian Churches' Forum for Global Mins.
CrossWorld Canada
EMAS Canada
ERRC Educational Society

Evangelical Free Church of Canada Mission
Evangelical Missionary Church of Canada
Global Outreach Mission Inc., Canada
Gospel Operation International for Chinese
 Christians Canada, Inc
Habitat for Humanity Canada
Hungry for Life International
InterAct Ministries of Canada
International Child Care (Canada), Inc.
Into All The World
Jusqu'aux Extremites de la Terre (JET)
Medical Ministry Canada, Inc.
Missionary Ventures Canada
MSC Canada
Operation Mobilization Canada
Pioneers Canada
Presbyterian Church in Canada
Samaritan's Purse—Canada
SEND International of Canada
TEAM of Canada
Teen Missions in Canada, Inc.
The Master's Foundation
Venture Teams International
Youth with a Mission Canada, Inc.

Sports program ministry
Power to Change

Supplying equipment
Crossroads Christian Communications, Inc.
CSM Canada Intl. (Christian Salvage Msn.)
Hope Haven Canada Ministries

Support of national workers
African Enterprise Association of Canada
Commission to Every Nation—Canada
Evangelical Christian Church in Canada,The
FRIENDS in Action International—Canada
Global Outreach Mission, Inc., Canada
Global Recordings Network Canada
Gospel for Asia
I. N. (International Needs) Network Canada
Intercede International
Into All The World
Jusqu'aux Extremites de la Terre (JET)
Latin America Mission (Canada), Inc.
Leprosy Mission Canada, The
Link International Ministries
Mustard Seed Mission Canada, Inc.
OMS International—Canada
Partners International Canada
Slavic Gospel Association—Canada
South Am. Missionary Society in Canada
Trans World Radio Canada
WorldServe Ministries Canada
YUGO Canada Ministries

Technical assistance
Africa Community Technical Service (ACTS)
Galcom International, Inc.
Mennonite Economic Dev. Associates

Tentmaking & related
Christar Canada
Christian and Missionary Alliance in Can.
Christian Studies International of Canada
Frontiers Canada
InterServe Canada (Intl. Service Fellowship)
ReachAcross

TESOL
Evangelical Free Church of Canada Mission
Haiti Arise—Canada
ReachAcross
TEAM of Canada

Trafficking/Slavery Issues
Bible Holiness Movement, The
Compasio
World Hope Canada

Training, other
Action International Ministries—Canada
BCM International (Canada), Inc.
Child Evangelism Fellowship of Canada
Evangelical Christian Church in Canada,The
Fellowship of Companies for Christ Intl. Can.
HCJB Global—Canada
HOPE International Development Agency
InterAct Ministries of Canada
Medical Ministry Canada, Inc.
Open Doors with Brother Andrew Canada
Operation Mobilization Canada
Opportunity International Canada
The Wellspring Foundation for Education
Voice of the Martyrs, Inc., The
World Compassion Society
World Vision Canada
Youth for Christ, Canada

Training/Orientation
Arab World Ministries (Canada)
Asian Outreach International Canada
Canadian Churches' Forum for Global Mins.
Child Evangelism Fellowship of Canada
ERRC Educational Society
Fundamental Baptist Mission of Trinidad and
   Tobago (Canada)
Gateway Training for Cross-cultural Service
Gospel Operation International for Chinese
   Christians Canada, Inc
Liebenzell Mission of Canada
MBMS International

Missionary Internship Canada, Inc.
New Tribes Mission of Canada
Operation Mobilization Canada
People International—Canada
Presbyterian Church in Canada
Visionledd
WEC International (Canada)
Youth with a Mission Canada, Inc.

Translation, Bible
Canadian Bible Society / La Societe Biblique
   Canadienne
Evangelical Missionary Church of Canada
MSC Canada
New Tribes Mission of Canada
ReachAcross
World Team Canada
WorldServe Ministries Canada
Wycliffe Bible Translators of Canada, Inc.

Translation, other
Global Recordings Network Canada
New Tribes Mission of Canada
Wycliffe Bible Translators of Canada, Inc.

Video/Film
CSM Canada Intl. (Christian Salvage Msn.)
International Russian Radio/TV (IRR/TV)

Youth programs
Avant Ministries Canada
Canadian Assemblies of God, General Conf.
Fundamental Baptist Mission of Trinidad and
   Tobago (Canada)
Hope Haven Canada Ministries
International Teams, Canada (Evangelical
   International Crusades Canada, Inc.)
Inter-Varsity Christian Fellowship of Canada
Jusqu'aux Extremites de la Terre (JET)
MBMS International
Teen Missions in Canada, Inc.
Venture Teams International
World Mission Prayer League
World Vision Canada
Young Life of Canada
Youth for Christ, Canada

Chapter 7
Countries of Activity for Canadian Protestant Agencies

I n this chapter you will find the countries where agencies reported field personnel in answer to question #14 of the survey (see Appendix D). The few exceptions are agencies whose whole program supports (with funds raised in Canada, but which may not be designated to specific personnel on a regular basis) churches or other initiatives in a country.

All countries are listed in alphabetical order according to the name most commonly recognized in North America. In a few cases we have listed a territory or other administrative district of a country because it is commonly viewed as a separate entity and mission agencies report it that way.

We have separated the personnel totals for all agencies into five categories. Under the "personnel from Canada" heading, the term of expected service has been divided into three categories: 4+ years, 2-4 years, and 1-2 years for fully supported personnel. For non-Canadian personnel in the "Other Countries" heading, the categories are those who are citizens of that ministry country and those who are not citizens, and are fully or partially supported by funds raised in Canada by the associated agency. For example, a Korean with specific mission/ministry duties serving in Korea would be included in an agency's "citizens" column of the Korea section. A Korean serving in Russia would be listed in the "not citizen" column of the Russia section.

At the end of each country section, totals of each category for that country are given. Note that the totals for the "other countries" heading do not necessarily reflect all non-Canadian mission personnel who draw support from Canadian agencies. Some agencies give grants for ongoing institutions and other programs without specifying individual recipients. This may be in addition to Canadian mission personnel based in that country or the agency may not have Canadian personnel living in that country.

Note also that the totals will be minimum numbers only because of the bigger number of large agencies in this edition that reported their personnel only by general regions and not by specific countries. Their numbers are not included in this "countries of activity" section.

	First Year	Personnel from CAN			Other Countries	
		1-2 yrs.	2-4 yrs.	4+ yrs.	Citizens	Non-Citizens

Afghanistan

	First Year	1-2 yrs.	2-4 yrs.	4+ yrs.	Citizens	Non-Citizens
HOPE International Development Agency	2006	-	-	-	2	-
Mennonite Economic Dev. Associates (MEDA)	2007	-	-	-	18	2
Operation Mobilization Canada (Send the Light)		1	-	3	-	-
Samaritan's Purse—Canada	2002	-	-	-	-	-
Totals:		1	-	3	20	2

Africa—General

	First Year	1-2 yrs.	2-4 yrs.	4+ yrs.	Citizens	Non-Citizens
ABWE Canada		-	-	2	-	-
African Enterprise Association of Canada		-	-	3	3	-
Arab World Ministries (Canada)	1881	-	-	9	-	9
Arms of Jesus Children's Mission, Inc., The	1990	-	-	-	-	-
Bible League of Canada, The	1980	-	-	-	5	-
Canadian National Baptist Convention (CNBC)	2004	-	-	-	-	4
Christian and Missionary Alliance in Canada, The		-	-	11	-	-
Emmanuel International Canada		-	-	-	-	5
Evangelical Christian Church in Canada,The	1988	-	-	1	1	-
Frontiers Canada	1984	-	-	6	-	-
Global Aid Network, Inc.—Canada	2004	-	25	25	-	-
International Christian Ministries Canada (ICM)	1990	-	2	8	4	-
InterServe Canada (Intl. Service Fellowship)		-	4	-	-	-
MBMS International	1998	-	-	4	2	-
Mennonite Central Committee Canada	1975	-	-	-	7	5
Navigators of Canada, The	1973	-	-	3	-	-
New Tribes Mission of Canada		-	-	14	-	-
Operation Mobilization Canada (Send the Light)		2	-	5	-	-
Pentecostal Assemblies of Canada, The	2003	-	-	4	-	-
Power to Change	1998	-	-	2	-	-
ReachAcross	1949	-	-	-	8	-
Salvation Army		-	1	11	-	-
WEC International (Canada)		-	-	-	-	2
Wycliffe Bible Translators of Canada, Inc.		-	-	5	-	-
Totals:		2	32	113	30	25

Albania

	First Year	1-2 yrs.	2-4 yrs.	4+ yrs.	Citizens	Non-Citizens
Christar Canada		-	2	-	-	-
Totals:		-	2	-	-	-

Angola

	First Year	1-2 yrs.	2-4 yrs.	4+ yrs.	Citizens	Non-Citizens
Brethren Assemblies (Canada)	1958	-	-	1	-	-
Canadian Baptist Ministries	1956	-	-	1	1	-
EMAS Canada		-	-	-	-	-
MBMS International	1990	-	-	-	-	1
Mission Aviation Fellowship of Canada (MAFC)	1989	1	-	2	-	-
SIM Canada	1917	-	-	6	-	-
Totals:		1	-	10	1	1

Argentina

	First Year	1-2 yrs.	2-4 yrs.	4+ yrs.	Citizens	Non-Citizens
Brethren Assemblies (Canada)	1987	-	-	2	-	-
Canadian Baptist Ministries	2008	-	-	1	-	-

		Personnel from CAN			Other Countries	
	First Year	1-2 yrs.	2-4 yrs.	4+ yrs.	Citizens	Non-Citizens
Evangelical Lutheran Church in Canada		-	-	-	-	-
Gospel Mission of South America of Canada		-	-	1	-	1
Salvation Army		-	-	1	-	-
Youth for Christ, Canada		-	-	2	-	-
Totals:		-	-	7	-	1

Armenia

Pentecostal Assemblies of Canada, The	2001	-	-	2	-	-
Totals:		-	-	2	-	-

Asia—General

ABWE Canada		-	2	1	-	-
Asian Outreach International Canada		-	-	-	20	-
Baptist General Conf. of Canada Global Mins.	1996	-	-	2	-	-
Bible League of Canada, The	1985	-	-	-	-	-
Canadian National Baptist Convention (CNBC)	1991	-	-	2	-	8
Child Evangelism Fellowship of Canada	2002	-	-	2	-	-
Christar Canada	1930	2	11	-	-	-
Christian and Missionary Alliance in Canada, The		-	-	12	-	-
Evangelical Free Church of Canada Mission	1999	1	-	6	-	-
Frontiers Canada	1984	-	-	10	1	-
InterServe Canada (Intl. Service Fellowship)	1975	-	15	-	-	-
MBMS International	1988	-	-	4	-	-
Navigators of Canada, The	1988	-	2	2	-	-
New Tribes Mission of Canada		2	-	39	-	-
OMF International—Canada	1865	-	-	23	-	-
OMS International—Canada		-	-	4	-	-
Operation Mobilization Canada (Send the Light)		-	-	3	-	-
Pentecostal Assemblies of Canada, The	1919	8	-	25	-	-
Power to Change	1997	12	4	12	-	-
SEND International of Canada	1988	-	-	2	-	-
SIM Canada		6	-	6	1	-
TEAM of Canada	1992	-	1	5	-	-
WEC International (Canada)		-	-	10	1	10
World Team Canada		-	-	6	-	-
Wycliffe Bible Translators of Canada, Inc.		-	-	11	-	-
Totals:		31	35	187	23	18

Australia

Mission Aviation Fellowship of Canada (MAFC)		-	-	3	-	-
Salvation Army	1996	-	3	-	-	-
Totals:		-	3	3	-	-

Austria

Avant Ministries Canada	1966	-	-	1	-	-
Brethren Assemblies (Canada)	1983	-	-	8	-	-
International Teams, Canada		-	-	2	-	-
MBMS International	1953	-	-	2	-	-
Operation Mobilization Canada (Send the Light)	1960	2	-	-	-	-
Trans World Radio Canada		-	-	3	-	-

	Personnel from CAN				Other Countries	
	First Year	1-2 yrs.	2-4 yrs.	4+ yrs.	Citizens	Non-Citizens
Wycliffe Bible Translators of Canada, Inc.		-	-	1	-	-
Totals:		2	-	17	-	-
Azerbaijan	-					-
Inter-Varsity Christian Fellowship of Canada	2004	-	-	-	-	-
Totals:		-	-	-	-	-
Bangladesh						-
Christian Reformed Wld. Relief Committee Can.	1972	-	-	1	-	1
Gospel for Asia		-	-	-	-	-
I. N. (International Needs) Network Canada	1974	-	-	-	168	-
Liebenzell Mission of Canada	2004	-	-	1	-	1
Mennonite Central Committee Canada	1970	-	-	-	63	7
Partners International Canada	2005	-	-	-	-	-
Salvation Army	1994	-	2	1	-	-
World Relief Canada		-	-	-	-	-
Totals:			2	3	231	9
Belarus						
TeachBeyond		-	-	-	-	-
Totals:		-	-	-	-	-
Belgium						
Brethren Assemblies (Canada)	1970	-	-	6	-	-
Global Outreach Mission Inc., Canada		-	-	1	-	-
Link International Ministries	2008	-	-	-	-	1
Totals:		-	-	7	-	1
Belize						
Evangelical Mennonite Mission Conference	1965	-	-	2	-	-
Into All The World	1990	-	-	1	-	-
Totals:		-	-	3	-	-
Benin						
SIM Canada	1946	-	-	7	-	-
Totals:		-	-	7	-	-
Bhutan						
Gospel for Asia	1995	-	-	-	-	-
Partners International Canada	2007	-	-	-	-	-
Totals:		-	-	-	-	-
Bolivia						
Apostolic Church of Pentecost of Canada, Inc.	2007	-	-	2	-	-
Avant Ministries Canada	1928	-	-	6	-	-
Brethren Assemblies (Canada)	1976	-	-	6	-	-
Canadian Baptist Ministries	1898	-	-	3	2	-
Canadian South America Mission	1922	-	-	2	1	1
Child Evangelism Fellowship of Canada	2004	-	-	1	-	-
Evangelical Free Church of Canada Mission	2000	3	8	4	-	-
Evangelical Mennonite Mission Conference	1969	3	-	8	-	-

	First Year	Personnel from CAN 1-2 yrs.	2-4 yrs.	4+ yrs.	Other Countries Citizens	Non-Citizens
FH Canada	1998	-	-	2	-	-
International Teams, Canada		1	-	1	-	-
Into All The World	2005	-	-	2	-	-
Medical Ministry Canada, Inc.	2006	-	-	-	-	2
Mennonite Central Committee Canada	1959	-	-	-	27	25
Partners International Canada	2007	-	-	-	-	-
Pioneers Canada	2002	-	-	2	-	-
SIM Canada	1907	2	-	7	-	-
TeachBeyond		-	-	-	-	-
Totals:		9	8	46	30	28

Bosnia and Herzegovina

Operation Mobilization Canada (Send the Light)		1	-	-	-	-
Totals:		1	-	-	-	-

Botswana

						-
Brethren Assemblies (Canada)	1991	-	-	2	-	-
Canadian National Baptist Convention (CNBC)	2004	-	-	-	-	2
Mission Aviation Fellowship of Canada (MAFC)		2	-	2	-	-
SIM Canada	1973	1	-	1	-	-
Totals:		3	-	5	-	2

Brazil

ABWE Canada		-	-	4	-	-
Action International Ministries—Canada		-	-	2	2	-
Apostolic Church in Canada, The	1980	-	-	-	-	-
Apostolic Church of Pentecost of Canada, Inc.	1999	-	-	2	-	-
Avant Ministries Canada	1911	-	-	2	-	-
Brethren Assemblies (Canada)	1948	-	-	3	-	-
Canadian Baptist Ministries	1970	-	-	2	-	-
Canadian South America Mission	1913	-	2	-	-	2
Child Evangelism Fellowship of Canada	1970	-	-	2	-	-
Ch. of God (Anderson, Ind.) Can. Bd. of Msns.		-	-	-	-	-
CrossWorld Canada		1	1	6	-	-
Emmanuel International Canada		-	-	-	3	-
Evangelical Missionary Church of Canada	1998	1	5	-	-	-
FH Canada	1998	-	1	-	-	-
Global Outreach Mission Inc., Canada		-	-	1	-	-
Gospel Operation Intl. for Chinese Christians Can.	1999	-	-	-	2	-
Latin America Mission (Canada) Inc.	2008	-	-	2	-	-
MBMS International	1946	-	-	8	-	-
Mennonite Central Committee Canada	1947	-	-	-	12	15
Partners International Canada	2007	-	-	-	-	-
Pentecostal Assemblies of Canada, The	1965	-	-	6	-	-
Pioneers Canada	1991	-	-	2	-	-
TeachBeyond		-	3	-	3	-
United Church of Canada	2008	-	1	-	-	-
WEC International (Canada)	1930	-	-	1	1	-
Wycliffe Bible Translators of Canada, Inc.		-	-	3	-	-
Totals:		2	13	46	23	17

	Personnel from CAN				Other Countries	
	First Year	1-2 yrs.	2-4 yrs.	4+ yrs.	Citizens	Non-Citizens
Bulgaria		-	-	-	-	-
Far East Broadcasting Associates of Canada	2008	-	2	-	-	-
Pioneers Canada	2005	-	-	1	-	-
SEND International of Canada	1992	-	-	-	-	-
Totals:		-	2	1	-	-
Burkina Faso						
Apostolic Church of Pentecost of Canada, Inc.	1950	-	-	1	-	-
Evangelical Mennonite Conference		-	-	2	-	-
FRIENDS in Action International—Canada	2000	1	-	1	-	-
MBMS International	1994	-	-	4	1	-
SIM Canada	1930	2	-	9	-	-
Wycliffe Bible Translators of Canada, Inc.		-	-	7	-	-
Totals:		3	-	24	1	-
Burundi						
World Relief Canada		-	-	-	-	-
Totals:		-	-	-	-	-
Cambodia						
Christian and Missionary Alliance in Canada, The		-	-	6	-	-
Christian Reformed Wld. Relief Committee Can.	1998	-	-	2	-	-
EMAS Canada		-	-	-	-	-
Far East Broadcasting Associates of Canada	2009	-	2	-	-	-
FH Canada	2001	-	1	-	-	-
Gospel for Asia	2005	-	-	-	-	-
Gospel Operation Intl. for Chinese Christians Can.	1999	-	2	-	-	-
HOPE International Development Agency	1992	1	-	-	5	-
Mennonite Central Committee Canada	1979	-	-	-	9	10
OMF International—Canada	1994	-	-	3	-	-
Pentecostal Assemblies of Canada, The	2006	1	-	2	-	-
Pioneers Canada	2008	-	-	2	-	-
Samaritan's Purse—Canada	2003	-	-	-	-	-
The Free Methodist Church in Canada	1991	-	-	-	2	-
WEC International (Canada)	1993	-	-	1	-	3
World Relief Canada		-	-	-	-	-
World Team Canada		1	-	2	-	-
World Vision Canada	2006	-	-	-	-	-
Totals:		3	5	18	16	13
Cameroon						
Commission to Every Nation—Canada	2009	-	-	2	-	3
Evangelical Lutheran Church in Canada	1999	-	2	2	-	-
World Team Canada		-	-	4	-	-
Wycliffe Bible Translators of Canada, Inc.		-	-	21	-	-
Totals:		2	-	29	-	3
Caribbean—General						
Child Evangelism Fellowship of Canada	2005	-	-	1	-	-
Salvation Army		1	-	-	-	-
Totals:		1	-	1	-	-

		Personnel from CAN			Other Countries	
	First Year	1-2 yrs.	2-4 yrs.	4+ yrs.	Citizens	Non-Citizens
Central African Republic						
Arms of Jesus Children's Mission, Inc., The	1990	-	-	-	2	-
World Team Canada		-	-	-	-	1
Totals:		-	-	-	2	1
Central Asia—General						
Asian Outreach International Canada		-	-	1	11	7
Canadian National Baptist Convention (CNBC)	1992	-	-	-	-	2
Evangelical Free Church of Canada Mission	1999	-	-	2	-	-
Frontiers Canada	1984	-	-	9	-	-
InterServe Canada (Intl. Service Fellowship)		-	-	32	-	-
MBMS International	2001	-	-	2	-	-
Mission Aviation Fellowship of Canada (MAFC)		-	-	1	-	-
Operation Mobilization Canada (Send the Light)		-	4	2	-	-
Pentecostal Assemblies of Canada, The	2007	-	-	2	-	-
TEAM of Canada	1968	3	-	5	-	-
WEC International (Canada)	1990	-	-	4	-	6
Wycliffe Bible Translators of Canada, Inc.		-	-	45	-	-
Totals:		3	4	105	11	15
Chad						-
Mission Aviation Fellowship of Canada (MAFC)		-	1	-	-	-
TEAM of Canada	1945	-	-	2	-	-
WEC International (Canada)	1962	-	-	-	-	2
Wycliffe Bible Translators of Canada, Inc.		-	-	1	-	-
Totals:		-	1	3	-	2
Chile						
Brethren Assemblies (Canada)	1952	-	-	10	-	-
Far East Broadcasting Associates of Canada	2006	-	-	2	-	-
Gospel Mission of South America of Canada		-	-	2	2	2
Navigators of Canada, The	1983	-	-	2	-	-
Salvation Army		-	-	1	-	-
SIM Canada	1986	-	-	2	-	-
Totals:		-	-	19	2	2
China						
Canadian Baptist Ministries	1989	-	-	-	-	-
Christian Studies International of Canada	2000	-	-	1	-	-
EMAS Canada		-	-	-	-	-
ERRC Educational Society		1	-	-	-	46
Evangelical Christian Church in Canada,The	1975	-	-	1	1	-
Gospel for Asia	1998	-	-	-	-	-
Intercede International		-	-	-	-	2
Inter-Varsity Christian Fellowship of Canada	2008	-	-	-	-	-
Mennonite Central Committee Canada		-	-	-	-	18
Partners International Canada	2009	1	-	-	1	-
Pioneers Canada	1999	-	-	15	-	-
United Church of Canada	1998	-	-	2	-	-
World Relief Canada		-	-	-	-	-
Totals:		2	-	19	2	66

	Personnel from CAN				Other Countries	
	First Year	1-2 yrs.	2-4 yrs.	4+ yrs.	Citizens	Non-Citizens

Colombia

Action International Ministries—Canada		-	-	4	-	1
Brethren Assemblies (Canada)	1972	-	-	1	-	-
Brethren in Christ World Missions—Canada		-	-	-	-	-
Evangelical Lutheran Church in Canada		-	-	-	-	-
Far East Broadcasting Associates of Canada	1969	-	-	4	2	-
I. N. (International Needs) Network Canada	2005	-	-	-	271	-
Latin America Mission (Canada) Inc.	1961	-	-	2	4	-
MBMS International	1945	-	-	-	-	-
Mennonite Central Committee Canada	2001	-	-	-	2	5
Totals:		-	-	11	279	6

Congo, Democratic Republic of

Africa Inland Mission International (Canada)		2	-	2	-	-
Evangelical Free Church of Canada Mission	2008	2	-	-	-	-
MBMS International	1912	-	-	1	1	-
Mennonite Central Committee Canada	1960	-	-	-	10	6
Mennonite Mission Health Association	2001	-	-	-	-	-
Pentecostal Assemblies of Canada, The	1998	-	-	2	-	-
The Free Methodist Church in Canada	1960	-	-	1	-	-
WEC International (Canada)	1913	-	-	2	-	-
World Relief Canada		-	-	-	-	-
World Vision Canada	2006	-	-	-	-	-
Wycliffe Bible Translators of Canada, Inc.		-	-	6	-	-
Totals:	4	-		14	11	6

Congo, Republic of the

Christian and Missionary Alliance in Canada, The		-	-	3	-	-
Global Outreach Mission Inc., Canada		-	-	1	-	-
Totals:		-	-	4	-	-

Costa Rica

Brethren Assemblies (Canada)	1956	-	-	2	-	-
Commission to Every Nation—Canada	2009	-	3	-	-	3
International Teams, Canada		-	-	2	-	-
Latin America Mission (Canada) Inc.	1961	-	-	4	2	-
The Mission to Children	1978	-	-	-	-	-
Totals:		-	3	8	2	3

Cote d'Ivoire

Link International Ministries	2004	-	-	-	-	1
WEC International (Canada)	1934	-	-	-	1	-
Totals:		-	-	-	1	1

Croatia

ABWE Canada	2001	-	-	2	-	-
Canadian National Baptist Convention (CNBC)	1999	-	-	-	-	2
Greater Europe Mission (Canada)	1999	-	-	2	-	-
SEND International of Canada	1995	-	-	-	-	-
Totals:		-	-	4	-	2

	First Year	1-2 yrs.	2-4 yrs.	4+ yrs.	Citizens	Non-Citizens
		Personnel from CAN			Other Countries	

Cuba

	First Year	1-2 yrs.	2-4 yrs.	4+ yrs.	Citizens	Non-Citizens
Brethren in Christ World Missions—Canada		-	-	-	-	-
EMAS Canada		-	-	-	-	-
Evangelical Free Church of Canada Mission	2000	-	-	-	-	-
Evangelical Missionary Church of Canada	2005	-	-	-	-	-
I. N. (International Needs) Network Canada	2007	-	-	-	12	-
Partners International Canada	2007	-	-	-	-	-
World Team Canada		-	-	2	-	-
Totals:		-	-	2	12	-

Cyprus

	First Year	1-2 yrs.	2-4 yrs.	4+ yrs.	Citizens	Non-Citizens
Brethren Assemblies (Canada)		-	-	1	-	-
Totals:		-	-	1	-	-

Czech Republic

	First Year	1-2 yrs.	2-4 yrs.	4+ yrs.	Citizens	Non-Citizens
Avant Ministries Canada	2008	-	-	4	-	-
Brethren Assemblies (Canada)		-	-	2	-	-
I. N. (International Needs) Network Canada	2003	-	-	-	3	-
SEND International of Canada	1992	1	-	-	-	-
TEAM of Canada	1990	-	-	2	-	-
Totals:		1	-	8	3	-

Dominican Republic

	First Year	1-2 yrs.	2-4 yrs.	4+ yrs.	Citizens	Non-Citizens
Arms of Jesus Children's Mission, Inc., The	1993	-	-	-	5	-
Brethren Assemblies (Canada)	1947	-	-	3	-	-
Christian Reformed Wld. Relief Committee Can.	1982	-	-	-	-	1
I. N. (International Needs) Network Canada	2008	-	-	-	31	-
International Child Care (Canada), Inc.	1988	-	-	-	-	-
Into All The World	2001	-	-	1	-	-
Medical Ministry Canada, Inc.	1980	-	-	-	2	2
Pentecostal Assemblies of Canada, The	2000	-	-	2	-	-
Totals:		-	-	6	38	3

Eastern Europe—General

	First Year	1-2 yrs.	2-4 yrs.	4+ yrs.	Citizens	Non-Citizens
Bible League of Canada, The	1985	-	-	-	-	-
International Christian Ministries Canada (ICM)	2000	-	-	2	4	-
Trans World Radio Canada		-	-	-	2	-
Totals:		-	-	2	6	-

Ecuador

	First Year	1-2 yrs.	2-4 yrs.	4+ yrs.	Citizens	Non-Citizens
Action International Ministries—Canada		-	-	2	-	-
Avant Ministries Canada	1896	-	-	4	-	-
Brethren Assemblies (Canada)	1983	-	-	5	-	-
Christian and Missionary Alliance in Canada, The		-	-	5	-	-
Christian Reformed Wld. Relief Committee Can.	1983	-	-	-	-	2
Commission to Every Nation—Canada	2008	-	5	-	-	5
EMAS Canada		-	-	-	-	-
Evangelical Free Church of Canada Mission	2000	-	-	2	-	-
HCJB Global—Canada		-	-	9	2	2
International Teams, Canada		1	-	-	-	-

	Personnel from CAN				Other Countries	
	First Year	1-2 yrs.	2-4 yrs.	4+ yrs.	Citizens	Non-Citizens
Liebenzell Mission of Canada		-	-	-	-	-
Medical Ministry Canada, Inc.	2000	-	-	-	2	-
Totals:		1	5	27	4	9
Egypt						
Brethren Assemblies (Canada)		-	-	2	-	-
I. N. (International Needs) Network Canada	1975	-	-	-	1	-
Mennonite Central Committee Canada	1968	-	-	-	3	12
Totals:		-	-	2	4	12
El Salvador						
Apostolic Church of Pentecost of Canada, Inc.		-	-	2	-	-
Brethren Assemblies (Canada)	1991	-	-	8	-	-
Canadian Baptist Ministries	1992	-	-	-	-	-
Evangelical Lutheran Church in Canada	1988	-	-	1	-	-
Evangelical Missionary Church of Canada	2001	-	-	-	1	-
Mennonite Central Committee Canada	1982	-	-	-	-	7
Pentecostal Assemblies of Canada, The	2008	-	-	2	-	-
The Mission to Children	1977	-	-	-	-	-
Totals:		-	-	13	1	7
Equatorial Guinea						
WEC International (Canada)	1993	-	-	4	-	-
Totals:		-	-	4	-	-
Estonia						
Apostolic Church of Pentecost of Canada, Inc.	1991	-	-	2	-	-
Pentecostal Assemblies of Canada, The	1991	-	-	2	-	-
Totals:		-	-	4	-	-
Ethiopia						
Baptist General Conf. of Canada Global Mins.	1968	-	1	-	-	-
FH Canada	2005	-	1	-	-	-
HOPE International Development Agency	1985	-	-	-	14	-
Into All The World	1999	-	-	2	-	-
Mennonite Central Committee Canada	1972	-	-	-	8	5
Mennonite Economic Dev. Associates (MEDA)	2008	-	-	-	-	1
Pentecostal Assemblies of Canada, The	1992	-	-	4	-	-
SIM Canada	1927	10	-	15	-	-
World Relief Canada		-	-	-	-	-
Wycliffe Bible Translators of Canada, Inc.		-	-	3	-	-
Totals:		10	2	24	22	6
Europe—General						
ABWE Canada		-	-	3	-	-
Barry Moore Ministries, Inc.		-	-	-	-	-
Canadian Baptist Ministries	1911	-	-	1	-	1
Canadian National Baptist Convention (CNBC)	2000	-	-	2	-	-
Frontiers Canada	1984	-	-	4	1	-
Mennonite Central Committee Canada		-	-	-	2	12

	First Year	Personnel from CAN			Other Countries	
		1-2 yrs.	2-4 yrs.	4+ yrs.	Citizens	Non-Citizens
Outreach Canada	2006	-	-	2	-	-
Totals:		-	-	12	3	13
Fiji						
WEC International (Canada)	1985	-	-	2	-	-
Totals:		-	-	2	-	-
Finland						
Brethren Assemblies (Canada)	1982	-	-	1	-	-
Totals:		-	-	1	-	-
France						
Apostolic Church of Pentecost of Canada, Inc.	2004	-	-	2	-	-
Arab World Ministries (Canada)	1976	-	-	4	1	3
Brethren Assemblies (Canada)	1949	-	-	18	-	-
Christar Canada		1	3	-	-	-
Christian and Missionary Alliance in Canada, The		-	-	3	-	-
Far East Broadcasting Associates of Canada	1982	-	-	8	2	-
Global Outreach Mission Inc., Canada		-	-	6	-	-
Inter-Varsity Christian Fellowship of Canada	2008	-	-	-	-	-
Liebenzell Mission of Canada	2008	1	-	-	-	1
MBMS International	2000	-	-	2	-	-
Operation Mobilization Canada (Send the Light)		-	-	1	-	-
Salvation Army	1994	-	2	-	-	-
TEAM of Canada	1952	-	-	1	-	-
WEC International (Canada)	1950	-	-	2	-	-
Totals:		2	5	47	3	4
Gambia, The						
WEC International (Canada)	1958	-	-	2	-	1
Totals:		-	-	2	-	1
Germany						
Avant Ministries Canada	1966	-	-	2	-	-
Canadian National Baptist Convention (CNBC)		-	-	-	-	2
Christian and Missionary Alliance in Canada, The		-	-	6	-	-
Evangelical Free Church of Canada Mission	2001	-	-	-	-	-
Greater Europe Mission (Canada)	1990	-	-	4	-	-
MBMS International	1953	-	-	5	-	-
Pentecostal Assemblies of Canada, The	2005	-	-	2	-	-
Salvation Army	1991	-	-	4	-	-
TeachBeyond	1955	2	9	33	-	-
Totals:		2	9	56	-	2
Ghana						
Bible Holiness Movement, The	1987	-	-	-	5	-
Brethren Assemblies (Canada)		-	-	3	-	-
I. N. (International Needs) Network Canada	1986	-	-	-	1812	-
SIM Canada	1956	-	-	5	-	-
Wycliffe Bible Translators of Canada, Inc.		-	-	3	-	-
Totals:		-	-	11	1817	-

		Personnel from CAN			Other Countries	
	First Year	1-2 yrs.	2-4 yrs.	4+ yrs.	Citizens	Non-Citizens

Greece

	First Year	1-2 yrs.	2-4 yrs.	4+ yrs.	Citizens	Non-Citizens
Hellenic Ministries/Canada		2	2	-	-	-
International Teams, Canada		1	-	-	-	-
WEC International (Canada)	1989	-	-	-	-	1
Totals:		3	2	-	-	1

Grenada

	First Year	1-2 yrs.	2-4 yrs.	4+ yrs.	Citizens	Non-Citizens
Presbyterian Church in Canada	2000	-	2	-	-	-
Totals:		-	2	-	-	-

Guam

	First Year	1-2 yrs.	2-4 yrs.	4+ yrs.	Citizens	Non-Citizens
Ch. of God (Anderson, Ind.) Can. Bd. of Msns.		-	-	-	-	-
Totals:		-	-	-	-	-

Guatemala

	First Year	1-2 yrs.	2-4 yrs.	4+ yrs.	Citizens	Non-Citizens
Arms of Jesus Children's Mission, Inc., The	1992	2	-	-	28	-
Christian Aid for Under-Assisted Soc. Everywhere	1984	-	-	-	17	-
Christian and Missionary Alliance in Canada, The		-	4	2	-	-
Commission to Every Nation—Canada	2008	-	2	-	-	2
Global Outreach Mission Inc., Canada		-	-	4	-	-
Mennonite Central Committee Canada	1976	-	-	-	3	9
Pentecostal Assemblies of Canada, The	1991	-	-	4	2	-
Presbyterian Church in Canada	1985	-	2	-	-	-
Totals:		2	8	10	50	11

Guinea

	First Year	1-2 yrs.	2-4 yrs.	4+ yrs.	Citizens	Non-Citizens
Christian and Missionary Alliance in Canada, The		-	-	6	-	-
Pentecostal Assemblies of Canada, The	1988	-	-	2	-	-
Totals:		-	-	8	-	-

Guinea-Bissau

	First Year	1-2 yrs.	2-4 yrs.	4+ yrs.	Citizens	Non-Citizens
WEC International (Canada)	1939	-	-	-	-	2
Totals:		-	-	-	-	2

Guyana

	First Year	1-2 yrs.	2-4 yrs.	4+ yrs.	Citizens	Non-Citizens
Evangelical Lutheran Church in Canada		-	-	-	-	-
Totals:		-	-	-	-	-

Haiti

	First Year	1-2 yrs.	2-4 yrs.	4+ yrs.	Citizens	Non-Citizens
Arms of Jesus Children's Mission, Inc., The	1993	-	-	-	12	-
Christian Reformed Wld. Relief Committee Can.	1975	-	-	-	-	1
Crossroads Christian Communications Inc. (ERDF)	2004	-	-	-	-	-
CrossWorld Canada		-	-	1	-	-
EMAS Canada		-	-	-	-	-
Emmanuel International Canada		-	-	-	1	-
Evangelical Free Church of Canada Mission	2009	2	-	-	-	-
Evangelical Missionary Church of Canada	2002	-	-	-	-	-
Haiti Arise—Canada	2003	-	-	2	-	-
Intercede International		-	-	-	2	-
International Child Care (Canada), Inc.	1967	-	4	2	-	-

		Personnel from CAN			Other Countries	
	First Year	1-2 yrs.	2-4 yrs.	4+ yrs.	Citizens	Non-Citizens
Medical Ministry Canada, Inc.	2004	-	-	-	-	2
Mennonite Central Committee Canada	1958	-	-	-	19	10
Mission Aviation Fellowship of Canada (MAFC)		-	-	1	-	-
OMS International—Canada		4	-	8	-	-
Pentecostal Assemblies of Canada, The	1983	2	-	2	-	-
World Team Canada		-	-	2	-	-
Totals:		8	4	18	34	13

Honduras

Action International Ministries—Canada		-	-	-	-	1
Brethren Assemblies (Canada)		-	-	2	-	-
Brethren in Christ World Missions—Canada		-	-	-	-	-
Christian Aid for Under-Assisted Soc. Everywhere	1995	1	-	-	6	1
Christian Reformed Wld. Relief Committee Can.	1974	-	1	-	-	1
Far East Broadcasting Associates of Canada	2006	-	1	-	-	-
Latin America Mission (Canada) Inc.	2005	2	-	2	-	-
Mennonite Central Committee Canada	1981	-	-	-	2	9
Pentecostal Assemblies of Canada, The	2006	-	-	2	-	-
Totals:		3	2	6	8	12

Hong Kong

Brethren Assemblies (Canada)	1994	-	-	2	-	-
EMAS Canada		-	-	-	-	-
Evangelical Lutheran Church in Canada	2000	-	2	-	-	-
Global Outreach Mission Inc., Canada		-	-	1	-	-
Mennonite Central Committee Canada		-	-	-	-	2
Samaritan's Purse—Canada	2000	-	-	-	-	-
Totals:		-	2	3	-	2

Hungary

Christian and Missionary Alliance in Canada, The		-	-	4	-	-
Evangelical Free Church of Canada Mission	1990	-	-	4	1	-
Evangelical Missionary Church of Canada	2006	-	3	-	-	-
Greater Europe Mission (Canada)	1994	-	--	3	-	-
Navigators of Canada, The	1981	-	-	2	-	-
OMS International—Canada		-	-	1	-	-
Presbyterian Church in Canada	2006	-	-	1	-	-
SEND International of Canada	1994	-	-	-	-	-
Totals:		-	3	15	1	-

India

Action International Ministries—Canada		-	-	2	5	-
Apostolic Church in Canada, The	1994	-	-	-	-	-
Barry Moore Ministries, Inc.		-	-	-	1	-
Bible Holiness Movement, The	1982	-	-	-	3	-
Brethren Assemblies (Canada)	1982	-	-	4	-	-
Brethren in Christ World Missions—Canada		-	-	-	-	-
Canadian Baptist Ministries	1874	-	-	-	4	-
Crossroads Christian Communications Inc. (ERDF)	2005	-	-	-	-	-
Evangelical Christian Church in Canada,The	1989	-	-	1	1	-

	Personnel from CAN				Other Countries	
	First Year	1-2 yrs.	2-4 yrs.	4+ yrs.	Citizens	Non-Citizens
Far East Broadcasting Associates of Canada	2008	-	3	-	2	-
Global Outreach Mission Inc., Canada		1	-	17	-	-
Gospel for Asia	1979	-	-	-	-	-
I. N. (International Needs) Network Canada	1979	-	-	-	59	-
Intercede International		-	-	-	12	-
MBMS International	1898	-	-	8	-	-
Mennonite Central Committee Canada	1942	-	-	-	20	5
Mennonite Mission Health Association	2001	-	-	-	-	-
Mission of Mercy Canada	1954	1	3	-	-	-
Operation Mobilization Canada (Send the Light)		-	-	1	-	-
Partners International Canada	1975	-	-	-	-	-
Pioneers Canada	2006	-	-	4	-	-
Power to Change	1996	2	-	2	-	-
TEAM of Canada	1945	-	-	1	-	-
The Mission to Children	1979	-	-	-	-	-
World Relief Canada		-	-	-	-	-
Totals:	4	6	40		107	5

Indonesia

Canadian Baptist Ministries	1973	-	-	3	-	-
Christian and Missionary Alliance in Canada, The		-	-	10	-	-
Far East Broadcasting Associates of Canada	2008	-	-	2	-	-
FH Canada	2005	2	-	-	-	1
Intercede International		-	-	-	6	-
Mennonite Central Committee Canada	1948	-	-	-	13	12
Mission Aviation Fellowship of Canada (MAFC)		2	-	7	-	-
Navigators of Canada, The	2008	-	-	2	-	-
OMF International—Canada	1952	2	-	6	-	-
Partners International Canada	1978	-	-	-	-	-
WEC International (Canada)	1949	-	-	2	3	3
Totals:	6	-	32		22	16

Iran

Mennonite Central Committee Canada		-	-	-	-	2
Totals:	-	-	-		-	2

Iraq

Mennonite Central Committee Canada	1998	-	-	-	-	1
Totals:	-	-	-		-	1

Ireland

Apostolic Church of Pentecost of Canada, Inc.	2007	-	-	2	-	-
Brethren Assemblies (Canada)	1968	-	-	13	-	-
CrossWorld Canada		-	-	3	1	-
Evangelical Missionary Church of Canada	2005	-	1	-	-	-
Global Outreach Mission Inc., Canada		-	-	4	-	-
Greater Europe Mission (Canada)		1	-	-	-	-
Totals:	1	1	22		1	-

Israel

International Russian Radio/TV (IRR/TV)	2001	-	-	-	2	2

		Personnel from CAN			Other Countries	
	First Year	1-2 yrs.	2-4 yrs.	4+ yrs.	Citizens	Non-Citizens
Pentecostal Assemblies of Canada, The	1981	-	2	2	-	-
United Church of Canada	2003	1	-	-	-	-
Totals:		1	2	2	2	2

Italy

BCM International (Canada), Inc.	1951	-	-	-	-	2
Brethren Assemblies (Canada)	1987	-	-	4	-	-
CrossWorld Canada		-	-	1	-	-
Far East Broadcasting Associates of Canada	1980	-	-	2	-	-
TEAM of Canada	1981	-	-	3	-	-
World Team Canada		-	-	2	-	-
Totals:		-	-	12	-	2

Jamaica

Apostolic Church in Canada, The	1949	-	-	-	-	
Mennonite Central Committee Canada	1970	-	-	-	2	11
Pentecostal Assemblies of Canada, The	2006	-	-	2	-	-
Totals:		-	-	2	2	11

Japan

Brethren Assemblies (Canada)	1949	-	-	7	-	-
Brethren in Christ World Missions—Canada		-	-	-	-	-
Child Evangelism Fellowship of Canada		-	-	2	-	-
Christian and Missionary Alliance in Canada, The		-	-	8	-	-
Evangelical Free Church of Canada Mission		2	1	2	-	-
Far East Broadcasting Associates of Canada	1963	-	-	6	-	-
MBMS International	1950	5	-	2	-	-
OMF International—Canada	1951	2	-	6	-	-
Pentecostal Assemblies of Canada, The	2004	-	-	2	-	-
Pioneers Canada	2008	-	-	1	-	-
Power to Change	2002	-	-	2	-	-
SEND International of Canada	1945	-	-	2	-	-
TEAM of Canada	1945	-	-	8	-	-
United Church of Canada	1969	1	-	4	-	-
Totals:		10	1	52	-	-

Jordan

Evangelical Lutheran Church in Canada		-	-	-	-	-
Intercede International		-	-	-	2	-
Medical Ministry Canada, Inc.	2000	-	-	-	-	2
Mennonite Central Committee Canada	1985	-	-	-	2	4
Samaritan's Purse—Canada	2006	-	-	-	-	-
Totals:		-	-	-	4	6

Kazakhstan

Far East Broadcasting Associates of Canada	2001	-	-	2	-	-
Global Outreach Mission Inc., Canada		-	-	2	-	-
Inter-Varsity Christian Fellowship of Canada	2000	-	-	-	-	-
SEND International of Canada	2005	-	-	-	-	-
Totals:		-	-	4	-	-

	First Year	1-2 yrs.	2-4 yrs.	4+ yrs.	Other Countries Citizens	Other Countries Non-Citizens

Kenya

	First Year	1-2 yrs.	2-4 yrs.	4+ yrs.	Citizens	Non-Citizens
Africa Inland Mission International (Canada)	1895	-	11	18	-	-
Arms of Jesus Children's Mission, Inc., The	1990	-	-	-	5	-
Bible Holiness Movement, The	2002	-	-	-	1	-
Brethren Assemblies (Canada)	1963	-	-	2	-	-
Canadian Baptist Ministries	1970	-	-	5	-	-
Christian Reformed Wld. Relief Committee Can.	1983	-	-	1	2	2
Crossroads Christian Communications Inc. (ERDF)	2002	-	-	-	-	-
Far East Broadcasting Associates of Canada	1998	-	-	6	-	-
Global Recordings Network Canada		-	-	-	4	-
Intercede International		-	-	-	6	-
Into All The World	2001	-	-	2	-	-
Link International Ministries	1989	-	-	-	13	-
Mennonite Central Committee Canada	1962	-	-	-	4	6
Mission Aviation Fellowship of Canada (MAFC)		-	-	2	-	-
Pentecostal Assemblies of Canada, The	1918	2	-	14	-	-
Presbyterian Church in Canada	1983	-	-	1	-	-
The Free Methodist Church in Canada	1991	-	-	1	-	-
World Relief Canada		-	-	2	-	-
Wycliffe Bible Translators of Canada, Inc.		-	-	3	-	-
Totals:		2	11	57	35	8

Korea, South

	First Year	1-2 yrs.	2-4 yrs.	4+ yrs.	Citizens	Non-Citizens
Bible Holiness Movement, The	1985	-	-	-	25	-
Gospel Operation Intl. for Chinese Christians Can.	2004	1	-	-	-	-
Mennonite Central Committee Canada		-	-	-	-	3
United Church of Canada	1998	-	-	1	-	-
Totals:		1	-	1	25	3

Kosovo

	First Year	1-2 yrs.	2-4 yrs.	4+ yrs.	Citizens	Non-Citizens
Pioneers Canada	2006	-	-	2	-	-
Samaritan's Purse—Canada	2005	-	-	-	-	-
Totals:		-	-	2	-	-

Kyrgyzstan

	First Year	1-2 yrs.	2-4 yrs.	4+ yrs.	Citizens	Non-Citizens
Liebenzell Mission of Canada		-	-	-	-	-
Pentecostal Assemblies of Canada, The	2003	-	-	2	-	-
Totals:		-	-	2	-	-

Laos

	First Year	1-2 yrs.	2-4 yrs.	4+ yrs.	Citizens	Non-Citizens
Christian and Missionary Alliance in Canada, The		-	-	-	-	-
Gospel for Asia	2005	-	-	-	-	-
Mennonite Central Committee Canada	1975	-	-	-	11	10
Mission Aviation Fellowship of Canada (MAFC)		-	-	1	-	-
Totals:		-	-	1	11	10

Latin America—General

	First Year	1-2 yrs.	2-4 yrs.	4+ yrs.	Citizens	Non-Citizens
Bible League of Canada, The	1985	-	-	-	-	-
International Christian Ministries Canada (ICM)	2008	-	-	2	2	-
New Tribes Mission of Canada		-	-	31	-	-

		Personnel from CAN			Other Countries	
	First Year	1-2 yrs.	2-4 yrs.	4+ yrs.	Citizens	Non-Citizens
Wycliffe Bible Translators of Canada, Inc.		-	-	19	-	-
Totals:		-	-	52	2	-
Latvia						
Greater Europe Mission (Canada)	2003	-	-	4	-	-
Totals:		-	-	4	-	-
Lebanon						
Canadian Baptist Ministries	2005	-	-	2	-	-
Mennonite Central Committee Canada	1977	-	-	-	2	2
Partners International Canada	1994	-	-	-	-	-
Totals:		-	-	2	2	2
Lesotho						
Africa Inland Mission International (Canada)		-	1	-	-	-
Mission Aviation Fellowship of Canada (MAFC)		-	-	1	-	-
Totals:		-	1	1	-	-
Liberia						
ABWE Canada	2002	-	-	1	-	-
Equip, Canada	1997	-	-	2	-	-
High Adventure Gospel Communication Ministries		-	-	-	6	-
Intercede International		-	-	-	2	-
Samaritan's Purse—Canada	2006	-	-	-	-	-
World Relief Canada		-	-	-	-	-
Totals:		-	-	3	8	-
Lithuania						
Evangelical Free Church of Canada Mission	2000	-	2	-	-	-
MBMS International	1994	-	-	1	2	-
Totals:		-	2	1	2	-
Luxembourg						
Greater Europe Mission (Canada)	1977	-	-	2	-	-
Totals:		-	-	2	-	-
Macedonia						
SEND International of Canada	1993	-	-	3	-	-
Totals:		-	-	3	-	-
Madagascar						
Africa Inland Mission International (Canada)		-	2	-	-	-
Mission Aviation Fellowship of Canada (MAFC)		-	1	1	-	-
Totals:		-	3	1	-	-
Malawi						
Apostolic Church of Pentecost of Canada, Inc.	1955	-	-	2	-	-
Barry Moore Ministries, Inc.		-	-	-	2	1
Bible Holiness Movement, The	1990	-	-	-	20	-
Brethren in Christ World Missions—Canada		-	-	-	-	-

	First Year	Personnel from CAN 1-2 yrs.	Personnel from CAN 2-4 yrs.	Personnel from CAN 4+ yrs.	Other Countries Citizens	Other Countries Non-Citizens
Christian Reformed Wld. Relief Committee Can.	1989	-	-	-	-	2
Ch. of God (Anderson, Ind.) Can. Bd. of Msns.		-	-	-	-	-
EMAS Canada		-	-	-	-	-
Emmanuel International Canada		-	-	-	-	5
Liebenzell Mission of Canada		-	-	-	-	-
Pentecostal Assemblies of Canada, The	1982	2	-	6	-	-
Presbyterian Church in Canada	1969	-	-	4	-	-
Visionledd	2004	-	-	-	-	-
Totals:		2	-	12	22	8

Malaysia

	First Year	1-2 yrs.	2-4 yrs.	4+ yrs.	Citizens	Non-Citizens
Christian and Missionary Alliance in Canada, The		-	-	9	-	-
OMF International—Canada	1952	-	-	2	-	-
TeachBeyond		-	-	1	-	-
Trans World Radio Canada		-	-	1	-	-
Totals:		-	-	13	-	-

Mali

	First Year	1-2 yrs.	2-4 yrs.	4+ yrs.	Citizens	Non-Citizens
Avant Ministries Canada	1919	-	-	4	-	-
Christian Reformed Wld. Relief Committee Can.	1984	-	-	3	-	1
ReachAcross	1984	-	-	-	7	-
World Vision Canada	2006	-	-	-	-	-
Wycliffe Bible Translators of Canada, Inc.		-	-	2	-	-
Totals:		-	-	9	7	1

Mexico

	First Year	1-2 yrs.	2-4 yrs.	4+ yrs.	Citizens	Non-Citizens
Apostolic Church of Pentecost of Canada, Inc.		-	-	2	-	-
Avant Ministries Canada	1956	-	-	4	-	-
Brethren Assemblies (Canada)	1988	-	-	18	-	-
Brethren in Christ World Missions—Canada		-	-	-	-	-
CAM International of Canada	2007	-	2	2	-	-
Canadian National Baptist Convention (CNBC)	1985	-	-	-	-	4
Christian and Missionary Alliance in Canada, The		-	3	12	-	-
Evangelical Free Church of Canada Mission	1994	2	-	2	-	-
Evangelical Mennonite Conference		-	4	7	-	-
Evangelical Mennonite Mission Conference	1982	-	-	-	-	-
Evangelical Missionary Church of Canada	1998	-	-	6	-	-
Far East Broadcasting Associates of Canada	2005	-	-	4	-	-
Gospel Operation Intl. for Chinese Christians Can.	2005	-	-	2	-	-
Latin America Mission (Canada) Inc.	1961	-	-	1	-	-
MBMS International	1905	-	-	8	-	2
Mennonite Central Committee Canada	1981	-	-	-	3	13
TeachBeyond		-	-	-	-	-
WEC International (Canada)	1991	-	-	2	-	1
Wycliffe Bible Translators of Canada, Inc.		-	-	9	-	-
YUGO Canada Ministries	2004	2	2	6	1	-
Totals:		4	11	85	4	20

Micronesia, Federated States of

	First Year	1-2 yrs.	2-4 yrs.	4+ yrs.	Citizens	Non-Citizens
Liebenzell Mission of Canada		1	-	-	-	2
Totals:		1	-	-	-	2

	Personnel from CAN				Other Countries	
	First Year	1-2 yrs.	2-4 yrs.	4+ yrs.	Citizens	Non-Citizens

Middle East

ABWE Canada	1989	-	-	2	-	-
Arab World Ministries (Canada)	1983	-	-	9	-	4
Brethren in Christ World Missions—Canada		-	-	-	-	-
Canadian Baptist Ministries	1978	-	-	2	-	-
Canadian National Baptist Convention (CNBC)	2004	-	-	2	-	-
Christian and Missionary Alliance in Canada, The		-	2	26	-	-
Far East Broadcasting Associates of Canada	1990	-	2	-	-	-
Frontiers Canada	1984	-	-	8	-	-
InterServe Canada (Intl. Service Fellowship)		-	-	4	-	-
MBMS International	1996	-	-	4	-	-
Operation Mobilization Canada (Send the Light)		2	-	6	-	-
Pentecostal Assemblies of Canada, The	2007	-	-	9	-	-
ReachAcross	1951	2	-	8	9	-
TEAM of Canada	1960	2	-	-	-	-
Trans World Radio Canada		-	-	1	8	-
WEC International (Canada)		-	-	8	-	10
Totals:		6	4	89	17	14

Moldova

TeachBeyond		-	-	2	-	-
Totals:		-	-	2	-	-

Mongolia

Mission Aviation Fellowship of Canada (MAFC)		-	-	1	-	-
Totals:		-	-	1	-	-

Mozambique

Brethren in Christ World Missions—Canada		-	-	-	-	-
Christian Reformed Wld. Relief Committee Can.	1989	-	-	-	-	1
Ch. of God (Anderson, Ind.) Can. Bd. of Msns.		-	-	-	-	-
Mennonite Central Committee Canada	1982	-	-	-	2	5
Pentecostal Assemblies of Canada, The	1927	-	-	8	-	4
United Church of Canada	1998	-	-	2	-	-
Wycliffe Bible Translators of Canada, Inc.		-	-	6	-	-
Totals:		-	-	16	2	10

Myanmar/Burma

Gospel for Asia	1992	-	-	-	-	-
Gospel Operation Intl. for Chinese Christians Can.	2000	-	1	-	-	-
Intercede International		-	-	-	2	-
Operation Mobilization Canada (Send the Light)		1	-	-	-	-
Partners International Canada	1982	-	-	-	-	-
Samaritan's Purse—Canada	2007	-	-	-	-	-
Totals:		1	1	-	2	-

Namibia

Africa Inland Mission International (Canada)		1	2	-	-	-
Arms of Jesus Children's Mission, Inc., The	1990	-	-	-	2	-
Totals:		1	2	-	2	-

	First Year	Personnel from CAN 1-2 yrs.	2-4 yrs.	4+ yrs.	Other Countries Citizens	Non-Citizens
Nepal						
Brethren in Christ World Missions—Canada		-	-	-	-	-
Gospel for Asia	1988	-	-	-	-	-
I. N. (International Needs) Network Canada	1975	-	-	-	169	-
Intercede International		-	-	-	4	2
Mennonite Central Committee Canada	1956	-	-	-	3	4
Operation Mobilization Canada (Send the Light)		1	-	-	-	-
Partners International Canada	1999	-	-	-	-	-
Samaritan's Purse—Canada	2006	-	-	-	-	-
Totals:		1	-	-	176	6
Netherlands						
BCM International (Canada), Inc.	1950	-	-	-	-	1
Brethren Assemblies (Canada)		-	-	2	-	-
Christian and Missionary Alliance in Canada, The		-	-	1	-	-
Far East Broadcasting Associates of Canada	2003	2	-	-	-	-
Trans World Radio Canada		-	-	2	-	-
Wycliffe Bible Translators of Canada, Inc.		-	-	2	-	-
Totals:		2	-	7	-	1
New Zealand						
Action International Ministries—Canada		-	-	-	2	-
OMF International—Canada		-	-	-	-	1
Totals:		-	-	-	2	1
Nicaragua						
Brethren Assemblies (Canada)		-	-	2	-	
Brethren in Christ World Missions—Canada		-	-	-	-	-
Child Evangelism Fellowship of Canada	2002	-	-	1	-	-
Christian Reformed Wld. Relief Committee Can.	1973	-	-	1	-	-
Mennonite Central Committee Canada	1979	-	-	-	3	4
Mennonite Economic Dev. Associates (MEDA)	1995	-	-	-	47	1
Presbyterian Church in Canada	1985	-	-	2	-	-
Totals:		-	-	6	50	5
Niger						
Canadian National Baptist Convention (CNBC)	2004	-	-	-	-	2
Christian and Missionary Alliance in Canada, The		-	-	10	-	-
Christian Reformed Wld. Relief Committee Can.	1991	-	-	-	-	2
Samaritan's Purse—Canada	2005	-	-	-	-	-
SIM Canada	1924	1	-	13	-	2
The Free Methodist Church in Canada	2007	-	-	2	-	-
World Hope Canada	2008	-	-	-	3	-
Totals:		1	-	25	3	6
Nigeria						
Bible Holiness Movement, The	1959	-	-	-	41	-
Brethren Assemblies (Canada)	1954	-	-	4	-	-
Christian Reformed Wld. Relief Committee Can.	1969	-	-	2	-	1
Christian Studies International of Canada	2004	-	1	-	-	-

	Personnel from CAN			Other Countries	
	First Year	1-2 yrs.	2-4 yrs.	4+ yrs.	Citizens	Non-Citizens

	First Year	1-2 yrs.	2-4 yrs.	4+ yrs.	Citizens	Non-Citizens
Equip, Canada	2005	-	-	2	-	-
Evangelical Missionary Church of Canada	1998	-	2	-	-	-
Intercede International		-	-	-	2	-
Leprosy Mission Canada, The	2006	2	-	-	-	-
Link International Ministries	1989	-	-	-	12	-
Mennonite Central Committee Canada	1963	-	-	-	7	7
Partners International Canada	1999	-	-	-	-	-
Presbyterian Church in Canada	1954	-	-	1	-	-
SIM Canada	1893	-	-	10	-	-
Wycliffe Bible Translators of Canada, Inc.		-	-	4	-	-
Totals:		2	3	23	62	8

Norway

	First Year	1-2 yrs.	2-4 yrs.	4+ yrs.	Citizens	Non-Citizens
Brethren Assemblies (Canada)		-	-	2	-	-
Totals:		-	-	2	-	-

Oceania—General

	First Year	1-2 yrs.	2-4 yrs.	4+ yrs.	Citizens	Non-Citizens
Africa Inland Mission International (Canada)		-	2	-	-	-
New Tribes Mission of Canada		3	-	41	-	-
Totals:		3	2	41	-	-

Pakistan

	First Year	1-2 yrs.	2-4 yrs.	4+ yrs.	Citizens	Non-Citizens
					-	-
Far East Broadcasting Associates of Canada	1969	1	-	6	-	-
Intercede International		-	-	-	-	2
Mennonite Economic Dev. Associates (MEDA)	2007	-	-	-	6	1
Operation Mobilization Canada (Send the Light)		-	-	1	-	-
Partners International Canada	1975	-	-	-	-	-
Pioneers Canada	2005	-	-	1	-	-
ReachAcross	1972	-	-	-	7	-
Salvation Army	1997	-	1	-	-	-
Totals:		1	1	8	13	3

Palestine

	First Year	1-2 yrs.	2-4 yrs.	4+ yrs.	Citizens	Non-Citizens
Mennonite Central Committee Canada	1949	-	-	-	1	5
United Church of Canada	2003	-	-	-	-	-
Totals:		-	-	-	1	5

Panama

	First Year	1-2 yrs.	2-4 yrs.	4+ yrs.	Citizens	Non-Citizens
Christian and Missionary Alliance in Canada, The		-	-	2	-	-
Evangelical Free Church of Canada Mission	2000	-	-	2	-	-
MBMS International	1965	-	-	-	-	2
Pentecostal Assemblies of Canada, The	2008	-	-	2	-	-
Power to Change	2006	2	-	-	-	-
Totals:		2	-	6	-	2

Papua New Guinea

	First Year	1-2 yrs.	2-4 yrs.	4+ yrs.	Citizens	Non-Citizens
Evangelical Lutheran Church in Canada	2000	-	-	1	-	-
FRIENDS in Action International—Canada	1998	-	-	2	-	-
Into All The World	2008	1	-	-	-	-
Liebenzell Mission of Canada	2003	-	-	2	-	-

	Personnel from CAN			Other Countries	
	First Year	1-2 yrs.	2-4 yrs.	4+ yrs.	Citizens	Non-Citizens

	First Year	1-2 yrs.	2-4 yrs.	4+ yrs.	Citizens	Non-Citizens
Mission Aviation Fellowship of Canada (MAFC)		-	1	7	-	-
Salvation Army	1998	-	1	-	-	-
World Team Canada		-	-	4	-	-
Wycliffe Bible Translators of Canada, Inc.		-	-	23	-	-
Totals:		1	2	39	-	-

Paraguay

	First Year	1-2 yrs.	2-4 yrs.	4+ yrs.	Citizens	Non-Citizens
Evangelical Mennonite Conference		-	-	14	-	-
MBMS International	1940	-	-	-	2	-
Mennonite Mission Health Association	2005	-	-	-	-	-
SIM Canada	1987	-	-	2	-	-
TeachBeyond		-	-	-	-	-
Totals:		-	-	16	2	-

Peru

	First Year	1-2 yrs.	2-4 yrs.	4+ yrs.	Citizens	Non-Citizens
Brethren Assemblies (Canada)	1977	-	-	5	-	-
Canadian South America Mission	1926	-	-	1	-	2
Evangelical Lutheran Church in Canada	1994	-	-	1	-	-
FH Canada	2002	-	3	-	-	-
Gospel Operation Intl. for Chinese Christians Can.	2003	-	-	-	-	1
Into All The World	2009	-	1	-	-	-
MBMS International	1944	-	-	3	-	2
Medical Ministry Canada, Inc.	2005	-	-	-	2	-
Mennonite Economic Dev. Associates (MEDA)	1996	-	-	-	19	10
Partners International Canada	2007	-	-	-	-	-
Pioneers Canada	2001	-	-	2	-	-
TEAM of Canada	1961	-	-	3	-	-
United Church of Canada	1992	1	-	1	-	-
World Team Canada		-	-	4	-	-
Totals:		1	4	20	21	15

Philippines

	First Year	1-2 yrs.	2-4 yrs.	4+ yrs.	Citizens	Non-Citizens
Action International Ministries—Canada	1980	-	-	5	-	-
Baptist General Conf. of Canada Global Mins.	1999	-	-	2	-	-
Bible Holiness Movement, The	1961	-	-	-	2	-
Brethren Assemblies (Canada)		1	-	2	-	-
Christian and Missionary Alliance in Canada, The		-	-	1	-	-
Christian Reformed Wld. Relief Committee Can.	1970	-	1	-	1	-
EMAS Canada		-	-	-	-	-
Emmanuel International Canada		-	-	-	2	1
Far East Broadcasting Associates of Canada	2003	-	2	-	-	-
I. N. (International Needs) Network Canada	1977	-	-	-	139	-
Intercede International		-	-	-	8	-
MBMS International		-	-	1	-	-
Mennonite Central Committee Canada	1977	-	-	-	-	2
OMF International—Canada	1952	2	-	9	-	-
Pentecostal Assemblies of Canada, The	1987	-	-	1	-	-
Power to Change	1979	-	-	2	-	-
SEND International of Canada	1945	3	2	5	-	-
The Mission to Children	1978	-	-	-	-	-

	Personnel from CAN				Other Countries	
	First Year	1-2 yrs.	2-4 yrs.	4+ yrs.	Citizens	Non-Citizens
Wycliffe Bible Translators of Canada, Inc.		-	-	21	-	-
Totals:	6	5	49	152		3
Poland						
Brethren Assemblies (Canada)	1996	-	-	2	-	-
Christian and Missionary Alliance in Canada, The		-	-	4	-	-
Far East Broadcasting Associates of Canada	2005	-	-	3	-	-
SEND International of Canada	1991	-	-	-	-	-
Totals:	-	-	9		-	-
Portugal						
ABWE Canada		1	-	3	-	-
Baptist General Conf. of Canada Global Mins.	1998	-	-	1	-	-
Evangelical Missionary Church of Canada	1998	-	-	2	-	-
Greater Europe Mission (Canada)	1996	-	2	2	-	-
MBMS International	1986	-	-	2	-	-
Totals:	1	2	10		-	-
Puerto Rico						
Brethren Assemblies (Canada)	1967	-	-	1	-	-
Totals:	-	-	1		-	-
Romania						
ABWE Canada	2000	-	-	2	-	-
EMAS Canada		-	-		-	-
Evangelical Missionary Church of Canada	2001	6	-	-	-	-
FH Canada	2000	-	2	-	-	-
Global Outreach Mission Inc., Canada		-	-	1	-	-
I. N. (International Needs) Network Canada	1998	-	-		1	-
Pentecostal Assemblies of Canada, The	1998	-	-	5	-	-
Presbyterian Church in Canada	1997	-	-	1	-	-
Totals:	6	2	9	1		-
Russia						
Brethren Assemblies (Canada)	1998	-	-	3	-	-
Christian and Missionary Alliance in Canada, The		-	-	2	-	-
EMAS Canada		-	-	-	-	-
Evangelical Christian Church in Canada,The	1993	-	-	1	1	-
International Christian Ministries Canada (ICM)	2003	-	-	2	4	-
International Russian Radio/TV (IRR/TV)	1978	-	-	-	10	30
Liebenzell Mission of Canada	2008	-	-	-	-	-
MBMS International	1995	-	-	1	1	-
Mennonite Central Committee Canada		-	-	-	3	9
Outreach Canada	2002	-	-	2	-	-
Pentecostal Assemblies of Canada, The	1993	-	-	4	-	-
Power to Change	1994	-	-	1	-	-
Salvation Army	1990	-	1	-	-	-
SEND International of Canada	1992	-	-	5	-	-
WEC International (Canada)	2000	-	1	-	-	-
Totals:	-	2	21	19		39

| | Personnel from CAN | | | | Other Countries | |
	First Year	1-2 yrs.	2-4 yrs.	4+ yrs.	Citizens	Non-Citizens
Rwanda						
Canadian Baptist Ministries	1992	-	-	2	2	-
Evangelical Free Church of Canada Mission	2008	2	-	-	1	-
International Teams, Canada	-	-	-	2	-	-
Mennonite Central Committee Canada	1994	-	-	-	6	3
Pentecostal Assemblies of Canada, The	1998	2	-	2	-	-
The Wellspring Foundation for Education	2004	1	-	2	20	3
World Relief Canada	-	-	-	-	-	-
Totals:	5	-		8	29	6
Saint Vincent and the Grenadines						
Brethren Assemblies (Canada)	1990	-	-	1	-	-
Totals:	-	-		1	-	-
Senegal						
Christian and Missionary Alliance in Canada, The	-	-	1	-	-	
CrossWorld Canada	-	-	2	-	2	
Intercede International	-	-	-	-	2	
Partners International Canada	2000	-	-	-	-	-
Pentecostal Assemblies of Canada, The	1989	1	-	11	-	-
SIM Canada	1984	-	-	2	-	-
WEC International (Canada)	1936	-	-	1	-	1
World Vision Canada	2006	-	-	-	-	-
Wycliffe Bible Translators of Canada, Inc.	-	-	3	-	-	
Totals:	1	-		20	-	5
Serbia and Montenegro						
Christian and Missionary Alliance in Canada, The	-	-	2	-	-	
Totals:	-	-		2	-	-
Sierra Leone						
Christian Aid for Under-Assisted Soc. Everywhere	1987	2	2	-	55	1
Christian Reformed Wld. Relief Committee Can.	1979	-	-	-	-	1
World Hope Canada	2000	-	-	-	1	-
Totals:	2	2		-	56	2
Singapore						
HCJB Global—Canada	-	-	2	-	-	
OMF International—Canada	1950	1	-	4	-	-
Totals:	1	-		6	-	-
Slovakia						
Brethren Assemblies (Canada)	-	-	2	-	-	
Evangelical Lutheran Church in Canada	2001	1	-	-	-	-
Navigators of Canada, The	1975	-	-	2	-	-
Pentecostal Assemblies of Canada, The	2006	-	-	7	-	-
Totals:	1	-		11	-	-
Slovenia						
SEND International of Canada	1997	-	-	-	-	-
Totals:	-	-		-	-	-

	Personnel from CAN				Other Countries	
	First Year	1-2 yrs.	2-4 yrs.	4+ yrs.	Citizens	Non-Citizens

Somalia

Mennonite Central Committee Canada	1971	-	-	-	-	3
Totals:		-	-	-	-	3

South Africa

Africa Inland Mission International (Canada)		-	1	-	-	-
Barry Moore Ministries, Inc.		-	-	-	1	1
Brethren Assemblies (Canada)		-	-	2	-	-
Emmanuel International Canada		-	-	-	-	1
HOPE International Development Agency	1983	-	-	-	2	-
Into All The World	2003	-	-	4	-	-
MBMS International	2002	-	-	-	-	2
Mennonite Central Committee Canada	1971	-	-	-	13	8
Outreach Canada	2004	-	2	-	-	-
Partners International Canada	1975	-	-	-	-	-
Pentecostal Assemblies of Canada, The	1917	-	-	4	-	-
Power to Change	1988	-	-	2	-	-
SIM Canada	1989	-	-	7	-	-
TEAM of Canada	1945	-	-	2	-	-
Trans World Radio Canada		-	-	3	-	-
WEC International (Canada)	1955	-	-	2	-	4
Totals:		-	3	26	16	16

South America—General

Barry Moore Ministries, Inc.		-	-	-	1	-
Evangelical Christian Church in Canada,The	1978	-	-	1	1	-
Totals:		-	-	1	2	-

South Pacific

Wycliffe Bible Translators of Canada, Inc.		-	-	14	-	-
Totals:		-	-	14	-	-

Spain

		-	-	-	-	-
Avant Ministries Canada	1966	-	-	8	-	-
BCM International (Canada), Inc.	1949	-	-	-	-	1
Brethren Assemblies (Canada)	1975	-	-	2	-	-
Brethren in Christ World Missions—Canada		-	-	-	-	-
Christian and Missionary Alliance in Canada, The		-	-	1	-	-
Evangelical Missionary Church of Canada	1998	1	-	-	-	-
Far East Broadcasting Associates of Canada	1980	-	-	2	-	-
Liebenzell Mission of Canada	2009	-	-	1	-	1
Salvation Army	1998	-	-	2	-	-
SEND International of Canada	1987	-	-	-	-	-
TEAM of Canada	1952	-	2	2	-	-
WEC International (Canada)	1968	-	-	3	-	1
World Team Canada		-	-	2	-	-
Totals:		1	2	23	-	3

Sri Lanka

Gospel for Asia		-	-	-	-	-

	Personnel from CAN			Other Countries	
	First Year	1-2 yrs.	2-4 yrs.	4+ yrs. Citizens	Non-Citizens
I. N. (International Needs) Network Canada	1976	-	-	-	112	-
Mennonite Central Committee Canada		-	-	-	-	2
The Free Methodist Church in Canada	2003	-	-	2	-	-
Totals:	-	-	2	112	2

Sudan

Africa Inland Mission International (Canada)		-	3	2	-	-
Intercede International		-	-	-	2	-
Mennonite Central Committee Canada	1972	-	-	-	-	5
Pioneers Canada	2003	-	-	4	-	-
Samaritan's Purse—Canada	2006	-	-	-	-	-
SIM Canada	2006	2	-	1	-	-
World Relief Canada		-	-	-	-	-
Totals:	2	3	7	2	5

Sweden

Operation Mobilization Canada (Send the Light)		-	1	-	-	-
Totals:	-	1	-	-	-

Switzerland

Operation Mobilization Canada (Send the Light)		2	-	-	-	-
Pentecostal Assemblies of Canada, The	2008	-	-	2	-	-
TeachBeyond		-	-	-	-	-
United Church of Canada	2008	-	1	-	-	-
Totals:	2	1	2	-	-

Syria

Mennonite Central Committee Canada	1991	-	-	-	-	2
Pioneers Canada	2007	-	-	3	-	-
Totals:	-	-	3	-	2

Taiwan

Apostolic Church of Pentecost of Canada, Inc.	1950	-	-	2	-	-
Christian and Missionary Alliance in Canada, The		-	-	6	-	-
Presbyterian Church in Canada	1872	-	-	1	-	-
SEND International of Canada	1966	1	2	-	-	-
Totals:	1	2	9	-	-

Tajikistan

					-
Mennonite Economic Dev. Associates (MEDA)	2004	-	-	-	7	1
Totals:	-	-	-	7	1

Tanzania

Africa Inland Mission International (Canada)		-	4	5	-	-
Apostolic Church of Pentecost of Canada, Inc.	2009	-	-	2	-	-
Baptist General Conf. of Canada Global Mins.	2004	-	-	1	-	-
Barry Moore Ministries, Inc.		-	-	-	1	2
Bible Holiness Movement, The	1998	-	-	-	1	-
Christian Reformed Wld. Relief Committee Can.	1989	-	-	-	1	1
Emmanuel International Canada		-	-	-	-	1

	Personnel from CAN				Other Countries	
	First Year	1-2 yrs.	2-4 yrs.	4+ yrs.	Citizens	Non-Citizens
Evangelical Missionary Church of Canada	2004	-	1	-	-	-
I. N. (International Needs) Network Canada	1997	-	-	-	7	-
Into All The World	2005	-	-	2	-	-
Mennonite Central Committee Canada	1962	-	-	-	9	6
Mennonite Economic Dev. Associates (MEDA)	1991	-	-	-	68	2
Pentecostal Assemblies of Canada, The	1955	2	-	6	-	-
World Relief Canada		-	-	-	-	-
Wycliffe Bible Translators of Canada, Inc.		-	-	5	-	-
Totals:		2	5	21	87	12

Thailand

Brethren in Christ World Missions—Canada		-	-	-	-	-
Christian and Missionary Alliance in Canada, The		-	-	4	-	-
Compasio	2001	-	-	2	12	-
Evangelical Free Church of Canada Mission	2002	-	-	2	1	-
Evangelical Lutheran Church in Canada	2000	-	1	-	-	-
FH Canada	1998	-	2	2	-	-
Gospel for Asia		-	-	-	-	-
Gospel Operation Intl. for Chinese Christians Can.	2000	-	1	-	-	-
Intercede International		-	-	-	-	2
MBMS International	1992	-	-	6	-	-
Mennonite Central Committee Canada	1960	-	-	-	-	2
Navigators of Canada, The	2007	-	-	2	-	-
OMF International—Canada	1951	-	-	18	-	-
Partners International Canada	1965	-	-	-	-	-
Pentecostal Assemblies of Canada, The	1961	-	-	13	-	-
Samaritan's Purse—Canada	2002	-	-	-	-	-
WEC International (Canada)	1947	-	-	1	-	-
Totals:		-	4	50	13	4

Togo

ABWE Canada		-	-	4	-	-
Wycliffe Bible Translators of Canada, Inc.		-	-	1	-	-
Totals:		-	-	5	-	-

Trinidad and Tobago

ABWE Canada	2002	-	-	2	-	-
Apostolic Church of Pentecost of Canada, Inc.		-	-	1	-	-
Fundamental Baptist Msn. of Trinidad/Tobago	1960	-	-	-	1	-
Pentecostal Assemblies of Canada, The	2004	2	-	-	-	-
Totals:		2	-	3	1	-

Turkey

I. N. (International Needs) Network Canada	2001	-	-	-	1	-
Intercede International		-	-	-	2	-
Navigators of Canada, The	1991	-	-	2	-	-
People International—Canada	2008	1	-	-	-	-
Pioneers Canada	2008	-	-	1	-	-
Totals:		1	-	3	3	-

		Personnel from CAN			Other Countries	
	First Year	1-2 yrs.	2-4 yrs.	4+ yrs.	Citizens	Non-Citizens
Uganda						
Africa Community Technical Service (ACTS)	1978	-	-	2	29	-
Africa Inland Mission International (Canada)		2	1	2	-	-
Christian Reformed Wld. Relief Committee Can.	1983	-	-	-	2	3
Ch. of God (Anderson, Ind.) Can. Bd. of Msns.		-	-	-	-	-
Crossroads Christian Communications Inc. (ERDF)	2006	-	-	-	-	-
Emmanuel International Canada		-	-	-	-	4
Equip, Canada	2000	-	-	2	-	-
FH Canada	2002	-	-	1	-	-
High Adventure Gospel Communication Ministries		-	-	-	4	-
I. N. (International Needs) Network Canada	1994	-	-	-	769	-
Into All The World	2002	-	-	1	-	-
Mennonite Central Committee Canada	1979	-	-	-	6	9
Mission Aviation Fellowship of Canada (MAFC)		-	-	2	-	-
Pentecostal Assemblies of Canada, The	1969	-	-	9	-	-
World Vision Canada	2005	-	-	-	-	-
Totals:		2	1	19	810	16
Ukraine						
ABWE Canada	1993	-	-	2	-	-
Action International Ministries—Canada	2004	-	-	1	-	-
Crossroads Christian Communications Inc. (ERDF)	2007	-	-	-	-	-
Evangelical Free Church of Canada Mission	1992	2	2	5	3	-
Intercede International		-	-	-	-	2
International Russian Radio/TV (IRR/TV)	1986	-	-	-	4	-
Inter-Varsity Christian Fellowship of Canada	2000	-	-	-	-	-
MBMS International		-	-	-	-	-
Pentecostal Assemblies of Canada, The	1992	-	-	4	-	-
Presbyterian Church in Canada	2000	-	-	2	-	-
SEND International of Canada	1991	3	-	4	-	-
Slavic Gospel Association—Canada	1952	-	-	1	-	-
The Master's Foundation	1983	-	-	-	9	-
Ukrainian Children's Christian Fund		-	-	-	-	-
World Hope Canada	2001	-	-	2	8	-
World Team Canada		-	-	2	-	-
Totals:		5	2	23	24	2
United Kingdom						
ABWE Canada		-	-	2	-	-
Brethren in Christ World Missions—Canada		-	-	-	-	-
Christar Canada		-	2	-	-	-
Emmanuel International Canada		-	-	-	2	-
Global Outreach Mission Inc., Canada		-	-	2	-	-
InterServe Canada (Intl. Service Fellowship)		-	2	-	-	-
New Tribes Mission of Canada		-	-	1	-	-
OMF International—Canada	1865	-	-	-	-	1
Pentecostal Assemblies of Canada, The	2004	-	-	2	-	-
Power to Change	2008	1	-	-	-	-
Salvation Army	1985	-	4	2	-	-
WEC International (Canada)	1913	-	-	2	1	6

		Personnel from CAN			Other Countries	
	First Year	1-2 yrs.	2-4 yrs.	4+ yrs.	Citizens	Non-Citizens
Wycliffe Bible Translators of Canada, Inc.		-	-	5	-	-
Youth for Christ, Canada		2	-	-	-	-
Totals:		3	8	16	3	7

Unspecified Country

Brethren Assemblies (Canada)		-	-	22	-	-
Christian and Missionary Alliance in Canada, The		-	-	13	-	-
International Teams, Canada		-	-	3	-	-
Operation Mobilization Canada (Send the Light)	1970	20	5	3	-	-
Wycliffe Bible Translators of Canada, Inc.		-	-	16	-	-
Totals:		20	5	57	-	-

Uruguay

Brethren Assemblies (Canada)	1974	-	-	5	-	-
MBMS International	1950	-	-	-	-	-
Operation Mobilization Canada (Send the Light)		-	-	2	-	-
Totals:		-		7	-	-

Venezuela

Brethren Assemblies (Canada)	1947	-	-	7	-	-
Brethren in Christ World Missions—Canada		-	-	-	-	-
Christian and Missionary Alliance in Canada, The		-	-	5	-	-
Evangelical Free Church of Canada Mission	2000	-	-	2	-	-
Far East Broadcasting Associates of Canada	1990	-	-	3	-	-
MBMS International	1951	-	-	-	-	-
WEC International (Canada)	1954	-	-	-	-	2
Totals:		-	-	17	-	2

Vietnam

EMAS Canada		-	-	-	-	-
I. N. (International Needs) Network Canada	1991	-	-	-	42	-
Intercede International		-	-	-	-	2
Mennonite Central Committee Canada	1954	-	-	-	6	8
Samaritan's Purse—Canada	2007	-	-	-	-	-
World Relief Canada		-	-	-	-	-
Totals:		-	-	-	48	10

Western Europe—General

Operation Mobilization Canada (Send the Light)		-	5	4	-	-
Totals:		-	5	4	-	-

Zambia

Action International Ministries—Canada	2000	2	-	1	-	-
Apostolic Church of Pentecost of Canada, Inc.	2003	-	-	2	-	-
Bible Holiness Movement, The	1990	-	-	-	2	-
Brethren Assemblies (Canada)		-	-	36	-	-
Brethren in Christ World Missions—Canada		-	-	-	-	-
Christian Reformed Wld. Relief Committee Can.	1990	-	-	2	-	2
Ch. of God (Anderson, Ind.) Can. Bd. of Msns.		-	-	-	-	-
Crossroads Christian Communications Inc. (ERDF)	2000	-	-	-	-	-

		Personnel from CAN			Other Countries	
	First Year	1-2 yrs.	2-4 yrs.	4+ yrs.	Citizens	Non-Citizens
I. N. (International Needs) Network Canada	1985	-	-	-	91	-
Liebenzell Mission of Canada		-	-	-	-	-
Mennonite Central Committee Canada	1962	-	-	-	3	7
Mennonite Economic Dev. Associates (MEDA)	2008	-	-	-	3	-
Mission Aviation Fellowship of Canada (MAFC)		-	1	1	-	-
Pentecostal Assemblies of Canada, The	1962	2	-	5	-	-
SIM Canada	1910	-	-	11	-	-
United Church of Canada	2008	1	-	1	-	-
	Totals:	5	1	59	99	9

Zimbabwe

Apostolic Church of Pentecost of Canada, Inc.	1955	-	-	-	1	-
Brethren in Christ World Missions—Canada		-	-	-	-	-
Mennonite Central Committee Canada	1980	-	-	-	1	2
Mennonite Mission Health Association	2004	-	-	-	-	-
Pentecostal Assemblies of Canada, The	1948	-	-	8	-	-
TEAM of Canada	1945	-	-	1	-	-
WEC International (Canada)	2007	-	-	1	1	-
	Totals:	-	-	10	3	2

Appendix A
Mission Directories

The websites listed contain electronic directories of mission agencies. In most cases, the directories contain full contact information for the organizations which are included.

Worldwide
The Lausanne Movement
www.lausanne.org

The Network for Strategic Missions
www.strategicnetwork.org

World Evangelical Alliance—Mission Commission (Formerly World Evangelical Fellowship)
www.worldevangelicalalliance.org

Regions
Asia
Asia-Pacific Missions & Evangelism Network, Inc
www.amen21.net

Europe
European Evangelical Alliance
www.europeanea.org

European Evangelical Missionary Association
www.europeanema.org

Latin America
Ibero-America (Latin America, Spain, and Portugal) The Ibero-American Missions Handbook of COMIBAM Internacional
www.comibam.org

Individual Countries
Australia
Australian Evangelical Alliance—Missions Interlink
www.evangelicalalliance.org.au

Evangelical Missionary Alliance, New South Wales
www.pastornet.net.au

Canada
CCRDA: Canadian Christian Relief and Development Association
www.ccrda.ca

Canadian Tentmaking Network
www.tentmaking.org

EFC: Evangelical Fellowship of Canada —Global Initiatives
www.evangelicalfellowship.ca

Hong Kong
Hong Kong Association of Christian Missions
www.hkacm.org.hk

India
India Missions Association
www.imaindia.org

Japan
Japan Evangelical Missionary Association
www.jema.org

Korea
Korean World Missions Association
www.kwma.org

Malaysia
National Evangelical Christian Fellowship
www.necf.org.my

Mexico
Cooperacion Misionera de Mexico
www.COMIMEX.org

United Kingdom
Global Connections
www.globalconnections.co.uk

OSCAR: UK information service
for world mission
www.oscar.org.uk

United States of America
AERDO: Association of Evangelical
Relief and Development Organization
www.aerdo.org

AIMS: Accelerating International
Mission Strategies
www.aims.org

ANAM: Association of North American
Missions
www.anamissions.org

CrossGlobal Link (Formerly IFMA)
www.crossgloballink.org

CWS: Church World Service
www.churchworldservice.org

FOM: Fellowship of Missions
www.fellowshipofmissions.org

The Mission Exchange (Formerly EFMA)
www.themissionexchange.org

Non-Protestant
OCMC: Orthodox Christian Mission
Center
www.ocmc.org

USCMA: US Catholic Mission
Association
www.uscatholicmission.org

Appendix B
Associations

AERDO—Association of Evangelical Relief and Development Organizations

AERDO is made up of evangelical Christian relief and development agencies from North America. For information on AERDO agencies, please check the website at www.aerdo.net

ANAM—Association of North American Missions

The ANAM is made up of independent mission and ministry agencies serving in North America. For information on ANAM agencies, please check the website at www.anamissions.org

CCRDA—Canadian Christian Relief and Development Association

The CCRDA membership is made up of Canadian Christian organizations and individuals involved in relief, development, and justice who are committed to integrated, transformational development. For information on CCRDA agencies, please check the website at www.ccrda.org

CrossGlobal Link (formerly IFMA)

The CrossGlobal Link membership is made up primarily of nondenominational evangelical mission agencies in North America. For more information on CrossGlobal Link agencies, please check the website at www.crossglobal-link.org

CWS—Church World Service

CWS is the relief, development, and refugee assistance ministry of 35 Protestant, Orthodox, and Anglican denominations in the United States. For information on CWS agencies, please check the website at www.churchworldservice.org

FOM—Fellowship of Missions

The FOM membership is open to fundamental, premillennial agencies in North America. For more information on FOM agencies, please check the website at www.fellowshipofmissions.org

The Mission Exchange (formerly EFMA)

The Mission Exchange, the missions arm of the National Association of Evangelicals, has a membership made up of support and sending mission agencies and churches that send missionaries. For information on The Mission Exchange agencies, please check the website at www.themissionexchange.org

OCMC—Orthodox Christian Mission Center

The OCMC is the official mission agency of the Canonical Orthodox Bishops in the Americas (SCOBA). For information on OCMC agencies, check the website at www.ocmc.org

USCMA—US Catholic Mission Association

For information on USCMA agencies, please check the website at www.uscatholicmission.org

Appendix C

Mission Handbook
USA Protestant Ministries Overseas
Questionnaire

Please return to: EMIS, P. O. Box 794, Wheaton, IL 60187-5593
Fax: 630.752.7155 • Email: missionhandbook@wheaton.edu

1. What is your organization's name as you are known and would like to be listed in the *Mission Handbook*? [legal name]

_____

2. Mailing Address:

_____
(P. O. Box or Street)   (City)   (State)   (Zip)

3. Telephone number: (_____) _____

   Fax number: (_____) _____

   E-mail _____

   Web Site _____

4. Chief Executive Officer in the USA:

_____
(Name)   (Title of Position)

5. Year organization founded in USA: _____

6. Year Incorporated in USA if different from year founded: _____

7. Which one of the following is most used in describing your organization's denominational orientation?

   ❏ Denominational   ❏ Transdenominational
   ❏ Nondenominational   ❏ Prefer that denominational orientation not be used
   ❏ Interdenominational   ❏ Other _____

8. Which one (or two if needed) of the following terms most clearly describes the general doctrinal and/or ecclesiastical stance of your organization (or that of your supporters if more appropriate)?

   ❏ Adventist   ❏ Congregational   ❏ Methodist
   ❏ Anglican   ❏ Ecumenical   ❏ Pentecostal
   ❏ Baptist   ❏ Episcopal   ❏ Presbyterian
   ❏ Brethren   ❏ Evangelical   ❏ Reformed
   ❏ Christian ("Restoration ❏ Friends   ❏ Wesleyan
     Movement")   ❏ Fundamentalist   ❏ Other _____
   ❏ Christian/Plymouth   ❏ Holiness
     Brethren   ❏ Independent
   ❏ Charismatic   ❏ Lutheran
                            ❏ Mennonite

9. Select up to six descriptors from the following list which are primary activities of your organization. If actively involved in more than six, please indicate only the six for which the most resources are currently committed.

- ❏ Adoption
- ❏ Agricultural assistance
- ❏ Apologetics
- ❏ Association of Missions
- ❏ Audio recording/distribution
- ❏ Aviation services
- ❏ Bible distribution
- ❏ Bible memorization
- ❏ Broadcasting, radio and/or TV
- ❏ Business as Missions
- ❏ Camping programs
- ❏ Childcare/orphanage
- ❏ Children's programs
- ❏ Church construction/financing
- ❏ Church planting/establishing
- ❏ Correspondence courses
- ❏ Development, community or other
- ❏ Disability assistance programs
- ❏ Discipleship
- ❏ Education, church/sch. general Christian
- ❏ Education, missionary (certificate)
- ❏ Education, theological education by extension (TEE)
- ❏ Education, extension (other)
- ❏ Education, theological

- ❏ Evangelism, mass
- ❏ Evangelism, personal & small group
- ❏ Evangelism, student
- ❏ Funds transmission
- ❏ Furloughed missionary support
- ❏ HIV/AIDS
- ❏ Information service (mission related)
- ❏ Justice related
- ❏ Leadership development
- ❏ Linguistics
- ❏ Literacy
- ❏ Literature distribution
- ❏ Literature production
- ❏ Management consulting/ training
- ❏ Medical supplies
- ❏ Medicine, incl. dental & public health
- ❏ Member care
- ❏ National worker support
- ❏ Nurture/support of national churches
- ❏ Partnership development
- ❏ Psychological counseling
- ❏ Purchasing services

- ❏ Recruiting/mobilizing
- ❏ Relief and/or rehabilitation
- ❏ Research (missions related)
- ❏ Services for other agencies
- ❏ Short-term programs coordination
- ❏ Sports program ministry
- ❏ Supplying equipment
- ❏ Technical assistance
- ❏ Tentmaking and related
- ❏ TESOL
- ❏ Training/orientation, missionary
- ❏ Trafficking/Slavery issues
- ❏ Training/orientation, missionary
- ❏ Training, other
- ❏ Translation, Bible
- ❏ Translation, other
- ❏ Video/film production distribution
- ❏ Youth programs
- ❏ Other _____
  _____
  _____
  _____

Which **one** of the activities above is most commonly associated with your organization?

_____

10. Is your organization a member of an association of missions?
   ❏ AERDO   ❏ ANAM   ❏ CCRDA   ❏ CWS   ❏ The Mission Exchange
   ❏ FOM   ❏ CrossGlobal Link   ❏ Other:_____

FINANCIAL DATA

11. What was your organization's **grand total income** for all ministries in the USA and overseas, raised in the USA in the last fiscal year? (Denominations should report their board total.) $_____

12. Of the grand total for all ministries reported in Question 11, what was the amount of **income for overseas ministries**? $ _____

13. Of the amount reported in Question 12, what, if any, was the dollar amount of **gifts-in-kind commodities and/or services** that were donated for overseas activities to your organization? $ _____

COUNTRIES OF SERVICE AND FIELD PERSONNEL

14. Personnel **FROM USA and other** Countries:

NOTE: For personnel from the US, include:

- those engaged in cross-cultural ministry and fully supported under your organization from your most recent fiscal year
- those on furlough and those on loan to another organization if they are fully supported by your organization
- those on loan to your organization only if fully supported by you
- spouses, even if they don't have "official" ministry status but serve in a ministry or support role

NOTE: For personnel from countries other than the US, include:

- personnel with specific mission/ministry duties who are fully or partially supported by/through your organization from funds raised in the USA

PLEASE MAKE ADDITIONAL COPIES OF THIS PAGE IF NEEDED

Country of Service Note: Indicate a region only if a specific country is suitable	Year Work Began	**Number of personnel from USA:** Fully supported personnel with length of service expected to be:			**Number of personnel from countries other than USA:** Fully or partially supported personnel. Show the number on the appropriate country of service line.	
		From 1 up to 2 years	2 to 4 years	More than 4 years	**Citizens** of their country of service	**Not citizens** of their country of service

OTHER PERSONNEL (Categories other than those reported in Question 14)

15. Number of **nonresidential mission personnel** from the USA (persons not residing in the country(s) of their ministry focus but assigned to overseas duties and traveling overseas at least 12 weeks per year on operational aspects of the ministry) who are supported by your organization.

_____ Fully supported by your organization _____ Partially supported

16. Number of short-term personnel from the USA who went on overseas service projects or mission trips in your most recent fiscal year through your organization, either fully or partially supported including those raising their own support:

_____less than one year, but at least 2 weeks   _____ less than 2 weeks

If you have a short-term program, where are initial contacts usually made with potential participants?
_____ Churches _____ Individually _____ Conferences (other than in churches)
_____ Schools _____ Website _____ Other: _____

How many of your **regular staff** in the USA and overseas have **duties related to short-term programs**?
_____ Full-time on S-T program
_____Part-time on S-T program: 50%+ of total time _____ 10–49% _____

17. Number of **USA bi-vocational or "tentmaker" personnel sponsored or supervised by your organization** (persons who support themselves partially or fully through non-church/mission vocations and live overseas for the purpose of Christian witness, evangelism, and/or encouraging believers). _____

If you relate to "tentmakers," do you have staff assigned to maintain such contacts?
_____ Yes _____ No

Note: If countries of service for personnel in Items 14-16 are not already listed in the table in Item 14, please add the countries to the list. Also list countries with no personnel but with regular ongoing programs you support.

18. Number of **staff and/or other employees** assigned to ministry and/or office duties in the USA.
_____ Full-time paid staff _____ Part-time paid staff/associates

19. What is your organization's board approved mission statement? _____
_____
_____

20. Please list any periodicals published by your organization: _____
_____

21. Please give the name and title of the person in your organization in charge of one or all of the following departments: Recruiting, Training and Member Care.

Name: _____ Title: _____
Name: _____ Title: _____
If you have additional comments about your organization or this survey that you would like us to be aware of, please indicate here or enclose an additional sheet.

THANK YOU for responding to this survey! We appreciate it.

Submitted by: _____ Date: _____
Position: _____

Appendix D

Mission Handbook
Canadian Protestant Ministries Overseas
Questionnaire
Please return to: EMIS, P. O. Box 794, Wheaton, IL 60187-5593
Fax: 630.752.7155 • Email: missionhandbook@wheaton.edu

1. What is your organization's name as you are known and would like to be listed in the *Mission Handbook*? [legal name]

_____

2. Mailing Address:

_____
(P. O. Box or Street)   (City)   (Province)   (Postal code)

3. Telephone number: (_____) _____

   Fax number: (_____) _____

   E-mail _____

   Web Site _____

4. Chief Executive Officer in Canada:

_____
(Name)   (Title of Position)

5. Year organization founded in Canada: _____

6. Year Incorporated in Canada if different from year founded: _____

7. Which one of the following is most used in describing your organization's denominational orientation?

   ❏ Denominational   ❏ Transdenominational
   ❏ Nondenominational   ❏ Prefer that denominational orientation not be used
   ❏ Interdenominational   ❏ Other _____

8. Which one (or two if needed) of the following terms most clearly describes the general doctrinal and/or ecclesiastical stance of your organization (or that of your supporters if more appropriate)?

   ❏ Adventist   ❏ Episcopal   ❏ Presbyterian
   ❏ Anglican   ❏ Evangelical   ❏ Reformed
   ❏ Baptist   ❏ Friends   ❏ Wesleyan
   ❏ Brethren   ❏ Fundamentalist   ❏ Other _____
   ❏ Christian ("Restoration   ❏ Holiness
      Movement")   ❏ Independent
   ❏ Christian/Plymouth Brethren ❏ Lutheran
   ❏ Charismatic   ❏ Mennonite
   ❏ Congregational   ❏ Methodist
   ❏ Ecumenical   ❏ Pentecostal

9. Select up to six descriptors from the following list which are primary activities of your organization. If actively involved in more than six, please indicate only the six for which the most resources are currently committed.

❏ Adoption
❏ Agricultural assistance
❏ Apologetics
❏ Association of Missions
❏ Audio recording/distribution
❏ Aviation services
❏ Bible distribution
❏ Bible memorization
❏ Broadcasting, radio and/or TV
❏ Business as Missions
❏ Camping programs
❏ Childcare/orphanage
❏ Children's programs
❏ Church construction/financing
❏ Church planting/establishing
❏ Correspondence courses
❏ Development, community or other
❏ Disability assistance programs
❏ Discipleship
❏ Education, church/sch. general Christian
❏ Education, missionary (certificate)
❏ Education, theological education by extension (TEE)
❏ Education, extension (other)
❏ Education, theological

❏ Evangelism, mass
❏ Evangelism, personal & small group
❏ Evangelism, student
❏ Funds transmission
❏ Furloughed missionary support
❏ HIV/AIDS
❏ Information service (mission related)
❏ Justice related
❏ Leadership development
❏ Linguistics
❏ Literacy
❏ Literature distribution
❏ Literature production
❏ Management consulting/ training
❏ Medical supplies
❏ Medicine, incl. dental & public health
❏ Member care
❏ National worker support
❏ Nurture/support of national churches
❏ Partnership development
❏ Psychological counseling
❏ Purchasing services

❏ Recruiting/mobilizing
❏ Relief and/or rehabilitation
❏ Research (missions related)
❏ Services for other agencies
❏ Short-term programs coordination
❏ Sports program ministry
❏ Supplying equipment
❏ Technical assistance
❏ Tentmaking and related
❏ TESOL
❏ Training/orientation, missionary
❏ Trafficking/Slavery issues
❏ Training/orientation, missionary
❏ Training, other
❏ Translation, Bible
❏ Translation, other
❏ Video/film production distribution
❏ Youth programs
❏ Other _____
_____
_____
_____

Which **one** of the activities above is most commonly associated with your organization?

_____

10. Is your organization a member of an association of missions?
    ❏ AERDO   ❏ ANAM   ❏ CCRDA   ❏ CWS   ❏ The Mission Exchange
    ❏ FOM   ❏ CrossGlobal Link   ❏ Other:_____

FINANCIAL DATA

11. What was your organization's **grand total income** for all ministries in Canada and overseas, raised in Canada in the last calendar or fiscal year? (Denominations should report their board total.) $_____

12. Of the grand total for all ministries reported in Question 11, what was the amount of **income for overseas ministries**? $ _____

13. Of the amount reported in Question 12, what, if any, was the dollar amount of **gifts-in-kind commodities and/or services** that were donated for overseas activities to your organization? $ _____

COUNTRIES OF SERVICE AND FIELD PERSONNEL

14. Personnel **FROM Canada and other** Countries:

NOTE: For personnel from Canada, include:
- those engaged in cross-cultural ministry and fully supported under your organization from your most recent fiscal year
- those on furlough and those on loan to another organization if they are fully supported by your organization
- those on loan to your organization only if fully supported by you
- spouses, even if they don't have "official" ministry status but serve in a ministry or support role

NOTE: For personnel from countries other than the Canada, include:
- personnel with specific mission/ministry duties who are fully or partially supported by/through your organization from funds raised in Canada

PLEASE MAKE ADDITIONAL COPIES OF THIS PAGE IF NEEDED

Country of Service Note: Indicate a region only if a specific country is not suitable	Year Work Began	Number of personnel from Canada: Fully supported personnel with length of service expected to be:			Number of personnel from countries other than Canada: Fully or partially supported personnel. Show the number on the appropriate country of service line.	
		From 1 up to 2 years	2 to 4 years	More than 4 years	Citizens of their country of service	Not citizens of their country of service

266.0216

M67

2010

C.2

122289

OTHER PERSONNEL (Categories other than those reported in Question 14)

15. Number of **nonresidential mission personnel from Canada** (persons not residing in the country(s) of their ministry focus but assigned to overseas duties and traveling overseas at least 12 weeks per year on operational aspects of the ministry) who are
supported by your organization.

_____ Fully supported by your organization _____ Partially supported

16. Number of short-term personnel from Canada who went on overseas service projects
or mission trips in your most recent fiscal year through your organization, either fully
or partially supported including those raising their own support:

_____ less than one year, but at least 2 weeks _____ less than 2 weeks

If you have a short-term program, where are initial contacts usually made with potential participants?

_____ Churches _____ Individually _____ Conferences (other than in churches)
_____ Schools _____ Website _____ Other: _____

How many of your **re** **ed to
short-term progran**

_____ Full-time on S-T
_____ Part-time on S-T

17. Number of **Canada b. ed or su-
pervised by your organization** (persons who support themselves partially or fully
through non-church/mission vocations and live overseas for the purpose of Christian
witness, evangelism, and/or encouraging believers). _____

If you relate to "tentmakers," do you have staff assigned to maintain such contacts?
_____ Yes _____ No

Note: If countries of service for personnel in Items 14-16 are not already listed in the
table in Item 14, please add the countries to the list. Also list countries with no personnel but with regular ongoing programs you support.

18. Number of **staff and/or other employees** assigned to ministry and/or office duties
in Canada.

_____ Full-time paid staff _____ Part-time paid staff/associates

19. What is your organization's board approved mission statement? _____
_____
_____

20. Please list any periodicals published by your organization: _____
_____

21. Please give the name and title of the person in your organization in charge of one or
all of the following departments: Recruiting, Training and Member Care.

Name: _____ Title: _____
Name: _____ Title: _____

If you have additional comments about your organization or this survey that you would
like us to be aware of, please indicate here or enclose an additional sheet.

THANK YOU for responding   3 4711 00201 6790

Submitted by: _____ Date: _____
Position: _____